D1408492

ARIS™ *Assessment, Review and Instruction System*

ONLINE STUDY & HOMEWORK MATERIALS

IMPORTANT: Following are instructions to access online resources to support your McGraw-Hill textbook

The URL associated with your text is:
http://www.mhhe.com/nester5

Option 1: **ARIS LOGIN.** Your instructor may use **ARIS** as a homework and assessment tool. If so, you must register in order to ensure your assignments are recorded into your instructor's gradebook.

Option 2: If your instructor is **NOT** using **ARIS** as a homework and assessment tool, you are welcome to access the material on the site without registering. Simply go to the URL listed above. You are free to access these materials for your own self-study.

ARIS LOGIN. *To Register you need:*

1. **Section Code:** Provided by your instructor.
2. **Registration Code:** Provided in the gray scratch-off area below.
3. **URL:** Go to the URL listed at the top of this card and follow the directions for creating an ARIS account.

Scratch off for registration code

This registration code can be used by one individual and is not transferable.

IMPORTANT: The registration code printed above can only be used once to create a unique student account. Students do not need a registration code to access the content of the site. Students choosing "ARIS Login" must login each time they visit the site in order for their grades to be saved to their instructor's gradebook.

Mc Graw Hill **Higher Education**

T/A Nester: Microbiology, 5E
ISBN-13: 978-0-07-326284-0
ISBN-10: 0-07-326284-6

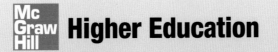

Selected Chapters from

MICROBIOLOGY

A HUMAN PERSPECTIVE

Fifth Edition

Eugene W. Nester
University of Washington

Denise G. Anderson
University of Washington

C. Evans Robert, Jr.
University of Washington

Martha T. Nester

McGraw Hill Custom Publishing

Boston Burr Ridge, IL Dubuque, IA New York San Francisco St. Louis
Bangkok Bogotá Caracas Lisbon London Madrid
Mexico City Milan New Delhi Seoul Singapore Sydney Taipei Toronto

The McGraw·Hill Companies

Selected Chapters from
Microbiology
A Human Perspective, Fifth Edition

3 4 5 6 7 8 9 0 QSR QSR 0 9 8 7 6

ISBN-13: 978-0-07-328367-8
ISBN-10: 0-07-328367-3

Editor: Nicole Young
Production Editor: Lynn Nagel
Printer/Binder: Quebecor World

BRIEF CONTENTS

PART I
LIFE AND DEATH OF MICROORGANISMS

PART II
THE MICROBIAL WORLD

PART III
MICROORGANISMS AND HUMANS

CONTENTS

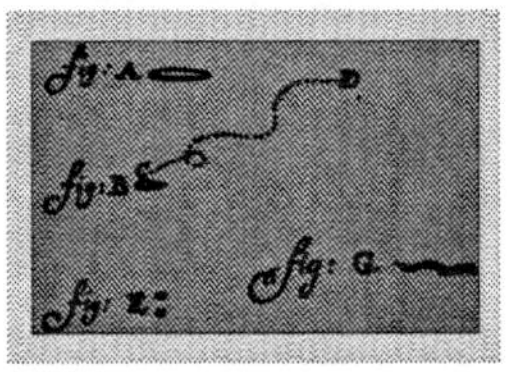

PART I
LIFE AND DEATH OF MICROORGANISMS

CHAPTER ONE
Humans and the Microbial World 1

CHAPTER TWO
The Molecules of Life 19

CHAPTER THREE

Microscopy and Cell Structure 41

CHAPTER FOUR

Dynamics of Prokaryotic Growth 87

CHAPTER FIVE
Control of Microbial Growth 111

CHAPTER SIX
Metabolism: Fueling Cell Growth 131

CHAPTER SEVEN

The Blueprint of Life, from DNA to Protein 167

CHAPTER EIGHT

Bacterial Genetics 191

CHAPTER NINE

Biotechnology and Recombinant DNA 219

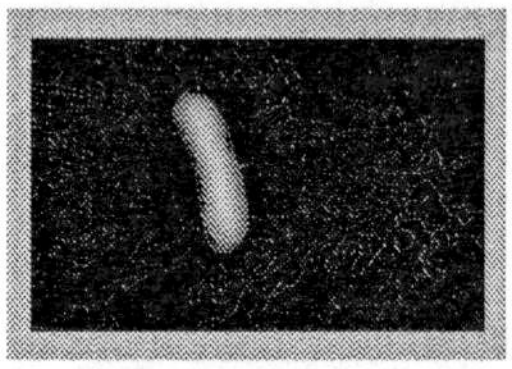

PART II
THE MICROBIAL WORLD

CHAPTER TEN

Identification and Classification of Prokaryotes 245

CHAPTER ELEVEN

The Diversity of Prokaryotic Organisms 265

CHAPTER TWELVE

The Eukaryotic Members of the Microbial World 295

CHAPTER THIRTEEN

Viruses of Bacteria 319

CHAPTER FOURTEEN

Viruses, Prions, and Viroids: Infectious Agents of Animals and Plants 337

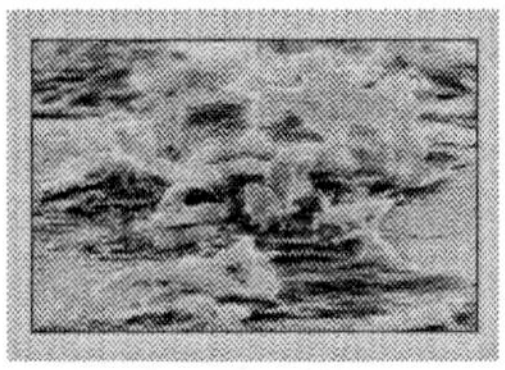

PART III
MICROORGANISMS AND HUMANS

CHAPTER FIFTEEN

The Innate Immune Response 365

CHAPTER SIXTEEN
The Adaptive Immune Response 387

CHAPTER SEVENTEEN
Applications of Immune Responses 413

CHAPTER EIGHTEEN
Immunologic Disorders 433

CHAPTER NINETEEN
Host-Microbe Interactions 451

CHAPTER TWENTY
Epidemiology 475

CHAPTER TWENTY-ONE
Antimicrobial Medications 495

ABOUT THE AUTHORS

Eugene Nester

Eugene (Gene) Nester performed his undergraduate work at Cornell University and received his Ph.D. in Microbiology from Case Western University. He then pursued postdoctoral work in the Department of Genetics at Stanford University with Joshua Lederberg. Since 1962, Gene has been a faculty member in the Department of Microbiology at the University of Washington. Gene's research has focused on gene transfer systems in bacteria. His laboratory demonstrated that *Agrobacterium* transfers DNA into plant cells, the basis for the disease, crown gall. He continues to study this unique system of gene transfer which has become a cornerstone of plant biotechnology.

In 1990, Gene Nester was awarded the inaugural Australia Prize along with an Australian and a German scientist for their work on *Agrobacterium* transformation of plants. In 1991, he was awarded the Cetus Prize in Biotechnology by the American Society of Microbiology. He has been elected to Fellowship in the National Academy of Sciences, the American Academy for the Advancement of Science, the American Academy of Microbiology, and the National Academy of Sciences in India. Throughout his career, Gene has been actively involved with the American Society for Microbiology and currently serves as Chair of the Board of Governors of the American Academy of Microbiology.

In addition to his research activities, Gene has taught an introductory microbiology course for students in the allied health sciences for many years. He wrote the original version of the present text, *Microbiology: Molecules, Microbes and Man,* with C. Evans Roberts and Nancy Pearsall more than 30 years ago because they felt no suitable text was available for this group of students. The original text pioneered the organ system approach to the study of infectious disease.

Gene enjoys traveling, museum hopping, and the study and collecting of Northwest Coast Indian Art. He and his wife, Martha, live on Lake Washington with a seldom used sailboat, but a well-used kayak. Their two children and four grandchildren live in the Seattle area.

Denise Anderson

Denise Anderson is a Senior Lecturer in the Department of Microbiology at the University of Washington, where she teaches a variety of courses including general microbiology, recombinant DNA techniques, medical bacteriology laboratory, and medical mycology/parasitology laboratory. Equipped with a diverse educational background, including undergraduate work in nutrition and graduate work in food science and in microbiology, she first discovered a passion for teaching when she taught microbiology laboratory courses as part of her graduate training. Her enthusiastic teaching style, fueled by regular doses of Seattle's famous caffeine, receives high reviews by her students.

Outside of academic life, Denise relaxes in the Phinney Ridge neighborhood of Seattle, where she lives with her husband, Richard Moore and one dog. When not planning lectures, grading papers, or writing textbook chapters, she can usually be found chatting with the neighbors, fighting the weeds in her garden, or enjoying a fermented beverage at the local pub.

C. Evans Roberts, Jr.

Evans Roberts was a marginally motivated mathematics student at Haverford College when a chance encounter landed him a summer job at the Marine Biological Laboratory in Woods Hole, Massachusetts. There, interaction with leading scientists awakened his interest in biology and medicine. After completing his undergraduate work in mathematics, he studied for his M.D. at Columbia University, completed an internship at the University of Rochester School of Medicine and Dentistry, and held a Residency in Medicine at the University of Washington. Further, he received a fellowship in Infectious Disease with Dr. William M. M. Kirby and fulfilled a traineeship in Diagnostic Microbiology with Dr. John Sherris.

Subsequently, Dr. Roberts has taught microbiology, directed diagnostic microbiology laboratories, worked on hospital infection control committees, and helped in a refugee camp for Karen people in northern Thailand. He has had extensive experience in the practice of medicine as it relates to infectious diseases. He is certified both by the American Board of Microbiology and the American Board of Internal Medicine, and is a member of the American Academy of Family Physicians.

Evans Roberts worked with Gene Nester in the early development of *Microbiology: A Human Perspective.* His professional publications concern susceptibility testing as a guide to treatment of infectious diseases, Whipple's disease, group A streptococcal epidemiology, use of fluorescent antibody in diagnosis, bacteriocin typing, antimicrobial resistance of tuberculosis and gonorrhea, viral encephalitis, and rabies. Dr. Roberts has traveled extensively around the world. For relaxation he enjoys hiking and gardening, especially the cultivation of flowers and exotic tropical fruits.

Martha Nester

Martha Nester received an undergraduate degree in biology from Oberlin College and a Master's degree in education from Stanford University. She has worked in university research laboratories and has taught elementary school. She currently works in an environmental education program at the Seattle Audubon Society. Martha has worked with her husband, Gene, for more than 40 years on microbiology textbook projects, at first informally as an editor and sounding board, and then as one of the authors of *Microbiology: A Human Perspective.* Martha's favorite activities include spending time with their four grandchildren, all of whom live in the Seattle area. She also enjoys playing the cello with a number of musical groups in the Seattle area.

PREFACE

This is an exciting yet challenging time to be teaching and learning about microbiology. With the horrendous events of September 11, 2001, and the subsequent attacks of bioterrorism in the United States, the need to provide accurate and current information about the good and bad microbes seems greater than ever. Almost every day newspaper reports discuss the possibility of another attack using microbial agents or their toxins. Of equal interest, however, are the frequent articles that describe the discovery of microbes in an environment considered impossible to sustain life, the sequencing of another microbial genome, or the death of an individual from a rare infectious disease. Anyone glancing at the front page cannot help but realize the impact that microorganisms have in our daily lives. The announcements of the many scientific advances being made about the microbial world often bring with them vehement arguments related to the science. Are plants that contain genes of microorganisms safe to eat? Is it wise to put antimicrobial agents in soaps and animal feed? What agents of biological warfare might the citizens of the world face? Are we facing another flu pandemic? This book presents what we believe are the most important facts and concepts about the microbial world and the important role its members play in our daily lives. With the information presented, students should be able to form reasoned opinions and discuss intelligently their views on these questions.

An important consideration in revising this textbook is the diverse interests among students who take an introductory microbiology course today. As always, many students take microbiology as a prerequisite for nursing, pharmacy, and dental programs. A suitable textbook must provide a solid foundation in health-related aspects of microbiology, including coverage of medically important bacteria, antimicrobial medications, and immunization. An increasing number of students take microbiology as a step in the pursuit of other fields, including biotechnology, food science, and ecology. For these students, topics such as recombinant DNA technologies, fermentation processes, and microbial diversity are essential. With the search for the source of the anthrax preparation used in the bioterrorism attacks in the United States, the subject of techniques of microbial identification become more relevant. Microbiology is also becoming more popular as an elective for biology students, who are particularly interested in topics that highlight the relevance of microorganisms to shaping the biological world. Because of the wide range of career goals and interests of students, we have made a particular effort to broaden the scope of previous editions, providing a more balanced approach, yet retaining our strength in medical microbiology.

Diversity in the student population is manifested not only in the range of career goals, but also in educational backgrounds. For some, microbiology may be their first college-level science course; for others, microbiology builds on an already strong background in biology and chemistry. To address this broad range of student backgrounds, we have incorporated numerous learning aids that will facilitate review for some advanced students, and will be a tremendous support to those who are seeing this material for the first time.

Preparing a textbook that satisfies such a broad range of needs and interests is a daunting task, but also extremely rewarding. We hope you will find that the approach and structure of this edition presents a modern and balanced view of microbiology in our world, acknowledging the profound and essential impact that microbes have on our lives today and their possible roles in our lives tomorrow.

Features of the Fifth Edition

Completely updated and including the most current topics in microbiology today, *Microbiology: A Human Perspective,* fifth edition, continues to be a classic. It has always been our goal to present sound scientific content that students can understand and rely upon for accuracy and currency, and thereby succeed in their preparation for meaningful careers. We have used constructive comments from numerous microbiology instructors and their students to continue to enhance the robust features of this proven text.

Expert Approach to Writing

We, as a strong and diverse team of scientists and teachers, solidly present the connection between microorganisms and humans. Because of our individual specializations and our research and educational backgrounds, we remain in the hub of the scientific community and can provide accurate and modern coverage spanning the breadth of microbiology. More importantly, as teachers, we constantly strive to present material that easily speaks to the students reading it.

We recognize that a textbook, no matter how exciting the subject matter, is not a novel. Few students will read the text from cover to cover and few instructors will include all of the topics covered in their course. We have used judicious redundancy to help present each major topic as a complete unit. We have avoided the chatty, superficial style of writing in favor of clarity and conciseness. The text is not "watered down" but rather provides students the depth of coverage needed to fully understand and appreciate the role of microorganisms in the biological sciences and human affairs.

> *"The writing style is very clear, precise, and student friendly. For example, the descriptions of innate and adaptive immunity, their roles and how they interact, are the best of their kind that I have encountered in any textbook."* (Kim Burnham, Oklahoma State University)

"I loved the analogies and the simplicity of the writing."
(Kathleen Lauber, College of Southern Maryland)

Instructive Art Program That Speaks a Thousand Words

Microorganisms, by definition, are invisible to the naked eye. It becomes ever more important to allow students to visualize organisms as well as processes to reinforce learning. The art program continues as a key element of the learning process. Each figure in *Microbiology: A Human Perspective* was developed as the narrative was written and is referenced in bold in the supporting text. Colors and symbols are used consistently throughout the text. Legends are short, clear, and descriptive. Various types of art styles are used as needed to bring concepts to life.

Overview Figures simplify complex interactions and provide a sound study tool. **Image Pathways** help students to follow the progression of a discussion over several pages by highlighting and visualizing in detail each step of an overview figure.

Process Figures include step-by-step descriptions and include supporting text so that the figure walks through a compact summary of important concepts.

Combination Figures tie together the features that can be illustrated by an artist with the appearance of organisms in the real world.

Stunning Micrographs used generously throughout the text bring the microbial world to life. In the chapters presenting infectious diseases (chapters 22 to 29), micrographs are often combined with photographs showing the symptoms that the organisms cause.

Unmatched Clinical Coverage

Evans Roberts, Jr.—a member of the author team who is licensed and board certified in internal medicine by the American Board of Internal Medicine, and in public health and medical laboratory microbiology by the American Board of Microbiology—ensures that clinical coverage is accurate, modern, and instructive to those planning to enter health careers. The incomparable treatment of infectious diseases, which are organized by human body systems, is supported with generous photographs, summary tables, case histories, and critical thinking questions. Elements of the unparalleled clinical coverage include:

- Consistent coverage of all diseases, including individual sections that describe the symptoms, pathogenesis, causative agent, epidemiology, prevention, and treatment.
- Disease summaries that feature a drawing of a human showing symptoms, portals of entry and exit, location of pathology, and a step-by-step description of the infection process for each major disease.
- Case presentations of realistic clinical situations.
- Modern coverage of topics such as emerging diseases, new vaccines, and nosocomial infections.
- Dedicated chapters covering wound infections and HIV.

Learning System That Actively Involves Students

In today's classroom, it is important to pursue active learning by students. This edition of *Microbiology* challenges students to think critically by providing several avenues of practice in analyzing data, drawing conclusions, synthesizing information, interpreting graphs, and applying concepts to practical situations. These learning tools, developed by critical thinking expert Robert Allen, will benefit students pursuing any discipline.

What's New in This Edition?

We have added several pedagogical features that should reduce what may seem to be an information overload to some students. First, a list of key terms, with definitions, is provided at the beginning of each chapter. Second, carefully designed questions, termed focus points, target the key concepts of each major section. Knowing the answers to these questions ensures that students have grasped the important concepts in the text that follows. Finally, cartoons relevant to the presented material are interspersed throughout the text in order to lighten up the scientific contents.

All Chapters

- A list of key terms and their definition was added at the beginning of each chapter (the page following the chapter opener).
- Each section now begins with a list of Focus Points (learning objectives).
- Cartoons are scattered throughout the chapters.

Chapter 1

- New figure showing students in 1918 wearing gauze masks to protect themselves against influenza
- Updated figure on emerging diseases
- Eliminated figure showing various bacterial shapes
- Eliminated figure on a microfossil
- Updated story in the Perspective, including new photograph

Chapter 2

- Shortened A Glimpse of History
- All figures have brighter and more contrasting colors.

Chapter 3

- Small photos have been added to the table that describes the different types of microscopes.
- Improved EMs that show typical Gram-positive/Gram-negative cell walls
- New mention that the role of metachromatic granules might be more complex than originally thought; they appear to resemble eukaryotic acidocalcisomes.
- Mitochondria and chloroplasts are now described more completely in separate sections.

- Improved illustrations of eukaryotic cells and organelles

Chapter 4

- The chapter was rearranged to increase the emphasis on biofilms. The section that describes biofilms, "Bacterial Growth in Nature," is now the second section of the chapter. To maintain the flow, the section "Bacterial Growth in Laboratory Conditions" was also moved so that it still follows "Bacterial Growth in Nature."
- New EM that shows a biofilm
- Updated to include the current record-holder for highest temperature growth (121°C)
- Improved photos of a lactose fermenter on MacConkey agar and beta hemolysis on blood agar

Chapter 5

- Updated to include mention of alcohol-based antiseptic hand gels and silver-containing bandages
- The chapter has been reorganized so that the methods of physical control are covered in adjacent sections.
- New table that compares the various physical methods of microbial control
- New section that describes the use of high pressure to pasteurize foods such as guacamole
- New section on methods used by water treatment facilities to control microbial growth in drinking water; mentions amended regulations that require facilities to minimize the level of disinfection by-products and *Cryptosporidium* oocysts
- *Giardia* cysts and *Cryptosporidium* oocysts are now mentioned in the list of microbes that must be considered when selecting a disinfection procedure.
- Composition of the item to be sterilized is now listed in the factors to consider when selecting an appropriate germicidal chemical.
- The figure that shows the electromagnetic spectrum has been revised so that it is now easier to interpret.

Chapter 6

- Photos have been added to the figure that shows fermentation end products.
- Figure that illustrates oxidation-reduction reactions was revised for clarity.

Chapter 7

- Section on genomics has been moved to the end of the chapter.
- The three-dimensional structure of tRNA has been incorporated into the figures that illustrate tRNA and the process of translation.
- The figure that illustrates the replication fork has been revised for increased clarity.

Chapter 8

- Changed the story introducing the chapter from the rise of multiple antibiotic resistance after WWII to the story of the rise of methicillin- and vancomycin-resistant *Staph* today in the United States. The explanation of how *Staph* became resistant is discussed at the end of the chapter.
- Added section on how methylation of DNA is important in DNA repair
- Eliminated the section on conditional lethal mutants
- Added a section on how reactive oxygen damages DNA and how this damaged DNA can be repaired
- The section on conjugation now focuses on the transfer of plasmids and the discussion of chromosome transfer is greatly reduced.
- Barriers to gene transfer was moved to Chapter 13 (bacterial viruses).

Chapter 9

- New figure showing fluorescence *in situ* hybridization (FISH) result
- New figure showing the exponential amplification of the PCR product
- Information about genetic engineering of eukaryotic cells has been moved to the Web.

Chapter 10

- Increased emphasis on classification using rRNA sequences
- Details about numerical taxonomy have been moved to the Web.
- Outline of the 2nd edition of *Bergey's Manual of Systematic Bacteriology* is now included.
- Phylogenetic tree of the bacteria based on 16S rRNA comparisons is now included.
- Increased emphasis on the complications of lateral gene transfer in taxonomy, along with a new diagram that depicts the "shrub of life"
- Expanded the introduction to the section that describes methods used to characterize strain differences, pointing out the role these play in tracing sources of foodborne illnesses as well as forensic investigations of biocrimes. Decreased the detail about the specific methods.

Chapter 11

- The summary table now lists the phylum of each organism, in order to emphasize the phylogeny of the various prokaryotes described.
- A new section on the recently discovered *Nanoarchaea* has been added.

Chapter 12

- New A Glimpse of History, about the effect of the late blight of potatoes especially on the history of the United States
- New Perspective, about phytoplankton and global warming
- New Future Challenges, about developing malaria vaccines and new drugs

Chapter 13

- Eliminated tail fibers on phage lambda
- Corrected Figure 13.11
- Eliminated Figure 13.13 (restriction-modification of DNA)

Chapter 14

- Changed A Glimpse of History from the role of viruses in animal tumors to discovery of prions
- Moved the section on "Methods Used to Study Viruses" to end of chapter
- Eliminated Table 14.5 (relationship of virus size to dependency on host cell enzymes)
- Eliminated section on viruses and animal tumors
- Eliminated section on phenotypic mixing and the two correlating figures
- Expanded the discussion on prions

Chapter 15

- Moved the information on interferons into the section, "Sensor Systems"
- Rearranged the section on activation of the complement system so that the alternative pathway, which comes into play first and provides an essential "early warning system," is described first
- Added NOD receptors to the section, "Sensor Systems"

Chapter 16

- Updated and simplified information on T_H cells
- Moved the section on T-cell activation; it now precedes the section that describes the roles of T cells.
- Revised general overview photo so that it now includes T-cell activation
- New table that summarizes the characteristics of cytotoxic T cells and helper T cells
- Revised detailed overview figure that is now larger and more engaging

Chapter 17

- Extensive revision of the section on immunological testing:
  - Some of the less common but historically important tests have been moved to the Web (such as complement fixation), increasing emphasis on the more routine tests such as ELISA and Western blotting.
  - The section is now divided into three general parts—Principles of Immunological Testing, Observing Antigen-Antibody Aggregations, and Using Labeled Antibodies to Detect Antigen-Antibody Interactions.
- Section on obtaining antibodies (for immunoassays) has been added to the section, "Principles of Immunological Testing"
- New figure that illustrates how immunoassays can be used to either identify an unknown antigen (using antibodies of known specificity) or identify specific antibodies in a patient's serum (using known antigen)
- New photo showing latex agglutination results
- Photo of an Ouchterlony test is now included; the line drawing has been revised to correlate to the photo.
- New simplified line drawing of the radial immunodiffusion test
- Improved photo showing Western blotting results

Chapter 18

- New chapter opener showing asthmatic
- Added role of regulatory T cells
- Expanded and updated type 1 diabetes
- Added section on Graves' disease
- Added leukocyte adhesion deficiency
- Added effect of feeding parasitic worms
- Revised figures 18.1, 18.3, 18.4, 18.5, and 18.7
- New photo of tuberculin test

Chapter 19

- Updated figure of a type III secretion system
- Simplified line drawing showing the role of Fc receptors in pathogenesis

Chapter 20

- New figure shows the decline in infectious diseases in the 20th century (CDC figure).

Chapter 21

- Added information about daptomycin
- Added information about echinocandins

Chapter 22

- Added section on cutaneous leishmaniasis
- Pediculosis and scabies cross-referenced
- Added importance of *P. acnes* sequencing
- Updated and clarified varicella
- Updated measles vaccination
- Added monograph on smallpox to OLC
- Revised figures 22.1, 22.3, 22.7, 22.10, 22.12, 22.14, and 22.16

Chapter 23

- Wound infections chapter moved next to skin infections chapter
- Replaced chapter opener with wound photo
- Updated vancomycin-resistant *Staphylococcus aureus*
- Updated invasive *Streptococcus pyogenes*
- Added *Pseudomonas aeruginosa* infections from ear piercing
- Updated neonatal tetanus
- Revised rat bite fever
- Updated *S. aureus,* Future Challenges
- Revised figures 23.1, 23.9, 23.10, and 23.15

Chapter 24

- New chapter opener showing strep throat
- Cross-referenced necrotizing fasciitis
- Added streptolysin and streptokinase importance
- Added importance of *S. pyogenes* genome sequencing
- Added *Moraxella* as cause of otitis media

- Added small effect of *H. influenzae* and *S. pneumoniae* vaccination on otitis media
- Updated pathogenesis of adenoviral infection
- Added mode of action of pneumolysin
- Updated anthrax by mail episode
- Added monograph on anthrax for OLC
- Updated pertussis in adults and increasing incidence
- Updated new pertussis vaccine
- Added worldwide importance of tuberculosis
- Updated tuberculosis pathogenesis and treatment
- Updated *Legionella* epidemiology, pathogenesis, and genomic studies
- Updated influenza virus cell entry
- Updated avian influenza
- Updated prevention of hantavirus infection
- Added section on SARS
- Revision of figure 24.3 (streptococcal surface antigens)
- New figure, a photo of pinkeye
- Revised figures 24.16, 24.17, 24.21, 24.22, and 24.23

Chapter 25

- New chapter opener: individual with jaundice
- Added cross-reference to pork tapeworm; refer to OLC for other helminths
- Updated norovirus name, symptoms, epidemiology
- Added green onion epidemic of hepatitis A
- Updated treatment of hepatitis B
- Added to *Giardia*: mitochondrial remnants, cysts infectious upon passage
- Replaced figure 25.3 (dental plaque)
- Updated map of hepatitis A, and incidence curves of hepatitis viruses

Chapter 26

- Updated pathogenesis of urinary tract infection
- Added photo of gonococcal urethritis
- Added description of Tuskegee experiment
- Added HPV vaccine in prevention of cervical cancer
- Revised figures 26.2, 26.7, and 26.21
- New photo of clue cell

Chapter 27

- Updated West Nile virus
- New Perspective (a rabies survivor)
- Updated poliomyelitis eradication
- New photo showing *C. botulinum* spores
- New map, West Nile infections in the United States
- New photo (animal with scrapie)

Chapter 28

- Updated arteriosclerosis and *Chlamydia pneumoniae*
- Added *T. whippelii* cultivation
- Updated clinical use of TNF inhibitors
- Inhalation tularemia symptoms, therapy, in Europe, and as a bioweapon
- *Brucella* as a bioweapon
- Updated treatment of plague
- ARIS, leishmaniasis
- Updated malaria prevention and treatment
- New photograph of individual with tularemia
- Updated map of yellow fever
- Updated map of malaria

Chapter 29

- Updated global AIDS distribution
- Updated cost of AIDS medications to the poor
- Updated failure of prime-boost AIDS vaccine
- Revised figures 29.5 and 29.6
- Revised figure (AIDS deaths in the United States)
- Revised figure 29.11 (mode of action of AZT)

Chapter 30

- New photo showing endo- and ectomycorrhizae

Chapter 31

- New figure that summarizes the steps of municipal wastewater treatment
- New photo showing municipal composting

Teaching Supplements

Digital Content Manager CD-ROM

This cross-platform CD-ROM is a multimedia collection of visual resources that allows instructors to utilize artwork from the text in multiple formats and create customized classroom presentations, visually based tests and quizzes, dynamic course website content, or attractive printed support material. The assets on this CD-ROM are organized by chapter within the following easy to use folders:

Art Library Full-color digital files of all the illustrations in the book, plus the same art saved in black and white versions, can be readily incorporated into lecture presentations, exams, or custom-made classroom materials. These images are also pre-inserted into blank PowerPoint slides for ease of use.

Photo Library Digital files of most of the photographs from the text can be reproduced for multiple classroom uses.

Table Library Every table that appears in the text is provided in digital form.

PowerPoint Lecture Outline Library Ready-made presentations that combine art and lecture notes are provided for each of the 32 chapters of the text. These lecture outlines can be used as they are, or can be tailored to reflect preferred lecture topics and sequences.

Animation Library More than 50 full-color animations are available to harness the visual impact of processes in motion. Import these dynamic files into classroom presentations or online course materials.

TextEdit Art Library Every illustration from the textbook is provided in PowerPoint. Instructors may revise, move, or delete labels to create customized presentations and exams.

Video Library 36 dynamic motion sequences have been produced to bring microorganisms to life for students.

ARIS™

ARIS (www.mhhe.com/nester5) ARIS is a complete, online tutorial, electronic homework, and course management system, designed for greater ease of use than any other system available. Free on adoption of any McGraw-Hill microbiology text, instructors can create and share course materials and assignments with colleagues with a few clicks of the mouse. All PowerPoint lectures, assignments, and quizzes are directly tied to text-specific materials in *Nester/Microbiology, 5/e,* but instructors can also edit questions, import their own content, and create announcements and due dates for assignments. ARIS has automatic grading and reporting of easy-to-assign homework, quizzing, and testing. All student activity within McGraw-Hill's ARIS is automatically recorded and available to the instructor through a fully integrated grade book that can be downloaded to Excel.

Instructor's Testing and Resource CD-ROM This cross-platform CD-ROM provides a wealth of resources for the instructor. Supplement features on this CD-ROM include a computerized test bank, utilizing testing software, to quickly create customized exams. This user-friendly program allows you to search for questions by topic, format, or difficulty level; edit existing questions or add new ones; and scramble questions and answers keys for multiple versions of the same test. Word files of the test bank are included for instructors who prefer to work outside of the test-generator software.

Other assets on the Instructor's Testing and Resource CD-ROM are grouped within easy-to-use folders. These resources include the Instructor's Manual and the Laboratory Preparator's Manual.

Instructor's Manual This valuable resource includes Learning Objectives keyed to the Student Study Guide, correlations to the multimedia resources available with the text, and answers to questions in the text.

Transparencies A set of 300 images from the textbook is provided for classroom projection.

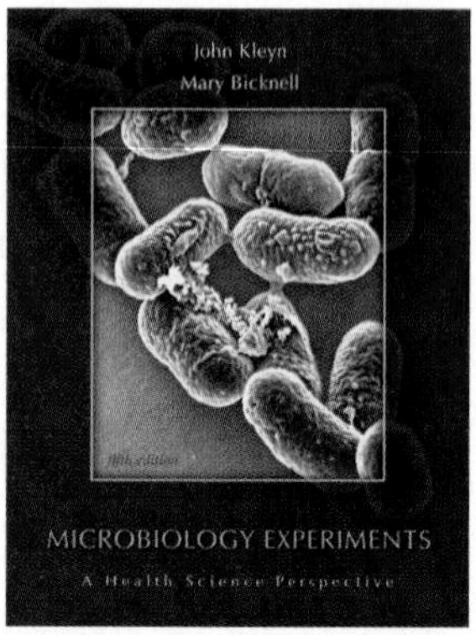

Laboratory Manual The fifth edition of *Microbiology Experiments: A Health Science Perspective,* by the late John Kleyn and Mary Bicknell, has been prepared to directly support the text (although it may also be used with other microbiology textbooks). The laboratory manual features health-oriented experiments and endeavors also to reflect the goals and safety regulation guidelines of the American Society for Microbiology. Engaging student projects introduce some more intriguing members of the microbial world and expand the breadth of the manual beyond health-related topics. Newer experiments introduce modern techniques in biotechnology such as use of restriction enzymes and use of a computer database to identify sequence information.

Preparator's Manual for the Laboratory Manual This invaluable guide includes answers to exercises, tips for successful experiments, lists of microbial cultures with sources and storage information, formulae and sources for stains and reagents, directions and recipes for preparing culture media, and sources of supplies. The Preparator's Manual is available to instructors through ARIS.

PageOut McGraw-Hill's exclusive tool for creating your own website for your Microbiology course. It requires no knowledge of coding and is hosted by McGraw-Hill.

Learning Supplements

ARIS www.mhhe.com/nester5 Student resources on ARIS support each chapter in the text. Some of the features include:

- Self-quizzing with immediate feedback
- Animations of key processes with self-quizzing
- Electronic flash cards to review key vocabulary
- Additional clinical case presentations
- Web exercises encouraging practice of use of the Web to gather and evaluate information

Microbes in Motion CD-ROM This interactive CD-ROM for both Windows and Mac brings microbiology to life through interactive video, audio, animations, and hyperlinking. This easy-to-use tutorial can go from the classroom to the resource center to the student's own personal computer. Ideal for self-quizzing, class preparation, or review of microbiological concepts.

Hyperclinic CD-ROM Students will have fun with this interactive CD-ROM while learning valuable concepts and gaining practical experience in clinical microbiology. Packed with over 100 case studies and over 200 pathogens supported with audio, video, and interactive screens, students will gain confidence as they take on the role of the professionals.

Student Study Guide This valuable student resource goes beyond the standard multiple choice and true-false self-quizzing. The authors have provided a wealth of study assets to help students truly master the material. In addition to unique learning activities, it includes key concepts, vocabulary review, self-tests, and more.

Reviewers of the Fifth Edition

Gene Nester, Evans Roberts, and Nancy Pearsall shared a vision many years ago to write a new breed of microbiology textbook especially for students planning to enter nursing and other health-related careers. Today there are other books of this type, but we were extremely gratified to learn that 85% of the students we surveyed intend to keep their copies of *Microbiology: A Human Perspective* because they feel it will benefit them greatly as they pursue their studies in these fields. We offer special thanks to the many students who used the fourth edition of *Microbiology: A Human Perspective* and who shared their thoughts with us about how to improve the presentation for the students who will use this edition of the text.

Rao Ayyagari's students at Lindenwood University

David Hurley's students at South Dakota State University

Steve Larsen's students at Indiana University–Purdue University at Indianapolis

Ellen Neidle's students at the University of Georgia

Jennifer Walker's students at the University of Georgia

We offer our sincere appreciation to the many gracious and expert professionals who helped us with this revision by offering helpful suggestions. In addition to thanking those individuals listed here who carefully reviewed revised chapters, we also thank those who responded to our informal surveys, those who participated in regional focus groups, and those participants who chose not to be identified. All of you have contributed significantly to this work and we thank you.

Karen L. Anderson, *Madison Area Technical College*
Lois C. Anderson, *Minnesota State University, Mankato*
Martha K. Bates, *Chattanooga State Technical Community College*
Barbara Beck, *Rochester Community and Technical College*
Benjie Blair, *Jacksonville State University*
Edward Braun, *Iowa State University*
Kathryn H. Brooks, *Michigan State University*
Alfred Brown, *Auburn University*
Katherine D. Buhrer, *Tidewater Community College*
Kim Burnham, *Victoria University*
Suzanne K. Butler, *Miami-Dade College*
Thomas R. Danford, *West Virginia Northern Community College*
Janet M. Decker, *University of Arizona*
Charles J. Dick, *Pasco-Hernando Community College*
Bob F. Drake, *Southwest Tennessee Community College*
Angela M. Edwards, *Trident Technical College*
Melissa J. Elliott, *Butler Community College*
Jeff S. Erikson, *Messiah College*
Teresa G. Fischer, *Indian River Community College*
Daniel C. Flynn, *West Virginia University*
Katherine Foreman, *Moraine Valley Community College*
S. Marvin Friedman, *Hunter College of CUNY*
Kathy Germain, *Southwest Tennessee Community College*
Ray Green, *Mercer University*
Michael T. Griffin, *Angelo State University*
Judy Haber, *California State University–Fresno*
Janelle M. Hare, *Morehead State University*
Margaret F. Hicks, *Pellissippi State Technical Community College*
Helmut Hirt, *Kansas State University*
James H. Holda, *University of Akron*
Robert D. Hunter, *Trident Technical College*
Ahmad Kamal, *Olive Harvey College*
Judith Marie Krey, *Waubunsee Community College*
Dawn Janich, *Community College of Philadephia*
H. Bruce Joetston, *Fresno City College*
Karen Kendal-Fite, *Columbia State Community College*
Lee H. Lee, *Montclair State University*
Jeff G. Leid, *Northern Arizona University*
Leslie Lichtenstein, *Massasoit Community College*
Roger Lightner, *University of Arkansas at Fort Smith*
David Lipson, *San Diego State University*
William Lorowitz, *Weber State University*
Thomas J. Lynch, *University of Arkansas, Little Rock*
Barry Margulies, *Towson University*
Elizabeth F. McPherson, *University of Tennessee, Knoxville*
Pamela Moolenaar-Wirsiy, *Georgia Perimeter College*
Karen Grandel Nakaoka, *Weber State University*
Murad M. Odeh, *South Texas Community College*
Clark L. Ovrebo, *University of Central Oklahoma*
Gregory E. Paquette, *University of Rhode Island*
Marcia Pierce, *Eastern Kentucky University*
Nirmala Prabhu, *Edison College*
R. Prade, *Oklahoma State University*
Davis W. Pritchett, *University of Louisiana at Monroe*
Kathy Romero, *Greenville Technical College*
Todd Sandrin, *University of Wisconsin–Oshkosh*
David J. Schwartz, *Houston Community College, SW*
Timothy E. Scott, *Minnesota State University, Mankato*
Teri Shors, *University of Wisconsin–Oshkosh*
Timothy A. Steele, *Des Moines University*
Luis Rodriquez, *San Antonio College*
Musau WaKabongo, *Des Moines University*
Valerie Watson, West Virginia University
Carola Wright, Mt. San Antonio College

Acknowledgments

We thank our colleagues in the Department of Microbiology at the University of Washington who have lent their support of this project over many years. Our special thanks go to: John Leigh for advice on the coverage of microbial diversity, Mary Bicknell, Mark Chandler, Kendall Gray, Jimmie Lara, Sharon Schultz, and James Staley for their general suggestions and encouragement.

Thanks also to David Hurley for serving as the "guardian" during the development of the substantially revised immunology chapters. He was instrumental in navigating the murky waters as we updated the coverage of innate and adaptive immunity.

We would also like to thank Denise's husband, Richard Moore, who was "forced" to proofread and critique many of the chapters. Although he has no formal scientific education, or perhaps because of that fact, his suggestions have been instrumental in making the text more "reader-friendly." Much to his own surprise, Richard has learned enough about the fundamentals of microbiology, and more recently immunology, to actually become intrigued with the subject.

Additionally, we would like to thank Joseph Gauthier, Elizabeth McPherson, and Donald Rubbelke for producing new media resources to support us and other instructors who lecture from our text.

We hope very much that this text will be interesting, educational for students, a help to their instructors, and will convey the excitement that we all feel for the subject. We would appreciate any comments and suggestions from our readers.

Eugene Nester
Denise Anderson
C. Evans Roberts, Jr.
Martha Nester

Instructive Artwork Makes the Difference

A picture is worth a thousand words—especially when learning microbiology. *Microbiology: A Human Perspective* employs a combination of art styles to bring concepts to life and to provide concrete, visual reinforcement of the topics discussed throughout the text.

Overview Figures

Overview figures simplify complex interactions and provide a sound study tool.

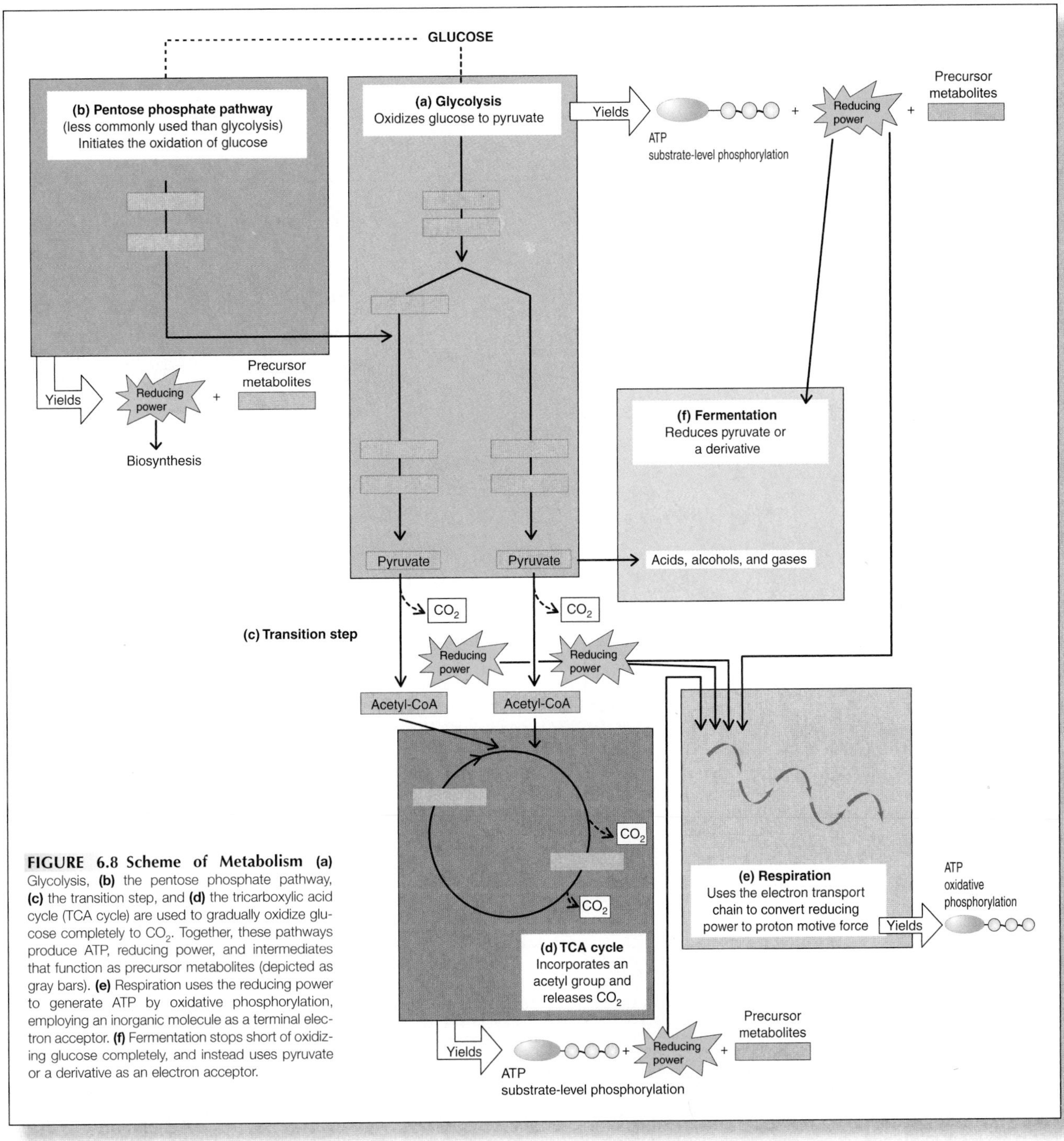

FIGURE 6.8 Scheme of Metabolism **(a)** Glycolysis, **(b)** the pentose phosphate pathway, **(c)** the transition step, and **(d)** the tricarboxylic acid cycle (TCA cycle) are used to gradually oxidize glucose completely to CO_2. Together, these pathways produce ATP, reducing power, and intermediates that function as precursor metabolites (depicted as gray bars). **(e)** Respiration uses the reducing power to generate ATP by oxidative phosphorylation, employing an inorganic molecule as a terminal electron acceptor. **(f)** Fermentation stops short of oxidizing glucose completely, and instead uses pyruvate or a derivative as an electron acceptor.

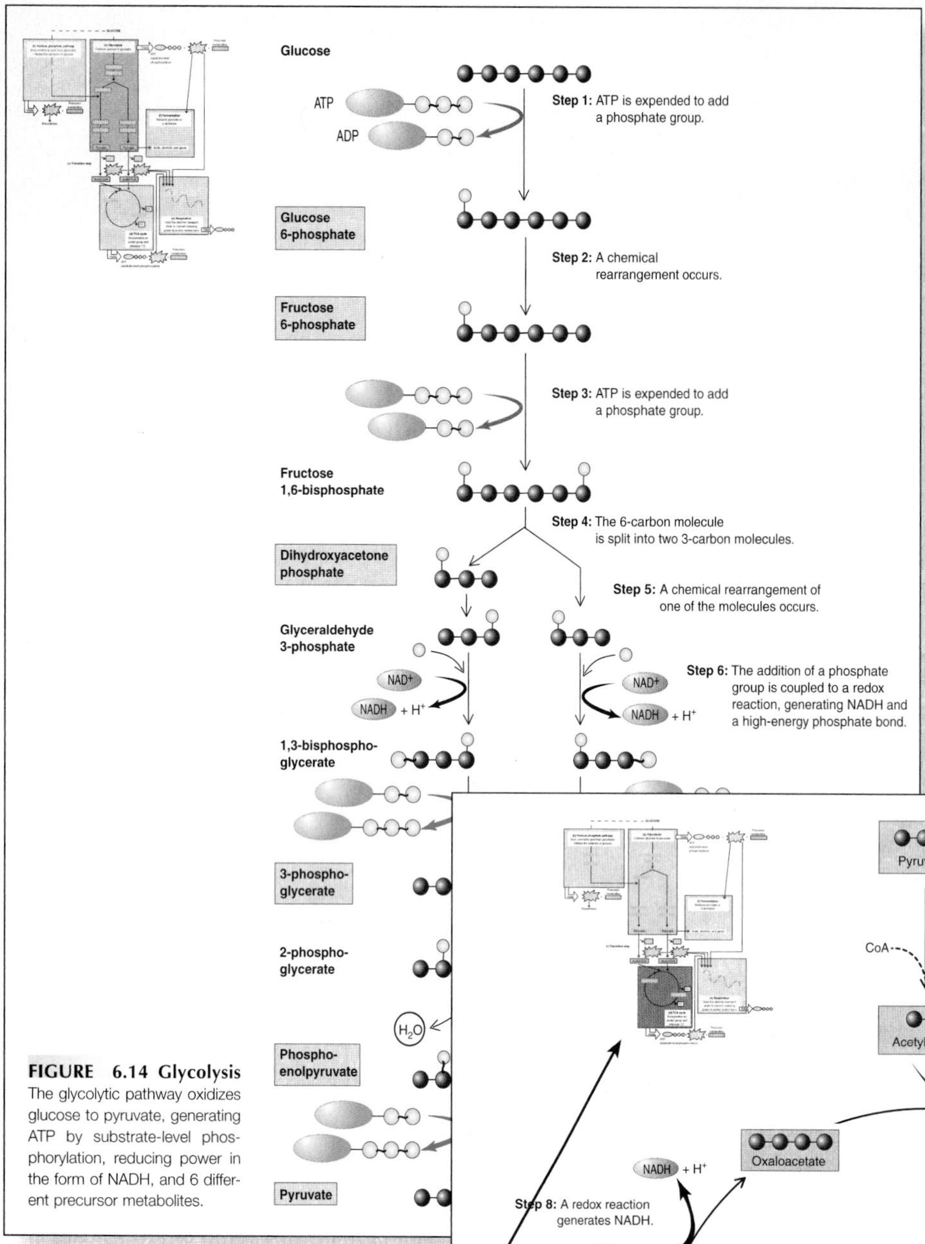
Glucose
ATP
ADP
Step 1: ATP is expended to add a phosphate group.
Glucose 6-phosphate
Step 2: A chemical rearrangement occurs.
Fructose 6-phosphate
Step 3: ATP is expended to add a phosphate group.
Fructose 1,6-bisphosphate
Step 4: The 6-carbon molecule is split into two 3-carbon molecules.
Dihydroxyacetone phosphate
Step 5: A chemical rearrangement of one of the molecules occurs.
Glyceraldehyde 3-phosphate
NAD+
NADH + H+
NAD+
NADH + H+
Step 6: The addition of a phosphate group is coupled to a redox reaction, generating NADH and a high-energy phosphate bond.
1,3-bisphospho-glycerate
3-phospho-glycerate
2-phospho-glycerate
H_2O
Phospho-enolpyruvate
Pyruvate

FIGURE 6.14 Glycolysis The glycolytic pathway oxidizes glucose to pyruvate, generating ATP by substrate-level phosphorylation, reducing power in the form of NADH, and 6 different precursor metabolites.

Image Pathways

Image pathways help students follow the progression of a discussion over several pages by highlighting and visualizing each step of an overview figure.

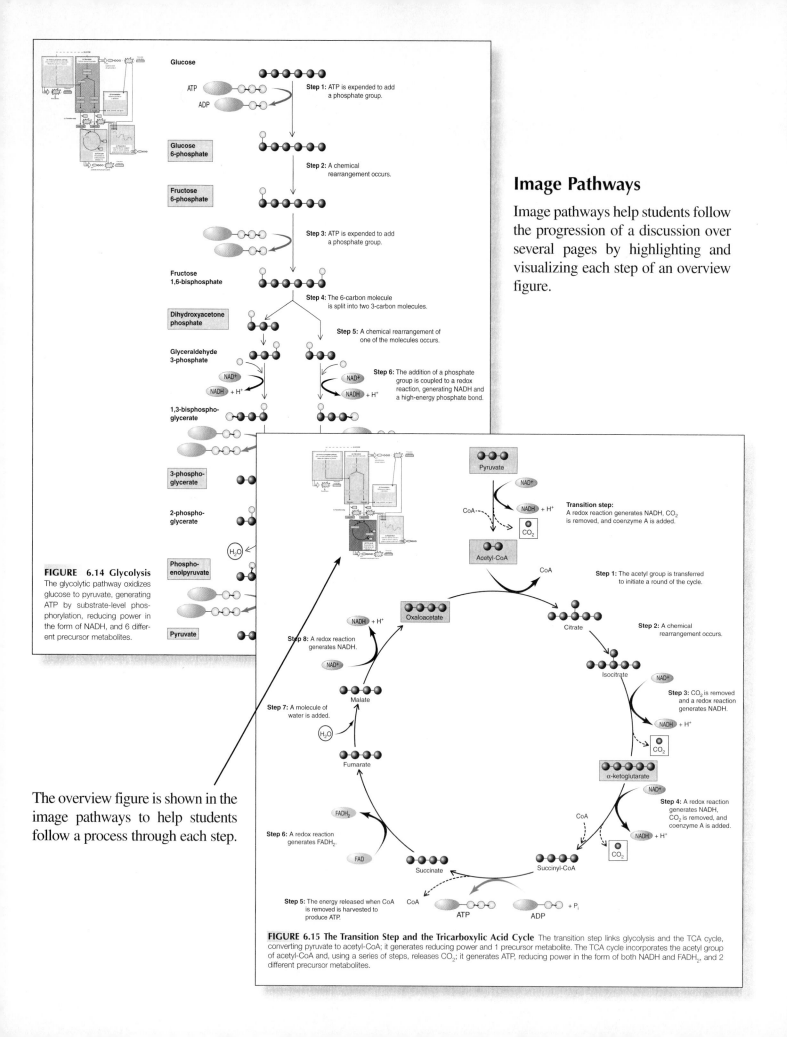

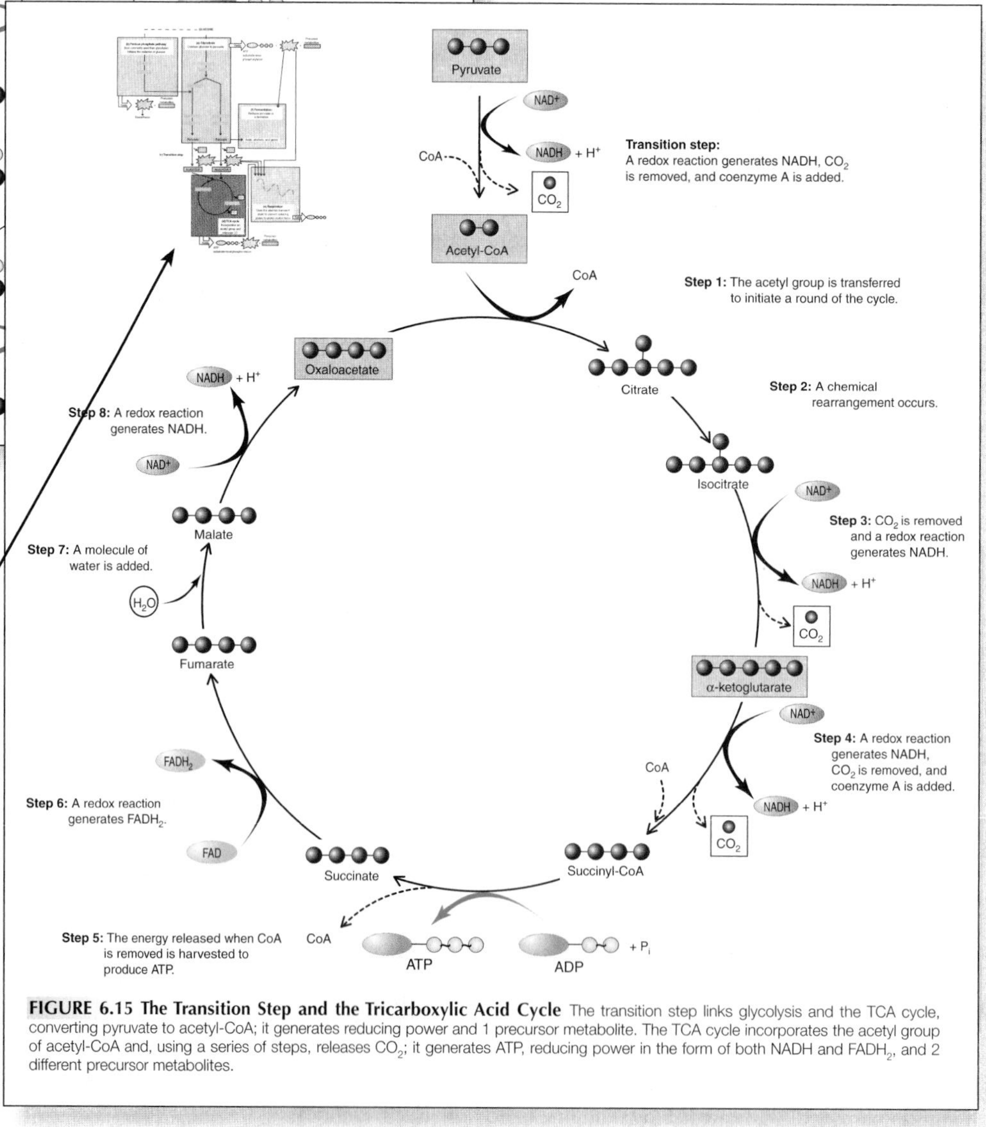
Pyruvate
NAD+
NADH + H+
CoA
CO_2
Transition step: A redox reaction generates NADH, CO_2 is removed, and coenzyme A is added.
Acetyl-CoA
CoA
Step 1: The acetyl group is transferred to initiate a round of the cycle.
Oxaloacetate
Citrate
Step 2: A chemical rearrangement occurs.
Isocitrate
NAD+
Step 3: CO_2 is removed and a redox reaction generates NADH.
NADH + H+
CO_2
α-ketoglutarate
NAD+
Step 4: A redox reaction generates NADH, CO_2 is removed, and coenzyme A is added.
CoA
NADH + H+
CO_2
Succinyl-CoA
Succinate
Step 5: The energy released when CoA is removed is harvested to produce ATP.
CoA
ATP
ADP
+ P_i
FAD
$FADH_2$
Step 6: A redox reaction generates $FADH_2$.
Fumarate
H_2O
Step 7: A molecule of water is added.
Malate
NAD+
NADH + H+
Step 8: A redox reaction generates NADH.

FIGURE 6.15 The Transition Step and the Tricarboxylic Acid Cycle The transition step links glycolysis and the TCA cycle, converting pyruvate to acetyl-CoA; it generates reducing power and 1 precursor metabolite. The TCA cycle incorporates the acetyl group of acetyl-CoA and, using a series of steps, releases CO_2; it generates ATP, reducing power in the form of both NADH and $FADH_2$, and 2 different precursor metabolites.

The overview figure is shown in the image pathways to help students follow a process through each step.

Process Figures

Process figures include step-by-step descriptions to walk the student through a compact summary of important concepts.

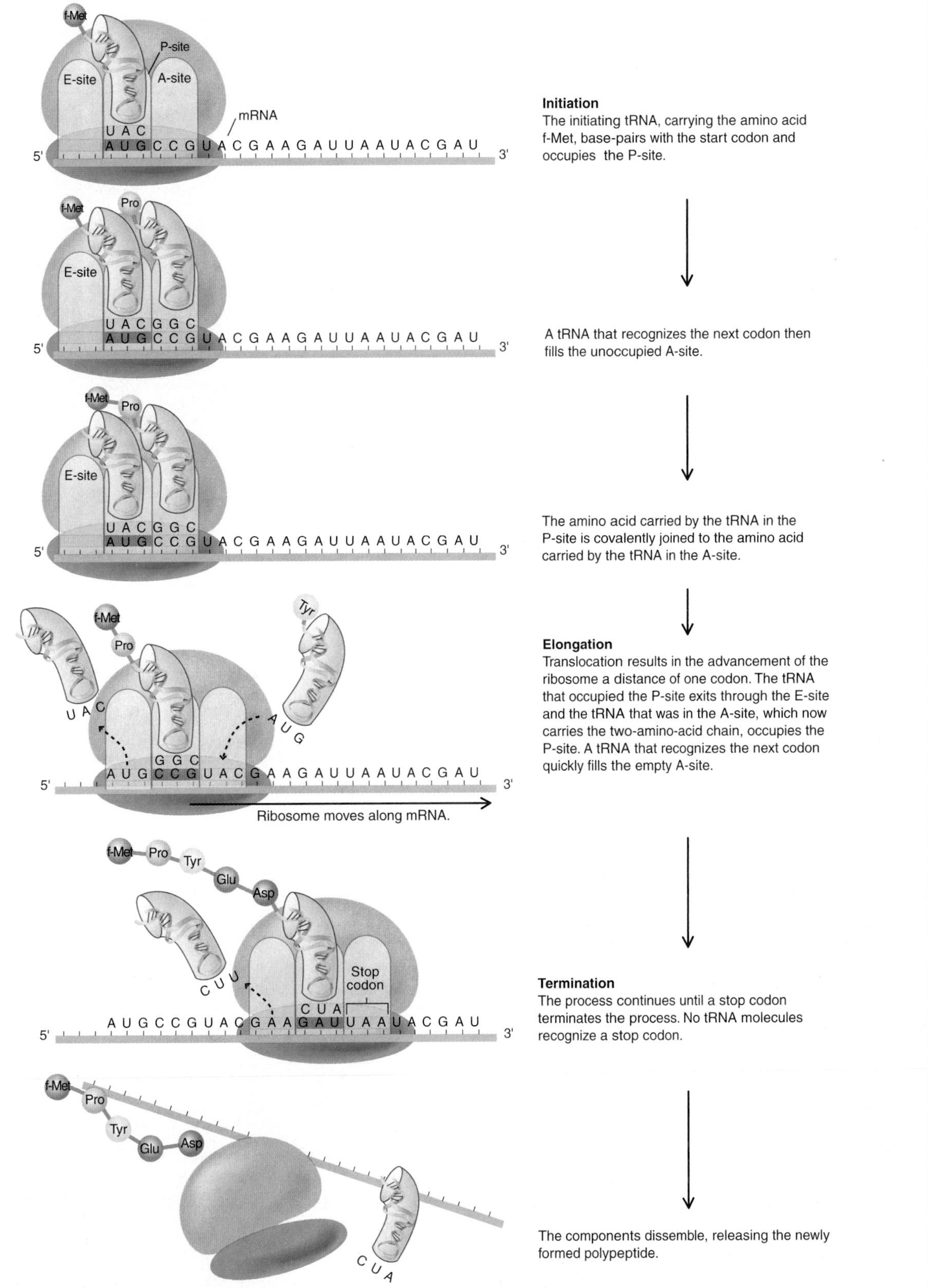
f-Met
P-site
E-site
A-site
mRNA
U A C
A U G C C G U A C G A A G A U U A A U A C G A U
5'
3'
Initiation
The initiating tRNA, carrying the amino acid f-Met, base-pairs with the start codon and occupies the P-site.
Pro
U A C G G C
A tRNA that recognizes the next codon then fills the unoccupied A-site.
The amino acid carried by the tRNA in the P-site is covalently joined to the amino acid carried by the tRNA in the A-site.
Tyr
Elongation
Translocation results in the advancement of the ribosome a distance of one codon. The tRNA that occupied the P-site exits through the E-site and the tRNA that was in the A-site, which now carries the two-amino-acid chain, occupies the P-site. A tRNA that recognizes the next codon quickly fills the empty A-site.
Ribosome moves along mRNA.
Glu
Asp
Stop codon
C U A
Termination
The process continues until a stop codon terminates the process. No tRNA molecules recognize a stop codon.
The components dissemble, releasing the newly formed polypeptide.

FIGURE 7.15 The Process of Translation For simplicity, this diagram shows a polypeptide only five amino acids long being synthesized. Note, however, that most polypeptides are over 100 amino acids long.

Combination Figures

Combination figures tie together the features that can be illustrated by an artist with the appearance of organisms in the real world.

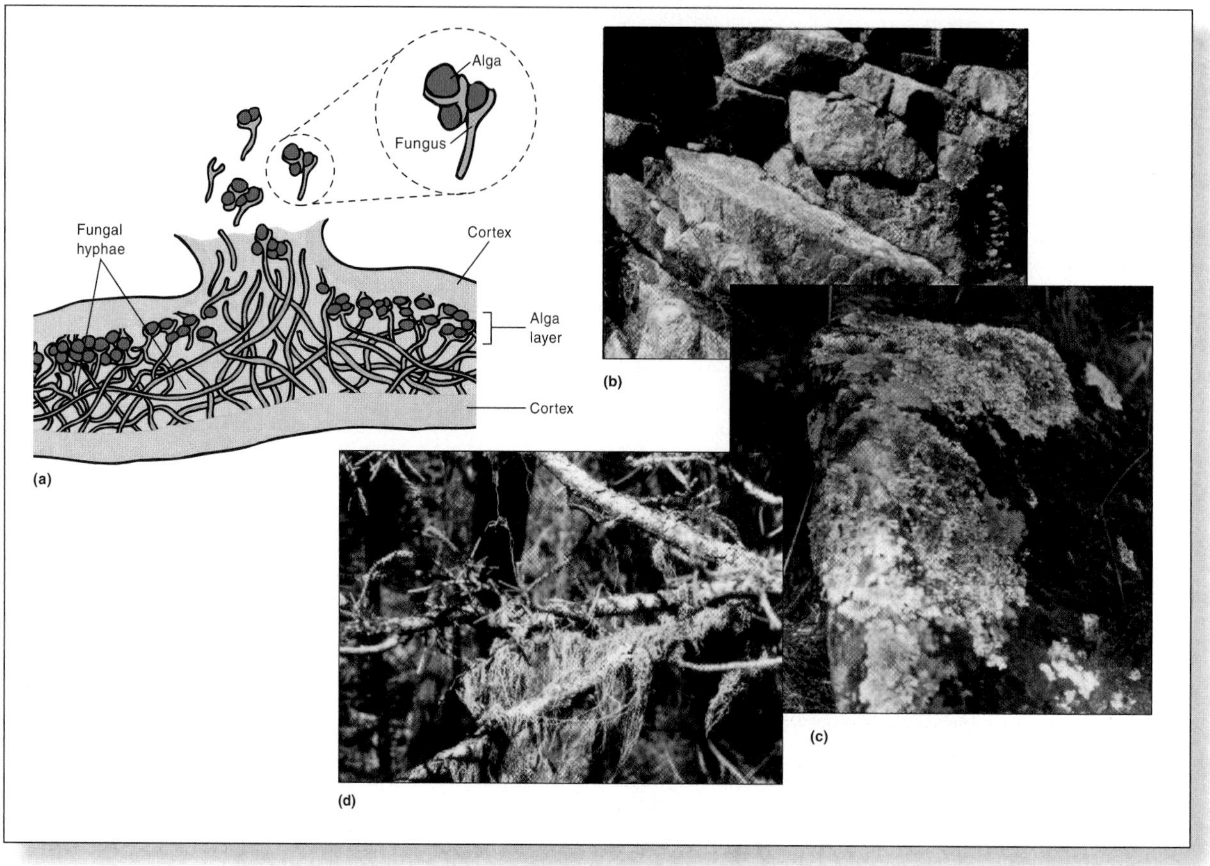

Micrographs

Stunning micrographs used generously throughout the text bring the microbial world to life.

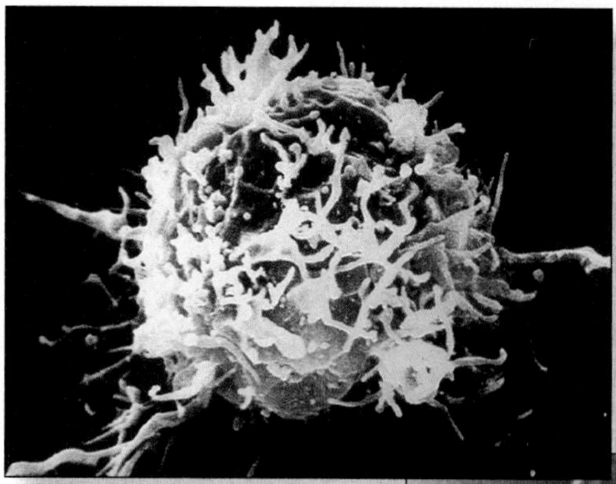

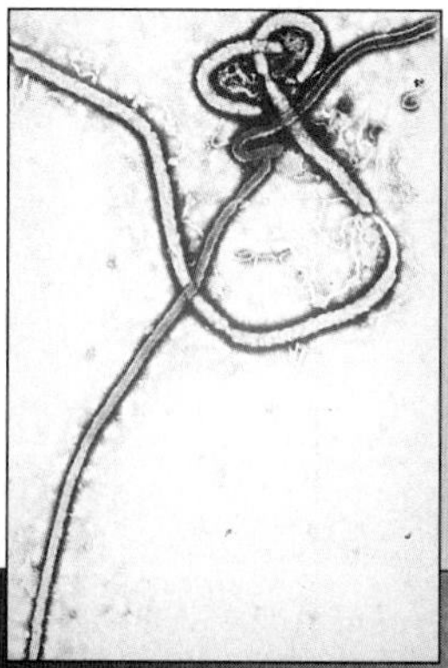

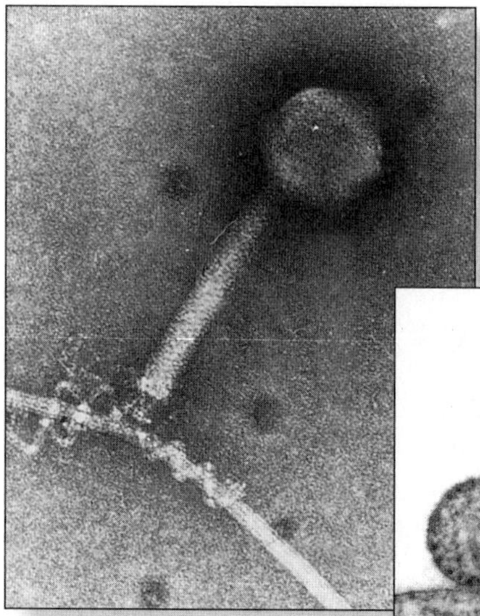

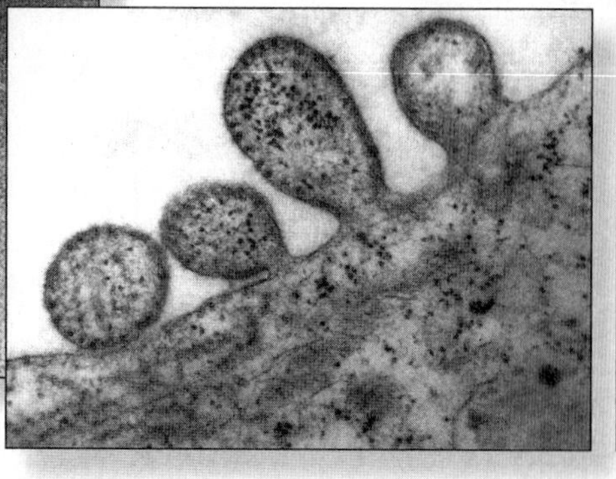

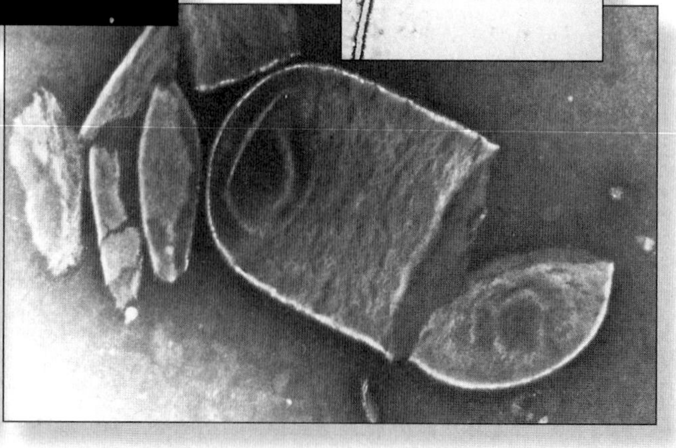

Unmatched Clinical Coverage

Organized by human body systems, the infectious disease chapters (Chapters 22-29) are highlighted with yellow shading in the top corner of the page for easy reference. Additional case presentations and clinical reference material are available through ARIS **(www.mhhe.com/nester5).**

Fungi very rarely invade the central nervous system of healthy people, but patients with cancer, diabetes, and AIDS, as well as those receiving immunosuppressive medications, risk serious disease. Common fungi from the soil and decaying vegetation sometimes infect the nose and sinuses of these patients; from there, they penetrate to the brain and cause the patient's death. These infections are dangerous because they are difficult to treat with antimicrobial medication. Cryptococcal meningoencephalitis differs somewhat from this general pattern, since about half the cases occur in apparently normal people, and many cases are cured by medication.

Cryptococcal Meningoencephalitis

Cryptococcal meningoencephalitis was an uncommon disease until the onset of the AIDS epidemic. Now 2 to 4 cases occur among every 1,000 AIDS patients, as opposed to 0.2 to 0.9 cases per 100,000 in the general population. The disease is among the top four life-threatening infectious complications in AIDS.

Symptoms

In apparently healthy people, symptoms of cryptococcal meningoencephalitis develop very gradually in most cases and generally consist of difficulty in thinking, dizziness, intermittent headache, and slight or no fever. After weeks or months of slow progression of these symptoms, vomiting, weight loss, paralysis, seizures, and coma may appear. In people with immunodeficiency, the disease generally progresses much faster; without treatment, death can occur in as little as 2 weeks.

Causative Agent

Cryptococcal meningoencephalitis is an infection of the meninges and brain by the encapsulated yeast form of *Filobasidiella neoformans,* a fungus previously placed in the genus *Cryptococcus.* In 1975, however, discovery of a sexual form was reported, showing that the fungus was closely related to a group of basidiomycetes pathogenic for plants. Due to this discovery, the organism was renamed *F. neoformans,* but the earlier genus name is still generally used. As can be seen in infected material from patients, the organism is a small, spherical yeast generally 3 to 7 μm in diameter surrounded by a large capsule **(figure 27.20).** ■ basidiomycetes, p. 304

Pathogenesis

The *C. neoformans* fungus becomes airborne with dust, enters the body by inhalation, and establishes an infection first in the lung. This infection causes mild or no symptoms in most people and is usually eliminated by body defenses, chiefly lung phagocytes. Phagocytic killing of *C. neoformans* is slow and inefficient in immunocompromised individuals, however. In some cases, the organisms continue to multiply, enter the blood-stream, and are then distributed throughout the body. The capsule is essential to pathogenicity, since non-encapsulated strains do not cause disease. Capsular material inhibits phagocytosis and migration of leukocytes. It also diffuses from the organism and neutralizes opsonins. Progressive infection and dissemination are much more likely to occur when a person's cell-mediated immunity is impaired, particularly in AIDS and certain cancers. Macrophage activation by immune lymphocytes, lacking in many immunodeficiencies, is essential for rapid phagocytic killing of *C. neoformans.* Meningoencephalitis is the most common infection outside of the lung, but organisms spread by the bloodstream can also infect skin, bones, or other body tissues. In meningoencephalitis, the organisms typically cause thickening of the meninges, sometimes impeding the flow of cerebrospinal fluid, thereby increasing the pressure within the brain. They also invade the brain tissue, producing multiple abscesses. ■ opsonins, pp. 376, 394

Epidemiology

Cryptococcus neoformans is distributed worldwide in soil and vegetation but is especially numerous in soil where pigeon droppings accumulate. Infection is contracted by inhaling contaminated dust. For every case of cryptococcal meningoencephalitis, millions of people are infected by the organism without harm. Symptomatic infection is often the first indication of AIDS. Person-to-person transmission of the disease does not occur.

Prevention and Treatment

There is no vaccine or other preventive measure available. Treatment with the antibiotic amphotericin B is often effective, particularly if given concurrently with flucytosine (5-fluorocytosine) or newer oral antifungal medicines such as itraconazole. Amphotericin B must be given intravenously and the dose carefully regulated to minimize the toxic effects of the antibiotic, mainly against the kidneys. Since amphotericin B does not reliably cross the blood-brain barrier, it is often necessary to administer it through a plastic tube inserted through the skull into a lateral ventricle of the brain. Except in AIDS patients, treatment is

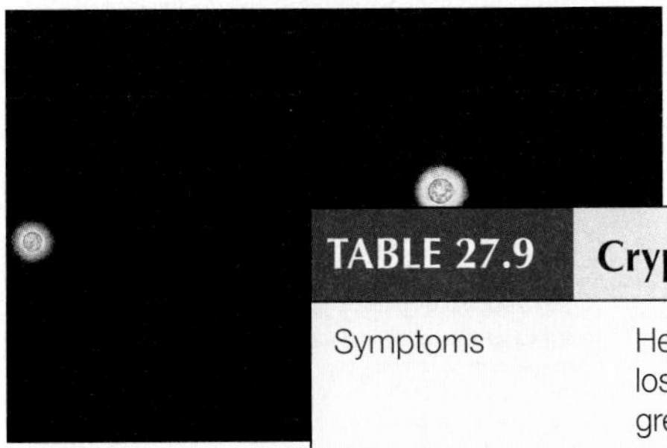

FIGURE 27.20 ***Cryptococcus*** **Individual with Cryptococcal** the fluid to outline the organism's c

A summary table follows the presentation for each particular disease.

TABLE 27.9	**Cryptococcal Meningoencephalitis**
Symptoms	Headache, vomiting, confusion, and weight loss; slight or no fever; symptoms may progress to seizures, paralysis, coma, and death
Incubation period	Widely variable, few to many weeks
Causative agent	*Filobasidiella (Cryptococcus) neoformans,* an encapsulated yeast
Pathogenesis	Infection starts in lung; encapsulated organisms multiply, enter bloodstream, and are carried to various parts of the body; phagocytosis inhibited and opsonins neutralized; meninges and adjacent brain tissue become infected.
Epidemiology	Inhalation of dust containing dried pigeon droppings contaminated with the fungus; most people resistant to the disease.
Prevention and treatment	No preventive measures. Treatment; amphotericin B with flucytosine or itraconazole.

Incomparable Treatment of Diseases

Each disease is presented systematically and predictably by including individual sections describing the symptoms, causative agents, pathogenesis, epidemiology, and prevention and treatment.

Disease Summaries

Major diseases are represented with a summary table, which includes an outline of pathogenesis keyed to a human figure showing the entry and exit of the pathogen.

TABLE 28.5 "Black Death" (Plague)

① Causative organism *Yersinia pestis* is contracted from the bite of an infected flea or scratching skin contaminated by the flea's feces.

② The bacteria are carried by the lymphatics to regional lymph nodes.

③ Phagocytes ingest the bacteria but the intracellular conditions activate capsule production and other genes responsible for virulence.

④ Fully virulent bacteria break out of the phagocytes, infect the nodes, producing buboes, bubonic plague.

⑤ The bacteria may be carried into the bloodstream, causing septicemic plague.

⑥ The lungs can become infected, producing the highly contagious and lethal pneumonic plague.

⑦ Bacteria exit with coughing.

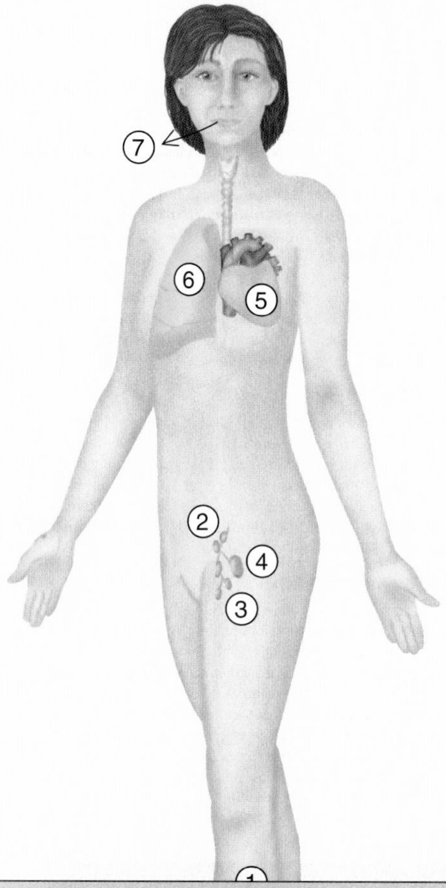

Symptoms	Sudden onset of high fever, large lymph nodes called buboes, skin hemorrhages; sometimes bloody sputum
Incubation period	Usually 1 to 6 days
Causative agent	*Yersinia pestis,* an encapsulated enterobacterium with multiple plasmid- and chromosome-coded virulence factors
Pathogenesis	Enters the body with bite of infected flea. Bacteria taken up by macrophages. Intracellular environment causes them to transform into encapsulated organisms capable of elaborating multiple virulence factors that allow attachment to host cells, and provide defense against phagocytes and the immune system.
Epidemiology	Endemic in rodents and other wild animals, and their fleas, particularly in the western states of the United States. Can be introduced into human habitations by pets, transmitted from human to human by fleas; with pneumonic plague, by coughing. Pneumonic plague is the most dangerous because *Y. pestis* is fully virulent at the time of transmission.
Prevention and	A vaccine is available for short- rm protection. Avoid contact with d rodents and their burrows. secticides and rat control. Prompt agnosis and antibacterial treat- ent necessary to prevent high ortality.

CASE PRESENTATION

The patient was a 24-year-old woman, a surgical nurse, seen in the clinic for evaluation of a needle puncture wound to the hand. Earlier in the day, while assisting in a frantic attempt to revive a man with cardiac arrest, she sustained a deep puncture wound to her right palm from a needle that had accidentally dropped into the bedclothes. The needle was visibly contaminated with blood. She immediately washed her hand thoroughly with soap and water, applied an antiseptic, and dressed the puncture site with a loose adhesive bandage.

She was married, with one 14-month-old child. There was no history of blood transfusion or injected-drug abuse. She had donated blood the previous month, and it was not rejected. Her tetanus immunization was up to date, but she had not been immunized against hepatitis B.

Two days after the clinic visit, tests for antibody in the cardiac arrest patient's blood revealed that he had a chronic viral infection.

1. What were the main diagnostic considerations?
2. What risk of infection did the patient face?
3. What measures could be taken to reduce the risk? How much time could expire before preventive measures became ineffective?
4. What was the nurse's prognosis?

Discussion

1. The viruses of concern are hepatitis B virus (HBV), human immunodeficiency virus (HIV), and hepatitis C virus (HCV). Each of these could be transmitted to the nurse by a needle stick and cause serious illness.
2. There are an estimated 750,000 to 1 million carriers of HBV in the United States. They typically have large amounts of circulating infectious virus, so that even a tiny amount of their blood can transmit the disease. The risk of infection from a needle puncture wound when the blood originates from a hepatitis B virus carrier is estimated to be 10% to 35%. The AIDS-causing human immunodeficiency virus (HIV) infects approximately 1 million Americans. The blood of these persons is also potentially infectious, but the risk of transmission by a needle stick is considerably lower than the risk for hepatitis B, averaging about 0.4%. The lower risk results from smaller amounts of circulating infectious virus in HIV-infected individuals. The risk is probably higher early in HIV disease, during the acute infection, and later, when AIDS develops, because much higher levels of circulating infectious virus are then present.

   Hepatitis C virus is also transmitted by blood. Transmission from surgeon to patient has been documented, presumably by the multiple pricks from surgical needles that often penetrate the surgeons' gloves during major surgery. The risk of transmission by needle stick from an HCV-positive individual is about 1.8%. The number of new hepatitis C virus infections in the United States each year has been estimated at between 150,000 and 170,000, but the mode of transmission is unknown in most cases.

   Other viruses, such as cytomegalovirus (CMV) and Epstein-Barr virus (EBV), can be transmitted by blood. The risk from a needle stick injury is unknown but is probably much lower than from the viruses already mentioned. Obviously, all blood should be considered potentially infectious.
3. In the case of needle puncture wounds that expose a person to HBV, hepatitis B immune globulin (HBIG) is given as soon as possible after the wound occurs. HBIG is gamma globulin obtained from individuals that have a high titer of antibody against HBV. At the same time, active immunization is started with hepatitis B vaccine. These measures must be initiated within 7 days of the injury to be effective. This nurse, as with all persons at high risk of blood exposure, should have already been immunized with hepatitis B vaccine; then, no other preventive measures would need to be taken.

   Those exposed to HIV by needle punctures should be given zidovudine (AZT), plus one or more other anti-HIV medications, immediately and for 4 weeks. There is probably little protective effect if therapy is delayed beyond 2 hours.

   There is no proven preventive measure for HCV exposure. Approaches similar to those for HBV may become available in the future.
4. Preventive measures for hepatitis B exposure are highly effective, reducing the risk of infection by 75% or more. Also, the already relatively low risk from needle puncture wound for HIV exposure can probably be reduced by 75% to 80% with preventive medication. The patient's prognosis for remaining free of infection was good. The small chance of becoming infected and the long incubation period of these diseases, however, add up to considerable worry. Every effort should be made to avoid needle puncture wounds in the first place.

Case Presentations

Each infectious disease chapter includes a case presentation of a realistic clinical situation.

An Active Learning System

In today's classroom, it is important to pursue active learning by students. Carefully devised questions and problem sets have been provided throughout the text and at the end of each chapter, allowing students to build their working knowledge of microbiology while also developing reasoning and analytical skills.

Microchecks

Major sections end with a short "Microcheck" that summarizes the major concepts in that section and offers both review questions and critical thinking questions (in blue) to assess understanding of the preceding section.

MICROCHECK 7.1

Replication is the process of duplicating double-stranded DNA. Transcription is the process of copying the information encoded in DNA into RNA. Translation is the process of interpreting the information carried by messenger RNA in order to synthesize the encoded protein.

✓ How does the 5′ end of DNA differ from the 3′ end?

✓ If the nucleotide sequence of one strand of DNA is 5′ ACGTTGCA 3′, what is the sequence of the complementary strand?

✓ Why is a short-lived RNA important in cell control mechanisms?

166 CHAPTER SIX Metabolism: Fueling Cell Growth

REVIEW QUESTIONS

Short Answer

1. Explain the difference between catabolism and anabolism.
2. How does ATP serve as a carrier of free energy?
3. How do enzymes catalyze chemical reactions?
4. Explain how precursor molecules serve as junctions between catabolic and anabolic pathways.
5. How do cells regulate enzyme activity?
6. Why do the electrons carried by $FADH_2$ result in less ATP production than those carried by NADH?
7. Name three food products produced with the aid of microorganisms.
8. In photosynthesis, what is encompassed by the term light-independent reactions?
9. Unlike the oxygenic phototrophs, the anoxygenic phototrophs do not evolve oxygen (O_2). Why not?
10. What is the role of transamination in amino acid biosynthesis?

Multiple Choice

1. Which of these environmental factors does not affect general enzyme activity?
   a) Temperature
   b) Inhibitors
   c) Coenzymes
   d) Humidity
   e) pH
2. Which of the following statements is false? Enzymes
   a) bind to substrates.
   b) lower the energy of activation.
   c) convert coenzymes to products.
   d) speed up biochemical reactions.
   e) can be named after the kinds of reaction they catalyze.
3. Which of these is not a coenzyme?
   a) FAD
   b) Coenzyme A
   c) NAD^+
   d) ATP
   e) $NADP^+$
4. What is the end product of glycolysis?
   a) Glucose
   b) Citrate
   c) Oxaloacetate
   d) α-ketoglutarate
   e) Pyruvate
5. The major pathway(s) of central metabolism are
   a) glycolysis and the TCA cycle only.
   b) glycolysis, the TCA cycle, and the pentose phosphate pathway.
   c) glycolysis only.
   d) glycolysis and the pentose phosphate pathway only.
   e) the TCA cycle only.
6. Which of these pathways has the potential to produce the most ATP?
   a) TCA cycle
   b) Pentose phosphate pathway
   c) Lactic acid fermentation
   d) Glycolysis
7. In fermentation, the terminal electron acceptor is
   a) oxygen (O_2).
   b) hydrogen (H_2).
   c) carbon dioxide (CO_2).
   d) an organic compound.
8. In the process of oxidative phosphorylation, the energy of proton motive force is used to generate
   a) NADH.
   b) ADP.
   c) ethanol.
   d) ATP.
   e) glucose.
9. In the TCA cycle, the carbon atoms contained in acetate are converted into
   a) lactic acid.
   b) glucose.
   c) glycerol.
   d) CO_2.
   e) all of these.
10. Degradation of fats as an energy source involves all of the following, *except*
    a) β-oxidation.
    b) acetyl-CoA.
    c) glycerol.
    d) lipase.
    e) transamination.

Applications

1. A worker in a cheese-making facility argues that whey, a nutrient-rich by-product of cheese, should be dumped in a nearby pond where it could serve as fish food. Explain why this proposed action could actually kill the fish by depleting the oxygen in the pond.
2. Scientists working with DNA *in vitro* often store it in solutions that contain EDTA, a chelating agent that binds magnesium (Mg^{2+}). This is done to prevent enzymes called DNases from degrading the DNA. Explain why EDTA would interfere with enzyme activity.

Critical Thinking

1. A student argued that aerobic and anaerobic respiration should produce the same amount of ATP. He reasoned that they both use basically the same process; only the terminal electron acceptor is different. What is the primary error in this student's argument?
2. Chemolithotrophs near hydrothermal vents support a variety of other life forms there. Explain how their role there is analogous to that of photosynthetic organisms in terrestrial environments.

End-of-Chapter Review

- ***Short Answer*** questions review major chapter concepts.
- ***Multiple Choice*** questions allow self-testing; answers are provided in Appendix V.
- ***Applications*** provide an opportunity to use knowledge of microbiology to solve real-world problems.
- ***Critical Thinking*** questions, written by leading critical thinking expert, Robert Allen, encourage practice in analysis and problem solving that can be used in the study of any subject.

Applications Promote Further Interest

Applications throughout *Microbiology: A Human Perspective* not only help students understand microbiology's history but also how microbiology influences their daily lives and their futures.

Glimpse of History

Each chapter opens with an engaging story about the men and women who pioneered the field of microbiology.

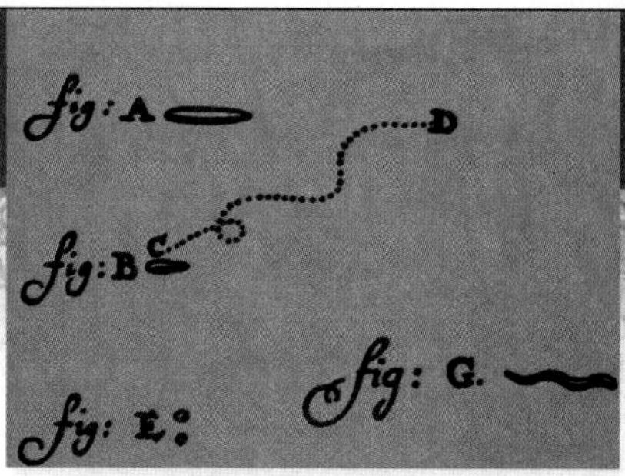

Van Leeuwenhoek's engravings (1.5x), 1695 Drawings that van Leeuwenhoek made in 1695 of the shapes of microorganisms he saw through his single lens microscope. He also observed the movement of organism B moving from C to D.

CHAPTER ONE

Humans and the Microbial World

A Glimpse of History

Microbiology as a science was born in 1674 when Antony van Leeuwenhoek (1632–1723), an inquisitive Dutch drapery merchant, peered at a drop of lake water through a glass lens that he had carefully ground. It was known for several centuries previous that curved glass would magnify objects, but it took the skillful hands of a craftsman coupled with the questioning mind of an amateur scientist to revolutionize the understanding of the world in which we live. What he observed through this simple magnifying glass was undoubtedly one of the most startling and amazing sights that humans have ever beheld—the first glimpse of the world of microbes. As van Leeuwenhoek wrote in a letter to the Royal Society of London, he saw

> "Very many little animalcules, whereof some were roundish, while others a bit bigger consisted of an oval. On these last, I saw two little legs near the head, and two little fins at the hind most end of the body. Others were somewhat longer than an oval, and these were very slow a-moving, and few in number. These animalcules had diverse colours, some being whitish and transparent; others with green and very glittering little scales, others again were green in the middle, and before and behind white; others yet were ashed grey. And the motion of most of these animalcules in the water was so swift, and so various, upwards, downwards, and round about, that 'twas wonderful to see."

Although van Leeuwenhoek was the first to observe bacteria, Robert Hooke, an English microscopist was the first to observe a microorganism. In 1665, he published a description of a microfungus which he called a "microscopical mushroom." His drawing was so accurate that his specimen could later be identified as the common bread mold. Hooke also described how to make the kind of microscope that van Leeuwenhoek made almost 10 years later. In light of their almost simultaneous discovery of the microbial world, both men should be given equal credit for first describing the organisms you are about to study.

Microorganisms are the foundation for all life on earth. It has been said that the twentieth century was the age of physics. Now we can say that the twenty-first century will be the age of biology and biotechnology, with microbiology as the most important branch.

Perspective Boxes

Perspective boxes introduce a "human" perspective by showing how microorganisms and their products influence our lives in a myriad of different ways.

PERSPECTIVE 9.1

Science Takes the Witness Stand

After serving more than 10 years on a rape charge, a wrongfully convicted young man was released from prison when a new DNA typing technique exonerated him. The new technique, which used polymerase chain reaction (PCR) to amplify specific sequences, showed that the semen sample taken from the rape victim did not contain the man's DNA. Indeed, a database indicated a DNA match with a man currently in prison for an unrelated rape charge.

Stories abound about the growing power of DNA evidence for obtaining convictions and also clearing the wrongly accused, but how is DNA used in forensics? It is not feasible to compare the entire nucleotide sequence of two people; instead, specific regions that vary significantly between individuals are analyzed. In the past, forensics labs commonly looked at restriction fragment length polymorphisms, employing Southern blot hybridization to detect the differences (see figures 9.9 and 9.10). This provides valuable information but cannot be used on small or degraded samples and is quite time-consuming. Most forensics labs have now switched to using a PCR-based method because results can be obtained in less than 5 hours from a sample as small as a drop of blood the size of a pinhead. In fact, the FBI now catalogs PCR-based DNA profiles from unsolved crimes and convicted violent offenders, making it easier to track or link the crimes of serial offenders. The national database is called CODIS (**Co**mbined **D**NA **I**ndex **S**ystem).

PCR-based DNA typing amplifies certain chromosomal regions that contain **short tandem repeats (STRs)**. These consist of a core sequence of 2 to 6 base pairs that repeat a variable number of times in different people. On chromosome 2, for example, in an intron within the thyroid peroxidase gene, the sequence AATG is repeated sequentially between 5 to 14 times. In one individual, there may be 9 of these STRs in one copy of that chromosome and 7 in the other, whereas another individual may have 11 and 5 **(figure 1).** This variation, or polymorphism, makes tandem repeats a useful genetic marker for distinguishing individuals. With PCR, using primers that bind regions flanking the repeating sequences, the number of repeats can be determined. A fragment that contains 9 repeats, for example, will be longer than one that contains only 7. The PCR-amplified fragments can be quickly separated using a rapid type of gel electrophoresis called capillary electrophoresis. Their size can then be determined by comparing their positions as they move out of the gel to those of known standards.

The FBI's CODIS database catalogs the amplification pattern of 13 different STR loci (chromosomal locations). Commercially available kits contain fluorescently-labeled primers that allow simultaneous amplification and subsequent recognition of each of the 13 loci. A laser detects the color of each amplified fragment as it moves out of the capillary gel, and computer analysis generates a pattern of

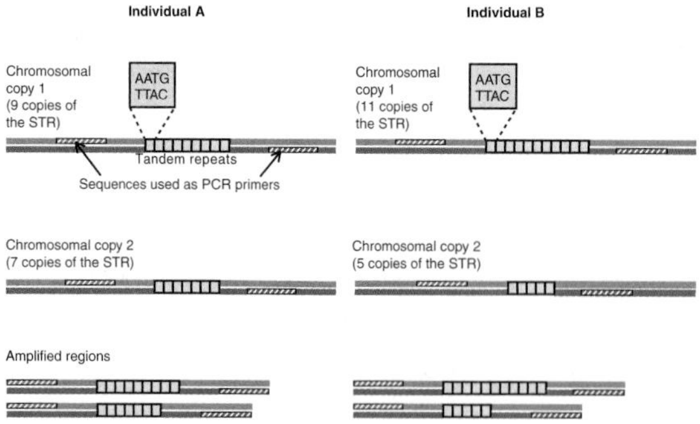

FIGURE 1 Using PCR to Type ("Fingerprint") DNA PCR is used to amplify chromosomal regions containing short tandem repeats (STRs). The number of copies of a given STR vary among people, resulting in corresponding differences in the length of the amplified fragments. Typically, at least 13 d…

FUTURE CHALLENGES

Astrobiology: The Search for Life on Other Planets

If life as we know it exists on other planets, one form it will likely take will be microbial. The task, then, is to figure out how to find and detect such extraterrestrial microorganisms.

Considering that we still know relatively little about the microbial life on our own planet, coupled with the extreme difficulty of obtaining or testing extraterrestrial samples, this is a daunting challenge with many as yet unanswered questions. For example, what is the most likely source of life on other planets? What is the best way to preserve specimens for study on earth? What will be the culture requirements to grow such organisms? **Astrobiology,** the study of life in the universe, is a new field that is bringing together scientists from a wide range of disciplines, including microbiology, geology, astronomy, biology, and chemistry, to begin answering some of these questions. The goal is to determine the origin, evolution, distribution, and destiny of life in the universe. These astrobiologists are also given the task of developing lightweight, dependable, and meaningful testing devices to be used in future space missions.

Astrobiologists believe that within our solar system, life would most likely be found either on Europa, a moon of Jupiter, or on Mars. This is because Europa and Mars appear to have, or have had, water, which is crucial for all known forms of life. Europa has an icy crust, beneath which may be liquid water or even a liquid ocean. Mars is the planet that is closest to earth, and it has the most similar environment. Images and data from the recent Mars missions indicate that flowing water once existed there.

To prepare for researching life on other planets, microbiologists have turned to some of the most extreme environments here on earth. These include glaciers and ice shelves, hot springs, deserts, volcanoes, deep ocean hydrothermal vents, and subterranean features such as caves. Because select microorganisms can survive in these environs, which are analogous to conditions expected on other planets, they are good testing grounds for the technology to be used on future missions.

Future Challenges

Each chapter ends with a pending challenge facing microbiologists and future microbiologists.

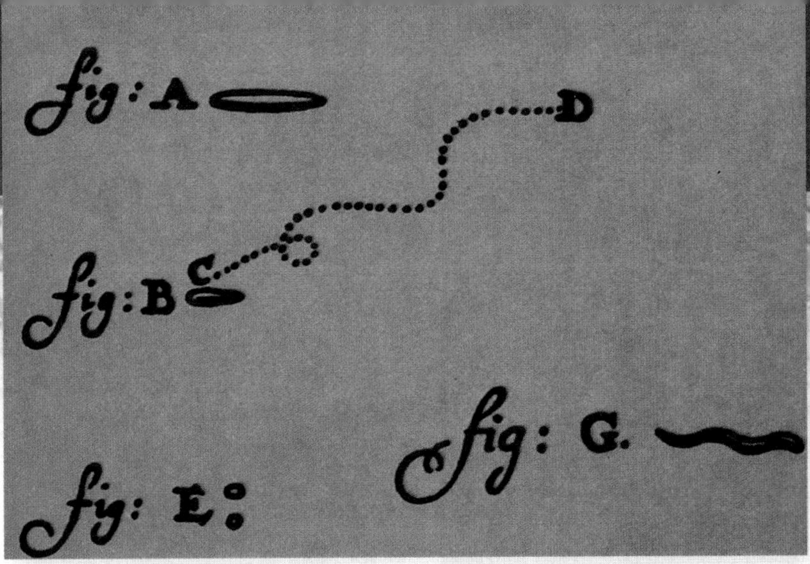

Van Leeuwenhoek's engravings (1.5×), 1695. Drawings that van Leeuwenhoek made in 1695 of the shapes of microorganisms he saw through his single lens microscope. He also observed the movement of organism B moving from C to D.

CHAPTER ONE

Humans and the Microbial World

A Glimpse of History

Microbiology as a science was born in 1674 when Antony van Leeuwenhoek (1632–1723), an inquisitive Dutch drapery merchant, peered at a drop of lake water through a glass lens that he had carefully ground. It was known for several centuries previous that curved glass would magnify objects, but it took the skillful hands of a craftsman coupled with the questioning mind of an amateur scientist to revolutionize the understanding of the world in which we live. What he observed through this simple magnifying glass was undoubtedly one of the most startling and amazing sights that humans have ever beheld—the first glimpse of the world of microbes. As van Leeuwenhoek wrote in a letter to the Royal Society of London, he saw

> "Very many little animalcules, whereof some were roundish, while others a bit bigger consisted of an oval. On these last, I saw two little legs near the head, and two little fins at the hind most end of the body. Others were somewhat longer than an oval, and these were very slow a-moving, and few in number. These animalcules had diverse colours, some being whitish and transparent; others with green and very glittering little scales, others again were green in the middle, and before and behind white; others yet were ashed grey. And the motion of most of these animalcules in the water was so swift, and so various, upwards, downwards, and round about, that 'twas wonderful to see."

Although van Leeuwenhoek was the first to observe bacteria, Robert Hooke, an English microscopist was the first to observe a microorganism. In 1665, he published a description of a microfungus which he called a "microscopical mushroom." His drawing was so accurate that his specimen could later be identified as the common bread mold. Hooke also described how to make the kind of microscope that van Leeuwenhoek made almost 10 years later. In light of their almost simultaneous discovery of the microbial world, both men should be given equal credit for first describing the organisms you are about to study.

Microorganisms are the foundation for all life on earth. It has been said that the twentieth century was the age of physics. Now we can say that the twenty-first century will be the age of biology and biotechnology, with microbiology as the most important branch.

1.1 The Origin of Microorganisms

Focus Points

- Describe the key experiments that disproved spontaneous generation. Name the scientists who carried them out.
- Explain why endospores confused the studies on spontaneous generation.

It is generally believed that microorganisms have existed on earth for about 3.5 billion years, and over this time, plants and animals have evolved from these microscopic forms.

The discovery of microorganisms raised an intriguing question: "Where did these microscopic forms originate?" The theory of **spontaneous generation** suggested that organisms, such as tiny worms, can arise spontaneously from non-living material. It was completely debunked by Francesco Redi, an Italian biologist and physician, at the end of the seventeenth century. By a simple experiment, he demonstrated conclusively that worms found on rotting meat originated from the eggs of flies, not directly from the decaying meat as proponents of spontaneous generation believed. To prove this, he simply covered the meat with gauze fine enough to prevent flies from depositing their eggs. No worms appeared.

KEY TERMS

Biodiversity The variety of species inhabiting a particular environment.

Bioremediation The degradation of environmental pollutants by living organisms.

Biotechnology The application of biology to solve practical problems and produce useful products.

Domain The highest level in classification above the level of kingdom. All organisms can be assigned to one of three domains: *Bacteria, Archaea*, and *Eucarya*.

Emerging diseases Diseases that have increased in incidence in the past 20 years.

Genetic engineering Deliberately altering an organism's genetic information using *in vitro* techniques.

Genomics The complete analysis of all the genetic information of an organism or virus, done by determining the order of the subunits (nucleotides).

Obligate intracellular parasite An organism or agent that can only multiply inside living cells.

Pathogen An organism or virus causing disease.

Spontaneous generation The creation of living organisms from non-living material.

Theory of Spontaneous Generation Revisited

Despite Redi's findings, the theory of spontaneous generation was difficult to disprove, and it took about 200 years more to refute this idea to everyone's satisfaction.

Experiments of Pasteur

One giant in science who did much to disprove the theory of spontaneous generation was the French chemist Louis Pasteur, considered by many to be the father of modern microbiology. In 1861, Pasteur refuted spontaneous generation by a series of clever experiments. First, he demonstrated that air is filled with microorganisms. He did this by filtering air through a cotton plug, trapping organisms that he then examined with a microscope. Many of these trapped organisms looked identical microscopically to those that had previously been observed by others in many **infusions.** Infusions are liquids that contain nutrients in which microorganisms can grow. Pasteur further showed that if the cotton plug was then dropped into a sterilized infusion, it became cloudy because the organisms quickly multiplied.

Most importantly, Pasteur's experiment demonstrated that sterile infusions would remain sterile in specially constructed flasks even when they were left open to the air. Organisms from the air settled in the bends and sides of these swan-necked flasks, never reaching the fluid in the bottom of the flask **(figure 1.1).** Only when the flasks were tipped would bacteria be able to enter the broth and grow. These simple and elegant experiments ended the arguments that unheated air or the infusions themselves contained a "vital force" necessary for spontaneous generation.

Experiments of Tyndall

Although most scientists were convinced by Pasteur's experiments, others were not. This skepticism in part stemmed from the fact that some scientists could not reproduce Pasteur's results. One of these was an English physicist, John Tyndall. It was Tyndall who finally explained differences in experimental results obtained in different laboratories and, in turn, proved Pasteur correct. Tyndall concluded that different infusions required different boiling times to be sterilized. Thus, boiling for 5 minutes

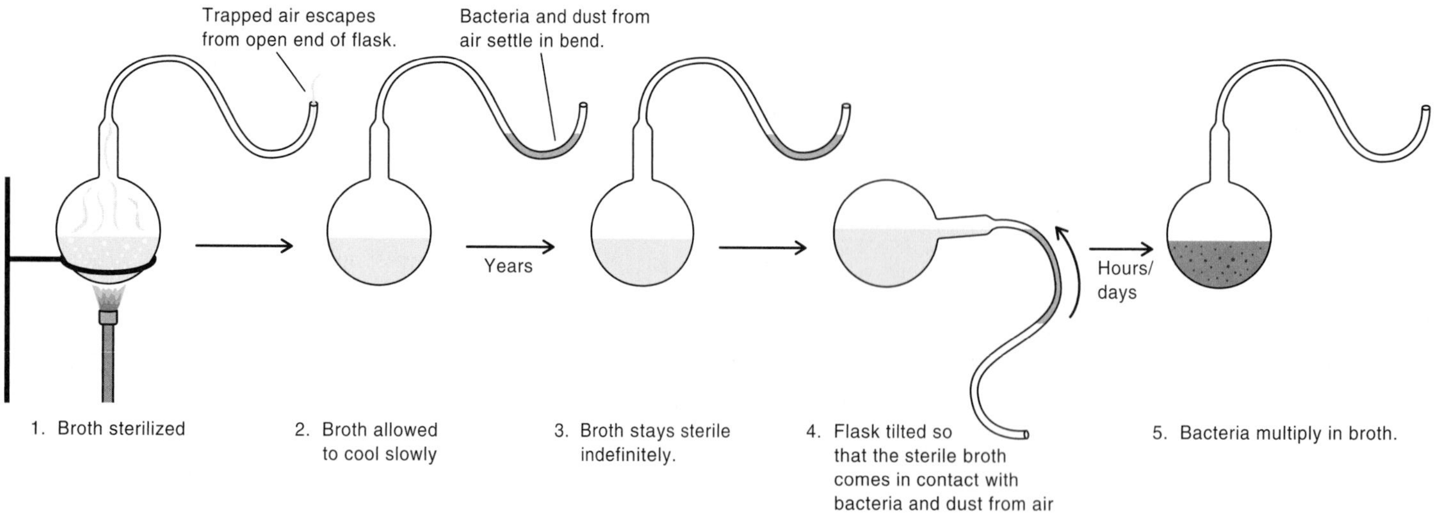

Trapped air escapes from open end of flask.
Bacteria and dust from air settle in bend.
Years
Hours/ days
1. Broth sterilized
2. Broth allowed to cool slowly
3. Broth stays sterile indefinitely.
4. Flask tilted so that the sterile broth comes in contact with bacteria and dust from air
5. Bacteria multiply in broth.

FIGURE 1.1 Pasteur's Experiment with the Swan-Necked Flask If the flask remains upright, no microbial growth occurs. **(1–3)** If the flask is tipped, the microorganisms trapped in the neck reach the sterile liquid and grow. **(4, 5)** Why did bacteria grow in the flask only after the flask was tipped?

would sterilize some materials, whereas others, most notably hay infusions, could be boiled for 5 hours and they still contained living organisms! Furthermore, if hay was present in the laboratory, it became almost impossible to sterilize the infusions that had previously been sterilized by boiling for 5 minutes. What did hay contain that caused this effect? Tyndall finally realized that heat-resistant forms of life were being brought into his laboratory on the hay. These heat-resistant life forms must then have been transferred to all other infusions in his laboratory on dust particles, thereby making everything difficult to sterilize. Tyndall concluded that some microorganisms could exist in two forms: a cell that is readily killed by boiling, and one that is heat resistant. In the same year (1876), a German botanist, Ferdinand Cohn, also discovered the heat-resistant forms of bacteria, now termed **endospores.** The following year (1877), Robert Koch demonstrated that anthrax was caused by *Bacillus anthracis* and that the usual means of transmission in animals was by means of resistant spores. In 2001, the deliberate transmission of anthrax to humans by means of spores was instigated by bioterrorists in the United States. ■ **endospores, p. 71**

The extreme heat resistance of endospores explains the differences between Pasteur's results and those of other investigators. Organisms that produce endospores are commonly found in the soil and most likely were present in hay infusions. Because Pasteur used only infusions prepared from sugar or yeast extract, his broth most likely did not contain endospores. At the time these experiments on spontaneous generation were performed, the importance of the source of the infusion was not appreciated. In hindsight, the infusion source was critical to the results observed and conclusions drawn.

These experiments on spontaneous generation point out an important lesson for all scientists. In repeating an experiment and comparing results with previous experiments, it is absolutely essential to reproduce all conditions of an experiment as closely as possible. It may seem surprising that the concept of spontaneous generation was disproved less than a century and a half ago. **Table 1.1** lists some

TABLE 1.1 Some Major Milestones in Microbiology

Date	Event
1500 B.C.	Egyptians ferment cereal grains to make beer.
A.D. 1546	Italian physician Girolamo Fracastoro suggests that invisible organisms may cause disease.
1665	Robert Hooke publishes his discovery of cells in cork and sees the first microorganism.
1676	Antony van Leeuwenhoek observes bacteria and protozoa using his homemade microscope.
1796	Edward Jenner introduces a vaccination procedure for smallpox.
1838–1839	Mathias Schleiden and Theodor Schwann independently propose that all organisms are composed of cells, the basic unit of life.
1840	J. Henle presents a clear exposition of the germ theory of disease.
1847–1850	Ignaz Semmelwels demonstrates that puerperal or childbed fever is a contagious disease transmitted by physicians to their patients during childbirth.
1853–1854	John Snow demonstrates the epidemic spread of cholera through a water supply contaminated with human sewage.
1857	Louis Pasteur demonstrates that yeast can degrade sugar to ethanol and carbon dioxide as they multiply.
1861	Louis Pasteur publishes experiments that refute the theory of spontaneous generation.
1864	Louis Pasteur develops pasteurization as a method to destroy unwanted organisms in wine.
1867	Joseph Lister publishes the first work on antiseptic surgery, beginning the trend toward modern aseptic techniques in medicine.
1876	Robert Koch demonstrates that anthrax is caused by a bacterium.
1881	Robert Koch introduces the use of pure culture techniques for handling bacteria in the laboratory.
	Walter and Fanny Hesse introduce agar-agar as a solidifying gel for culture media.
1882	Koch identifies the causative agent of tuberculosis.
1884	Koch states Koch's Postulates.
	Elie Metchnikoff discovers phagocytic cells and their role in engulfing bacteria.
	Christian Gram publishes a paper describing the Gram stain.
1892	Dmitri Iwanowski discovers that tobacco-mosaic disease is caused by a filterable agent—a virus.
1908	Paul Ehrlich develops the drug salvarsan to treat syphilis, thereby starting the use of chemotherapy to treat diseases.
1911	F. Peyton Rous discovers that a virus can cause cancer in chickens.
1928	Frederick Griffith discovers genetic transformation in bacteria, thereby raising a key question in genetics: What chemical caused the transformation?
1929	Alexander Fleming discovers and describes the properties of the first antibiotic, penicillin.
1944	Oswald Avery, Colin MacLeod, and Maclyn McCarty demonstrate that Griffith's transforming principle is DNA.
1944	Joshua Lederberg and Edward Tatum demonstrate that DNA can be transferred from one bacterium to another.
1948	Barbara McClintock demonstrates transposable elements in maize, and almost two decades later they are discovered in bacteria.

TABLE 1.1 Some Major Milestones in Microbiology (*continued*)

Date	Event
1953	James Watson, Francis Crick, Rosalind Franklin, and Maurice Wilkins determine the structure of DNA.
1957	D. Carlton Gajdusek demonstrates the slow infectious nature of the disease kuru, which is later shown to be caused by a prion.
1970	Hamilton Smith reports the discovery of the first restriction enzyme.
1971	Theodor Diener demonstrates the fundamental differences between viroids and viruses.
1973	Herbert Boyer and Stanley Cohen, using plasmids, are the first to clone DNA.
1975	Cesar Milstein, Georges Kohler, and Niels Kai Jeme develop the technique for making monoclonal antibodies.
1976	Michael Bishop and Harold Varmus discover the cancer-causing genes, called oncogenes, and find that such genes are in normal tissues.
1977	Carl Woese classifies all organisms into three domains.
1980	A rare cancer in humans is shown to be caused by a retrovirus.
	World Health Organization declares eradication of smallpox in the world.
1982	Stanley Prusiner isolates a protein from a slow disease infection and suggests that it might direct its own replication. He suggests the agent be termed a prion.
	Barry Marshall demonstrates that a bacterium, *Helicobacter pylori*, causes ulcers.
	First product of genetic engineering introduced—human insulin.
1983	Luc Montagnier of France and Robert Gallo of the United States independently isolate and characterize the human immunodeficiency virus (HIV), the cause of AIDS.
	Kary Mullis invents the polymerase chain reaction.
1994	The Food and Drug Administration approves the first genetically engineered food for human consumption, a slow ripening tomato.
1995	The Food and Drug Administration approves the first protease inhibitor, a major weapon against the progression of AIDS.
	The first complete nucleotide sequence of a chromosome of a bacterium, *Haemophilus influenzae*, is reported.
1997	The first complete nucleotide sequence of all of the chromosomes of a eukaryote (yeast) is reported.
1999	Ford Doolittle proposes that evolution proceeded through horizontal gene transfer between the three domains.
2000	The first new antibiotic in 35 years, Zyvox or linezolid, is approved by the Food and Drug Administration.
2001	Bioterrorism in the form of mailed anthrax spores is waged against the United States.
2002	The genomes of the mosquito that transmits malaria, and the organism that causes it, are sequenced.
2003	Outbreak of SARS in Southeast Asia occurs
2004	Use of interfering RNA to control gene expression and thereby treat a variety of diseases is actively studied.
2005	Avian influenza considered a major threat in the world.

of the other important advances in microbiology that have been made in the course of history. Rather than cover the entire history of microbiology here, we will return to many of these major milestones in more detail as our study of microbiology continues. How far the science of microbiology and all biological sciences have advanced over the last 145 years!

MICROCHECK 1.1

Antony van Leeuwenhoek first observed bacteria about 300 years ago. Pasteur and Tyndall refuted the theory of spontaneous generation less than 150 years ago.

- ✓ Give two reasons why it took so long to disprove the theory of spontaneous generation.
- ✓ What experiment disproved the notion that a "vital force" in air was responsible for spontaneous generation?
- ✓ If Pasteur's swan-necked flasks had contained endospores, what results would have been observed?

1.2 Microbiology: A Human Perspective

Focus Points

- List the reasons life on earth could not exist without microorganisms.
- Describe five applications of microbiology.
- Discuss why emerging diseases are appearing in industrialized countries.

Microoganisms have had, and continue to have, an enormous impact on the lives of all living things. On the one hand, microorganisms and other infectious agents, the viruses, have killed far more people than have ever been killed in war. On the other hand, without microorganisms, life as we know it could not exist on the

earth. They are responsible for continually recycling the oxygen and nitrogen that all living beings require.

Which organisms are included in the microbial world? Microbiology encompasses the study of many diverse organisms. These include bacteria, viruses, protozoa, algae, fungi, and some multicellular parasites.

The most common feature of most members of the microbial world is that they cannot be seen without the aid of a microscope. Other than their small size, microorganisms share few other properties. They are extremely diverse in their appearance, metabolism, physiology and genetics. Genes of particular ribonucleic acid (RNA) molecules, which are found in all organisms, reveal that plants are more closely related to animals than certain bacteria are to one another. There is tremendous **biodiversity** in the microbial world, biodiversity being the variety of species present in a particular environment. The visible forms, the plants and animals, by which biodiversity is usually measured, represent only a tiny fraction of the organisms that contribute to biodiversity. Microorganisms not only represent the most forms of life on earth in terms of weight, or **biomass,** but they are also the oldest and therefore have had the longest time to evolve. One needs to view and measure biodiversity in a different light with this information, since the most important and underappreciated forms of life are those that cannot be seen. Yet, the true contribution and biological role of microorganisms is underestimated because less than 1% of the total number of microorganisms in any environment can be studied in the laboratory.

Let us now consider some of the roles that microorganisms play in our lives, both beneficial and harmful. In large part this section and the remainder of this chapter will introduce you to what will be covered in more detail in later chapters.

Vital Activities of Microorganisms

The activities of microorganisms are responsible for the survival of all other organisms, including humans on this planet. A few examples readily prove this point. Nitrogen is an essential part of most of the important molecules in our bodies, such as nucleic acids and proteins. Nitrogen is also the most common gas in the atmosphere. Neither plants nor animals, however, can use nitrogen gas. Without certain bacteria that are able to convert the nitrogen in air into a chemical form that plants can use, life as we know it would not exist on earth.

All animals including humans require oxygen (O_2) to breathe. The supply of O_2 in the atmosphere, however, would be depleted in about 20 years, were it not replenished. On land, plants are important producers of O_2, but when all land and aquatic environments are considered, microorganisms are primarily responsible for continually replenishing the supply of O_2.

Microorganisms can also break down a wide variety of materials that no other forms of life can degrade. For example, the bulk of the carbohydrate in terrestrial (land) plants is in the form of cellulose, which humans and most animals cannot digest. Certain microorganisms can, however. As a result, leaves and downed trees do not pile up in the environment. Cellulose is also degraded by billions of microorganisms in the digestive tracts of cattle, sheep, deer, and other ruminants. The digestion products are used by the cattle for energy. Without these bacteria, ruminants would not survive. Microorganisms also play an indispensable role in degrading a wide variety of materials in sewage and wastewater.

Applications of Microbiology

In addition to the crucial roles that microorganisms play in maintaining all life on earth, they also have made life more comfortable for humans over the centuries. **Biotechnology** is the application of biology to solve practical problems and produce useful products economically.

Food Production

By taking advantage of what microorganisms do naturally, Egyptian bakers as early as 2100 B.C. used yeast to make bread. Today, bakeries use essentially the same technology. ■ **breadmaking, p. 804**

The excavation of early tombs in Egypt revealed that by 1500 B.C., Egyptians employed a highly complex procedure for fermenting cereal grains to produce beer. Today, brewers use the same fundamental techniques to make beer and other fermented drinks. ■ beer, p. 802

Virtually every human culture that has domesticated milk-producing animals such as cows and goats also has developed the technology to ferment milk to produce foods such as yogurt, cheeses, and buttermilk. Today, the bacteria added to some fermented milk products are being touted by nutritionists as protecting against intestinal infections and bowel cancer, the field of **probiotics.** ■ milk products, p. 798

Bioremediation

The use of living organisms to degrade environmental pollutants is termed **bioremediation.** Bacteria are being used to destroy such dangerous chemical pollutants as polychlorinated biphenyls (PCBs), dichlorodiphenyltrichloroethane (DDT), and trichloroethylene, a highly toxic solvent used in dry cleaning. All three organic compounds and many more have been detected in soil and water. Bacteria are also being used to degrade oil, assist in the cleanup of oil spills, and treat radioactive wastes. A bacterium was discovered recently that can live on trinitrotoluene (TNT). ■ bioremediation, p. 790

Useful Products from Bacteria

Bacteria can synthesize a wide variety of different products in the course of their metabolism. Many of these products have great commercial value. Although these same products can be synthesized in factories, bacteria often can do it faster and cheaper. For example, different bacteria produce:

- Cellulose used in stereo headsets
- Hydroxybutyric acid used in the manufacture of disposable diapers and plastics
- Ethanol, which is added to gasoline to make it burn cleaner
- Chemicals poisonous to insects
- Antibiotics used in the treatment of disease
- Amino acids, which are used as dietary supplements

Genetic Engineering

It is now possible to introduce genes from one organism into an unrelated organism and confer new properties on that organism. This is the process of **genetic engineering.** Genetically engineered microorganisms often appear in the popular press because they are being used to solve many problems associated with an industrial society. Genetic engineering has expanded the power of biotechnology enormously. Here are examples of the roles that microorganisms play in this new biotechnology:

- Microorganisms can be genetically engineered to produce a variety of medically important products. These include interferon, insulin, human growth hormone, blood clotting factors, and enzymes that dissolve blood clots. ■ genetic engineering, p. 219
- Microorganisms are being modified so that they will produce vaccines against rabies, gonorrhea, herpes, leprosy, malaria, and hepatitis. ■ vaccines, p. 415
- A bacterium can be used to genetically engineer plants so they become resistant to insect attacks and viral diseases, and produce large amounts of β-carotene **(figure 1.2).** ■ genetically engineered plants, p. 226

FIGURE 1.2 Pest-Resistant Transgenic Plant The plant in back has been genetically engineered by a bacterium to produce Bt-toxin, which kills insects when they feed on the plant. The control plant in front has been ravaged by insects.

- A bacterium can be used to transfer antibody eliciting genes into bananas which then confer resistance to certain diarrheal diseases. ■ vaccines, p. 415
- Viruses are being studied as a means of delivering genes into humans to correct conditions such as cystic fibrosis, heart disease, and cancer. This is the process of **gene therapy.** ■ gene therapy, p. 361

These examples represent only a few of the ways that microorganisms and viruses are being used to promote human welfare. In the past, microorganisms were considered only as dangerous organisms because they caused disease. The current and future use of microorganisms to increase the quality of human life, however, will receive increasing attention in scientific laboratories.

Genomics

The DNA in bacteria carries all of the information that gives the organism its unique characteristics and the ability to carry out the activities that are essential to life on earth. To fully understand the basis for their remarkable diversity and what makes them tick, we need to sequence their DNA and thereby reveal this storehouse of information. This is the science of **genomics.** The DNA of about 200 different bacteria has now been sequenced, revealing the innermost secrets of these organisms. Scientists are now better able to understand how bacteria can live in widely diverse environments and their relationships to other organisms. This will allow scientists to improve organisms' usefulness in biotechnology.

Medical Microbiology

In addition to the useful roles that microorganisms play in our daily lives, some also play a sinister role. For example, more Americans died of influenza in 1918–1919 than were killed in World War I, World War II, the Korean War, and the Vietnam War combined **(figure 1.3).** Modern sanitation, vaccination, and effective antibiotic treatments have reduced the incidence of some of the worst diseases,

FIGURE 1.3 Students wearing gauze masks to protect themselves against becoming infected with the influenza virus in 1918.

such as smallpox, bubonic plague, and influenza, to a small fraction of their former numbers. Another disease, acquired immunodeficiency syndrome (AIDS), however, has risen as a modern day plague.

Past Triumphs

About the time that spontaneous generation was finally disproved to everyone's satisfaction, the Golden Age of medical microbiology was born. Between the years 1875 and 1918, most disease-causing bacteria were identified, and early work on viruses had begun. Once people realized that some of these invisible agents could cause disease, they tried to prevent their spread from sick to healthy people. The great successes in the area of human health in the last 100 years have resulted from the prevention of infectious diseases with vaccines and treatment of these diseases with antibiotics. The results have been astounding!

The viral disease smallpox was one of the greatest killers the world has ever known. Approximately 10 million people have died from this disease over the past 4,000 years. It was brought to the New World by the Spaniards and made it possible for Hernando Cortez, with fewer than 600 soldiers, to conquer the Aztec Empire, whose subjects numbered in the millions. During a crucial battle in Mexico City, an epidemic of smallpox raged, killing only the Aztecs who had never been exposed to the disease before. In recent times, an active worldwide vaccination program has resulted in no cases being reported since 1977. Although the disease will probably never reappear on its own, its potential use as an agent in bioterrorist attacks is raising great concern.

Plague has been another great killer. One-third of the entire population of Europe, approximately 25 million people, died of this bacterial disease between 1346 and 1350. Now, generally less than 100 people in the entire world die each year from plague. In large part, this dramatic decrease is a result of controlling the population of black rats that harbor the bacterium. Further, the discovery of antibiotics in the early twentieth century made the isolated outbreaks treatable and the disease no longer the scourge it once was.

Epidemics are not limited to human populations. In 2001, a catastrophic outbreak of foot-and-mouth disease of animals ran out of control in England. To control this disease, one of the most contagious diseases known, almost 4 million pigs, sheep, and cattle were destroyed.

Present and Future Challenges

Although progress has been very impressive against bacterial diseases, a great deal still remains to be done, especially in the treatment of viral diseases and diseases that are prevalent in developing countries. Even in wealthy developed countries with their sophisticated health care systems, however, infectious diseases remain a serious threat. For example, about 750 million cases of infectious diseases of all types occur in the United States each year. Every year these diseases lead to 200,000 deaths and cost tens of billions of health care dollars. Respiratory infections and diarrheal diseases cause most illness and deaths in the world today.

Emerging Diseases In addition to the well-recognized diseases, seemingly "new" **emerging diseases** continue to arise. In the last several decades, they have included:

- Legionnaires' disease, p. 595
- Toxic shock syndrome, p. 658
- Lyme disease, p. 532
- Acquired immunodeficiency syndrome (AIDS), p. 734
- Hantavirus pulmonary syndrome, p. 601
- Hemolytic uremic syndrome, p. 627
- Mad cow disease (Bovine spongiform encephalopathy), p. 337
- West Nile virus disease, p. 693
- Severe acute respiratory syndrome (SARS), p. 606

Few of these diseases are really new, but an increased occurrence and wider distribution have brought them to the attention of health workers. Using the latest techniques, biomedical scientists have isolated, characterized, and identified these agents of disease. Now, methods need to be developed to prevent them.

A number of factors account for these emerging diseases arising even in industrially advanced countries. One reason is that changing lifestyles bring new opportunities for infectious agents to cause disease. For example, the vaginal tampons used by women provide an environment in which the organism causing toxic shock syndrome can grow and produce a toxin. In another example, the suburbs of cities are expanding into rural areas, bringing people into closer contact with animals previously isolated from humans. Consequently, people become exposed to viruses and infectious organisms that had been far removed from their environment. A good example is the hantavirus. This virus infects rodents, usually without causing disease. The infected animals, however, shed virus in urine, feces, and saliva; from there, it can be inhaled by humans as an aerosol. This disease, as well as Lyme disease, are only two of many emerging human diseases associated with small-animal reservoirs.

Some emerging diseases arise because the infectious agents change abruptly and gain the ability to infect new hosts. It is possible that HIV (Human Immunodeficiency Virus), the cause of

AIDS, arose from a virus that once could infect only monkeys. The virus causing SARS is related to viruses found in animals and may have been transmitted from animals to humans. Some bacterial **pathogens,** organisms capable of causing disease, differ from their non-pathogenic relatives in that the pathogens contain large pieces of DNA that confer on the organism the ability to cause disease. These pieces of DNA may have originated in unrelated organisms.

Figure 1.4 shows the countries in the world where, since 1976, new infectious diseases of humans and animals have first appeared. Are there other agents out there that may cause "new" diseases in the future? The answer is undoubtedly yes!

Resurgence of Old Diseases Not only are "new" diseases emerging, but many infectious diseases once on the wane in the United States have begun to increase again. Further, many of these diseases are more serious today because the causative agents resist the antibiotics once used to treat them. One reason for this resurgence is that thousands of foreign visitors and U.S. citizens returning from travel abroad enter this country daily. About one in five comes from a country where such diseases as malaria, cholera, plague, and yellow fever still exist. In developed countries these diseases have been eliminated largely through sanitation, vaccination, and quarantine. An international traveler incubating a disease in his or her body, however, could theoretically circle the globe, touch down in several countries, and expose many people before he or she became ill. As a result these diseases are recurring in countries where they had been virtually eliminated.

A second reason that certain diseases are on the rise is that in both developed and developing countries many childhood diseases have been so effectively controlled by childhood vaccinations that some parents have become lax about having their children vaccinated. The unvaccinated children are highly susceptible, and the number of those infected has increased dramatically. These diseases include measles, polio, mumps, whooping cough, and diphtheria.

A third reason for the rise in infectious diseases is that the population contains an increasing proportion of elderly people, who have weakened immune systems and are susceptible to diseases that younger people readily resist. In addition, individuals infected with HIV are especially susceptible to a wide variety of diseases, such as tuberculosis and Kaposi's sarcoma.

Chronic Diseases Caused by Bacteria In addition to the diseases long recognized as being caused by microorganisms or viruses, some illnesses once attributed to other causes may in fact be caused by bacteria. The best-known example is peptic ulcers. This common affliction has been shown to be caused by a bacterium, *Helicobacter pylori*, and is treatable with antibiotics. Chronic indigestion, which affects 25% to 40% of the people in the Western world, may also be caused by the same bacterium. Some scientists have also suggested that a bacterium is involved in cardiovascular disease, but evidence in favor is weak.

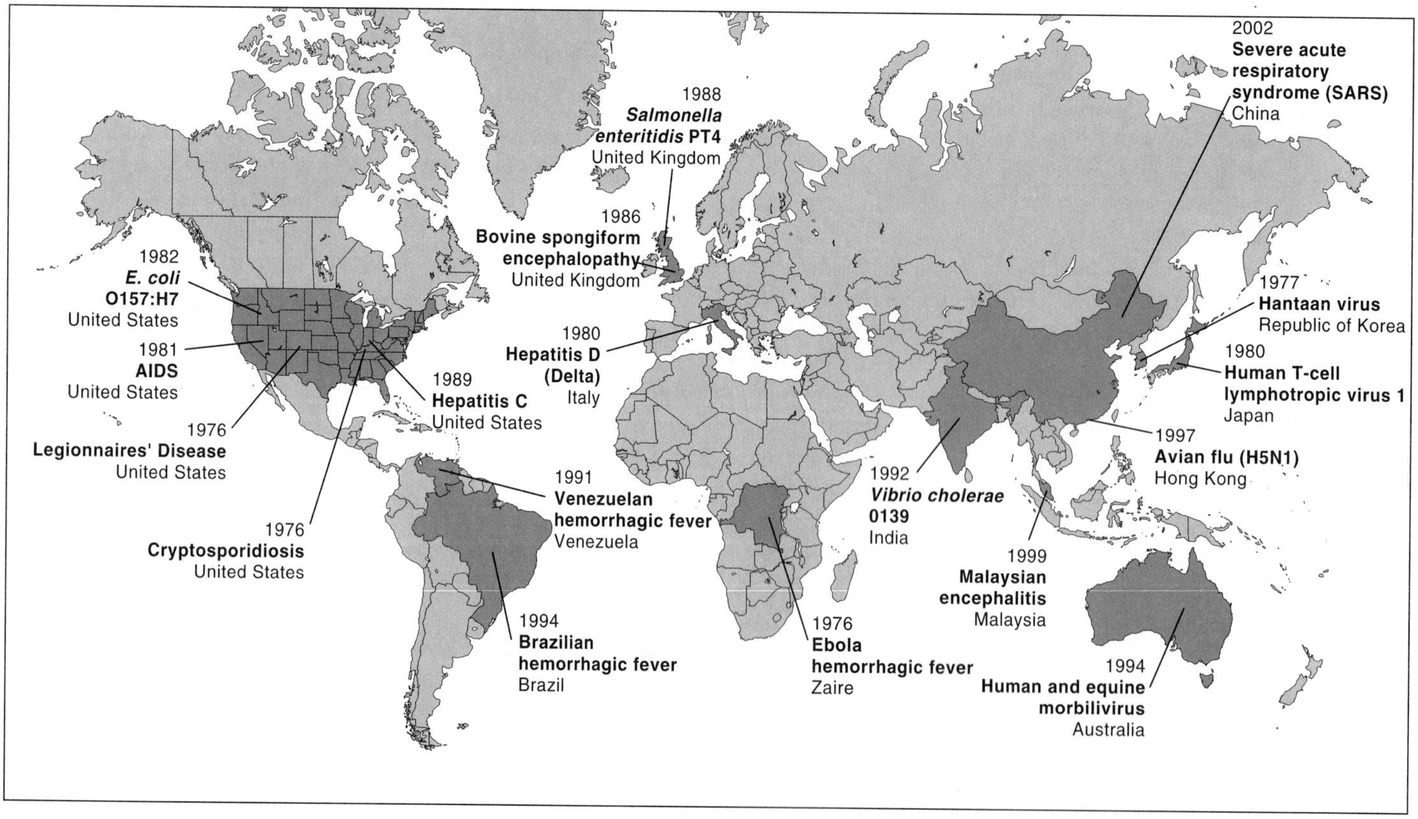

FIGURE 1.4 "New" Infectious Diseases in Humans and Animals Since 1976 Countries where cases first appeared or were identified appear in a darker shade. Why are the United States and Western European countries so prominent?

In 2002, it was shown that the worm responsible for the tropical disease, river blindness, must contain a specific bacterium which apparently causes the disease. Infectious agents likely play roles in other diseases of unknown origin.

Host-Bacterial Interactions

All surfaces of the human body are populated with bacteria, most of which protect against disease. It has been estimated that 500 to 1,000 species of bacteria reside within the human body and for every cell in the body, there are 10 bacteria. These bacteria play a number of indispensable roles in the life of the body. They successfully compete with occasional disease-causing bacteria and keep them from breaching host defenses that prevent disease. Further, they play important roles in the development of the intestine. Bacteria apparently also process foodstuffs in the intestine that the body cannot digest.

Certain bacteria, the pathogens, can cause damage to tissues in the body leading to symptoms of disease. These microbes, bacteria, and viruses, use the human body as a habitat for multiplication, persistence, and transmission to other hosts. The disease symptoms are often offshoots of the body's defense mechanisms, which may damage the host as well as the pathogen.

Microorganisms As Subjects for Study

Microorganisms are wonderful model organisms to study because they display the same fundamental metabolic and genetic properties found in higher forms of life. For example, all cells synthesize protein from the same amino acids by the same mechanism. They all duplicate their DNA by similar processes, and they degrade food materials to harvest energy via the same metabolic pathways. To paraphrase a Nobel Prize-winning microbiologist, Dr. Jacques Monod, what is true of an elephant is also true of bacteria. Bacteria are easy to study and results can be obtained very quickly because they grow rapidly and form billions of cells per milliliter on simple inexpensive media. Thus, most of the major advances that have been made in the last century toward understanding life have come through the study of microorganisms. The number of Nobel Prizes that have been awarded to microbiologists, and especially the ones awarded in 2001, proves this point (see inside cover). Such studies constitute basic research, and they continue today.

MICROCHECK 1.2

Microorganisms are essential to all life on earth and affect the life of humans in both beneficial and harmful ways. Microorganisms have been used for food production for thousands of years using essentially the same techniques that are used today. They are now being used to degrade toxic pollutants and produce a variety of compounds more cheaply than can be done in the chemical laboratory. The genetic engineering of microorganisms has expanded these capabilities greatly. Enormous progress has been made in preventing and curing most infectious diseases, but new ones continue to emerge around the world. Microbes represent wonderful model organisms, and many principles of biochemistry and genetics have been discovered from studying bacteria.

✓ Discuss activities that microbes carry out that are essential to life on earth.

✓ Discuss several reasons for the reemergence of old diseases.

✓ Why would it seem logical, even inevitable, that at least some bacteria would attack the human body and be disease-causing agents?

1.3 The Microbial World

Focus Points

- Name the three domains of all living organisms and the properties that distinguish them from one another.
- Compare and contrast the three eukaryotic members of the microbial world.

The microbial world includes the kinds of cells that van Leeuwenhoek observed looking through his simple microscope **(figure 1.5).** Although he could not realize it at the time, the microbial world, in fact all living organisms, can be classified into one of three major groups called **domains.** Organisms in each domain share properties of their cells that distinguish them from members of the other domains. Many properties, however, are shared among members of different domains because genes were transferred between domains billions of years ago, and the three domains may have a common ancestor. The three

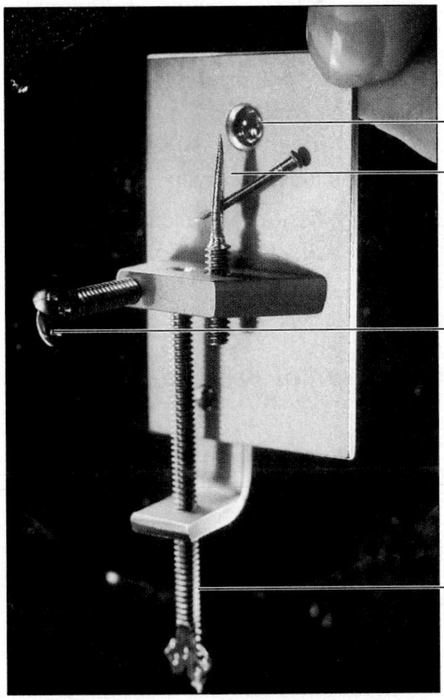

FIGURE 1.5 Model of van Leeuwenhoek's Microscope The original made in 1673 could magnify the object being viewed almost 300 times. The object being viewed is brought into focus with the adjusting screws. Note the small size.

domains are the ***Bacteria*** (formerly called Eubacteria), the ***Archaea*** (meaning ancient), and the ***Eucarya.*** Microscopically, members of the *Bacteria* and *Archaea* look identical. Both are single-celled organisms that do not contain a membrane-bound nucleus nor any other intracellular lipid-bound **organelles.** Their genetic information is stored in deoxyribonucleic acid (DNA) in a region called the **nucleoid.** These simple cell types have their cytoplasm surrounded by a rigid cell wall and are termed **prokaryotes,** which means "prenucleus." All bacteria and archaea are prokaryotes. Although all members of these two domains are prokaryotes, they are totally unrelated. In fact, the *Archaea* are as closely related to humans as they are to the *Bacteria*.

Members of the *Eucarya*, termed **eukaryotes,** which means "true nucleus," are distinctly different from members of the *Bacteria* and *Archaea*. Eukaryotes may be single-celled or multicellular, but they always contain a true membrane-bound nucleus and other internal cell organelles, making them far more complex than the simple prokaryotes. These structures include **mitochondria,** organelles which harvest chemical energy, from foods and in some organisms **chloroplasts,** which harvest light energy. Eukaryotes also have an internal scaffolding, the **cytoskeleton,** which gives the cells their shape. All algae, fungi, protozoa, and multicellular parasites are eukaryotes.

The *Bacteria*

Most of the prokaryotes covered in this text are members of the Domain *Bacteria*. Even within this group, much diversity is seen in the shape and properties of the organisms. Their most prominent features are:

- They are all single-celled prokaryotes.
- Most have specific shapes, most commonly cylindrical (rod-shaped), spherical (round), or spiral ■ bacterial shapes, p. 53
- Most have rigid cell walls, which are responsible for the shape of the organism. The walls contain an unusual chemical compound called **peptidoglycan,** which is not found in organisms in the other domains (see figure 3.32).
- They multiply by **binary fission** in which one cell divides into two cells, each generally identical to the original cell. ■ binary fission, p. 87
- Many can move using appendages extending from the cell, called **flagella** (sing: **flagellum**). ■ flagella, p. 66

The *Archaea*

The *Archaea* have the same shape, size, and appearance as the *Bacteria*. Like the *Bacteria*, the *Archaea* multiply by binary fission and move primarily by means of flagella. They also have rigid cell walls. The chemical composition of their cell wall, however, differs from that in the *Bacteria*. The *Archaea* do not have peptidoglycan as part of their cell walls. Other chemical differences also exist between these two groups.

An interesting feature of many members of the *Archaea* is their ability to grow in extreme environments in which most organisms cannot survive. For example, some archaea can grow in salt concentrations 10 times higher than that found in seawater. These organisms grow in such habitats as the Great Salt Lake and the Dead Sea. Other archaea grow best at extremely high temperatures. One member can grow at a temperature of 121°C. (100°C is the temperature at which water boils at sea level). Some archaea can be found in the boiling hot springs at Yellowstone National Park. Members of the *Archaea*, however, are spread far beyond extreme environments. They are widely distributed in the oceans, and they are found in the cold surface waters of Antarctica and Alaska.

The *Eucarya*

All members of the living world except the prokaryotes are in the Domain *Eucarya*, and all members of this domain consist of eukaryotic cells. The microbial world is composed of single-celled members of the *Eucarya* as well as their close multicellular relatives. These members include **algae** (sing: **alga**), **fungi** (sing: **fungus**), and **protozoa** (sing: **protozoan**). Algae and protozoa are also referred to as **protists.** In addition, some multicellular organisms are considered in this text because they kill millions of people around the world, especially in developing nations. Since they derive nutrients from the host organism they are termed **parasites.** They are given the general name of **helminths** and include organisms such as roundworms and tapeworms.

The *Bacteria, Archaea*, and *Eucarya* are compared in **table 1.2.**

TABLE 1.2 Comparison of *Bacteria, Archaea*, and *Eucarya*

	Bacteria	*Archaea*	*Eucarya*
Typical Size	0.3–2 μm	0.3–2 μm	5–50 μm
Nuclear Membrane	No	No	Yes
Cell Wall	Peptidoglycan present	No peptidoglycan	No peptidoglycan
Cytoplasmic Structures			
Mitochondria	No	No	Yes
Chloroplasts	No	No	In plant and algal cells
Cytoskeleton	No	No	Yes
Where Found	In all environments	In all environments	In environments that are not extreme

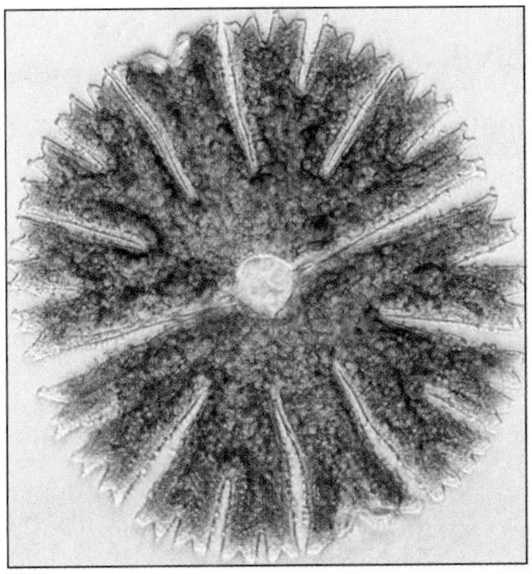

FIGURE 1.6 Alga *Micrasterias*, a green alga composed of two symmetrical halves (100×).

Algae

The algae are a diverse group of eukaryotes; some are single-celled and others are multicellular. Many different shapes and sizes are represented, but they all share some fundamental characteristics **(figure 1.6).** They all contain chloroplasts, some of which have a green pigment, **chlorophyll.** Some also contain other pigments that give them characteristic colors. The pigments absorb light, a source of energy in **photosynthesis.** Algae are usually found near the surface of either salt or fresh water. Their cell walls are rigid, but their chemical composition is quite distinct from that of the *Bacteria* and the *Archaea.* Many algae move by means of flagella, which are structurally more complex and unrelated to flagella in prokaryotes.

Fungi

Fungi are also a diverse group of eukaryotes. Some are single-celled yeasts, but many are large multicellular organisms including molds and mushrooms **(figure 1.7).** In contrast to algae, which derive energy from sunlight, fungi gain their energy from organic materials. Interestingly, fungi are found wherever organic materials are present. Unlike algae, which live primarily in water, fungi live mostly on land.

Protozoa

Protozoa are a diverse group of microscopic, single-celled organisms that live in both aquatic and terrestrial environments. Although microscopic, they are very complex organisms and much larger than prokaryotes **(figure 1.8).** Unlike algae and fungi, protozoa do not have a rigid cell wall. However, many do have a specific shape based on a rigid covering just beneath the outer membrane of the cell. Most protozoa require organic compounds as sources of food, which they ingest as particles. Most groups of protozoa are motile, and a major feature of their classification is their means of locomotion.

The eukaryotic members of the microbial world are compared in **table 1.3.**

Nomenclature

In biology, the Binomial System of Nomenclature refers to a two word naming system. The first word in the name is the **genus,**

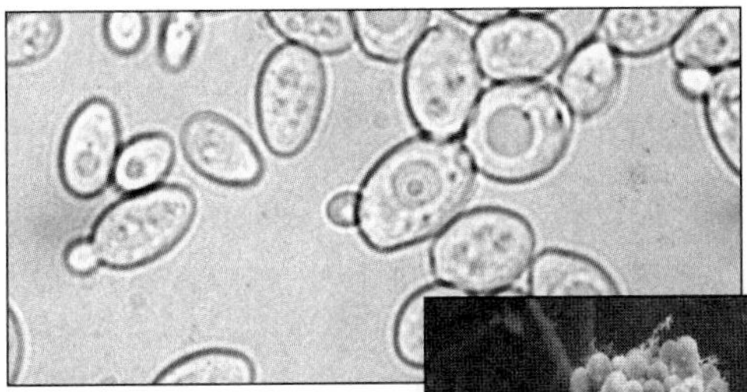
(a)

(b)

FIGURE 1.7 Two Forms of Fungi (a) Living cells of yeast form *Cryptococcus neoformans* stained with India ink to reveal the large capsules that surround the cell. **(b)** *Aspergillus*, a typical mold form whose dark reproductive structures rise above the mycelium.

with the first letter always capitalized; the second is the **species** name, which is not capitalized. Both words are always italicized or underlined. For example, *Escherichia coli* is a member of the genus *Escherichia*. The genus name is commonly abbreviated, with the first letter capitalized: that is, *E. coli*. A number of different species are included in the same genus. Members of the same

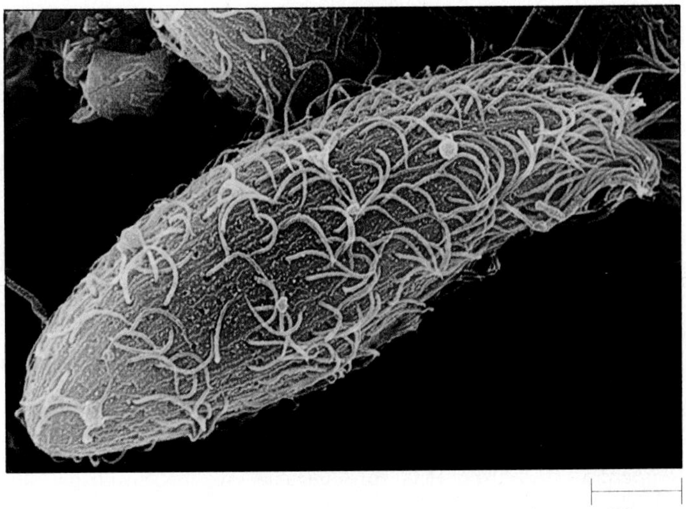

FIGURE 1.8 Protozoan A paramecium moves with the aid of cilia on the cell surface.

TABLE 1.3 Comparison of Eukaryotic Members of the Microbial World

	Algae	Fungi	Protozoa
Cell Organization	Single- or multicellular	Single- or multicellular	Single-celled
Source of Energy	Sunlight	Organic compounds	Organic compounds
Size	Microscopic or macroscopic	Microscopic or macroscopic	Microscopic

species may vary from one another in minor ways, but not enough to give the organisms different species names. These differences, however, may result in the organism being given different **strain designations,** for example, *E. coli* strain B or *E. coli* strain K12.

MICROCHECK 1.3

All organisms fall into one of three large groups based on their cell structure and chemical composition: the *Bacteria,* the *Archaea,* or the *Eucarya.* The *Bacteria* and the *Archaea* have a simple cell type and are termed prokaryotes. Both are identical in appearance but distinctly different in many aspects of their chemical composition. The *Eucarya* have a complex cell structure and are termed eukaryotes. The algae, fungi, protozoa, and multicellular parasites belong to this group. Bacteria, like all organisms, are classified according to the Binomial System of Nomenclature.

- ✓ Name one feature that distinguishes the *Bacteria* from the *Archaea.*
- ✓ List four groups of organisms in the eukaryotic world.
- ✓ List two features that distinguish prokaryotes from eukaryotes.
- ✓ The binomial system of classification uses both a genus and a species name. Why bother with two names? Wouldn't it be easier to use a single, unique name for each different kind of microorganism?

1.4 Viruses, Viroids, and Prions

Focus Points

- Distinguish between viruses, viroids, and prions.
- Discuss the reasons why viruses, viroids, and prions are not organisms.

The organisms discussed so far are living members of the microbial world. In order to be alive, an organism must be composed of one or more cells. Viruses, viroids, and prions are not living and are termed **agents.** Many infectious agents consist of only a few of the molecules typically found in cells. ■ viroids, p. 361 ■ prions, p. 359

Viruses consist of a piece of nucleic acid surrounded by a protein coat. They come in a variety of shapes **(figure 1.9).** Viruses need to reproduce copies of themselves, otherwise they would not exist in nature. Viruses can only multiply inside living host cells, whose multiplication machinery and nutrients they must borrow for reproduction. Outside the hosts, they are inactive. Thus, viruses may be considered **obligate intracellular parasites.** All forms of life including members of the *Bacteria,*

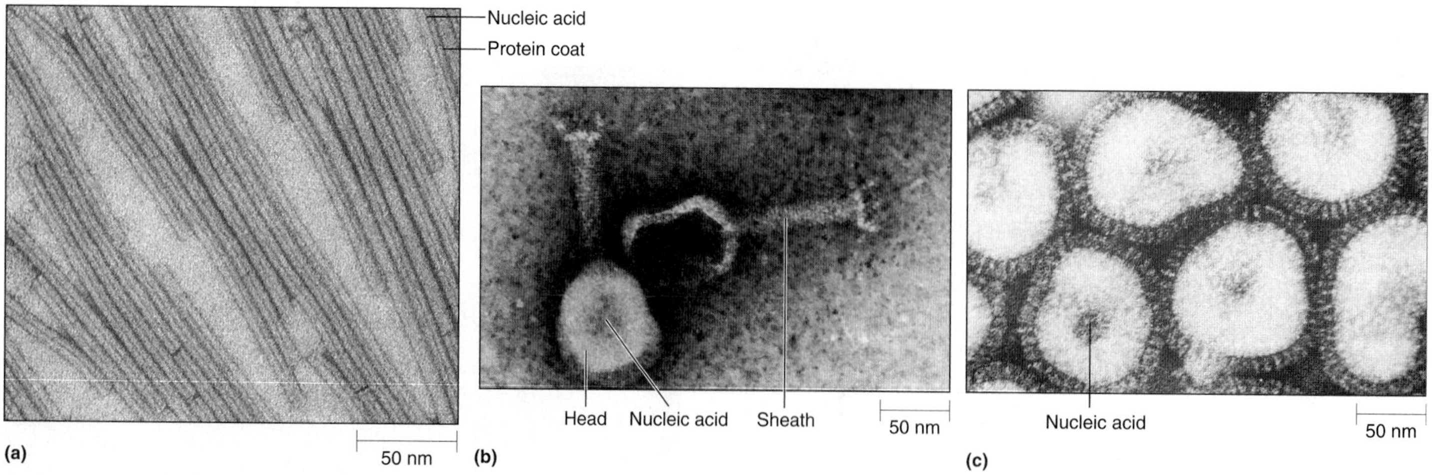

FIGURE 1.9 Viruses That Infect Three Kinds of Organisms (a) Tobacco mosaic virus that infects tobacco plants. A long hollow protein coat surrounds a molecule of RNA. **(b)** A bacterial virus (bacteriophage), which invades bacteria. Nucleic acid is surrounded by a protein coat (head). **(c)** Influenza virus, thin section. This virus infects humans and causes flu.

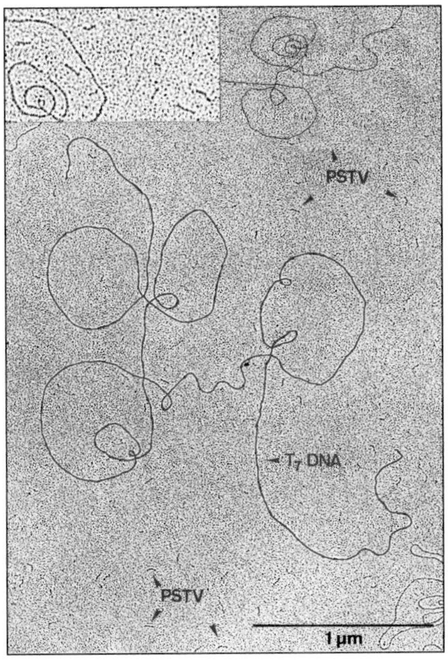

FIGURE 1.10 The Size of a Viroid Compared with a Molecule of DNA from a Virus That Infects Bacteria (T_7) The red arrow points to the potato spindle tuber viroids (PSTV); the other arrow points to bacterial virus T_7 DNA.

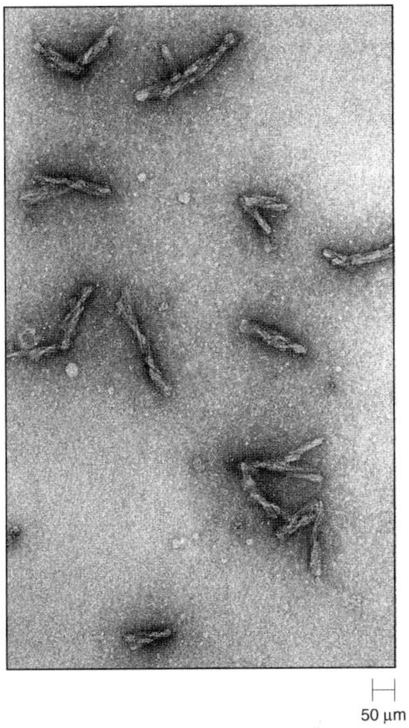

FIGURE 1.11 Prion Prions isolated from the brain of a scrapie-infected hamster. This neurodegenerative disease is caused by a prion.

Archaea, and *Eucarya* can be infected by viruses. Although viruses frequently kill the cells in which they multiply, some viruses exist harmoniously within the host cell without causing obvious ill effects.

Viroids are simpler than viruses, consisting of a single, short piece of nucleic acid, specifically ribonucleic acid (RNA), without a protective coat. They are much smaller than viruses **(figure 1.10)**, and, like viruses, they can reproduce only inside cells. Viroids cause a number of plant diseases, and some scientists speculate that they may cause diseases in humans.

Prions are very unusual agents that are responsible for at least seven neurodegenerative diseases in humans and animals; these are always fatal. Prions consist of only protein, without any nucleic acid **(figure 1.11)**.

The distinguishing features of the non-living members of the microbial world are given in **table 1.4.** The relationships of the major groups of the microbial world to one another are presented in **figure 1.12.**

MICROCHECK 1.4

The acellular agents are viruses, viroids, and prions, all of which can be considered to be obligate intracellular parasites.

- ✓ Compare the chemical composition of viruses, viroids, and prions.
- ✓ What groups of organisms are infected by each of the following: viruses, viroids, prions?
- ✓ How might one argue that viruses are actually living organisms?

TABLE 1.4 Distinguishing Characteristics of Viruses, Viroids, and Prions

Viruses	Viroids	Prions
Obligate intracellular agents	Obligate intracellular agents	Obligate intracellular agents
Consist of either DNA or RNA, surrounded by a protein coat	Consist only of RNA; no protein coat	Consist only of protein; no DNA or RNA

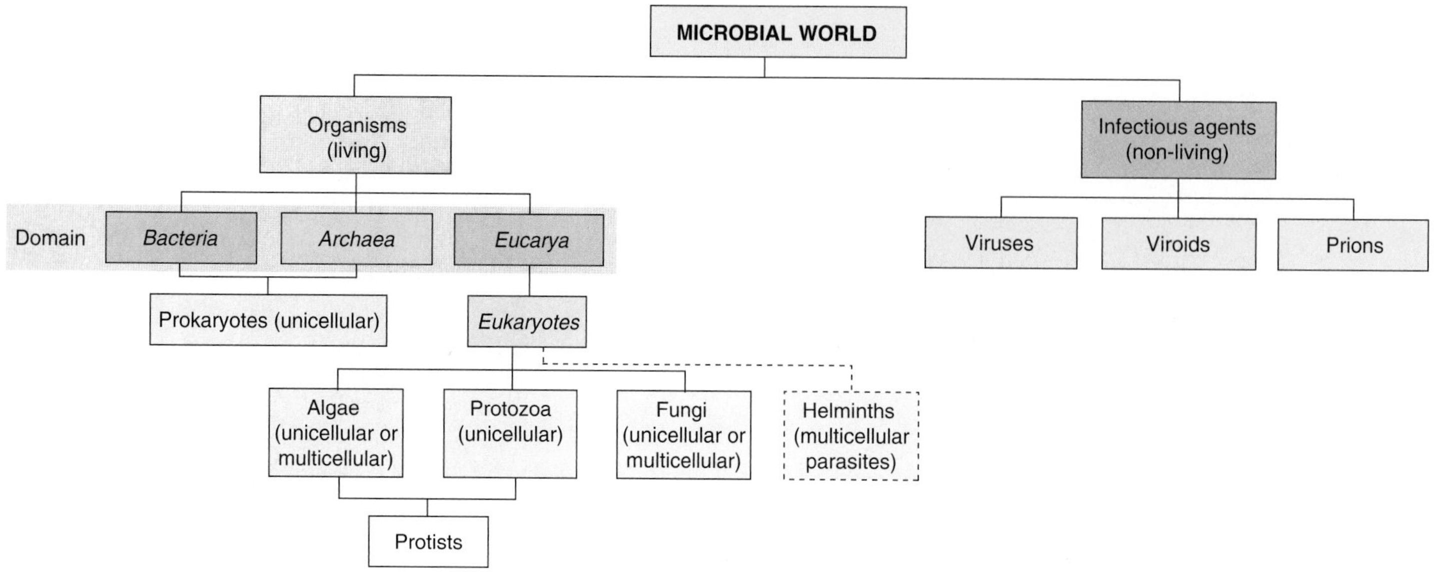

FIGURE 1.12 The Microbial World Although adult helminths are generally not microscopic, some stages in the life cycle of many disease-causing helminths are.

1.5

Size in the Microbial World

Focus Point

- Compare the differences in sizes between members of the microbial world.

Members of the microbial world cover a tremendous range in their sizes, as is seen in **figure 1.13.** The smallest viruses are about 1 million times smaller than the largest eukaryotic cells. Even within a single group, wide variations exist. For example, *Bacillus megaterium* and *Mycoplasma* are both bacteria, but they differ enormously in size (see figure 1.13). The variation in size of bacteria was recently expanded when a bacterium longer than 0.5 mm was discovered (see **Perspective 1.1**). In fact, it is so big that it is visible to the naked eye. More recently, an even larger bacterium, round in shape, was discovered. Its volume is 70 times larger than the previous record holder. Likewise, a eukaryotic cell was recently discovered that is not much larger than a typical bacterium. These, however, are rare exceptions to the rule that

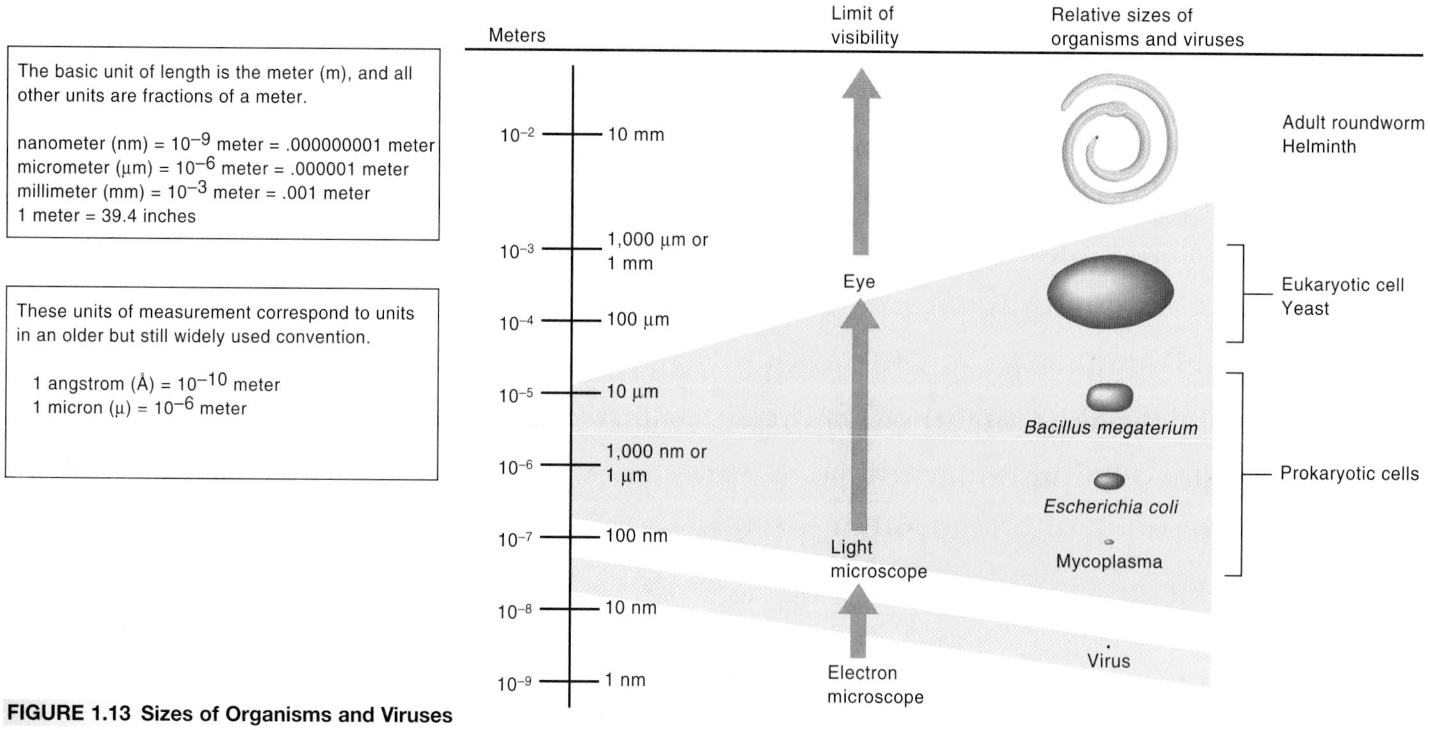

FIGURE 1.13 Sizes of Organisms and Viruses

PERSPECTIVE 1.1

The Long and the Short of It

We might assume that because prokaryotes have been so intensively studied over the past hundred years, no major surprises are left to be discovered. This, however is far from the truth. In the mid-1990s, a large peculiar-looking organism was seen when the intestinal tracts of certain fish from both the Red Sea in the Middle East and the Great Barrier Reef in Australia were examined. This organism, named *Epulopisicium* cannot be cultured in the laboratory **(figure 1).** Its large size, 600 μ m long and 80 μ wide, which makes it clearly visible without any magnification, suggested that this organism was a eukaryote. It did not, however have a nuclear membrane. A chemical analysis of the cell confirmed that it was a prokaryote and a member of the Domain *Bacteria.* This very long, slender organism is an exception to the rule that prokaryotes are always smaller than eukaryotes.

In 1999, an even larger prokaryote in volume was isolated from the sulfurous muck of the ocean floor off the coast of Namibia in Africa. It is a spherical organism 70 times larger in volume than *Epulopisicium.* Since it grows on sulfur compounds and contains glistening globules of sulfur, It was named *Thiomargarita namibiensis,* which means "sulfur pearl of Namibia" **(figure 2).** Although scientists were initially skeptical that prokaryotes could be so large, there is no question in their minds now. In contrast to these large bacteria, a cell was isolated in the Mediterranean Sea that is 1 μ m in width. It is a eukaryote because it contains a nucleus and a mitochondrion even though it is about the size of a typical bacterium.

On the other side of the coin, investigators are asking how small can a living organism be. An answer to this question may be at hand as a result of a new microorganism discovered off the coast of Iceland. The organism, found in an ocean vent where the temperature was close to the boiling point of water, cannot be grown in the laboratory by itself, but only grows when it is attached to another much larger member of the *Archaea* **(figure 3).** These tiny organisms, also members of the *Archaea,* have been named *Nanoarchaeum equitans,* which means "riding the fire sphere." The organism to which *N. equitans* is attached is *Ignicoccus,* which means "fire ball." It grows very well without its rider. *N. equitans* is spherical and only about 400 nanometers in diameter, about a quarter the diameter of *Ignicoccus.* Also, the amount of genetic information (DNA) contained in *N. equitans* is less than in any known organism, and only about one-tenth the amount found in the common gut organism, *Escherichia coli.* This sets the record for the smallest amount of DNA in any organism. Thus, this organism may contain only the essential DNA required for life. Further analysis of these cells suggests that they may resemble the earliest cells and therefore the ancestor of all life on earth. The scientists who discovered *N. equitans* suggest that many more unusual organisms related to *N. equitans* will be discovered. They are probably right!

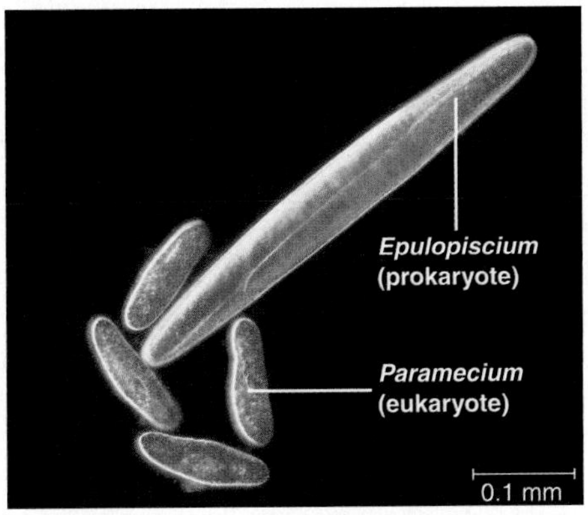

FIGURE 1 Longest Known Bacterium, *Epulopisicium* Mixed With Paramecia Note how large this prokaryote is compared with the four eukaryotic paramecia.

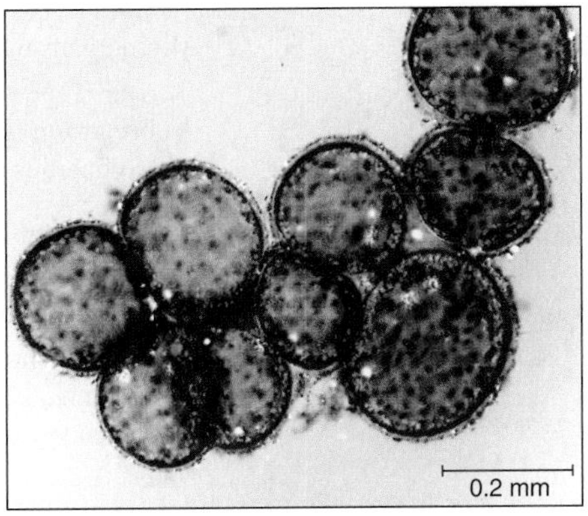

FIGURE 2 *Thiomargarita namibiensis* The average *Thiomargarita namibiensis* is two-tenths of a millimeter, but some reach three times that size. ■ **Thiomargarita, p. 268**

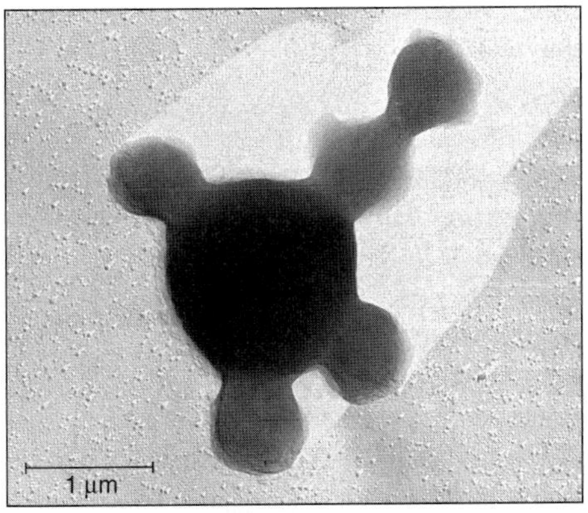

FIGURE 3 Five Cells of "N. equitans," Attached on the Surface of the (Central) Ignicoccus Cell. Platinum shadowed.

eukaryotes are larger than prokaryotes, which in turn are larger than viruses.

As you might expect, the small size and broad size range of some members of the microbial world have required the use of measurements not commonly used in everyday life. The use of logarithms has proved to be enormously helpful, especially in designating the sizes of prokaryotes and viruses. A brief discussion of measurements and logarithms is given in Appendix I.

MICROCHECK 1.5

The range in size of the members of the microbial world is tremendous. As a general rule, the obligate intracellular parasites are the smallest and the eukaryotes the largest.

- ✓ Why do eukaryotic cells generally need to be larger than prokaryotic cells?
- ✓ What factor limits the size of free-living cells?

FUTURE CHALLENGES

Entering a New Golden Age

For all the information that has been gathered about the microbial world, it is remarkable how little we know about its prokaryotic members. This is not surprising in view of the fact that less than 1% of the prokaryotes have ever been studied. In large part, this is because only one in a hundred of the prokaryotes in the environment can be cultured in the laboratory. Part of the current revolution in microbiology, however, will allow us to inventory the millions of species that are out there waiting to be discovered. This is now being done. Using techniques that helped decipher the human genome, scientists have begun to analyze the biological content of the oceans. In a small volume of water from the Sargasso Sea, an area of the ocean that contains few nutrients and therefore presumably few organisms, scientists found 1,800 species of bacteria that were previously unknown. The biodiversity of the microbial world is astounding!

Exploring the unknowns in the microbial world is a major challenge and should answer many intriguing questions fundamental to understanding the biological world. What are the extremes of temperature, salt, pH, radioactivity, and pressure in which prokaryotes can live? Are there organisms growing in even more extreme environments? If life can exist on this planet under such extreme conditions, what does this mean about the possibility of finding living organisms on other planets? Although considered highly unlikely, is it possible that living organisms exist whose chemical structure is not based on the carbon atom? Will living organisms be found whose genetic information is coded in a chemical other than deoxyribonucleic acid? What new metabolic pathways remain to be discovered? Who would have thought that some organisms, members of the *Archaea,* could live at temperatures above boiling water and a pH of sulfuric acid? As extreme environments are mined for their living biological diversity, there seems little doubt that many surprises will be found. In many cases these surprises will be translated into new biotechnology products on this planet, and they will help shape the way we look for life on other planets.

One hundred years ago we were in the Golden Age of medical microbiology. We are now entering the Golden Age of microbial biodiversity.

SUMMARY

1.1 The Origin of Microorganisms

Theory of Spontaneous Generation Revisited

The experiments of Pasteur refuted the theory of spontaneous generation. (Figure 1.1)

The experiments of Tyndall and Cohn demonstrated the existence of heat-resistant forms of bacteria that could account for the growth of bacteria in infusions that had been heated.

1.2 Microbiology: A Human Perspective

Vital Activities of Microorganisms

The activities of microorganisms are vital for the survival of all other organisms, including humans.

Microorganisms represent the most diverse forms of life on earth.

Bacteria are necessary to convert the nitrogen gas in air into a form that plants and other organisms can use.

Microorganisms replenish the oxygen on earth.

Microorganisms degrade organic waste materials.

Applications of Microbiology

For thousands of years, bread, wine, beer, and cheeses have been made by using technology still applied today.

Bacteria are being used to degrade dangerous toxic pollutants.

Bacteria are used to synthesize a variety of different products, such as cellulose, hydroxybutyric acid, ethanol, antibiotics, and amino acids.

Genetic engineering is the process in which genes from one organism are introduced into related or unrelated organisms resulting in new properties. (Figure 1.2)

Genetic engineering has expanded the capabilities of microorganisms enormously.

Microorganisms produce medically important products and can produce vaccines against a variety of diseases.

A bacterium can transfer genes into plants and modify their properties.

Medical Microbiology

Many devastating diseases such as smallpox, bubonic plague, and influenza have determined the course of history. (Figure 1.3)

"New" emerging diseases are arising. Partly, this is because people are engaging in different lifestyles and living in regions where formerly only animals lived. (Figure 1.4)

"Old" diseases that were on the wane have begun to reemerge. Many are brought to this country by people visiting foreign lands.

Several chronic diseases such as ulcers and perhaps, but unlikely, heart disease are caused by bacteria.

Bacteria use the body as an ecological habitat and interact with other bacteria on its surface. Pathogens gain entrance to the body and find a protected habitat inside host cells.

Microorganisms As Subjects for Study

Microorganisms are excellent model organisms to study because they grow rapidly on simple, inexpensive media, but follow the same genetic, metabolic, and biochemical principles as higher organisms.

1.3 The Microbial World (Figure 1.12)

Members of the microbial world consist of two major cell types: the simple **prokaryotic** and the complex **eukaryotic**.

All organisms fall into one of three **domains**, based on their chemical composition and cell structure. These are the ***Bacteria***, the ***Archaea***, and the ***Eucarya***. (Table 1.2)

The Bacteria

The *Bacteria* are single-celled prokaryotes that have peptidoglycan in their cell wall.

The Archaea

Archaea are single-celled prokaryotes that are identical in appearance to the *Bacteria*. They do not have peptidoglycan in their cell walls and are unrelated to the *Bacteria*.

Many of the *Archaea* grow in extreme environments such as hot springs and salt flats.

The Eucarya

Eucarya have eukaryotic cell structures and may be single-celled or multicellular.

Microbial members of the *Eucarya* are the **algae, fungi,** and **protozoa.**

Algae can be single-celled or multicellular, and they can use sunlight as a source of energy. (Figure 1.6, Table 1.3)

Fungi are either single-celled yeasts or multicellular molds and mushrooms. They use organic compounds as food. (Figure 1.7, Table 1.3)

Protozoa are single-celled organisms that are motile by a variety of means. They use organic compounds as food. (Figure 1.8, Table 1.3)

Nomenclature

Organisms are named according to a binomial system.

Each organism has a **genus** and a **species** name, written in italics.

1.4 Viruses, Viroids, and Prions

The non-living members of the microbial world are not composed of cells. They are considered **obligate intracellular parasites** and include **viruses, viroids,** and **prions.**

Viruses are a piece of nucleic acid surrounded by a protein coat. They can infect members of all three domains. (Figure 1.9, Table 1.4)

Viroids are composed of a single, short RNA molecule. Thus far, they are only known to cause diseases in plants. (Figure 1.10, Table 1.4)

Prions consist only of protein, without any nucleic acid. They cause several different neurodegenerative diseases of humans and animals. (Figure 1.11, Table 1.4)

1.5 Size in the Microbial World

Sizes of members of the microbial world vary enormously, (Figure 1.13)

REVIEW QUESTIONS

Short Answer

1. Name the prokaryotic groups in the microbial world.
2. List five beneficial applications of bacteria.
3. Name three non-living groups in the microbial world and describe their major properties.
4. In the designation *Escherichia coli* O157:H7, what is the genus? What is the species? What is the strain?
5. Where would you go to isolate members of the *Archaea*?
6. How might you distinguish a prokaryotic cell from a eukaryotic cell?
7. Give three reasons why life could not exist on earth without the activities of microorganisms.
8. Differentiate between biotechnology and genetic engineering.
9. Name two diseases that have been especially destructive in the past. What is the status of those diseases today?
10. State three reasons that there is a resurgence of infectious diseases today.

Multiple Choice

1. The prokaryotic members of the microbial world include
   1. algae. 2. fungi. 3. prions.
   4. bacteria. 5. archaea.
   a) 1, 2 b) 2, 3 c) 3, 4 d) 4, 5 e) 1, 5
2. The *Archaea*
   1. are microscopic.
   2. are commonly found in extreme environments.
   3. contain peptidoglycan.
   4. contain mitochondria.
   5. are most commonly found in the soil.
   a) 1, 2 b) 2, 3 c) 3, 4 d) 4, 5 e) 1, 5
3. The most fundamental division of cell types is between the
   a) algae, fungi, and protozoa.
   b) eukaryotes and prokaryotes.
   c) viruses and viroids.
   d) bacteria and archaea.
   e) *Eucarya, Bacteria,* and *Archaea.*
4. The number of bacteria in the human body compared to the number of non-bacterial cells is estimated to be
   a) About 10 times more non-bacterial cells than bacteria.
   b) About equal numbers of bacteria and non-bacterial cells.
   c) About 10 times more bacteria than non-bacteria.
5. An organism isolated from a hot spring in an acidic environment is most likely a member of the
   a) *Bacteria.* b) *Archaea.* c) *Eucarya.*
   d) virus family. e) Fungi.
6. The agent that contains no nucleic acid is a
   a) virus. b) prion. c) viroid.
   d) bacterium. e) fungus.
7. Prokaryotes do not have
   a) cell walls. b) flagella. c) a nuclear membrane.
   d) specific shapes. e) genetic information.
8. Nucleoids are associated with
   1. genetic information. 2. prokaryotes. 3. eukaryotes.
   4. viruses. 5. prions.
   a) 1, 2 b) 2, 3 c) 3, 4 d) 4, 5 e) 1, 5

9. Which of the following are eukaryotes?
   1. Algae 2. Viruses 3. Bacteria
   4. Prions 5. Protozoa
   a) 1, 2 b) 2, 3 c) 3, 4 d) 4, 5 e) 1, 5
10. The person best known for his microscopy of microorganisms is
    a) Antony van Leeuwenhoek.
    b) Louis Pasteur.
    c) John Tyndall.
    d) Ferdinand Cohn.

Applications

1. The American Society of Microbiology is preparing a "Microbe-Free" banquet to emphasize the importance of microorganisms in the diet. What foods would not be on the menu if microorganisms were not available for our use?
2. If you were asked to nominate one of the individuals mentioned in this chapter for the Nobel Prize, who would it be? Make a statement supporting your choice.

Critical Thinking

1. An early microbiologist, who was inclined to accept the theory of spontaneous generation, criticized Pasteur's experiments (see figure 1.1). He claimed that a few spontaneously generated bacteria would be present in the boiled and cooled broth but shaking the broth was necessary to stimulate these few to start dividing. Pasteur had not included this step, and bacteria had not started dividing until the flask was tipped and the broth agitated. Does this microbiologist have a valid criticism? What experiment would eliminate this possibility?
2. A microbiologist obtained two pure isolated biological samples: one of a virus, and the other of a viroid. Unfortunately, the labels had been lost from the two samples. The microbiologist felt she could distinguish the two by analyzing for the presence or absence of a single chemical element. What element would she search for and why?
3. Chlamydias and rickettsias were once classified as viruses because of their small size and obligate intracellular growth requirement. What techniques can be used to show that they are really bacteria?
4. Why are the spores of *Bacillus anthracis* such an effective agent of bioterrorism?

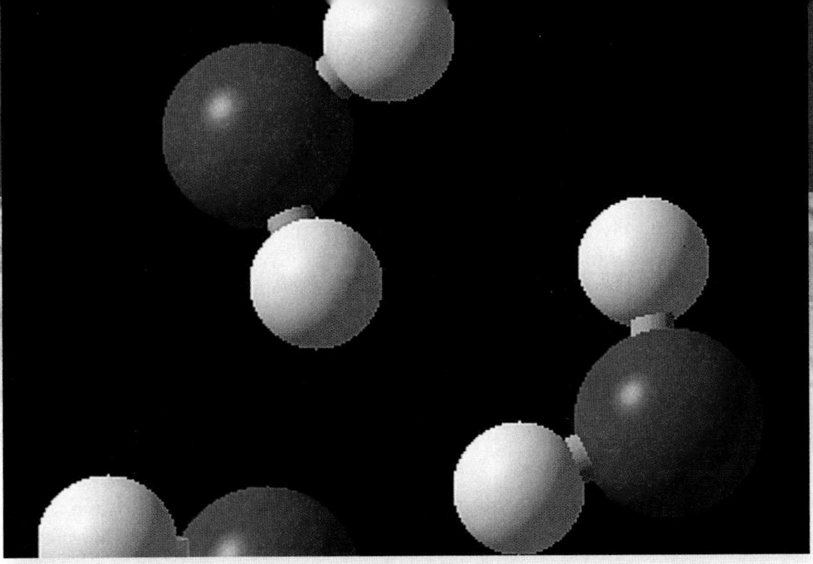

Ball-and-stick model of water molecules

CHAPTER TWO

The Molecules of Life

A Glimpse of History

Louis Pasteur (1822–1895) is often considered the father of bacteriology. His contributions to this science, especially in its early formative years, were enormous and are discussed in many of the succeeding chapters. Pasteur started his scientific career as a chemist, initially working in the science of crystallography.

He first studied two compounds, tartaric and paratartaric acids, which formed thick crusts within wine barrels. These two substances form crystals that have the same number and arrangement of atoms, yet they twist (rotate) a plane of light differently when that light passes through the crystal. Tartaric acid twists the light; paratartaric acid does not. Therefore, the two molecules must differ in some way, even though they are chemically identical. Pasteur was intrigued by these observations and set about to understand how the crystals differed. Looking at them under a microscope, he saw that the crystals of tartaric acid all looked identical but paratartaric acid consisted of two different kinds of crystals. Using tweezers, he carefully separated the two kinds into two piles and dissolved each kind in a separate flask of water. When he shone polarized light through each solution, one solution twisted the light to the left and the other twisted it to the right. When he mixed equal numbers of each kind of crystal into water and shone polarized light through the solution, the light was not twisted. Apparently, the two components of the mixture counteracted each other, and as a result, the mixture did not rotate the light. Pasteur concluded that paratartaric acid is a mixture of two compounds, each being the mirror image, or **optical isomer,** of the other. Optical isomers are often called **stereoisomers.** This mixture of two optical isomers can be viewed as a mixture of right- and left-handed molecules, represented as a right and left hand facing each other (see figure 2.14). They cannot be superimposed on each other, much as a right-handed glove cannot fit the left hand.

Stereoisomers of the same molecule have greatly different properties. For example, the amino acid phenylalanine, one of the key ingredients in the artificial sweetener aspartame, makes aspartame sweet when it is in one optical form but bitter when in the other form. Thus, what Pasteur studied as a straightforward problem in chemistry has implications far beyond what he ever imagined. It is often difficult to predict where research will lead or the significance of interesting but seemingly unimportant observations.

To understand how cells live and interact with one another and with their environment, we must be familiar with the molecules that compose all living matter. For some, this information may serve as a review of material already encountered. For others, it may be a first encounter with the chemistry of biological molecules. In this case, you likely will return to this chapter frequently. The discussion proceeds from the lowest level of organization, the atoms and elements, to the highly complex associations between small molecules which often form large molecules, the macromolecules.

2.1 Atoms and Elements

Focus Point

- Name the three major components of atoms and describe their properties.

Atoms, the basic units of all matter, are made up of three major components: the negatively charged **electrons;** positively charged **protons;** and uncharged **neutrons (figure 2.1).** The protons and

KEY TERMS

ATP An abbreviation for adenosine triphosphate, the form in which chemical energy is stored in the cell.

Carbohydrate A compound characterized by a large number of —OH groups and containing principally carbon, hydrogen, and oxygen in a ratio of 1:2:1.

Covalent bond A strong chemical bond formed by the sharing of electrons between atoms.

Dehydration synthesis A chemical reaction that joins two molecules to form a larger molecule by removing water.

Hydrogen bond A weak bond resulting from the attraction between a positively charged hydrogen atom in one compound and a negatively charged atom in another compound.

Lipid A heterogenous group of organic molecules characterized by being insoluble in water, but soluble in organic solvents such as ether, chloroform, and benzene.

Macromolecule A very large molecule usually consisting of repeating subunits.

Nucleic acid A macromolecule consisting of chains of nucleotide subunits to form either DNA or RNA, the two types of nucleic acid.

Peptide bond A covalent bond formed between the —COOH group of one amino acid and the $—NH_2$ group of another amino acid; their formation is an important reaction in the synthesis of a protein.

pH The abbreviation for potential hydrogen, a measure on a scale of 0 to 14 of acidity of a solution.

Protein A macromolecule consisting of one or more chains of amino acids.

Stereoisomers Two compounds that are mirror images of one another.

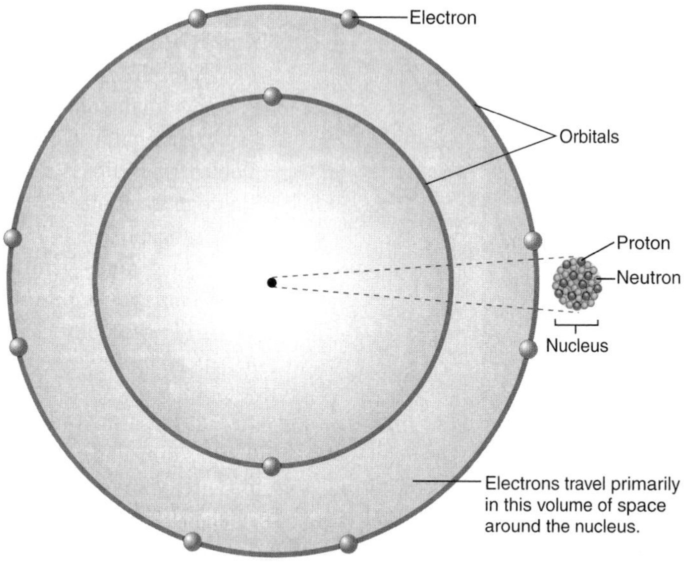

FIGURE 2.1 Atom The proton has a positive charge, the neutron has a neutral charge, and the electron has a negative charge. The electrons that orbit the nucleus are arranged in orbitals of different energy levels.

neutrons, the heaviest components, are found in the heaviest part of the atom, the nucleus. The very light electrons orbit the nucleus. The number of protons normally equals the number of electrons, and so the atom as a whole is uncharged. The relative sizes and motion of the parts of an atom can be illustrated by the following analogy. If a single atom were enlarged to the size of a football stadium, the nucleus would be the size of a marble and it would be positioned somewhere above the 50-yard line. The electrons would resemble fruit flies zipping around the stands. Their orbits would be mostly inside the stadium, but on occasion they would travel outside it.

An **element** is a substance that consists of a single type of atom. Although 92 naturally occurring elements exist, four elements make up over 99% of all living material by weight. These elements are carbon (abbreviated C), hydrogen (H), oxygen (O), and nitrogen (N). Two other elements, phosphorus (P), and sulfur (S), together make up an additional 0.5% of the elements in living systems **(table 2.1).** All of the remaining elements together account for less than 0.5% of living material. In general, the basic chemical composition of all living cells is remarkably similar.

Each element is identified by two numbers: its **atomic number** and its **atomic weight** or **mass.** The atomic number is the number of protons, which equals the number of electrons. For example, hydrogen has 1 proton, and thus its atomic number is 1; oxygen has 8 protons, and its atomic number is 8. The atomic weight is the sum of the number of protons and neutrons, since electrons are too light to contribute to the weight. The atomic weight of hydrogen is 1, which is abbreviated ^{1}H, reflecting 1 proton and no neutrons. It is the lightest element known. The atomic weight of oxygen is approximately 16 and is abbreviated ^{16}O, reflecting 8 protons and 8 neutrons.

It is convenient to consider electrons as being arranged in **orbitals** of differing energy levels. The electrons farthest from the nucleus with its positive charge travel the fastest and have the highest energy level. Electrons can move from one orbital to another as they gain or lose energy (see figure 2.1). Each orbital can contain only a certain number of electrons. The first orbital closest to the nucleus contains a maximum of 2 electrons, the next 8, and the next also 8. Other atoms, which have little biological importance, have additional electrons. Each orbital must be filled, starting with the one closest to the nucleus, before electrons can occupy the next outer orbital.

MICROCHECK 2.1

All living organisms contain the same elements. The four most important are carbon, hydrogen, oxygen, and nitrogen. The basic unit of all matter, the atom, is composed of protons, electrons, and neutrons.

✓ Of all the elements found in cells, which element is found most frequently?

TABLE 2.1 Atomic Structure of Elements Commonly Found in the Living World

Element	Symbol	Atomic Number (Total Number of Protons)	Atomic Weight (Protons + Neutrons)	Number of Possible Covalent Bonds*	Approximate % of Atoms in Cells
Hydrogen	H	1	1	1	49
Carbon	C	6	12	4	25
Nitrogen	N	7	14	3	0.5
Oxygen	O	8	16	2	25
Phosphorus	P	15	31	3	0.1
Sulfur	S	16	32	2	0.4

*The number of electrons required to fill the outer orbital equals the number of possible covalent bonds.
The number of electrons in a completed outer orbital varies depending on the distance of the orbital from the nucleus.

2.2

Chemical Bonds and the Formation of Molecules

Focus Points

- Name the strongest bond between atoms and two weak bonds.
- Explain the difference between polar and non-polar covalent bonds and explain why polar bonds are important in biology.
- Describe the properties of the carbon atom that make it the most important atom in all organisms.

All atoms seek maximum stability. For an atom to be very stable, its outer orbital must contain the maximum number of electrons. If an atom does not have its outer orbital full, then it tends to fill its outer orbital by bonding with other atoms in order to become maximally stable.

Most atoms do not have their outer orbitals filled with the maximum number of electrons and therefore must either gain electrons from, or lose electrons to, other atoms. The number of electrons that an atom must gain or lose to fill its outer orbital is its **valence.** This is the number of covalent bonds that the atom can form (see table 2.1). To gain or lose electrons, atoms bond with other atoms to form **molecules.** A molecule consists of two or more atoms held together by **chemical bonds.** The atoms that make up a molecule may be of the same or different elements. For example, H_2 is a molecule of hydrogen gas formed from two atoms of hydrogen; water (H_2O) is an association of two hydrogen atoms with one oxygen atom. A **compound** consists of two or more different elements.

The chemical bonds that hold atoms together are of various types, which differ in strength. These include covalent bonds, ionic bonds, and hydrogen bonds.

Covalent Bonds

Atoms often achieve stability by sharing electrons with other atoms, thereby filling the outer orbitals of both atoms simultaneously. This sharing creates strong bonds, called **covalent bonds.** Carbon (C), the most important single atom in biology, is frequently involved in covalent bonding. Carbon has four electrons but requires a total of eight to fill its outer orbital. A hydrogen (H) atom has one electron and requires an additional one to fill its outer orbital. Thus, the C atom can fill its outer orbital by sharing electrons with four H atoms. Each H atom has its outer orbital filled by sharing two electrons with the C atom. The compound CH_4 is methane, and its formation involves one carbon atom sharing eight electrons with four hydrogen atoms (**figure 2.2,** and see table 2.1) The outer orbitals of both C and H are filled with shared electrons. Since a C atom can bond with four other atoms, it can build up a large number of different molecules, which explains why it is the key atom in all cells. When C forms covalent bonds with C or H atoms, an **organic** compound is formed. **Inorganic** compounds do not contain C to C bonds.

A single covalent bond is designated by a dash between the two atoms sharing the electrons and is written as C—H. Sometimes two pairs of electrons are shared between atoms in order for their outer orbitals to be filled. This forms a double covalent bond indicated by two lines between the atoms—for example O=C=O (CO_2).

All covalent bonds are strong. The stronger the bond, the more difficult it is to break. Consequently, covalent bonds do not break unless they are exposed to strong chemicals or large amounts of energy, generally as heat. Molecules formed by covalent bonds never break apart spontaneously at temperatures compatible with life. Since most biological systems cannot tolerate the high temperatures required to break these covalent bonds, cells utilize protein catalysts called **enzymes,** which can break these covalent bonds at the lower temperatures found in living systems. How enzymes function is covered in chapter 6.

■ Enzymes, pp. 134, 139

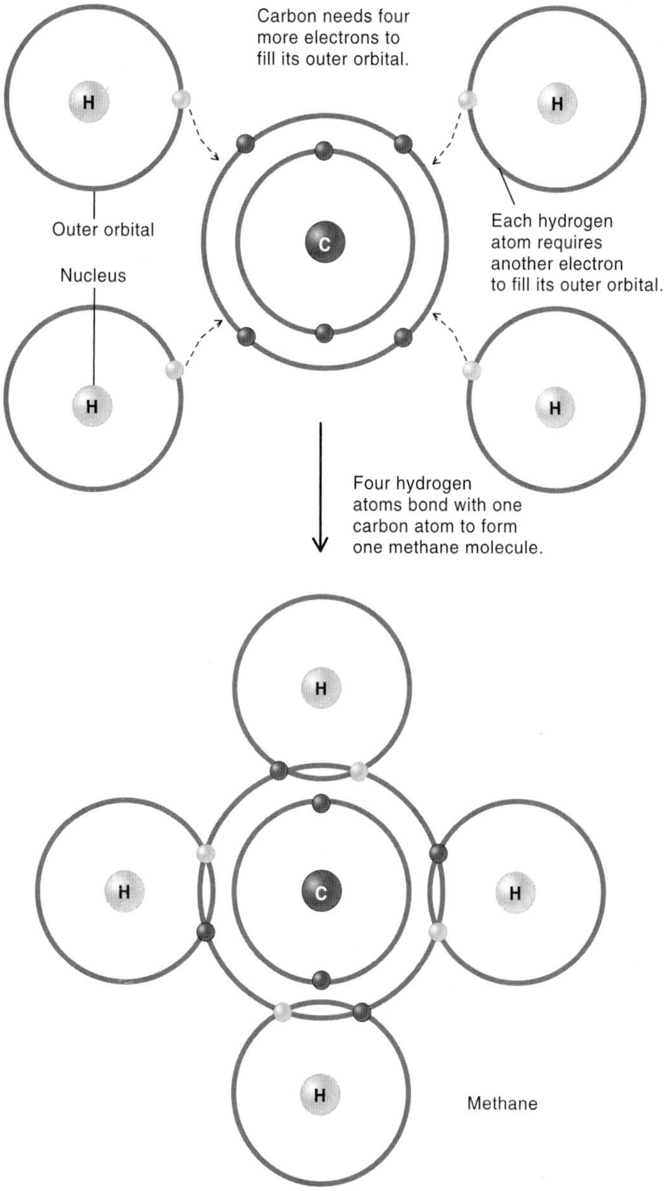
Carbon needs four more electrons to fill its outer orbital.
H
H
Outer orbital
C
Each hydrogen atom requires another electron to fill its outer orbital.
Nucleus
H
H
Four hydrogen atoms bond with one carbon atom to form one methane molecule.
H
H
C
H
H
Methane

FIGURE 2.2 Covalent Bonds The carbon atom fills its outer electron orbital by sharing a total of 8 electrons. Four belong to the four H atoms and four belong to the one carbon atom. The outer orbitals of each of these atoms are then filled—2 in the case of the H atom and 8 in the case of the C atom.

Non-Polar and Polar Covalent Bonds

Two atoms connected by a covalent bond may exert the same or different attractions for the shared electrons of the bond. In covalent bonds between identical atoms, such as H—H, the electrons are shared equally. Equal sharing also exists between different atoms, such as C—H, if both atoms have a similar attraction for electrons **(table 2.2).** This bond is termed a **non-polar covalent bond.** If, however, one atom has a much greater attraction for electrons than the other, the electrons are shared unequally, and

TABLE 2.2 Non-Polar and Polar Covalent Bonds

Type of Covalent Bond	Atoms Involved and Charge Distribution	
Non-polar	C—C C—H H—H	C and H have equal attractions for electrons, so there is an equivalent charge on each atom.
Polar	O—H N—H O—C N—C	The O and N atoms have a stronger attraction for electrons than do C and H, so the O and N have a slight negative charge; the C and H have a slight positive charge.

polar covalent bonds are formed. One part of the molecule has a slightly positive charge and another part a slightly negative charge. An example of a polar molecule is water, in which the oxygen atom has a greater attraction for the shared electrons than do the hydrogen atoms **(figure 2.3).** Consequently, the oxygen atom has a slight negative charge and the hydrogen atoms a slight positive charge. Polar covalent bonds play a key role in biological systems because they allow weak bonds, termed **hydrogen bonds,** to be formed. Hydrogen bonds will be covered in more detail in this chapter. These weak bonds allow different molecules to recognize one another and join together to carry out biological functions.

Ionic Bonds

Ionic bonds join charged atoms termed **ions** together **(figure 2.4).** As we have already mentioned, an atom can fill its outer orbital by either gaining or losing electrons. If electrons from one atom are attracted very strongly by another nearby atom, the electrons completely leave the first atom and become a part of the outer electron orbital of the second, without any sharing. The loss or gain of electrons leads to an atom that is electrically charged. The attraction of the positively charged atom to the negatively charged atom forms the ionic bond. The atom that gains the electrons becomes negatively charged, while the atom that gives up the electrons becomes positively charged. Ions that are positively charged are termed **cations;** negatively charged ions are **anions.** The difference between the number of protons and electrons in the ion is indicated by a superscript number. If only a + or – is indicated, then the charge is 1. For example, Na^+ indicates a Na ion with one positive charge. Note that the charge is much greater when electrons are transferred from one atom to another than when polar covalent bonds are formed. Ionic bonds are an example of extreme polarity.

Ionic bonds are important in biology because they are common among the weak forces holding ions, atoms, and molecules together. In water (aqueous solutions), ionic bonds are about 100 times weaker than covalent bonds, because water molecules tend to move between the ions and thereby greatly reduce their attraction for one another. Thus, in aqueous solution, which is

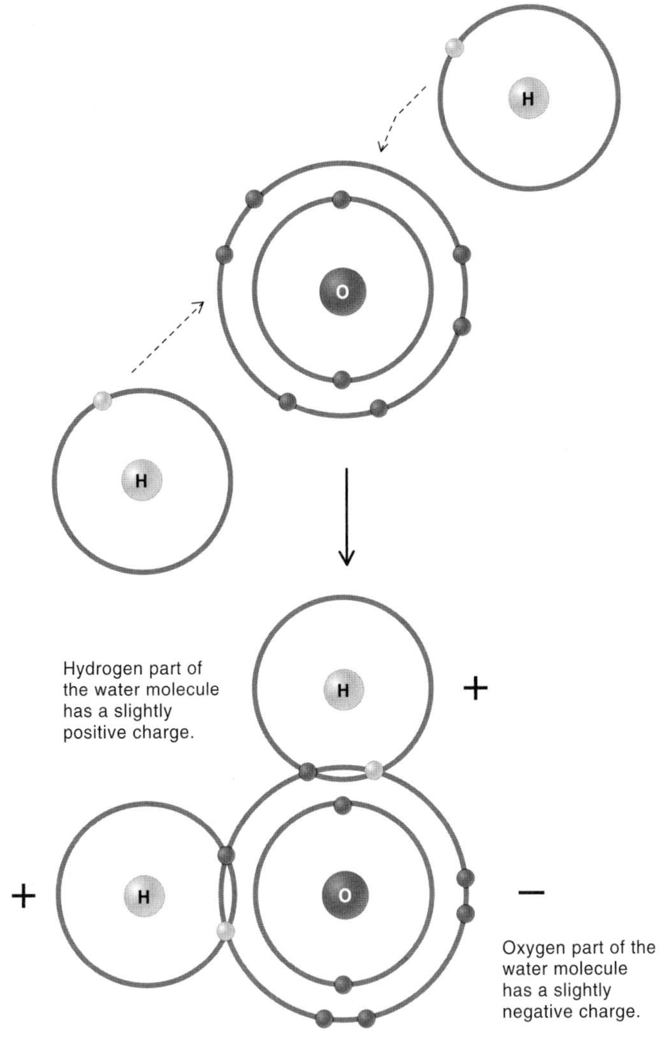

FIGURE 2.3 Formation of Polar Covalent Bonds in a Water Molecule In a water molecule the oxygen atom has a greater attraction for the shared electrons than do the hydrogen atoms. Hence, the electron is closer to the oxygen and confers a slight negative charge on a portion of this atom. Each of the hydrogen atoms has a slight positive charge on a portion of the atom. Because of these charges, water is a polar molecule.

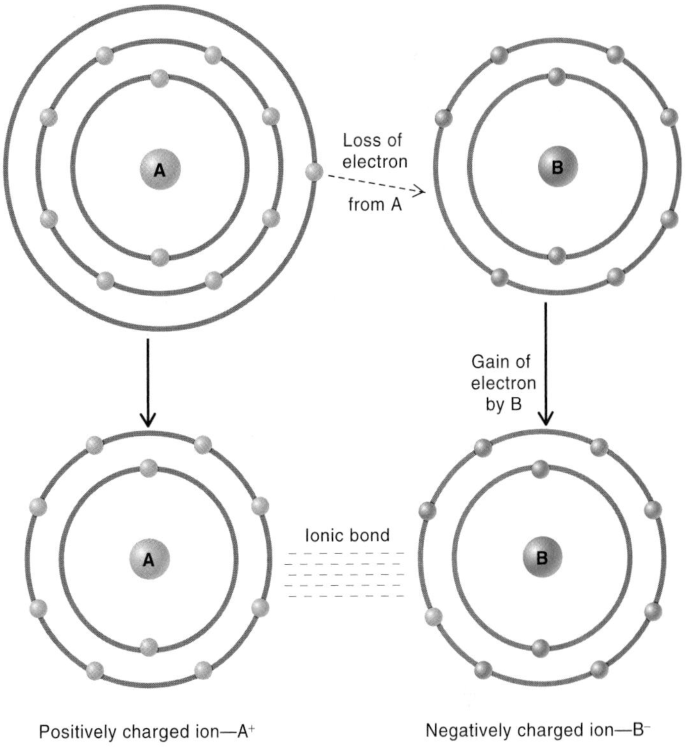

FIGURE 2.4 Ionic Bond Atom A gives up an electron to atom B; hence, atom A acquires a positive charge and atom B a negative charge. Both atoms then have their outer orbitals filled with the maximum number of electrons leading to maximum stability. The attraction of the positively charged A^+ ion to the negatively charged B^- ion forms the bond.

common in all biological systems, the weak ionic bonds are readily broken at room temperature. Ionic bonds play another important role in biology. In all biological systems, molecules must recognize one another. This recognition depends on large numbers of atoms on the surfaces of molecules matching each other precisely. Large numbers of weak bonds, which include ionic bonds, are necessary to hold the molecules together.

Hydrogen Bonds

Hydrogen bonds are weak bonds formed by the attraction of a positively charged hydrogen atom in a polar molecule to a negatively charged atom, frequently oxygen (O) or nitrogen (N) in another polar molecule (**figure 2.5,** and see table 2.2). Oxygen and nitrogen attract electrons within a molecule, and therefore they often have a slightly negative charge. Note that hydrogen bonds form between molecules such as water molecules or within molecules such as DNA, whereas covalent bonds occur between the atoms that make up these molecules.

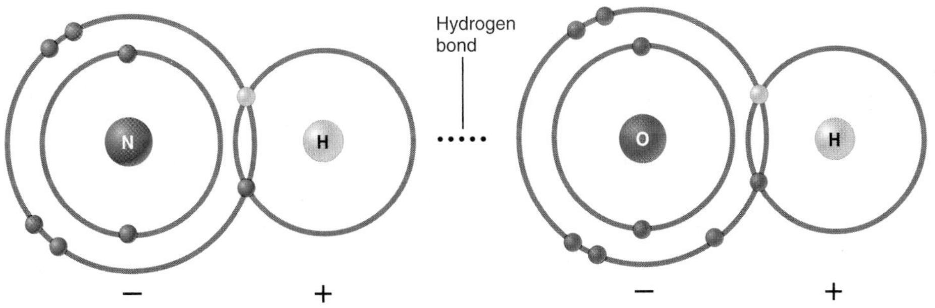

FIGURE 2.5 Hydrogen Bond Formation The N atom has a greater attraction for electrons than the H atom, thereby conferring a slight positive charge on the H atom. The O atom has a greater attraction for electrons than the H atom to which it is covalently bonded, thereby gaining a slight negative charge. The bonds between N—H and O—H are polar covalent bonds. The positively charged H atom weakly bonds to the negatively charged O atom, thereby forming a hydrogen bond.

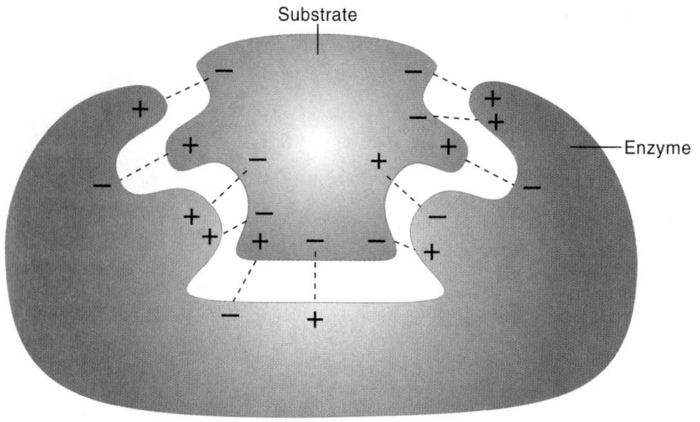

FIGURE 2.6 Weak Ionic Bonds and Molecular Recognition Weak bonds, such as ionic and hydrogen bonds, are important for molecules to recognize each other. Many weak bonds are required to hold the two molecules together, in this case, the substrate binding to an enzyme.

Hydrogen bonds are important in biological systems since organisms are composed of many molecules that contain hydrogen atoms bonded to nitrogen or oxygen atoms, thereby creating the possibility for many hydrogen bonds. Like ionic bonds, these weak bonds are important in recognizing matching surfaces and holding molecules on these surfaces together **(figure 2.6).** For example, in order for an enzyme to break covalent bonds of a compound, the substrate, the enzyme first binds to the substrate through many weak non-covalent bonds.

In contrast to covalent bonds, hydrogen bonds involving water molecules are constantly being formed and broken at room temperature because the energy produced by the movement of water is enough to break these bonds. The average lifetime of a single hydrogen bond is only a fraction of a second at room temperature, so enzymes are not necessary to form or break hydrogen bonds.

Although a single hydrogen bond is too weak to bind molecules together, a large number can hold molecules together firmly. A good example is the double-stranded DNA molecule. The two strands of this molecule are held together by many hydrogen bonds up and down the length of the molecule. The two strands will only come apart if energy is supplied, usually in the form of heat approaching temperatures of 100°C.

MICROCHECK 2.2

Molecules are formed by bonding between atoms. Bonds are formed when electrons from one atom interact with another atom. The bonds between the atoms which make up a molecule are strong covalent bonds; bonds between molecules are generally weak bonds such as ionic and hydrogen bonds.

- ✓ Compare the relative strengths of covalent, hydrogen, and ionic bonds.
- ✓ Which of these bonds requires an enzyme to break it?
- ✓ Why does an atom that gives up electrons become positively charged? What causes the positive charge?

2.3

Chemical Components of the Cell

Focus Points

- Describe the bonding properties of water and explain why they are important in biology.
- Define pH and state what the pH numbers tell you about the acidity of a solution.
- Name the four macromolecules found in all cells.

The most important molecule in the cell is water; the life of all organisms depends on its special properties.

Water

Unquestionably, water is the most important molecule in the world. Water makes up over 70% of all living organisms by weight. Most of the compounds of living beings are in solution inside cells. The importance of water to life on earth in large part depends on its unusual properties.

Bonding Properties of Water

Hydrogen bonding plays a very important role in giving water the properties which are required for life **(figure 2.7a).** Since water is a polar molecule, the positive H portion of the molecule is attracted to the negative O portion of other water molecules, thereby creating hydrogen bonds. The extent of hydrogen bond formation between water molecules depends on the temperature. At room temperature, when water is in a liquid state, the weak bonds continually form and break. As the temperature is lowered, the breakage and formation decreases, and in ice, a crystalline structure is formed. Each water molecule bonds to four other molecules to form a rigid lattice structure (figure 2.7b). When ice melts, the water molecules can move closer together. Consequently, liquid water is more dense than ice, which explains why ice floats. This explains how fish and bacteria can apparently live in frozen bodies of water. They actually live in the water, which remains liquid below the ice.

The polar nature of water also accounts for its ability to dissolve a large number of compounds. Water has been referred to as *the universal solvent of life* because it dissolves so many compounds. To dissolve in water, compounds must consist of atoms with positive or negative charges. In water, they ionize or split into their component charged atoms. For example, NaCl dissolves in water to form Na^+ ions, and Cl^- ions. In solution, ions such as Na^+ and Cl^- tend to be surrounded by water molecules such that the OH^- of HOH forms weak bonds with Na^+, and the H^+ forms weak bonds with Cl^- **(figure 2.8).** The Na^+ and the Cl^- cannot come together, and this accounts for the solubility of NaCl in water.

Water containing dissolved substances freezes at a lower temperature than pure water and in nature, most water does not freeze unless the temperature drops below 0°C. Consequently, microorganisms can usually grow in liquids below 0°C, because the water remains liquid.

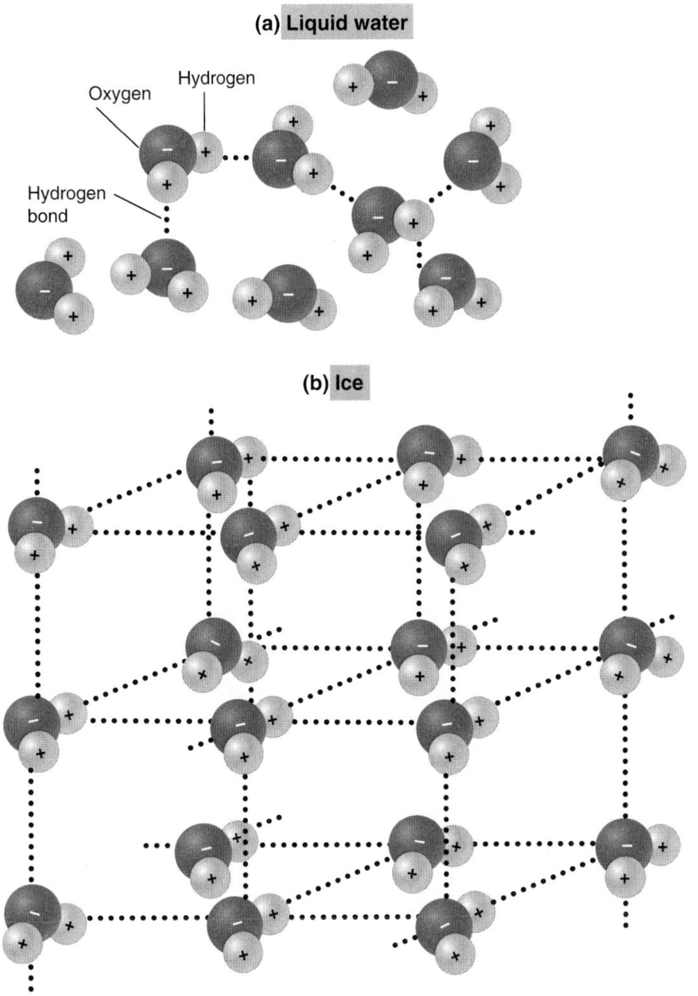

FIGURE 2.7 Water (a) In liquid water, each H_2O molecule hydrogen bonds to one or more H_2O molecules. These bonds continuously break and re-form. **(b)** In ice, each H_2O molecule is hydrogen bonded to four other H_2O molecules, forming a rigid crystalline structure. The bonds do not break continuously.

pH

An important property of every aqueous solution is its degree of acidity. This property is measured as the **pH** of the solution (an abbreviation for **p**otential **H**ydrogen), defined as the concentration of H^+ in moles per liter. pH is measured on a logarithmic scale of 0 to 14 in which the lower the number, the more acid the solution. The acidity of a solution is based on several properties of water. Water has a slight tendency to split (ionize) into hydrogen ions H^+ (protons), which are acidic, and OH^- ions (hydroxyl), which are basic or alkaline.

When water splits into its component parts, the number of H^+ and OH^- ions is equal, and in pure water, the concentration of each is 10^{-7} molar (10^{-7} M). The product of the concentration of H^+ and OH^- must always be 10^{-14} M ($10^{-7} \times 10^{-7}$). (Exponents are added when numbers are multiplied.) Thus, if H^+ ions are added to an aqueous solution so that the concentration of H^+ increases tenfold to 10^{-6} M, then the concentration of OH^- must decrease by a factor of 10 (to 10^{-8} M).

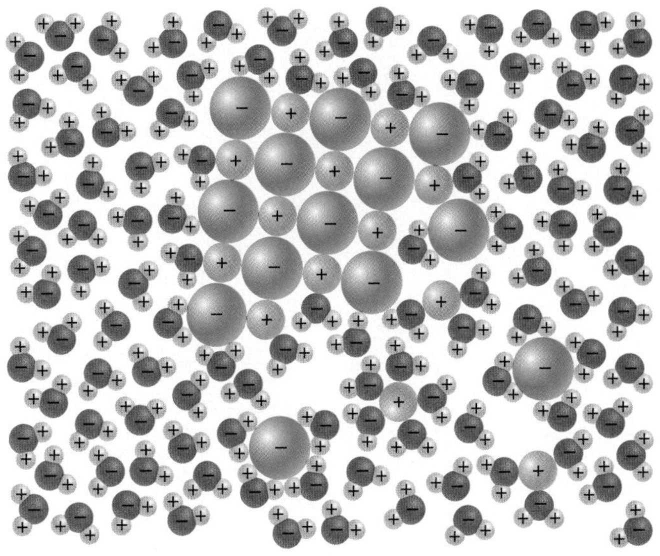

FIGURE 2.8 Salt (NaCl) Dissolving in Water In water, the Na^+ and Cl^- are separated by H_2O molecules. The Na^+ hydrogen bonds to the slightly negatively charged O^- and the Cl^- hydrogen bonds to the slightly positively charged H^+ portion of the water molecules. In the absence of water, the salt is highly structured because of ionic bond formation between Na^+ and Cl^- ions.

The pH scale, ranges from 0 to 14 because the concentrations of H^+ and OH^- ions varies within these limits **(figure 2.9).** When the concentration of H^+ and OH^- are equal, the pH of the solution is 7 and is neutral. However, for every unit on the log scale, the concentration of H^+ ions changes by a factor of 10. Most bacteria can live within only a narrow pH range, near neutrality. Some, however, can live under very acidic conditions **(acidophiles)** and a few under alkaline conditions **(alkalophiles).** ■ acidophiles, p. 96 ■ alkalophiles, p. 97

Bacteria often produce acids and, less commonly, bases when they degrade compounds to gain energy. To prevent drastic shifts in pH, which would be deleterious to growth, compounds, called **buffers** are commonly added to growth medium to maintain the pH near neutrality. A common buffer is a mixture of two salts of phosphoric acid, Na_2HPO_4 and NaH_2PO_4. These salts can combine chemically with the H^+ ions of acids and the OH^- of bases to produce neutral compounds, thereby maintaining the pH near neutrality.

Small Molecules in the Cell

All cells contain a variety of small organic and inorganic molecules, many of which occur in the form of ions. About 1% of the weight of a bacterial cell, once the water is removed (dry weight), is composed of inorganic ions, principally Na^+ (sodium), K^+ (potassium), Mg^{2+} (magnesium), Ca^{2+} (calcium), Fe^{2+} (iron), Cl^- (chloride), PO_4^{3-} (phosphate), and SO_4^{2-} (sulfate). Certain enzymes require positively charged ions in minute amounts to function. The negatively charged phosphate ion plays a key role in energy metabolism. This will be discussed in chapter 6.

The organic small molecules include compounds that accumulate in the process of metabolism of sugars. These are **precursor metabolites,** which are converted to the building blocks of large

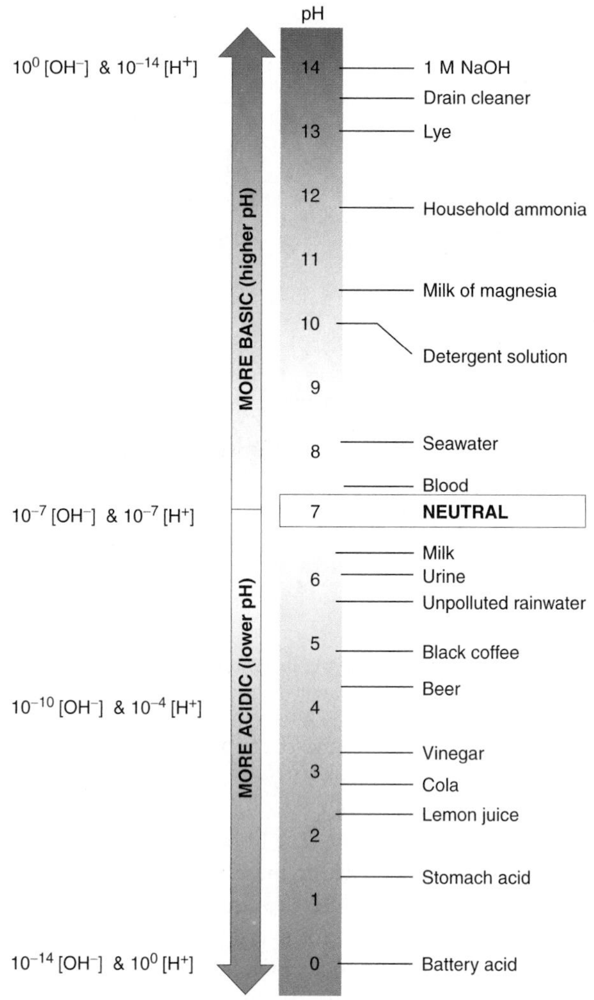

FIGURE 2.9 pH Scale The concentration of H⁺ ions varies by a factor of 10 between each pH number since the scale is logarithmic.

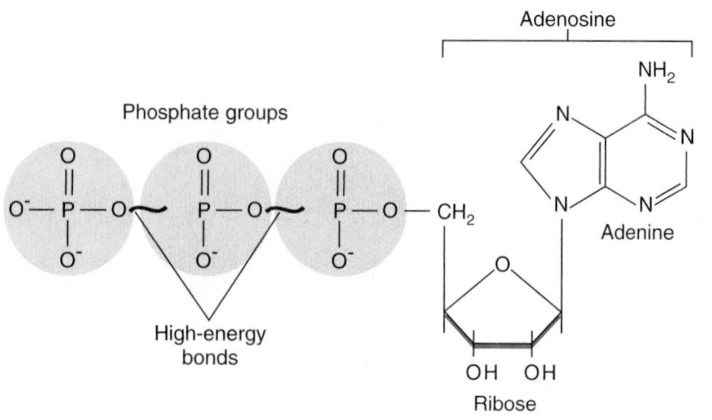

FIGURE 2.10 ATP Adenosine triphosphate (ATP) serves as the energy currency of a cell. The bonds are high energy because of the tandem arrangement of the negatively charged phosphate groups.

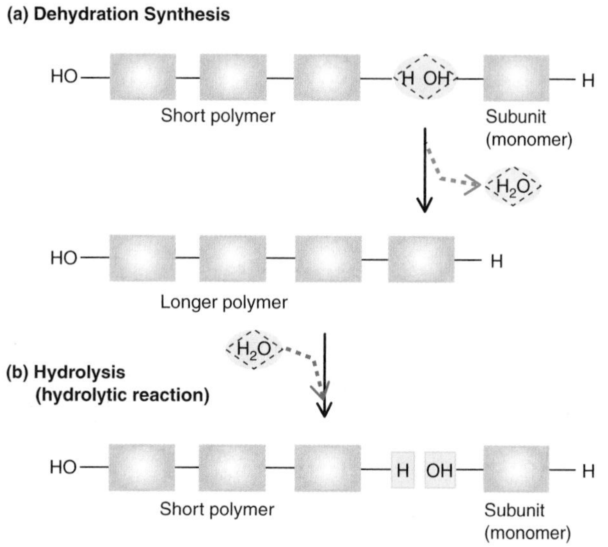

FIGURE 2.11 The Synthesis and Breakdown of Polymers (a) Subunits are joined (polymerized) by removal of water, a dehydration reaction. **(b)** In the reverse reaction, hydrolysis, the addition of water breaks bonds between the subunits. These reactions take place in the formation of many different polymers (macromolecules).

molecules, the **macromolecules**, which will be considered in the next section. The building blocks, also small molecules, include amino acids, purines and pyrimidines, and various sugars.

An especially important small organic molecule is **adenosine triphosphate (ATP),** the storage form of energy in the cell. The molecule is composed of the sugar ribose, the purine adenine, and three phosphate groups, arranged in tandem **(figure 2.10).** This is an energy-rich molecule because two of the bonds which join the three phosphate molecules are readily broken with the release of energy. The breakage of the terminal high-energy bond of ATP results in the formation of **adenosine diphosphate (ADP),** inorganic phosphate, and the release of energy. The role of ATP in energy metabolism is covered more fully in chapter 6.

Macromolecules and Their Component Parts

Macromolecules are very large molecules (*macro* means "large") consisting of several thousand atoms each. The four major classes of biologically important macromolecules are **proteins, polysaccharides, nucleic acids,** and **lipids.** These four groups of macromolecules differ from each other in their chemical structure. However, other aspects of their structure as well as how they are synthesized have features in common. Understanding these common features makes the structure of these large molecules surprisingly simple to learn and understand.

All macromolecules are **polymers** (*poly* means "many"), large molecules formed by joining together small molecules, the **subunits.** Each different class of macromolecules is composed of different subunits, although the subunits of the same macromolecule have a similar structure.

The synthesis of macromolecules involves two steps: first, the subunits are synthesized from different precursor metabolites and then, they are joined together, one by one. The synthesis of the various subunits is very complex and involves almost 100 different chemical reactions. An overview of how some of these subunits are synthesized is given in chapter 6.

The overall process of joining two subunits involves a chemical reaction in which H_2O is removed, a reaction termed **dehydration synthesis (figure 2.11a).** When the macromolecule is broken down into its subunits, the reverse reaction occurs, and H_2O is added back, a **hydrolytic reaction,** or **hydrolysis** (figure 2.11b). This type of reversible reaction, involving the removal and addition of H_2O molecules, is common to the synthesis and degradation of all macromolecules and requires the action of specific enzymes.

PERSPECTIVE 2.1

Isotopes: Valuable Tools for the Study of Biological Systems

One important tool in the analysis of living cells is the use of **isotopes,** variant forms of the same element that have different atomic weights. The nuclei of certain elements can have greater or fewer neutrons than usual and thereby be heavier or lighter than is typical. For example, the most common form of the hydrogen atom contains 1 proton and 0 neutrons and has an atomic weight of 1 (^{1}H). Another form, however, also exists in nature in very low amounts. This isotope, ^{2}H (deuterium), contains 1 neutron. A third, even heavier isotope, ^{3}H (tritium), is not found in nature but can be made by a nuclear reaction in which stable atoms are bombarded with high-energy particles. This latter isotope is unstable and gives off radiation (decays) in the form of rays or electrons, which can be very sensitively measured by a radioactivity counter. Once the atom has finished disintegrating, it no longer gives off radiation and is stable.

An important feature of radioactive isotopes is that their other properties are very similar to their non-radioactive counterparts. For example, tritium combines with oxygen to form water and with carbon to form hydrocarbons, and both molecules have biological properties very similar to their non-radioactive counterparts. The only difference is that the molecules containing tritium can be detected by the radiation they emit.

Isotopes are used in numerous ways in biological research. They are frequently added to growing cells in order to label particular molecules, thereby making them detectable. For example, tritiated thymidine (a component of DNA) added to growing bacteria will specifically label DNA and no other molecules. Tritiated uridine, a component of RNA, will label RNA. Isotopes are also used in medical diagnosis. For example, to evaluate proper functioning of the human thyroid gland, which produces the iodine containing hormone thyroxin, doctors often administer radioactive iodine and then scan the gland later to locate the gland and determine if the amount and distribution of the iodine in the gland is normal **(figure 1)**.

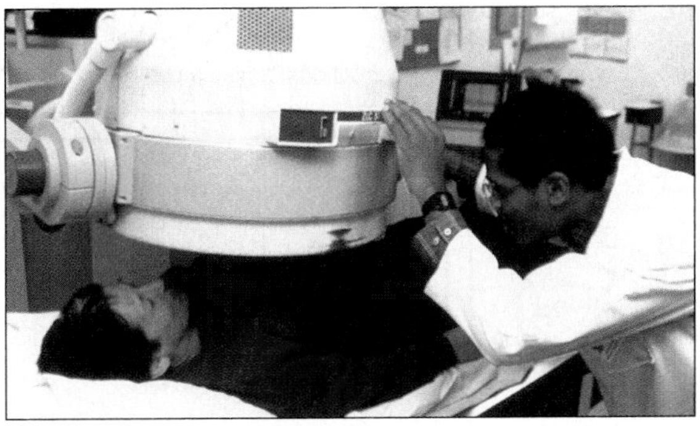
(a)

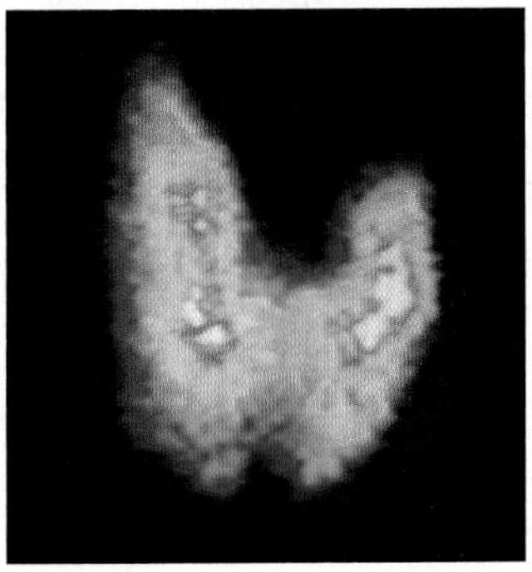
(b)

FIGURE 1 Radioactive Isotopes (a) Physicians use scintillation counters such as this to detect radioactive isotopes. **(b)** A scan of the thyroid gland 24 hours after the patient receives radioactive iodine.

MICROCHECK 2.3

The weak polar bonds of water molecules are responsible for the many properties of water required for life on earth. The degree of acidity of an aqueous solution is also an important property in biological systems. Macromolecules consist of many repeating subunits, each subunit being similar or identical to the other subunits.

✓ Why is water a polar molecule? Give three examples of why this property is important in microbiology.

✓ Name the four important classes of large molecules in cells.

✓ In pure water, what must be done to decrease the OH^- concentration? To decrease the H^+ concentration?

2.4

Proteins and Their Functions

Focus Points

- Name the subunits of protein molecules and the bonds that join them.
- Name the four levels of protein structure and what distinguishes each level.

Proteins constitute more than 50% of the dry weight of cells and a typical bacterial cell contains 600 to 800 different kinds of proteins at any one time. Of all the macromolecules, they are the most versatile in what they do in cells.

In the microbial world, proteins are responsible for:

- Catalyzing all reactions of the cell required for life. ■ enzymes, pp. 134, 139
- The structure and shape of certain structures such as ribosomes, the protein-building machinery in all cells. ■ ribosomes, p. 70
- Cell movement by flagella. ■ flagella, p. 66
- Taking nutrients into the cell. ■ transport proteins, p. 58
- Turning genes on and off. ■ gene regulation, p. 182
- Certain properties of various membranes in the cell. ■ inner cytoplasmic membrane, p. 56 ■ outer membrane, p. 62

Amino Acid Subunits

Proteins are macromolecules that are composed of numerous combinations of 20 major amino acids. The properties of a protein depend mainly on its shape, which in turn depends on the arrangement of the **amino acids** that make up the protein.

All amino acids have at one end a carbon atom to which a carboxyl group and an amino group are bonded **(figure 2.12).** This carbon atom also is bonded to a side chain or backbone (labeled R), which gives each amino acid its characteristic properties. In solution at pH 7, both the amino and carboxyl groups are ionized such that the $—NH_2$ group is $—NH_3^+$ and the —COOH group is $—COO^-$, with the overall charge being zero. The amino acids are subdivided into several different groups based on similarities in their side chains **(figure 2.13).** One

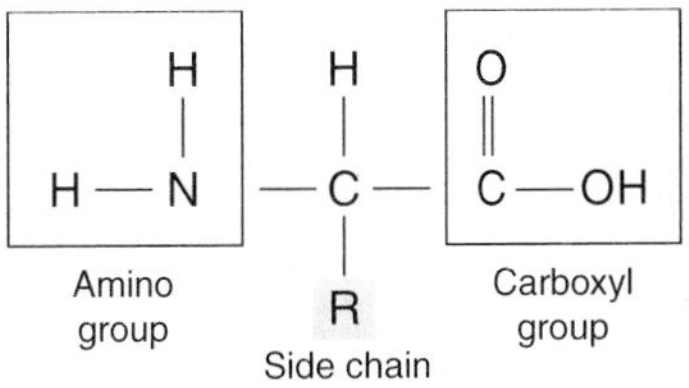

FIGURE 2.12 Generalized Amino Acid This figure illustrates the three groups that all amino acids possess. The R side chain differs with each amino acid and determines the properties of the amino acid.

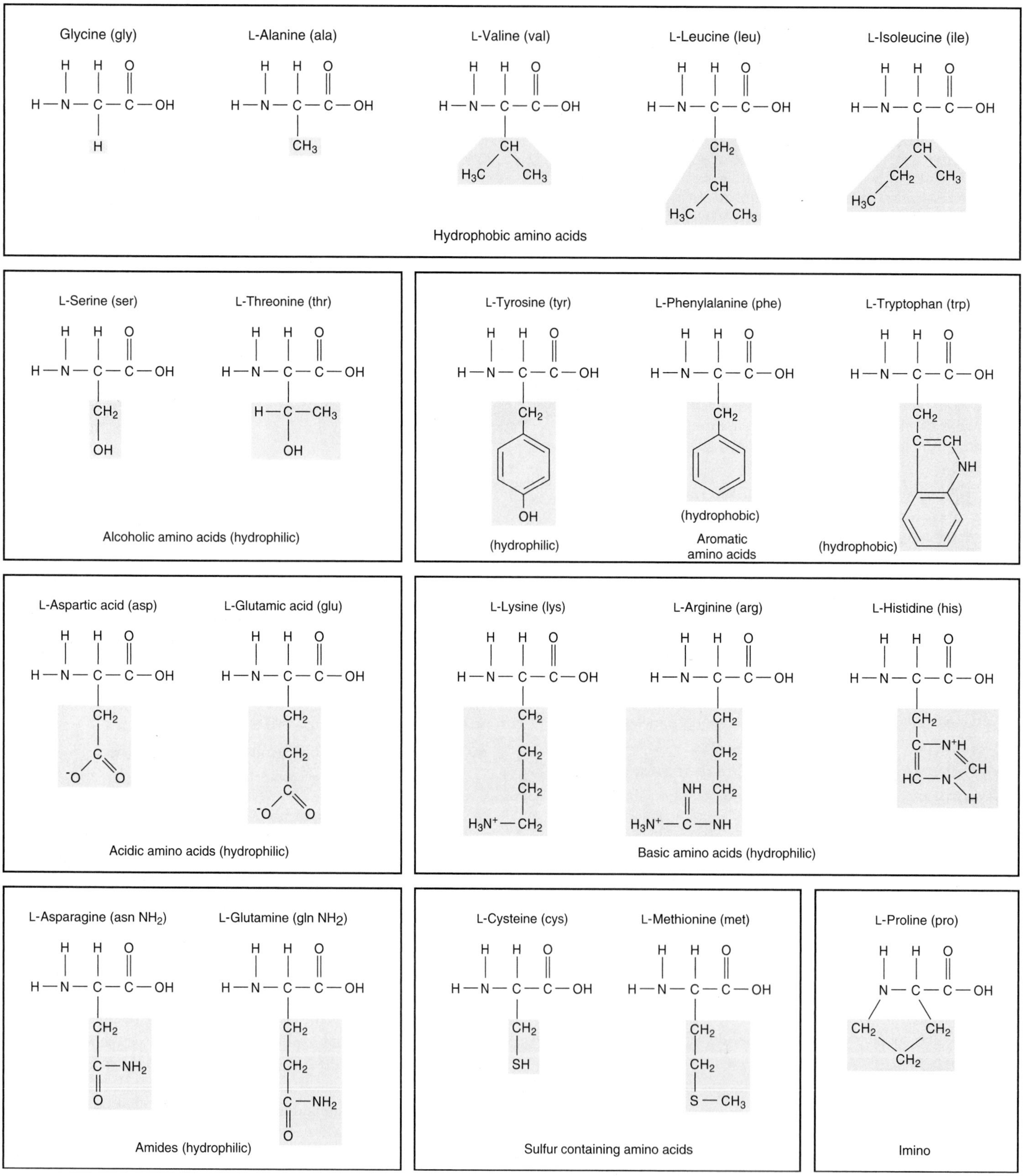

FIGURE 2.13 Common Amino Acids All amino acids have one feature in common—a carboxyl group and an amino group bonded to the same carbon atom. This carbon atom is also bonded to a side chain (shaded). In solution, the —COOH group is ionized to $—COO^-$ and the $—NH_2$ group to $—NH_3$ giving a net charge of zero to the amino acid. The basic and acidic amino acids have a net positive or negative charge, respectively. The three-letter code name for each amino acid is given.

important property of the side chains is whether they are polar or non-polar; this feature determines the solubility properties of the protein, its shape, and how it interacts with other proteins inside the cell. Amino acids that contain many methyl (CH_3) groups are non-polar and therefore do not interact with water molecules. Thus, they are poorly soluble in water and are termed **hydrophobic** ("water-fearing"). These amino acids tend to be on the inside of protein molecules. Other amino acids contain polar side chains, which make them more soluble in water. They are termed **hydrophilic** ("water-loving"). They usually occur on the surface of protein molecules.

All amino acids except glycine can exist in two stereoisomeric forms, a D (right-handed) or L (left-handed) form. Each is a mirror image of the other (**figure 2.14**; see **A Glimpse of History**). Only L-amino acids occur in proteins, and accordingly, they are designated the **natural amino acids.** D-amino acids are rare in nature and are found in only a few compounds mostly associated with bacteria. They are found primarily in the cell walls and in certain antimicrobial medications termed antibiotics that many bacteria produce. The bacterium *Bacillus anthracis*, which causes the disease anthrax and has been used as an agent of bioterrorism in the United States, has an outer coat of D-glutamic acid.

Peptide Bonds and Their Synthesis

Proteins are made up of amino-acids held together by **peptide bonds,** a unique type of covalent linkage formed when the carboxyl group of one amino acid reacts with the amino group of another amino acid, with the release of water (dehydration synthesis) **(figure 2.15).**

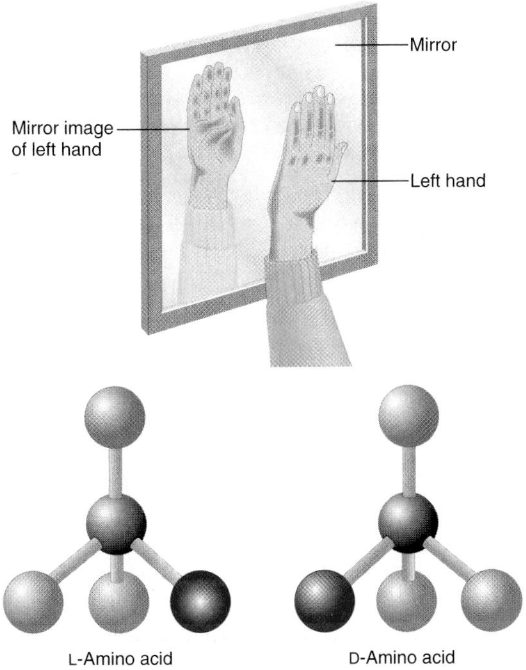

FIGURE 2.14 Mirror Images (Stereoisomers) of an Amino Acid The joining of a carbon atom to four different groups leads to asymmetry in the molecule. The molecule can exist in either the L- or D-form, each being the mirror image of the other. There is no way that the two molecules can be rotated in space to give two identical molecules.

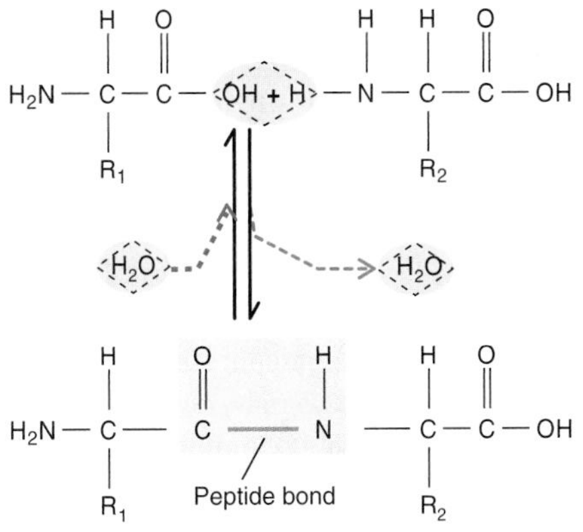

FIGURE 2.15 Peptide Bond Formation by Dehydration Synthesis

The chain of amino acids formed when a large number of amino acids are joined by peptide bonds is called a **polypeptide chain.** A protein is a long polypeptide chain. One end of the chain has a free amino ($—NH_2$) group, which is termed the **N terminal,** or **amino terminal,** end. The other end has a free carboxyl ($—COOH$) group, which is termed **the C terminal,** or **carboxyl terminal,** end. Proteins are always synthesized in cells starting from the N terminal end. Some proteins consist of a single polypeptide chain, whereas others consist of one or more chains joined together by weak bonds. Sometimes, the chains are identical; in other cases, they are different. One or more polypeptide chains make up the protein. In proteins that consist of several chains, the individual polypeptide chains generally do not have biological activity by themselves. Proteins vary greatly in size, but an average-size protein consists of a single polypeptide chain of about 400 amino acids. ■ protein synthesis, p. 176

Protein Structure

Proteins have four levels of structure: primary, secondary, tertiary, and quaternary. The number and arrangement or sequence of amino acids in the polypeptide chain determines its **primary structure (figure 2.16a).** The primary structure in large part determines the other features of the protein. Some amino acids are especially important to functioning of the protein. The substitution of such a critical amino acid with another often destroys the ability of the protein to carry out its function. This will be discussed in greater detail in chapter 8.

Depending on the specific amino acids that make up the primary structure, the amino acid chain form several different arrangements. This is the protein's **secondary structure** (figure 2.16b). Certain sequences of amino acids will arrange themselves into a helical structure termed an **alpha (α) helix.** Others will form a **pleated structure** termed a **beta (β) sheet** (figure 2.16b). These structures result from the amino acids forming weak bonds, such as hydrogen bonds, with other amino acids. This is why certain sequences of amino acids lead to distinctive secondary structures in various parts of the molecule.

The protein next folds into its distinctive three-dimensional shape, its **tertiary structure** (figure 2.16c). Two major shapes exist: **globular,** which tends to be spherical; and **fibrous,** which has an

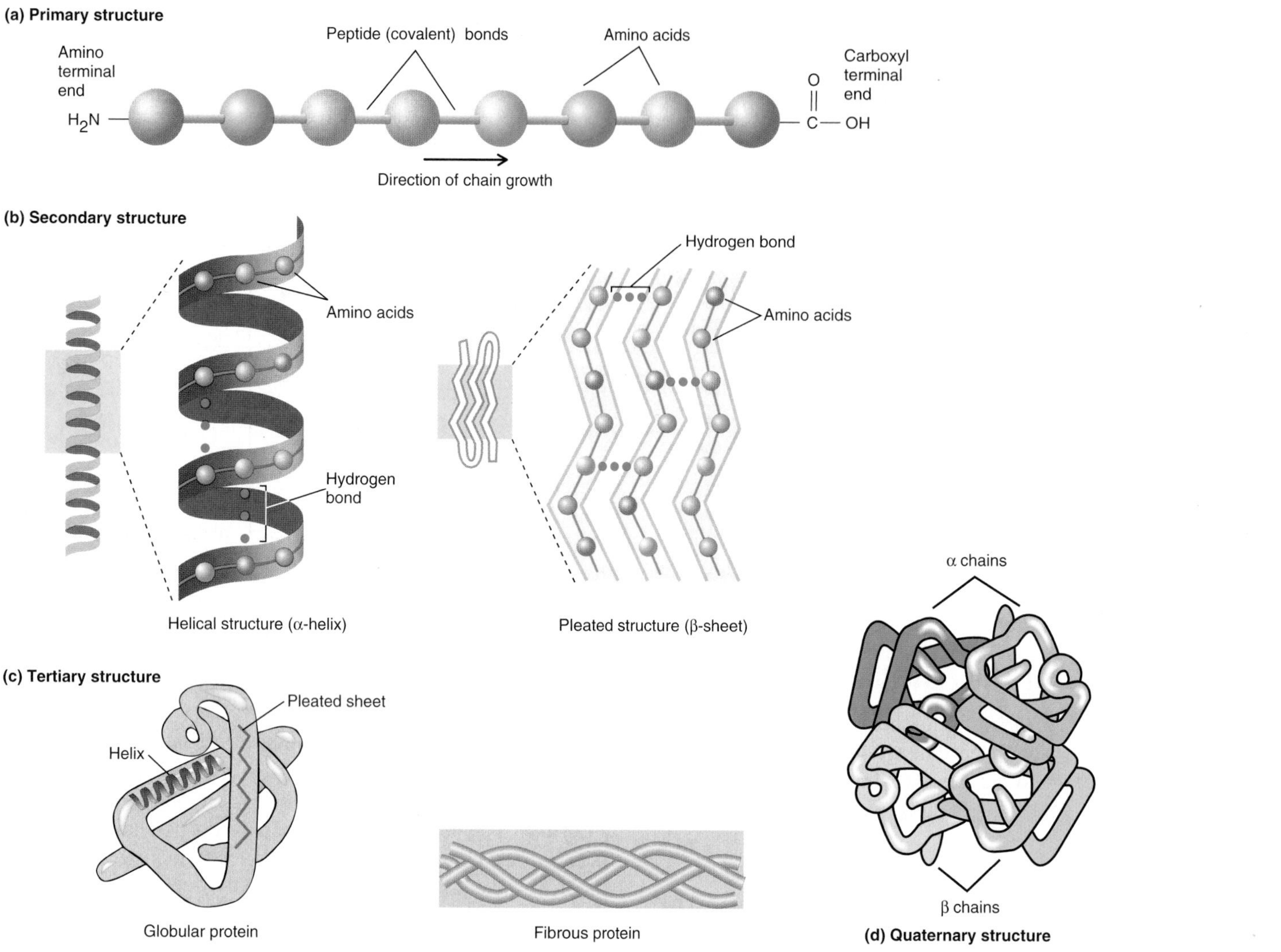

FIGURE 2.16 Protein Structures (a) The primary structure is determined by the amino acid composition. **(b)** The secondary structure results from folding of the various parts of the protein into two major patterns—helices and sheets. **(c)** The tertiary structure is the overall shape of the molecule, globular and fibrous. **(d)** Quaternary structure results from several polypeptide chains interacting to form the protein. This protein is hemoglobin and consists of two pairs of identical chains, α and β.

elongated structure (figure 2.16c). The shape is determined in large part by the sequence of the amino acids and whether or not they interact with water. Hydrophilic amino acids are located on the outside of the protein molecule, where they can interact with charged polar water molecules. Hydrophobic amino acids are pushed together and cluster inside the molecule to avoid water molecules. This phenomenon also explains why non-polar molecules of fat form droplets in an aqueous environment. The non-polar amino acids form weak interactions with each other, termed **hydrophobic interactions.** In addition to these weak bonds, some amino acids can form strong covalent bonds with other amino acids. One example is the formation of bonds between sulfur atoms (S—S bonds) in different cysteine molecules. The combination of strong and weak bonds between the various amino acids results in the proteins' tertiary structure.

Proteins often consist of more than one polypeptide chain, either identical or different, held together by many weak bonds. The chains also assume a specific shape, termed the **quaternary structure** of the protein (figure 2.16d). Of course, only proteins that consist of more than one polypeptide chain have a quaternary structure.

Sometimes different proteins, each having different functions, associate with one another to make even larger structures termed **multiprotein complexes.** For example, sometimes enzymes involved in the pathway of synthesis of the same amino acid are joined in a **multi-enzyme complex.** Sometimes, enzymes involved in the degradation of a particular compound form a multi-enzyme complex.

Proteins form extremely rapidly. Within seconds, amino acids are joined together inside cells to yield a polypeptide chain. This process will be discussed in chapter 7. The polypeptide chain then folds into its correct shape. Although many shapes are possible, only one is functional. Most proteins will fold spontaneously into their most stable state correctly. To help some proteins assume the proper shape, however, cells have proteins called **chaperones** that help specific proteins fold correctly. Incorrectly folded proteins are degraded into their amino acid subunits that can then be used to make more proteins.

Protein Denaturation

A protein must have its proper shape to function. When proteins encounter different conditions such as high temperature, high or low

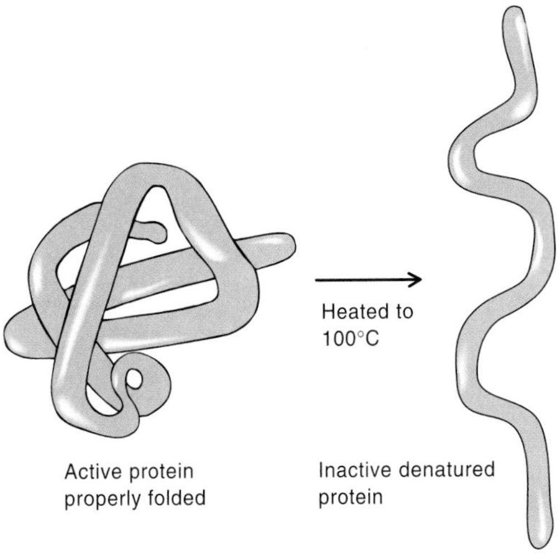

FIGURE 2.17 Denaturation of a Protein

pH, or certain solvents, bonds within the protein are broken and its shape changes **(figure 2.17).** The protein becomes **denatured** and no longer functions. Most bacteria cannot grow at very high temperatures because their enzymes are denatured by the heat. Denaturation may be reversible in some cases; in other cases, it is irreversible. For example, boiling an egg denatures the egg white protein, an irreversible process since cooling the egg does not restore the protein to its original appearance. If the denaturating agent is a chemical and is removed, the protein may refold spontaneously into its original shape.

Substituted Proteins

The proteins that play important roles in certain structures of the cell often have other molecules covalently bonded to the side chains of amino acids. These are called **substituted proteins.** The proteins are named after the molecules that are covalently joined to the amino acids. If **sugar** molecules are bonded, the protein is termed a **glycoprotein.** If **lipids** are bonded, then the protein is termed a **lipoprotein.** Sugars and lipids are covered later in this chapter.

MICROCHECK 2.4

The side chains of amino acids are responsible for their properties. The sequence of amino acids in a protein determines how the protein folds to its three-dimensional shape.

- ✓ What type of bond joins amino acids to form proteins?
- ✓ Name two groups of amino acids that are hydrophilic.
- ✓ What elements must all amino acids contain? What elements will only some amino acids contain?

2.5 Carbohydrates

Focus Points

- Distinguish between the various carbohydrates based on the number of their subunits.
- Name the most distinguishing feature of carbohydrates in terms of their chemical composition.

Carbohydrates comprise a heterogeneous group of compounds of various sizes that play important roles in the life of all organisms. These include:

- Carbohydrates are a common food source from which organisms can obtain energy and make cellular material. ■ metabolism, p. 131
- Two sugars form a part of the nucleic acids, DNA and RNA. ■ nucleic acids, p. 33
- Certain carbohydrates serve as a reserve source of food in bacteria. ■ storage granules, p. 70
- Sugars form a part of the bacterial cell wall. ■ cell wall structure, p. 60

All carbohydrates contain carbon, hydrogen, and oxygen atoms in an approximate ratio of 1:2:1. This is because they contain a large number of alcohol groups (—OH) in which the C is also bonded to an H atom to form H—C—OH. **Polysaccharides** are high molecular weight compounds and are linear or branched polymers of their subunits. **Oligosaccharides** are short chains. The term **sugar** is often applied to both **monosaccharides** (*mono* means "one"), a single subunit, and **disaccharides** (*di* means "two"), which are two monosaccharides joined together by covalent bonds.

Carbohydrates also usually have an aldehyde group

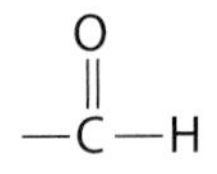

and less commonly, a keto group

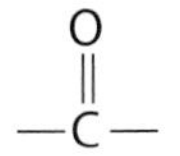

The —OH groups on sugars can be replaced by many other groups such as carboxyl, amino, and acetyl groups to form molecules that are important in the structures of the cell. For example, acetyl glucosamine is an important component of the cell wall of bacteria. ■ bacterial cell wall, p. 60

Monosaccharides

Monosaccharides are classified by the number of carbon atoms they contain. The most common monosaccharides are those with 5- or 6-carbon atoms. The 5-carbon sugars, **ribose** and **deoxyribose,** are the sugars in nucleic acids **(figure 2.18).** Note that these monosaccharides are identical except that deoxyribose has one less molecule of oxygen than does ribose (*de* means "away from"). Thus, deoxyribose is ribose "away from" oxygen. Common 6-carbon sugars include glucose, galactose, and fructose. It is convenient to number the carbon atoms with carbon atom 1 being closest to the aldehyde or keto group.

Sugars can be illustrated in two forms, a linear and a ring form. The linear form of ribose, the ring form, and the relationship between the two representations are shown in figure 2.18. Both forms naturally occur in the cell, but most molecules are in the ring form. The forms are interconvertible.

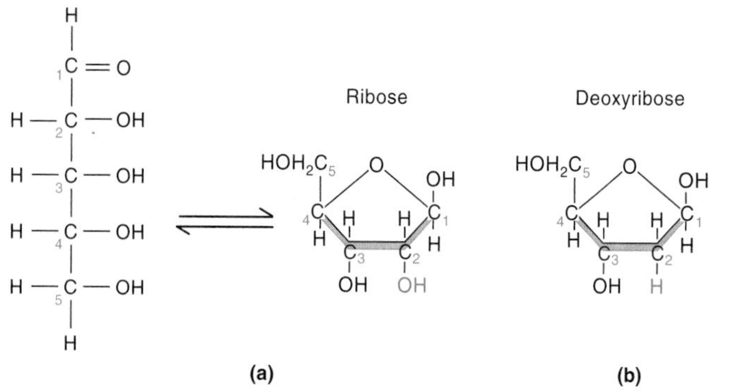

FIGURE 2.18 Ribose and Deoxyribose with the Carbon Atoms Numbered **(a)** Ribose in linear and ring form. **(b)** Deoxyribose in ring form. Although both structures occur in the cell, the ring form predominates. The plane of the ring is perpendicular to the plane of the paper with the shaded line on the ring closest to the reader.

Sugars can form two different **stereoisomers** (mirror images). These stereoisomers result because the —OH group on the C atom involved in the formation of the ring can be above or below the plane of the ring **(figure 2.19a).** The two different forms are termed alpha (α) and beta (β). These two different positions yield molecules with different properties when this —OH is linked to another monosaccharide to form larger molecules.

Every sugar can also exist in two different forms, D and L, which also are mirror images of one another (figure 2.19b). Most monosaccharides in living organisms are of the D-configuration, which is opposite to the situation observed with amino acids. The sugars of different isomeric forms still have the same name.

Sugars also form **structural isomers,** molecules that contain the same elements but in different arrangements that are not mirror images. They are different sugars and have different names. For example, common hexoses of biological importance include glucose, galactose, and mannose. They all contain the same atoms but differ in the arrangements of the —H and —OH groups relative to the carbon atoms. Glucose and galactose are identical except for the arrangement of the —H and —OH groups attached to carbon 4. Mannose and glucose differ in the arrangement of the —H and —OH groups joined to carbon 2. Structural isomers result in three distinct sugars with different properties and different names. For example, glucose has a sweet taste as does mannose, but mannose has a bitter aftertaste.

Disaccharides

The two most common disaccharides in nature are the milk sugar, **lactose,** and the common table sugar, **sucrose.** Lactose consists of glucose and galactose, while sucrose, which comes from sugar cane or sugar beets, is composed of glucose and fructose. The monosaccharides are joined together by a dehydration reaction between hydroxyl groups of two monosaccharides, with the loss of a molecule of water. Note that this reaction is similar to the joining of two amino acids. The reaction is reversible, so that the addition of a water molecule, the process of hydrolysis, yields the two original molecules. Great diversity is possible in molecules formed by joining monosaccharides. The carbon atoms involved in the joining together of the monosaccharides may differ and the position of the —OH groups, α and β, involved in the bonding may also differ.

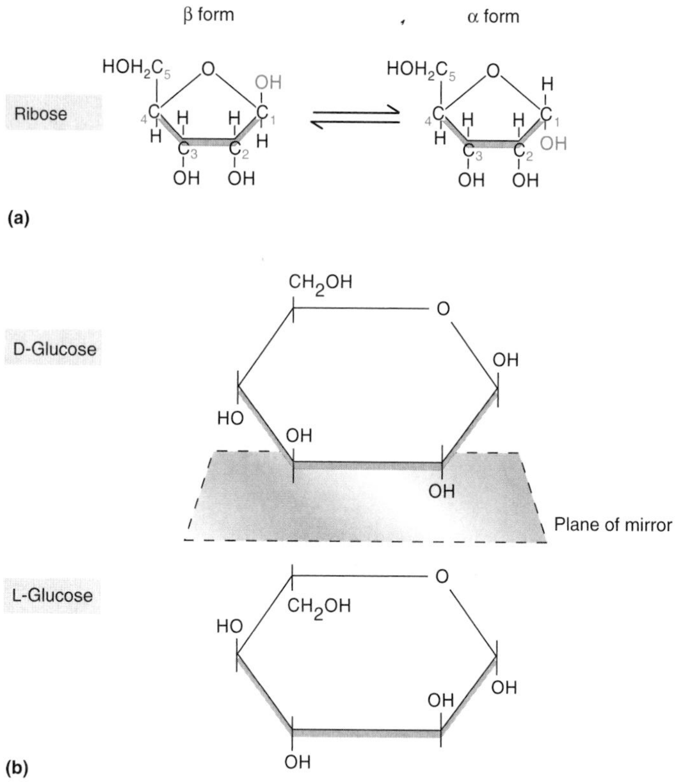

FIGURE 2.19 Stereoisomers **(a)** The α and β forms of ribose are interconvertible and only differ in whether the OH group on carbon 1 is above or below the plane of the ring. **(b)** As shown in these stereoisomers of glucose, the carbon atoms at the intersections of the lines in the ring structure are understood to be present and are not labeled.

Polysaccharides

Polysaccharides, which are found in many different places in nature, serve different functions. **Cellulose,** the most abundant organic molecule on earth, is a polymer of glucose subunits and is the principal constituent of plant cell walls. Some bacteria synthesize cellulose in the form of fibrils that attach the bacteria to various surfaces. **Glycogen,** a carbohydrate storage product of animals and some bacteria, and **dextran,** which is also synthesized by bacteria as a storage product for carbon and energy, resemble cellulose in some ways.

These three polysaccharides, cellulose, glycogen, and dextran, are composed of glucose subunits, but they differ from one another in many important ways. These include (1) the size of the polymer; (2) the degree of chain branching, since the side chains of monosaccharides can branch from the main chain; (3) the particular carbon atoms of the two sugar molecules involved in covalent bond formation, such as a 1, 4 linkage when the carbon atom number 1 of one sugar is joined to the number 4 carbon atom of the adjacent sugar; and (4) the orientation of the covalent bond between the sugar molecules. Thus, these subunits can yield a large variety of polysaccharides that have different properties but are composed of the same subunits. How these various aspects of the structure of a polysaccharide fit into the structures of cellulose, glycogen, and dextran are shown in **figure 2.20.**

Polysaccharides and oligosaccharides can also contain different monosaccharide subunits in the same molecule. For example,

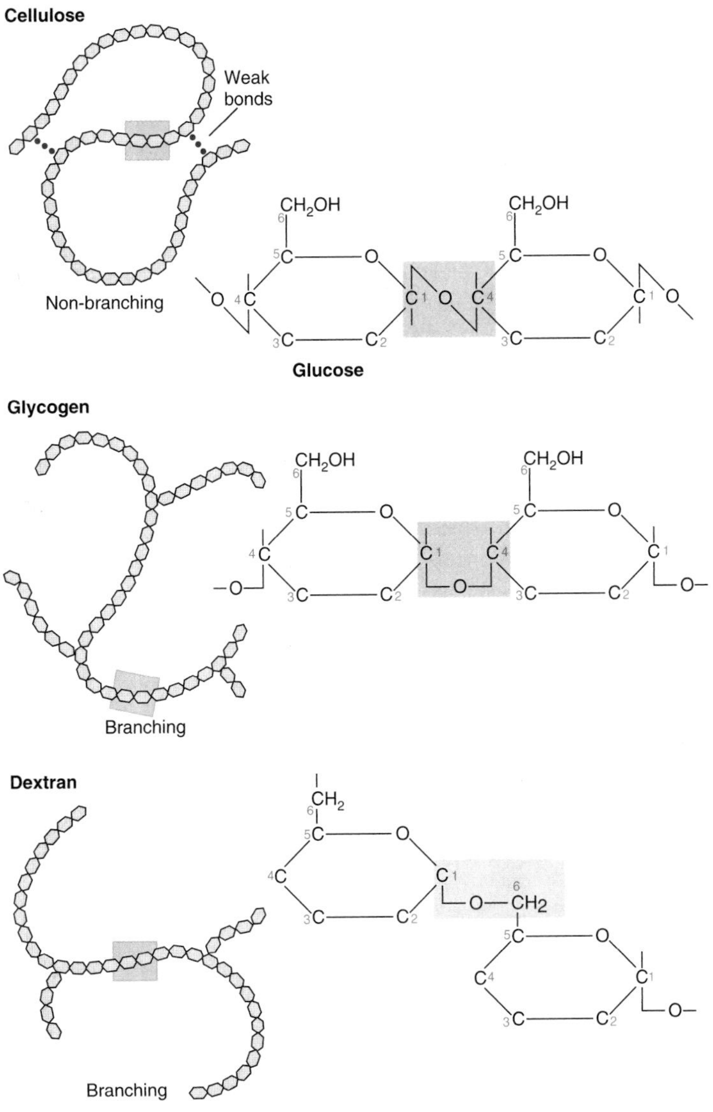

FIGURE 2.20 Structures of Three Important Polysaccharides The three molecules shown consist of the same subunit, D-glucose, yet they are distinctly different molecules because of differences in linkage that join the molecules (α and β; 1,4 or 1,6), the degree of branching, and the bonds involved in branching (not shown). Weak hydrogen bonds are also involved.

the cell walls of the Domain *Bacteria* contain a polysaccharide consisting of alternating subunit molecules of two different amino sugars.

MICROCHECK 2.5

Carbohydrates perform a variety of functions in cells, including serving as a source of energy and forming part of the cells' structures. Carbohydrates with the same subunit composition can have distinct properties because of different arrangements of the atoms in the molecules.

✓ Distinguish between structural isomers and stereoisomers.
✓ What is the general name given to a single sugar?
✓ How could you distinguish sucrose and lactose from protein by analyzing the elements in the molecules?

2.6 Nucleic Acids

Focus Points

- Compare and contrast the chemical composition of RNA and DNA.
- Describe the major functions of RNA and DNA.

Nucleic acids carry the genetic information in all cells. That information is decoded into the sequence of amino acids in protein molecules. There are two types of nucleic acids: **deoxyribonucleic acid (DNA)** and **ribonucleic acid (RNA),** and their subunits are **nucleotides.**

DNA

DNA is the master molecule of the cell—all of the cell's properties are determined by its DNA. This information is coded in the sequence of nucleotides. The code is then converted into a specific arrangement of amino acids that make up the protein molecules of the cell. The details of this process are covered in chapter 7.

In addition to their role in the structure of DNA, nucleotides play additional roles in the cell.

- They carry chemical energy in their bonds. ■ adenosine triphosphate, p. 134
- They are part of certain enzymes. ■ CoA, p. 141
- They serve as specific signaling molecules. ■ cyclic AMP, p. 185

The nucleotides of DNA are composed of three units: a nitrogen-containing ring compound, called a **base;** which is covalently bonded to a 5-carbon sugar molecule, **deoxyribose;** which in turn is bonded to a **phosphate** molecule **(figure 2.21).** The four different nitrogen-containing bases can be divided into two groups according to their

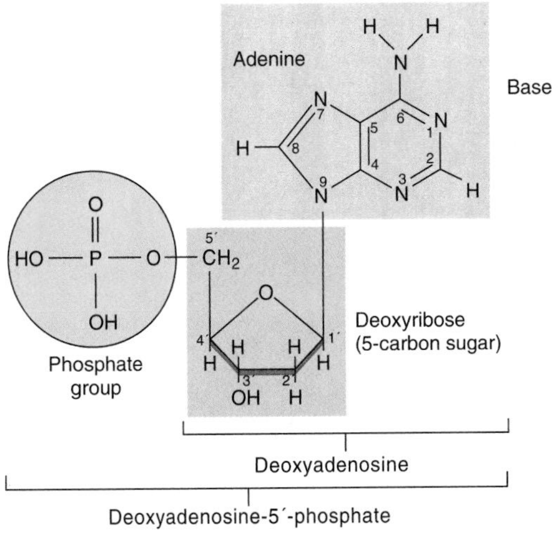

FIGURE 2.21 A Nucleotide This is one subunit of DNA. This subunit is called adenylic acid or deoxyadenosine-5′-phosphate because the base is adenine. If the base is thymine, the nucleotide is thymidylic acid; if guanine, guanylic acid; and if cytosine, cytidylic acid. If the nucleotide lacks the phosphate molecule, it is called a nucleoside, in this case, deoxyadenosine.

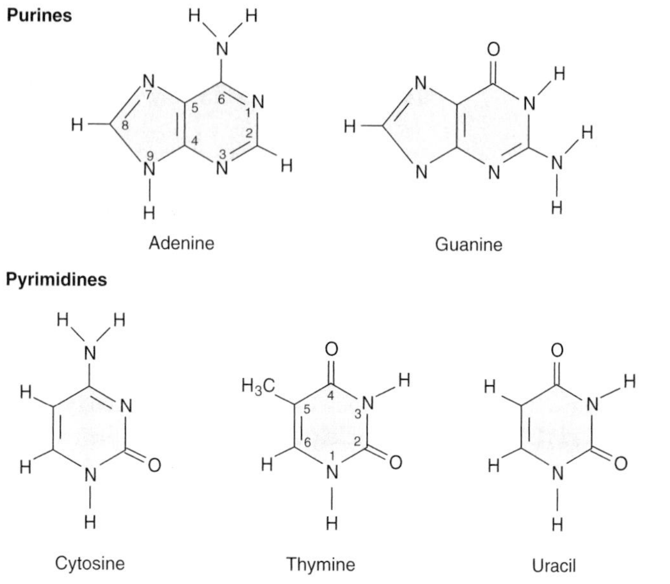

FIGURE 2.22 Formulas of Purines and Pyrimidines Both N and C atoms are numbered consecutively.

ring structures: two **purines,** adenine and guanine, which consist of two rings; and two **pyrimidines,** cytosine and thymine, which consist of a single ring **(figure 2.22).**

The nucleotide subunits are joined by a covalent bond between the phosphate of one nucleotide and the sugar of the adjacent nucleotide **(figure 2.23a).** Thus, the phosphate is a bridge that joins the number 3 carbon atom (termed 3′) of one sugar to the number 5 carbon atom (termed 5′) of the other. The result is a molecule with a backbone of alternating sugar and phosphate molecules. The two ends of the molecule are different. The 5′ end has a phosphate molecule attached to the sugar; the 3′ end has a hydroxyl group (figure 2.23b). Accordingly, the end of the chain that grows by adding more nucleotides is always the 3′ end. The synthesis of DNA is covered in chapter 7.

The DNA of a typical bacterium is a single molecule composed of nucleotides joined together and arranged in a double-stranded helix, with about 4 million nucleotides in each strand **(figure 2.24).** This double-stranded helical molecule can be pictured as a spiral staircase with two railings and stairs split in half. The railings represent the sugar-phosphate backbone of the molecule, and the stairs attached to the railings are the bases. One half of each stair is strongly attached to one railing, and the other half is strongly attached to the other railing. Each pair of stairs (bases) is held together by weak hydrogen bonds. A specificity exists in the bonding between bases, however, in that adenine (A) can only hydrogen bond to thymine (T), and guanine (G) to cytosine (C). The pair of bases that bond are **complementary** to each other. Thus, G is complementary to C, and A to T. As a result, one entire strand of DNA is complementary to the other strand. This explains why in all DNA molecules, the total number of adenine molecules is equal to the number of thymine molecules and the number of guanines equals the number of cytosines.

Three hydrogen bonds join each G to C, but only two join A to T. Each of the hydrogen bonds is weak, but their large number

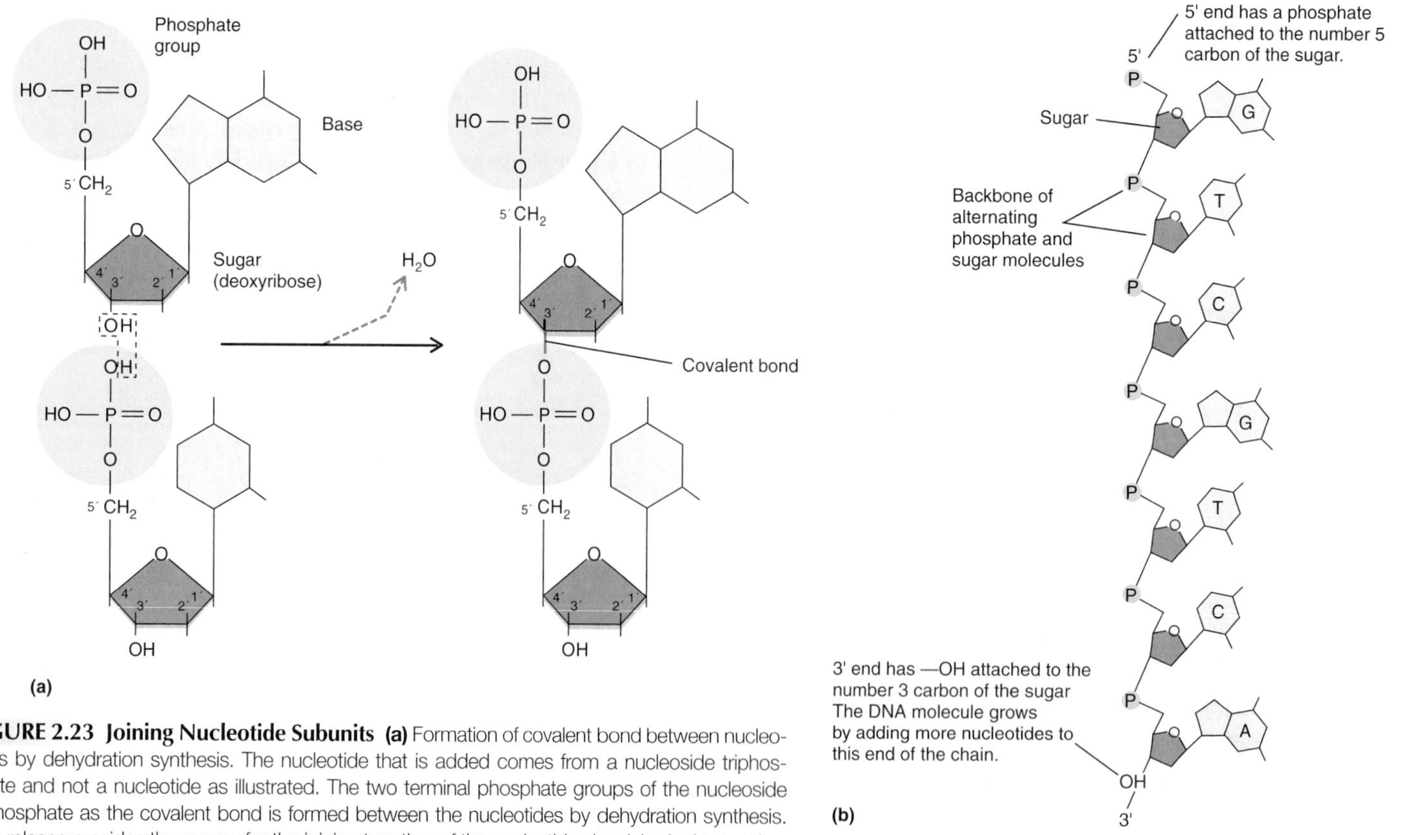

FIGURE 2.23 Joining Nucleotide Subunits (a) Formation of covalent bond between nucleotides by dehydration synthesis. The nucleotide that is added comes from a nucleoside triphosphate and not a nucleotide as illustrated. The two terminal phosphate groups of the nucleoside triphosphate as the covalent bond is formed between the nucleotides by dehydration synthesis. This release provides the energy for the joining together of the nucleotides by dehydration synthesis. **(b)** Chain of nucleotides showing the differences between 5′ end and 3′ end. The chain always is extended at the 3′ end, which has the unbonded —OH hydroxyl group.

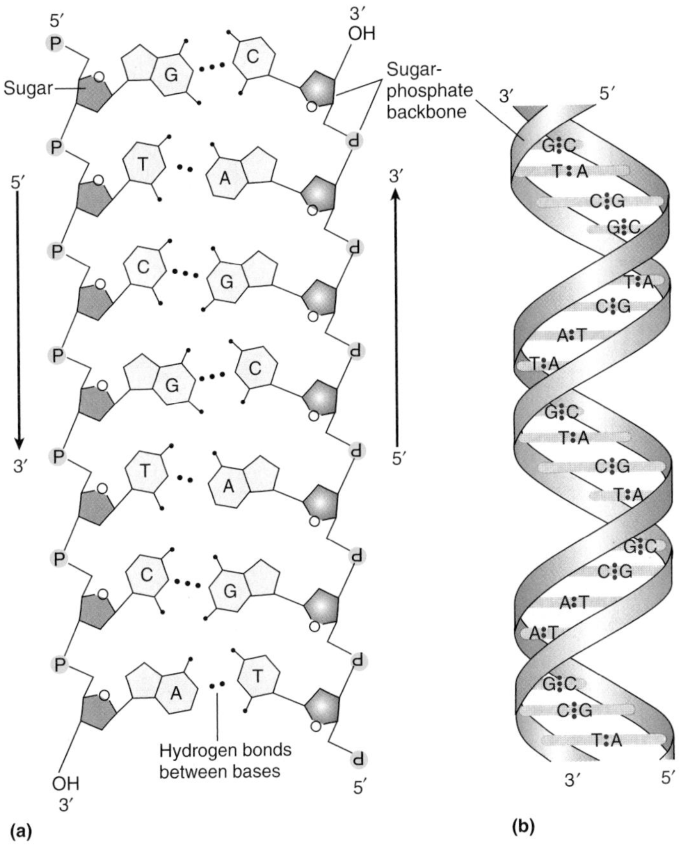

FIGURE 2.24 DNA Double-Stranded Helix (a) The sugar-phosphate backbone and the hydrogen bonding between bases. There are two hydrogen bonds between adenine and thymine and three between guanine and cytosine. **(b)** The spiral staircase of the sugar-phosphate backbone with the bases on the inside. The railings go in opposite directions.

in a DNA molecule holds the two strands together. In addition to the differences in their sequence of bases, the two complementary strands differ from each other in their orientation. The two strands are arranged in opposite directions. One goes in the 3′ to the 5′ direction; the other in the 5′ to 3′ direction. Consequently, the two ends of the strands opposite each other differ; one is a 5′ end, the other, a 3′ end (see figure 2.24).

RNA

RNA is involved in decoding the information in the DNA into a sequence of amino acids in protein molecules. This complex multi-step process will be examined in chapter 7.

Although the structure of RNA is similar to that of DNA, it differs in several ways. First, RNA contains the pyrimidine **uracil** in place of thymine and the sugar **ribose** in place of deoxyribose (see figures 2.22 and 2.18). Also, whereas DNA is a long, double-stranded helix, RNA is considerably shorter and exists as a single chain of nucleotides that may form short double-stranded stretches as a result of hydrogen bonding between complementary bases in the single strand.

MICROCHECK 2.6

DNA carries the genetic code in the sequence of purine and pyrimidine bases in its double-helical structure. The information is transferred to RNA and then into a sequence of amino acids in proteins.

✓ What are the two types of nucleic acids?

✓ If the DNA molecule were placed in boiling water, how would the molecule change?

2.7 Lipids

Focus Points

- Name the one property common to all lipids.
- Explain how the chemical structure of a phospholipid prevents the entry and exit of substances into and out of the cell.

Lipids play an indispensable role in all living cells. They are critically important in the structure of all membranes. These membranes act as the gatekeepers of the cells. They keep a cell's internal contents inside the cell and keep many molecules from entering the cell. ■ cytoplasmic membranes, p. 56

Lipids are a very heterogeneous group of molecules. Their defining feature is their slight solubility in water contrasted with great solubility in most organic solvents such as ether, benzene, and chloroform. These solubility properties result from their non-polar, hydrophobic nature. Lipids have molecular weights of no more than a few thousand and so are the smallest of the macromolecules we have discussed. Further, unlike the other macromolecules, they are not composed of similar subunits; rather, they consist of a wide variety of substances that differ in their chemical structure. Lipids can be divided into two general classes: the **simple** and the **compound lipids,** which differ in important aspects of their chemical composition.

Simple Lipids

Simple lipids contain only carbon, hydrogen, and oxygen. The most common are the **fats,** a combination of **fatty acids** and **glycerol** that are solid at room temperature **(figure 2.25).** Fatty acids are molecules with long chains of C atoms bonded to H atoms with an acidic group (—COOH) on one end **(figure 2.26).**

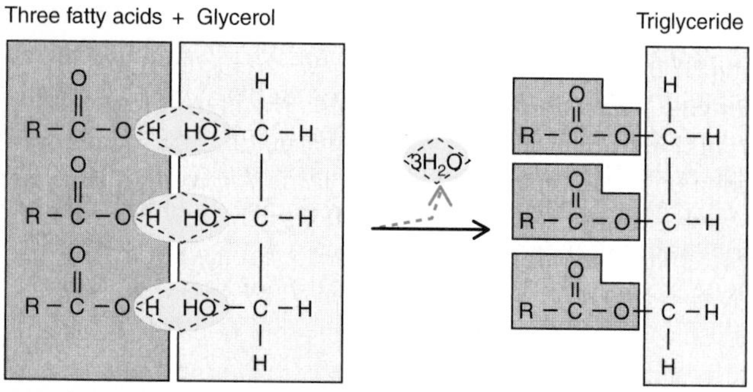

FIGURE 2.25 Formation of a Fat The R group of the fatty acids commonly contains 16 or 18 carbon atoms bonded to hydrogen atoms.

Since glycerol has three hydroxyl groups, a maximum of three fatty acid molecules, either the same or different, can be linked through covalent bonds between the —OH group of glycerol and the —COOH group of the fatty acid. If only one fatty acid is bound to glycerol, the fat is called a **monoglyceride;** when two fatty acids are joined, it is a **diglyceride;** when three fatty acids are bound, a **triglyceride** is formed. Fatty acids are stored in the body as an energy reserve by forming triglycerides.

Although hundreds of different fatty acids exist, they can be divided into two groups based on whether or not any double bonds are present in the portion of the molecule containing only carbon and hydrogen atoms. If there are no double bonds, the fatty acid is termed **saturated** with H atoms. If it contains one or more double bonds, it is **unsaturated.** Unsaturated fats tend to be liquid and are then called **oils.** Oils are liquid because these unsaturated fatty acids develop kinks in their long tails that prevent tight packing. The saturated fats can pack their straight long tails tightly together and therefore are solid (figure 2.26a). Two of the most common saturated fatty acids in nature are **palmitic acid** (16 carbon atoms), and **stearic acid** (18 carbon atoms). A common unsaturated fatty acid is oleic acid (18 carbon atoms and one double bond in the molecule). Oleic acid, with its one double bond, is a **monounsaturated** fatty acid (figure 2.26b). Other fatty acids containing numerous double bonds are **polyunsaturated.** Different lipids are called highly saturated or highly unsaturated when they contain mostly saturated or unsaturated fatty acids.

Another very important group of simple lipids is the **steroids.** All members of this group have the four-membered ring structure shown in **(figure 2.27a).** These compounds differ from the fats in chemical structure, but both are classified as lipids because they are both insoluble in water. If a hydroxyl group is attached to one of the rings, the steroid is called a **sterol,** an example being **cholesterol** (figure 2.27b).

Other important compounds in this group of lipids are certain hormones such as cortisone, progesterone, and testosterone.

Compound Lipids

Compound lipids contain fatty acids and glycerol as well as elements other than carbon, hydrogen, and oxygen. Some of the most important members of this group in biology are the **phospholipids,** which contain a phosphate molecule in addition to the fatty acids and glycerol **(figure 2.28).** The phosphate is further linked to a variety of other polar molecules, such as an alcohol, a sugar, or one of certain amino acids. This entire group is often referred to as a **polar head group** and is soluble in water.

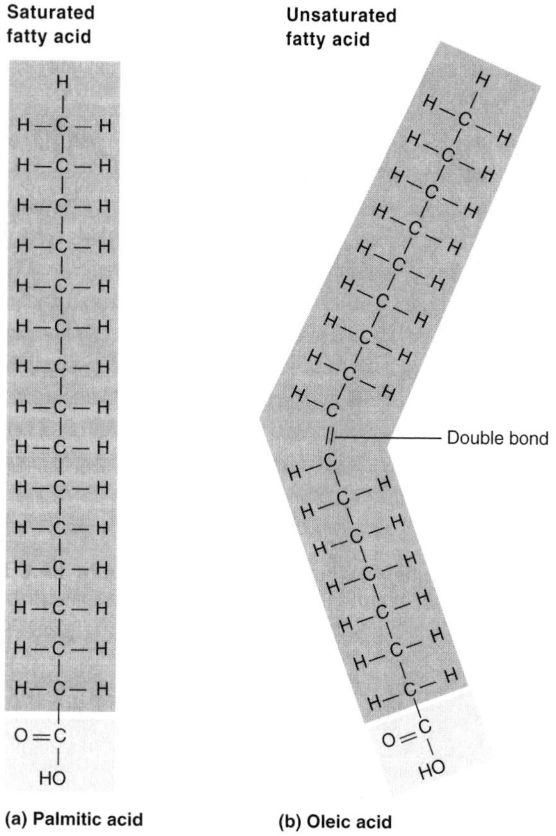

FIGURE 2.26 Fatty Acids The saturated fatty acids **(a)** are solids, and the unsaturated fatty acids **(b)** are liquids.

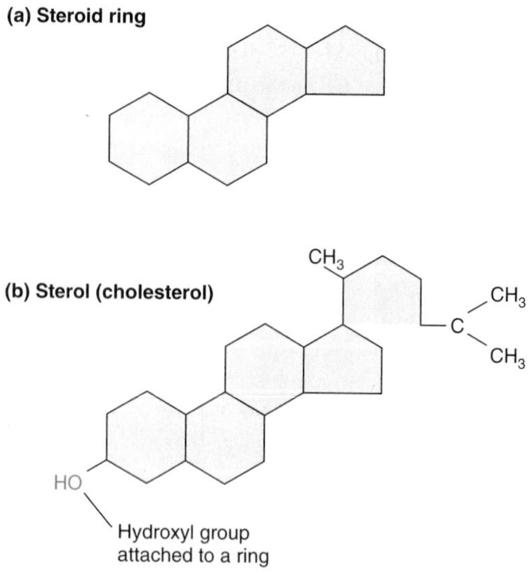

FIGURE 2.27 Steroid (a) General formula showing the four-membered ring and **(b)** the —OH group that make the molecule a sterol. The sterol shown here is cholesterol. The carbon atoms in the ring structures and the attached hydrogen atoms are not shown.

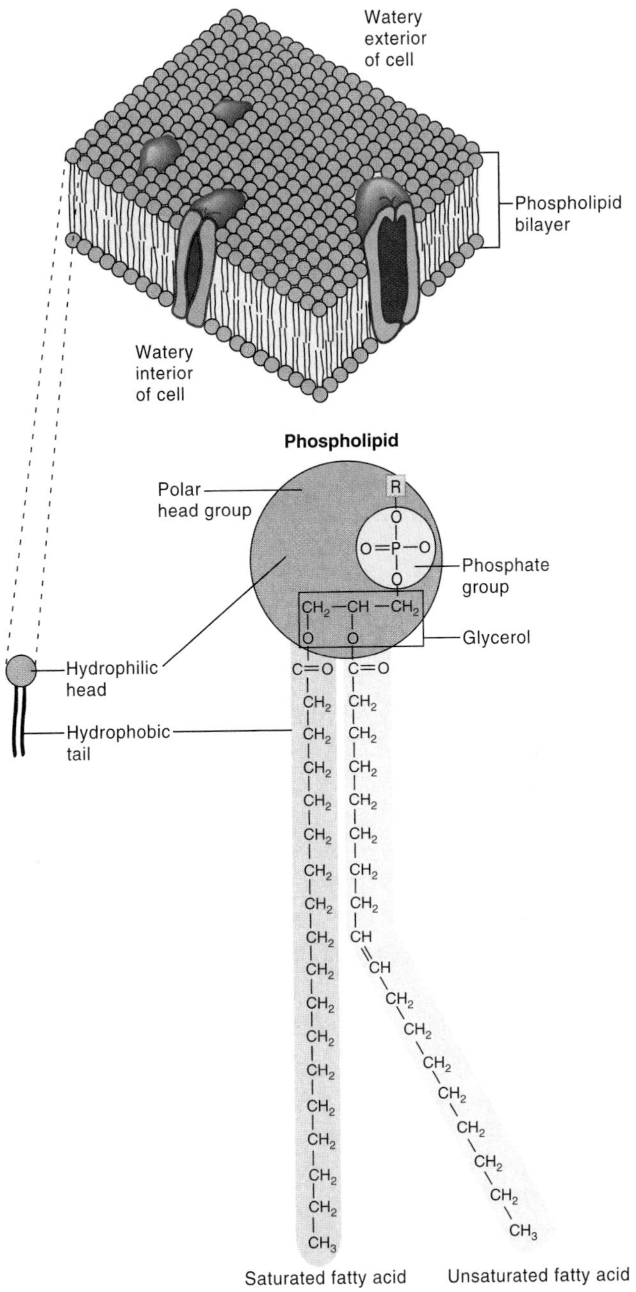

FIGURE 2.28 Phospholipid and the Bilayer That Phospholipids Form in the Membrane of Cells In phospholipids, two of the —OH groups of glycerol are linked to fatty acids and the third —OH group is linked to a hydrophilic head group, which contains a phosphate ion and a polar molecule, labeled R.

Phospholipids occur as a double layer, termed a **bilayer** or **unit membrane,** in the cytoplasmic membrane, a structure that separates the outside of the cell from its internal contents (see figure 2.28). The chemical structure of the bilayer is responsible for the properties of the cytoplasmic membrane. This membrane acts as the major barrier to the entry and exit of substances from the cell. The structure of the phospholipids is responsible for this barrier. A phospholipid consists of two parts, each with unique properties. The end with the phosphate bonded to the polar head group is hydrophilic and therefore soluble in water. The long fatty acid chains consisting of only C and H atoms are hydrophobic and therefore water insoluble. The hydrophilic regions orient themselves toward the external or internal (cytoplasmic) environments with their high concentration of water. The long-chain fatty acids orient themselves away from the aqueous areas and inward interacting hydrophobically with the long hydrocarbon chains of other phospholipid molecules (see figure 2.28). Water-soluble substances, which are the most common and important in the cell's environment, cannot pass through the hydrophobic portion. Therefore, the cell has special mechanisms to bring these molecules into the cell. These will be discussed in chapter 3.

Other compound lipids are found in the outer covering of bacterial cells and will be discussed in chapter 3. These include the **lipoproteins,** covalent associations of proteins and lipids, and the **lipopolysaccharides,** molecules of lipid linked with polysaccharides through covalent bonds.

Some of the most important properties of macromolecules of biological importance are summarized in **table 2.3.**

MICROCHECK 2.7

Phospholipids, with one end polar and the other non-polar, form a major part of cell membranes. They limit the entry and exit of molecules into and out of cells.

- ✓ What are the two main types of lipids and how do they differ from one another?
- ✓ What are the main functions of lipids in cells?
- ✓ Some molecules such as many alcohols are soluble in water and in hydrophobic liquids such as oils. How easily do you think these molecules would cross the cell membrane?

TABLE 2.3 Structure and Function of Macromolecules

Name	Subunit	Some Functions of Macromolecules
Protein	Amino acid	Catalysts; structural portion of many cell components
Nucleic acids	Nucleotide	RNA—Various roles in protein synthesis; DNA—Carrier of genetic information
Polysaccharide	Monosaccharide	Structural component of plant cell wall; storage products
Lipids	Varies—Subunits are not similar	Important in structure of cell membranes

FUTURE CHALLENGES

Fold Properly: Do Not Bend or Mutilate

The properties of all organisms depend on the proteins they contain. These include the structural proteins as well as enzymes. Even though a cell may be able to synthesize a protein, unless that protein is folded correctly and achieves its correct shape, it will not function properly. A major challenge associated with the molecules of life is to understand how proteins fold correctly. This is the **protein folding problem.** Not only is this an important problem from a purely scientific point of view, but a number of serious neurodegenerative diseases appear to be a result of protein misfolding. These include Alzheimers disease and the neurodegenerative diseases caused by prions. If we could understand how proteins fold correctly, we might be able to prevent such diseases.

The information that determines how a protein folds into its three-dimensional configuration is contained in the sequence of its amino acids. It is not yet possible, however, to predict accurately how a protein will fold from its amino acid sequence. The folding occurs in a matter of seconds after the protein is synthesized. The protein folds rapidly into its secondary structure and then more slowly into its tertiary structure. In these slower reactions, many different adjustments of the amino acid side chains are tried out before the protein assumes the correct tertiary structure. The proteins that help other proteins fold correctly, the chaperones, play their role in the slow stage. The cell discards improperly folded proteins. Enzymes, called **proteases,** recognize improperly folded proteins and degrade them. The protein-folding problem has such important implications for medicine and is so challenging a scientific question, that a super-computer is being built to help solve the problem of predicting the three-dimensional structure of a protein from its amino acid sequence. ■ **prions, pp. 13, 359**

SUMMARY

2.1 Atoms and Elements

Atoms are composed of **electrons, protons,** and **neutrons.** (Figure 2.1)

An element consists of a single type of atom.

2.2 Chemical Bonds and the Formation of Molecules

For maximum stability, the outer **orbital** of electrons of an atom must be filled. The electrons in different orbitals have different energy levels. **Bonds** form between atoms to fill their outer orbitals with electrons.

Covalent Bonds

Covalent bonds are strong bonds formed by atoms sharing electrons. (Figure 2.2)

Non-Polar and Polar Covalent Bonds

When atoms have an equal attraction for electrons, a **non-polar covalent bond** is formed between them. (Table 2.2)

When one atom has a greater attraction for electrons than another atom, **polar covalent bonds** are formed between them. (Figure 2.3)

Ionic Bonds

When electrons leave the orbitals of one atom and enter the orbitals of another atom, an **ionic bond** forms between the atoms. (Figure 2.4)

Hydrogen Bonds

Hydrogen bonds are weak bonds that result from the attraction of a positively charged hydrogen atom in a polar molecule to a negatively charged atom in another polar molecule. (Figure 2.5)

Hydrogen bonds are important in the weak association of enzymes with their substrate. (Figure 2.6)

2.3 Chemical Components of the Cell

Water

Water is the most important molecule in the cell.

Water makes up over 70% of all living organisms by weight.

Hydrogen bonding plays a very important role in the properties of water. Figures 2.7, 2.8)

pH

pH is the degree of acidity of a solution; it is measured on a scale of 0 to 14. Buffers prevent the rise or fall of pH. (Figure 2.9)

Small Molecules in the Cell

All cells contain a variety of small organic and inorganic molecules.

A key element in all cells is carbon; it occurs in all organic molecules.

ATP, the energy currency of the cell, stores energy in two high-energy phosphate bonds which, when broken, release energy. (Figure 2.10)

Macromolecules and Their Component Parts

Macromolecules are large molecules usually composed of **subunits** with similar properties.

Synthesis of macromolecules occurs by **dehydration synthesis**, the removal of water, and their degradation occurs by **hydrolysis,** the addition of water.

2.4 Proteins and Their Functions

Proteins are the most versatile of the macromolecules in what they do.

Activities of proteins include catalyzing reactions, being a component of cell structures, moving cells, taking nutrients into the cell, turning genes on and off, and being a part of cell membranes.

Amino Acid Subunits

Proteins are composed of 20 major **amino acids.** (Figure 2.13)

All amino acids consists of a **carboxyl group** at one end and an **amino group** bonded to the same carbon atom as the carboxyl group and a side chain which confers unique properties on the amino acid. (Figure 2.12)

Peptide Bonds and Their Synthesis

Amino acids are joined through **peptide bonds,** joining an amino with a carboxyl group and splitting out water. (Figure 2.15)

Protein Structure (Figure 2.16)

The **primary structure** of a protein is its amino acid sequence.

The **secondary structure** of a protein is determined by intramolecular bonding between amino acids to form **helices** and **sheets.**

The **tertiary structure** of a protein describes the three-dimensional shape of the protein, either **globular** or **fibrous.**

The **quaternary structure** describes the structure resulting from the interaction of several **polypeptide** chains.

When the intramolecular bonds within the protein are broken, the protein changes shape and no longer functions; the proteins are **denatured.** (Figure 2.17)

Substituted Proteins

Substituted proteins contain other molecules such as **sugars** and **lipids,** bonded to the side chains of amino acids in the protein.

2.5 Carbohydrates

Carbohydrates comprise a heterogeneous group of compounds that perform a variety of functions in the cell.

Carbohydrates have carbon, hydrogen, and oxygen atoms in a ratio of approximately 1:2:1.

Monosaccharides

Monosaccharides are classified by the number of carbon atoms they contain, most commonly 5 or 6.

Two different isomers can exist in sugars: **stereoisomers** and **structural isomers.** (Figure 2.19)

Disaccharides

Disaccharides consist of two monosaccharides joined by a covalent bond between their hydroxyl groups.

Polysaccharides

Polysaccharides are macromolecules consisting of monosaccharide subunits, sometimes identical, other times not. (Figure 2.20)

2.6 Nucleic Acids

Nucleic acids are macromolecules whose subunits are **nucleotides.** (Figure 2.21)

There are two types of nucleic acid: **deoxyribonucleic acid (DNA)** and **ribonucleic acid (RNA).**

DNA

DNA is the master molecule of the cell and carries all of the cell's genetic information in its sequence of nucleotides.

DNA is a double-stranded helical molecule with a backbone composed of covalently bonded sugar and phosphate groups. The **purine** and **pyrimidine** bases extend into the center of the helix. (Figure 2.24a)

The two strands of DNA are **complementary** and are held together by hydrogen bonds between the bases. (Figure 2.24b)

RNA

RNA is involved in decoding the genetic information contained in DNA.

RNA is a single-stranded molecule and contains **uracil** in place of the **thymine** in DNA. (Figure 2.22)

2.7 Lipids

Lipids are a heterogeneous group of molecules that are slightly soluble in water and very soluble in most organic solvents.

They comprise two groups: **simple** and **compound lipids.**

Simple Lipids

Simple lipids contain carbon, hydrogen, and oxygen and may be liquid or solid at room temperature.

Fats are common simple lipids and consist of **glycerol** bound to **fatty acids.** (Figure 2.25)

Fatty acids may be **saturated,** in which the fatty acid contains no double-bonds between carbon atoms, or **unsaturated,** in which one or more double bonds exist. (Figure 2.26)

Some simple lipids consist of a four-membered ring, and include **steroids** and **sterols.** (Figure 2.27)

Compound Lipids

Compound lipids contain elements other than carbon, hydrogen, and oxygen.

Phospholipids are common and important examples of compound lipids. They are essential components of bilayer membranes in cells. (Figure 2.28)

REVIEW QUESTIONS

Short Answer

1. Differentiate between an atom, an element, an ion, and a molecule.
2. Which solution is more acidic, one with a pH of 4 or a pH of 5? What is the concentration of H^+ ions in each? The concentration of OH^- ions?
3. How do the two types of nucleic acids differ from one another in (a) composition, (b) size, and (c) function?
4. Name the subunits of proteins, polysaccharides, and nucleic acids.
5. What are the two major groups of lipids? Give an example of each group. What feature is common to all lipids?
6. How does the primary structure of a protein determine its overall structure?
7. Why is water a good solvent?
8. Give an example of a dehydration synthesis reaction. Give an example of a hydrolysis reaction. How are these types of reactions related?
9. List four functions of proteins.
10. What is a steroid?

Multiple Choice

1. Choose the list that goes from the lightest to the heaviest:
   a) Proton, atom, molecule, compound, electron
   b) Atom, proton, compound, molecule, electron
   c) Electron, proton, atom, molecule, compound
   d) Atom, electron, proton, molecule, compound
   e) Proton, atom, electron, molecule, compound

2. The strongest chemical bonds between two atoms in solution are
   a) covalent. b) ionic.
   c) hydrogen bonds. d) hydrophobic interactions.
3. Dehydration synthesis is involved in the synthesis of all of the following, *except*
   a) DNA b) proteins c) polysaccharides
   d) lipids e) monosaccharides
4. The primary structure of a protein relates to its
   a) sequence of amino acids b) length c) shape
   d) solubility e) bonds between amino acids
5. Pure water has all of the following properties, *except*
   a) polarity. b) ability to dissolve lipids. c) pH of 7.
   d) covalent joining of its atoms. e) ability to form hydrogen bonds.
6. The macromolecules that are composed of carbon, hydrogen, and oxygen in an approximate ratio of 1 : 2 : 1 are
   a) proteins. b) lipids. c) polysaccharides.
   d) DNA. e) RNA.
7. In proteins, α helices and β pleated structures are associated with the
   a) primary structure. b) secondary structure.
   c) tertiary structure. d) quaternary structure.
   e) multiprotein complexes.
8. Complementarity plays a major role in the structure of
   a) proteins. b) lipids. c) polysaccharides.
   d) DNA. e) RNA.
9. A bilayer is associated with
   a) proteins. b) DNA. c) RNA.
   d) complex polysaccharides. e) phospholipids.
10. Isomers are associated with
    1. carbohydates. 2. amino acids. 3. nucleotides.
    4. RNA. 5. fatty acids.
    a) 1, 2 b) 2, 3 c) 3, 4 d) 4, 5 e) 1, 5

Applications

1. A group of bacteria known as thermophiles thrive at high temperatures that would normally destroy other bacteria. Yet these thermophiles cannot survive well at the lower temperatures normally found on the earth. Propose a plausible explanation for this observation.
2. Microorganisms use hydrogen bonds to attach themselves to the surfaces that they live upon. Many of them lose hold of the surface because of the weak nature of these bonds and end up dying. Contrast the benefits and disadvantages of using covalent bonds as a means of attaching to surfaces.

Critical Thinking

1. What properties of the carbon atom make it ideal as the key atom for all molecules in organisms?
2. A biologist determined the amounts of several amino acids in two separate samples of pure protein. His data are shown here:

Amino Acid	Leucine	Alanine	Histidine	Cysteine	Glycine
Protein A	7%	12%	4%	2%	5%
Protein B	7%	12%	4%	2%	5%

   He concluded that protein A and protein B were the same protein. Do you agree with this conclusion? Justify your answer.
3. This table indicates the freezing and boiling points of several molecules:

Molecule	Freezing Point (°C)	Boiling Point (°C)
Water	0	100
Carbon tetrachloride (CCl_4)	– 23	77
Methane (CH_4)	– 182	– 164

   Carbon tetrachloride and methane are non-polar molecules. How does the polarity and non-polarity of these molecules explain why the freezing and boiling points for methane and carbon tetrachloride are so much lower than those for water?

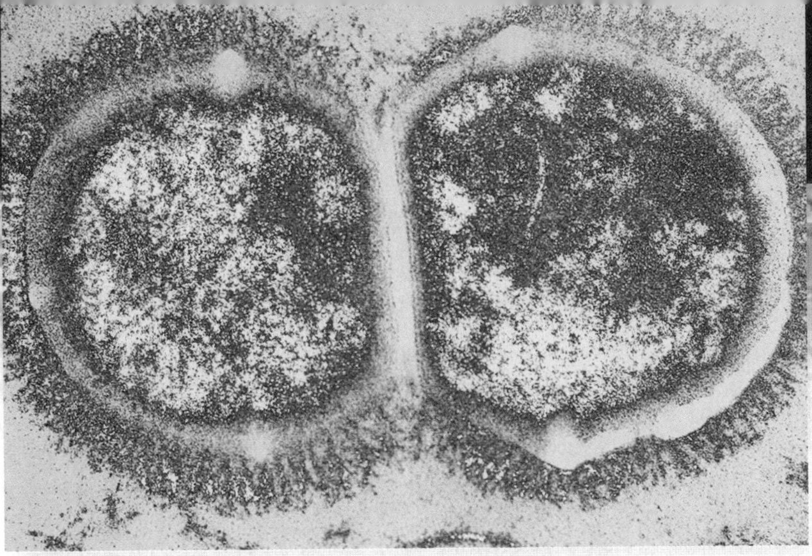

Color-enhanced TEM of bacterial cells.

CHAPTER THREE

Microscopy and Cell Structure

A Glimpse of History

Hans Christian Joachim Gram (1853–1938) was a Danish physician working in a laboratory at the morgue of the City Hospital in Berlin, microscopically examining the lungs of patients who had died of pneumonia. He was working under the direction of Dr. Carl Friedlander, who was trying to identify the cause of pneumonia by studying patients who had died of it. Gram's task was to stain the infected lung tissue to make the bacteria easier to see under the microscope. Strangely, one of the methods he developed did not stain all bacteria equally; some types retained the first dye applied in this multistep procedure, whereas others did not. Gram's staining method revealed that two different kinds of bacteria were causing pneumonia, and that these types retained the dye differently. We now recognize that this important staining method, called the **Gram stain,** efficiently identifies two large, distinct groups of bacteria: Gram-positive and Gram-negative. The variation in the staining outcome of these two groups reflects a fundamental difference in the structure and chemistry of their cell walls.

For a long time, historians thought that Gram did not appreciate the significance of his discovery. In more recent years, however, several letters show that Gram did not want to offend the famous Dr. Friedlander under whom he worked; therefore, he played down the importance of his staining method. In fact, the Gram stain has been used as a key test in the initial identification of bacterial species ever since the late 1880s.

Imagine the astonishment Antony van Leeuwenhoek must have felt in the 1600s when he first observed microorganisms with his handcrafted microscopes, instruments that could magnify images approximately 300-fold (300×). Even today, observing diverse microbes interacting in a sample of stagnant pond water can provide enormous education and entertainment.

Microscopic study of cells has revealed two fundamental types: prokaryotic and eukaryotic. The cells of all members of the Domains *Bacteria* and *Archaea* are prokaryotic. In contrast, cells of all animals, plants, protozoa, fungi, and algae are eukaryotic. The similarities and differences between these two basic cell types are important from a scientific standpoint and also have significant consequences to human health. For example, chemicals that interfere with processes unique to prokaryotic cells can be used to selectively destroy bacteria without harming humans. ■ prokaryotic cells, p. 10

Prokaryotic cells are generally much smaller than most eukaryotic cells—a trait that carries with it certain advantages as well as disadvantages. On one hand, their high surface area relative to their low volume makes it easier for these cells to take in nutrients and excrete waste products. Because of this, they can multiply much more rapidly than their eukaryotic counterparts. On the other hand, their small size makes them vulnerable to an array of threats. Predators, parasites, and competitors constantly surround them. Prokaryotic cells, although simple in structure, have developed many unique attributes that enhance their evolutionary success.

Eukaryotic cells are considerably more complex than prokaryotic cells. Not only are they larger, but many of their cellular processes take place within membrane-bound compartments. Eukaryotic cells are defined by the presence of a membrane-bound nucleus, which contains the chromosomes. Although eukaryotic cells share many of the same characteristics as prokaryotic cells, many of their structures and cellular processes are fundamentally different. ■ eukaryotic cells, p. 10

KEY TERMS

Capsule A distinct thick gelatinous material that surrounds some types of bacteria.

Chemotaxis Directed movement of an organism toward or away from a certain chemical in the environment.

Cytoplasmic membrane A phospholipid bilayer embedded with proteins that surrounds the cytoplasm and defines the boundary of the cell.

Endospore A type of dormant cell that is extraordinarily resistant to damaging conditions including heat, desiccation, ultraviolet light, and toxic chemicals.

Flagellum A structure that provides a mechanism for motility.

Gram-negative bacteria Bacteria that have a cell wall composed of a thin layer of peptidoglycan surrounded by an outer membrane; when Gram stained, these cells are pink.

Gram-positive bacteria Bacteria that have a cell wall composed of a thick layer of peptidoglycan; when Gram stained, these cells are purple.

Lipopolysaccharide (LPS) Molecule that makes up the outer leaflet of the outer membrane of Gram-negative bacteria.

Peptidoglycan A macromolecule found only in bacteria that provides rigidity to the cell wall.

Periplasm The gel-like material that fills the region between the cytoplasmic membrane and the outer membrane of Gram-negative bacteria.

Pili Cell surface structures that generally enable cells to adhere to certain surfaces; some types are involved in a mechanism of DNA transfer.

Ribosome Structure intimately involved in protein synthesis.

Transport systems Mechanisms used to transport nutrients and other small molecules across the cytoplasmic membrane.

MICROSCOPY AND CELL MORPHOLOGY

3.1

Microscopic Techniques: The Instruments

Focus Points

- Describe the importance of magnification, resolution, and contrast in microscopy.
- Compare and contrast light microscopes, electron microscopes, and atomic force microscopes.

One of the most important tools for studying microorganisms is the **light microscope,** which uses visible light for observing objects. These instruments can magnify images approximately 1,000×, making it relatively easy to observe the size, shape, and motility of prokaryotic cells. The **electron microscope,** introduced in 1931, can magnify images in excess of 100,000×, revealing many fine details of cell structure. A major advancement came in the 1980s with the development of the **atomic force microscope,** which allows scientists to view individual atoms. The types of microscopes discussed in this section are summarized in **table 3.1.**

Principles of Light Microscopy: The Bright-Field Microscope

In light microscopy, light typically passes through a specimen and then through a series of magnifying lenses. The most common type of light microscope, and the easiest to use, is the **bright-field microscope,** which evenly illuminates the field of view.

Magnification

The modern light microscope has two magnifying lenses—an **objective lens** and an **ocular lens**—and is called a **compound microscope (figure 3.1).** These lenses in combination visually enlarge an object by a factor equal to the product of each lens' magnification. For example, an object is magnified 1,000-fold when it is viewed through a 10× ocular lens in conjunction with a 100× objective lens. Most compound microscopes have a selection of objective lenses that are of different powers—typically 4×, 10×, 40×, and 100×. This makes a choice of different magnifications possible with the same instrument.

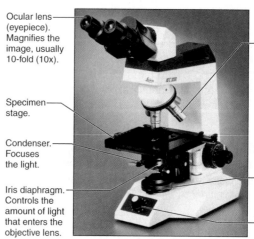

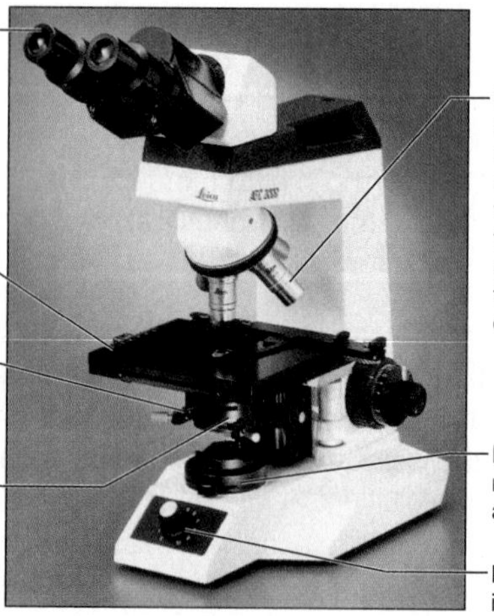

Ocular lens (eyepiece). Magnifies the image, usually 10-fold (10x).
Specimen stage.
Condenser. Focuses the light.
Iris diaphragm. Controls the amount of light that enters the objective lens.
Objective lens. A selection of lens options provide different magnifications. The total magnification is the product of the magnifying power of the ocular lens and the objective lens.
Light source with means to control amount of light.
Knob to control intensity of light.

FIGURE 3.1 A Modern Light Microscope The compound microscope employs a series of magnifying lenses.

TABLE 3.1 A Summary of Microscopic Instruments and Their Characteristics

Instrument	Mechanism	Uses/Comment
Light Microscopes	Visible light passes through a series of lenses to produce a magnified image.	Relatively easy to use. Considerably less expensive than confocal and electron microscopes.
Bright-field 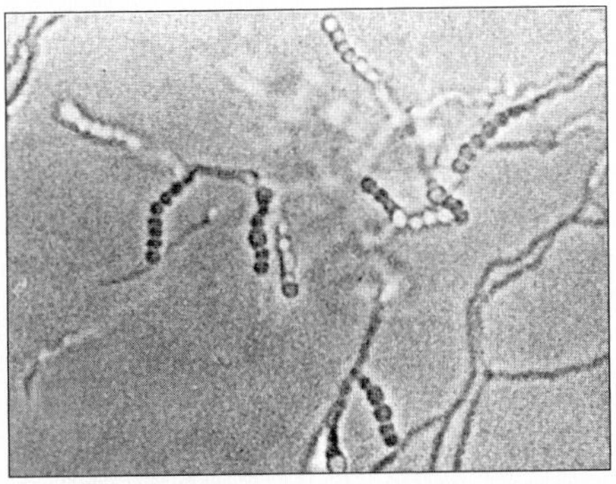	Illuminates the field of view evenly.	Most common type of microscope.
Phase-contrast 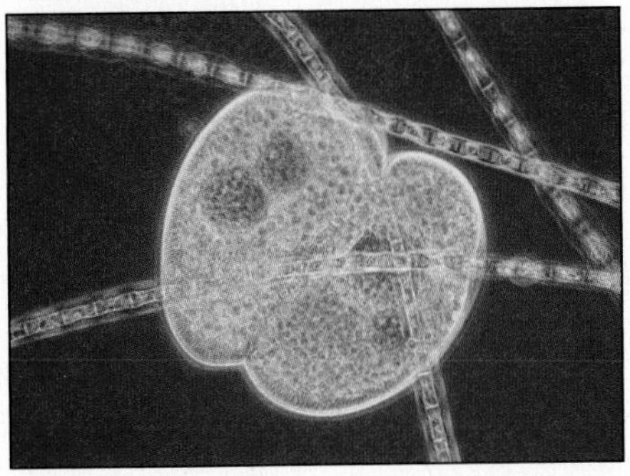	Amplifies differences in refractive index to create contrast.	Makes unstained cells more readily visible.
Interference 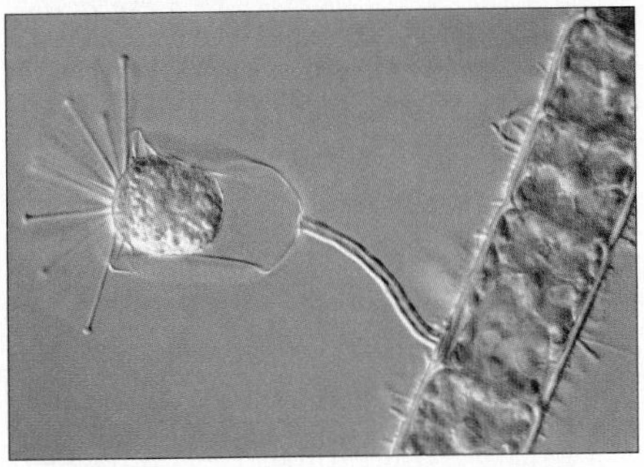	Two light beams pass through the specimen and then recombine.	Causes the specimen to appear as a three-dimensional image.
Dark-field 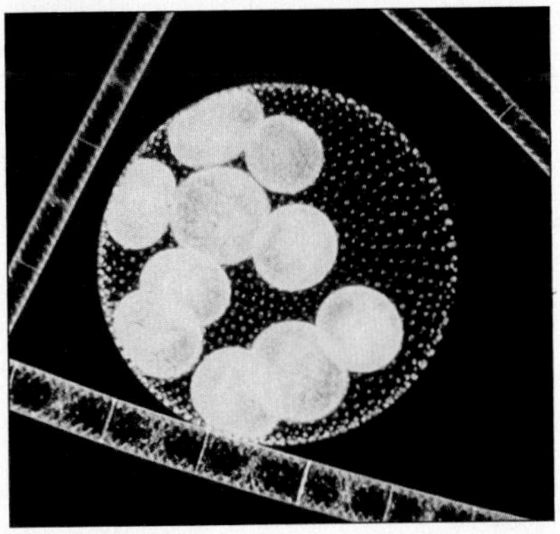	Light is directed toward the specimen at an angle.	Makes unstained cells more readily visible; organisms stand out as bright objects against a dark background.

TABLE 3.1 A Summary of Microscopic Instruments and Their Characteristics (*continued*)

Instrument	Mechanism	Uses/Comment
Fluorescence 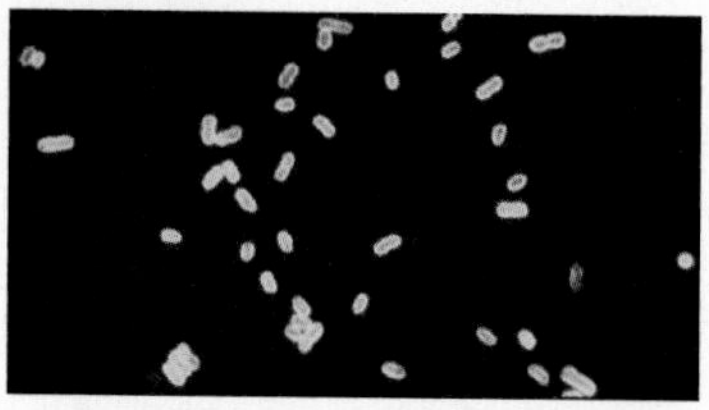	Projects ultraviolet light, causing fluorescent molecules in the specimen to emit longer wavelength light.	Used to observe cells that have been stained or tagged with a fluorescent dye.
Confocal 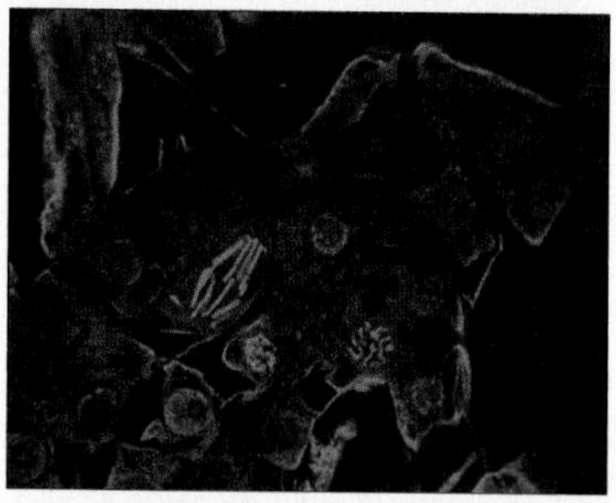	Mirrors scan a laser beam across successive regions and planes of a specimen. From that data, a computer constructs an image.	Used to construct a three-dimensional image of a structure; provides detailed sectional views of intact cells.
Electron Microscopes	Electron beams are used in place of visible light to produce the magnified image.	Can clearly magnify images 100,000×.
Transmission 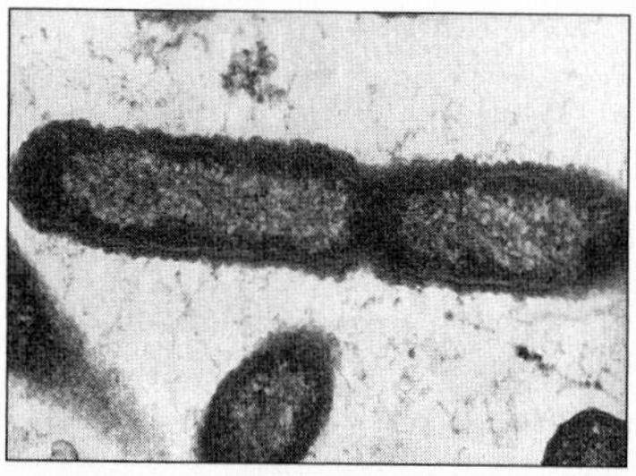	Transmits a beam of electrons through a specimen.	Elaborate specimen preparation, which may introduce artifacts, is required.
Scanning 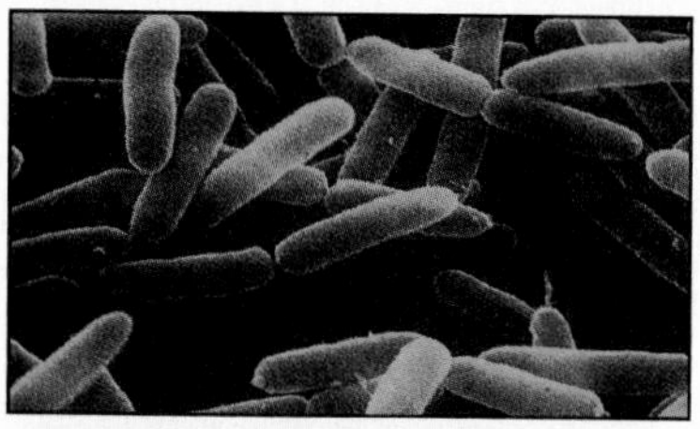	A beam of electrons scans back and forth over the surface of a specimen.	Used for observing surface details; produces a three-dimensional effect.
Atomic Force Microscope 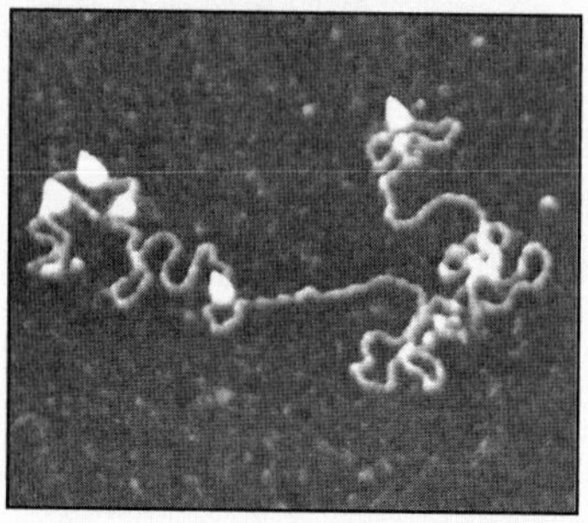	A probe moves in response to even the slightest force between it and the sample.	Produces a map showing the bumps and valleys of the atoms on the surface of the sample.

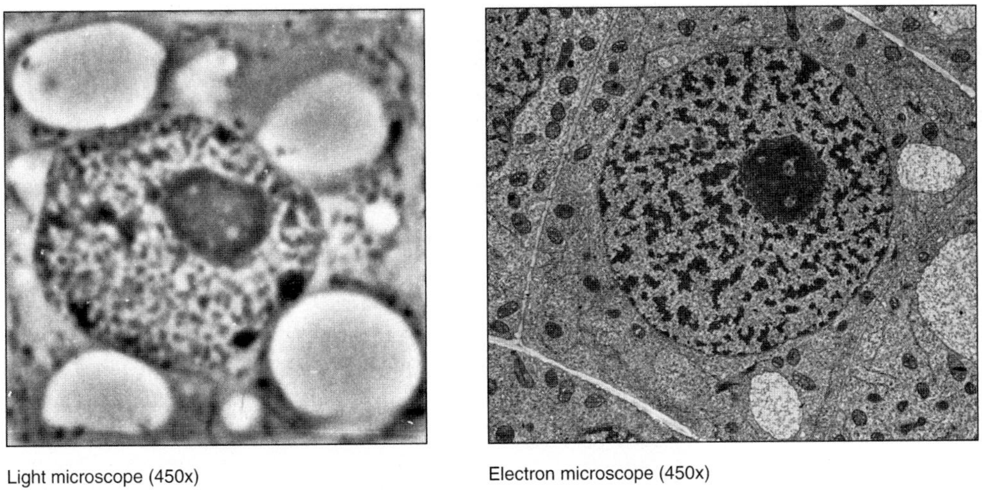

FIGURE 3.2 Comparison of the Resolving Power of the Light Microscope and an Electron Microscope In this case, an onion root tip was magnified 450×. Note the difference in the degree of detail that can be seen at the same magnification.

The **condenser lens** does not affect the magnification but, positioned between the light source and the specimen, is used to focus the illumination on the specimen.

Resolution

The usefulness of a microscope depends not so much on its degree of magnification, but on its ability to clearly separate, or **resolve,** two objects that are very close together. The **resolving power** is defined as the minimum distance existing between two objects when those objects can still be observed as separate entities. The resolving power therefore determines how much detail actually can be seen **(figure 3.2).**

Resolving power of a microscope depends on the quality and type of lens, wavelength of the light, magnification, and how the specimen under observation has been prepared. The maximum resolving power of the best light microscope is 0.2 μm. This is sufficient to observe the general morphology of a prokaryotic cell but too low to distinguish a particle the size of a virus.

To obtain maximum resolution when using certain high-power objectives such as the 100× lens, oil must be used to displace the air between the lens and the specimen. This avoids the bending of light rays, or **refraction,** that occurs when light passes from glass to air **(figure 3.3).** Refraction can prevent those rays from entering the relatively small openings of higher-power objective lenses. The oil has nearly the same **refractive index** as glass. Refractive index is a measure of the relative velocity of light as it passes through a medium. As light travels from a medium of one refractive index to another, those rays are bent. When oil displaces air at the interface of the glass slide and glass lens, light rays pass with little refraction occurring.

Contrast

Contrast reflects the number of visible shades in a specimen—high contrast being just two shades, black and white. Different specimens require various degrees of contrast to reveal the most information. One example is bacteria, which are essentially transparent against

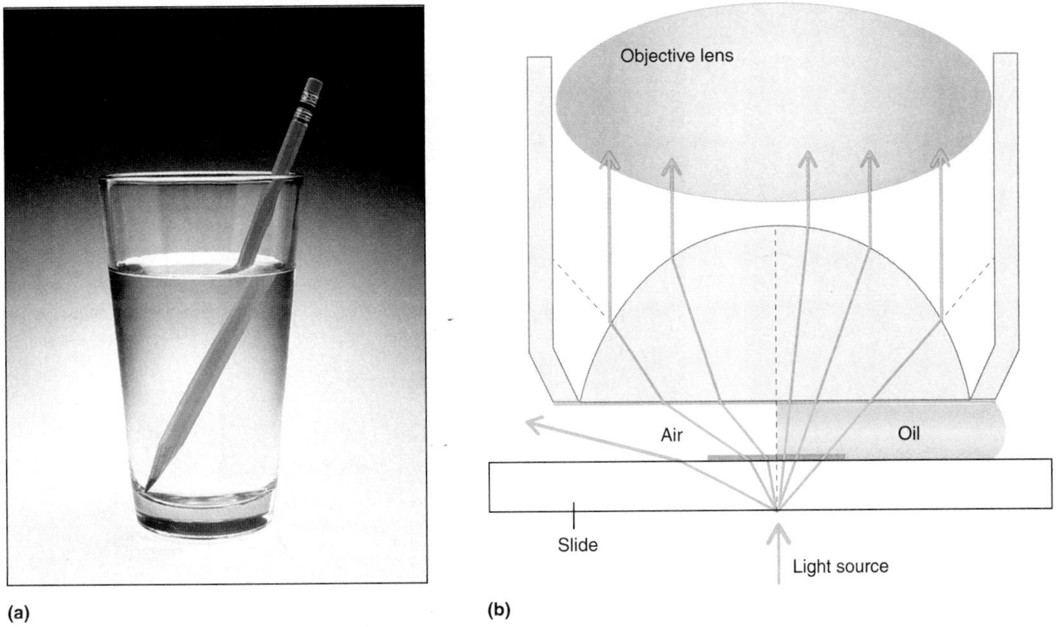

FIGURE 3.3 Refraction As light passes from one medium to another, the light rays may bend, depending on the refractive index of the two media. **(a)** The pencil in water appears bent because the refractive index of water is different from that of air. **(b)** Light rays bend as they pass from air to glass because of the different refractive indexes of these media; some rays are lost to the objective. Oil and glass have the same refractive index, and therefore the light rays are not bent.

a bright colorless background. The lack of contrast presents a problem when viewing objects (see figure 11.18). One way to overcome this problem is to stain the bacteria with any one of a number of dyes. The types and characteristics of these stains will be discussed shortly.

Light Microscopes That Increase Contrast

Special light microscopes that increase the contrast between microorganisms and their surroundings overcome some of the difficulties of observing unstained bacteria. Staining kills microbes; therefore, some of these microscopes are invaluable when the goal is to examine characteristics of living organisms such as motility.

The Phase-Contrast Microscope

The **phase-contrast microscope** amplifies the slight difference between the refractive index of cells and the surrounding medium, resulting in a darker appearance of the denser material **(figure 3.4).** As light passes through cells, it is refracted slightly differently than when it passes through its surroundings. Special optical devices boost those differences, thereby increasing the contrast.

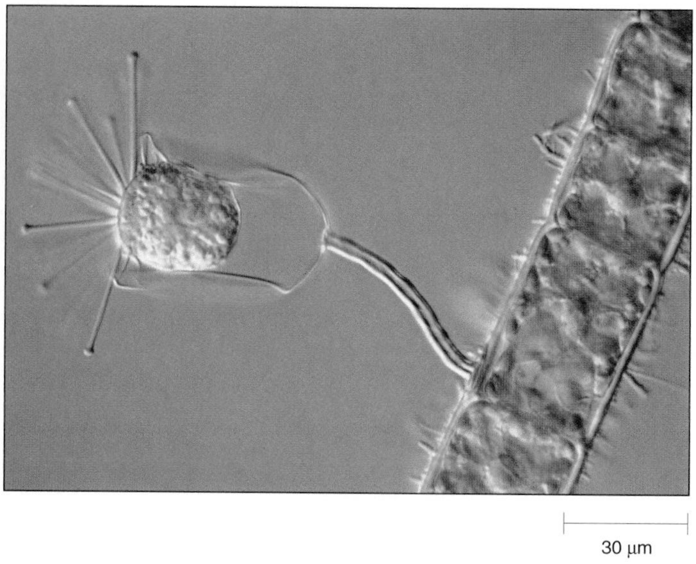

FIGURE 3.5 Nomarski Differential Interference Contrast (DIC) Microscopy Protozoan (*Paracineta*) attached to a green alga (*Spongomorpha*).

The Interference Microscope

The **interference microscope** causes the specimen to appear as a three-dimensional image **(figure 3.5).** This microscope, like the phase-contrast microscope, depends on differences in refractive index as light passes through different materials. The most frequently used microscope of this type is the **Nomarski differential interference contrast (DIC) microscope,** which has a device for separating light into two beams that pass through the specimen and then recombine. The light waves are out of phase when they recombine, thereby yielding the three-dimensional appearance of the specimen.

The Dark-Field Microscope

Organisms viewed through a **dark-field microscope** stand out as bright objects against a dark background **(figure 3.6).** The microscope operates on the same principle that makes dust visible when a beam of bright light shines into a dark room. A special mechanism directs light toward the specimen at an angle, so that only light scattered by the specimen enters the objective lens. Dark-field microscopy can detect *Treponema pallidum*, the causative agent of syphilis. These thin, spiral-shaped organisms stain poorly and are difficult to see via bright-field microscopy (see figure 11.26).

The Fluorescence Microscope

The **fluorescence microscope** is used to observe cells or other material that are either naturally fluorescent or have been stained or tagged with fluorescent dyes. A **fluorescent** molecule absorbs light at one wavelength (usually ultraviolet light) and then emits light of a longer wavelength.

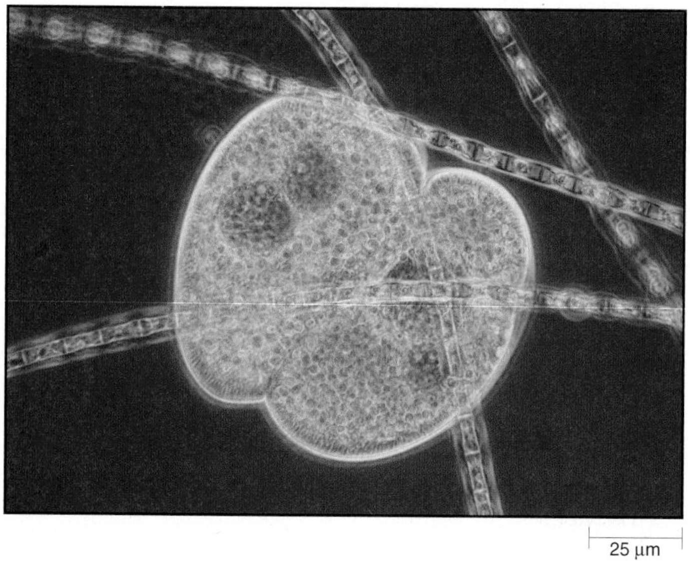

FIGURE 3.4 Phase-Contrast Photomicrograph *Paramecium bursaria* containing endosymbiotic *Chlorella* (a green alga).

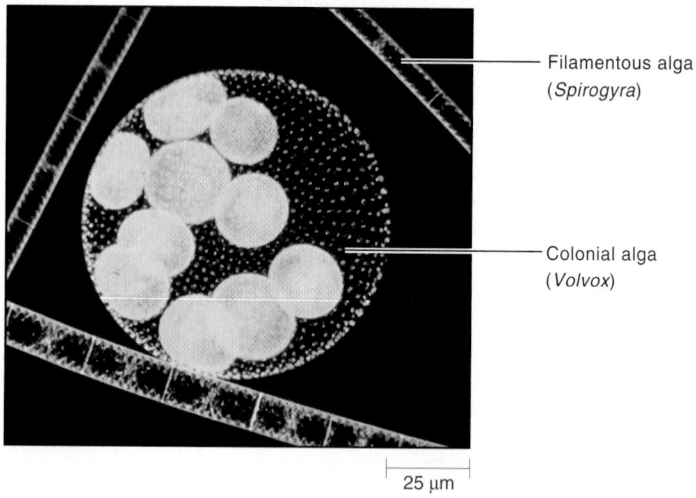

FIGURE 3.6 Dark-Field Photomicrograph *Volvox* (sphere) and *Spirogyra* (filaments), both of which are eukaryotes.

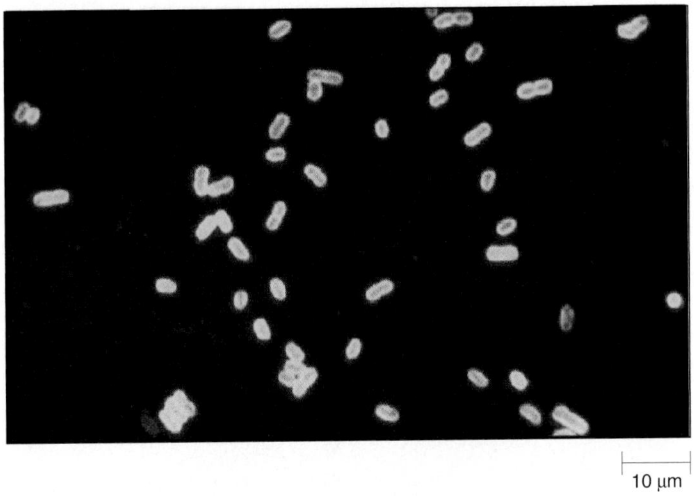

FIGURE 3.7 Fluorescence Photomicrograph A rod-shaped bacterium tagged with fluorescent marker.

The fluorescence microscope projects ultraviolet light through a specimen, but then captures only the light emitted by the fluorescent molecules to form the image. This allows fluorescent cells to stand out as illuminated objects against a dark background **(figure 3.7).** The types and characteristics of fluorescent dyes and tags will be discussed shortly. ■ fluorescent dyes and tags, p. 52

A common variation of the standard fluorescence microscope is the **epifluorescence microscope,** which projects the ultraviolet light through the objective lens and onto the specimen. Because the light is not transmitted through the specimen, cells attached to soil particles or other opaque materials can be observed.

The Confocal Scanning Laser Microscope

The **confocal scanning laser microscope** is used to construct a three-dimensional image of a thick structure such as a community of microorganisms **(figure 3.8).** The instrument can also provide detailed sectional views of the interior of an intact cell. In confocal microscopy, lenses focus a laser beam to illuminate a given point on one vertical plane of a specimen. Mirrors then scan the laser beam across the specimen, illuminating successive regions and planes until the entire specimen has been scanned. Each plane corresponds to an image of one fine slice of the specimen. A computer then assembles the data and constructs a three-dimensional image, which is displayed on a screen. In effect, this microscope is a miniature CAT scan for cells.

Frequently, the specimens are first stained or tagged with a fluorescent dye. By using certain fluorescent tags that bind specifically to a given protein or other compound, the precise cellular location of that compound can be determined. In some cases, multiple different tags that bind to specific molecules are used, each having a distinct color.

Electron Microscopes

Electron microscopy is in some ways comparable to light microscopy. Rather than using glass lenses, visible light, and the eye to observe the specimen, the electron microscope uses electromagnetic lenses, electrons, and a fluorescent screen to produce the magnified image **(figure 3.9).** That image can be captured on photographic film to create an **electron photomicrograph.** Sometimes, the black and white images are artificially enhanced with color to add visual clarity. ■ electrons, p. 19

Since the electrons have a wavelength about 1,000 times shorter than visible light, the resolving power increases about 1,000-fold, to about 0.3 nanometers (nm) or 0.3×10^3 μm. Consequently, considerably more detail can be observed due to the much higher resolution. These instruments can clearly magnify an image 100,000×. One of the biggest drawbacks of the microscope is that the lenses and specimen must all be in a vacuum. Otherwise, the molecules composing air would interfere with the path of the electrons. This results in an expensive, bulky unit and requires substantial and complex specimen preparation.

The Transmission Electron Microscope

The **transmission electron microscope (TEM)** is used to observe fine details of cell structure, such as the number of layers that

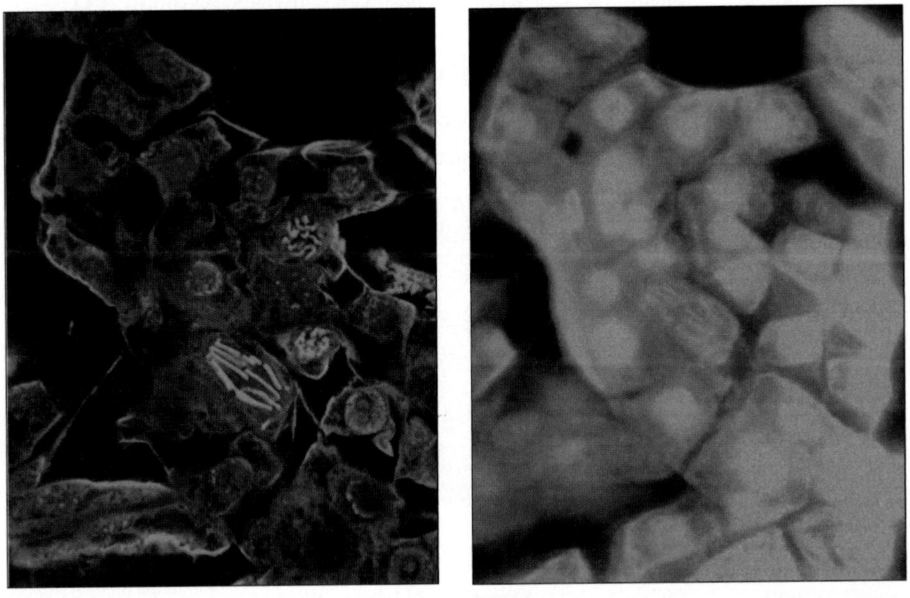

FIGURE 3.8 Confocal Microscopy This can be used to produce a clear image of a single plane in a thick structure. **(a)** Confocal photomicrography of fava bean mitosis. **(b)** Regular photomicrograph.

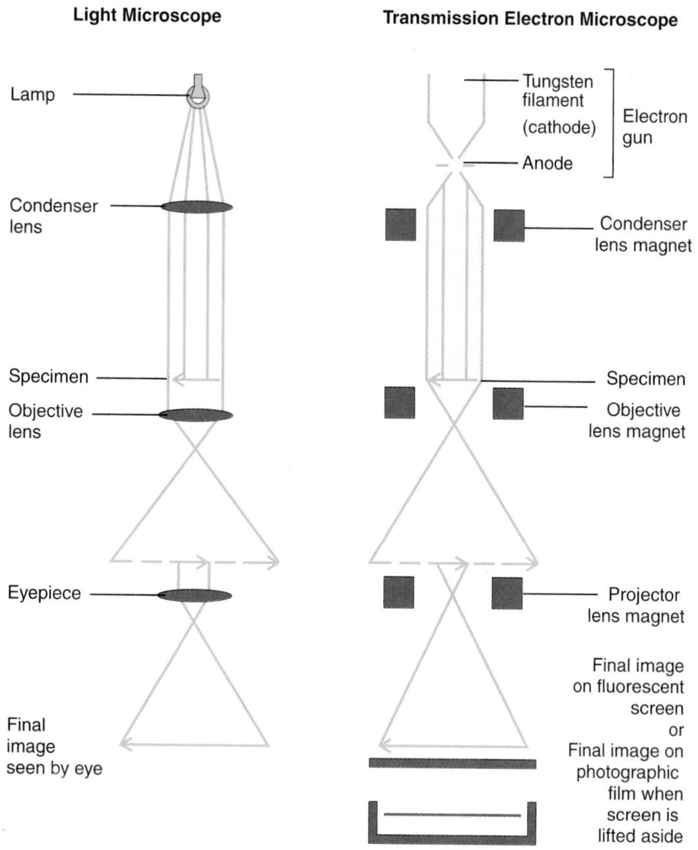

FIGURE 3.9 Comparison of the Principles of Light and the Electron Microscopy For the sake of comparison, the light source for the light microscope has been inverted (the light is shown at the top and the eyepiece, or ocular lens, at the bottom).

envelop a cell. The instrument directs a beam of electrons at a specimen. Depending on the density of a particular region in the specimen, electrons will either pass through or be scattered to varying degrees. The darker areas of the resulting image correspond to the denser portions of the specimen **(figure 3.10).**

Transmission electron microscopy requires elaborate and painstaking specimen preparation. To view details of internal structure, a process called **thin sectioning** is used. Cells are carefully treated with a preservative and dehydrated in an organic solvent before being embedded in a plastic resin. Once embedded, they can be cut into exceptionally thin slices with a diamond or glass knife and then stained with heavy metals. Even a single bacterial cell must be cut into slices this way to be viewed via TEM. Unfortunately, the procedure can severely distort the cells. Consequently, a major concern in using TEM is distinguishing actual cell components from artifacts occurring as a result of specimen preparation.

A process called **freeze fracturing** is used to observe the shape of structures within the cell. The specimen is rapidly frozen and then fractured by striking it with a knife blade. The cells break open, usually along the middle of internal membranes. Next, the surface of the section is coated with a thin layer of carbon to create a replica of the surface. This replica is then examined in the electron microscope. A variation of freeze fracturing is **freeze etching.** In this process, the frozen surface exposed by fracturing is dried slightly under vacuum, which allows underlying regions to be exposed.

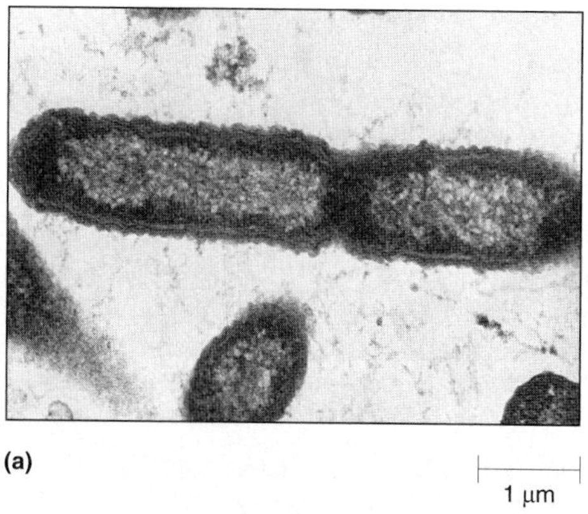

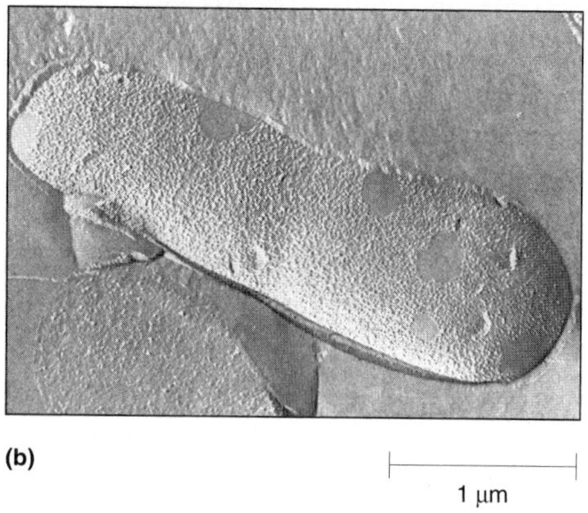

FIGURE 3.10 Transmission Electron Photomicrograph A rod-shaped bacterium prepared by **(a)** thin section; **(b)** freeze etching.

The Scanning Electron Microscope

The **scanning electron microscope (SEM)** is used for observing surface details of cells. A beam of electrons scans back and forth over the surface of a specimen coated with a thin film of metal. As those beams move, electrons are released from the specimen and reflected back into the viewing chamber. This reflected radiation is observed with the microscope. Relatively large specimens can be viewed, and a dramatic three-dimensional effect is observed with the SEM **(figure 3.11).**

Atomic Force Microscopy

The **atomic force microscope (AFM)** makes it possible to view images at an atomic scale **(figure 3.12).** The resolving power is much greater

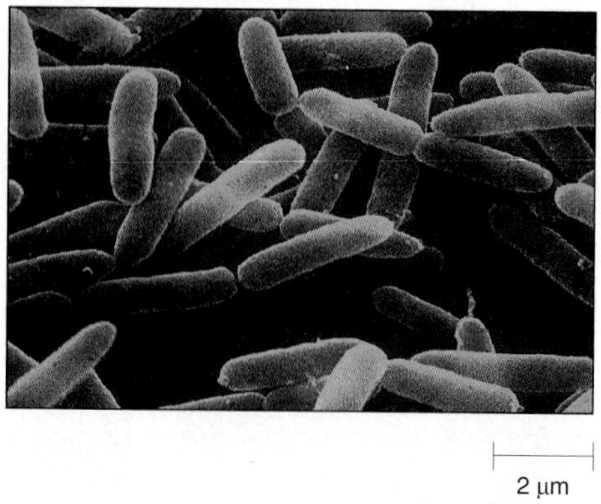

FIGURE 3.11 Scanning Electron Photomicrograph A rod-shaped bacterium.

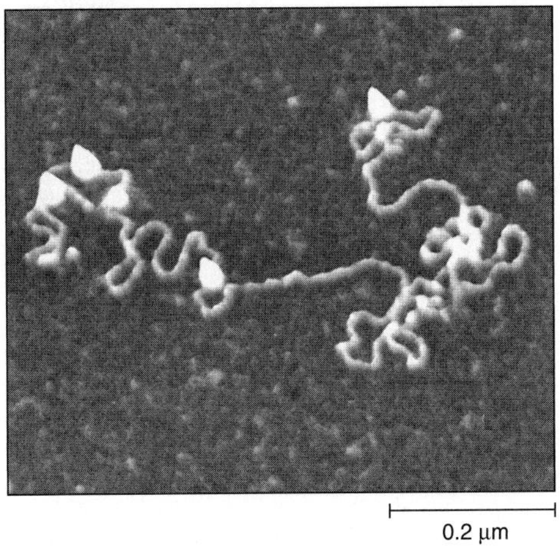

FIGURE 3.12 Atomic Force Microscopy 3-D micrograph of a fragment of DNA. The bright peaks are enzymes attached to the DNA.

than that of an electron microscope, and the samples do not need the special preparation that is required for electron microscopy. In fact, the instrument can inspect samples either in air or submerged in liquid.

The mechanics of AFM can be compared to that of a stylus mounted on the arm of a record player. A very sharp probe (stylus) is attached to a cantilever that moves across the surface of the sample, "feeling" the bumps and valleys of the atoms on that surface. As the probe scans the sample, a laser measures its motion, and a computer produces a topographic map of the sample's surface.

MICROCHECK 3.1

The usefulness of a microscope depends on its resolving power. The most common type of microscope is the bright-field microscope. Variations of light microscopes are designed to increase contrast between a bacterium and its surroundings. The fluorescence microscope is used to observe microbes stained with special dyes. The confocal scanning laser microscope is used to construct a three-dimensional image of a thick structure. Electron microscopes can magnify images 100,000×. The atomic force microscope maps images on an atomic scale.

- ✓ Why must oil be employed when using the 100× lens?
- ✓ Why are microscopes that enhance contrast used to view live rather than stained specimens?
- ✓ If an object being viewed under the phase-contrast microscope has the same refractive index as the background material, how would it appear?

3.2

Microscopic Techniques: Dyes and Staining

Focus Points

- Describe the principles of the Gram stain and the acid-fast stain.
- Describe the techniques used to observe capsules, endospores, and flagella.
- Describe the benefits of using fluorescent dyes and tags to stain cells.

It can be difficult with the bright-field microscope to observe living microorganisms. Most are nearly transparent and often move rapidly about the slide. To remedy this problem, cells are frequently immobilized and stained with dyes. Many different dyes and staining procedures can be used; each has specific applications **(table 3.2).**

Basic dyes, which carry a positive charge, are more commonly used for staining than are negatively charged **acidic dyes.** Because

TABLE 3.2 A Summary of Stains and Their Characteristics

Stain	Characteristics
Simple Stains	Employ a basic dye to impart a color to a cell. Easy way to increase the contrast between otherwise colorless cells and a transparent background.
Differential Stains	Distinguish one group of microorganisms from another.
Gram stain	Used to separate bacteria into two major groups, Gram-positive and Gram-negative. The staining characteristics of these groups reflect a fundamental difference in the chemical structure of their cell walls. This is by far the most widely used staining procedure.
Acid-fast stain	Used to detect members of the genus *Mycobacterium* in a specimen. Due to the lipid composition of their cell walls, these organisms do not readily take up stains.
Special Stains	Stain specific structures inside or outside of a cell.
Capsule stain	Capsule stains exploit the fact that viscous capsules do not readily take up certain stains; the capsules stand out against a stained background. This is an example of a negative stain.
Endospore stain	Stains endospores, a type of dormant cell that does not readily take up stains. These are produced by *Bacillus* and *Clostridium* species.
Flagella stain	The staining agent adheres to and coats the otherwise thin flagella, enabling them to be seen with the light microscope.
Fluorescent Dyes and Tags	Fluorescent dyes and tags absorb ultraviolet light and then emit light of a longer wavelength. They are used in conjunction with a fluorescence microscope.
Fluorescent dyes	Some fluorescent dyes bind to compounds found in all cells; others bind to compounds specific to only certain types of cells.
Fluorescent tags	Antibodies to which a fluorescent molecule has been attached are used to tag specific molecules.

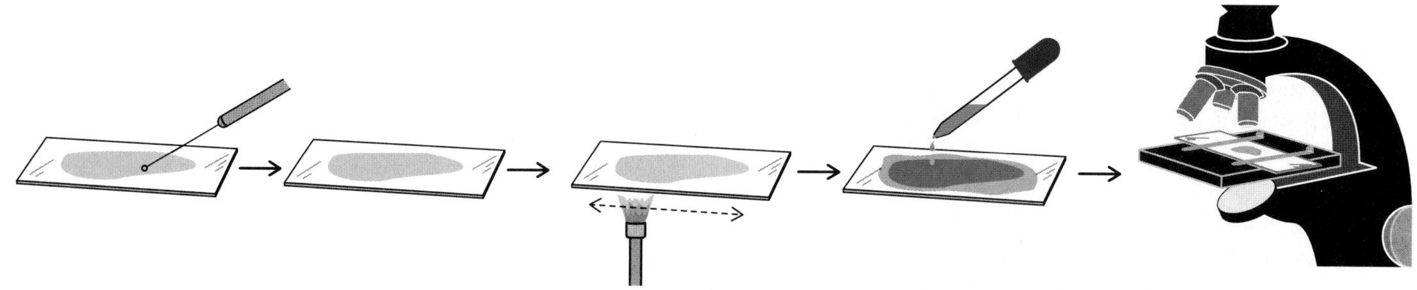

FIGURE 3.13 Staining Bacteria for Microscopic Observation

opposite charges attract, basic dyes stain the negatively charged components of cells, including nucleic acid and many proteins, whereas acidic dyes are repelled. Common basic dyes include methylene blue, crystal violet, safranin, and malachite green. **Simple staining** employs one of these basic dyes to stain the cells. Acidic dyes are sometimes used to stain backgrounds against which colorless cells can be seen, a technique called **negative staining.**

To stain microorganisms, a drop of a liquid containing the microbe is placed on a glass microscope slide and allowed to air dry. The resulting specimen forms a film, or **smear.** The organisms are then attached, or **fixed,** to the slide, usually by passing the slide over a flame **(figure 3.13).** Dye is then applied and washed off with water. Heat fixing and subsequent staining steps kill the microorganisms and may distort their shape.

Differential Stains

Differential staining techniques are used to distinguish one group of bacteria from another. The two most frequently used differential staining techniques are the **Gram stain** and the **acid-fast stain.**

Gram Stain

The **Gram stain** is by far the most widely used procedure for staining bacteria. The basis for it was developed over a century ago by Dr. Hans Christian Gram (see **Glimpse of History**). His observations led to procedures by which bacteria can be separated into two major groups: **Gram-positive** and **Gram-negative.** We now know that the difference in the staining properties of these two groups reflects a fundamental difference in the chemical structure of their cell walls.

Gram staining involves four basic steps **(figure 3.14).**

1. The smear is first flooded with the **primary stain,** crystal violet in this case. The primary stain is the first dye applied in any multistep staining procedure and generally stains all of the cells.
2. The smear is rinsed to remove excess crystal violet and then flooded with a dilute solution of iodine, called **Gram's iodine.** Iodine is a **mordant,** a substance that increases the affinity of cellular components for a dye. The iodine combines with the crystal violet to form a dye-iodine complex, thereby decreasing the solubility of the dye within the cell.

	Steps in Staining	State of Bacteria
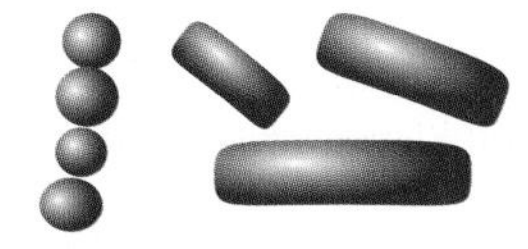	Step 1: Crystal violet (primary stain)	Cells stain purple.
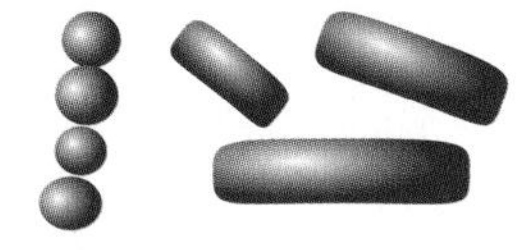	Step 2: Iodine (mordant)	Cells remain purple.
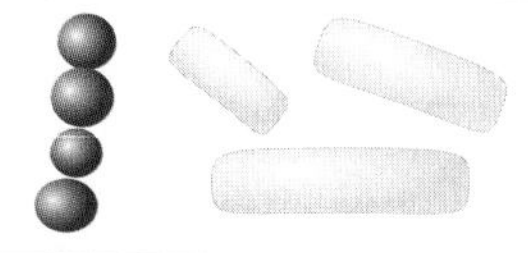	Step 3: Alcohol (decolorizer)	Gram-positive cells remain purple; Gram-negative cells become colorless.
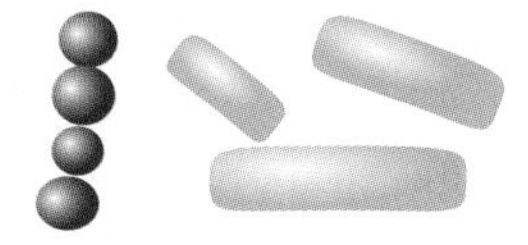	Step 4: Safranin (counterstain)	Gram-positive cells remain purple; Gram-negative cells appear red.

(a)

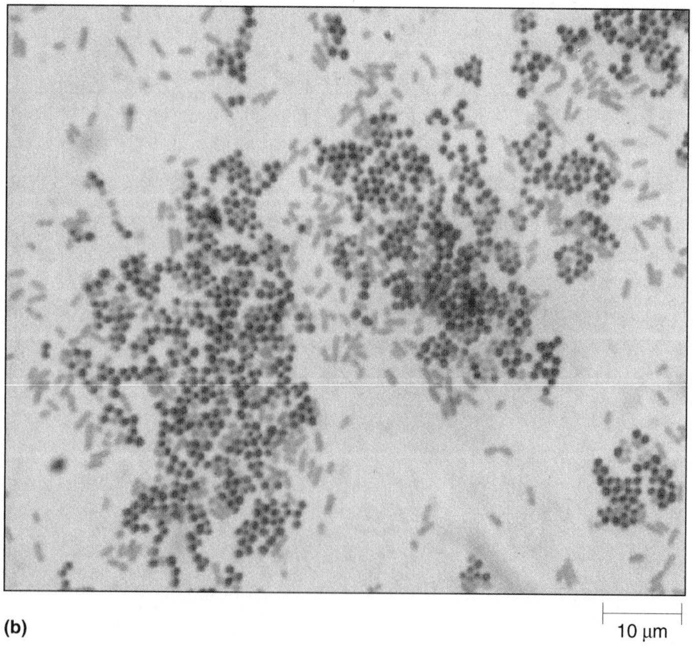

(b)

FIGURE 3.14 Gram Stain (a) Steps in the Gram stain procedure. **(b)** Results of a Gram stain. The Gram-positive cells (purple) are *Staphylococcus aureus;* the Gram-negative cells (reddish-pink) are *Escherichia coli.*

3. The stained smear is rinsed again, and then 95% alcohol or a mixture of alcohol and acetone is briefly added. These solvents act as **decolorizing agents** and readily remove the dye-iodine complex from Gram-negative, but not Gram-positive, bacteria.
4. A **counterstain** is then applied to impart a contrasting color to the now colorless Gram-negative bacteria. For this purpose, the red dye safranin is used. This dye stains Gram-negative as well as Gram-positive bacteria, but because the latter are already stained purple, it imparts little difference to those cells.

To obtain reliable results, the Gram stain must be done properly. One of the most common mistakes is to decolorize a smear for too long a time period. Even Gram-positive cells can lose the crystal violet-iodine complex during prolonged decolorization. An over-decolorized Gram-positive cell will appear pink after counterstaining. Another important consideration is the age of the culture. As bacterial cells age, they lose their ability to retain the crystal violet–iodine dye complex, presumably because of changes in their cell wall. This also causes the cells to appear pink. Thus, the Gram stain results of fresh cultures (less than 24 hours old) are more reliable.

Acid-Fast Stain

The **acid-fast stain** is a procedure used to stain a small group of organisms that do not readily take up stains. Among these are members of the genus *Mycobacterium*, including a species that causes tuberculosis and one that causes Hansen's disease (leprosy). The cell wall of these bacteria contains high concentrations of lipid, preventing the uptake of dyes, including those used in the Gram stain. Therefore, harsh methods are needed to stain these organisms. Once stained, however, these same cells are very resistant to decolorization. Because mycobacteria are among the few organisms that retain the stain in this procedure, the acid-fast stain can be used to presumptively identify them in clinical specimens that might contain a variety of different bacteria. ■ tuberculosis, p. 593 ■ Hansen's disease, p. 688

The acid-fast stain, like the Gram stain, requires multiple steps. The primary stain in this procedure is carbol fuchsin, a red dye. In the classic procedure, the stain-flooded slide is heated over boiling water, which facilitates the staining. A current variation does not use heat, instead using a prolonged application of a more concentrated solution of dye. The slide is then rinsed briefly to remove the residual stain before being flooded with acid-alcohol, a potent decolorizing agent. This step removes the carbol fuchsin from nearly all cells, including tissue cells and most bacteria. Those few unusual organisms that retain the dye are called **acid-fast.** Methylene blue is then used as a counter-stain, imparting a blue color to non-acid-fast cells. Acid-fast organisms, which do not take up the methylene blue, appear a bright reddish-pink **(figure 3.15).**

Special Stains to Observe Cell Structures

Dyes can also be used to stain specific structures inside or outside the cell. The staining procedure for each component of the cell is different, being geared to the chemical composition and properties of that structure. The function of each of these structures will be discussed in more depth later in the chapter.

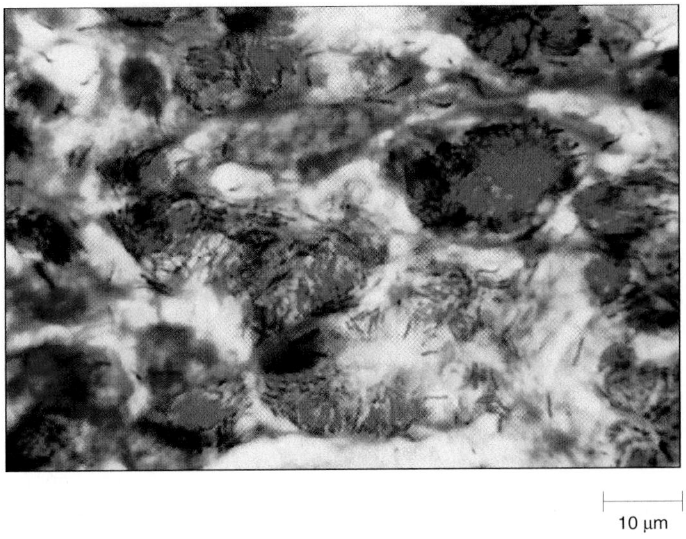

FIGURE 3.15 Acid-Fast Stain *Mycobacterium* species retain the red primary stain, carbol fuchsin. Counterstaining with methylene blue imparts a blue color to cells that are not acid-fast.

Capsule Stain

A **capsule** is a viscous layer that envelops a cell and is sometimes correlated with an organism's ability to cause disease. Capsules stain poorly, a characteristic exploited with a **capsule stain,** an example of a negative stain. It colors the background, allowing the capsule to stand out as a halo around an organism **(figure 3.16).**

In one method to observe capsules, a liquid specimen is placed on a slide next to a drop of India ink. A thin glass coverslip is then placed over the two drops, causing them to flow together. This creates a gradient of India ink concentration across the specimen. Unlike the stains discussed previously, this capsule stain is done as a **wet mount**—a drop of liquid on which a coverslip has been placed—rather than as a smear. At the optimum concentration of India ink, the fine dark particles of the stain color the background enough to allow the capsule to be visible.

Endospore Stain

Members of certain Gram-positive genera including *Bacillus* and *Clostridium* form a special type of dormant cell, an **endospore,** that

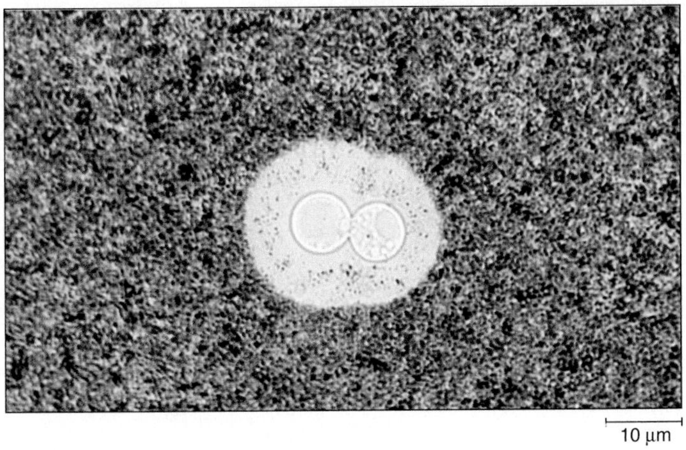

FIGURE 3.16 Capsule Stain Capsules stain poorly, and so they stand out against the India ink-stained background as a halo around the organism. This photomicrograph shows *Cryptococcus neoformans,* an encapsulated yeast.

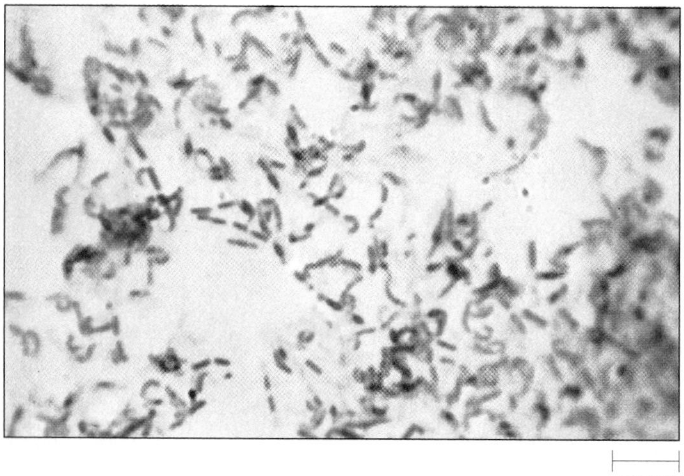

FIGURE 3.17 Endospore Stain Endospores retain the green primary stain, malachite green. Counterstaining with safranin imparts a red color to other cells.

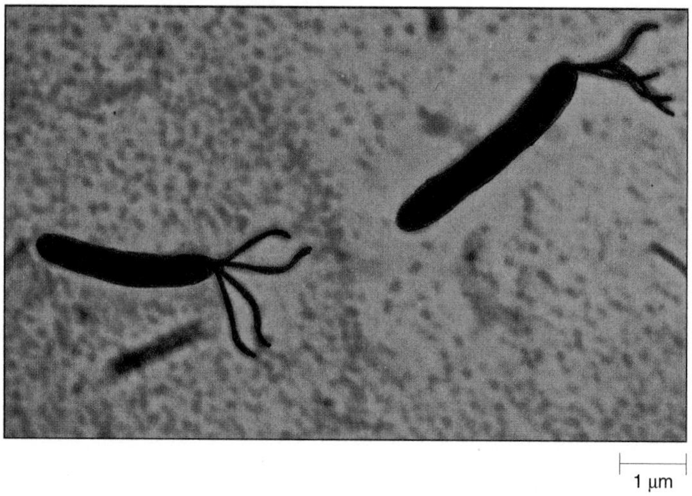

FIGURE 3.18 Flagella Stain The staining agent adheres to and coats the flagella. This increases their diameter to they can be seen with the light microscope.

is resistant to destruction and to staining. Although these structures do not stain with the Gram stain, they can often be seen as clear smooth objects within otherwise purple-stained cells. To make endospores more readily noticeable, a **spore stain** is used. This stain, like the classic acid-fast staining procedure, uses heat to facilitate staining.

The endospore stain is a multistep procedure that employs a primary stain as well as a counterstain. Generally, malachite green is used as a primary stain. Its uptake by endospores is facilitated by gentle heat. When water is then used to rinse the smear, only endospores retain the malachite green. The smear is then counterstained, most often with the red dye safranin. The endospores appear green amid a background of pink cells **(figure 3.17).**

Flagella Stain

Flagella are appendages that provide the most common mechanism of motility for prokaryotic cells, but they are ordinarily too thin to be seen with the light microscope. The **flagella stain** employs a mordant that allows the staining agent to adhere to and coat the thin flagella, effectively increasing their diameter—which makes them visible using light microscopy. Not all bacteria have flagella, but those that do can have them in different arrangements around a cell, so that the presence and distribution of these appendages can be used to identify bacteria **(figure 3.18).** Unfortunately, the staining procedure is difficult and requires patience and expertise.

Fluorescent Dyes and Tags

Depending on the procedure employed, fluorescence can be used to observe total cells, a subset of cells, or cells with certain proteins on their surface **(figure 3.19).**

Fluorescent Dyes

Some fluorescent dyes bind to compounds found in all cells. For example, acridine orange binds DNA, making it useful for deter-

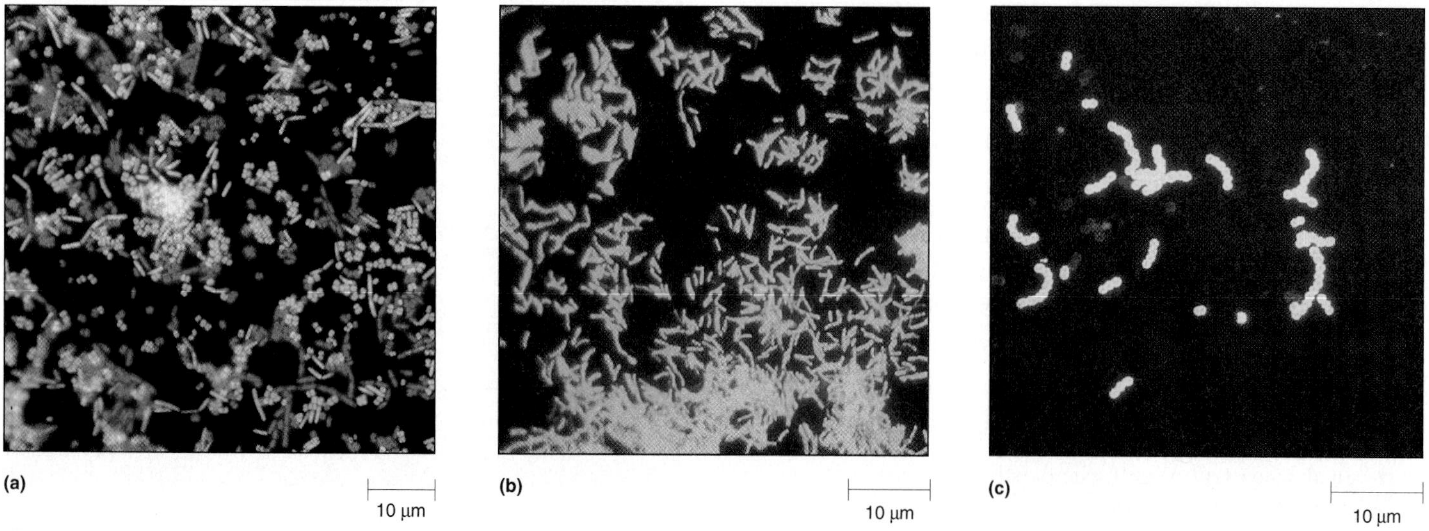

FIGURE 3.19 Fluorescent Dyes and Tags **(a)** Dyes that cause live cells to fluoresce green and dead ones red. **(b)** Auramine is used to stain *Mycobacterium* species in a modification of the acid-fast technique. **(c)** Fluorescent antibodies tag specific molecules—in this case, the antibody binds to a molecule that is unique to *Streptococcus pyogenes.*

mining the number of total microorganisms in a sample. Other fluorescent dyes are changed by cellular processes of living cells, enabling microbiologists to distinguish between cells that are alive and those that are dead. For example, the dye CTC is made fluorescent by cellular proteins involved in respiration. Consequently, CTC only fluoresces when bound to live cells. There are also fluorescent dyes that bind to compounds primarily found in certain types of cells. For example, **calcofluor white** binds to a component of the cell walls of fungi, causing those cells to fluoresce bright blue. The fluorescent dyes **auramine** and **rhodamine** bind to a compound found in the cell walls of members of the genus *Mycobacterium*. These two dyes can be used in a staining procedure analogous to the acid-fast stain; cells of *Mycobacterium* will emit a bright yellow or orange fluorescence. ■ respiration, p. 148

Immunofluorescence

Immunofluorescence is a technique used to tag specific proteins with a fluorescent compound. By tagging a protein unique to a given microbe, immunofluorescence can be used to detect that specific organism in a sample containing a mixture of cells. Immunofluorescence uses an **antibody** to deliver the fluorescent tag (see figure 17.10). An antibody is produced by the immune system in response to a foreign compound, usually a protein; it binds specifically to that compound. Immunofluorescence simply exploits the natural function of antibodies. ■ antibody, p. 392

MICROCHECK 3.2

Dyes can be used to stain cells so they stand out against the unstained background. The Gram stain is by far the most widely used differential stain. The acid-fast stain detects species of *Mycobacterium*. Specific dyes and techniques can be used to observe cell structures such as capsules, endospores, and flagella. Fluorescent dyes and tags can be used to observe total cells, a subset of cells, or cells that have certain proteins on their surface.

- ✓ What are the functions of a primary stain and a counterstain?
- ✓ Describe one error in the staining procedure that would result in a Gram-positive bacterium appearing pink.
- ✓ What color would a Gram-negative bacterium be in an acid-fast stain?

3.3 Morphology of Prokaryotic Cells

Focus Points

- Describe the common shapes of bacteria.
- Describe the common groupings of bacteria.
- Describe two multicellular associations of bacteria.

Prokaryotic cells come in a variety of simple shapes and often form characteristic groupings. Some aggregate, living as multicellular associations.

Shapes

Most common bacteria are one of two shapes: spherical, called a **coccus** (plural: cocci); and cylindrical, called a **rod (figure 3.20).** A

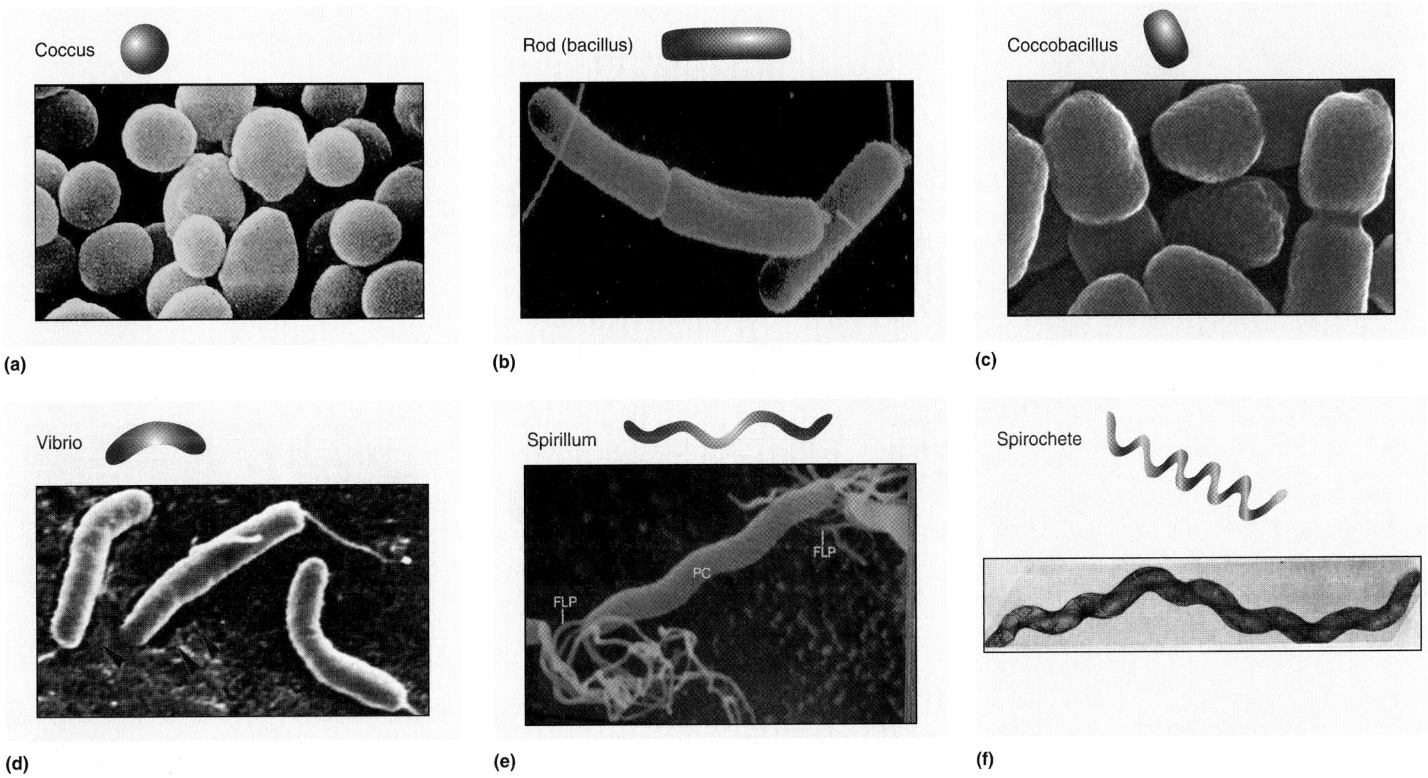

FIGURE 3.20 Typical Shapes of Common Bacteria **(a)** Coccus; **(b)** rod; **(c)** coccobacillus; **(d)** vibrio; **(e)** spirillum; **(f)** spirochete. Electron micrographs.

rod-shaped bacterium is sometimes called a **bacillus** (plural: bacilli). The descriptive term bacillus should not be confused with *Bacillus*, the name of a genus. While members of the genus *Bacillus* are rod-shaped, so are many other bacteria, including *Escherichia coli*.

Cells have a variety of other shapes. A rod-shaped bacterium so short that it can easily be mistaken for a coccus is often called a **coccobacillus.** A short curved rod is called a **vibrio** (plural: vibrios), whereas a curved rod long enough to form spirals is called a **spirillum** (plural: spirilla). A long helical cell with a flexible cell wall and a unique mechanism of motility is a **spirochete.** Bacteria that characteristically vary in their shape are called **pleomorphic** (*pleo* meaning many and *morphic* referring to shape).

Perhaps the greatest diversity in cell shapes is found in aquatic environments, where maximizing their surface area helps microbes absorb dilute nutrients **(figure 3.21).** Some aquatic bacteria have extensions on their surface, **prosthecae.** In some cases these give the organisms a starlike appearance. Square, tilelike archaeal cells have been found in the salty pools of the Sinai Peninsula in Egypt. ■ prosthecate bacteria, p. 283

Groupings

Most prokaryotes divide by **binary fission,** a process in which one cell divides into two cells. Cells adhering to one another following division form a characteristic arrangement that depends on the planes in which the organisms divide. This is seen especially in the cocci because they may divide in more than one plane **(figure 3.22).** Cells that divide in one plane may form chains of varying length. Cocci that typically occur in pairs are routinely called **diplococci.** An important clue in the identification of *Neisseria gonorrhoeae* is its characteristic diplococcus arrangement. Some cocci form long chains; this characteristic is typical of some, but not all, members of the genus *Streptococcus*.

Cocci that divide in two or three planes perpendicular to one another form cubical packets. Members of the genus *Sarcina* form such packets. Cocci that divide in several planes at random may form clusters. Species of *Staphylococcus* typically form characteristic grapelike clusters.

The various groupings are sometimes described with a Latin word. For example, chains of cocci may be called streptococci, cubical packets may be called sarcinae, and clusters may be called staphylococci. Unfortunately, these same words have also been assigned as genus names. Many microbiologists intentionally avoid using these words as descriptive terms because they are so easily confused with the genus names *Streptococcus, Sarcina*, and *Staphylococcus*.

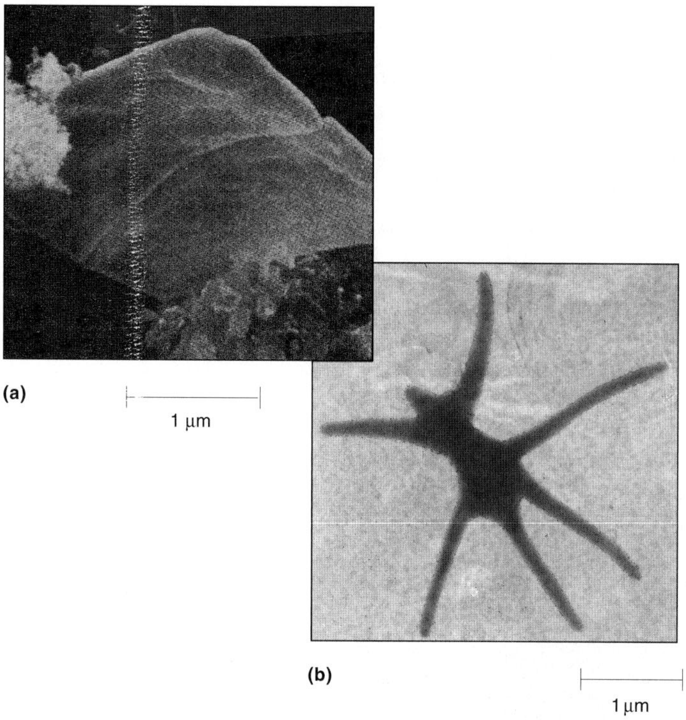

FIGURE 3.21 Diverse Shapes of Aquatic Bacteria (a) Square, tile-like archaeal cell. **(b)** *Ancalomicrobium*, an example of a prosthecate bacterium. Note that the cytoplasmic membrane and the cytoplasm are a part of each arm.

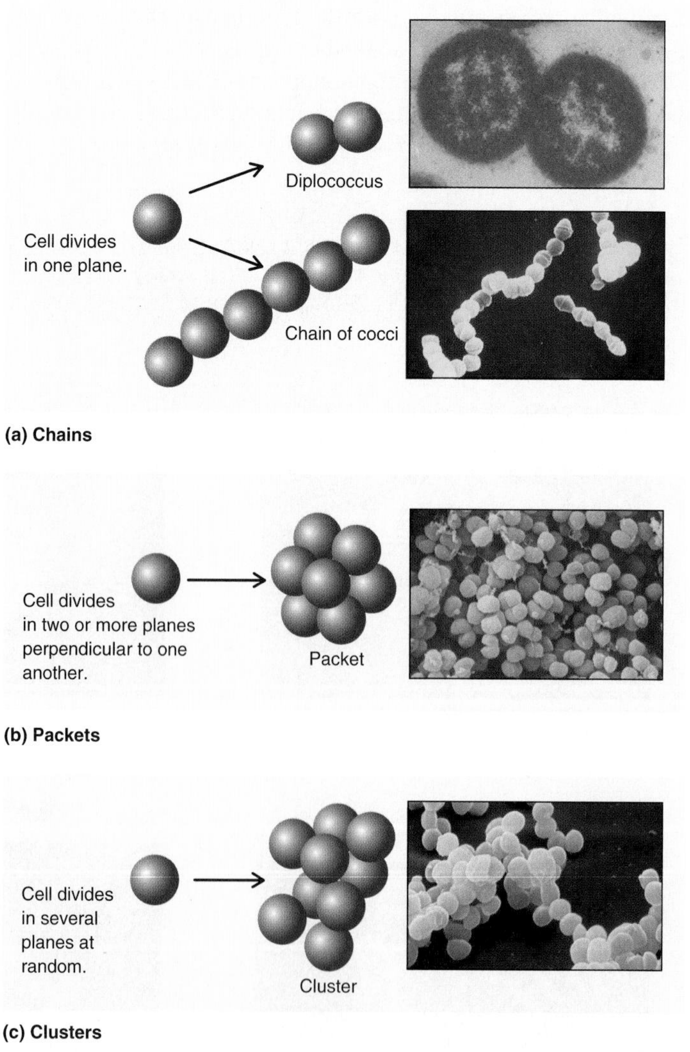

FIGURE 3.22 Typical Cell Groupings The planes in which cells divide determine the arrangement of the cells. These characteristic arrangements can provide important clues in the identification of certain bacteria: **(a)** chains; **(b)** packets; **(c)** clusters.

Multicellular Associations

Some types of bacteria typically live as multicellular associations. For example, members of a group of bacteria called myxobacteria glide over moist surfaces together, forming a swarm of cells that move as a pack. These cells release enzymes, which enables the pack to degrade organic material, including other bacterial cells. When water or nutrients are depleted, cells aggregate to form a structure called a **fruiting body,** which is visible to the naked eye (see figure 11.17). ■ myxobacteria, p. 280

Many types of bacteria live on surfaces in associations called **biofilms.** Cells within these aggregates alter their activities when a critical number of cells are present. ■ biofilms, p. 89

MICROCHECK 3.3

Most common prokaryotes are cocci or rods, but as a group, they come in a variety of shapes and sizes. Cells may form characteristic arrangements such as chains or clusters. Some types of bacteria form multicellular associations.

✓ Which environmental habitat has the greatest diversity of bacterial shapes?

✓ What causes some bacteria to form characteristic cell arrangements?

THE STRUCTURE OF THE PROKARYOTIC CELL

The overall structure of the prokaryotic cell is deceptively simple **(figure 3.23).** The **cytoplasmic membrane** surrounds the cell, acting as a barrier between the external environment and the interior of the cell. This membrane permits the passage of only certain molecules into and out of the cell. Enclosing the cytoplasmic membrane is the **cell wall,** a rigid barrier that functions as a tight corset to keep the cell contents from bursting out. Cloaking the wall may be additional layers, some of which serve to protect the cell from predators and environmental assaults. The cell may also have appendages giving it useful traits, including motility and the ability to adhere to certain surfaces.

The capsule (if present), cell wall, and cytoplasmic membrane together make up the **cell envelope.** Enclosed within this envelope are the contents of the cell—the cytoplasm and nucleoid. The **cytoplasm** is a viscous fluid composed of a variety of substances including water, enzymes and other proteins, carbohydrates, lipids, and various inorganic molecules. Structures within the cytoplasm include ribosomes and various storage granules. The **nucleoid** is the gel-like region where the chromosome resides. Unlike the nucleus that characterizes eukaryotic cells, the nucleoid is not enclosed within a membrane.

The structures of a prokaryote, together, enable the cell to survive and multiply in a given environment. Some structures are essential for survival and, as such, are common among all prokaryotic cells; others might be considered optional. Without these "optional" structures, the cell might be able to exist in the protected confines of a laboratory, but it may not be suited for the competitive surroundings of the outside world. The characteristics of typical structures of prokaryotic cells are summarized in **table 3.3.**

The components of the prokaryotic cell have important consequences for human health. Recall that structures and processes unique to bacteria are potential targets for selective toxicity. By interfering with these, bacteria can be killed or their growth inhibited without harming the human host. More importantly, the

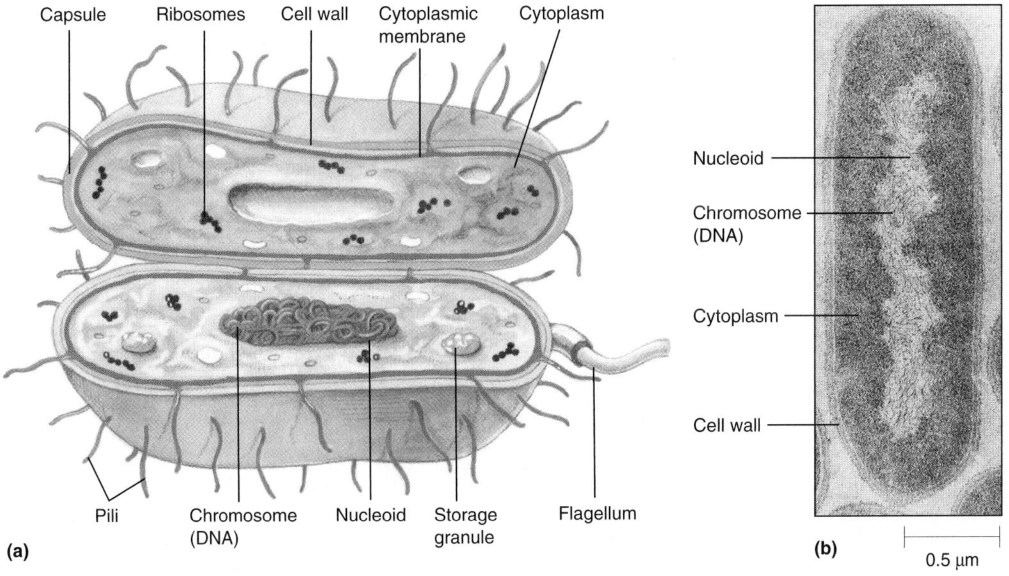

FIGURE 3.23 Typical Prokaryotic Cell A representation of typical structures within and outside a bacterial cell. **(a)** Diagrammatic representation. **(b)** Electron micrograph.

TABLE 3.3 A Summary of Prokaryotic Cell Structures

Structure	Characteristics
Extracellular	
Filamentous appendages	Composed of subunits of proteins that form a helical chain.
Flagella	Provides the most common mechanism of motility.
Pili	Different types of pili have different functions. The common types, often called fimbriae, enable cells to adhere to surfaces. A few types mediate twitching or gliding motility. Sex pili are involved in a mechanism of DNA transfer.
Surface layers	
Capsules and slime layers	Layers outside the cell wall, usually made of polysaccharide.
Capsule	Distinct and gelatinous. Enables bacteria to adhere to specific surfaces; allows some organisms to thwart innate defense systems and thus cause disease.
Slime layer	Diffuse and irregular. Enables bacteria to adhere to specific surfaces.
Cell wall	Peptidoglycan provides rigidity to bacterial cell walls, preventing the cells from lysing.
Gram-positive	Thick layer of peptidoglycan that contains teichoic adds and lipoteichoic acids.
Gram-negative	Thin layer of peptidoglycan surrounded by an outer membrane. The outer leaflet of the outer membrane is lipopolysaccharide.
Cell Boundary	
Cytoplasmic membrane	Phospholipid bilayer embedded with proteins. A barrier between the cytoplasm and the outside environment. Also functions as a discriminating conduit between the cell and its surroundings.
Intracellular	
DNA	Contains the genetic information of the cell.
Chromosomal	Carries the genetic information that is essential to a cell, Typically a single, circular, double-stranded DNA molecule.
Plasmid	Carries genetic information that may be advantageous to a cell in certain situations.
Endospore	A type of dormant cell that is extraordinarily resistant to damaging conditions including heat, desiccation, ultraviolet light, and toxic chemicals.
Gas vesicles	Small, rigid structures that provides buoyancy to a cell.
Granules	Accumulations of high molecular weight polymers, synthesized from a nutrient that a cell has in relative excess.
Ribosomes	Intimately involved in protein synthesis. Two subunits, 30S and 50S, join to form the 70S ribosome.

defense systems of our bodies have evolved to recognize specific bacterial surface components as the sign of danger. For example, certain cell wall components shared by nearly all bacteria are found nowhere else in nature. The body's defenses are poised to mount an attack against them. When these molecules that signify danger enter our body, our defense systems respond rapidly, generally eliminating the invader before it has a chance to multiply. Because of this, the vast majority of bacteria cannot cause disease in a healthy person. Those that do are able to disguise their surface components or otherwise interfere with our immune defenses. This complex interaction between our immune defenses and microbes will be discussed in detail in later chapters.

Cell structures are also important in identifying bacteria. Certain components are characteristic of select groups of microbes and can be used as identifying markers.

3.4

The Cytoplasmic Membrane

Focus Points

- Describe the structure and chemistry of the cytoplasmic membrane, focusing on how it relates to membrane permeability.
- Briefly describe how the electron transport chain generates a proton motive force, focusing on how it relates to membrane permeability.

The **cytoplasmic membrane** is a delicate thin fluid structure that surrounds the cytoplasm and defines the boundary of the cell. It serves as an important semipermeable barrier between the cell and its external environment. Although the membrane's chemical composition primarily allows only water, gases, and some small hydrophobic molecules to pass through freely, specific proteins embedded within the membrane act as selective gates. These permit nutrients to enter the cell, and waste products to exit. Other proteins within the membrane serve as sensors of environmental conditions. Thus, while the cytoplasmic membrane acts as a barrier, it also functions as an effective and highly discriminating conduit between the cell and its surroundings.

Structure and Chemistry of the Cytoplasmic Membrane

The structure of the bacterial cytoplasmic membrane is typical of other biological membranes—a lipid bilayer embedded with proteins **(figure 3.24).** The bilayer consists of two opposing **leaflets** composed of phospholipids. At one end of each phospholipid molecule are two fatty acid chains, which act as **hydrophobic tails.** The other end, containing glycerol, a phosphate group, and other polar molecules, functions as a **hydrophilic head.** The phospholipid molecules are arranged in each leaflet of the bilayer so that their hydrophobic tails face in, toward the other leaflet. Their hydrophilic heads face outward. As a consequence, the inside of the bilayer is water insoluble whereas the two surfaces interact freely with aqueous solutions.

■ **phospholipids, p. 36** ■ **hydrophobic, p. 29** ■ **hydrophilic, p. 29**

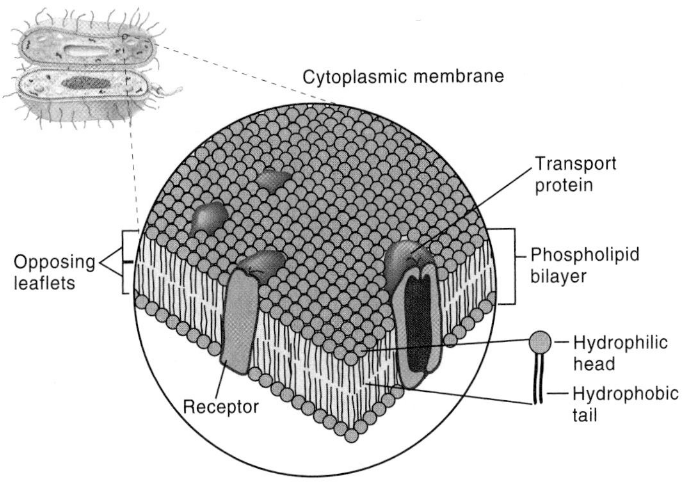

FIGURE 3.24 The Structure of the Cytoplasmic Membrane Two opposing leaflets make up the phospholipid bilayer. Embedded within the bilayer are a variety of different proteins, some of which span the membrane.

More than 200 different **membrane proteins** have been found in *E. coli*. Many function as **receptors,** binding to specific molecules in the environment. This, in turn, provides a mechanism for the cell to sense and adjust to its surroundings. Proteins are not stationary within the fluid bilayer; rather, they constantly change position. Such movement is necessary for the functions the membrane performs. This structure, with its resulting dynamic nature, is called the **fluid mosaic model.**

Members of the *Bacteria* and *Archaea* have the same general structure of their cytoplasmic membranes, but the lipid compositions are distinctly different. The side chains of the membrane lipids of *Archaea* are connected to glycerol by a different type of chemical linkage. In addition, the side chains are hydrocarbons rather than fatty acids. These differences represent important distinguishing characteristics between these two domains of prokaryotes.

Permeability of the Cytoplasmic Membrane

The cytoplasmic membrane is **selectively permeable;** relatively few types of molecules can pass through freely. Those that do so, move through by a process called **simple diffusion.** Other molecules must be transported across the membrane by specific transport mechanisms. These mechanisms, which generally require an expenditure of energy, will be discussed in detail later.

Simple Diffusion

Simple diffusion is the process by which some molecules move freely into and out of the cell. Water, small hydrophobic molecules, and gases such as oxygen and carbon dioxide are among the few compounds that move through the cytoplasmic membrane by simple diffusion. The speed and direction of diffusion depend on the relative concentration of molecules on each side of the membrane. The greater the difference in concentration, the higher the rate of diffusion. The molecules continue to pass through at a diminishing rate until their concentration is the same on both sides of the membrane.

The ability of water to move freely through the membrane has important biological consequences. The cytoplasm of a cell is a concentrated solution of inorganic salts, sugars, amino acids, and various other molecules. However, the environments in which prokaryotes normally grow contain only small amounts of some salts and other small molecules. Since the concentration of dissolved molecules, or **solute,** tends to equalize inside and outside the cell, water flows from the surrounding medium into the cell, thereby reducing the concentration of solute inside the cell **(figure 3.25).** This is the process of **osmosis.** This inflow of water exerts tremendous **osmotic pressure** on the cytoplasmic membrane, much more than it generally can resist. However, the rigid cell wall surrounding the membrane generally withstands such high pressure. The cytoplasmic membrane is forced up against the wall but cannot balloon further. Damage to the cell wall weakens the structure, and consequently, cells may burst or **lyse.**

The Role of the Cytoplasmic Membrane in Energy Transformation

The cytoplasmic membrane of prokaryotic cells plays an indispensable role in converting energy to a usable form. This is an important distinction between prokaryotic and eukaryotic cells; in eukaryotic cells energy is transformed in membrane-bound organelles, which will be discussed later in this chapter.

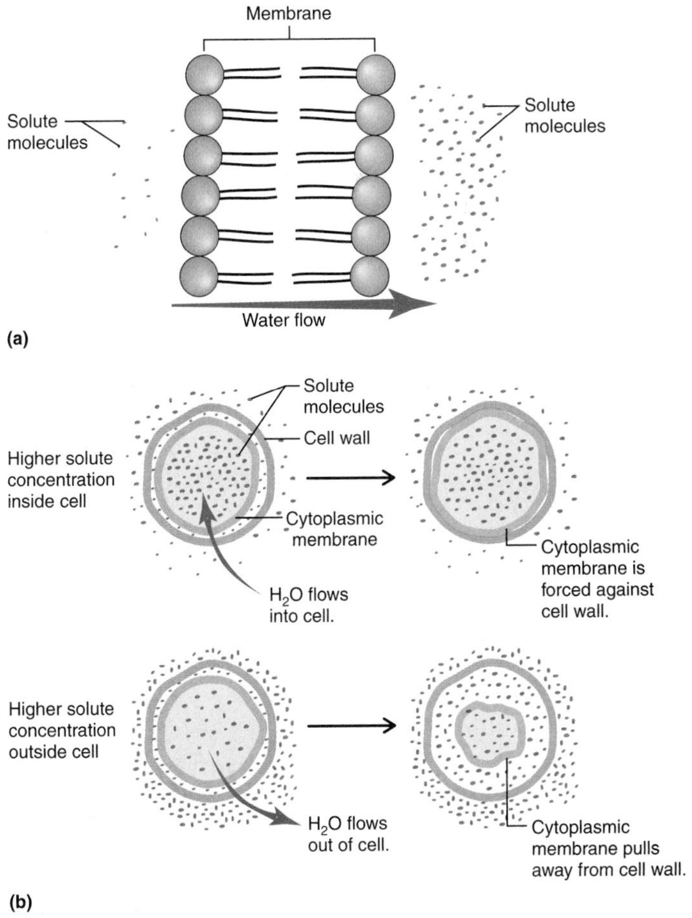

FIGURE 3.25 Osmosis (a) Water flows across a membrane toward the side that has the highest concentration of molecules and ions, thereby equalizing the concentrations on both sides. **(b)** The effect of osmosis on cells.

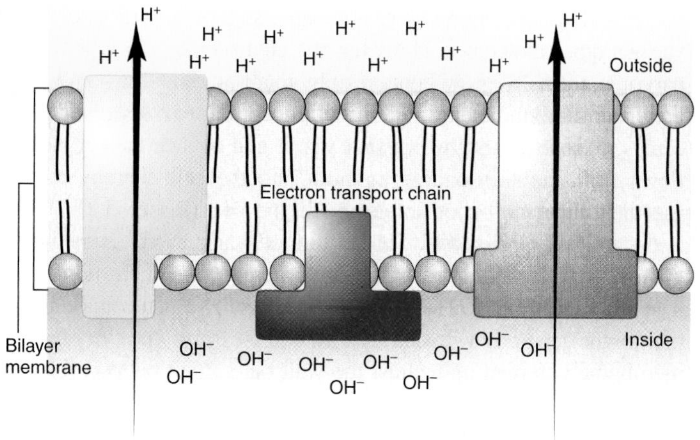

FIGURE 3.26 Proton Motive Force The electron transport chain, a series of protein complexes within the membrane, ejects protons from the cell. This creates an electrochemical gradient, which is a form of energy called proton motive force. The controlled flow of protons back into the cell releases energy. This is used to drive flagella and certain transport systems. It can also be used to synthesize ATP.

As part of their energy-harvesting processes, most prokaryotes have a series of protein complexes, the **electron transport chain,** embedded in their membrane. These sequentially transfer electrons and, in the process, eject protons from the cell. The details of these processes will be explained in chapter 6. The expulsion of protons by the electron transport chain results in the formation of a proton gradient across the cell membrane. Positively charged protons are concentrated immediately outside the membrane, whereas negatively charged hydroxyl ions accumulate directly inside the membrane **(figure 3.26).** This separation of charged ions creates an **electrochemical gradient** across the membrane; inherent in it is a form of energy, called **proton motive force.** This is analogous to the energy stored in a battery. ■ electron transport chain, p. 148

Energy of the proton motive force can be harvested when protons are allowed to move back into the cell. This is used directly to drive certain cellular processes, including some transport mechanisms that carry small molecules across the membrane and some forms of motility. It is also used to synthesize ATP. ■ ATP, p. 26

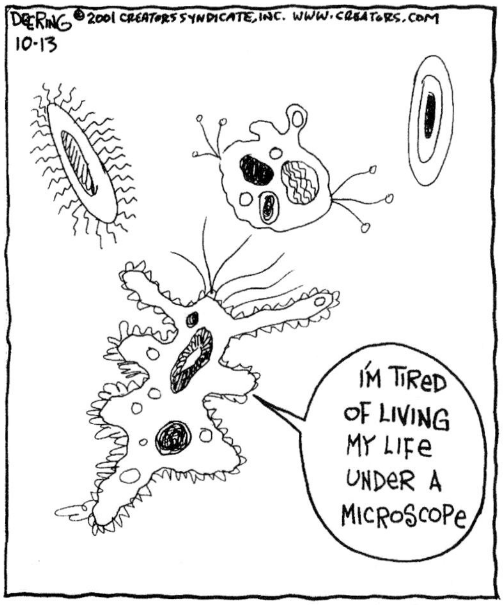

MICROCHECK 3.4

The cytoplasmic membrane is a phospholipid bilayer embedded with a variety of different proteins. It serves as a barrier between the cell and the surrounding environment, allowing relatively few types of molecules to pass through freely. The electron transport chain within the membrane expels protons, generating a proton motive force.

- ✓ Explain the fluid mosaic model.
- ✓ Name three molecules that can pass freely through the lipid bilayer.
- ✓ Why is the word fluid in fluid mosaic model an appropriate term?

3.5 Directed Movement of Molecules Across the Cytoplasmic Membrane

Focus Points

- Compare and contrast facilitated diffusion and active transport.
- Describe the role of signal sequences in secretion.

Nearly all molecules that enter or exit a cell must cross the otherwise impermeable cytoplasmic membrane through proteins that function as selective gates. Mechanisms allowing nutrients and other small molecules to enter the cell are called **transport systems.** Some of these systems are used to expel wastes and compounds such as antibiotics and disinfectants that are otherwise deleterious to the cell.

Cells actively move certain proteins they synthesize out of the cell—a process called **secretion.** Some of these secreted proteins make up structures such as flagella, which are appendages used for motility. Others are enzymes secreted to break down substances that would otherwise be too large to transport into the cell.

Transport Systems

Mechanisms used to transport molecules across the membrane employ highly specific proteins called **transport proteins, permeases,** or **carriers.** These proteins span the membrane, so that one end projects into the surrounding environment and the other into the cell. The interaction between the transport protein and the molecule it carries is highly specific. Consequently, a single carrier generally transports only a specific type of molecule. As a carrier transports a molecule, its shape changes, facilitating the passage of the molecule **(figure 3.27).**

Cells do not produce all of the transport proteins continuously. Instead, regulatory mechanisms sense the presence of specific compounds and, based on the concentration of those compounds

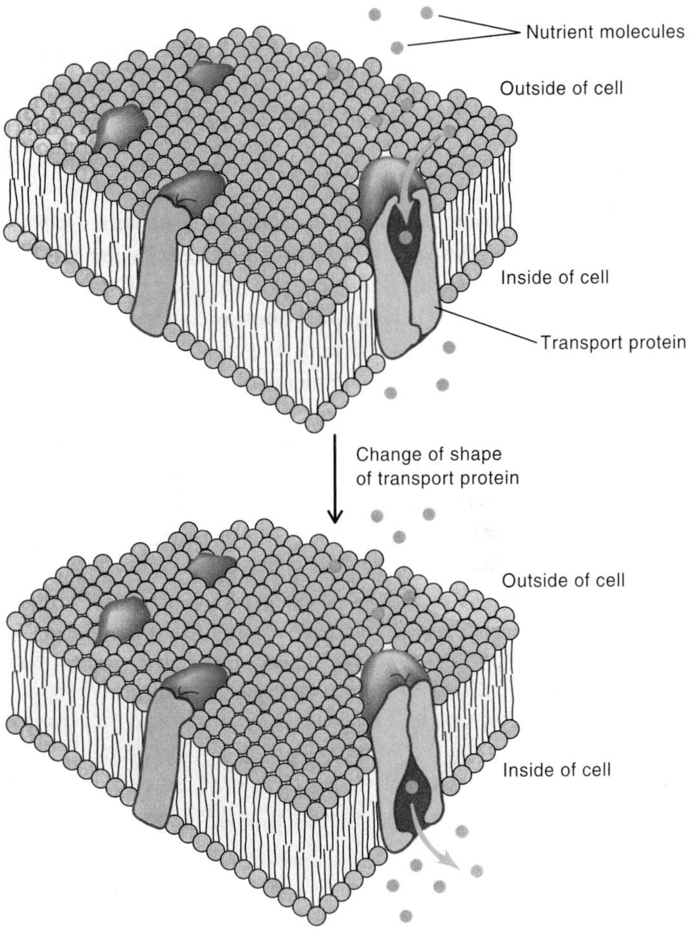

FIGURE 3.27 Transport Protein A transport protein changes its shape to facilitate passage of a compound across the cytoplasmic membrane.

TABLE 3.4 A Summary of Transport Mechanisms Used by Prokaryotic Cells

Transport Mechanism	Characteristics
Facilitated Diffusion	Rarely used by prokaryotes. Exploits a concentration gradient to move molecules; can only eliminate a gradient, not create one. No energy is expended.
Active Transport	Energy is expended to accumulate molecules against a concentration gradient.
Major facilitator superfamily	In bacteria, the proton motive force drives these transporters. As a proton is allowed into the cell another substance is either brought along or expelled.
ABC transporters	ATP is used as an energy source. Extracellular binding proteins deliver a molecule to the transporter.
Group Translocation	The transported molecule is chemically altered as it passes into the cell. Consequently, uptake of that molecule does not affect its concentration gradient.

and availability of other molecules, determine which transport proteins are synthesized. The mechanisms of transport are summarized in **table 3.4.** ■ regulation of gene expression, p. 182

Facilitated Diffusion

Facilitated diffusion, or **passive transport,** moves impermeable compounds from one side of the membrane to the other by exploiting a concentration gradient. Molecules are transported across until their concentration is the same on both sides of the membrane. This mechanism can only eliminate a difference in concentration, it cannot create one. As prokaryotes typically grow in relatively nutrient-poor environments, they generally cannot rely on facilitated diffusion to take in nutrients. Glycerol is one of the few nutrients known to enter *E. coli* cells this way.

Active Transport

Active transport moves compounds against a concentration gradient. This requires an expenditure of energy. There are two primary mechanisms of active transport, each utilizing a different form of energy.

Transport Systems That Use Proton Motive Force Many bacterial transport systems can accumulate or extrude small molecules and ions using the energy of a proton motive force. Transporters of this type allow a proton into the cell and simultaneously either bring along or expel another substance **(figure 3.28).** For example, the permease that transports lactose brings the sugar into the cell along with a proton. Expulsion of waste products, on the other hand, relies on transporters that eject the compound as a proton passes in. **Efflux pumps,** which are used by some bacteria to oust antimicrobial drugs, use this latter mechanism. These systems are part of a large group of transporters, collectively known as the **major facilitator superfamily (MFS),** found in prokaryotes as well as eukaryotes.

Transport Systems That Use ATP **ABC transport systems** require ATP as an energy source (ABC stands for ATP Binding-Cassette). These systems are relatively elaborate, involving multiple protein components **(figure 3.29).** ABC transport systems use **binding proteins**

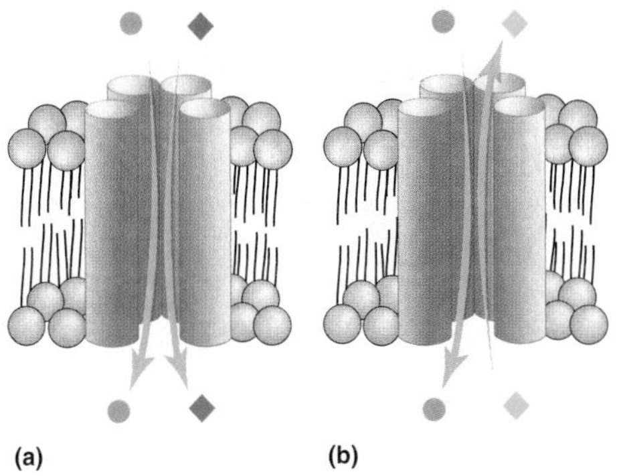

FIGURE 3.28 Active Transport Systems That Use Proton Motive Force Transporters of this type allow a proton into cell and simultaneously either **(a)** bring along another substance or **(b)** expel a substance.

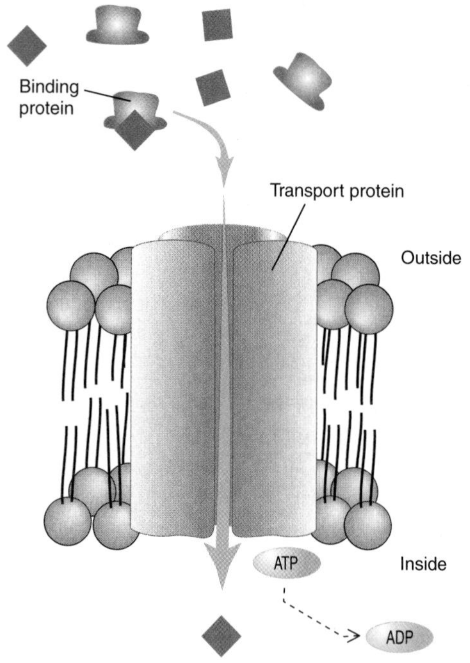

FIGURE 3.29 Active Transport Systems That Use ATP ABC transport systems require energy in the form of ATP. A binding protein that resides outside of the cytoplasmic membrane delivers a given molecule to a specific transport protein.

that reside immediately outside of the cytoplasmic membrane. These proteins each scavenge and deliver a given molecule to a specific transport complex within the membrane. The sugar maltose is an example of a molecule that is transported by an ABC transport system.

Group Translocation

Group translocation is a transport process that chemically alters a molecule during its passage through the cytoplasmic membrane **(figure 3.30).** Consequently, uptake of that molecule does not alter the concentration gradient. As an example, glucose and several other sugars are phosphorylated during their transport into the cell by the **phosphotransferase system.** The energy expended to phosphorylate the sugar can be regained when that sugar is later broken down to provide energy.

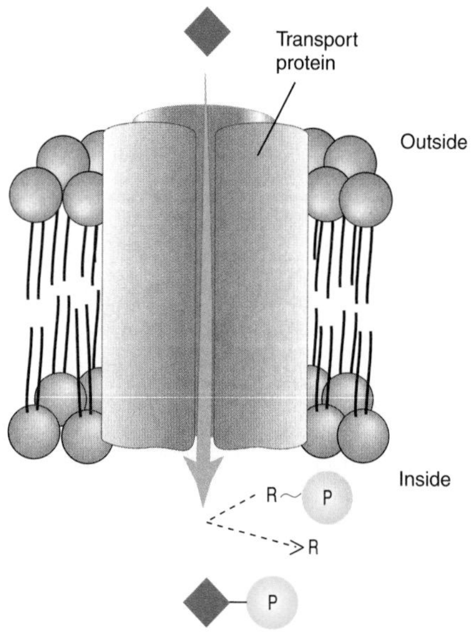

FIGURE 3.30 Group Translocation This process chemically alters a molecule during its passage through the cytoplasmic membrane. Consequently, uptake of that molecule does not alter the concentration gradient.

Secretion

The **general secretory pathway** is the primary mechanism used to secrete proteins synthesized by the cell. It recognizes the proteins destined for secretion by their characteristic sequence of amino acids that make up one end. This **signal sequence** consists of 20 or so hydrophobic amino acids and functions as a tag, which is specifically removed by an enzyme during the process of secretion.

The general secretory pathway requires at least 11 different proteins and uses ATP to drive the process. However, the precise mechanism by which the proteins move across the membrane is still poorly understood.

MICROCHECK 3.5

Facilitated transport does not require energy but is rarely used by bacteria. Active transport via the major facilitator superfamily uses proton motive force. Active transport via an ABC transporter uses ATP as an energy source. Group translocation chemically modifies a molecule as it enters the cell. Proteins that have a leader sequence are secreted from a cell by the general secretory pathway.

- ✓ Transport proteins may be referred to as what two other terms?
- ✓ Describe the role of binding proteins in an ABC transport system.
- ✓ Can you argue that group translocation is a form of active transport?

3.6

Cell Wall

Focus Points

- Describe the chemistry and structure of peptidoglycan.
- Compare and contrast the structure and chemistry of the Gram-positive and Gram-negative cell walls, and how the differences account for the Gram staining characteristics.
- Explain why Gram-negative bacteria are typically less susceptible to penicillin and lysozyme, and why *Mycoplasma* species are not affected by the agents.
- Describe the cell walls of members of the *Archaea*.

The cell wall of most common prokaryotes is a rigid structure that determines the shape of the organism. A primary function of the wall is to hold the cell together and prevent it from bursting. If the cell wall is somehow breached, undamaged parts maintain their original shape **(figure 3.31).** The cell wall is composed of unique structures and molecules, some of which are recognized by our immune system as the sign of an invader. Antimicrobial medications target some of the unique structures.

The type of cell wall distinguishes two main groups of bacteria—Gram-positive and Gram-negative. A comparison of the features of these groups is presented in **table 3.5.**

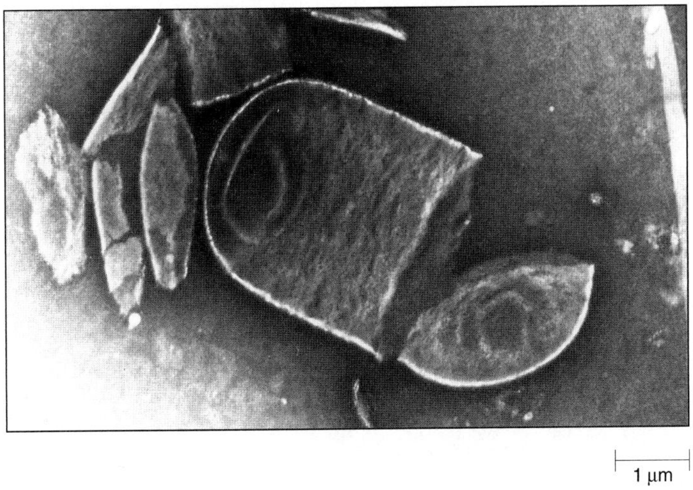

FIGURE 3.31 The Rigid Cell Wall Determines the Shape of the Bacterium Even though the cell has split apart, the cell wall maintains its original shape.

Peptidoglycan

Although the structure varies in Gram-positive and Gram-negative cells, the rigidity of bacterial cell walls is due to a layer of **peptidoglycan,** a macromolecule found only in bacteria. The basic structure of peptidoglycan is an alternating series of two major subunits, **N-acetylmuramic acid (NAM)** and **N-acetylglucosamine (NAG)**. These subunits, which are related to glucose in their structure, are covalently joined to one another to form a **glycan chain (figure 3.32).** This high molecular weight linear polymer serves as the backbone of the peptidoglycan molecule.

Attached to each of the NAM molecules is a string of four amino acids, a **tetrapeptide chain,** that plays an important role in the structure of the peptidoglycan molecule. Cross-linkages can form between tetrapeptide chains, thus joining adjacent glycan chains to form a single, very large three-dimensional molecule. In Gram-negative bacteria, tetrapeptides are joined directly. In Gram-positive bacteria, they are usually joined indirectly by a **peptide interbridge,** the composition of which may vary among species.

An assortment of only a few different amino acids make up the tetrapeptide chain. One of these, diaminopimelic acid, which is related to the amino acid lysine, is not found in any other place in nature. Some of the others are D-isomers, a form not found in proteins. ■ **D-Isomer, p. 29** ■ **lysine, p. 28**

The Gram-Positive Cell Wall

A relatively thick layer of peptidoglycan characterizes the cell wall of Gram-positive bacteria **(figure 3.33).** As many as 30 layers, or sheets, of interconnected glycan chains make up the polymer. Regardless of its thickness, peptidoglycan is fully permeable to many substances including sugars, amino acids, and ions.

TABLE 3.5 Comparison of Features of Gram-Positive and Gram-Negative Bacteria

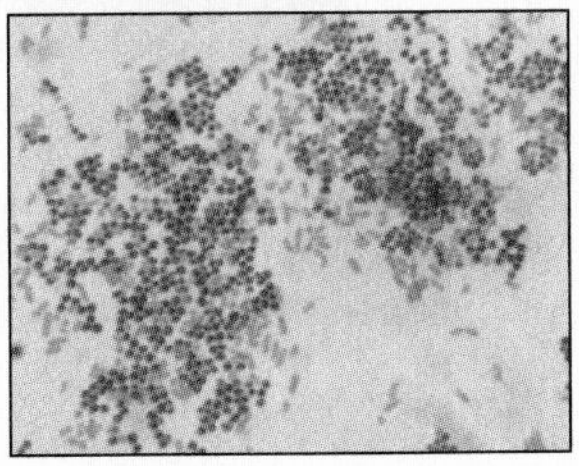

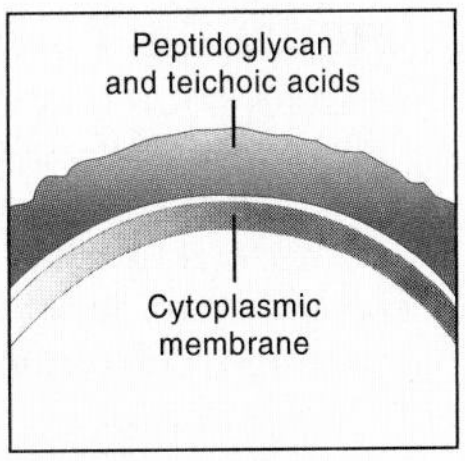

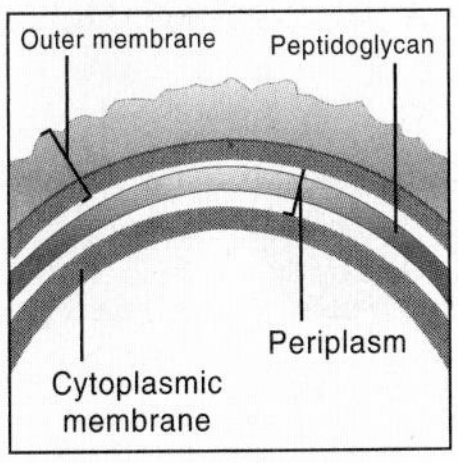

	Gram-Positive	Gram-Negative
Color of Gram Stained Cell	Purple	Reddish-pink
Representative Genera	*Bacillus, Staphylococcus, Streptococcus*	*Escherichia, Neisseria, Pseudomonas*
Distinguishing Structures/Components		
Peptidoglycan	Thick layer	Thin layer
Teichoic acids	Present	Absent
Periplasm	Absent	Present
Outer membrane	Absent	Present
Lipopolysaccharide (endotoxin)	Absent	Present
Porin proteins	Absent (unnecessary because there is no outer membrane)	Present; allow passage of molecules through outer membrane
General Characteristics		
Sensitivity to penicillin	Generally more susceptible (with notable exceptions)	Generally less susceptible (with notable exceptions)
Sensitivity to lysozyme	Yes	No (unless also treated with EDTA)
Form that results from removal of peptidoglycan	Protoplast	Spheroplast

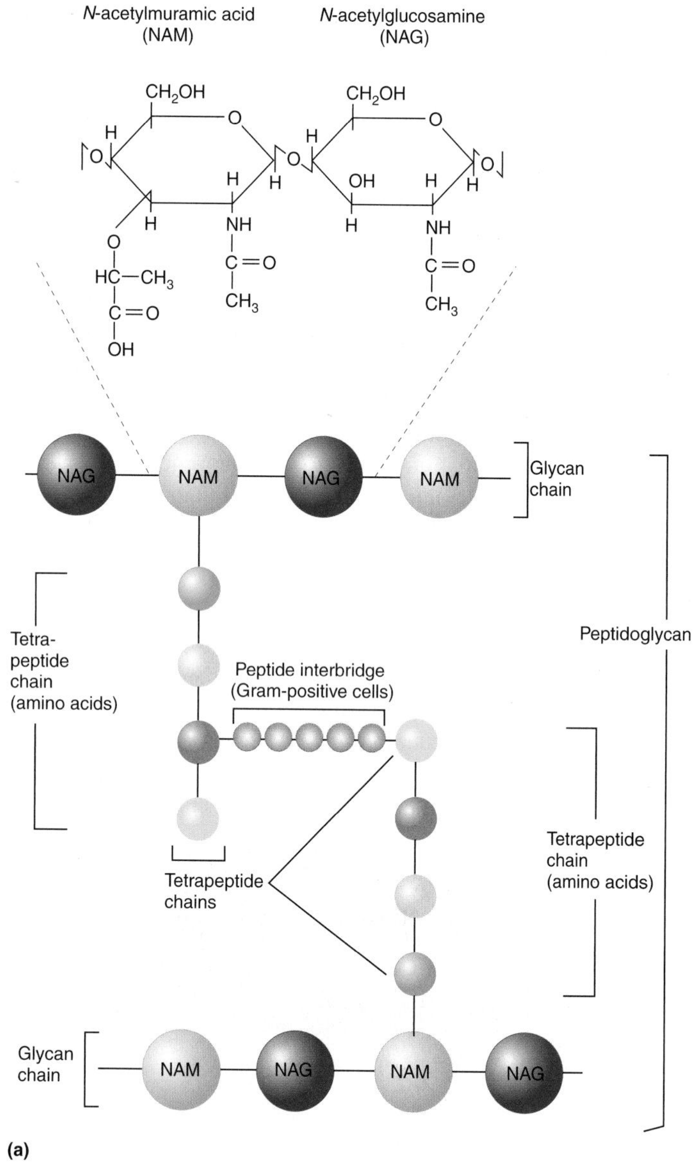

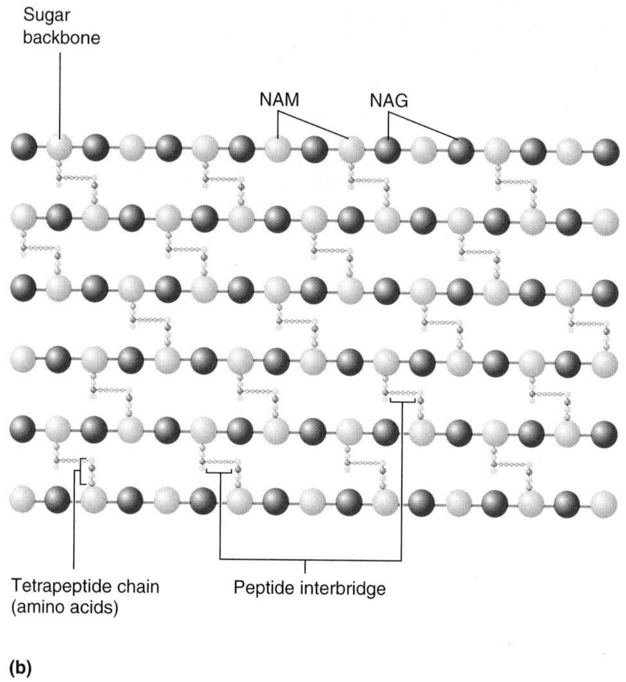

FIGURE 3.32 Components and Structure of Peptidoglycan **(a)** Chemical structure of *N*-acetylglucosamine (NAG) and *N*-acetylmuramic acid (NAM); the ring structures of the two molecules are glucose. Glycan chains are composed of alternating subunits of NAG and NAM joined by covalent bonds. Adjacent glycan chains are cross-linked via their tetrapeptide chains to create peptidoglycan. **(b)** Interconnected glycan chains form a very large three-dimensional molecule of peptidoglycan.

A prominent component of the Gram-positive cell wall is a group of molecules called **teichoic acids** (from the Greek word *teichos*, meaning wall). These are chains of a common subunit, either ribitol-phosphate or glycerol-phosphate, to which various sugars and D-alanine are usually attached. Teichoic acids are joined to the peptidoglycan molecule through covalent bonds to *N*-acetylmuramic acid. Some, which are called **lipoteichoic acids,** are linked to the cytoplasmic membrane. Teichoic acids and lipoteichoic acids both stick out above the peptidoglycan layer and, because they are negatively charged, give the cell its negative polarity.

The Gram-Negative Cell Wall

The cell wall of **Gram-negative bacteria** is far more complex than that of Gram-positive organisms **(figure 3.34).** It contains only a thin layer of peptidoglycan. Outside of that layer is the **outer membrane,** a unique lipid bilayer embedded with proteins. The peptidoglycan layer is sandwiched between the cytoplasmic membrane and the outer membrane.

The Outer Membrane

Like the cytoplasmic membrane, which in Gram-negative bacteria is sometimes called the **inner membrane,** the outer membrane serves as a barrier to the passage of most molecules. Thus, it serves as a protective barrier, excluding many compounds that are deleterious to the cell, including certain antimicrobial medications. This is one reason why Gram-negative bacteria are generally less sensitive to many such medications. Small molecules and ions can cross the membrane through **porins,** specialized channel-forming proteins that span the outer membrane. Some porins are specific for certain molecules; others allow many different molecules to pass. Proteins produced by the cell that are destined for secretion are translocated to the outside of the outer membrane by mechanisms known as **secretion systems.**

The outer membrane is unlike any other membrane in nature. Its lipid bilayer structure is typical of other membranes, but the outside leaflet is made up of **lipopolysaccharides** rather than phospholipids. For this reason, the outer membrane is also called the **lipopolysaccharide layer** or **LPS.** The outer membrane

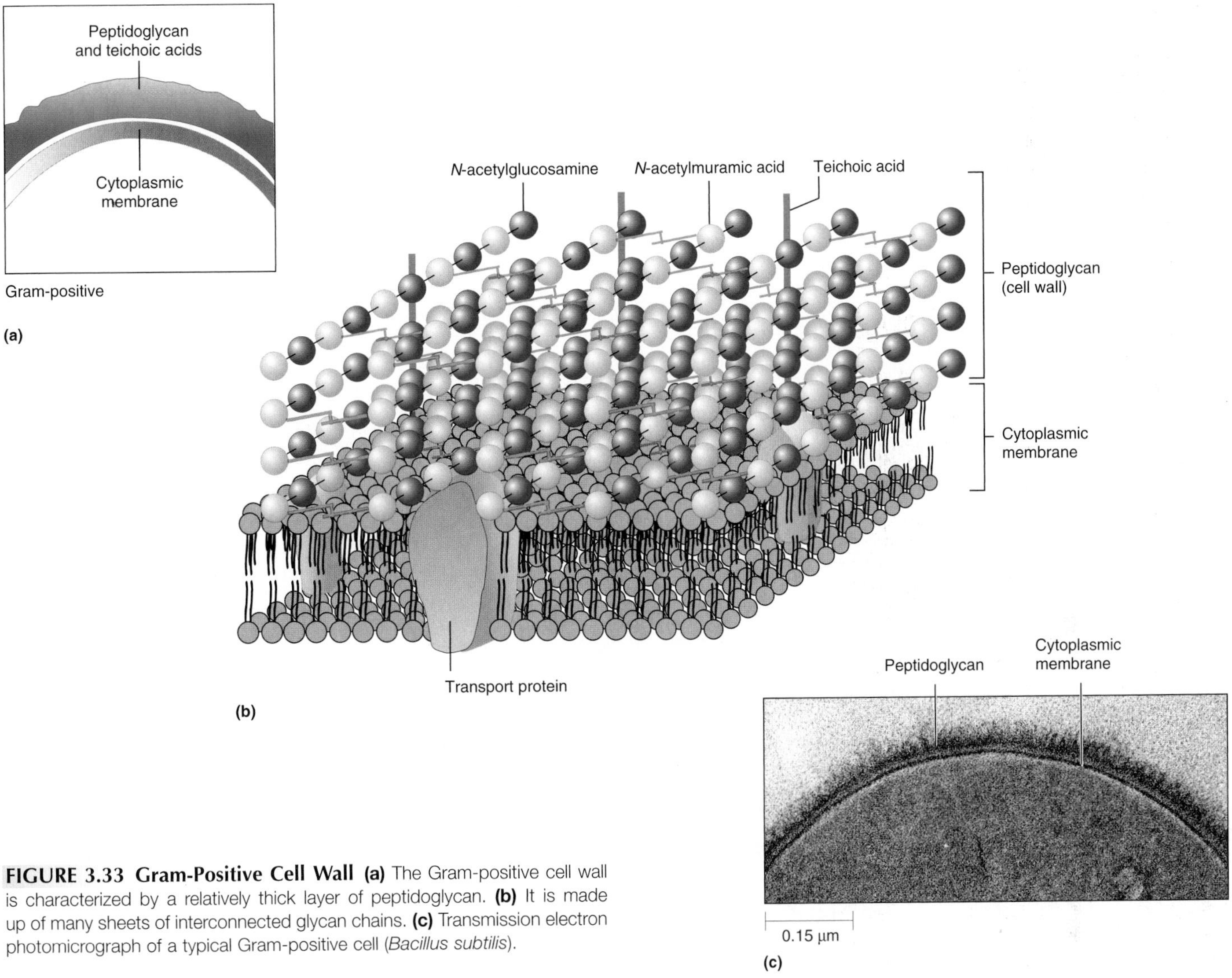

FIGURE 3.33 Gram-Positive Cell Wall **(a)** The Gram-positive cell wall is characterized by a relatively thick layer of peptidoglycan. **(b)** It is made up of many sheets of interconnected glycan chains. **(c)** Transmission electron photomicrograph of a typical Gram-positive cell (*Bacillus subtilis*).

is joined to peptidoglycan by means of lipoprotein molecules. ■ lipoproteins, p. 31

The Lipopolysaccharide Molecule The lipopolysaccharide molecule is extremely important from a medical standpoint. When purified lipopolysaccharide is injected into an animal, it elicits symptoms characteristic of infections caused by live bacteria. The same symptoms occur regardless of the bacterial species. To reflect the fact that the toxic activity is an inherent part of the cell wall, it is called **endotoxin.** ■ endotoxin, p. 467

Two parts of the LPS molecule are notable for their medical significance (see figure 3.34c):

- **Lipid A** is the portion that anchors the LPS molecule in the lipid bilayer. Its chemical make-up plays a significant role in the body's ability to recognize the presence of invading bacteria. When lipid A is introduced into the body in small amounts, such as when microbes contaminate a small lesion, the defense system responds at an appropriate level to effectively eliminate the invader. If, however, large amounts of lipid A are present, such as when Gram-negative bacteria are actively growing in the bloodstream, the magnitude of the response damages even our own cells. This response to lipid A is responsible for the symptoms associated with endotoxin.
- The **O-specific polysaccharide** side chain is the portion of LPS directed away from the membrane, at the end opposite that of lipid A. It is made up of a chain of sugar molecules, the number and composition of which varies among different species of bacteria. The differences can be exploited to identify certain species or strains. For example, the "O157" in *E. coli* O157:H7 refers to the characteristic O-side chain of the strains.

Periplasm

The region between the cytoplasmic membrane and the outer membrane is filled with a gel-like fluid called **periplasm.** In Gram-negative bacteria, all secreted proteins are contained within the periplasm unless they are specifically translocated across the outer membrane as well. Thus, the periplasm is filled with proteins involved in a variety of cellular activities, including nutrient degradation and transport. For example, the enzymes that cells secrete to break down peptides and other molecules are found in

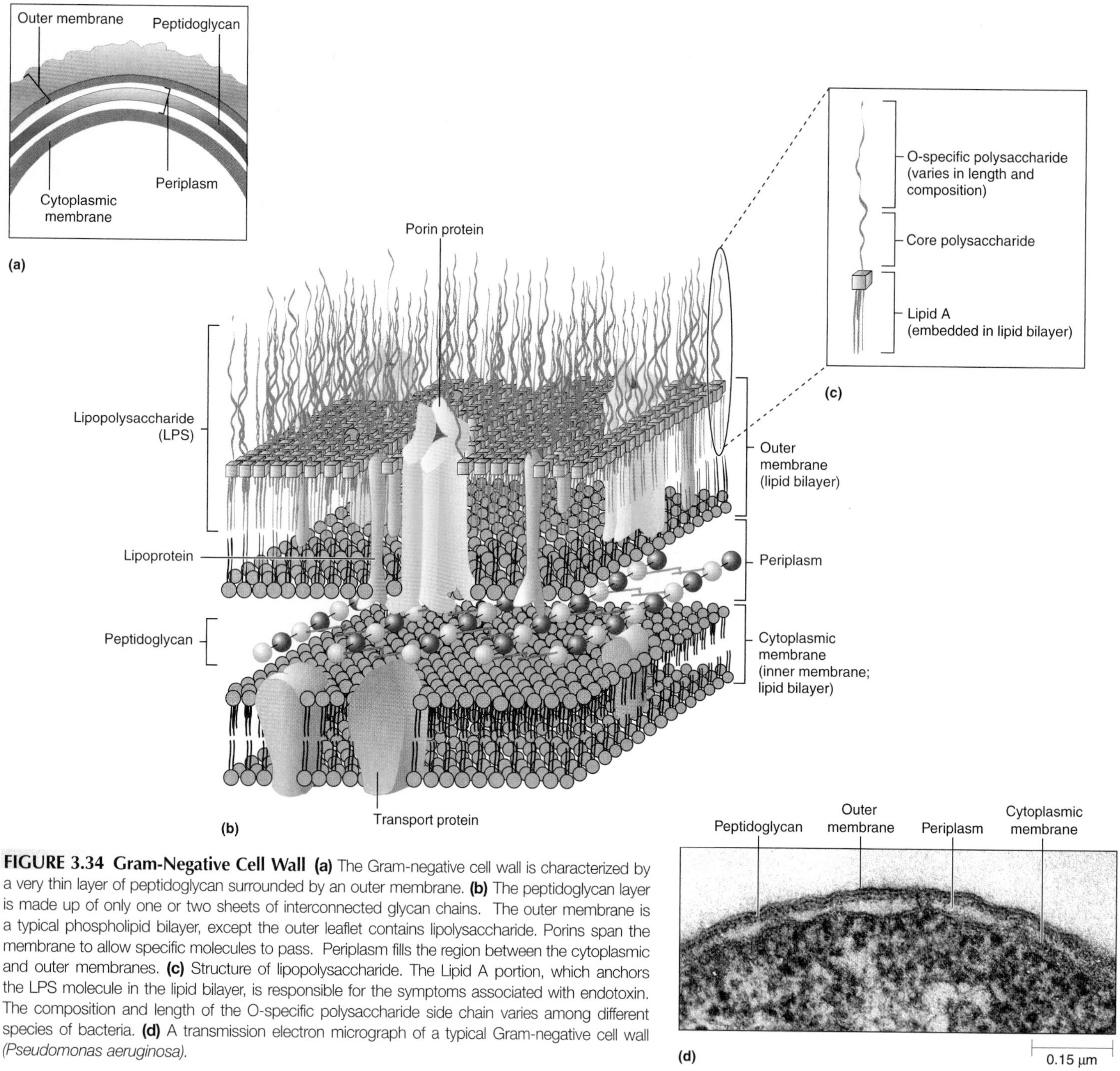

FIGURE 3.34 Gram-Negative Cell Wall (a) The Gram-negative cell wall is characterized by a very thin layer of peptidoglycan surrounded by an outer membrane. **(b)** The peptidoglycan layer is made up of only one or two sheets of interconnected glycan chains. The outer membrane is a typical phospholipid bilayer, except the outer leaflet contains lipolysaccharide. Porins span the membrane to allow specific molecules to pass. Periplasm fills the region between the cytoplasmic and outer membranes. **(c)** Structure of lipopolysaccharide. The Lipid A portion, which anchors the LPS molecule in the lipid bilayer, is responsible for the symptoms associated with endotoxin. The composition and length of the O-specific polysaccharide side chain varies among different species of bacteria. **(d)** A transmission electron micrograph of a typical Gram-negative cell wall *(Pseudomonas aeruginosa).*

the periplasm. Similarly, the binding proteins of the ABC transport systems are found there.

Antibacterial Compounds That Target Peptidoglycan

Compounds that interfere with the synthesis of peptidoglycan or alter its structural integrity weaken the rigid molecule to a point where it cannot prevent the cell from bursting. Examples of compounds that target peptidoglycan include the antibiotic penicillin and the enzyme lysozyme.

Penicillin

Penicillin is the most thoroughly studied of a group of antibiotics that interfere with peptidoglycan synthesis. Penicillin binds proteins involved in cell wall synthesis and, subsequently, prevents the cross-linking of adjacent glycan chains. ■ penicillin, p. 501

Generally, but with notable exceptions, penicillin is far more effective against Gram-positive cells than Gram-negative cells. This is because the outer membrane of Gram-negative cells prevents the medication from reaching its site of action, the peptidoglycan layer. However, the structure of penicillin can be modified to create penicillin derivatives that pass through porin channels.

These drugs are effective against a range of Gram-negative bacteria. ■ penicillin-derivatives, p. 502

Lysozyme

Lysozyme, an enzyme found in many body fluids including tears and saliva, breaks the bond that links the alternating *N*-acetylglucosamine and *N*-acetylmuramic acid molecules of peptidoglycan. This destroys the structural integrity of the glycan chain, the backbone of the peptidoglycan molecule.

Lysozyme is sometimes used in the laboratory to remove the peptidoglycan layer from bacteria for experimental purposes. Treating a Gram-positive bacterium with the enzyme creates a **protoplast,** which completely lacks a cell wall. The process is more complicated when working with Gram-negative bacteria, however, because their outer membrane naturally excludes lysozyme. To counter this problem, the cells must first be treated with a compound called EDTA (ethylenediaminetetraacetic acid). This interacts with ions that otherwise stabilize the outer membrane, allowing lysozyme access to the peptidoglycan. The action of lysozyme on an EDTA-treated Gram-negative cell creates a **spheroplast,** which retains part of the outer membrane. Because they lack their rigid cell wall, protoplasts and spheroplasts both become spherical regardless of the original cell shape. Due to osmosis, they will burst unless maintained in a solution that has the same relative concentration of ions and small molecules as the cytoplasm.

Differences in Cell Wall Composition and the Gram Stain

Differences in the cell wall composition of Gram-positive and Gram-negative bacteria account for their staining characteristics. It is not the cell wall, however, but the inside of the cell that is stained by the crystal violet-iodine complex. The Gram-positive cell wall somehow retains the crystal violet-iodine complex within the cell even when subjected to the trauma of acetone-alcohol treatment, whereas the Gram-negative cell wall cannot.

The precise mechanism that accounts for the differential aspect of the Gram stain is not entirely understood. Presumably, the decolorizing agent dehydrates the thick layer of peptidoglycan; in this dehydrated state the wall acts as a permeability barrier, holding the dye within the cell. In contrast, the solvent action of acetone-alcohol easily damages the outer membrane of Gram-negative bacteria, and the relatively thin layer of peptidoglycan cannot retain the dye complex. These bacteria lose the dye complex more readily than their Gram-positive counterparts.

As Gram-positive cells age, they often lose their ability to retain the dye. This probably results from damage to their peptidoglycan layer that occurs as a consequence of aging.

Characteristics of Bacteria That Lack a Cell Wall

Some bacteria naturally lack a cell wall. Species of *Mycoplasma*, one of which causes a mild form of pneumonia, have an extremely variable shape because they lack a rigid cell wall **(figure 3.35).** As expected, neither penicillin nor lysozyme affects these organisms. *Mycoplasma* and related bacteria can survive without a cell wall because their cytoplasmic membrane is stronger than that of most other bacteria. They have **sterols** in their membrane; these rigid, planar molecules stabilize membranes, making them stronger.

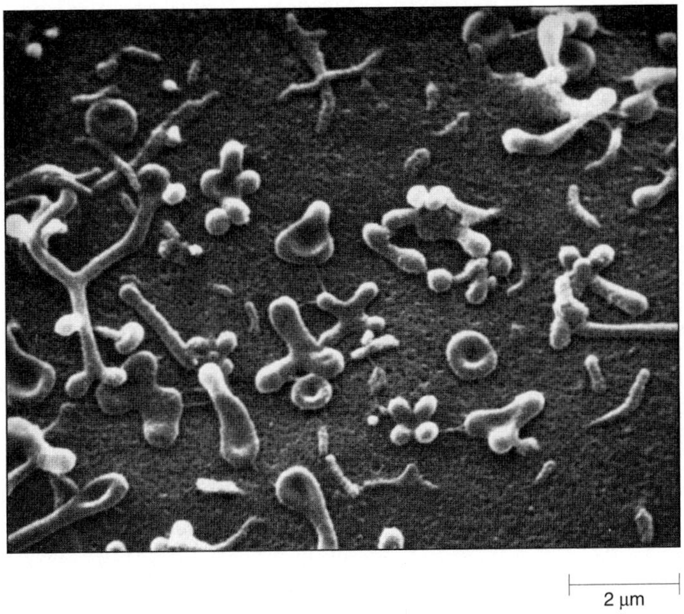

FIGURE 3.35 ***Mycoplasma pneumoniae*** These cells vary in shape because they lack a cell wall.

Cell Walls of the Domain *Archaea*

As a group, members of the *Archaea* inhabit a wide range of extreme environments, and so it is not surprising they contain a greater variety of cell wall types than do members of the *Bacteria*. However, because most of these organisms have not been studied as extensively as the *Bacteria*, less is known about the structure of their walls. None contain peptidoglycan, but some do have a similar molecule, **pseudopeptidoglycan.**

MICROCHECK 3.6

Peptidoglycan is a molecule unique to bacteria that provides rigidity to the cell wall. The Gram-positive cell wall is composed of a relatively thick layer of peptidoglycan as well as teichoic acids. The Gram-negative cell wall has a thin layer of peptidoglycan and an outer membrane, which contains lipopolysaccharide. The outer membrane excludes molecules with the exception of those that pass through porins; proteins are secreted via special mechanisms. Penicillin and lysozyme interfere with the structural integrity of peptidoglycan. *Mycoplasma* species lack a cell wall. Members of the *Archaea* have a variety of cell wall types.

- ✓ What is the significance of lipid A?
- ✓ How does the action of penicillin differ from that of lysozyme?
- ✓ Explain why penicillin will kill only actively multiplying cells, whereas lysozyme will kill cells in any stage of growth.

3.7

Surface Layers External to the Cell Wall

Focus Point

- Compare and contrast the structure and function of capsules and slime layers.

Some bacteria have layers of material outside of the cell wall.

Capsules and Slime Layers

Many bacteria envelop themselves with a gel-like layer that generally functions as a mechanism of either protection or attachment **(figure 3.36).** If the layer is distinct and gelatinous, it is called a **capsule.** If, instead, the layer is diffuse and irregular, it is called a **slime layer.** Colonies of bacteria that form either of these often appear moist and glistening.

Capsules and slime layers vary in their chemical composition depending on the species of bacteria. Most are composed of polysaccharides, and are commonly referred to as a **glycocalyx** (*glyco* means "sugar" and *calyx* means "shell"). A few capsules consist of polypeptides made up of repeating subunits of only one or two amino acids. Interestingly, the amino acids are generally of the D-stereoisomeric form, one of the few places D-amino acids are found in nature. ■ **polysaccharide, p. 32** ■ **D-amino acid, p. 29**

Some types of capsules and slime layers enable bacteria to adhere to specific surfaces, including teeth, rocks, and other bacteria. These often enable microorganisms to grow as a biofilm, a polysaccharide-encased mass of bacteria coating a surface. One example is **dental plaque,** a biofilm on teeth. *Streptococcus mutans* uses sucrose to synthesize a capsule, which enables it to adhere to and grow in the crevices of the tooth. Other bacteria can then adhere to the layer created by *S. mutans*. Acid production by bacteria in the biofilm damages the tooth surface. ■ ***Streptococcus mutans,* p. 614** ■ **sucrose, p. 32** ■ **dental caries, p. 614**

Some capsules enable bacteria to thwart innate defense systems that otherwise protect against infection. For example, *Streptococcus pneumoniae*, the organism that causes bacterial pneumonia, can only cause disease if it has a capsule. Unencapsulated cells are quickly engulfed and killed by phagocytes, an important cell of the body's defense system. ■ ***Streptococcus pneumoniae,* p. 588** ■ **phagocytes, p. 378**

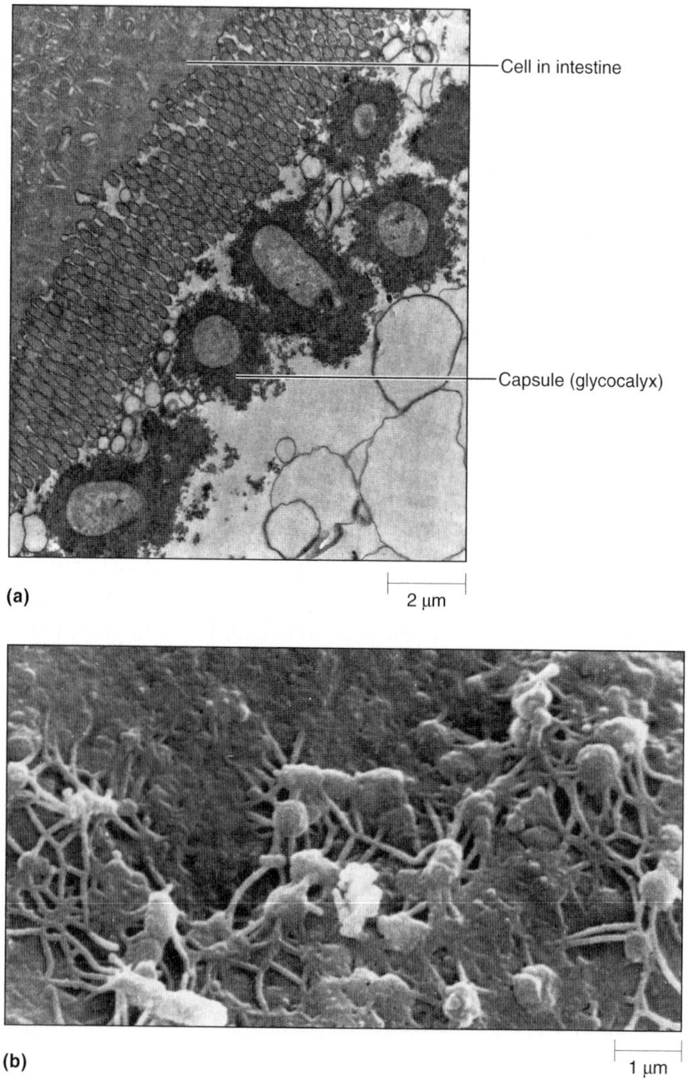

FIGURE 3.36 Capsules and Slime Layers These layers enable bacteria to attach to specific surfaces. **(a)** Capsules facilitating the attachment of bacteria to cells in the intestine (EM). **(b)** Masses of cells of *Eikenella corrodens* adhering in a layer of slime (SEM).

MICROCHECK 3.7

Capsules and slime layers enable organisms to adhere to surfaces and sometimes protect bacteria from our innate defense system.

✓ How do capsules differ from slime layers?
✓ What is dental plaque?
✓ Explain why a sugary diet can lead to tooth decay.

3.8

Filamentous Protein Appendages

Focus Points

- Describe the structure and function of flagella, and explain how the direction of their rotation is involved in chemotaxis.
- Compare and contrast the structure and function of fimbriae and sex pili.

Many bacteria have protein appendages that are anchored in the membrane and protrude out from the surface. These structures are not essential to the life of the cell, but they do allow some bacteria to exist in certain environments in which they otherwise might not survive.

Flagella

The **flagellum** is a long protein structure responsible for most types of bacterial motility **(figure 3.37).** By spinning like a propel-

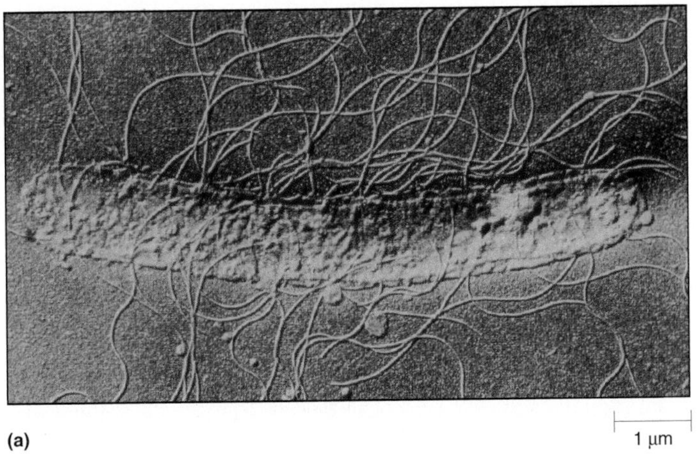

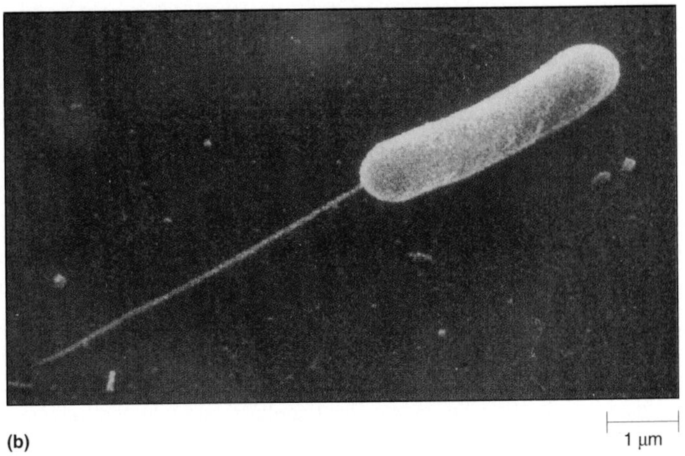

FIGURE 3.37 Flagella (a) Peritrichous flagella (SEM); **(b)** polar flagellum (SEM).

ler, using proton motive force as energy, the flagellum pushes the bacterium through liquid much as a ship is driven through water. Flagella must work very hard to move a cell, since water has the same relative viscosity to bacteria as molasses has to humans. Nevertheless, their speed is quite phenomenal; flagella can rotate more than 100,000 revolutions per minute (rpm), propelling the cell at a rate of 20 body lengths per second. This is the equivalent of a 6-foot man running 82 miles per hour!

In some cases, flagella are important in the ability of an organism to cause disease. For example, *Helicobacter pylori*, the bacterium that causes gastric ulcers, has powerful multiple flagella at one end of its spiral-shaped cell. These flagella allow *H. pylori* to penetrate the viscous mucous gel that coats the stomach epithelium. ■ *Helicobacter pylori*, p. 617

Structure and Arrangement of Flagella

Flagella are composed of three basic parts **(figure 3.38).** The **filament** is the portion extending into the exterior environment. It is composed of identical subunits of a protein called **flagellin.** These subunits form a chain that twists into a helical structure with a hollow core. Connecting the filament to the cell surface is a curved structure, the hook. The **basal body** anchors the flagellum to the cell wall and cytoplasmic membrane.

The numbers and arrangement of flagella can be used to characterize flagellated bacteria. For example, *E. coli* have flagella distributed over the entire surface, an arrangement called **peritrichous** (*peri* means "around"). Other common bacteria have a **polar flagellum,** a single flagellum at one end of the cell. Other arrangements include a tuft of flagella at one or both ends of a cell (see figures 3.18 and 3.20e).

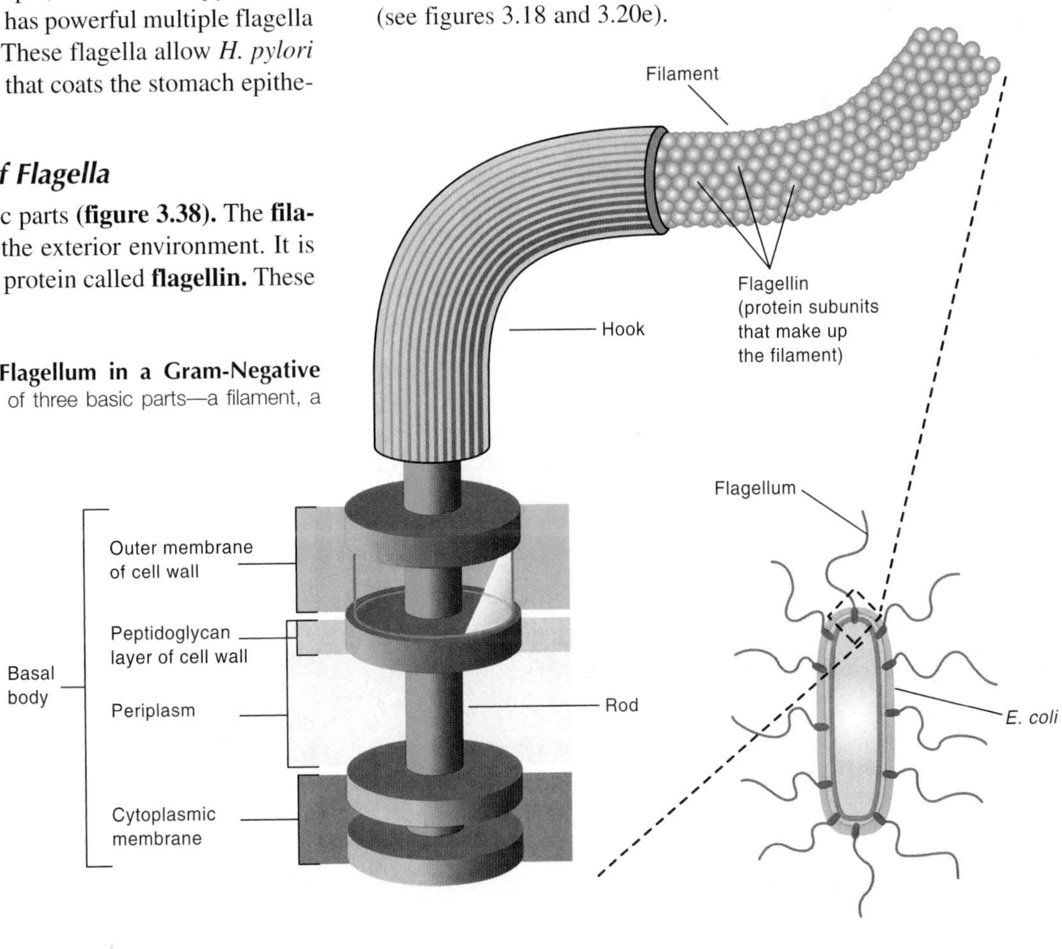

FIGURE 3.38 The Structure of a Flagellum in a Gram-Negative Bacterium The flagellum is composed of three basic parts—a filament, a hook, and a basal body.

Chemotaxis

Motile bacteria sense the presence of chemicals and respond by moving in a certain direction—a phenomenon called **chemotaxis.** If a compound is a nutrient, it may serve as an **attractant,** enticing cells to move toward it. On the other hand, if the compound is toxic, it may act as a **repellent,** causing cells to move away.

The movement of a bacterium toward an attractant is anything but direct **(figure 3.39).** When *E. coli* travels, it progresses in a given direction for a short time, then stops and tumbles for a fraction of a second, and then moves again in a relatively straight line. But after rolling around, the cell is often oriented in a completely different direction. The seemingly odd pattern of movement is due to the rotation of the flagella. When the flagella rotate counterclockwise, the bacterium is propelled in a forward movement called a **run.** The flagella of *E. coli* and other peritrichously flagellated bacteria rotate in a coordinated fashion, forming a tight propelling bundle. After a brief period, the direction of rotation of the flagella is reversed. This abrupt change causes the cell to stop and roll, called a **tumble.** Movement toward an attractant is due to runs of longer duration that occur when cells are going in the right direction; this occurs because cells tumble less frequently when they sense they are moving closer to an attractant. In contrast, they tumble more frequently when they sense they are moving closer to a repellent.

In addition to reacting to chemicals, some bacteria can respond to variations in light, **phototaxis.** Other bacteria can respond to the concentration of oxygen, **aerotaxis.** Organisms that require oxygen for growth will move toward it, whereas bacteria that grow only in its absence tend to be repelled by it. Certain motile bacteria can react to the earth's magnetic field by the process of **magnetotaxis.** They actually contain a row of magnetic particles that cause the cells to line up in a north-to-south direction much as a compass does **(figure 3.40).** The magnetic forces of the earth attract the organisms so that they move downward and into sediments where the concentration of oxygen is low, which is the environment best suited for their growth.

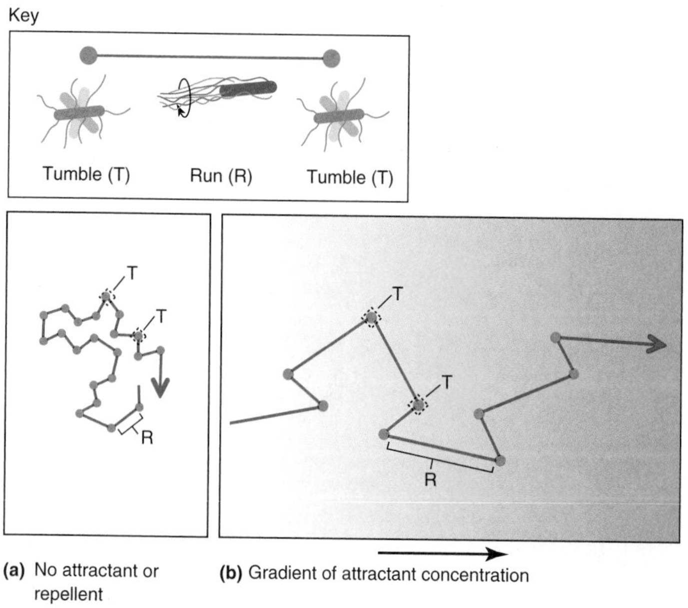

(a) No attractant or repellent (b) Gradient of attractant concentration

FIGURE 3.39 Chemotaxis (a) A cell moves via a random series of short runs and tumbles when the attractant or repellent is uniformly distributed. **(b)** The cell tumbles less frequently resulting in longer runs when it senses that it is moving closer to the attractant.

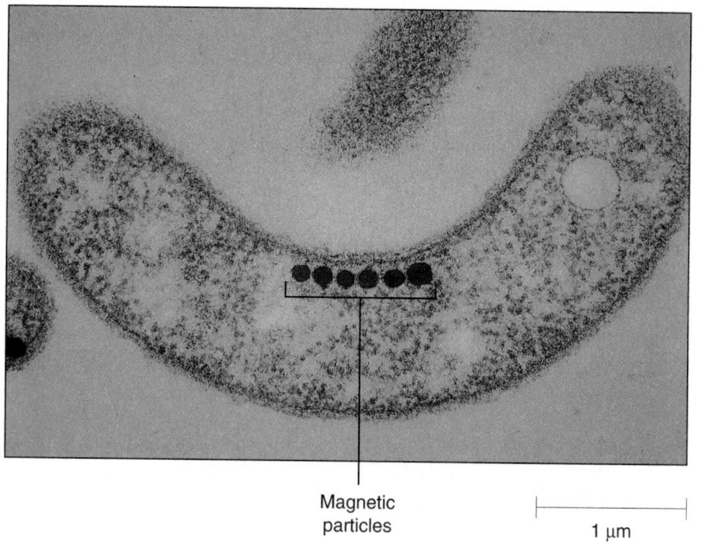

FIGURE 3.40 Magnetic Particles Within a Magnetotactic Bacterium The chain of particles of magnetite (Fe_3O_4) within the spirillum *Magnetospirillum magnetotacticum* serve to align the cell along geomagnetic lines (TEM).

Pili

Pili are considerably shorter and thinner than flagella, but they have a similar structural theme to the filament of flagella—a string of protein subunits arranged helically to form a long cylindrical molecule with a hollow core **(figure 3.41).** The functions of pili, however, are distinctly different from those of flagella.

Many types of pili enable attachment of cells to specific surfaces; these pili are also called **fimbriae.** At the tip or along the length of the molecule is located another protein, an **adhesin,** that adheres by binding to a very specific molecule. For example, certain strains of *E. coli* that cause a severe watery diarrhea can attach to the cells that line the small intestine. They do this through specific interactions between adhesins on their pili and the intestinal cell surface. Without the ability to attach, these cells would simply be propelled through the small intestine along with the other intestinal contents. ■ enterotoxigenic *E. coli,* p. 627

Pili also appear to play a role in the movement of populations of cells on solid media. **Twitching motility,** characterized by short, jerking movements, and some types of **gliding motility,** characterized by smooth sliding motion, involve pili.

Another type of pilus is involved in **conjugation,** a mechanism of DNA transfer from one bacterial cell to another. A **sex pilus** is used to join those two cells. An example is the **F pilus** of *E. coli.* Typically, sex pili are somewhat longer than other types of pili. ■ conjugation, p. 211

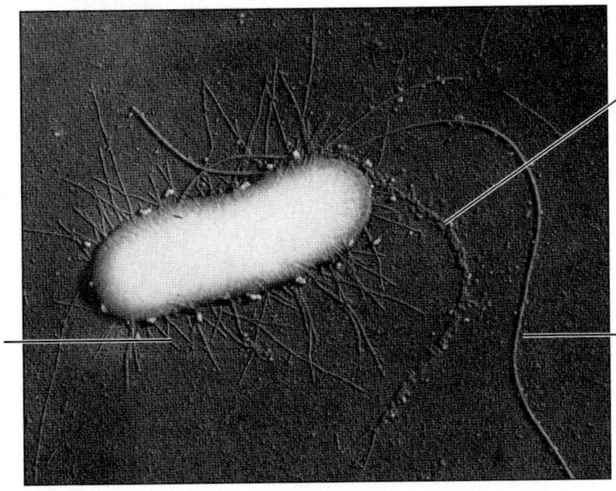

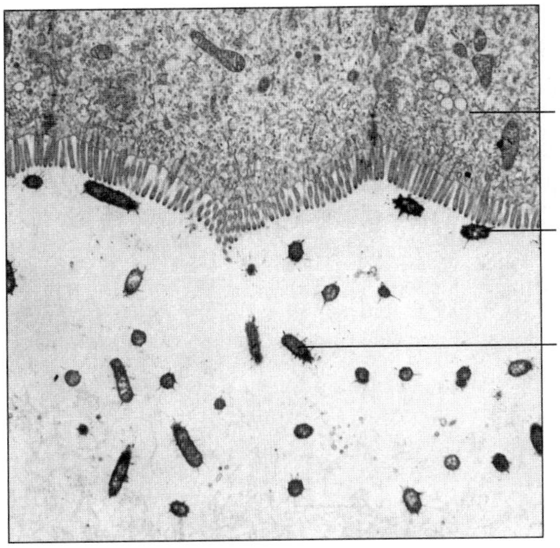

FIGURE 3.41 Pili (a) Pili on an *Escherichia coli* cell. The short pili (fimbriae) mediate adherence; the F pilus is involved in DNA transfer. **(b)** *Escherichia coli* attaching to epithelial cells in the small intestine of a pig.

MICROCHECK 3.8

Flagella are the most common mechanism for bacterial motility. Chemotaxis is the directed movement of cells toward an attractant or away from a repellent. Pili provide a mechanism for attachment to specific surfaces and, in some cases, a type of motility. Sex pili are involved in the transfer of DNA from one bacterium to another.

- ✓ What role does a series of runs and tumbles play in chemotaxis?
- ✓ What energy source is used to rotate flagella?

3.9 Internal Structures

Focus Points

- Describe the structure and function of the chromosomes, plasmids, ribosomes, storage granules, gas vesicles, and endospores.
- Describe the processes of sporulation and germination.

Prokaryotic cells have a variety of structures within the cell. Some, such as the chromosome and ribosomes, are essential for the life of all cells. Others, such as plasmids, are optional but confer certain selective advantages. Storage granules, vesicles, and endospores are characteristic of only certain types of bacteria.

The Chromosome

The chromosome of prokaryotes resides as an irregular mass within the cytoplasm, forming a gel-like region called the **nucleoid.** Typically, it is a single, circular double-stranded DNA molecule that contains all the genetic information required by a cell.

Chromosomal DNA is tightly packed into about 10% of the total volume of the cell **(figure 3.42).** Rather than being a loose circle it is typically in a twisted form called **supercoiled,** which appears to be stabilized by the binding of positively charged proteins. Supercoiling can be visualized by cutting a rubber band and twisting one end several times before rejoining the ends. The resulting circle will twist and coil in response.

Plasmids

Most **plasmids** are circular, supercoiled, double-stranded DNA molecules. They are generally 0.1% to 10% of the size of the chromosome and carry from a few to several hundred genes. A single cell can harbor multiple types of plasmids.

A cell does not absolutely require the genetic information carried by a plasmid. However, the encoded genetic characteristics may be advantageous in certain situations. For example, many plasmids code for the production of one or more enzymes that destroy certain antibiotics, enabling the organism to resist the otherwise lethal effect of these medications. Because a bacterium can sometimes transfer a copy of a plasmid to another bacterial cell, this accessory genetic information can spread, which accounts in large part for the increasing frequency of antibiotic-resistant organisms worldwide. At the same time, excess genetic information can be disadvantageous to a cell, slowing its multiplication. Occasionally, a cell will divide without evenly distributing its plasmids, giving rise to one cell that lacks a plasmid. If that cell can multiply faster as a consequence of losing that plasmid, and that plasmid is not essential to viability in that environment, then progeny of the cell will eventually predominate. Thus, populations can gain and lose plasmids. In the laboratory, cells can

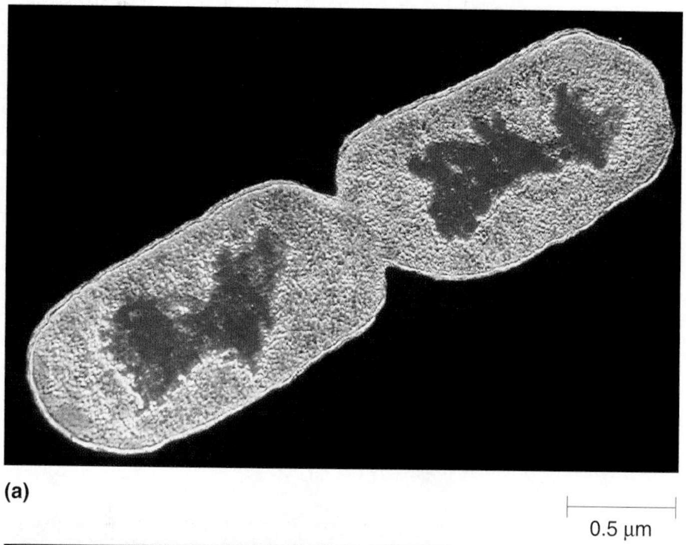

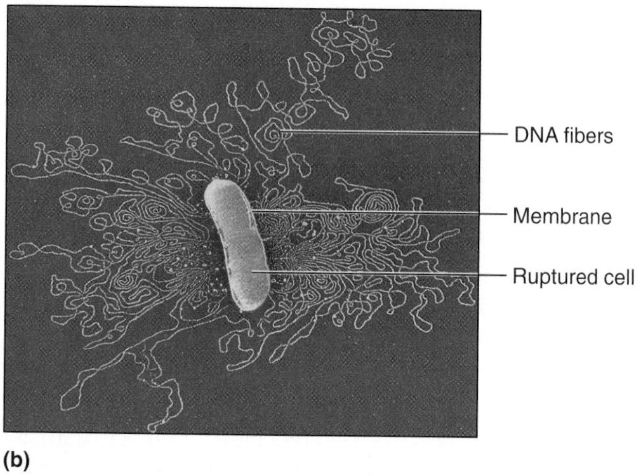

FIGURE 3.42 The Chromosome **(a)** Color-enhanced transmission electron micrograph of a thin section of *Escherichia coli*, with the DNA shown in red. **(b)** Chromosome released from a gently lysed cell of *E. coli*. Note how tightly packed the DNA must be inside the bacterium.

be grown under conditions that increase the likelihood that a plasmid will be lost. The resulting population has been **cured** of the plasmid.

Ribosomes

Ribosomes are intimately involved in protein synthesis, where they serve as the structures that facilitate the joining of amino acids. Each ribosome is composed of a large and a small subunit, which are made up of **ribosomal proteins** and **ribosomal RNAs.** ■ function of ribosomes, p. 177

The relative size and density of ribosomes and their subunits is expressed as a distinct unit, **S** (for Svedberg), that reflects how fast they move when they are spun at very high speeds in an **ultracentrifuge.** The faster they move toward the bottom, the higher the S value and the greater the density. Prokaryotic ribosomes are 70S ribosomes. Note that S units are not strictly arithmetic; the 70S ribosome is composed of a 30S and a 50S subunit **(figure 3.43).**

Prokaryotic ribosomes differ from the eukaryotic ribosomes, which are 80S. Differences in the structures serve as targets for certain antibiotics, which preferentially bind to the 70S ribosome and thus inhibit protein synthesis in bacteria.

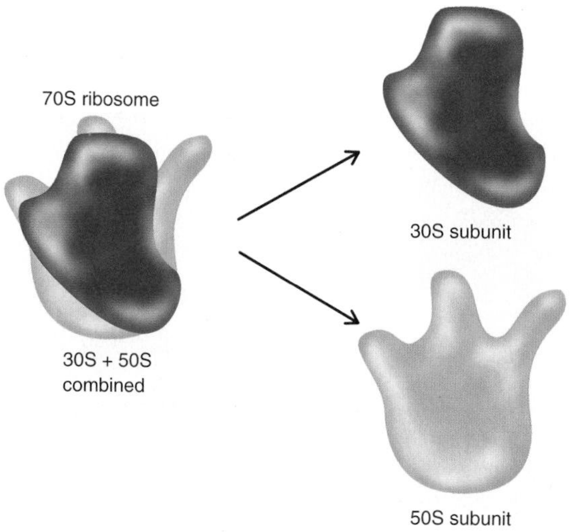

FIGURE 3.43 The Ribosome The 70S ribosome is composed of 50S and 30S subunits.

Storage Granules

Storage granules are accumulations of high molecular weight polymers synthesized from a nutrient that a cell has in relative excess. For example, if nitrogen and/or phosphorus are lacking, *E. coli* cannot multiply even if a carbon and energy source such as glucose is plentiful. Rather than waste the carbon/energy source, cells use it to produce **glycogen,** a glucose polymer. A single large molecule such as glycogen has little osmotic effect on the cell. Later, when conditions are appropriate, cells degrade and use the glycogen granule. Other bacterial species store carbon and energy as **poly-β-hydroxybutyrate (figure 3.44).** This microbial compound is now being employed to produce a biodegradable polymer, which can be used in place of petroleum-based plastics.

Some types of granules can be readily detected by light microscopy. **Volutin** granules, a storage form of phosphate, stain red with blue dyes such as methylene blue, whereas the surrounding cellular material stains blue. Because of this, they are often called **metachromatic**

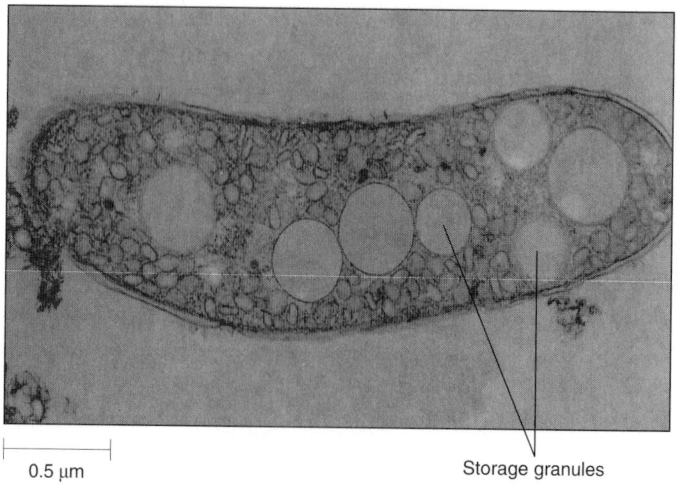

FIGURE 3.44 Storage Granules The large unstained areas in the photosynthetic bacterium *Rhodospirillum rubrum* are granules of poly-β-hydroxybutyrate.

granules (*meta* means "change" and *chromatic* means "color"). Recent evidence suggests that the role of these granules is more complex than originally thought. The volutin granules of *Agrobacterium tumefaciens* are membrane-bound and appear to resemble eukaryotic organelles called acidocalcisomes, which are thought to be involved with energy storage and pH balance within the cell. Regardless of the precise function of the granules, bacteria that produce them are beneficial in wastewater treatment because they scavenge phosphate, which is an environmental pollutant.

Gas Vesicles

Some aquatic bacteria produce **gas vesicles,** small rigid protein-bound compartments that provide buoyancy to the cell. Gases, but not water, flow freely into the vesicles, thereby decreasing the density of the cell. By regulating the number of gas vesicles within the cell, an organism can float or sink to its ideal position in the water column. For example, bacteria that use sunlight as a source of energy float closer to the surface, where light is available.

Endospores

An **endospore** is a unique type of dormant cell produced by a process called **sporulation** within cells of certain bacterial species, primarily members of the genera *Bacillus* and *Clostridium* (**figure 3.45**). The structures may remain dormant for perhaps 100 years, or even longer, and are extraordinarily resistant to damaging conditions including heat, desiccation, toxic chemicals, and ultraviolet irradiation. Immersion in boiling water for hours may not kill them. Endospores that survive these treatments can **germinate,** or exit the dormant stage, to become a typical, actively multiplying cell, called a **vegetative cell.**

The consequences of these resistant dormant forms are far-reaching. Because endospores can survive so long in a variety of conditions, they can be found virtually anywhere. They are common in soil, which can make its way into environments such as laboratories and hospitals and onto products such as food, media used to cultivate microbes, and medical devices. Because the exclusion of microbes in these environments and on these products is of paramount importance, special precautions must be taken to destroy these resistant structures.

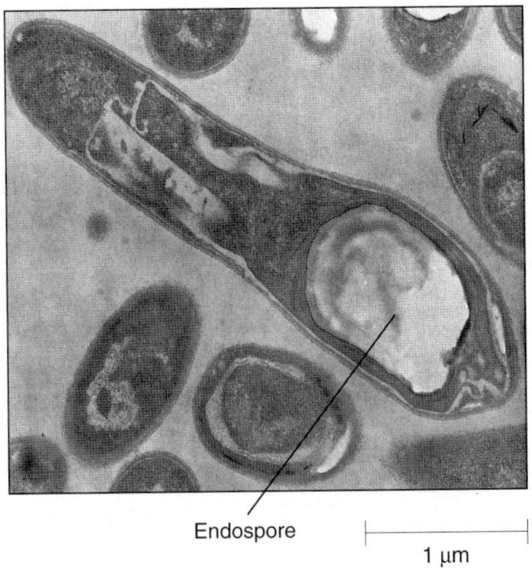
Endospore
1 μm

FIGURE 3.45 Endospores Endospore inside a vegetative cell of a *Clostridium* species (TEM).

Endospores are sometimes called **spores.** However, this latter term is also used to refer to the structures produced by unrelated microorganisms such as fungi. Bacterial endospores are much more resistant to environmental conditions than are other types of spores.

Several species of endospore-formers can cause disease. For example, botulism results from the ingestion of a deadly toxin produced by vegetative cells of *Clostridium botulinum*. Other disease-causing species of endospore-formers include *Clostridium tetani*, which causes tetanus; *Clostridium perfringens*, which causes gas gangrene; and *Bacillus anthracis*, which causes anthrax. ■ botulism, p. 690 ■ tetanus, p. 557 ■ gas gangrene, p. 559 ■ anthrax, p. 490

Sporulation

Endospore formation is a complex, highly ordered sequence of changes that initiates when cells are grown in low amounts of carbon or nitrogen (**figure 3.46**). Apparently the bacteria sense

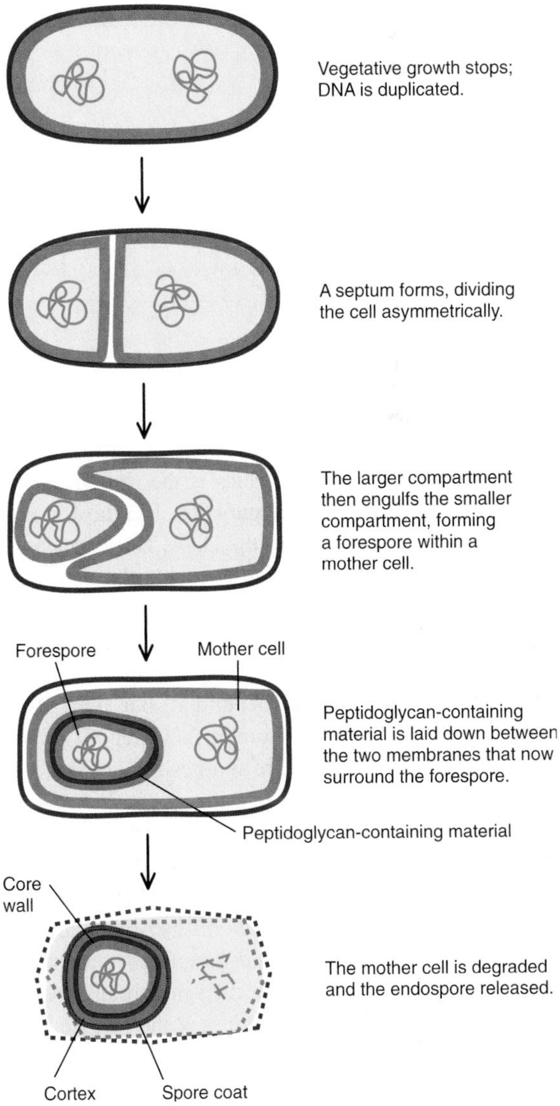
Vegetative growth stops; DNA is duplicated.
A septum forms, dividing the cell asymmetrically.
The larger compartment then engulfs the smaller compartment, forming a forespore within a mother cell.
Forespore
Mother cell
Peptidoglycan-containing material is laid down between the two membranes that now surround the forespore.
Peptidoglycan-containing material
Core wall
The mother cell is degraded and the endospore released.
Cortex
Spore coat

FIGURE 3.46 The Process of Sporulation

starvation conditions and therefore begin the 8-hour process that prepares them for rough times ahead.

After vegetative growth stops, DNA is duplicated and then a septum forms between the two chromosomes, dividing the cell asymmetrically. The larger compartment then engulfs the smaller compartment, forming a **forespore** within a **mother cell.** These two portions take on different roles in synthesizing the components that will make up the endospore. The forespore, which is enclosed by two membranes, will ultimately become the **core** of the endospore. Peptidoglycan-containing material is laid down between these two membranes, forming the **core wall** and the **cortex.** Meanwhile, the mother cell makes proteins that will form the **spore coat.** Ultimately, the mother cell is degraded and the endospore released.

The layers of the completed endospore function together, protecting the structure from damage. The spore coat is thought to function as a sieve, excluding molecules such as lysozyme. The cortex helps maintain the core in a dehydrated state, protecting it from the effects of heat. In addition, the core has small, acid-soluble proteins that bind DNA, altering its conformation and protecting it from damage. The core is rich in an unusual compound called dipicolinic acid, which combines with calcium ions. This complex appears to also play an important role in spore resistance.

Germination

Germination can be triggered by a brief exposure to heat or certain chemicals. Following such exposure, the endospore takes on water and swells. The spore coat and cortex then crack open, and a vegetative cell grows out. Since one vegetative cell gives rise to one endospore, sporulation is not a means of cell reproduction.

MICROCHECK 3.9

The prokaryotic chromosome is usually a circular, double-stranded DNA molecule that contains all of the genetic information required by a cell. Plasmids encode information that is advantageous to a cell in certain conditions. Ribosomes are the structures that facilitate the joining of amino acids to form a protein. Storage granules are polymers synthesized from a nutrient a cell has in relative excess. Gas vesicles provide buoyancy to a cell. An endospore is a highly resistant dormant stage produced by *Bacillus* and *Clostridium species*.

- ✓ Explain how glycogen granules benefit a cell.
- ✓ Explain why endospores are an important consideration for the canning industry.
- ✓ Why are the processes of sporulation and germination not considered a mechanism of multiplication?

THE EUKARYOTIC CELL

Eukaryotic cells are generally much larger than prokaryotic cells, and their internal structures are far more complex **(figure 3.47).** One of their most distinguishing characteristics is the abundance of membrane-enclosed compartments or **organelles.** The most important of these is the nucleus, which contains the DNA. The organelles, which can take up half the total cell volume, enable the cell to perform complex functions in separated regions. For example, degradative enzymes contained within an organelle digest food and other material without posing a threat to the integrity of the cell itself.

Organelles are functionally beneficial, but they also create transit problems. Each organelle contains a variety of proteins and other molecules, many of which are synthesized at other locations. To deliver these to the **lumen,** or interior, of another organelle, an elaborate transportation system is required. To transfer material, a section of an organelle will bud or pinch off, forming a small membrane-enclosed **vesicle (figure 3.48).** This mobile vesicle, containing a sampling of the contents of the organelle, can move to other parts of the cell. When that vesicle encounters the lipid membrane of another organelle, the two membranes will fuse to become one contiguous unit. By doing so, the vesicle introduces its contents to the lumen of that organelle. A similar process is used to export molecules synthesized within an organelle to the external environment.

As a group, eukaryotic cells are highly variable in many aspects. For example, protozoa, which are single-celled organisms, must function exclusively as self-contained units that seek and ingest food. These cells must be mobile and flexible to take in food particles. Consequently, they lack a cell wall that would otherwise provide rigidity. Animal cells also lack a cell wall, because they too must be flexible to accommodate movement. Fungi, on the other hand, are stationary and benefit from the protection provided by a rigid cell wall. Compounds that make up their cell walls include glucan and mannan, which are polysaccharides, and chitin, a polymer of *N*-acetylglucosamine that is also found in crustaceans and insects. Plant cells, which are also stationary, have cell walls composed of cellulose, a polymer of glucose. ■ polysaccharides, p. 32

The individual cells of a multicellular organism can be distinctly different from one another. Mammals, for example, are composed of several hundred different types of cells, and it is obvious that a liver cell is quite different from a bone cell. Cells of plants and animals function in cooperative associations called **tissues.** The tissues in your body include muscle, con-

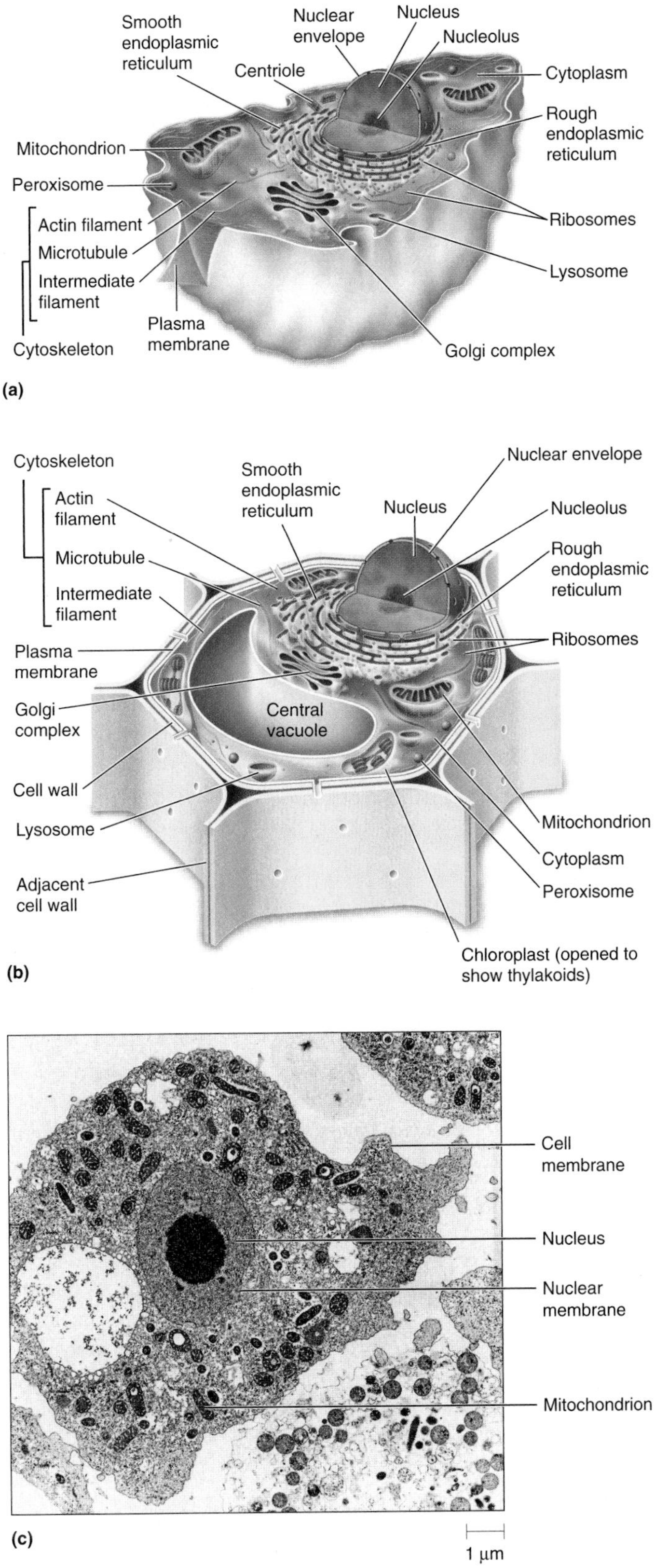

FIGURE 3.47 Eukaryotic Cells **(a)** Diagrammatic representation of an animal cell. **(b)** Diagrammatic representation of a plant cell. **(c)** Micrograph of an animal cell shows several membrane-bound structures including mitochondria and a nucleus.

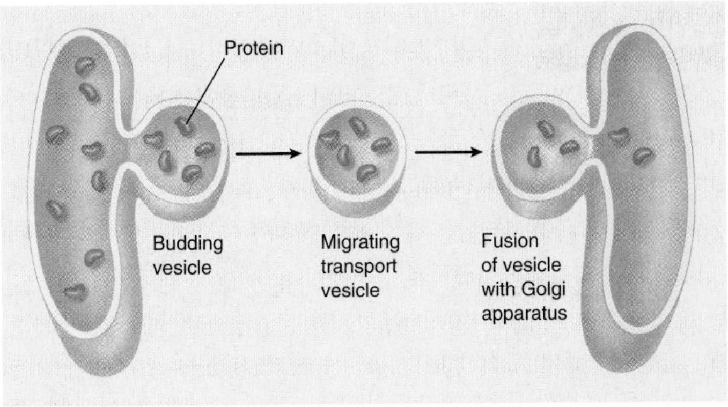

FIGURE 3.48 Vesicle Formation and Fusion A vesicle forms when a section of an organelle buds off. The mobile vesicle can then move to other parts of the cell, ultimately fusing with the membrane of another organelle.

nective, nerve, epithelial, blood, and lymphoid. Each of these provides a different function. Connective tissue, for example, which includes bone and cartilage, provides structure and support. Muscle provides movement. Combinations of various tissues function together to make up larger units, **organs.** These include skin, heart, and liver. Organs and the tissues that constitute them will be covered in detail in chapters 22 through 29 on infectious diseases. At this point, however, it is helpful to recognize that a generic discussion of eukaryotic cells encompasses many functional varieties. ■ types of epithelium, p. 367 ■ lymphoid tissue, p. 390

A comprehensive coverage of all aspects of eukaryotic cells is beyond the scope of this textbook. Instead, this section will focus on key characteristics, particularly those that directly affect the interaction of a microbe with a human host. These characteristics are summarized in **table 3.6.** A comparison of functional aspects of prokaryotic and eukaryotic cells is presented in **table 3.7.**

3.10 The Plasma Membrane

Focus Point

- Describe the structure of the eukaryotic plasma membrane, comparing and contrasting it with the bacterial cytoplasmic membrane.

All eukaryotic cells have a cytoplasmic membrane, or **plasma membrane,** which is similar in chemical structure and function to that of prokaryotic cells. It is a typical phospholipid bilayer embedded with proteins. The lipid and protein composition of the leaflet that faces the cytoplasm, however, differs significantly from that facing the outside of the cell. The same is true for membranes that surround the organelles. The leaflet facing the lumen of the organelle is similar to its counterpart facing the cell exterior. This lack of symmetry reflects

TABLE 3.6 A Summary of Eukaryotic Cell Structures

	Characteristics
Plasma Membrane	Asymmetric lipid bilayer embedded with proteins. Selective permeability, conduit to external environment.
Internal Protein Structures	
Cilia	Appear to project out of a cell. Beat in synchrony to provide movement. Composed of microtubules in a 9 + 2 arrangement.
Cytoskeleton	Dynamic filamentous network that provides structure to the cell.
Flagella	Appear to project out of a cell. Propel or push the cell with a whiplike or thrashing motion. Composed of microtubules in a 9 + 2 arrangement.
Ribosomes	Two subunits, 60S and 40S, join to form the 80S ribosome.
Membrane-Bound Organelles	
Chloroplasts	Site of photosynthesis; the organelle harvests the energy of sunlight to generate ATP, which is then used to convert CO_2 to carbohydrates. Within the stroma are chlorophyll-containing, disclike thylakoids. The membranes of these contain the components of the electron transport chain and the proteins that use proton motive force to synthesize ATP.
Endoplasmic reticulum	Site of synthesis of macromolecules destined for other organelles or the external environment.
Rough	Attached ribosomes extrude the proteins they are synthesizing through pores leading into the lumen of the organelle.
Smooth	Site of lipid synthesis and degradation, and Ca^{2+} storage.
Golgi apparatus	Site where macromolecules synthesized in the endoplasmic reticulum are modified before they are transported in vesicles to other destinations.
Lysosome	Digestion of foodstuffs.
Mitochondria	Harvest the energy released during the degradation of organic compounds to generate ATP. Within the highly folded inner membrane are the components of the electron transport chain and the proteins that use proton motive force to synthesize ATP.
Nucleus	Contains the DNA.
Peroxisome	Oxidation of lipids and toxic chemicals occurs.

the important role these membranes play in the complex processes occuring within the eukaryotic cell.

The proteins in the lipid bilayer perform a variety of functions. Some are involved in transport and others are attached to internal structures, helping to maintain cell integrity. Those in the outer leaflet often function as receptors. Typically, these receptors are **glycoproteins,** proteins that have various sugars attached. A given receptor binds a specific molecule, which is referred to as its **ligand.** These receptor-ligand interactions are extremely important in multicellular organisms because they allow cells to communicate with each other—a process called **signaling.** For example, in our bodies, some cells secrete a specific protein when they encounter certain compounds perceived as dangerous. Other cells of the immune system have receptors for that protein on their surface. When the protein binds its receptor, those cells recognize the signal as a call for help and respond accordingly. This type of cell-to-cell communication enables the multicellular organism to function as a cohesive unit. ■ glycoproteins, p. 31

The membranes of many eukaryotic cells contain sterols, which provide strength to the otherwise fluid structure. Recall that *Mycoplasma*, a group of bacteria lacking a cell wall, also have sterols in their membrances. The sterol found in animal cell membranes is **cholesterol,** whereas fungal membranes contain **ergosterol.** This difference is exploited by antifungal medications that act by interfering with ergosterol synthesis or function. ■ antifungal medications, p. 515 ■ oligosaccharides, p. 31

The plasma membrane plays no role in ATP synthesis; instead, that task is performed by mitochondria (discussed later). Although proton motive force is not generated across the membrane, an electrochemical gradient is maintained by energy-consuming mechanisms that expel either sodium ions or protons. ■ electrochemical gradient, p. 58

MICROCHECK 3.10

The plasma membrane is an asymmetric lipid bilayer embedded with proteins. Specific receptors on the outer leaflet mediate cell-to-cell signaling. Sterols provide strength to the fluid membrane.

- ✓ What is the medical significance of ergosterol in the fungal membranes?
- ✓ Describe why signaling is important in animal cells.
- ✓ How could one argue that the lumen of an organelle is "outside" of a cell?

TABLE 3.7 Comparison of Prokaryotic and Eukaryotic Cell Structures/Functions

	Prokaryotic	Eukaryotic
General Characteristics		
Size	Generally 0.3– 2 μm in diameter.	Generally 5– 50 μm in diameter.
Cell Division	Chromosome replication followed by binary fission.	Mitosis followed by division.
Chromosome location	Located in the nucleoid, which is not membrane-bound.	Contained within the membrane-bound nucleus.
Structures		
Cell membrane	Relatively symmetric with respect to the lipid content of the bilayers.	Highly asymmetric; lipid composition of outer leaflet differs significantly from that of inner leaflet.
Cell wall	Composed of peptidoglycan (*Bacteria*); Gram-negative bacteria have an outer membrane as well.	Absent in animal cells; composition in other cell types may include: chitin, glucans and mannans (fungi), and cellulose (plants).
Chromosome	Single, circular DNA molecule is typical.	Multiple, linear DNA molecules. DNA is wrapped around histones.
Flagella	Composed of protein subunits.	Made up of a 9 + 2 arrangement of microtubules.
Membrane-bound organelles	Absent.	Present; includes the nucleus, mitochondria, chloroplasts (only in plant cells), endoplasmic reticulum, Golgi apparatus, lysosomes, and peroxisomes.
Nucleus	Absent; DNA resides as an irregular mass forming the nucleoid region.	Present.
Ribosomes	70S ribosomes, which are made up of 50S and 30S subunits.	80S ribosomes, which are made up of 60S and 40S subunits. Mitochondria and chloroplasts have 70S ribosomes.
Functions		
Degradation of extracellular substances	Enzymes are secreted that degrade macromolecules outside of the cell. The resulting small molecules are transported into the cell.	Macromolecules are brought into the cell by endocytosis. Lysosomes carry digestive enzymes.
Motility	Generally involves flagella, which are composed of protein subunits. Flagella rotate like propellers, using proton motive force for energy.	Involves cilia and flagella, which are made up of a 9 + 2 arrangement of microtubules, Cilia move in synchrony; flagella propel a cell with a whiplike motion or thrash back and forth to pull a cell forward. Both use ATP for energy.
Protein secretion	A characteristic signal sequence marks proteins for secretion by the general secretory pathway. The precise mechanisms of translocation are still poorly understood.	Secreted proteins are translocated to the lumen of the rough endoplasmic reticulum as they are being synthesized. From there, they are transported to the Golgi apparatus for processing and packaging.
Strength and rigidity	Peptidoglycan-containing cell wall (*Bacteria*)	Cytoskeleton composed of microtubules, intermediate filaments, and microfilaments. Some have a cell wall; some have sterols in the membrane.
Transport	Primarily active transport. Group translocation.	Facilitated diffusion and active transport. Ion channels.

3.11 Transfer of Molecules Across the Plasma Membrane

Focus Points

- Compare and contrast the roles of channels and carriers in transport.
- Describe the processes of endocytosis and exocytosis.
- Describe the role of the endoplasmic reticulum in secretion.

Foodstuffs, signaling molecules, and waste products pass through the plasma membrane. Some of these enter and exit the cell via transport proteins. Others are taken in through a process called **endocytosis. Exocytosis,** which is the reverse of endocytosis, can be used to expel material.

Transport Proteins

The transport proteins of eukaryotic cells function as either carriers or channels. **Carriers** are analogous to proteins in prokaryotic cells that mediate facilitated diffusion and active transport. **Channels** are pores in the membrane. These pores are so small that only specific ions can diffuse through. They allow ions to move with the concentration gradient; they do not create such a gradient. To control ion passage, the channel has a gate, which can be either opened or closed, depending on environmental conditions.

Cells of multicellular organisms can often take up nutrients by facilitated diffusion, because the nutrient concentration of surrounding environments can be controlled. For example, glucose levels in the blood are maintained at a concentration higher than in most tissues. Consequently, animal cells generally do not need to expend energy transporting glucose.

The active transport mechanisms of eukaryotic cells are structurally analogous to those of prokaryotic cells. Some are of medical interest because they can eject drugs from the cell. For example, some human cancer cells use an ABC transporter that ejects therapeutic drugs intended to kill those cells.

Endocytosis and Exocytosis

Endocytosis is the process by which eukaryotic cells take up material from the surrounding environment **(figure 3.49).** The type of endocytosis common to most animal cells is **pinocytosis.** In this process a cell internalizes and pinches off small pieces of its own membrane, bringing along a small volume of liquid and any material attached to the membrane. This **endocytic vesicle** becomes a membrane-enclosed, low-pH compartment called an **endosome.** This then fuses with digestive organelles called **lysosomes.** The characteristics of lysosomes will be discussed shortly.

Animal cells often take up material by **receptor-mediated endocytosis,** which can be viewed as a variation of pinocytosis that allows cells to internalize extracellular ligands that bind to receptors on the cell's surface. When the receptors bind their ligand, the region is internalized to form an endocytic vesicle that contains the receptors along with their bound ligands. The low pH of the endosome frees the ligands from the receptors, which are often recycled. The endosome then fuses with lysosomes. Many viruses, including those that cause influenza and rabies, exploit receptor-mediated endocytosis to enter animal cells. By binding to a specific receptor, they too are taken up. ■ influenza, p. 597 ■ rabies, p. 697

Protozoa and phagocytes, both of which ingest bacteria and large debris, use a specific type of endocytosis called **phagocytosis.** Phagocytes are important cells of the body's defense system. The cells send out armlike extensions, **pseudopods,** which surround and enclose extracellular material, including bacteria. This action envelops the material, bringing it into the cell in an enclosed compartment called a **phagosome.** These ultimately fuse with lysosomes to form a **phagolysosome.** Phagocytes have a greater abundance of lysosomes than do other animal cells, which reflects their specialized function. In addition, their lysosomes contain a wider array of powerful digestive enzymes. Thus, most microbes are readily dispatched within the phagolysosome. Those that resist the killing effects are able to cause disease. ■ phagocytes, p. 378 ■ survival within a phagocyte, p. 462

The process of **exocytosis** is the reverse of endocytosis. Membrane-bound vesicles inside the cell fuse with the plasma membrane and release their contents into the external medium. The processes of endocytosis and exocytosis result in the exchange of material between the inside and outside of the cell.

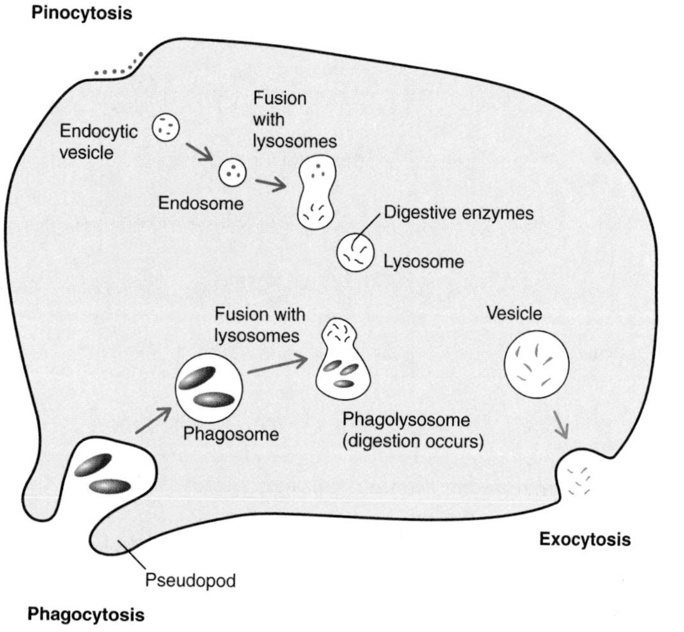

FIGURE 3.49 Endocytosis and Exocytosis Endocytosis includes pinocytosis and phagocytosis.

Secretion

Proteins destined for a non-cytoplasmic region, either outside of the cell or the lumen of an organelle, must be translocated across a membrane. Ribosomes synthesizing a protein that will be secreted attach to the membrane of the **endoplasmic reticulum (ER).** The characteristics of this organelle will be described shortly. As the protein is being made, it is threaded through the membrane and into the lumen of the ER. The lumen of any organelle can be viewed as equivalent to an extracellular space. Once a protein or any substance is there, it can readily be transported by vesicles to the lumen of another organelle, or to the exterior of the cell.

MICROCHECK 3.11

Gated channels allow specific ions to pass across the membrane. Carriers facilitate the passage of molecules across the membrane and often use energy. Pinocytosis allows cells to internalize small molecules. Protozoa and phagocytes internalize bacteria and debris by phagocytosis. Exocytosis is used to expel material. Secreted proteins are translocated across the membrane of the endoplasmic reticulum as they are being made.

- ✓ How does a cell bring in ligands?
- ✓ How is the formation of an endocytic vesicle different from that of a phagosome?
- ✓ How might a bacterium resist the killing effects of a phagolysosome?

3.12

Protein Structures Within the Cell

Focus Point

- Describe the structure and function of the eukaryotic cytoskeleton, flagella, and cilia.

Eukaryotic cells have unique protein structures that distinguish them from prokaryotic cells. These include the cytoskeleton, and optional flagella and cilia. The latter two appear to project out of the cell, but are actually covered by an extension of the cytoplasmic membrane. Another protein structure that characterizes the eukaryotic cell is the 80S ribosome, which is made up of a 60S and 40S subunit. Recall that the prokaryotic ribosomes are 70S. Like prokaryotic ribosomes, these are composed of ribosomal RNA and protein.

Cytoskeleton

The threadlike proteins that make up the cytoskeleton continually reconstruct to adapt to the cell's constantly changing needs. The network is composed of three elements: microtubules, actin filaments, and intermediate filaments **(figure 3.50).**

Microtubules, the thickest of the cytoskeleton structures, are long hollow cylinders composed of protein subunits called **tubulin.** Microtubules form the **mitotic spindles,** the machinery that partitions chromosomes between two cells in the process of cell division. Without mitotic spindles, cells could not reproduce. Microtubules also are the main structures that make up the **cilia** and **flagella,** the mechanisms of locomotion in certain eukaryotic cells. In addition, microtubules also function as the framework along which organelles and vesicles move within a cell. Organelles called **centrioles** are involved in the assembly of microtubules. The antifungal drug griseofulvin is thought to interfere with the structural integrity of the microtubules of some fungi. ■ mitosis, p. 299

Actin filaments enable the cell cytoplasm to move. They are composed of a polymer of **actin,** which can rapidly assemble and subsequently disassemble, causing motion. For example, pseudopod formation relies on actin polymerization in one part of the cell and depolymerization in another. Some intracellular pathogens exploit the process and trigger a rapid polymerization of actin, propelling them within that cell. This can move the pathogens with enough force to be ejected into an adjacent cell.

Intermediate filaments function like ropes, strengthening the cell mechanically. They enable cells to resist physical stresses.

Flagella and Cilia

Flagella and **cilia** are flexible structures that appear to project out of a cell yet are covered by an extension of the plasma membrane **(figure 3.51).** Both are composed of long microtubules grouped in what is called a 9 + 2 arrangement: nine pairs of microtubules surrounding two individual ones. They originate from a basal body within the cell; the basal body has a slightly different arrangement of microtubules.

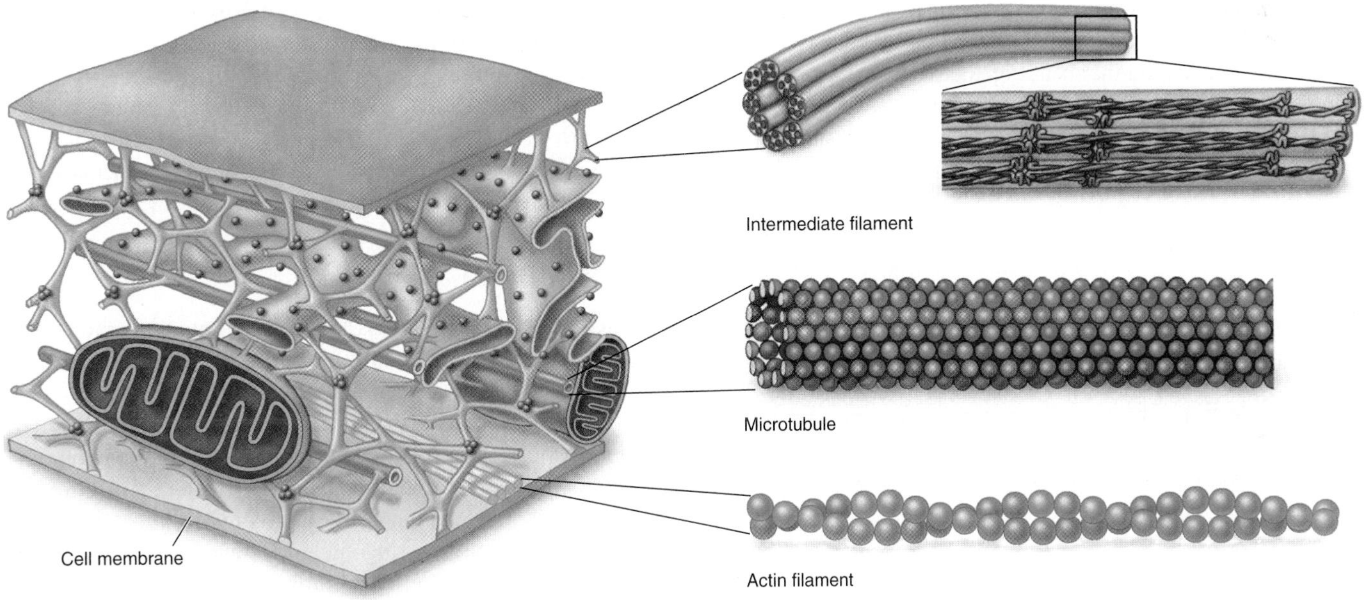

FIGURE 3.50 Cytoskeleton Diagrammatic representation of the dynamic filamentous network that provides structure to the cell; the cytoskeleton is composed of three elements—microtubules, actin filaments, and intermediate filaments.

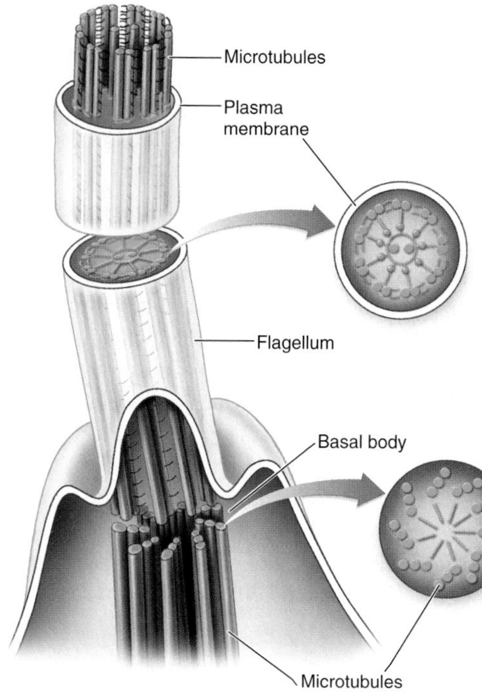

FIGURE 3.51 Flagella Flexible structures involved in movement.

Eukaryotic flagella function in motility, but are otherwise completely different from their prokaryotic counterparts. Using ATP as a source of energy, they either propel the cell with a whip-like motion or thrash back and forth to pull the cell forward.

Cilia are shorter than flagella, often covering a cell and moving in synchrony (see figure 1.8). This motion can move a cell forward in an aqueous solution, or propel surrounding material along a stationary cell. For example, epithelial cells that line the respiratory tract have cilia that beat together in a directed fashion. This moves the mucus film that covers those cells, directing it upward toward the mouth, where it can be swallowed. This action removes microorganisms that have been inhaled before they can enter the lungs.

MICROCHECK 3.12

The 80S eukaryotic ribosome is composed of 60S and 40S subunits. The cytoskeleton is a dynamic filamentous network that provides structure to the cell; it is composed of microtubules, actin filaments, and intermediate filaments. Flagella function in motility. Cilia either propel a cell or move material along a stationary cell.

- ✓ Explain how actin filaments are related to phagocytosis.
- ✓ Explain what is meant by the 9 + 2 structure of cilia and flagella.

3.13 Membrane-Bound Organelles

Focus Point

- Describe the function of the nucleus, mitochondria, chloroplasts, endoplasmic reticulum, Golgi apparatus, lysosomes, and peroxisomes.

The presence of membrane-bound organelles is an important feature that sets eukaryotic cells apart from their prokaryotic counterparts.

The Nucleus

The predominant distinguishing feature of the eukaryotic cell is the **nucleus,** which contains the DNA. The boundary of this structure is the **nuclear envelope,** which is composed of two lipid bilayer membranes: the **inner membrane** and the **outer membrane.** Spanning the envelope are complex protein structures that form **nuclear pores,** allowing large molecules such as ribosomal subunits and proteins to be transported into and out of the nucleus **(figure 3.52).** The **nucleolus** is a region within the nucleus where ribosomal RNAs are synthesized.

The nucleus contains multiple chromosomes, each one encoding different genetic information. Unlike the situation in most prokaryotic cells, double-stranded chromosomal DNA is linear. To add structure and order to the long DNA molecule, it is packed by winding it around positively charged proteins called **histones.** These bind tightly to the negatively charged DNA molecule. One packing unit, called a **nucleosome,** consists of a complex of histones around which the linear DNA wraps twice. The complex of DNA and proteins that together form the chromosomes is called **chromatin.**

Events that take place in the nucleus during cell division distinguish eukaryotes from prokaryotes. In eukaryotic cells, after DNA is replicated, chromosomes go through a nuclear division process called **mitosis,** which ensures the daughter cells receive the same number of chromosomes as the original parent. Through mitosis, a cell that is **diploid,** or has two copies of each chromosome, will generate two diploid daughter cells. A different process, **meiosis,** generates haploid daughter cells, which each have a single copy of each chromosome.

Mitochondria

Mitochondria function as ATP-generating powerhouses, and are found in nearly all eukaryotic cells. They are highly complex structures about the size of a bacterial cell, and are bounded by two lipid bilayer membranes **(figure 3.53).** These are referred to as the outer and inner membranes. The inner membrane is smooth, but the outer membrane is highly folded, forming invaginations called **cristae.** These folds increase the surface area of the membrane, maximizing the ATP-generating capabilities of the organelle (the processes will be discussed in chapter 6).

Enclosed by the inner membrane is the **matrix,** which contains DNA, ribosomes, and other molecules necessary for protein synthesis. Notably, the ribosomes are 70s rather than the 80S ribosome found in the cytoplasm of eukaryotic cells. These observations, along with the fact that mitochondria elongate and divide in a fashion similar to bacteria, were among the first pieces of

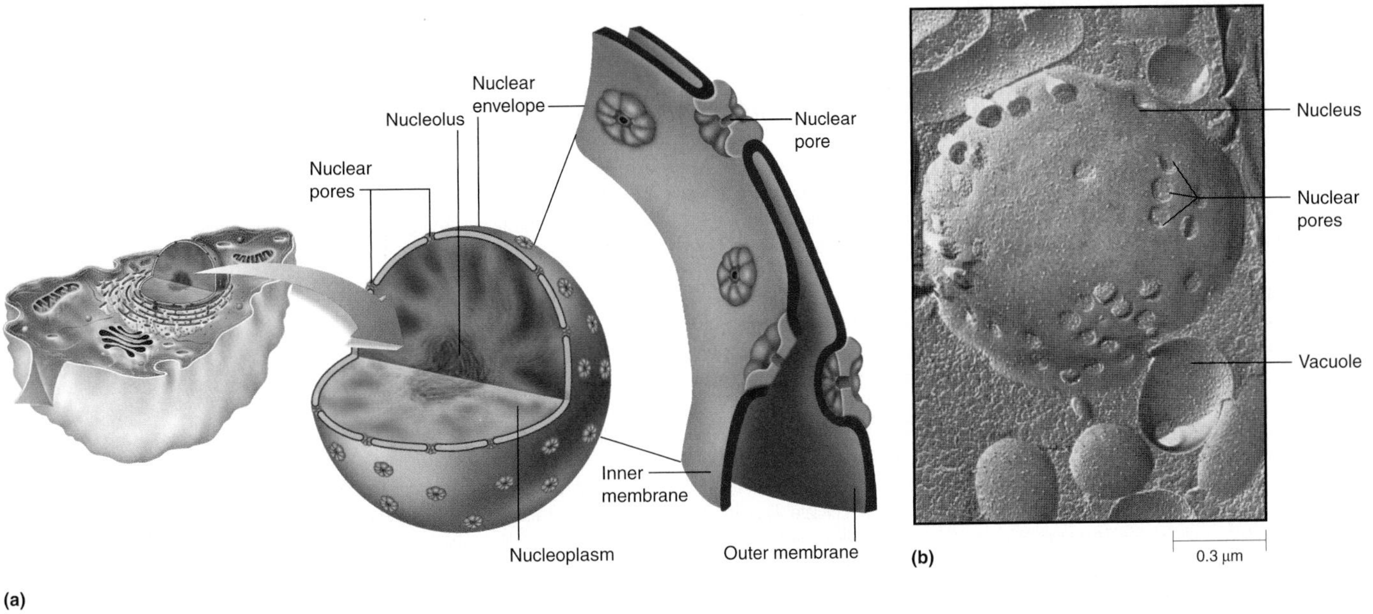

FIGURE 3.52 Nucleus Organelle that contains the DNA. **(a)** Diagrammatic representation. **(b)** Electron micrograph of a yeast cell (*Geotrichum candidium*) by freeze-fracture technique.

evidence that led scientists to speculate that mitochondria evolved from bacterial cells (see **Perspective 3.1**).

Chloroplasts

Chloroplasts, found exclusively in plants and algae, are the site of photosynthesis in eukaryotic cells. They harvest the energy of sunlight to generate ATP, which is then used to convert CO_2 to organic compounds like sugar and starch. Like mitochondria, chloroplasts are bounded by two membranes (**figure 3.54**). Within the chloroplast's **stroma,** the region analogous to the mitochondrial matrix, are membrane-bound disclike structures, called **thylakoids.** Chlorophyll and other pigments that capture radiant energy are embedded in the thylakoid membranes.

Like mitochondria, chloroplasts appear to have evolved from bacterial cells (see Perspective 3.1). They contain DNA and 70S ribosomes, elongate and divide, and have photosynthetic mechanisms similar to a group of bacteria called cyanobacteria.

Endoplasmic Reticulum (ER)

The **endoplasmic reticulum (ER)** is a complex three-dimensional internal membrane system of flattened sheets, sacs, and tubes **(figure 3.55).** The **rough endoplasmic reticulum** has a characteristic bumpy appearance due to the multitude of ribosomes coating it. It is the site where proteins not destined for the cytoplasm are synthesized. These include proteins targeted for the lumen of an organelle or for secretion outside the cell. Membrane proteins such as receptors are also synthesized on the rough ER. The ribosomes making these proteins attach to the ER surface. As the ribosomes synthesize the proteins, they thread them through gated pores in the membrane, delivering the proteins to the lumen of the ER. There, the proteins fold to assume their three-dimensional shapes. Vesicles that bud off from the ER transfer the newly synthesized molecules to the Golgi apparatus for further modification and sorting.

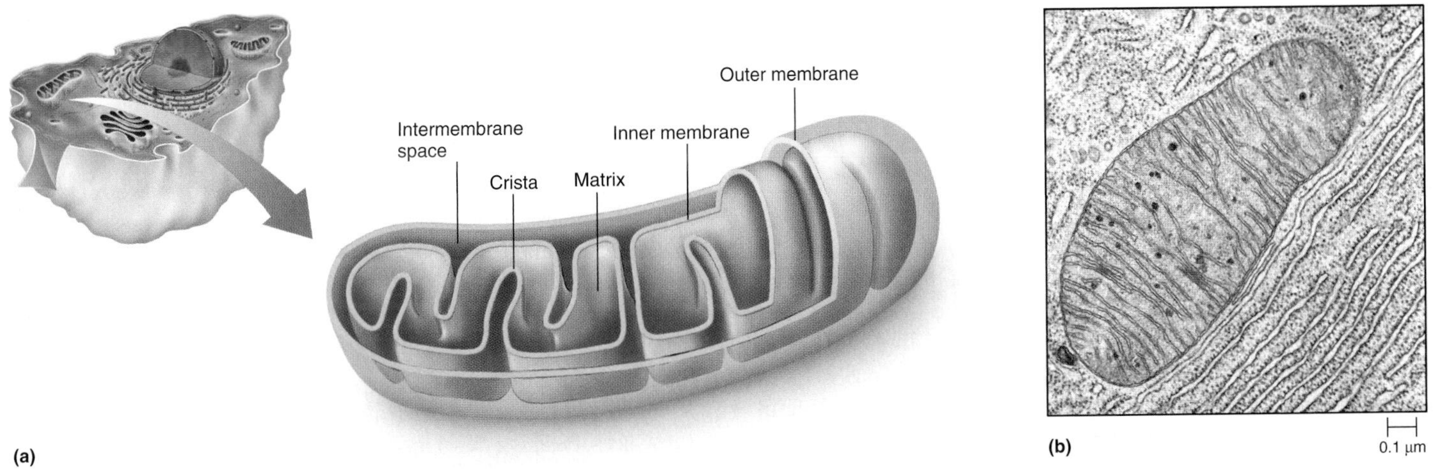

FIGURE 3.53 Mitochondria These harvest the energy released during the degradation of organic compounds to synthesize ATP. **(a)** Diagrammatic representation. **(b)** Electron micrograph.

PERSPECTIVE 3.1

The Origins of Mitochondria and Chloroplasts

Mitochondria and chloroplasts bear such a striking similarity to prokaryotic cells that it is no wonder scientists have speculated for many decades that these organelles evolved from bacteria. The **endosymbiont theory** states that the ancestors of mitochondria and chloroplasts were bacteria residing within other cells in a mutually beneficial partnership. The intracellular bacterium in such a partnership is called an **endosymbiont.** As time went on each partner became indispensable to the other, and the endosymbiont eventually lost key features such as a cell wall and the ability to replicate independently.

Several early observations have supported the endosymbiont theory. Mitochondria and chloroplasts, unlike other eukaryotic organelles, both carry some of the genetic information necessary for their function. These include genes for some of the ribosomal proteins and ribosomal RNAs that make up their 70S ribosomes. These ribosomes contrast with the typical 80S ribosomes that characterize eukaryotic cells and, in fact, are equivalent to the prokaryotic 70S ribosomes. Interestingly, cellular DNA encodes some of the components that make up these ribosomes. Another characteristic that supports the model that mitochondria and chloroplasts were once intracellular bacteria is the double membrane that surrounds these organelles. Present-day endosymblonts retain their cytoplasmic membranes and live within membrane-bound compartments in their eukaryotic host cell.

Evidence in favor of the endosymbiont theory continues to accumulate. Recent technology enables scientists to readily determine the precise order or **sequence,** of nucleotides that make up DNA. This allows comparison of the nucleotide sequences of organelle DNA with genomes of different bacteria. It has become apparent that some mitochondrial DNA sequences bear a striking resemblance to DNA sequences of members of a group of obligate intracellular parasites, the rickettsias. These are quite likely relatives of modern-day mitochondria.

A tremendous effort is now under way to determine the nucleotide sequence of mitochondria from a wide variety of eukaryotes, including plants, animals, and protists. While the size of mitochondrial DNA varies a great deal among these different eukaryotic organisms, common sequence themes are emerging. Today, researchers are no longer discussing "if" but "when" these organelles evolved from intracellular prokaryotes.

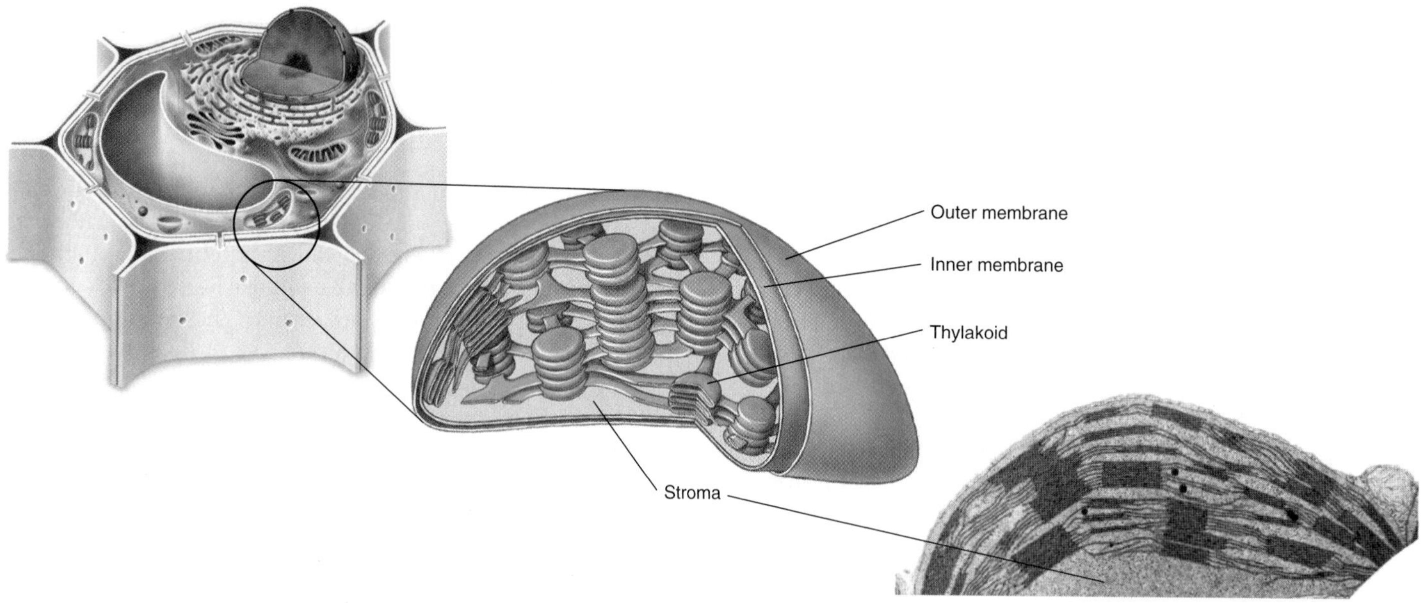

FIGURE 3.54 Chloroplasts These harvest the energy of sunlight to generate ATP. The ATP is then used to convert CO_2 to an organic form.

Some regions of the ER are smooth. This **smooth endoplasmic reticulum** provides a variety of functions including lipid synthesis and degradation, and calcium ion storage. As with material made in the rough ER, vesicles transfer compounds from the smooth ER to the Golgi apparatus.

The Golgi Apparatus

The **Golgi apparatus** consists of a series of membrane-bound flattened sacs **(figure 3.56).** It is the site where macromolecules synthesized in the endoplasmic reticulum are modified before they are transported to other destinations. These modifications, such as the addition of carbohydrate and phosphate groups, take place in a sequential order in different Golgi sacs. Much like an assembly line, the molecules are transferred in vesicles from one Golgi sac to another. These various molecules are then sorted and delivered in vesicles destined either for specific cellular compartments or to the outside of the cell.

Lysosomes and Peroxisomes

Lysosomes are organelles that contain a number of powerful degradative enzymes. These include various proteases and nucleases that could destroy the cell if not contained within the organelle. Recall that material brought into the cell through endocytosis is digested when the endosome or phagosome fuses with lysosomes. In a similar manner, exhausted organelles can fuse with lysosomes so that their contents are digested.

Peroxisomes are the organelles in which oxygen is used to oxidize substances, breaking down lipids and detoxifying certain chemicals. As a consequence, their enzymes generate highly reactive molecules such as hydrogen peroxide and superoxide. The peroxisome contains these

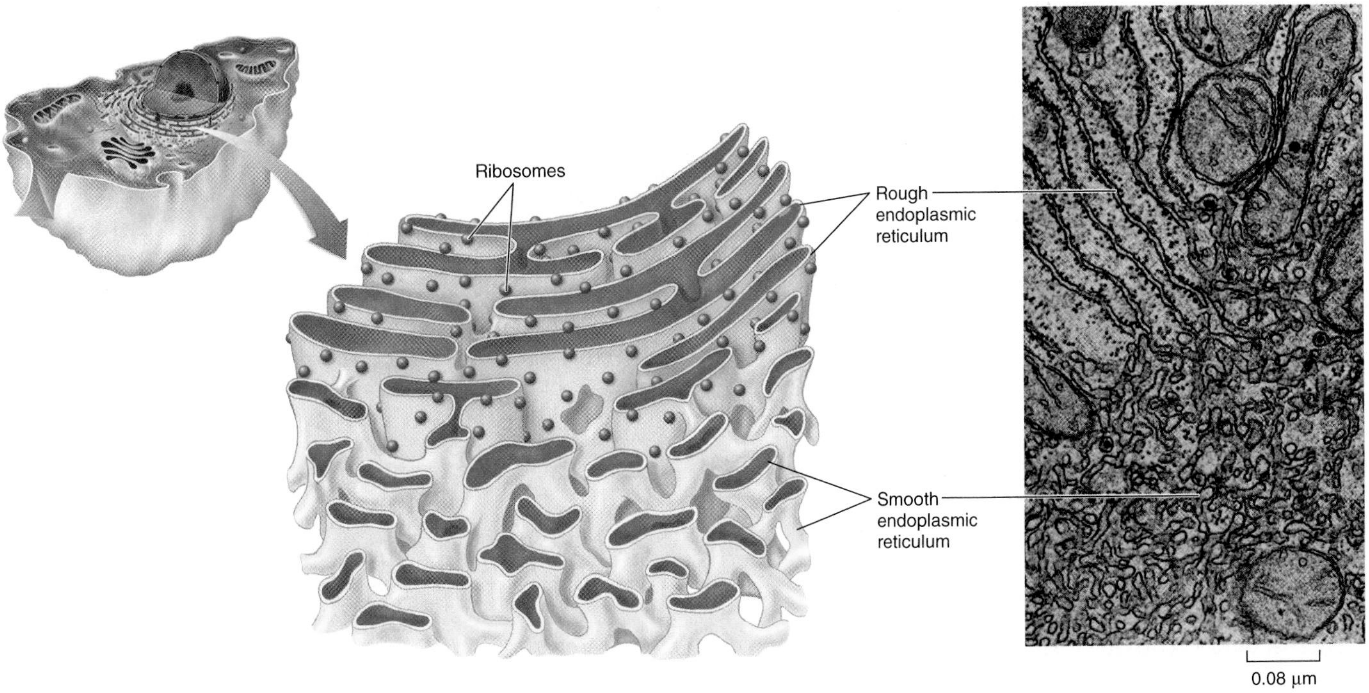

FIGURE 3.55 Endoplasmic Reticulum Site of synthesis of macromolecules destined for other organelles or the external environment.

molecules and ultimately degrades them, protecting the cell from their toxic effects. ■ hydrogen peroxide, p. 96 ■ superoxide, p. 96

MICROCHECK 3.13

The nucleus, which contains DNA, is the predominant distinguishing feature of eukaryotes. Mitochondria and chloroplasts generate energy in the form of ATP; mitochondria oxidize organic compounds to obtain energy, whereas chloroplasts harvest the energy of sunlight. The rough endoplasmic reticulum is the site where proteins not destined for the cytoplasm are synthesized. The smooth endoplasmic reticulum functions in lipid synthesis and degradation, and calcium ion storage. The Golgi apparatus modifies and sorts molecules synthesized in the rough ER. Lysosomes are the structures within which digestion takes place; peroxisomes are the organelles in which oxygen is used to oxidize substances.

- ✓ Describe the structure of the nucleus.
- ✓ How does the function of the rough endoplasmic reticulum differ from that of the smooth endoplasmic reticulum?
- ✓ If enzymes contained in a peroxisome are to act on a substrate, what must first occur?

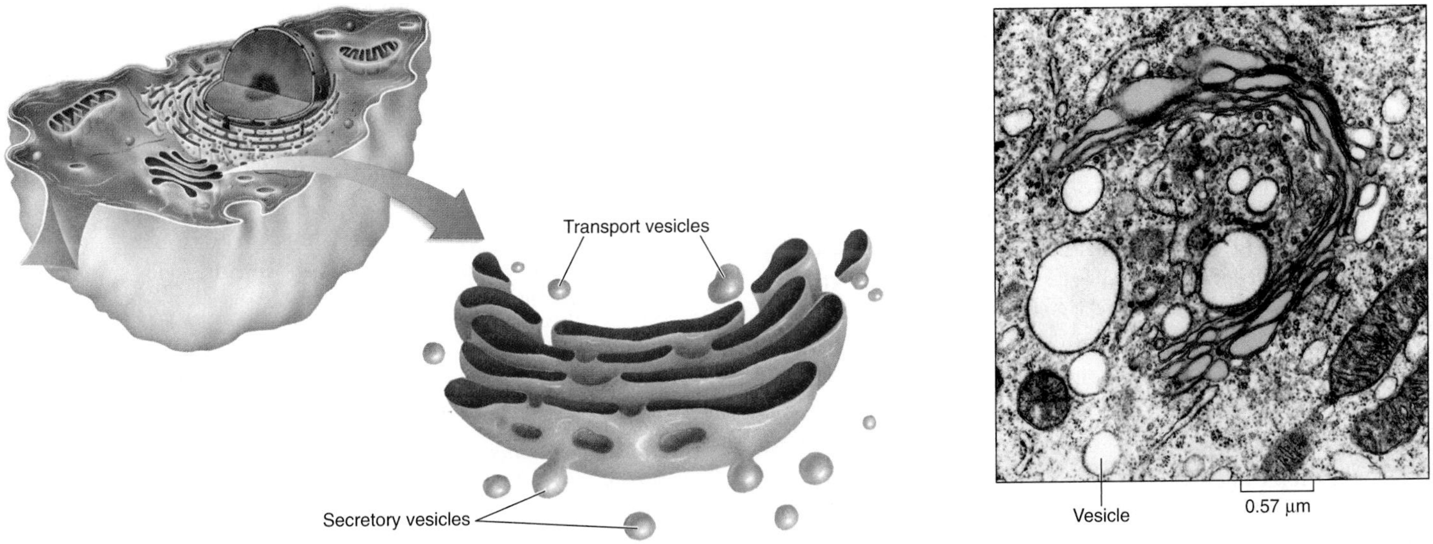

FIGURE 3.56 Golgi Apparatus Site where macromolecules synthesized in the endoplasmic reticulum are modified before being transported to other destinations in vesicles.

FUTURE CHALLENGES

A Case of Breaking and Entering

Unraveling the complex mechanisms that prokaryotic and eukaryotic cells use to transport materials across their membranes can potentially aid in the development of new antimicrobial medications. Armed with a precise model of the structure and function of bacterial transporter proteins, scientists might be able to design new drugs that exploit these systems. One strategy would be to design compounds that irreversibly bind to transporter molecules and jam the mechanism. If the microbes can be prevented from bringing in nutrients and removing wastes, their growth would cease. Another strategy would be to enhance the uptake or decrease the efflux of a specific compound that interferes with intracellular processes. This is already being done to some extent as new derivatives of current antibiotics are being produced, but more precise understanding of the processes by which bacteria take up or remove compounds could expedite drug development.

A more thorough understanding of eukaryotic uptake systems could be used to develop better antiviral drugs. Recall that viruses exploit the process of receptor-mediated endocytosis to gain entry into the cell. Once they are enclosed within the endosome, their protective protein coat is removed, releasing their genetic material. New drugs can potentially be developed that block these steps, preventing the entry or uncoating of infectious viral particles.

SUMMARY

Microscopy and Cell Morphology

3.1 Microscopic Techniques: The Instruments (Table 3.1)

Principles of Light Microscopy: The Bright-Field Microscope

The most common type of microscope is the **bright-field** microscope. (Figure 3.1)

The **objective lens** and the **ocular lens** in combination magnify an object by a factor equal to the product of the magnification of each of the individual lenses.

The usefulness of a microscope depends on its **resolving power.** (Figure 3.2)

Light Microscopes That Increase Contrast

The **phase-contrast** microscope amplifies differences in refraction. (Figure 3.4)

The **interference microscope** causes the specimen to appear as a three-dimensional image.(Figure 3.5)

The **dark-field microscope** makes organisms stand out as bright objects against a dark background. (Figure 3.6)

The **fluorescence microscope** is used to observe cells that have been stained with fluorescent dyes. (Figure 3.7)

The **confocal scanning laser microscope** is used to construct a three-dimensional image of a thick structure and to provide detailed sectional views of the interior of an intact cell. (Figure 3.8)

Electron Microscopes.

Electron microscopes use electromagnetic lenses, electrons, and fluorescent screens to produce a magnified image. (Figure 3.9)

Transmission electron microscopes (TEMs) transmit electrons through a specimen that has been prepared by **thin sectioning, freeze fracturing,** or **freeze etching.** (Figure 3.10)

Scanning electron microscopes (SEM) scan a beam of electrons back and forth over the surface of a specimen, producing a three-dimensional effect. (Figure 3.11)

Atomic Force Microscopes

Atomic force microscopes map the bumps and valleys of a surface on an atomic scale. (Figure 3.12)

3.2 Microscopic Techniques: Dyes and Staining (Table 3.2)

Differential Stains

The **Gram stain** is the most widely used procedure for staining bacteria; Gram-positive bacteria stain purple and Gram-negative bacteria stain pink. (Figure 3.14)

The **acid-fast stain** is used to stain organisms such as *Mycobacteria* species; **acid-fast** organisms stain pink and all other organisms stain blue. (Figure 3.15)

Special Stains to Observe Cell Structures

The **capsule stain** allows the **capsule** to stand out as a halo around an organism. (Figure 3.16)

The **spore stain** uses heat to facilitate the staining of **endospores.** (Figure 3.17)

The **flagella stain** employs a **mordant** that enables the stain to adhere to and coat the otherwise thin **flagella.** (Figure 3.18)

Fluorescent Dyes and Tags

Some fluorescent dyes bind compounds that characterize all cells; others bind compounds specific to certain cell types. (Figure 3.19)

Immunofluorescence is used to tag a specific protein of interest with a fluorescent compound.

3.3 Morphology of Prokaryotic Cells

Shapes

Most common prokaryotes are either **cocci** or **rods;** other shapes include **coccobacilli, vibrios, spirilla,** and **spirochetes. Pleomorphic** bacteria have variable shapes. (Figure 3.20)

Groupings

Cells adhering to one another following division form characteristic arrangements such as chains, packets, and clusters. (Figure 3.22)

Multicellular Associations

Cells within **biofilms** often alter their activities when a critical number of cells are present.

The Structure of the Prokaryotic Cell (Figure 3.23, Table 3.3)

3.4 The Cytoplasmic Membrane

Structure and Chemistry of the Cytoplasmic Membrane (Figure 3.24)

The cytoplasmic membrane is a **phospholipid bilayer** embedded with a variety of different proteins including transport proteins and receptors.

Permeability of the Cytoplasmic Membrane

The cytoplasmic membrane is selectively permeable; water, gases, and small hydrophobic molecules are among the few compounds that can pass through by **simple diffusion.**

The Role of the Cytoplasmic Membrane in Energy Transformation

The **electron transport chain** within the membrane expels protons, generating an **electrochemical gradient,** a form of energy called **proton motive force.** (Figure 3.26)

3.5 Directed Movement of Molecules Across the Cytoplasmic Membrane

Transport Systems (Table 3.4)

Facilitated diffusion, or **passive transport,** moves compounds from one side of the membrane to the other by exploiting the concentration gradient. (Figure 3.27)

Active transport uses energy, either proton motive force or ATP, to accumulate compounds against a concentration gradient.

Group translocation chemically modifies a molecule during its passage through the cytoplasmic membrane. (Figure 3.30)

Secretion

The presence of a characteristic **signal sequence** targets proteins for secretion.

3.6 Cell Wall

Peptidoglycan (Figure 3.32)

Peptidoglycan is found only in the *Bacteria* and provides rigidity to the cell wall.

Peptidoglycan is composed of **glycan strands,** which are alternating subunits of ***N*-acetylmuramic acid (NAM)** and ***N*-acetylglucosamine (NAG),** interconnected via the tetrapeptide chains on NAM.

The Gram-Positive Cell Wall (Figure 3.33)

The Gram-positive cell wall contains a relatively thick layer of peptidoglycan. **Teichoic acids** stick out of the peptidoglycan layer.

The Gram-Negative Cell Wall (Figure 3.34)

The Gram-negative cell wall has a relatively thin layer of peptidoglycan sandwiched between the cytoplasmic membrane and an **outer membrane.**

The outer membrane contains **lipopolysaccharides.** The **lipid A** portion of the lipopolysaccharide molecule is responsible for the toxic effects, which is why LPS is called **endotoxin.**

Porins form small channels that permit small molecules to pass through the outer membrane.

Periplasm contains a variety of proteins, including those involved in nutrient degradation and transport.

Antibacterial Compounds That Target Peptidoglycan

Penicillin prevents peptidoglycan synthesis.

Lysozyme destroys the structural integrity of peptidoglycan.

Differences in Cell Wall Composition and the Gram Stain

The Gram-positive, but not the Gram-negative, cell wall hold the crystal violet-iodine dye complex within the cell even when subjected to the trauma of acetone-alcohol treatment.

Characteristics of Bacteria That Lack a Cell Wall

Mycoplasma species are extremely variable in shape and are not affected by lysozyme or penicillin. (Figure 3.35)

Cell Walls of the Domain Archaea

Archaea have a greater variety of cell wall types than do the *Bacteria.*

3.7 Surface Layers External to the Cell Wall

Capsules and Slime Layers

Capsules and **slime layers** enable bacteria to adhere to surfaces. Some capsules allow disease-causing microorganisms to thwart the innate defense system. (Figure 3.36)

3.8 Filamentous Protein Appendages

Flagella (Figure 3.37)

The **flagellum** is a long protein structure responsible for most types of bacterial motility. (Figure 3.38)

Chemotaxis is the directed movement toward an attractant or away from a repellent. (Figure 3.39)

Phototaxis, aerotaxis, and **magnetotaxis** are directed movements toward light, oxygen, and a magnetic field, respectively.

Pili (Figure 3.41)

Many types of **pili (fimbriae)** enable attachment of cells to specific surfaces.

Sex pili are involved in a form of DNA transfer called **conjugation.**

3.9 Internal Structures

The Chromosome (Figure 3.42)

The **chromosome** of prokaryotes resides in the **nucleoid** rather than within a membrane bound nucleus; it contains all the genetic information required by a cell.

Plasmids

Plasmids encode genetic information that may be advantageous, but not required by the cell.

Ribosomes (Figure 3.43)

Ribosomes facilitate the joining of amino acids. The 70S bacterial ribosome is composed of a 50S and a 30S subunit.

Storage Granules (Figure 3.44)

Storage granules are synthesized from a nutrient that a cell has in relative excess.

Gas Vesicles

Gas vesicles provide buoyancy to aquatic cells.

Endospores

Endospores are a dormant stage produced by members of *Bacillus* and *Clostridium*; they can **germinate** to become **vegetative cells.** (Figures 3.45, 3.46)

Endospores are extraordinarily resistant to heat, desiccation, toxic chemicals, and ultraviolet irradiation.

The Eukaryotic Cell (Figure 3.47, Table 3.6)

3.10 The Plasma Membrane

The **plasma membrane** is a phospholipid bilayer embedded with proteins.

Proteins in the membrane are involved in transport, structural integrity, and **signaling.**

3.11 Transfer of Molecules Across the Plasma Membrane

Transport Proteins

Carriers mediate facilitated diffusion and active transport.

Channels are pores in the membrane that are so small that only specific ions can pass through. These channels are gated.

Endocytosis and Exocytosis (Figure 3.49)

Pinocytosis is the most common form of endocytosis in animal cells. The **endocytic vesicle** fuses with an **endosome,** which then fuses with a **lysosome.**

Protozoa and phagocytes take up bacteria and debris through the process of **phagocytosis.** The **phagosome** fuses with the **lysosome,** where the material is digested.

Exocytosis expels material.

Secretion

Proteins destined for a non-cytoplasmic region are made by ribosomes bound to the **endoplasmic reticulum.**

3.12 Protein Structures Within the Cell

The **80S** ribosome is composed of **60S** and **40S subunits.**

Cytoskeleton (Figure 3.50)

The cytoskeleton is composed of **microtubules, actin filaments, and intermediate filaments.**

Flagella and Cilia (Figure 3.51)

Flagella propel a cell or pull the cell forward.

Cilia move in synchrony to either propel a cell or move material along a stationary cell.

3.13 Membrane-Bound Organelles

The Nucleus (Figure 3.52)

The **nucleus** is the predominant distinguishing feature of eukaryotes.

Mitochondria

Mitochondria use the energy released during the degradation of organic compounds to generate ATP. (Figure 3.53)

Chloroplasts

Chloroplasts capture the energy of sunlight; this is then used to synthesize ATP that is expended to convert CO_2 to an organic form. (Figure 3.54)

Endoplasmic Reticulum (ER) (Figure 3.55)

The **rough endoplasmic reticulum** is the site where proteins not located in the cytoplasm are synthesized.

Within the **smooth endoplasmic reticulum,** lipids are synthesized and degraded, and calcium is stored.

The Golgi Apparatus (Figure 3.56)

The **Golgi apparatus** modifies and sorts molecules synthesized in the endoplasmic reticulum.

Lysosomes and Peroxisomes

Lysosomes carry digestive enzymes.

Peroxisomes are the organelles in which oxygen is used to oxidize certain substances.

REVIEW QUESTIONS

Short Answer

1. Explain why resolving power is important in microscopy.
2. Explain why basic dyes are used more frequently than acidic dyes in staining.
3. Describe what happens at each step in the Gram stain.
4. Compare and contrast ABC transport systems with group translocation.
5. Give two reasons that the outer membrane of Gram-negative bacteria is significant medically.
6. Compare and contrast penicillin and lysozyme.
7. Describe how a plasmid can help and hinder a cell.
8. How is an organ different from tissue?
9. How is receptor-mediated endocytosis different from phagocytosis?
10. Explain how the Golgi apparatus cooperatively functions with the endoplasmic reticulum.

Multiple Choice

1. Which of the following is most likely to be used in a typical microbiology laboratory?
   a) Bright-field microscope
   b) Confocal scanning microscope
   c) Phase-contrast microscope
   d) Scanning electron microscope
   e) Transmission electron microscope
2. Which of the following stains is used to detect *Mycobacterium* species?
   a) Acid-fast stain b) Capsule stain c) Endospore stain
   d) Gram stain e) Simple stain
3. Penicillin
   1. is most effective against Gram-positive bacteria.
   2. is most effective against Gram-negative bacteria.
   3. functions in the cytoplasm of the cell.

4. is effective against mycoplasma.
5. kills only growing cells.

a) 1,2 b) 2,3 c) 3,4 d) 4,5 e) 1,5

4. Endotoxin is associated with
   1. Gram-positive bacteria. 2. Gram-negative bacteria.
   3. the cell wall. 4. the endospore.
   5. the cytoplasmic membrane.

   a) 1,2 b) 2,3 c) 3,4 d) 4,5 e) 1,5

5. In prokaryotes, lipid bilayers are associated with the
   1. Gram-positive cell wall. 2. Gram-negative cell wall.
   3. cytoplasmic membrane. 4. capsule.
   5. nuclear membrane.

   a) 1,2 b) 2,3 c) 3,4 d) 4,5 e) 1,5

6. In bacteria, the cytoplasmic membrane functions in
   1. protein synthesis. 2. ribosome synthesis.
   3. generation of ATP. 4. transport of molecules.
   5. attachment.

   a) 1,2 b) 2,3 c) 3,4 d) 4,5 e) 1,5

7. Attachment is mediated by the
   1. capsule. 2. cell wall. 3. cytoplasmic membrane.
   4. periplasm. 5. pilus.

   a) 1,2 b) 2,3 c) 3,4 d) 4,5 e) 1,5

8. Endocytosis is associated with
   a) mitochondria. b) prokaryotic cells. c) eukaryotic cells.
   d) chloroplasts. e) ribosomes.

9. Protein synthesis is associated with
   1. lysosomes. 2. the cytoplasmic membrane.
   3. the Golgi apparatus. 4. rough endoplasmic reticulum.
   5. ribosomes.

   a) 1,2 b) 2,3 c) 3,4 d) 4,5 e) 1,5

10. All of the following are composed of tubulin, *except*:
    a) actin b) cilia c) flagella
    d) microtubules e) more than one of these

Applications

1. You are working in a pharmaceutical laboratory producing new antibiotics for human and veterinary use. One compound with potential value functions by inhibiting the action of prokaryotic ribosomes. The compound, however, was shown to inhibit the growth of animal cells in culture. What is one possible explanation for its effect on animal cells?
2. A research laboratory is investigating environmental factors that would inhibit the growth of *Archaea*. One question they have is if adding the antibiotic penicillin would be effective in controlling their growth. Explain the probable results of an experiment in which penicillin is added to a culture of *Archaea*.

Critical Thinking

1. This graph shows facilitated diffusion of a compound across a cytoplasmic membrane and into a cell. As the external concentration of the compound is increased, the rate of uptake increases until it reaches a point where it slows and then begins to plateau. This is not the case with passive diffusion, where the rate of uptake continually increases. Why does the rate of uptake slow and then eventually plateau with facilitated diffusion?

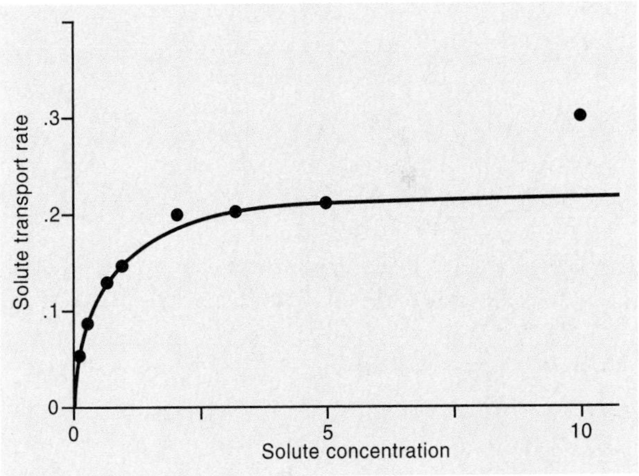

2. Most medically useful antibiotics interfere with either peptidoglycan synthesis or ribosome function. Why would the cytoplasmic membrane be a poor target for antibacterial medications?

Bacteria on an agar plate.

CHAPTER FOUR

Dynamics of Prokaryotic Growth

A Glimpse of History

The greatest contributor to methods of culturing bacteria was Robert Koch (1843–1910), a German physician who combined a medical practice with a productive research career for which he received a Nobel Prize in 1905. Koch was primarily interested in identifying disease-causing bacteria. To do this, however, he soon realized it was necessary to have simple methods to isolate and grow these particular species. He recognized that a single bacterial cell could multiply on a solid medium in a limited area and form a distinct visible mass of descendants.

Koch initially experimented with growing bacteria on the cut surfaces of potatoes, but he found that a lack of nutrients in the potatoes prevented growth of some species. To overcome this difficulty, Koch realized it would be advantageous to be able to solidify any liquid nutrient medium. Gelatin was used initially, but there were two major drawbacks—it melts at the temperature preferred by many medically important organisms and some bacteria can digest it. In 1882, Koch and others experimented with using agar. This solidifying agent was used to harden jelly at the time and proved to be the perfect answer.

Today, we take pure culture techniques for granted because of their relative ease and simplicity. Their development in the late 1800s, however, had a major impact on microbiology. Within 20 years, the agents causing most of the major bacterial diseases of humans were isolated and characterized.

Prokaryotes can be found growing even in the harshest climates and the most severe conditions. Environments that no unprotected human could survive, such as the ocean depths, volcanic vents, and the polar regions, have thriving species of prokaryotes. Indeed many scientists believe that if life exists on other planets, it may resemble these microorganisms. Each species, however, has a limited set of environmental conditions in which it can grow; even then, it will grow only if specific nutrients are available. Some prokaryotes can grow at temperatures above the boiling point of water but not at room temperature. Many species can only grow within an animal host, and then only in specific areas of that host.

Because of the medical significance of some bacteria, as well as the nutritional and industrial use of microbial by-products, microbiologists must be able to identify, isolate, and cultivate many species. To do this, one needs to understand the basic principles involved in prokaryotic growth while recognizing that a vast sea of information is yet to be discovered.

4.1 Principles of Prokaryotic Growth

Focus Point

- Describe binary fission and how it relates to generation time.

Prokaryotes generally multiply by the process of **binary fission (figure 4.1).** After a cell has increased in size and doubled all of its parts, it divides. One cell divides into two, those two divide to become four, those four become eight, and so on. In other words, the increase in cell numbers is exponential. Because it is neither practical, nor particularly relevant, to determine the relative size of the cells in a given population, **microbial growth** is defined as an increase in the number of cells in a population.

The time it takes for a population to double in number is the **generation** or **doubling time.** This varies greatly depending on the species of the organism and the conditions in which it is grown. Some common organisms, such as *Escherichia coli*, can double in approximately 20 minutes; others, such as the causative agent of tuberculosis, *Mycobacterium tuberculosis*, require at least 12 to 24 hours to double even under the most favorable conditions.

KEY TERMS

Biofilm Polysaccharide-encased community of microorganisms.

Chemically defined medium Bacteriological medium composed of precise mixtures of pure chemicals; generally used for specific experiments when nutrients must be precisely controlled.

Complex medium Bacteriological medium that contains protein digests, extracts, or other ingredients that vary in their chemical composition.

Differential medium Bacteriological medium that contains an ingredient which can be changed by certain bacteria in a recognizable way; used to differentiate organisms based on their metabolic traits.

Exponential (log) phase Stage of growth in which cells divide at a constant rate; generation time is measured during this period of active multiplication.

Facultative anaerobe Organism that grows best if O_2 is available, but can also grow without it.

Generation time The time it takes for a population to double in number.

Obligate aerobe Organism that requires molecular oxygen (O_2).

Obligate anaerobe Organism that cannot multiply, and is often killed, in the presence of O_2.

Plate count Method to measure the concentration of viable cells by determining the number of colonies that arise from a sample added to an agar plate.

Pure culture A population of organisms descended from a single cell and therefore separated from all other species.

Selective medium Bacteriological medium to which additional ingredients have been added that inhibit the growth of many organisms other than the one being sought.

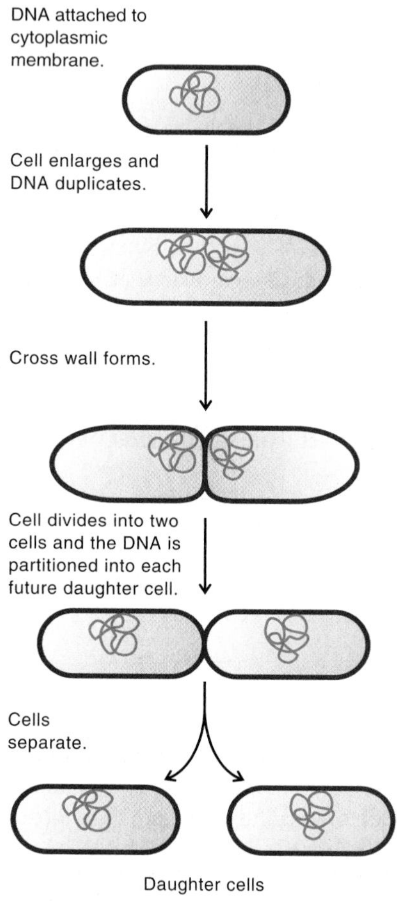

DNA attached to cytoplasmic membrane.
Cell enlarges and DNA duplicates.
Cross wall forms.
Cell divides into two cells and the DNA is partitioned into each future daughter cell.
Cells separate.
Daughter cells

FIGURE 4.1 Binary Fission The chromosomal DNA is attached to the cytoplasmic membrane. As the cell increases in length, the DNA is replicated and then partitioned into each of the two daughter cells.

The environmental and nutritional factors that affect the rate of growth will be discussed shortly.

The exponential multiplication of bacteria has important health consequences. For example, a mere 10 cells of a foodborne pathogen in a potato salad, sitting for 4 hours in the warm sun at a picnic, may multiply to more than 40,000 cells. A simple equation expresses the relationship between the number of cells in a population at a given time (N_t), the original number of cells in the population (N_0), and the number of divisions those cells have undergone during that time (n). If any two values are known, the third can be easily calculated from the equation:

$$N_t = N_0 \times 2^n$$

In this example, let us assume that we know that 10 cells of a disease-causing organism were initially added to the potato salad and we also know that the organism has a generation time of 20 minutes. The first step is to determine the number of cell divisions that will occur in a given time. Because the organism divides every 20 minutes, 3 times every hour, we know that in 4 hours it will divide 12 times. Now that we know the original number of cells and the number of divisions, we can solve for N_t:

$$10 \times 2^{12} = N_t = 40{,}960$$

Thus, after 4 hours the potato salad in the example will have 40,960 cells of our pathogen. Keep this in mind, and your potato salad in a cooler, the next time you go to a picnic!

MICROCHECK 4.1

Most prokaryotes multiply by binary fission. Microbial growth is an increase in the number of cells in a population. The time required for a population to double in number is the generation time.

- ✓ Explain why microbial growth refers to a population rather than a cell size.
- ✓ If a bacterium has a generation time of 30 minutes, and you start with 100 cells at time 0, how many cells will you have in 30, 60, 90, and 120 minutes?
- ✓ Why would placing potato salad in a cooler affect cell growth?

4.2

Bacterial Growth in Nature

Focus Points

- Describe a biofilm and give one positive and one negative impact that biofilms have on humans.
- Explain why bacteria that grow naturally in mixed communities sometimes cannot yet be grown in pure culture.

Historically, microorganisms have been studied by growing them in the laboratory, but scientists now recognize that the dynamic and complex conditions of the natural environment, which differ greatly from the conditions in the laboratory, have profound effects on microbial growth and behavior. When growing in a running stream, for example, prokaryotes frequently synthesize slime layers or other structures that allow them to attach to rocks or other solid surfaces. They may not produce these adherent structures when growing in the laboratory. In fact, research has shown that cells actually sense various surrounding chemicals and then respond by synthesizing compounds useful for growth in that particular environment. Cells can even grow in multicellular associations that function cooperatively to increase the chance of survival of the population as a whole. Only in the last decade have technologies been developed that allow scientists to study microorganisms in their natural environment. ■ slime layer, p. 66

Biofilms

In nature, prokaryotes can live suspended in an aqueous environment, but many attach to surfaces and live in polysaccharide-encased communities called **biofilms (figure 4.2).** Biofilms cause the slipperiness of rocks in a stream bed, the slimy "gunk" that coats kitchen drains, the scum that gradually accumulates in toilet bowls, and the dental plaque that forms on teeth. Biofilm formation begins when **planktonic,** or free-floating, bacteria adhere to a surface where they multiply and synthesize slime layers to which unrelated cells can attach and grow.

FIGURE 4.2 Biofilm on a Stainless Steel Surface A biofilm is a polysaccharide-encased community of microorganisms.

Surprisingly, biofilms are not generally haphazard mixtures of microbes in a layer of slime, but instead have characteristic architectures with open channels through which nutrients and waste materials can pass **(figure 4.3).** Cells communicate with one another by synthesizing and responding to chemical signals, an exchange that appears to be important in establishing structure. Cells move within the biofilm, often by pili-mediated twitching motility. ■ pili, p. 68 ■ twitching motility, p. 68

Biofilms are more than just an unsightly annoyance. Dental plaque leads to tooth decay and gum disease. Even troublesome persistent ear infections and the complications of cystic fibrosis are thought to be due to bacteria that grow as a biofilm. In fact, it is estimated that 65% of human bacterial infections involve biofilms. Treatment of these infections is difficult because microorganisms growing within the protective slime of a biofilm are often able to resist the effects of antibiotics, as well as the body's defenses. Biofilms are also important in industry, where their growth in pipes, drains, and cooling water towers can interfere with processes and damage equipment. Again, the structure of the biofilm shields the microbes growing within it, and bacteria in a biofilm may be hundreds of times more resistant to disinfectants than are their planktonic counterparts. ■ disinfectants, p. 112

While biofilms can be damaging, they also can be beneficial. Many **bioremediation** efforts, which use bacteria to degrade harmful chemicals, are enhanced by biofilms. Thus, as some industries are exploring ways to destroy biofilms, others, such as wastewater treatment facilities, are looking for ways to foster their development. ■ bioremediation, p. 790 ■ wastewater treatment, p. 780

Interactions of Mixed Microbial Communities

Prokaryotes in the environment regularly grow in close associations with many different species. Sometimes the interactions are cooperative, even fostering the growth of members that otherwise could not survive. For example, organisms that cannot multiply in the presence of O_2 can grow in the mouth. This is because other

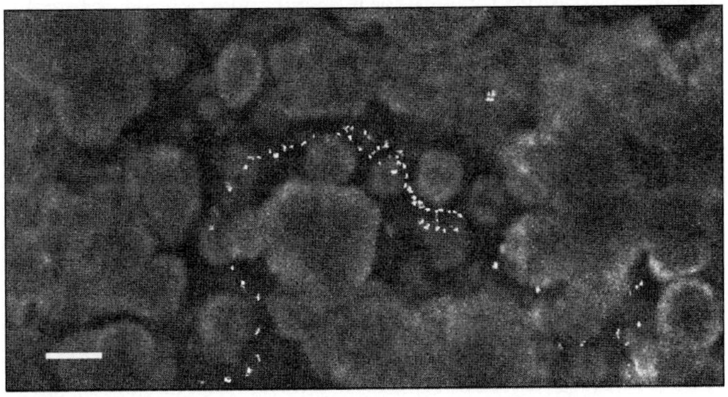

FIGURE 4.3 Architecture of a Biofilm Superimposed time sequence image shows a single latex bead moving through a biofilm water channel. The large light gray shapes are clusters of bacteria (scale bar = 50μm)

microbes found there consume O_2 during their metabolism, creating microenvironments that lack O_2. In addition, the metabolic wastes of one species may serve as a nutrient for another. Often, however, cells in these communities compete for nutrients, and some even resort to a type of biological warfare, synthesizing toxic compounds that inhibit competitors. Understandably, the conditions in these close associations are exceedingly difficult to reproduce in the laboratory. ■ microbial competition and antagonism, p. 761

MICROCHECK 4.2

Biofilms have a characteristic architecture with open channels through which nutrients and waste products can pass. In nature, prokaryotes often grow in close associations with many different species.

- ✓ Give three examples of biofilms.
- ✓ Describe a situation in which the activities of one species benefit another.
- ✓ Why would bacteria in a biofilm be more resistant to harmful chemicals?

4.3 Obtaining a Pure Culture

Focus Point

- Describe how the streak-plate method is used to obtain a pure culture, and how the resulting culture can be stored.

In the laboratory, prokaryotes are generally isolated and grown in **pure culture** in order to identify them and study the functions of a particular species. A pure culture is defined as a population of organisms descended from a single cell and therefore separated from all other species. Results obtained using pure cultures are much easier to interpret, but as discussed earlier, the organisms sometimes behave differently than they do in their natural environment. Another complicating issue is that only an estimated 1% of all prokaryotes can currently be cultured successfully. This makes it exceedingly difficult to study the vast majority of environmental microorganisms. Fortunately for humanity, most known medically significant bacteria can be grown in pure culture.

Pure cultures are obtained using a variety of special techniques. All glassware, media, and instruments must be **sterile,** or free of microbes, prior to use. These are then handled using **aseptic techniques,** which are procedures that minimize the chance of other organisms being accidentally introduced. The medium that the cells are grown in, or on, is a mixture of nutrients dissolved in water and may be in a liquid broth or a solidified gel-like form. The medium is called a **culture medium.** ■ aseptic techniques, p. 114 ■ sterilization, p. 112

Cultivating Bacteria on a Solid Culture Medium

The basic requirements for obtaining a pure culture are a solid culture medium, a media container that can be maintained in an aseptic condition, and a method to separate individual cells. A single bacterium, supplied with the right nutrients, will multiply on the solid medium in a limited area to form a **colony,** which is a mass of cells all descended from the original one **(figure 4.4).** About 1 million cells are required for a colony to be easily visible to the naked eye.

Agar, a polysaccharide extracted from marine algae, is used to solidify a liquid culture medium. Unlike other gelling agents such as gelatin, very few bacteria can degrade agar. It is not destroyed at high temperatures and can therefore be sterilized by heating, a process that also liquefies it. Melted agar will stay liquid until it is cooled to a temperature below 45°C. Therefore, nutrients that would be destroyed at high temperatures can be added at lower temperatures before the agar hardens. Once solidified, an agar medium will remain so until it is heated above 95°C. Thus, unlike gelatin, which is liquid at 37°C, agar remains solid over the entire temperature range at which the majority of bacteria grow. Agar is also translucent, enabling colonies embedded in the solid medium to be seen more easily. ■ polysaccharide, p. 32

The culture medium is contained in a **Petri dish** a two-part covered container made of glass or plastic. While not airtight, the Petri dish does exclude airborne microbial contaminants. A Petri dish containing a medium is commonly referred to as a plate of that medium type—for example, a nutrient agar plate or, more simply, an **agar plate.**

The Streak-Plate Method

The **streak-plate** method is the simplest and most commonly used technique for isolating bacteria **(figure 4.5).** A sterilized inoculating loop is dipped into a solution containing the organism of interest and is then lightly drawn several times across an agar plate, creating a set of parallel streaks covering approximately one-third of the plate. The loop is then sterilized and a new series of parallel streaks are made across and at an angle to the previous

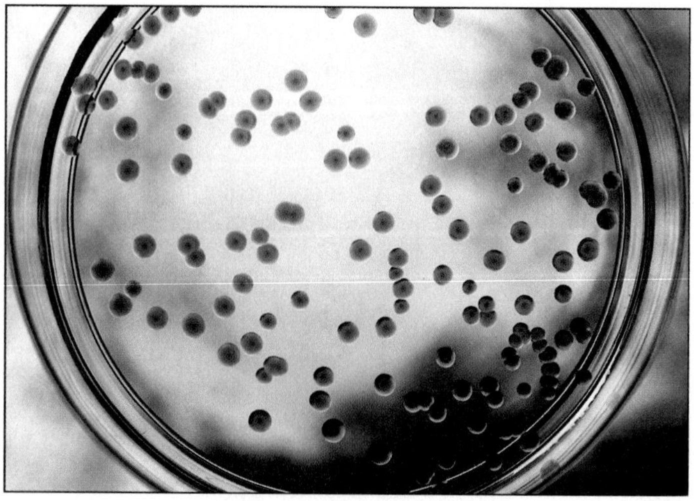

FIGURE 4.4 Colonies Growing on Agar Medium

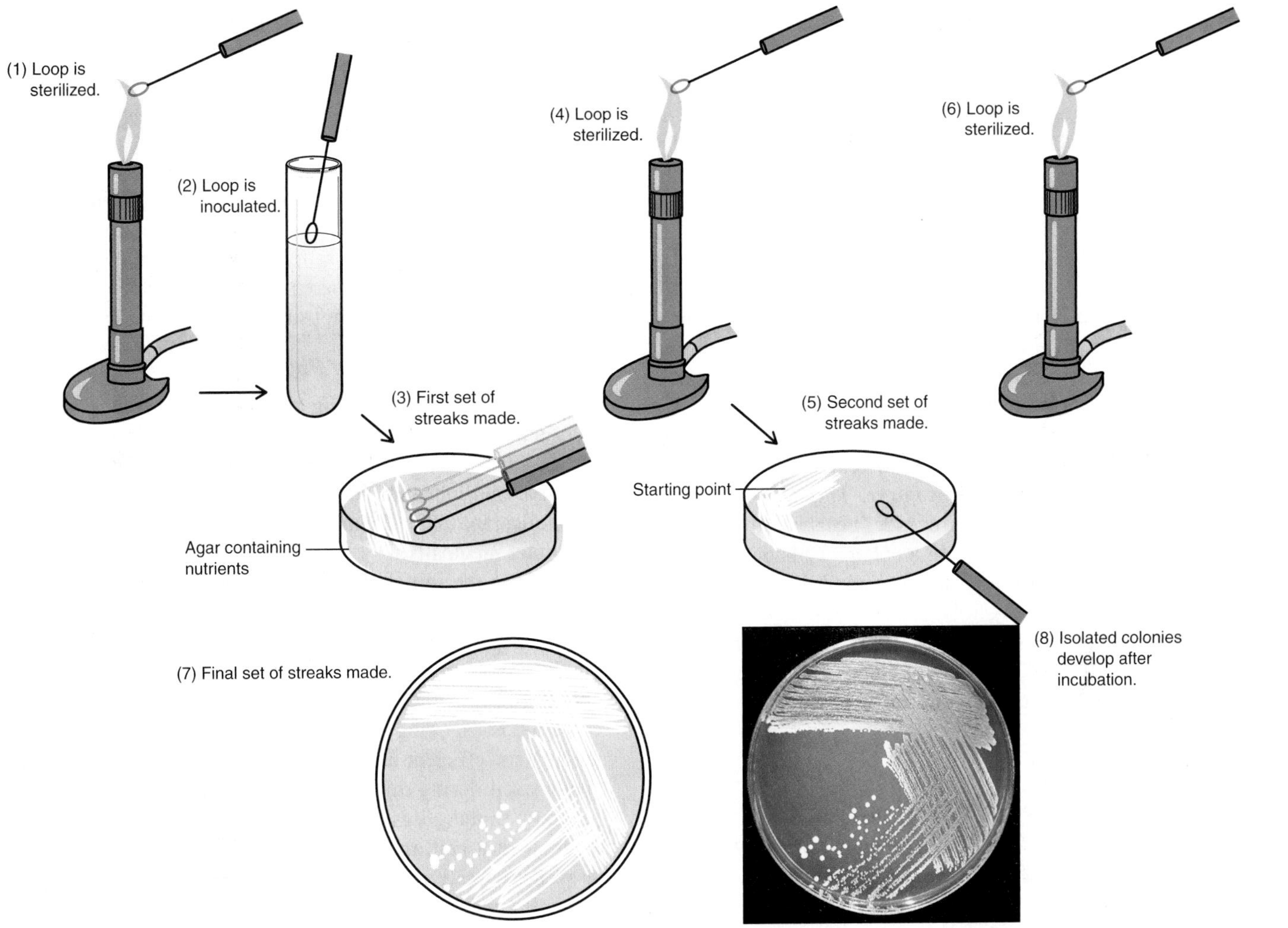

FIGURE 4.5 The Streak-Plate Method A sterilized inoculating loop **(1)** is dipped into a culture **(2)** and is then lightly drawn several times across an agar plate **(3).** The loop is sterilized again **(4),** and a new series of streaks is made at an angle to the first set **(5).** The loop is sterilized a final time **(6),** and another set of parallel streaks is made **(7).** The successive streaks dilute the concentration of cells. By the third set of streaks, cells should be separated enough so that isolated colonies develop after incubation **(8).**

ones, covering another third of the plate. This drags some of those cells streaked onto the first portion of the plate over to a previously uninoculated portion, creating a region containing a more dilute inoculum. The loop is sterilized again, and another set of parallel streaks are made, dragging into a third area some of the organisms that had been moved into the second section. The object is to reduce the number of cells being spread with each successive series of streaks, effectively diluting the sample. By the third set of streaks, cells should be separated enough so that distinct well-isolated colonies will form.

Maintaining Stock Cultures

Once a pure culture has been obtained, it can be maintained as a **stock culture,** a culture stored for use as an inoculum in later procedures. Often, stock cultures are stored in the refrigerator on an **agar slant.** This is agar medium in a tube that was held at a shallow angle as the medium solidified, creating a larger surface area. For long-term storage, stock cultures can be frozen at −70°C in a glycerol solution. The glycerol prevents ice crystals from damaging cells. Alternatively, cells can be **lyophilized,** or freeze-dried.

■ lyophilization, p. 127

MICROCHECK 4.3

Only an estimated 1% of prokaryotes can be cultured in the laboratory. Agar is used to solidify nutrient-containing broth. The streak-plate method is used to obtain a pure culture.

- ✓ What properties of agar make it ideal for use in bacteriological media?
- ✓ How does the streak-plate method separate individual cells?
- ✓ What might be a reason that medically significant bacteria can be grown in pure culture more often than environmental organisms?

4.4

Bacterial Growth in Laboratory Conditions

Focus Point

- Describe the five distinct stages of a growth curve, and compare this closed system to colony growth and continuous culture.

In the laboratory, bacteria are typically grown in broth contained in a tube or flask, or on an agar plate. These are considered **closed** or **batch systems** because nutrients are not renewed, nor are waste products removed. Under these conditions, the cell population increases in number in a predictable fashion and then eventually declines. As the population in a closed system grows, it follows a pattern of stages, called a **growth curve.** This growth pattern is most distinct in a shaken broth culture, because all cells are exposed to the same environment. In a colony, cells on the outer edge of a colony experience very different conditions from those at the center.

To maintain cells in a state of continuous growth, nutrients must be continuously added and waste products removed. This is called an **open system,** or **continuous culture.**

The Growth Curve

This growth curve is characterized by five distinct stages—the lag phase, the exponential or log phase, the stationary phase, the death phase, and the phase of prolonged decline **(figure 4.6).**

Lag Phase

When a culture of bacteria is diluted and then transferred into a different medium, the number of viable cells does not immediately increase. They go through a "tooling up" or **lag phase** prior to active multiplication. During this time they synthesize macromolecules required for multiplication, including enzymes, ribosomes, and nucleic acids, and they generate energy in the form of ATP.

The length of the lag phase depends on conditions in the original culture and the medium into which the bacteria are transferred. If cells are transferred from a nutrient rich medium to one containing fewer nutrients, the lag time tends to be longer. This is because cells must begin making enzymes to synthesize components missing in the new medium. A similar situation occurs when a stock culture stored in the refrigerator for several weeks is inoculated into fresh medium. In contrast, if young cells are transferred to a medium similar in composition, the lag time is quite short.

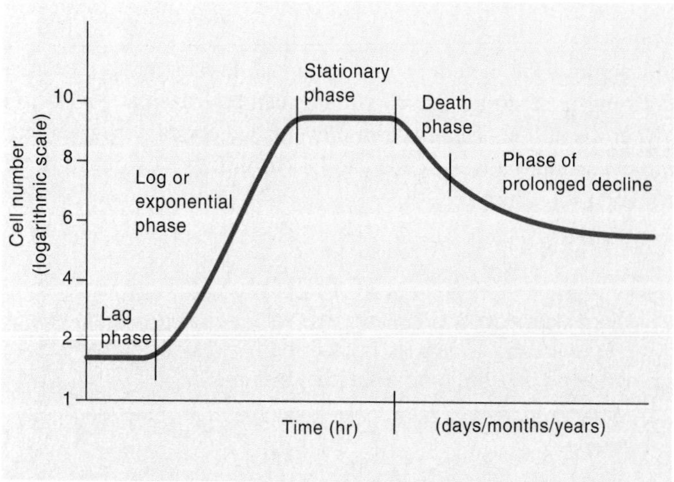

FIGURE 4.6 Growth Curve The growth curve is characterized by five distinct stages: lag phase, exponential or log phase, stationary phase, death phase, and phase of prolonged decline.

Exponential Phase (Log Phase)

During the **exponential** or **log phase** cells divide at a constant rate and their numbers increase by the same percentage during each time interval. The generation time is measured during this period of active multiplication. Because bacteria are most susceptible to antibiotics and other chemicals during this time, the log phase is important medically.

During the initial phase of exponential growth, all the cells' activities are directed toward increasing cell mass. Cells produce compounds such as amino acids and nucleotides, the respective building blocks of proteins and nucleic acids. Cells are remarkably precise in their ability to regulate the synthesis of these compounds, ensuring that each is made in the appropriate relative amount for efficient assembly into macromolecules. Compounds synthesized during this period of active multiplication are called **primary metabolites.** A metabolite is any product of a chemical reaction in a cell and includes compounds required for growth, as well as waste materials. Some primary metabolites are commercially valuable as flavoring agents and food supplements. Understandably, industries that harvest these compounds are working to develop methods to manipulate bacteria to overproduce certain primary metabolites. ■ regulation of gene expression, p. 182

Cells' activities shift as they enter a stage called **late log phase** which marks the transition to stationary phase. This change occurs in response to multiple factors that are inevitable in a closed system, such as depletion of nutrients and buildup of waste products. If the cells are able to form endospores, they initiate the process of sporulation. If they cannot, they still "hunker down" in preparation for the starvation conditions ahead. The cells become rounder in shape and more resistant to harmful chemicals and radiation. Changes in the composition of their cell walls and cytoplasmic membranes also occur. As their surrounding environment changes, cells begin synthesizing different enzymes and other proteins, which collectively give rise to a new group of metabolites, termed **secondary metabolites (figure 4.7).** Commercially, the most important secondary metabolites are antibiotics. These are produced by many members of the genus *Streptomyces*, and inhibit the growth of, or kill other organisms.

Stationary Phase

Cells enter the **stationary phase** when they have exhausted their supply of energy and nutrients. The total number of viable cells in the overall population remains relatively constant, but some cells are dying while others are multiplying. How can cells multiply when they have exhausted their supply of nutrients? Cells

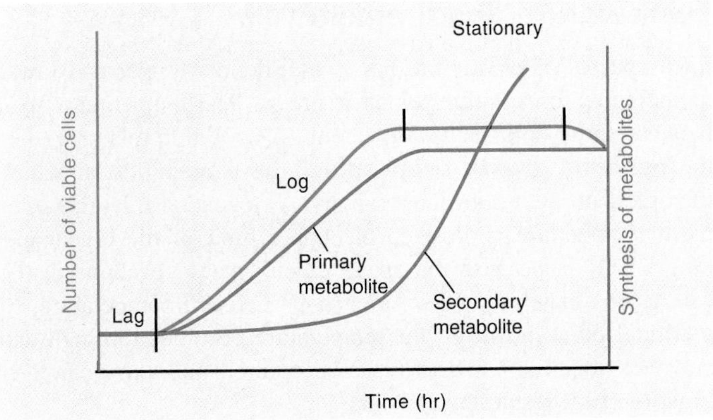

FIGURE 4.7 Primary and Secondary Metabolite Production Primary metabolites are synthesized during the period of active multiplication. Late in the log phase, cells begin synthesizing secondary metabolites. These compounds, which continue to be synthesized in stationary phase, appear to make the cells more resistant to environmental conditions.

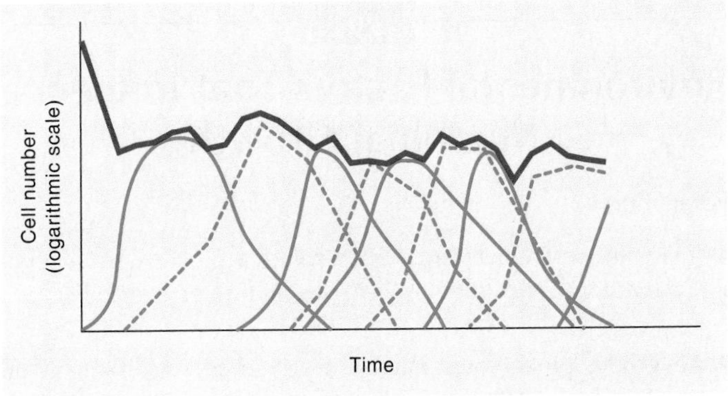

FIGURE 4.8 Dynamic Population Changes in the Phase of Prolonged Decline Many members of the population are dying and releasing their nutrients, while a few "fitter" cells are actively multiplying.

that die release peptides and nucleic acids, providing a source of nutrients and energy to fuel the growth of other cells. During the stationary phase, the viable cells continue to synthesize secondary metabolites and maintain the altered chemical properties they demonstrated in late log phase.

The length of time cells remain in the stationary phase varies depending on the species and on environmental conditions. Some populations remain in the stationary phase for only a few hours, whereas others remain for days.

Death Phase

The **death phase** is the period when the total number of viable cells in the population decreases as cells die off at a constant rate. Like bacterial growth, death is exponential. However, the cell population usually dies off much more slowly than it multiplies during the log phase. Once about 99% of the cells have died off, the remaining members of the population enter a different phase.

Phase of Prolonged Decline

The **phase of prolonged decline** is marked by a very gradual decrease in the number of viable cells in the population, lasting for days to years. Superficially, it might seem like a gradual march towards death of the population, but dynamic changes are actually occurring. Many members of the population are dying and releasing their nutrients, while a few "fitter" cells that are more able to cope with the deteriorating environmental conditions are actively multiplying. This dynamic process generates successive waves of slightly modified populations, each more fit to survive than the previous ones **(figure 4.8).** Thus, the statement "survival of the fittest" even holds true for closed cultures of bacteria.

Colony Growth

Growth of a bacterial colony on a solid medium involves many of the same features as bacteria growing in liquid, but it is marked by some important differences. After a lag phase, cells multiply exponentially and eventually compete with one another for available nutrients and become very crowded. Unlike a liquid culture, the position of a single cell within a colony markedly determines its environment. Cells multiplying on the edge of the colony face relatively little competition and can use O_2 in the air and obtain nutrients from the agar medium. In contrast, in the center of the colony the high density of cells rapidly depletes available O_2 and nutrients. Toxic metabolic wastes such as acids accumulate. As a consequence, cells at the edge of the colony may be growing exponentially, whereas those in the center may be in the death phase. Cells in locations between these two extremes may be in stationary phase.

Continuous Culture

Bacteria can be maintained in a state of continuous exponential growth by using a **chemostat.** This device continually drips fresh medium into a liquid culture contained in a growth chamber. With each drop that enters, an equivalent volume, containing cells, wastes, and spent medium, leaves through an outlet. By manipulating the concentration of nutrients in the medium and the rate at which it enters the growth chamber, a constant cell density and generation time of log phase cells can be maintained. This makes it possible to study a uniform population of cells over a long period of time. The effect of adding various supplements to the medium or altering the cellular environment on long-term cell growth can be determined.

MICROCHECK 4.4

When grown in a closed system, a population of bacteria goes through five distinct phases: lag, log, stationary, death, and prolonged decline. Cells within a colony may be in any one of the growth phases, depending on their relative location.

- ✓ Explain the difference between the two stages of the exponential phase.
- ✓ Describe how a chemostat keeps a culture in a continuous stage of growth.
- ✓ Why would bacteria be more susceptible to antibiotics during the log phase?

4.5

Environmental Factors That Influence Microbial Growth

Focus Point

- List the descriptive terms that express a prokaryote's requirements for temperature, oxygen, pH, and water availability.

As a group, prokaryotes inhabit nearly every environment on earth. Those we associate with disease and rapid food spoilage live in habitats that humans consider quite comfortable. Some prokaryotes, however, live in harsh environments that would kill most other organisms. Most of these, called **extremophiles** (*phile* means "loving"), are members of the Domain *Archaea*.

Recognizing the environmental factors that influence microbial growth—such as temperature, amount of oxygen, pH, and water availability—helps scientists study microorganisms in the laboratory and aids in understanding their role in the complex ecology of the planet. The major environmental conditions that influence the growth of microorganisms are summarized in **table 4.1.**

Temperature Requirements

Each species of prokaryote has a well-defined upper and lower temperature limit within which it grows. The temperature span between these limits is usually about 25°C. Within this range lies the **optimum growth temperature,** the temperature at which the organism multiplies most rapidly. As a general rule, this optimum temperature is close to the upper limit of the organism's range. This is because the speed of enzymatic reactions in the cell approximately doubles for each 10°C rise in temperature. At a critical point, however, the temperature becomes too high and enzymes required for growth are denatured and can no longer function. As a result, the cells die.

Prokaryotes are commonly divided into five groups based on their optimum growth temperatures **(figure 4.9).** Note, however, that this merely represents a convenient organization scheme. In reality, there is no sharp dividing line between each group. Furthermore, not every organism in a group can grow in the entire temperature range typical for its group.

- **Psychrophiles** have their optimum between –5°C and 15°C. These organisms are usually found in such environments as the Arctic and Antarctic regions and in lakes fed by glaciers.

TABLE 4.1 Environmental Factors That Influence Microbial Growth

Environmental Factor/ Descriptive Terms	Characteristics
Temperature	Thermostability appears to be due to protein structure.
Psychrophile	Optimum temperature between –5°C and 15°C
Psychrotroph	Optimum temperature between 20°C and 30°C, but grows well at lower temperatures.
Mesophile	Optimum temperature between 25°C and 45°C.
Thermophile	Optimum temperature between 45°C and 70°C.
Hyperthermophile	Optimum temperature of 70°C or greater.
Oxygen (O_2) Availability	Oxygen (O_2) requirement/tolerance reflects the organism's energy-converting mechanisms (aerobic respiration, anaerobic respiration, and fermentation) and its ability to detoxify O_2 derivatives.
Obligate aerobe	Requires O_2.
Obligate anaerobe	Cannot multiply in the presence of O_2.
Facultative anaerobe	Grows best if O_2 is present, but can also grow without it.
Microaerophile	Requires small amounts of O_2, but higher concentrations are inhibitory.
Aerotolerant anaerobe (obligate fermenter)	Indifferent to O_2.
pH	Prokaryotes that live in pH extremes appear to maintain a near neutral internal pH by pumping protons out of or into the cell.
Neutrophile	Multiplies in the range of pH 5 to 8.
Acidophile	Grows optimally at a pH below 5.5.
Alkalophile	Grows optimally at a pH above 8.5.
Water Availability	Prokaryotes that can grow in high solute solutions maintain the availability of water in the cell by increasing their internal solute concentration.
Osmotolerant	Can grow in relatively high salt solutions, up to approximately 10% NaCl.
Halophile	Requires high levels of sodium chloride.

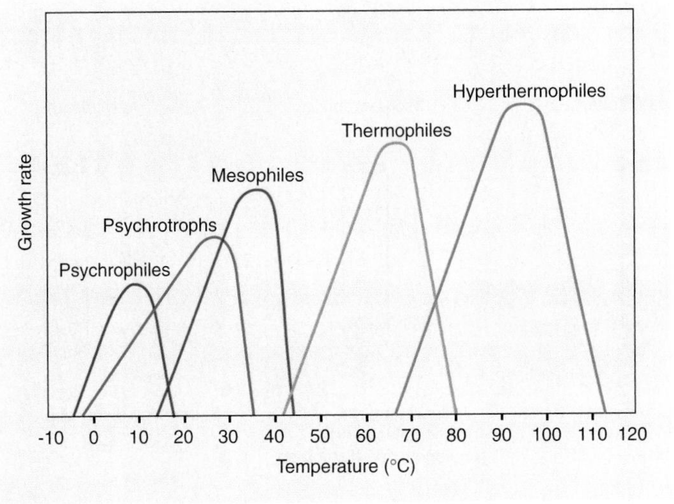

FIGURE 4.9 Temperature Requirements for Growth Prokaryotes are commonly divided into five groups based on their optimum growth temperatures. This graph depicts the typical temperature ranges of these groups. Note that the optimum temperature, the point at which the growth rate is highest, is near the upper limit of the range.

- **Psychrotrophs** have a temperature optimum between 20°C and 30°C, but grow well at lower temperatures. They are an important cause of food spoilage. ■ food spoilage, p. 805
- **Mesophiles** which include *E. coli* and most other common bacteria, have their optimum temperature between 25°C and about 45°C. Disease-causing bacteria, which are adapted to growth in the human body, typically have an optimum between 35°C and 40°C. Mesophiles that inhabit soil, a colder environment, generally have a lower optimum, close to 30°C.
- **Thermophiles** have an optimum temperature between 45°C and 70°C. These organisms commonly occur in hot springs and compost heaps. They also are found in artificially created thermal environments such as water heaters and nuclear power plant cooling towers. ■ composting, p. 789
- **Hyperthermophiles** have an optimum growth temperature of 70°C or greater. These are usually members of the *Archaea*. One member, isolated from the wall of a hydrothermal vent deep in the ocean, has a maximum growth temperature of 121°C, the highest yet recorded.

Why can some prokaryotes withstand such high temperatures but most cannot? As a general rule, proteins from thermophiles are not denatured at high temperatures. This thermostability is due to the sequence of the amino acids in the protein. This controls the number and position of the bonds that form within the protein, which in turn determines its three-dimensional structure. For example, the formation of many covalent bonds, as well as many hydrogen and other weak bonds, prevents denaturation of proteins. Heat-stable enzymes that degrade fats and other proteins are being used in high-temperature detergents. ■ protein denaturation, p. 30

Temperature and Food Preservation

Storage of fruits, vegetables, and cheeses at refrigeration temperatures (approximately 4°C) retards food spoilage because it limits the growth of otherwise fast-growing mesophiles. Psychrophiles and psychrotrophs, however, can still multiply and consequently spoilage will still occur, albeit more slowly. Because of this, foods and other perishable products that can withstand below-freezing temperatures should be frozen for long-term storage. Microorganisms, which require liquid water to grow, cannot multiply under these conditions. It is important to recognize, however, that freezing is not an effective means of destroying microbes. Recall that freezing is routinely used to preserve stock cultures. ■ low-temperature storage, p. 126 ■ food spoilage, p. 805

Temperature and Disease

Significant variations exist in the temperature of various parts of the human body. Although the heart, brain, and gastrointestinal tract are near 37°C, the temperature of the extremities may be much lower. For these reasons, some microorganisms can cause disease in certain body parts but not in others. For example, Hansen's disease (leprosy) typically involves the coolest regions of the body (ears, hands, feet, and fingers) because the causative organism, *Mycobacterium leprae*, grows best at these lower temperatures. The same situation applies to syphilis, in which lesions appear on the genitalia and then on the lips, tongue, and throat. Indeed, for more than 30 years the major treatment of syphilis was to induce fever by deliberately introducing the agent that causes malaria, which induces very high fevers. ■ Hansen's disease, p. 688 ■ syphilis, p. 664

Oxygen (O_2) Requirements

The oxygen (O_2) level in different environments varies greatly, providing many different habitats with respect to its availability. Gaseous oxygen accounts for about 20% of the earth's atmosphere. Beneath the surface of soil and in swamps, however, very limited amounts, if any, may be available. The human body alone provides many different habitats. While the surface of the skin is exposed to the atmosphere, the stomach and intestines are **anaerobic,** or contain no O_2.

Like humans, some bacteria have an absolute requirement for O_2. Others thrive in anaerobic environments, and many of these are killed if O_2 is present. The O_2 requirements of some organisms can be determined by growing them in **shake tubes.** To prepare a shake tube, a tube of nutrient agar is boiled, which both melts the agar and drives off the O_2. The agar is then allowed to cool to 50°C. Next, the test organism is added and dispersed by gentle shaking or swirling. The agar is allowed to harden and the tube is incubated at an appropriate temperature. Because the solidified agar impedes the diffusion of O_2, the level of O_2 in the tube is stratified—O_2 levels are high at the top, whereas the bottom portion is anaerobic. The bacteria grow in the region that has the level of O_2 that suits their requirements **(table 4.2).**

Based on their O_2 requirements, prokaryotes can be separated into these groups:

- **Obligate aerobes** have an absolute or obligate requirement for oxygen (O_2). They use it to transform energy in the

TABLE 4.2 Oxygen (O_2) Requirements of Prokaryotes

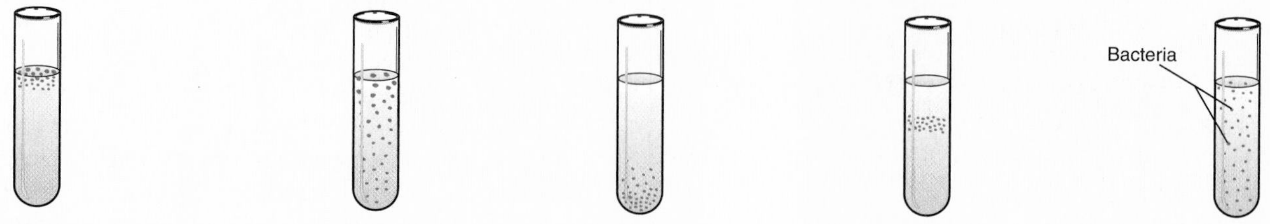

Obligate aerobe	Facultative anaerobe	Obligate anaerobe	Microaerophile	Aerotolerant
Enzymes in Cells for O_2 Detoxification Catalase: $2H_2O_2 \rightarrow 2H_2O + O_2$ Superoxide dismutase: $2O_2^- + 2H^+ \rightarrow O_2 + H_2O_2$	Catalase, superoxide dismutase	Neither catalase nor superoxide dismutase in most	Small amounts of catalase and superoxide dismutase	Superoxide dismutase

process of aerobic respiration. This and other ATP-generating pathways will be discussed in detail in chapter 6. Obligate aerobes include *Micrococcus* species, Gram-positive cocci that are common in the environment. ■ aerobic respiration, pp. 137, 150 ■ ATP, p. 26

- **Obligate anaerobes** cannot multiply if any O_2 is present; in fact, they are often killed in environments that have even traces of O_2 because of its toxic derivatives, which will be discussed shortly. Obligate anaerobes transform energy by fermentation or anaerobic respiration; the details of these processes will be discussed in chapter 6. Obligate anaerobes include members of the genus *Bacteroides* (the major inhabitants of the large intestine), *Clostridium botulinum* (the causative agent of botulism), and many others. In fact, it is estimated that one-half of all the cytoplasm on earth is in anaerobic bacteria! ■ fermentation, pp. 138, 152 ■ anaerobic respiration, pp. 137, 151
- **Facultative anaerobes** grow better if O_2 is present, but can also grow without it. The term facultative means that the organism is flexible, in this case in its requirements for O_2. Facultative anaerobes use aerobic respiration if oxygen is available, but use fermentation or anaerobic respiration in its absence. Growth is more rapid when oxygen is present because aerobic respiration yields the most ATP of all these processes. Examples of facultative anaerobes include *E. coli,* a common inhabitant of the large intestine, and the yeast *Saccharomyces* (a eukaryote), which is used to make bread and alcoholic beverages.
- **Microaerophiles** require small amounts of O_2 (2% to 10%) for aerobic respiration; higher concentrations are inhibitory. Examples include *Spirillum volutans,* which is common in aquatic habitats, and *Helicobacter pylori,* which causes gastric and duodenal ulcers.
- **Aerotolerant anaerobes** are indifferent to O_2. They can grow in its presence, but they do not use it to transform energy. Because they do not use aerobic or anaerobic respiration, they are also called **obligate fermenters**. An example is *Streptococcus pyogenes,* which causes strep throat.

Toxic Derivatives of Oxygen (O_2)

Although not toxic itself, O_2 can be converted into a number of compounds that are highly toxic. Some of these, such as **superoxide** (O_2^-), are produced both as a part of normal metabolic processes and as chemical reactions involving oxygen and light. Others, such as **hydrogen peroxide** (H_2O_2), result from metabolic processes involving oxygen. To survive in an environment containing O_2, cells must have enzymes that can convert these toxic compounds to non-toxic forms. The enzyme **superoxide dismutase** degrades superoxide to produce hydrogen peroxide. **Catalase** breaks down hydrogen peroxide to H_2O and O_2. Together, these two enzymes detoxify these reactive products of O_2.

Although most strict anaerobes do not have superoxide dismutase, some do, while a few aerobes lack it. Therefore, other unknown factors must also be playing a role in protecting organisms from the toxic forms of oxygen.

pH

Each bacterial species can survive within a range of pH values; within this range is its pH optimum. Despite the pH of the external environment, cells maintain a constant internal pH, typically near neutral. ■ pH, p. 25

Most bacteria can live and multiply within the range of pH 5 (acidic) to pH 8 (basic) and have a pH optimum near neutral (pH 7). These bacteria are called **neutrophiles.** Preservation methods that acidify foods, such as pickling, are intended to inhibit these organisms. Surprisingly, some neutrophiles have adapted special mechanisms that enable them to grow at a very low pH. For example, *Helicobacter pylori* grows in the stomach, where it can cause ulcers. To maintain the pH close to neutral in its immediate surroundings, *H. pylori* produces the enzyme **urease,** which splits urea in the stomach into carbon dioxide and ammonia. The ammonia neutralizes the stomach acid in the bacterium's immediate surroundings. ■ pickling, p. 800

Acidophiles grow optimally at a pH below 5.5. For example, *Thiobacillus ferroxidans,* a member of the *Bacteria,* grows best at a pH of approximately 2. This bacterium obtains its energy by oxidizing sulfur compounds, producing sulfuric acid in the process. It maintains its internal pH near neutral by pumping out protons (H^+) as quickly as they enter the cell. *Picrophilus oshimae*, a member of the *Archaea*, has an optimum pH of less than 1! This prokaryote, which was isolated from the dry, acid soils of a gas-emitting volcanic fissure in Japan, has an unusual cytoplasmic membrane that is unstable at a pH above 4.0.

Alkalophiles grow optimally at a pH above 8.5. For instance, *Bacillus alcalophilus* grows best at pH 10.5. It appears alkalophiles maintain a relatively neutral internal pH by exchanging internal sodium ions for external protons. Alkalophiles often live in alkaline lakes and soils.

Water Availability

All microorganisms require water for growth. Even if water is present, however, it may not be available in certain environments. For example, dissolved substances such as salt (NaCl) and sugars interact with water molecules and make the water unavailable to the cell. In any environment, particularly in certain natural habitats such as salt marshes, prokaryotes are faced with this situation. If the solute concentration is higher in the medium than in the cell, water diffuses out of the cell due to osmosis. This causes the cytoplasm to dehydrate and shrink from the cell wall, a phenomenon called **plasmolysis (figure 4.10).** ■ solute p. 57 ■ osmosis, p. 57

Prokaryotes able to live in high salt environments maintain the availability of water in the cell by increasing their internal solute concentration. For example, some bacteria synthesize certain small organic compounds such as the amino acid proline that have no detrimental effect on normal cellular activity. ■ proline, p. 28

Bacteria that can tolerate high salt concentrations, up to approximately 10% NaCl, are called **osmotolerant.** *Staphylococcus* species, which reside on the dry salty environment of the skin, are an example. Organisms that require high levels of sodium chloride to grow are called **halophiles** (*halo* means "salt"). Many marine bacteria are mildly halophilic, requiring concentrations of approximately 3% sodium chloride. Certain members of the *Archaea* are **extreme halophiles,** requiring 9% sodium chloride or more; some can even grow in saturated salt solutions. Extreme halophiles are found in environments such as the salt flats of Utah and the Dead Sea.

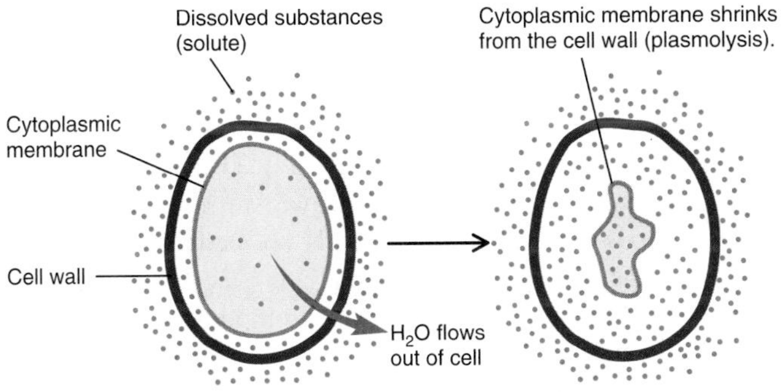

FIGURE 4.10 Effects of Solute Concentration on Cells The cytoplasmic membrane allows water molecules to pass through freely. If the solute concentration is higher outside of the cell, water moves out. The dehydrated cytoplasm shrinks from the cell wall, a process called plasmolysis.

The growth-inhibiting effect of high concentrations of salt and sugars is used in food preservation. High levels of salt are added to preserve such foods as bacon, salt pork, and anchovies. High concentrations of sugars can also inhibit the growth of bacteria. Many foods with a high sugar content, such as jams, jellies, honey, preserves, and sweetened condensed milk, are naturally preserved. ■ drying of foods, p. 127

MICROCHECK 4.5

A prokaryotic species can be grouped according to its optimum growth temperature. A species can also be grouped according to its oxygen requirements. Most species grow best near neutral pH, although some prefer acidic conditions and others grow best in alkaline conditions. All organisms require water for growth, but halophiles grow best in high-salt conditions.

- ✓ Describe four environmental factors that influence the growth of bacteria.
- ✓ List the categories into which bacteria can be classified according to their requirements for oxygen.
- ✓ Why would small organic compounds affect the water content of cells?

4.6

Nutritional Factors That Influence Microbial Growth

Focus Points

- Give an example of a bacterium that is fastidious.
- Define the terms *photoautotroph, chemolithoautotroph, photoheterotroph,* and *chemoorganoheterotroph.*

Growth of any prokaryote depends not only on a suitable physical environment, but also an available source of chemicals to use as nutrients. From these, the cell must synthesize all of the cell components discussed in chapter 3, including lipid membranes, cell walls, proteins, and nucleic acids. These components are made from building blocks such as fatty acids, sugars, amino acids, and nucleotides. In turn, each of these building blocks is composed of a variety of elements, including carbon and nitrogen. What sets the prokaryotic world apart from all other forms of life is their remarkable ability to use diverse sources of these elements. For example, prokaryotes are the only organisms able to use atmospheric nitrogen (N_2) as a nitrogen source.

Required Elements

Elements that make up cell constituents are called **major elements.** These include carbon, oxygen, hydrogen, nitrogen, sulfur, phosphorus, potassium, magnesium, calcium, and iron. They are the essential components of proteins, carbohydrates, lipids, and nucleic acids **(table 4.3).** ■ elements, p. 19

PERSPECTIVE 4.1

Can Prokaryotes Live on Only Rocks and Water?

Prokaryotes have been isolated from diverse environments that previously were thought to be incapable of sustaining life. For example, members of the *Archaea* have been isolated from environments 10 times more acidic than that of lemon juice. Other *Archaea* have been isolated from oil wells a mile below the surface of the earth at temperatures of 70°C and pressures of 160 atmospheres (at sea level, the pressure is 1 atmosphere). The isolation of these organisms suggests that thermophiles may be widespread in the earth's crust.

Perhaps the most unusual environment from which prokaryotes have been isolated are the volcanic rocks 1 mile below the earth's surface near the Columbia River in Washington State. What do these organisms use for food? They apparently get their energy from hydrogen gas that is produced chemically in a reaction between the iron-rich minerals in the rock and the groundwater. The groundwater also contains dissolved CO_2, which the bacteria can use as a source of carbon. Thus, these bacteria apparently exist on nothing more than rocks and water.

The source of carbon, the most abundant of the major elements, distinguishes different groups of prokaryotes. Those that use organic carbon are called **heterotrophs** (*hetero* means "different" and *troph* means "nourishment"). Medically important bacteria are typically heterotrophs, using organic carbon sources such as glucose. **Autotrophs** (*auto* means "self") use inorganic carbon in the form of carbon dioxide. They play a critical role in the cycling of carbon in the environment because they can convert inorganic carbon (CO_2) to an organic form, the process of **carbon fixation.** Without carbon fixation, the earth would quickly run out of organic carbon, which is essential to humans and other animals. ■ carbon cycle, p. 767

In addition to carbon, organisms require that the other major elements be supplied; often these are provided as organic salts. For example, ammonium sulfate supplies both nitrogen and sulfur. Some prokaryotes can convert inorganic nitrogen gas (N_2) to ammonia, the process of **nitrogen fixation.** Like carbon fixation, this process is essential to life on this planet. ■ nitrogen cycling, p. 769

Some elements, termed **trace elements,** are required in very minute amounts by all cells. They include cobalt, zinc, copper, molybdenum, and manganese. These elements form parts of enzymes or may be required for enzyme function. Very small amounts of these trace elements are found in most natural environments, including water.

TABLE 4.3 Representative Functions of the Major Elements

Chemical	Function
Carbon, oxygen, and hydrogen	Component of cellular constituents including amino acids, lipids, nucleic acids, and sugars.
Nitrogen	Component of amino acids and nucleic acids.
Sulfur	Component of some amino acids.
Phosphorus	Component of nucleic acids, membrane lipids, and ATP.
Potassium, magnesium, and calcium	Required for the functioning of certain enzymes; additional functions as well.
Iron	Part of certain enzymes.

Growth Factors

Some bacteria cannot synthesize some of their cell constitutents, such as amino acids, vitamins, purines, and pyrimidines, from the major elements. Consequently, these organisms can only grow in environments that contain these compounds. Low molecular weight compounds that must be provided to a particular bacterium are called **growth factors.** ■ purines, p. 34 ■ pyrimidines, p. 34

Microorganisms display a wide spectrum in their growth factor requirements, reflecting differences in their biosynthetic capabilities. For example, *E. coli* is quite versatile and does not require any growth factors. It grows in a medium containing only glucose and six different inorganic salts. In contrast, species of *Neisseria* require at least 40 additional ingredients, including 7 vitamins and all of the 20 amino acids. Bacteria such as *Neisseria* that require many growth factors are called **fastidious.**

Fastidious bacteria are exploited to determine the quantity of specific vitamins in food products. To do this, a well-characterized species of *Lactobacillus* is grown in a medium that lacks a specific vitamin, but has been supplemented with a measured amount of the food product. The amount of growth of the bacterium is related to the amount of test vitamin in the product.

Energy Sources

Organisms derive energy either from sunlight or by metabolizing chemical compounds. These processes will be discussed in chapter 6. Organisms that harvest the energy of sunlight are called **phototrophs** (*photo* means "light"). These include plants, algae, and photosynthetic bacteria. Organisms that obtain energy by metabolizing chemical compounds are called **chemotrophs** (*chemo* means "chemical"). Mammalian cells, fungi, and many types of bacteria metabolize organic compounds such as sugars, amino acids, and fatty acids. Some prokaryotes can extract energy from seemingly unlikely sources such as hydrogen sulfide, hydrogen gas, and other inorganic compounds, an ability that distinguishes them from eukaryotes.

TABLE 4.4 Energy and Carbon Sources Used by Different Groups of Prokaryotes

Type	Energy Source	Carbon Source
Photoautotroph	Sunlight	CO_2
Photoheterotroph	Sunlight	Organic compounds
Chemolithoautotroph	Inorganic chemicals (H_2, NH_3, NO_2^-, Fe^{2+}, H_2S)	CO_2
Chemoorganoheterotroph	Organic compounds (sugars, amino acids, etc.)	Organic compounds

Nutritional Diversity

Microbiologists often group prokaryotes according to the energy and carbon sources they utilize **(table 4.4)**:

- **Photoautotrophs** use the energy of sunlight and the carbon in the atmosphere to make organic compounds. These are eventually consumed by other organisms, including humans. Because of this, photoautotrophs are called **primary producers.** Cyanobacteria are important examples that inhabit both freshwater and saltwater environments. Many can fix nitrogen, providing another indispensable role in the biosphere.
- **Chemolithoautotrophs** (*lith* means "stone"), commonly referred to simply as **chemoautotrophs** or **chemolithotrophs,** use inorganic compounds for energy and derive their carbon from CO_2. These prokaryotes live in seemingly inhospitable environments such as sulfur hot springs, which are rich in reduced inorganic compounds such as hydrogen sulfide. In some regions of the ocean depths, hydrothermal vents have been discovered. Here, chemoautotrophs serve as the primary producers, supporting rich communities of life in these habitats utterly devoid of sunlight (see figure 30.11). ■ **hydrothermal vents, p. 771**
- **Photoheterotrophs** use the energy of sunlight and derive their carbon from organic compounds. Some are facultative in their nutritional capabilities. For example, some members of a group of bacteria called the purple nonsulfur bacteria can grow anaerobically using light as an energy source and organic compounds as a carbon source (photoheterotrophs). They can also grow aerobically in the dark using organic sources of carbon and energy (chemoheterotrophs). ■ **purple nonsulfur bacteria, p. 273**
- **Chemoorganoheterotrophs,** commonly referred to as **chemoheterotrophs** or **chemoorganotrophs** use organic compounds for energy and as a carbon source. They are by far the most common group associated with humans and other animals. Individual species of chemoheterotrophs differ in the number of organic compounds they can use. For example, certain members of the genus *Pseudomonas* can derive carbon and/or energy from more than 80 different organic compounds, including such unusual compounds as naphthalene (the ingredient associated with the smell of mothballs). At the other extreme, some organisms can degrade only a few compounds. For example, *Bacillus fastidiosus* can use only urea and certain of its derivatives as a source of both carbon and energy.

MICROCHECK 4.6

Organisms require a source of major and trace elements. Heterotrophs use an organic carbon source, and autotrophs use CO_2. Phototrophs harvest the energy of sunlight, and chemotrophs obtain energy by degrading chemicals.

✓ List the major elements other than carbon required for growth of bacteria.

✓ What is the carbon source of a photoautotroph? Of a chemoautotroph?

✓ Why would human-made materials (such as plastics) be degraded only slowly or not at all?

4.7 Cultivating Prokaryotes in the Laboratory

Focus Points

- Compare and contrast complex, chemically defined, selective, and differential media.
- Explain how the correct atmospheric conditions are provided to cultivate obligate aerobes, capnophiles, microaerophiles, and obligate anaerobes.
- Describe the purpose of an enrichment culture.

By knowing the environmental and nutritional factors that influence growth of specific prokaryotes, it is often possible to provide appropriate conditions for their cultivation. These include a medium on which to grow the organisms and a suitable atmosphere.

General Categories of Culture Media

Considering the diversity of bacteria, it is not surprising that a wide variety of media is used to culture them. For routine purposes, one of the many types of **complex media** is used. In contrast, **chemically defined media** are generally used for specific research experiments

TABLE 4.5 Characteristics of Representative Media Used to Cultivate Bacteria

Medium	Characteristic
Blood agar	Complex medium used routinely in clinical labs. Not selective. Differential because colonies of hemolytic organisms are surrounded by a zone of clearing of the red blood cells.
Chocolate agar	Complex medium used to culture fastidious bacteria, particularly those found in clinical specimens. Not selective or differential.
Glucose-salts	Chemically defined medium. Used in laboratory experiments to study nutritional requirements of bacteria. Not selective or differential.
MacConkey agar	Complex medium used to isolate Gram-negative rods that typically reside in the intestine. Selective because bile salts and dyes inhibit Gram-positive organisms and Gram-negative cocci. Differential because the pH indicator turns pink-red when the sugar in the medium, lactose, is fermented.
Nutrient agar	Complex medium used for routine laboratory work. Supports the growth of a variety of nonfastidious bacteria.
Thayer-Martin	Complex medium used to isolate *Neisseria* species, which are fastidious. Selective—contains antibiotics that inhibit most organisms except *Neisseria* species.

when nutrients must be precisely controlled. **Table 4.5** summarizes the characteristics of various types of media.

Complex Media

A **complex medium** contains a variety of ingredients such as meat juices and digested proteins, making what might be viewed as a tasty soup for microbes. Although a specific amount of each ingredient is in the medium, the exact chemical composition of these can be highly variable. One common ingredient is **peptone.** This is protein taken from any of a variety of sources that has been hydrolyzed to amino acids and short peptides by treatment with enzymes, acids, or alkali. **Extracts** which are the water-soluble components of a substance, are also common ingredients. For example, beef extract is a water extract of lean meat and provides vitamins, minerals, and other nutrients. A commonly used complex medium, **nutrient broth** consists of only 5 grams of peptone and 3 grams of beef extract per liter of distilled water. If agar is added, then **nutrient agar** results.

Many medically important bacteria are fastidious, requiring a medium that is even richer than nutrient agar. One rich medium commonly used in clinical laboratories is **blood agar.** This contains red blood cells, which supply a variety of nutrients including hemin, in addition to other ingredients. A medium used to culture even more fastidious bacteria is **chocolate agar,** named for its appearance rather than the ingredients. Chocolate agar contains lysed red blood cells and additional nutrients.

Additional ingredients are often incorporated into complex media to counteract compounds that may be toxic to some exquisitely sensitive bacteria. For example, cornstarch is included in some types of media used to culture *Neisseria* species because it binds fatty acids, which can be toxic to these organisms.

Several biological supply companies manufacture hundreds of different types of media, each one specially formulated to permit the plentiful growth of one or several groups of organisms. Even with the availability of all of these different media, however, many organisms, including *Treponema pallidum*, the spirochete that causes syphilis, have yet to be successfully grown on culture media. ■ **syphilis, p. 664**

Chemically Defined Media

Chemically defined media are composed of precise amounts of pure chemicals. This type of medium is generally not practical for use in most routine laboratory work, but is invaluable when studying nutritional requirements of bacteria. **Glucose-salts**, which supports the growth of *E. coli*, contains only those chemicals listed in **table 4.6.** More elaborate recipes containing as many as 46 different ingredients can be used to make chemically defined media that support the growth of fastidious bacteria such as *Neisseria gonorrhoeae*, the organism that causes gonorrhea. ■ **gonorrhea, p. 661**

To maintain the pH near neutrality, buffers are often added to the medium. They are usually important in a defined medium because some bacteria produce so much acid as a by-product of their metabolism that they inhibit their own growth. This typically is not as much of a problem in complex media because the amino acids and other natural components provide at least some buffering function. ■ **buffer, p. 25**

TABLE 4.6 Ingredients in Two Representative Types of Media that Support the Growth of *E. coli*

Nutrient Broth (complex medium)	Glucose-Salts (defined medium)
Peptone	Glucose
Meat extract	Dipotassium phosphate
Water	Monopotassium phosphate
	Magnesium sulfate
	Ammonium sulfate
	Calcium chloride
	Iron sulfate
	Water

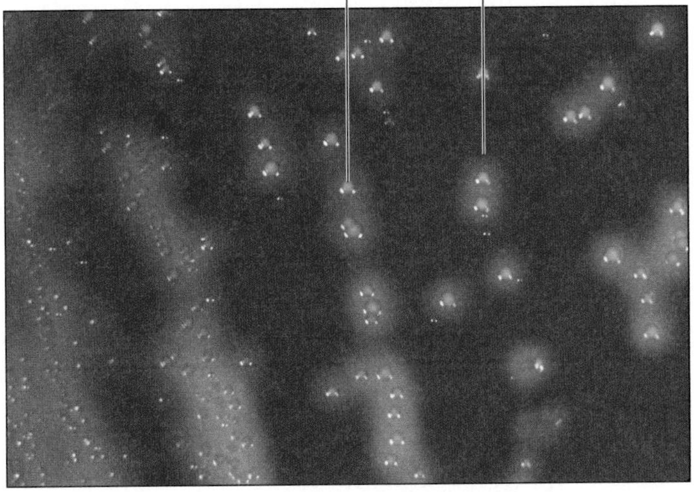

(a)

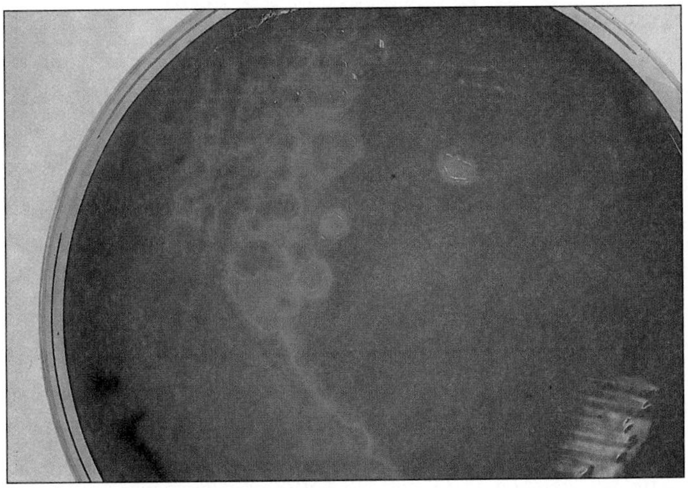

(b)

FIGURE 4.11 Blood Agar This complex medium is differential for hemolysis. **(a)** A zone of complete clearing around a colony growing on blood agar is called beta hemolysis. **(b)** A zone of greenish clearing is called alpha hemolysis.

Special Types of Culture Media

To detect or isolate an organism that is part of a mixed bacterial population, it is often necessary to make it more prevalent or more obvious. For these purposes **selective** and **differential media** are used. These can be either complex or chemically defined, depending on the needs of the microbiologist.

Selective Media

Selective media inhibit the growth of organisms other than the one being sought. For example, **Thayer-Martin agar** is used to isolate *Neisseria gonorrhoeae* from clinical specimens. This is chocolate agar to which three or more antimicrobial drugs have been added. The antimicrobials inhibit fungi, Gram-positive bacteria, and Gram-negative rods. Because these drugs do not inhibit most strains of *N. gonorrhoeae*, they allow those strains to grow with little competition from other organisms.

MacConkey agar is used to isolate Gram-negative rods that typically reside in the intestine from various clinical specimens such as urine. This complex medium contains, in addition to peptones and other nutrients, two inhibitory compounds: crystal violet, a dye, inhibits Gram-positive bacteria, and bile salts inhibit most non-intestinal bacteria.

Differential Media

Differential media contain a substance that certain bacteria change in a recognizable way. For example, blood agar, in addition to being nutritious, is differential; it is used to detect bacteria that produce a **hemolysin,** which lyses red blood cells **(figure 4.11).** The lysis appears as a zone of clearing around the colony growing on the blood agar plate. The type of hemolysis is used as an identifying characteristic. For example, species of *Streptococcus* that reside harmlessly in the throat often cause a type of hemolysis called **alpha hemolysis,** characterized by a zone of greenish clearing around the colonies. In contrast, *Streptococcus pyogenes*, which causes strep throat, causes **beta hemolysis,** characterized by a clear zone of hemolysis. Still other bacteria have no effect on red blood cells. ■*Streptococcus pyogenes, p. 577*

MacConkey agar, which is selective, is also differential **(figure 4.12).** In addition to containing peptones and other nutrients, it has lactose and a pH indicator. Bacteria that ferment the sugar produce acid, which turns the pH indicator pink. Thus, *E. coli* and other lactose-fermenting bacteria growing on MacConkey agar form pink colonies. Lactose-negative bacteria form tan or colorless colonies. ■ lactose, p. 32

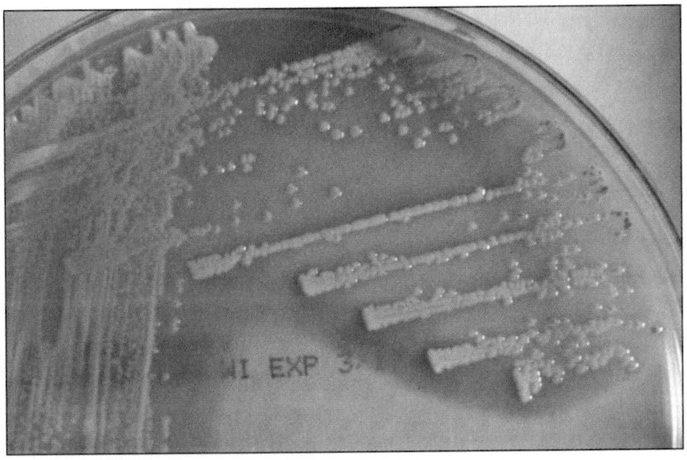

FIGURE 4.12 MacConkey Agar This complex medium is differential for lactose fermentation and selective for Gram-negative rods that typically reside in the intestine. Bacteria that ferment the sugar produce acid, which turns the pH indicator pink, resulting in pink colonies. Lactose-negative colonies are tan or colorless. The bile salts and dyes in the media inhibit all but certain Gram-negative rods.

Providing Appropriate Atmospheric Conditions

To cultivate bacteria in the laboratory, appropriate atmospheric conditions must be provided. For instance, broth cultures of obligate aerobes grow best when tubes or flasks containing the media are shaken, providing maximum aeration. Special methods create atmospheric environments such as increased CO_2, microaerophilic, and anaerobic conditions.

Increased CO_2

Providing an environment with increased levels of CO_2 enhances the growth of many medically important bacteria, including species of *Neisseria* and *Haemophilus*. Organisms requiring increased CO_2, along with approximately 15% oxygen, are called **capnophiles.** One of the simplest ways to provide this atmosphere is to incubate them in a closed **candle jar.** A lit candle in the jar consumes some of the O_2 in the air, generating CO_2 and H_2O; it soon extinguishes because of insufficient oxygen. Although a candle jar atmosphere contains about 3.5% CO_2, enough O_2 remains to support the growth of obligate aerobes and prevents growth of obligate anaerobes. Special incubators are also available that maintain CO_2 at prescribed levels.

Microaerophilic

Microaerophilic bacteria typically require O_2 concentrations less than what is achieved in a candle jar. Therefore, these bacteria are often incubated in a gastight jar with a special disposable packet containing chemicals that react to generate hydrogen and carbon dioxide. A catalyst in the jar speeds up the reaction of hydrogen with atmospheric oxygen to form water. The amount of hydrogen generated, however, is not enough to combine with all of the O_2, so that conditions do not become anaerobic.

Anaerobic

Cultivation of obligate anaerobes presents a great challenge to the microbiologist, because the cells may be killed if they are exposed to O_2 for even a short time. Obviously, special techniques to exclude O_2 are required.

Anaerobes that can tolerate a brief exposure to O_2 are cultivated in an **anaerobe jar (figure 4.13).** This is the same type of jar used to incubate microaerophiles, but the chemical composition of the disposable packet converts all the atmospheric oxygen to water.

Another method to cultivate anaerobes incorporates **reducing agents** into the culture medium. These react with O_2 and thus eliminate dissolved O_2; they include sodium thioglycollate, cysteine, and ascorbic acid. In some cases, immediately before the bacteria are inoculated, the medium is boiled to drive out dissolved O_2. Media that employ reducing agents frequently contain an O_2-indicating dye such as methylene blue.

A more stringent method for working with anaerobes is to use an anaerobic chamber, an enclosed compartment that can be maintained as an anaerobic environment **(figure 4.14).** A special port, which can be filled with an inert gas, is used to add or remove items. Airtight gloves enable researchers to handle items within the chamber.

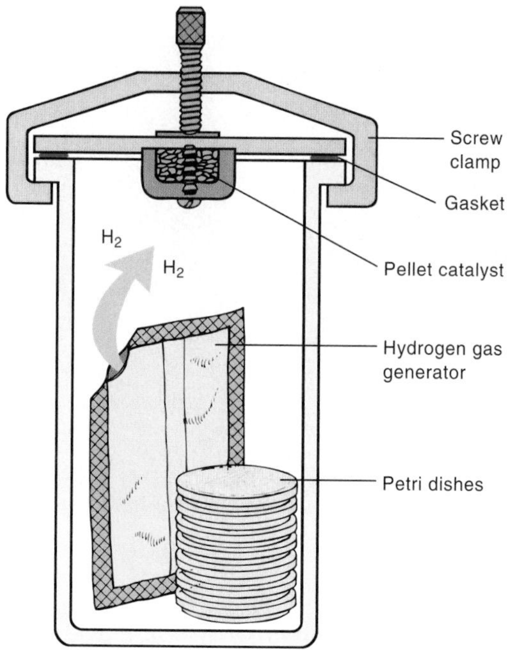

FIGURE 4.13 Anaerobe Jar The hydrogen released from the generator combines with any O_2 to form water, thereby producing an anaerobic environment.

Enrichment Cultures

An **enrichment culture** provides conditions in a broth that preferentially enhance the growth of one particular species in a mixed population **(figure 4.15).** This is helpful in isolating an organism from natural sources when the bacterium of interest is present in relatively small numbers. For example, if an organism is present at a concentration of only 1 cell/ml and it is outnumbered 10,000-fold by other organisms, isolating it using the streak-plate method would be difficult, even if a selective medium were used.

To enrich for a species, a sample such as pond water is placed into a liquid medium that favors the growth of the desired organism over others. For example, if the target organism can grow using atmospheric

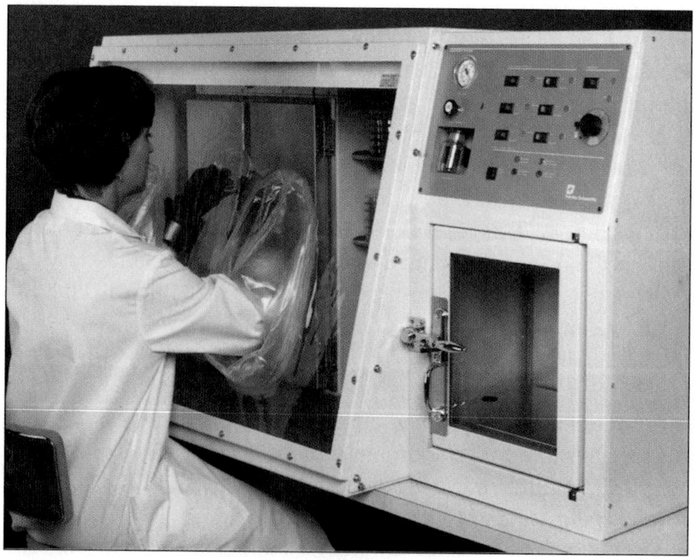

FIGURE 4.14 Anaerobic Chamber The enclosed compartment can be maintained as an anaerobic environment. A special port (visible on the right side of this device), which can be filled with inert gas, is used to add or remove items. The airtight gloves enable the researcher to handle items within the chamber.

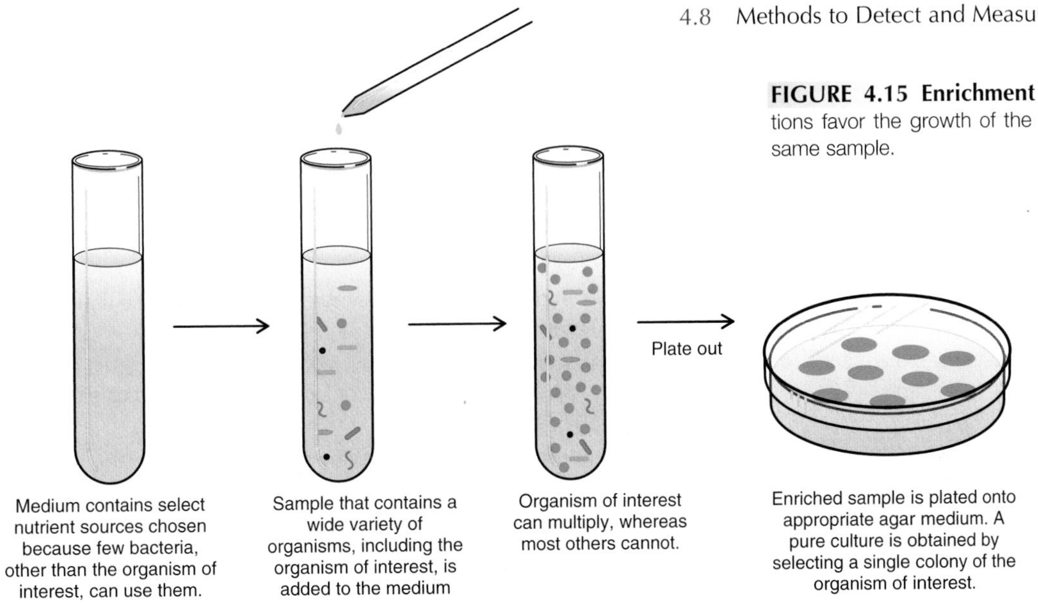

Plate out
Medium contains select nutrient sources chosen because few bacteria, other than the organism of interest, can use them.
Sample that contains a wide variety of organisms, including the organism of interest, is added to the medium
Organism of interest can multiply, whereas most others cannot.
Enriched sample is plated onto appropriate agar medium. A pure culture is obtained by selecting a single colony of the organism of interest.

FIGURE 4.15 Enrichment Culture Medium and incubation conditions favor the growth of the desired species over other bacteria in the same sample.

nitrogen as a source of nitrogen, then nitrogen is left out of the medium. If it can use an unusual carbon source such as phenol, then that is added as the only carbon source. In some cases selective agents such as bile are added: the procedure is then referred to as a **selective enrichment.** The culture is incubated under temperature and atmospheric conditions that preferentially promote the growth of the desired organism. During this time, the relative concentration of a microorganism that initially made up only a minor fraction of the population can increase dramatically. A pure culture can then be obtained by streaking the enrichment onto an appropriate agar medium and selecting a single colony.

MICROCHECK 4.7

Culture media can be either complex or chemically defined. Some media contain additional ingredients that make them selective or differential. Appropriate atmospheric conditions must be provided to isolate microaerophiles and anaerobes. An enrichment culture increases the relative concentration of an organism growing in a broth.

- ✓ Distinguish between a selective medium and a differential medium.
- ✓ Describe two methods used to create anaerobic conditions.
- ✓ Would bacteria that cannot utilize lactose be able to grow on MacConkey agar?

4.8 Methods to Detect and Measure Bacterial Growth

Focus Point

- Compare and contrast direct cell counts, viable cell counts, measuring biomass, and detecting cell products to measure bacterial growth.

A variety of techniques are available to monitor bacterial growth, either by determining the number of cells in the population or their total mass, or by detecting their products. The choice depends on various characteristics of the sample and the goals of the measurements. Characteristics of the common methods for measuring bacterial growth are summarized in **table 4.7.**

Direct Cell Counts

Direct cell counts are particularly useful for determining the total numbers of bacteria in a specimen, including those that cannot be grown in culture. Unfortunately, they generally do not distinguish between living and dead cells.

Direct Microscopic Count

One of the most rapid methods of determining the number of cells in a suspension is the direct microscopic count. The number of cells in a measured volume of liquid is counted using special glass slides, **counting chambers,** that hold a known volume of liquid (**figure 4.16).** These can be viewed under the light microscope, and the number of cells can be counted precisely. At least 10 million bacteria

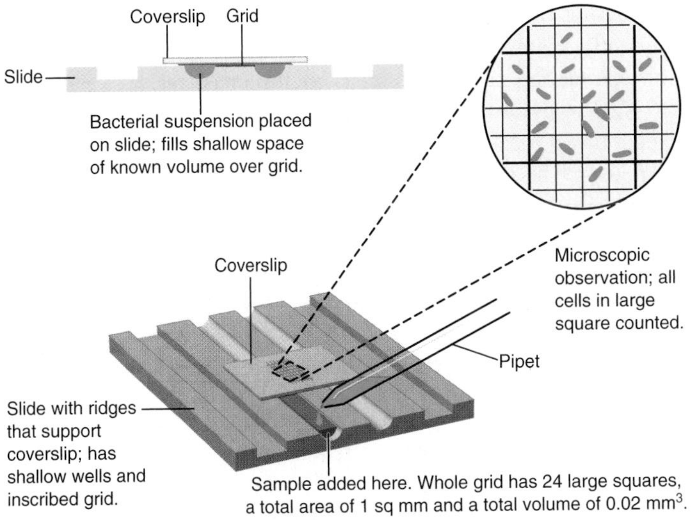

Bacterial suspension placed on slide; fills shallow space of known volume over grid.

Slide with ridges that support coverslip; has shallow wells and inscribed grid.
Sample added here. Whole grid has 24 large squares, a total area of 1 sq mm and a total volume of 0.02 mm3.

FIGURE 4.16 A Counting Chamber This special glass slide holds a known volume of liquid. The number of bacteria in that volume can be counted precisely.

TABLE 4.7 Methods Used to Measure Bacterial Growth

Method	Characteristics and Limitations
Direct Cell Counts	Used to determine total number of cells; counts include living and dead cells.
Direct microscopic count	Rapid, but at least 10^7 cells/ml must be present to be effectively counted.
Cell-counting instruments	Coulter counters and flow cytometers count total cells in dilute solutions. Flow cytometers can also be used to count organisms to which fluorescent dyes or tags have been attached.
Viable Cell Counts	Used to determine the number of viable bacteria in a sample, but that number only includes those that can grow in given conditions. Requires an incubation period of approximately 24 hours or longer. Selective and differential media can be used to enumerate specific species of bacteria.
Plate count	Time-consuming but technically simple method that does not require sophisticated equipment. Generally used only if the sample has at least 10^2 cells/ml.
Membrane filtration	Concentrates bacteria by filtration before they are plated; thus can be used to count cells in dilute environments.
Most probable number	Statistical estimation of likely cell number, it is not a precise measurement. Can be used to estimate numbers of bacteria in relatively dilute solutions.
Measuring Biomass	Biomass can be correlated to cell number.
Turbidity	Very rapid method; used routinely. A one-time correlation with plate counts is required in order to use turbidity for determining cell number.
Total weight	Tedious and time-consuming; however, it is one of the best methods for measuring the growth of filamentous microorganisms.
Chemical constituents	Uses chemical means to determine the amount of a given element, usually nitrogen. Not routinely used.
Measuring Cell Products	Methods are rapid but results must be correlated to cell number. Frequently used to detect growth, but not routinely used for quantitation.
Acid	Titration can be used to quantify acid production. A pH indicator is often used to detect growth.
Gases	Carbon dioxide can be detected by using a molecule that fluoresces when the medium becomes slightly more acidic. Gases can be trapped in an inverted Durham tube in a tube of broth.
ATP	Firefly luciferase catalyzes light-emitting reaction when ATP is present.

(10^7) per milliliter, however, are required to gain an accurate estimate. Otherwise, few, if any, cells will be seen in the microscope field.

Cell-Counting Instruments

A **Coulter counter** is an electronic instrument that counts cells in a suspension as they pass single file through a minute aperture **(figure 4.17).** The suspending liquid must be saline or another conducting fluid, because the machine actually detects and subsequently counts brief changes in resistance that occur when non-conducting particles such as bacteria pass by.

A **flow cytometer** is similar in principle to a Coulter counter except that it measures the scattering of light by cells as they pass by a laser. The instrument can be used to count either total cells or, by using special techniques, a specific population. This is done by first staining cells with a fluorescent dye or tag that binds only to the cells of interest; the flow cytometer then counts those cells that carry the fluorescent marker. ■ **fluorescent dyes and tags, p. 52**

Viable Cell Counts

Viable cell counts are used to quantify the number of cells capable of multiplying. These methods require knowledge of appropriate growth conditions for a particular microorganism as well as the time to allow growth to occur. By using selective and differential media, a particular species of bacteria can sometimes be enumerated. Viable cell counts are invaluable for monitoring bacterial growth in

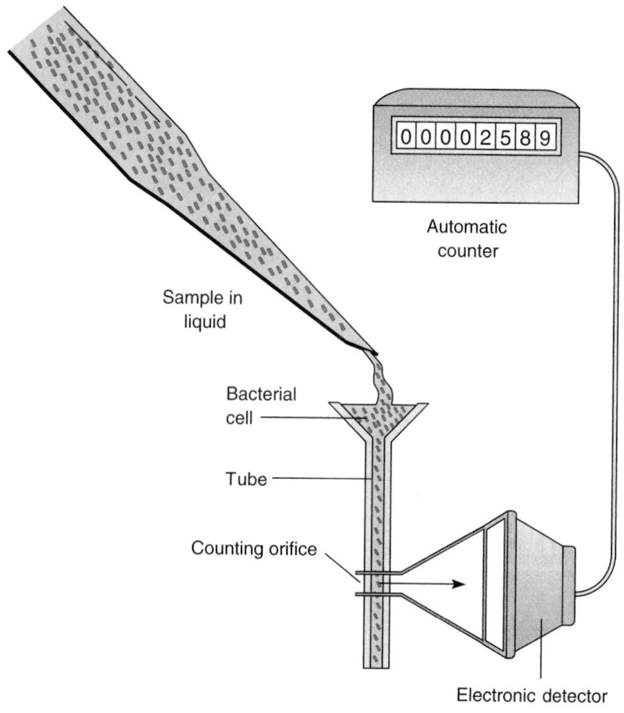

FIGURE 4.17 A Coulter Counter This instrument counts cells as they pass through a minute aperture. The bacteria, which are suspended in a conducting liquid, cause a brief change in resistance as they pass by the counter.

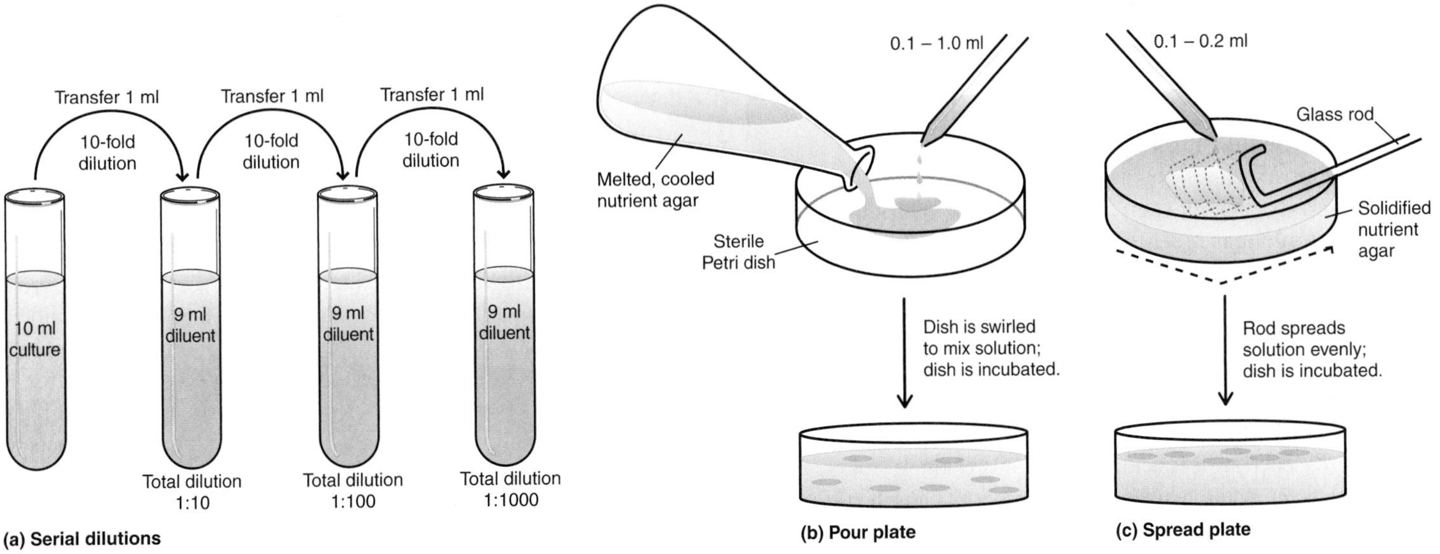

FIGURE 4.18 Plate Counts **(a)** A sample is first diluted in 10-fold increments. **(b)** In the pour-plate method, 0.1–1.0 ml of a dilution is transferred to a sterile Petri dish and mixed with melted, cooled nutrient agar. When the agar hardens, the plate is incubated and distinguishable colonies form on the surface and within the agar. **(c)** In the spread-plate method, 0.1–0.2 ml of a dilution is spread on a hardened agar plate with a sterile glass rod. After incubation, distinguishable colonies form only on the surface of the agar.

samples such as food and water that often contain numbers too low to be seen using a direct microscopic count.

Plate Counts

Plate counts measure the number of viable cells in a sample by exploiting the fact that an isolated cell on a nutrient agar plate will give rise to one colony. A simple count of the colonies determines how many cells were in the initial sample **(figure 4.18).** As the ideal number of colonies to count is between 30 and 300, and samples frequently contain many more bacteria than this, it is usually necessary to dilute the samples before plating the cells. The sample is normally diluted in 10-fold increments, making the resulting math relatively simple. The **diluent,** or sterile solution used to make the dilutions, is generally physiological saline (0.85% NaCl in water). Distilled water can be used, but some bacteria may lyse in this hypotonic environment.

In the **pour-plate** method, 0.1 to 1.0 ml of the final dilution is transferred into a sterile Petri dish and then overlaid with melted nutrient agar that has been cooled to 50°C. At this temperature, agar is still liquid. The dish is then gently swirled to mix the bacteria with the liquid agar. When the agar hardens, the individual cells are fixed in place and, after incubation, form distinguishable colonies.

In the **spread-plate** method, 0.1 to 0.2 ml of the final dilution is transferred directly onto a plate already containing a solidified nutrient agar medium. This solution is then spread over the surface of the agar with a sterilized bent glass rod, which resembles a miniature hockey stick.

In both methods the plates are then incubated for a specific time period to allow the colonies to form, which can then be counted. By knowing how much the sample was diluted prior to being plated, along with the amount of the dilution used in plating, the concentration of viable cells in the original sample can then be calculated. Cells attached to one another form a single colony and are counted as a single cell or **colony-forming unit.**

Pour plates and spread plates are generally only used if a sample contains more than 100 organisms/ml. Otherwise, few if any cells will be transferred to the plates. In these situations, alternative methods give more reliable results.

Membrane Filtration

Membrane filtration is used when the numbers of organisms in a sample are relatively low, as might occur in dilute environments such as natural waters. This method concentrates the bacteria by filtration before they are plated. A known volume of liquid is passed through a sterile membrane filter, which has a pore size that retains bacteria **(figure 4.19).** The filter is subsequently placed on an appropriate agar

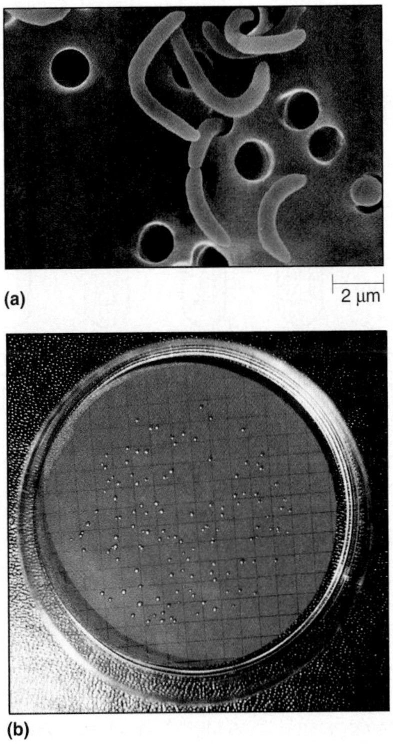

FIGURE 4.19 Membrane Filtration This technique concentrates bacteria before they are plated. **(a)** A known volume of liquid is passed through a sterile membrane filter, which has a pore size that retains bacteria. **(b)** The filter is then placed on an appropriate agar medium and incubated. The number of colonies that grow on the filter indicates the number of bacteria that were in the volume filtered.

medium and then incubated. The number of colonies that grow on the filter indicates the number of bacteria in the volume filtered.

Most Probable Number (MPN)

The **most probable number (MPN)** method is a statistical assay of cell numbers based on the theory of probability. The goal is to successively dilute a sample and determine the point at which subsequent dilutions receive no cells.

To determine the MPN, three sets of three or five tubes containing the same growth medium are prepared **(figure 4.20).** Each set receives a measured amount of a sample such as water, soil, or food. The amount added is determined, in part, by the expected bacterial concentration in that sample. What is important is that the second set receives 10-fold less than the first, and the third set 100-fold less. In other words, each set is inoculated with an amount 10-fold less than the previous set. After incubation, the presence or absence of growth in each tube in each set is noted; in some cases, growth along with a characteristic visible change such as gas production is noted. The results are then compared against an MPN table, which gives a statistical estimate of the cell concentration. The MPN method is most commonly used to determine the approximate number of **coliforms** in a water sample. Coliforms are lactose-fermenting, Gram-negative rods that typically reside in the intestine and thus serve as a bacterial indicator of fecal contamination. ■ coliforms, p. 787

Measuring Biomass

Instead of measuring the number of cells, the cell mass can be determined. This can be done by measuring the turbidity, the total weight, or the precise amount of chemical constituents such as nitrogen. These all relate to the number of cells present.

Turbidity

Cloudiness or **turbidity** of a bacterial suspension such as a broth culture is due to the scattering of light passing through the liquid by cells **(figure 4.21).** The amount scattered is proportional to the concentration of cells. To measure turbidity, a **spectrophotometer** is used. This instrument transmits light through a specimen and measures the percentage that reaches a light detector. That number is inversely proportional to the optical density. To use turbidity to estimate cell numbers, a one-time correlation between optical density and cell concentration for the specific organism under study must be made. Once this correlation has been determined, the turbidity measurement becomes a rapid and relatively accurate assay.

One limitation of assaying turbidity is that a medium must contain relatively high numbers of bacteria in order to be cloudy. One milliliter of a solution containing 1 million bacteria (10^6) is still perfectly clear, and if it contains 10 million cells (10^7), it is barely turbid. Thus, although a turbid culture indicates that bacteria are

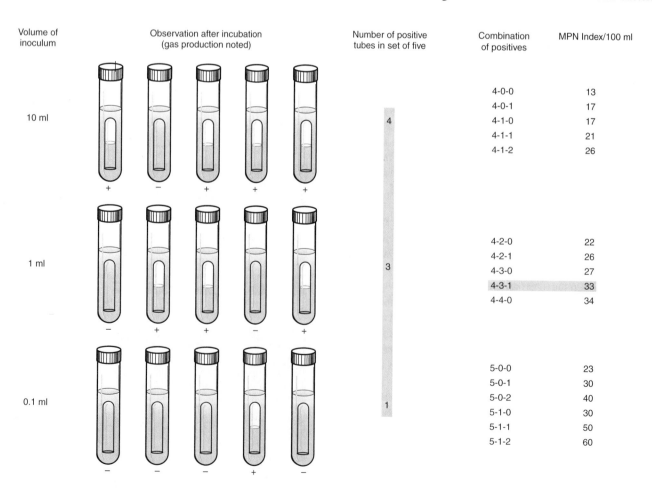

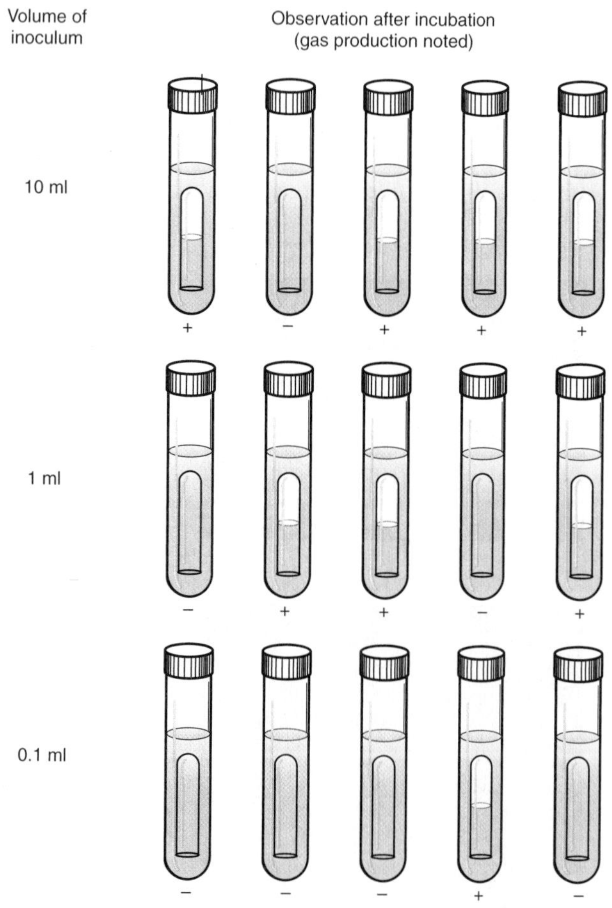

Number of positive tubes in set of five	Combination of positives	MPN Index/100 ml
4	4-0-0	13
	4-0-1	17
	4-1-0	17
	4-1-1	21
	4-1-2	26
3	4-2-0	22
	4-2-1	26
	4-3-0	27
	4-3-1	33
	4-4-0	34
1	5-0-0	23
	5-0-1	30
	5-0-2	40
	5-1-0	30
	5-1-1	50
	5-1-2	60

FIGURE 4.20 The Most Probable Number (MPN) Method Three sets of three or five tubes containing the same growth medium are prepared. Each set receives a measured amount of a sample; each set receives an amount 10-fold less than the first. After incubation the presence or absence of growth in each tube is noted. The results are then compared to an MPN table, which gives a statistical estimate of cell concentration.

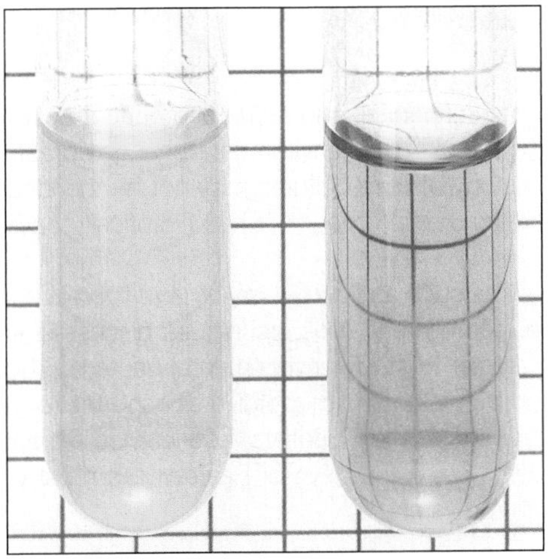

(a)

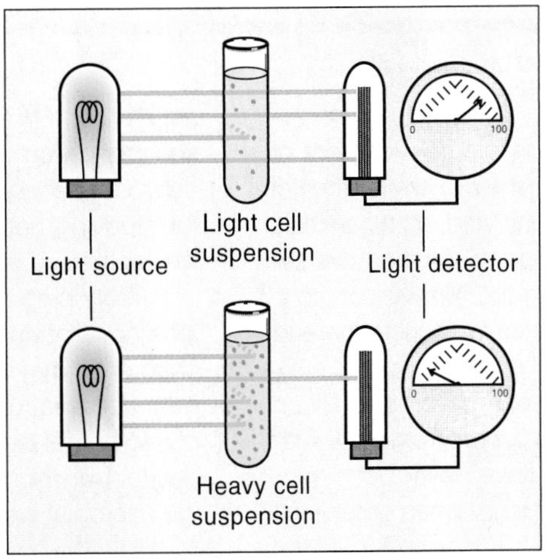

(b)

FIGURE 4.21 Measuring Turbidity with a Spectrophotometer **(a)** The cloudiness, or turbidity, of the liquid in the tube on the left is proportional to the concentration of cells. **(b)** The percentage of light that reaches the detector is inversely proportional to the optical density. To use turbidity to estimate cell number, a one-time experiment must be done to determine the correlation between cell concentration and optical density of a culture.

present, a clear solution does not guarantee their absence. Not recognizing these facts can have serious consequences in the laboratory as well as outside. Experienced hikers, for example, know that the clarity of mountain streams does not necessarily mean that the water is free of *Giardia* or other harmful organisms. ■ giardiasis, p. 638

Total Weight

Determining the total weight of a culture is a tedious and time consuming method that is not used routinely. It can be invaluable, however, for measuring the growth of filamentous organisms. These do not readily break up into individual cells, which are necessary for a valid plate count. To measure the **wet weight,** cells growing in liquid culture are centrifuged down and the liquid removed. The weight of the resulting packed cell mass is proportional to the number of cells in the culture. The **dry weight** can be determined by drying the centrifuged cells at approximately 100°C for 8 to 12 hours before weighing them. About 70% of the weight of a cell is water.

Chemical Constituents

The quantity of a chemical constituent of a cell, typically nitrogen, can be determined and then used to calculate the biomass. For example, cells can be treated with sulfuric acid, which converts cellular nitrogen to ammonia. The amount of ammonia can then be easily assayed. Because cells are typically composed of 14% nitrogen, the biomass can be mathematically derived from the amount of ammonia released.

Detecting Cell Products

Products of microbial growth can be used to estimate the number of microorganisms or, more commonly, to confirm their presence. These products include acids, gases, and ATP.

Acid Production

As a consequence of the breakdown of sugars, which are used as an energy source, microorganisms produce a variety of acids. The precise amount of acid can be measured using chemical means such as titration. Most commonly, however, acid production is used to detect growth by incorporating a **pH indicator** into a medium. A pH indicator changes from one color to another as the pH of a medium changes. Several pH indicators are available, and they differ in the value at which their color changes.

Gases

Production of gases such as CO_2 can be monitored in several ways. A method used in clinical labs employs a fluorescent molecule to detect bacteria growing in blood taken from patients who are suspected of having a bloodstream infection. The slight decrease in pH that accompanies the production of CO_2 increases the fluorescence.

ATP

The presence of ATP can be detected by adding the firefly enzyme luciferase. The enzyme catalyzes a chemical reaction that uses ATP as an energy source to produce light. This method is sometimes used to assess the effectiveness of chemical agents formulated to kill bacteria. Light is produced only if viable organisms remain.

MICROCHECK 4.8

Direct microscopic counts and cell-counting instruments generally do not distinguish between living and dead cells. Plate counts determine the number of cells capable of multiplying; membrane filtration can be used to concentrate the sample. The most probable number is a statistical assay based on the theory of probability. Turbidity of a culture is a rapid measurement that can be correlated to cell number. The total weight of a culture and the amount of certain cell constituents can be correlated to the number of cells present. Microbial growth can be detected by the presence of cell products such as acid, gas, and ATP.

- ✓ Why is an MPN an estimate rather than an accurate number?
- ✓ Why would a direct microscopic count yield a higher number than a pour plate if a sample of seawater was examined by both methods?
- ✓ The nitrogen in microorganisms will typically be present in what molecules?

FUTURE CHALLENGES

Seeing How the Other 99% Lives

One of the biggest challenges for the future is the development of methodologies to cultivate and study a wider array of environmental prokaryotes. Without these microbes, humans and other animals would not be able to exist. Yet considering their importance, we still know very little about most species, including the relative contributions of each to such fundamental processes as O_2 generation and nitrogen fixation.

Studying environmental microorganisms can be difficult. Much of our understanding of prokaryotic processes comes from work with pure cultures. Yet over 99% of prokaryotes have never been successfully grown in the laboratory. At the same time, when organisms are removed from their natural habital, and especially when they are separated from other organisms, their environment changes drastically. Consequently, the study of pure cultures may not be the ideal for studying natural situations, even though it has historically been the method of choice.

Technological advances such as flow cytometry and fluorescent labeling, along with the recombinant DNA techniques discussed in chapter 9, may make it easier to study environmental bacteria. This may well lead to a better understanding of the diversity and the roles of microorganisms in our ecosystem. Scientists have learned a great deal about microorganisms since the days of Pasteur, but most of the microbial world is still a mystery.

SUMMARY

4.1 Principles of Prokaryotic Growth

Most prokaryotes multiply by **binary fission.** (Figure 4.1)

Microbial growth is an increase in the number of cells in a population. The time required for a population to double in number is the **generation time.**

4.2 Bacterial Growth in Nature

Biofilms (Figure 4.2)

Prokaryotes often live in a **biofilm,** a polysaccharide-encased community.

Interactions of Mixed Microbial Communities

Prokaryotes often grow in close associations containing multiple different species: the metabolic activities of one organism may affect the growth of another.

4.3 Obtaining a Pure Culture

Only an estimated 1% of prokaryotes have been cultured in the laboratory.

Cultivating Bacteria on a Solid Medium

A single bacterial cell deposited on a solid medium will multiply to form a visible colony. (Figure 4.4)

The Streak-Plate Method (Figure 4.5)

The **streak-plate** method is used to isolate bacteria in order to obtain **a pure culture.**

Maintaining Stock Cultures

Stock cultures can be stored on an **agar slant** in the refrigerator, frozen in a glycerol solution, or **lyophilized.**

4.4 Bacterial Growth in Laboratory Conditions

The Growth Curve (Figure 4.6)

When grown in a **closed system,** a population of bacteria goes through five phases: **lag, log, stationary, death,** and **prolonged decline.**

Colony Growth

The position of a single cell within a colony markedly determines its environment.

Continuous Culture

Bacteria can be maintained in a state of continuous exponential growth by using a **chemostat.**

4.5 Environmental Factors That Influence Microbial Growth (Table 4.1)

Temperature Requirements (Figure 4.9)

Organisms can be grouped as **psychrophiles, psychrotrophs, mesophiles, thermophiles,** or **hyperthermophiles** based on their optimum growth temperatures.

Oxygen (O_2) Requirements (Table 4.2)

Organisms can be grouped as **obligate aerobes, obligate anaerobes, facultative anaerobes, microaerophiles** or **aerotolerant anaerobes based** on their oxygen (O_2) requirements.

Although O_2 itself is not toxic, it can be converted to **superoxide** and **hydrogen peroxide,** both of which are toxic. **Superoxide dismutase** and **catalase** can break these down.

pH

Organisms can be grouped as **neutrophiles, acidophiles,** or **alkalophiles** based on their optimum pH.

Water Availability

Halophiles are adapted to live in high salt environments.

4.6 Nutritional Factors That Influence Microbial Growth

Required Elements (Table 4.3)

The **major elements** make up cell constituents and include carbon, nitrogen, sulfur, and phosphorus. **Trace elements** are required in very minute amounts.

Growth Factors

Bacteria that cannot synthesize cell constituents such as amino acids and vitamins require these as **growth factors.**

Energy Sources

Organisms derive energy either from sunlight or from the oxidation of chemical compounds.

Nutritional Diversity (Table 4.4)

Photoautotrophs use the energy of sunlight and the carbon in the atmosphere to make organic compounds.

Chemolithoautotrophs use inorganic compounds for energy and derive their carbon from CO_2.

Photoheterotrophs use the energy of sunlight and derive their carbon from organic compounds.

Chemoorganoheterotrophs use organic compounds for energy and as a carbon source.

4.7 Cultivating Prokaryotes in the Laboratory

General Categories of Culture Media (Table 4.5)

A **complex medium** contains a variety of ingredients such as peptones and extracts; examples include **nutrient agar, blood agar,** and **chocolate agar.**

A **chemically defined** medium is composed of precise mixtures of pure chemicals; an example is **glucose-salts** medium.

Special Types of Culture Media

A **selective medium** inhibits organisms other than the one being sought; examples include **Thayer-Martin agar** and **MacConkey agar.**

A **differential medium** contains a substance that certain bacteria change in a recognizable way; examples include **blood agar** and **MacConkey agar.** (Figures 4.11, 4.12)

Providing Appropriate Atmospheric Conditions

A **candle jar** provides increased CO_2, which enhances the growth of many medically important bacteria.

Microaerophilic bacteria are incubated in a gastight jar along with a packet that generates low O_2 conditions.

Anaerobes may be incubated in an **anaerobe jar** or an anaerobic chamber. (Figures 4.13, 4.14)

Enrichment Cultures (Figure 4.15)

An **enrichment culture** provides conditions in a broth that enhance the growth of one particular organism in a mixed population.

4.8 Methods to Detect and Measure Bacterial Growth

(Table 4.7)

Direct Cell Counts

Direct cell counts generally do not distinguish between living and dead cells.

One of the most rapid methods of determining the number of cells is the **direct microscopic count.** (Figure 4.16)

Both a **Coulter counter** and a **flow cytometer** count cells as they pass through a minute aperture. (Figure 4.17)

Viable Cell Counts

Plate counts measure the number of viable cells by exploiting the fact that an isolated cell will form a single colony. (Figure 4.18)

Membrane filtration concentrates bacteria by filtration; the filter is then incubated on an agar plate. (Figure 4.19)

The **most probable number (MPN)** method is a statistical assay used to estimate cell numbers. (Figure 4.20)

Measuring Biomass

Turbidity of a culture can be correlated to the number of cells; a **spectrophotometer** is used to measure turbidity. (Figure 4.21)

Wet weight and **dry weight** are proportional to the number of cells in a culture.

The quantity of a cell constituent such as nitrogen can be used to calculate biomass.

Detecting Cell Products

Products including acid, gas, and ATP can be used to indicate growth.

REVIEW QUESTIONS

Short Answer

1. Define a pure culture.
2. If the number of bacteria in lake water were determined using both a direct microscopic count and a plate count, which method would most likely give a higher number? Why?
3. List the five categories of optimum temperature, and describe a corresponding environment in which a representative might thrive.
4. Explain why obligate anaerobes are significant to the canning industry.
5. Explain why O_2-containing atmospheres kill some bacteria.
6. Explain why photoautotrophs are the primary producers.
7. Distinguish between a selective medium and a differential medium.
8. Explain what occurs during each of the five phases of growth.
9. Explain how the environment of a colony differs from that of a liquid broth.
10. Describe a detrimental and a beneficial effect of biofilms.

Multiple Choice

1. *E. coli* is present in a liquid sample at a concentration of between 10^4 and 10^6 bacteria per ml. To determine the precise number of living bacteria in the sample, it would be best to
   a) use a counting chamber.
   b) plate out an appropriate dilution of the sample on nutrient agar.
   c) determine cell number by using a spectrophotometer.
   d) Any of these three methods would be satisfactory.
   e) None of these three methods would be satisfactory.
2. *E. coli*, a facultative anaerobe, is grown on the same solid medium, but under two different conditions: one aerobic, the other anaerobic. The size of the colonies that grow would be
   a) the same under both conditions.
   b) larger when grown under aerobic conditions.
   c) larger when grown under anaerobic conditions.
3. A soil sample is placed in liquid and the number of bacteria in the sample determined in two ways: (1) by colony count and (2) by counting the cells in a counting chamber (slide). How would the results compare?
   a) Methods 1 and 2 would give approximately the same number of bacteria.
   b) Many more bacteria would be estimated by method 1.
   c) Many more bacteria would be estimated by method 2.
   d) Depending on the soil sample, sometimes method 1 would be higher and sometimes method 2 would be higher.

4. Nutrient broth is an example of a
   a) synthetic medium. b) complex medium. c) selective medium.
   d) indicator medium. e) defined medium.
5. *E. coli* does not require vitamin E in the medium in which it grows. This is because *E. coli*
   a) does not require vitamin E for growth.
   b) gets vitamin E from its host.
   c) can substitute another vitamin for vitamin E in its metabolism.
   d) can synthesize vitamin E from the simple compounds provided in the medium.
   e) is a chemoheterotroph.
6. Cells are most sensitive to penicillin during which phase of the growth curve?
   a) lag b) log c) stationary
   d) death e) more than one of these.
7. *Streptomyces* cells would most likely synthesize antibiotics during which phase of the growth curve?
   a) lag b) log c) stationary
   d) death e) more than one of these.
8. In general, bacteria in nature, compared with their growth in the laboratory,
   a) grow more slowly.
   b) grow faster.
   c) usually grow at the same rate.
9. If there are 10^3 cells per ml at the middle of log phase, and the generation time of the cells is 30 minutes, how many cells will there be 2 hours later?
   a) 2×10^3 b) 4×10^3 c) 8×10^3
   d) 1.6×10^4 e) 1×10^7
10. The major effect of a temperature of 60°C on a mesophile is to
   a) destroy the cell wall.
   b) denature proteins.
   c) destroy nucleic acids.
   d) destroy the cytoplasmic membrane.
   e) cause the formation of endospores.

Applications

1. You are a microbiologist working for a pharmaceutical company and discover a new metabolite that can serve as a medication. Your company asked you to oversee the production of the metabolite. What are some factors you must consider if you need to grow 5,000-liter cultures of bacteria?
2. High-performance boat manufacturers know that bacteria can collect on a boat, ruining the boat's hydrodynamic properties. Periodic cleaning of the boat's surface and repainting eventually ruin that surface and do not solve the problem. A boat-manufacturing facility recently hired you to help with this problem because of your microbiology background. What strategies can you use to come up with a long-term remedy for the problem?

Critical Thinking Questions

1. This figure shows a growth curve plotted on a non-logarithmic, or linear, scale. Compare this with figure 4.6. In both figures, the number of cells increases dramatically during the log or exponential phase. In this phase, the cell number increases more and more rapidly (this effect is more apparent in the accompanying figure). Why should the increase be speeding up?
2. In question 1, how would the curve appear if the availability of nutrients were increased?

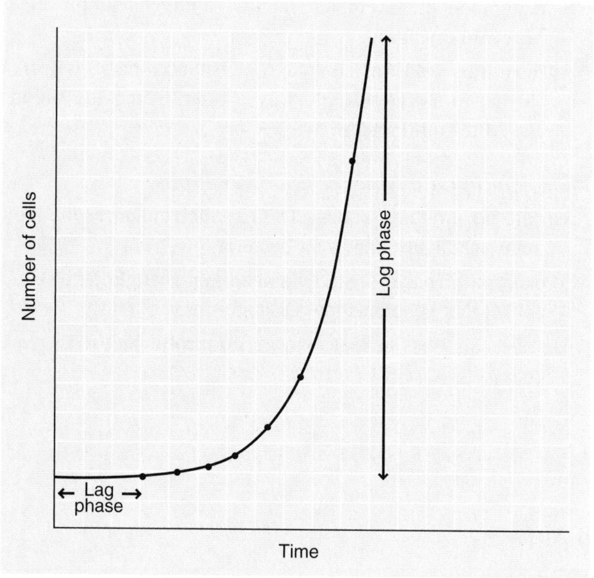

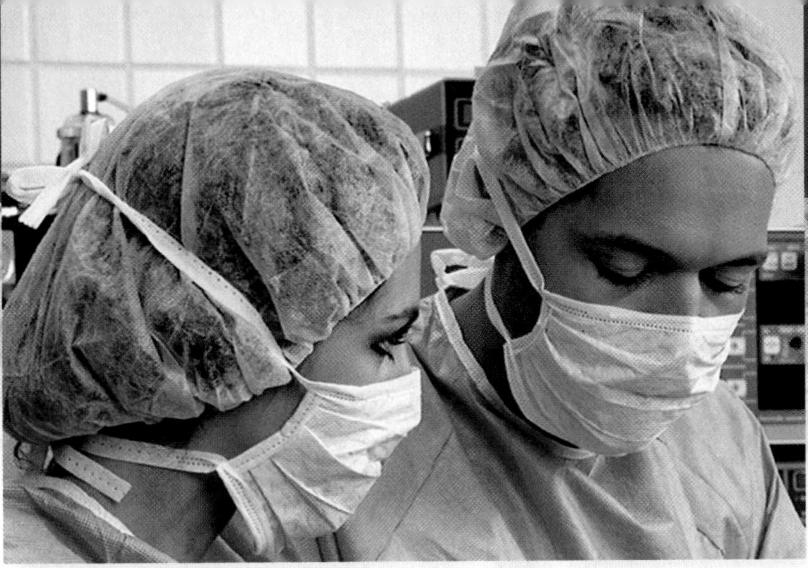

Medical settings warrant a high level of microbial control.

CHAPTER FIVE

Control of Microbial Growth

A Glimpse of History

The British Medical Journal stated that the British physician Joseph Lister (1827–1912) "saved more lives by the introduction of his system than all the wars of the 19th century together had sacrificed." He revolutionized surgery by developing effective methods that prevent surgical wounds from becoming infected. Impressed with Pasteur's work on fermentation (said to be caused by "minute organisms suspended in the air"). Lister wondered if "minute organisms" might be responsible also for the pus that forms in surgical wounds. He then experimented with a phenolic compound, carbolic acid, introducing it at full strength into wounds by means of a saturated rag. Lister was particularly proud of the fact that, after carbolic acid wound dressings became standard in his practice, his patients no longer developed gangrene. Lister's work provided impressive evidence for the germ theory of disease, even though microorganisms specific for various diseases were not identified for another decade.

Later, Lister improved his methods by introducing surgical procedures that excluded bacteria from wounds by maintaining a clean environment in the operating room and by sterilizing instruments. These procedures were preferable to killing the bacteria after they had entered wounds because they avoided the toxic effects of the disinfectant on the wound.

Lister was knighted in 1883 and subsequently became a baron and a member of the House of Lords.

Until the late nineteenth century, patients undergoing even minor surgery were at great risk of developing fatal infections due to unsanitary medical practices and hospital conditions. Physicians did not know that their hands could pass diseases from one patient to the next. Nor did they understand that airborne microscopic organisms could infect open wounds. Fortunately, today's modern hospitals use rigorous procedures to avoid microbial contamination, allowing surgical operations to be performed with relative safety.

The growth of microorganisms affects more than our health. Producers of a wide variety of goods recognize that unless microbial growth is controlled, the quality of their products can be compromised. This ranges from undesirable changes in the safety, appearance, taste, or odor of food products to the decay of untreated lumber.

This chapter covers the methods that have been developed to destroy, remove, and inhibit the growth of microorganisms on inanimate objects and some body surfaces. Most of these approaches are non-selective in that they can adversely impact all forms of life. Antibiotics and other antimicrobial medications will be discussed in chapter 21. These compounds are particularly valuable in combating infectious diseases because their toxicity is specifically targeted to microbes.

5.1 Approaches to Control

Focus Points

- Define the terms *sterile, disinfection, disinfectant, biocide, germicide, antiseptic, degerming, pasteurization, decontamination, sanitize,* and *preservation.*
- Compare and contrast the rigor of the methods used to control microbial growth in daily life, hospitals, microbiology laboratories, food and food production facilities, water treatment facilities, and other industries.

The processes used to control microorganisms are either physical or chemical, though a combination of both may be used. **Physical methods** include heat treatment, irradiation, filtration, and mechanical removal (washing). **Chemical methods** use any

KEY TERMS

Antiseptic A disinfectant that is non-toxic enough to be used on skin.

Aseptic technique Procedures that minimize the chance of unwanted microbes being accidentally introduced.

Bactericidal Kills bacteria.

Bacteriostatic Prevents the growth of, but does not kill, bacteria.

Degerm Treatment used to decrease the number of microbes in an area, usually skin.

Disinfectant A chemical used to destroy many microorganisms and viruses.

Germicide Kills microorganisms and viruses.

Pasteurization A treatment, usually brief heating, used to reduce the number of spoilage organisms and to kill disease-causing microbes.

Preservation The process of inhibiting the growth of microorganisms in products to delay spoilage.

Sterilant A chemical used to destroy all microorganisms and viruses in a product, rendering it sterile.

Sterile Completely free of all microbes; an absolute term.

Sterilization The process of destroying or removing all microorganisms and viruses, through physical or chemical means.

one of a variety of antimicrobial chemicals. The method chosen depends on the circumstances and resulting degree of control required.

Principles of Control

The process of removing or destroying all microorganisms and viruses on or in a product is called **sterilization.** These procedures include removing microbes by filtration, or destroying them using heat, certain chemicals, or irradiation. Destruction of microorganisms means they cannot be "revived" to multiply even when transferred from the sterilized product to an ideal growth medium. A **sterile** item is one that is absolutely free of microbes, including endospores and viruses. It is important to note, however, that the term *sterile* does not consider prions. These infectious protein particles are not destroyed by standard sterilization procedures. ■ endospores, p. 71 ■ prions, p. 13

Disinfection is the process that eliminates most or all pathogens on or in a material. Unlike sterilization, disinfection suggests that some viable microbes may persist. In practice, the term disinfection generally implies the use of antimicrobial chemicals. Those used for disinfecting inanimate objects are called **disinfectants.** Disinfectants are **biocides** (*bio* means "life," and *cida* means "to kill"). Although they are at least somewhat toxic to many forms of life, they are typically used in a manner that targets microscopic organisms, including bacteria and their endospores, fungi, and viruses. Thus, they are often called **germicides.** When disinfectants are formulated for use on skin they are called **antiseptics.** Antiseptics are routinely used to decrease the number of bacteria on skin to prepare for invasive procedures such as surgery. ■ pathogen, p. 8

Pasteurization uses a brief heat treatment to reduce the number of spoilage organisms and kill pathogens. Foods and inanimate objects can be pasteurized.

Decontamination is a treatment used to reduce the number of pathogens to a level considered safe to handle. The treatment can be as simple as thorough washing, or it may involve the use of heat or disinfectants.

Degerming is a treatment used to decrease the number of microbes in an area, particularly the skin. In other words, antiseptics are degerming agents.

Sanitized generally implies a substantially reduced microbial population that meets accepted health standards. Most people also expect a sanitized object to be clean in appearance. Note that this term does not denote any specific level of control.

Preservation is the process of delaying spoilage of foods or other perishable products. This is done by adding growth-inhibiting ingredients or adjusting storage conditions to impede growth of microorganisms.

Situational Considerations

Methods used to control microbial growth vary greatly depending on the situation and degree of control required **(figure 5.1).** Control measures adequate for routine circumstances of daily life might not be sufficient for situations such as hospitals, microbiology laboratories, foods and food production facilities, water treatment facilities, and other industries.

Daily Life

Washing and scrubbing with soaps and detergents achieves routine control of undesirable microorganisms and viruses. In fact, simple handwashing with plain soap and water is considered the single most important step in preventing the spread of many infectious diseases. Plain soap itself generally does not destroy many organisms; it simply aids in the mechanical removal of transient microbes, including most pathogens, as well as dirt, organic material, and cells of the outermost layer of skin. Regular handwashing and bathing does not adversely impact the beneficial normal skin flora, which reside more deeply on underlying layers of skin cells and in hair follicles. ■ normal flora of the skin, p. 522

Other methods used to control microorganisms in daily life include cooking foods, cleaning surfaces, and refrigeration.

Hospitals

Minimizing the numbers of microorganisms in a hospital is particularly important because of the danger of hospital-acquired, or **nosocomial,** infections. Hospitalized patients are often more susceptible to infectious agents because of their weakened condition. In addition, patients may be subject to invasive procedures such as surgery, which breaches the intact skin that would otherwise help prevent infection. Finally, pathogens are more likely to be found in

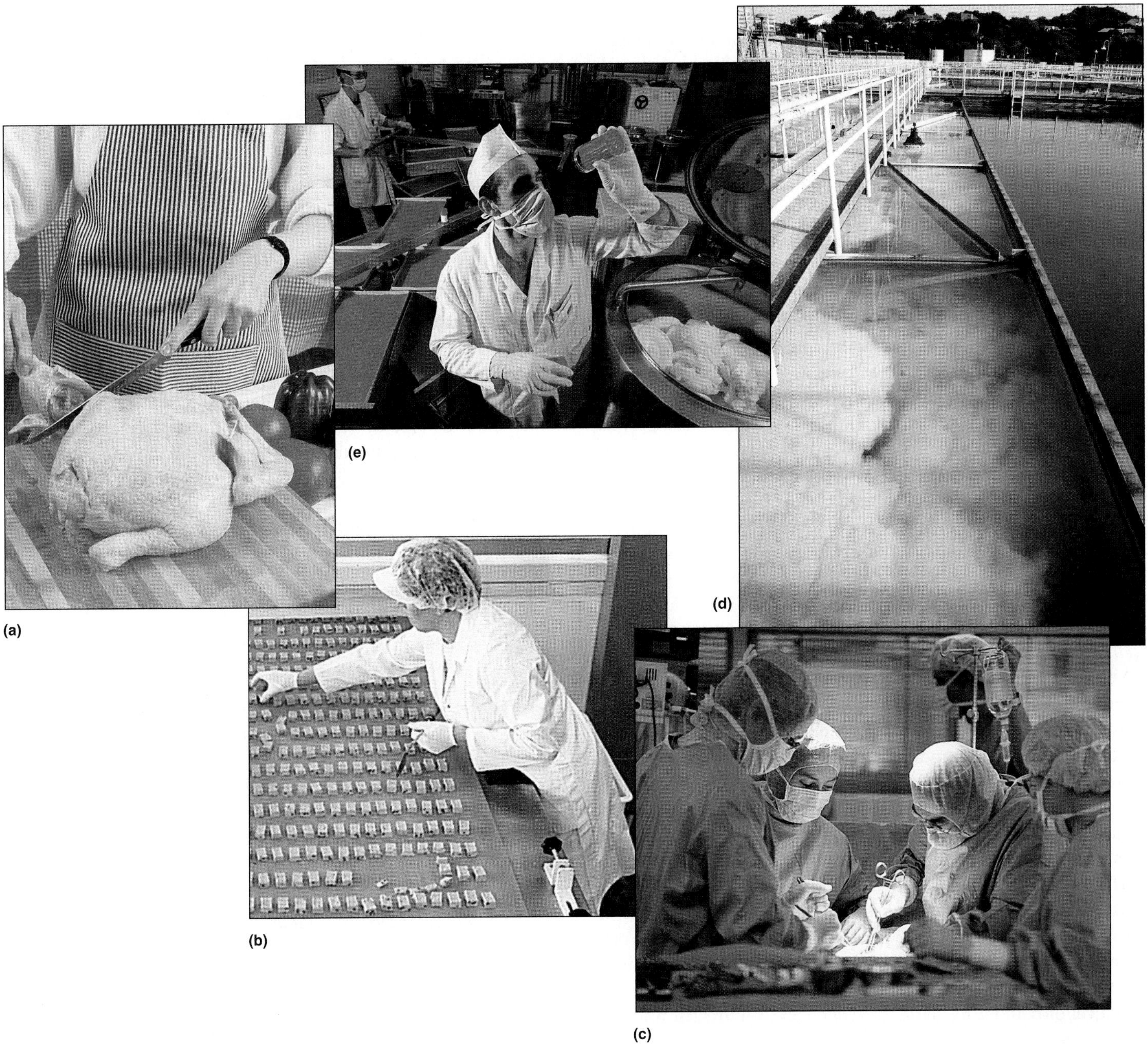

FIGURE 5.1 Situations that Warrant Different Levels of Microbial Control **(a)** Daily home life; **(b)** foods and food production facilities; **(c)** hospitals; **(d)** water treatment facilities; **(e)** other industries.

hospitals because of the high concentration of patients with infectious disease. These patients may shed pathogens in their feces, urine, respiratory droplets, or other body secretions. Thus, hospitals must be scrupulous in their control of microorganisms. Nowhere is this more important than in the operating rooms, where instruments used in invasive procedures must be sterile to avoid introducing even normally benign microbes into deep body tissue where they could easily establish infection. ■ nosocomial infections, p. 487

Prions are a relatively new concern for hospitals. Fortunately, disease caused by prions is thought to be exceedingly rare, less than 1 case per 1 million persons per year. Hospitals, however, must take special precautions when handling tissue that may be contaminated with prions, because these infectious particles are more difficult to destroy.

Microbiology Laboratories

Microbiology laboratories routinely work with microbial cultures and consequently must use rigorous methods of controlling microorganisms. To work with pure cultures, all media and instruments that contact the culture must first be rendered sterile to avoid contaminating the culture with environmental bacteria. All materials used to grow microorganisms must again be treated before disposal to avoid contamination of workers and the environment. The use of specific methods to exclude contaminating microorganisms from an environment is called **aseptic technique.** Although all microbiology laboratory personnel must use these prudent measures, those who work with known disease-causing microbes must be even more diligent.

Foods and Food Production Facilities

Foods and other perishable products retain their quality longer when the growth of contaminating microorganisms is prevented. This can be accomplished by physically removing or destroying microorganisms or by adding chemicals that impede their growth. Heat treatment is the most common and reliable method used, but heating can alter the flavor and appearance of food. Irradiation can be used to kill microbes without causing perceptible changes in food, but the Food and Drug Administration (FDA) has approved this technology to treat only certain foods. Chemicals can prevent the growth of microorganisms, but the risk of toxicity must always be a concern. Because of this, the FDA regulates chemical additives used in food and must deem them safe for consumption.

Food-processing facilities need to keep surfaces relatively free of microorganisms to avoid contamination. Machinery used to grind meat for example, if not cleaned properly, can create an environment in which bacteria multiply, eventually contaminating large quantities of product.

Water Treatment Facilities

Water treatment facilities need to ensure that drinking water is free of gastrointestinal pathogens including bacteria, protozoa, and viruses. Chlorine has traditionally been used to disinfect water, saving hundreds of thousands of lives by preventing transmission of waterborne illnesses such as cholera. Disinfectants including chlorine, however, can react with naturally occurring chemicals in the water to form compounds called **disinfection by-products (DBPs).** Some of these have been linked to long-term health risks. In addition, certain pathogens, particularly the oocysts of *Cryptosporidium parvum*, are resistant to traditional chemical disinfection procedures. To address these problems, water treatment regulations have been amended to require that facilities minimize the level of both DBPs and *C. parvum* oocysts in treated water.

Other Industries

Many diverse industries have specialized concerns regarding microbial growth. Manufacturers of cosmetics, deodorants, or any other product that will be applied to the skin must avoid microbial contamination that could affect the product's quality or safety. Even finished products that are impervious to microbial actions may have steps or processes during their manufacture that could be affected by the growth of microorganisms.

MICROCHECK 5.1

The methods used to control microbial growth depend on the situation and the degree of control required.

- ✓ How is sterilization different from disinfection?
- ✓ What is an antiseptic?
- ✓ Why would the term sterilization not encompass prions?

5.2

Selection of an Antimicrobial Procedure

Focus Point

- Explain why the type of microbe, number of microbes initially present, environmental conditions, potential risk of infection, and composition of the item influence the selection of an antimicrobial procedure.

Selection of an effective antimicrobial procedure is complicated by the fact that every procedure has parameters and drawbacks that limit its use. An ideal, multipurpose, non-toxic method simply does not exist. The ultimate choice depends on many factors including the type of microbes present, extent of contamination, environmental conditions, potential risk of infection associated with use of the item, and the composition of the item.

Type of Microorganism

One of the most critical considerations in selecting a method of destroying microorganisms and viruses is the type of microbial population present on or in the product. Products contaminated with microorganisms more resistant to killing require a more rigorous heat or chemical treatment. Some of the more resistant microbes include:

- Bacterial endospores. The endospores of *Bacillus* and *Clostridium* are by far the most resistant forms of life. Only extreme heat or chemical treatment ensures their complete destruction. Chemical treatments that kill vegetative bacteria in 30 minutes may require 10 hours to destroy their endospores. ■ endospores, p. 71
- Protozoan cysts and oocysts. Cysts and oocysts are stages in the life cycle of the intestinal protozoan pathogens *Giardia lamblia* and *Cryptosporidium parvum*, respectively. These disinfectant-resistant forms are excreted in the feces of infected animals, including humans, and can cause diarrheal disease if ingested. They are of particular concern in water treatment. Unlike endospores, they are readily destroyed by boiling. ■ *Cryptosporidium parvum*, p. 639 ■ *Giardia lamblia*, p. 638
- *Mycobacterium* species. The waxy cell walls of mycobacteria make them resistant to many chemical treatments. Thus, stronger, more toxic disinfectants must be used to disinfect environments that may contain *Mycobacterium tuberculosis*, the causative agent of tuberculosis. ■ tuberculosis, p. 593
- *Pseudomonas* species. These common environmental organisms are not only resistant to some chemical disinfectants, but in some cases can actually grow in them. *Pseudomonas* species are of particular importance in a hospital setting, where they are a common cause of infection. ■ *Pseudomonas* infections, p. 555
- Naked viruses. Viruses such as poliovirus that lack a lipid envelope are more resistant to disinfectants. Conversely, enveloped viruses, such as HIV, tend to be very sensitive to heat and chemical disinfectants. ■ naked viruses, p. 320 ■ enveloped viruses, p. 320

Numbers of Microorganisms Initially Present

The time it takes for heat or chemicals to kill a population of microorganisms is dictated in part by the number of cells initially present. It takes more time to kill a large population than it does to kill a small population, because only a fraction of organisms die during a given time interval. For example, if 90% of a bacterial population is killed during the first 3 minutes, then approximately 90% of those remaining will be killed during the next 3 minutes, and so on.

In the commercial canning industry, the **decimal reduction time,** or **D value,** is the time required for killing 90% of a population of bacteria under specific conditions **(figure 5.2).** The temperature of the process may be indicated by a subscript, for example D_{121}. A one D process reduces the number of cells by one exponent. Thus, if the D value for an organism is 2 minutes, then it would take 4 minutes (2 D values) to reduce a population of 100 (10^2) cells to only one (10^0) survivor. It would take 20 minutes (10 D values) to reduce a population of 10^{10} cells to only one survivor. Removing organisms by washing or scrubbing can minimize the time necessary to sterilize or disinfect a product.

Environmental Conditions

Factors such as pH, temperature, and presence of fats and other organic materials strongly influence microbial death rates. A solution of sodium hypochlorite (household bleach) can kill a suspension of *M. tuberculosis* in 150 seconds at a temperature of 50°C; whereas it takes only 60 seconds to kill the same suspension with chlorine if the temperature is increased to 55°C. The hypochlorite solution is even more effective at a low pH.

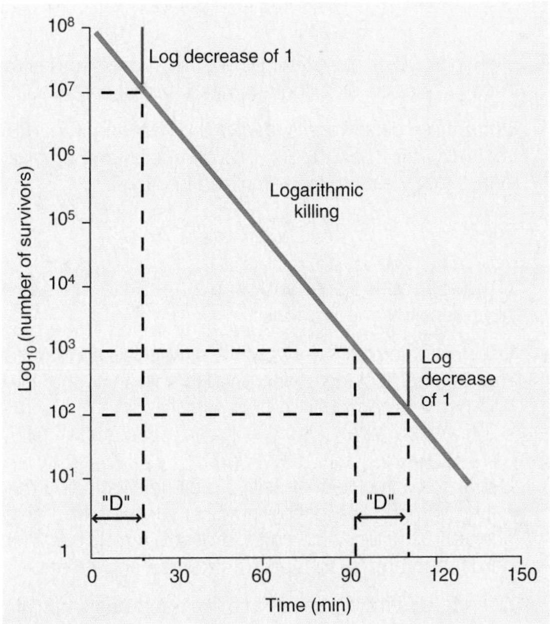

FIGURE 5.2 D Value The D value is the time it takes to reduce the population by 90%.

The presence of dirt, grease, and organic compounds such as blood and other body fluids can interfere with heat penetration and the action of chemical disinfectants. For this reason, it is important to thoroughly clean items before disinfection or sterilization. Meticulously cleaning a product also substantially decreases the number of microorganisms, which, as mentioned previously, shortens the time required to sterilize or disinfect the product.

Potential Risk of Infection

To guide medical biosafety personnel in their selection of germicidal procedures, medical items such as surgical instruments, endoscopes, and stethoscopes are categorized according to their potential risk of transmitting infectious agents. Those that pose the greatest threat of transmitting disease must be subject to more rigorous germicidal procedures.

- **Critical instruments** come into direct contact with body tissues. These items, including needles, scalpels, and biopsy forceps, must be sterilized to avoid transmission of all infectious agents.
- **Semicritical instruments** come into contact with mucous membranes, but do not penetrate body tissue. These items, including gastrointestinal endoscopes and endotracheal tubes, must be free of all viruses and vegetative bacteria including mycobacteria. Low numbers of endospores that may remain on semicritical instruments pose little risk of infection because mucous membranes are effective barriers against their entry into deeper tissue.
- **Non-critical instruments** and surfaces pose little risk of infection because they only come into contact with unbroken skin. Countertops, stethoscopes, and blood pressure cuffs are examples of non-critical items.

Composition of the Item

Some sterilization and disinfection procedures are inappropriate for certain types of material. For example, although heat treatment is generally the method of choice because it is so dependable and relatively inexpensive, many plastics and other materials are heat-sensitive. In addition, moist heat corrodes metals, dulling some instruments. Heat-sensitive material can be irradiated, but the process may damage some types of plastics. Moisture-sensitive material cannot be treated with liquid chemical disinfectants.

MICROCHECK 5.2

The types and numbers of microorganisms initially present, environmental conditions, the potential risks associated with use of the item, and the composition of the item must all be considered when determining which sterilization or disinfection procedure to employ.

✓ What form of microbial life is the most difficult to destroy?

✓ Define the term D value.

✓ Would it be safe to say that if all bacterial endospores had been killed, then all other medically important microorganisms had also been killed?

5.3

Using Heat to Destroy Microorganisms and Viruses

Focus Points

- Compare and contrast pasteurization, sterilization using pressurized steam, and the commercial canning process.
- Explain the drawbacks and benefits of using dry heat rather than moist heat to kill microorganisms.

Heat treatment is one of the most useful methods of microbial control because it is reliable, safe, relatively fast and inexpensive, and it does not introduce potentially toxic substances into the material being treated. Some heat-based methods sterilize the product, whereas others decrease the numbers of microorganisms and viruses. **Table 5.1** summarizes the characteristics of heat treatment and other physical methods of control.

Moist heat

Moist heat destroys microorganisms by irreversibly coagulating their proteins. Examples of moist heat treatment include boiling, pasteurization, and pressurized steam.

Boiling

Boiling (100°C at sea level) easily destroys most microorganisms and viruses. Because of this, drinking water that has potentially been contaminated because of floods or other emergency situations should be boiled for at least 5 minutes. Boiling is not an effective means of sterilization, however, because endospores can survive many hours of the treatment.

TABLE 5.1 Physical Methods Used to Destroy Microorganisms and Viruses

	Characteristics	Uses
Moist Heat	Denatures proteins. Relatively fast, reliable, safe, and inexpensive.	Widely used.
Boiling	Boiling for 5 minutes destroys most microorganisms and viruses; a notable exception is endospores.	Boiling for at least 5 minutes can be used to treat drinking water.
Pasteurization	Significantly decreases the numbers of heat-sensitive microorganisms, including spoilage microbes and pathogens (except sporeformers).	Milk is pasteurized by heating it to 72°C for 15 seconds. Juices are also routinely pasteurized.
Pressurized steam (autoclaving)	Typical treatment is 121°C/15 psi for 15 minutes or longer, a process that destroys endospores.	Widely used to sterilize microbiological media, laboratory glassware, surgical instruments, and other items that can be penetrated by steam. The canning process renders foods commercially sterile.
Dry Heat		
Incineration	Oxidizes cell components to ashes.	Flaming of wire inoculating loops. Also used to destroy medical wastes and contaminated animal carcasses.
Dry heat ovens	Oxidizes cell components and denatures proteins. Less efficient than moist heat, requiring longer times and higher temperatures.	Laboratory glassware is sterilized by heating it to 160°C to 170°C for 2 to 3 hours. Powders, oils, and other anhydrous materials are also sterilized in ovens.
Filtration	Filter retains microbes while letting the suspending fluid or air pass through small holes.	
Filtration of fluids	Various pore sizes are available; 0.2 μm is commonly used to remove bacteria.	Used to produce beer and wine, and to sterilize some heat-sensitive medications.
Filtration of air	HEPA filters are used to remove microbes that have a diameter greater than 0.3 μm.	Used in biological safety cabinets, specialized hospital rooms, and airplanes. Also used in some vacuum cleaners and home air purification units.
Radiation	Type of cell damage depends on the wavelength of the radiation.	
Ionizing radiation	Destroys DNA and possibly damages cytoplasmic membranes. Produces reactive molecules that damage other cell components. Items can be sterilized even after packaging.	Used to sterilize heat-sensitive materials including medical equipment, disposable surgical supplies, and drugs such as penicillin. Also used to destroy microbes in spices, herbs, and approved types of produce and meats.
Ultraviolet radiation	Damages DNA. Penetrates poorly.	Used to destroy microbes in the air and drinking water, and to disinfect surfaces.
High Pressure	Treatments of 130,000 psi are thought to denature proteins and alter the permeability of the cell. Products retain color and flavor.	Used to extend the shelf life of certain commercial food products such as guacamole.

Pasteurization

Louis Pasteur developed the brief heat treatment we now call pasteurization as a way of avoiding spoilage of wine. The process does not sterilize substances but significantly reduces the numbers of heat-sensitive organisms, including pathogens. Today, pasteurization is still used to destroy spoilage organisms in wine, vinegar, and a few other foods, but it is most widely used for killing pathogens in milk and juices. It increases the shelf life of foods and protects consumers by killing organisms that cause diseases such as tuberculosis, brucellosis, salmonellosis, and typhoid fever, without significantly altering the quality of the food. ■ food spoilage, p. 805

Today, most pasteurization protocols employ the **high-temperature-short-time (HTST) method.** Using this method, milk is heated to 72°C and held for 15 seconds. The parameters must be adjusted to the individual food product. For example, ice cream, which is richer than milk in fats, requires a pasteurization process of 82°C for about 20 seconds.

The single-serving containers of cream served in restaurants are processed using the **ultra-high-temperature (UHT) method.** Because this process is designed to render the product free of all microorganisms that can grow under normal storage conditions, it is technically not a type of pasteurization. The milk is rapidly heated to a temperature of 140°C to 150°C, held for several seconds, then rapidly cooled. The product is then aseptically packaged in containers that have been treated with the chemical germicide hydrogen peroxide. Boxed juices are processed and packaged in a similar manner.

Although one does not think of pasteurizing items such as cloth and rubber, this can easily be done by regulating the temperature of the water in a washing machine. For example, hospital anesthesia masks can be pasteurized at 80°C for 15 minutes. The temperatures and times used vary according to the organisms present and the heat stability of the material.

Sterilization Using Pressurized Steam

Pressure cookers and their commercial counterpart, the **autoclave,** heat water in an enclosed vessel that achieves temperatures above 100°C **(figure 5.3).** As heated water in the vessel forms steam, the steam causes the pressure in the vessel to increase beyond atmospheric pressure. The higher pressure, in turn, increases the temperature at which steam forms. Whereas steam produced at atmospheric pressure never exceeds 100°C, steam produced at an additional 15 psi (pounds/square inch) is 121°C, a temperature that kills endospores. Note that the pressure itself plays no direct role in the killing.

Autoclaving is generally the preferred method to sterilize items that can be penetrated by steam and withstand the heat and moisture. Examples include surgical instruments, most microbiological media, reusable glassware and other supplies. Autoclaving is also used to sterilize microbial cultures and other biohazards before disposal.

Typical conditions used for sterilization are 15 psi and 121°C for 15 minutes. Longer time periods are necessary when sterilizing large volumes because it takes longer for heat to completely penetrate the liquid. For example, it takes longer to sterilize 4 liters of liquid in a flask than it would if the same volume were

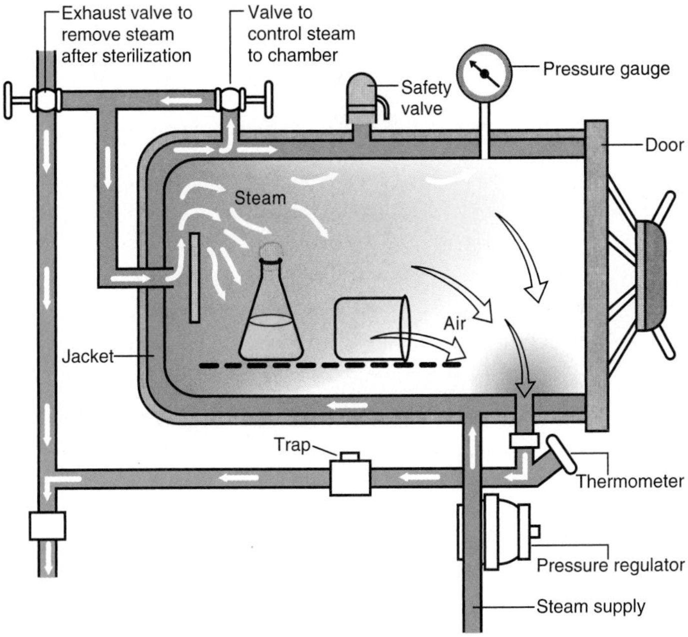

FIGURE 5.3 Autoclave Steam first travels in an enclosed layer, or jacket, surrounding the chamber. It then enters the autoclave, displacing the air downward and out through a port in the bottom of the chamber.

distributed into small tubes. When rapid sterilization is important, such as in operating rooms when sterile instruments must always be available, **flash autoclaving** at higher temperature can be used. By increasing the temperature to 135°C, sterilization is achieved in only 3 minutes. A temperature of 132°C applied for 4.5 hours is thought to destroy prions.

Autoclaving is a consistently effective means of sterilizing most objects, provided the process is done correctly. The temperature and pressure gauge should both be monitored to ensure proper operating conditions. It is also critical that steam enter items and displace the air. Long, thin containers should be placed on their sides. Likewise, containers and bags should never be closed tightly.

Attaching tape that contains a heat-sensitive indicator to objects when they are autoclaved can provide a visual signal that items have been heated. The indicator turns black during autoclaving **(figure 5.4a).** A changed indicator, however, does not always mean that the object is sterile, because heating may not have been uniform.

Biological indicators are used to ensure that the autoclave is working properly (figure 5.4b). A tube containing the heat-resistant endospores of *Geobacillus (Bacillus) stearothermophilus* is placed near the center of an item or package being autoclaved. After autoclaving, the endospores are mixed with a growth medium by crushing a container within the tube. Following incubation, a change of color of the medium indicates growth of the organisms and thus faulty autoclaving.

The Commercial Canning Process

The commercial canning process uses pressurized steam in an industrial-sized autoclave called a **retort.** Conditions of the process are designed to ensure that endospores of *Clostridium*

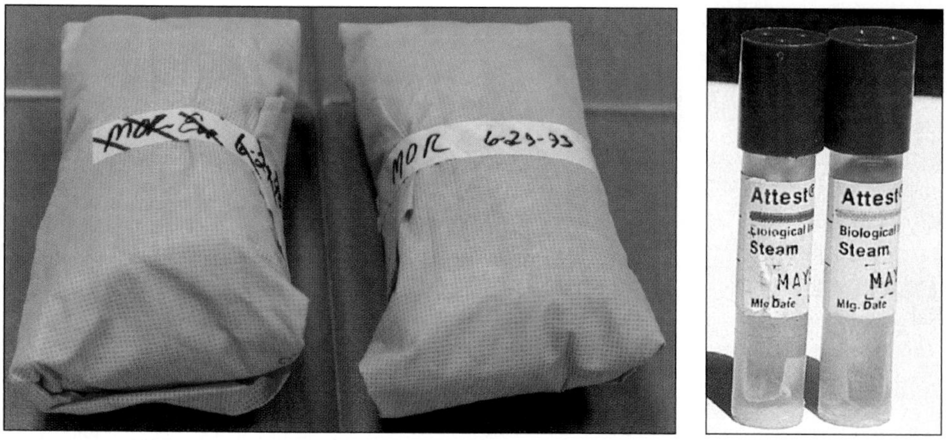

(a) (b)

FIGURE 5.4 Indicator Used in Autoclaving
(a) Chemical indicators. The pack on the left has been autoclaved. Diagonal marks on the tape have turned black, indicating that the object was exposed to heat. **(b)** Biological indicators. Following incubation, a change of color to yellow indicates growth of endospore-forming organisms. Why would a biological indicator be better than other indicators to detect if sterilization had been completely effective?

botulinum are destroyed. This is critical because surviving spores can germinate and the resulting vegetative cells can grow in the anaerobic conditions of low-acid canned foods, such as vegetables and meats, and produce botulinum toxin, one of the most potent toxins known. Because ingestion of even minute amounts of botulinum toxin can be lethal, the canning process of low-acid foods is designed to kill all endospores of *C. botulinum*. In doing so, the process also kills all other organisms capable of growing under normal storage conditions. Endospores of some thermophilic bacteria may survive the canning process, but these are usually of no concern because they only can grow at temperatures well above those of normal storage. Because of this, canned foods are called **commercially sterile** to reflect the fact that the endospores of some thermophiles may survive. **Figure 5.5** shows the steps involved in the commercial canning of foods. ■ botulism, p. 690

Several factors dictate the time and temperature of the canning process. First, as discussed earlier, the higher the temperature, the shorter the time needed to kill all organisms. Second, the higher the concentration of bacteria, the longer the heat treatment required to kill all organisms. To provide a wide margin of safety, the commercial canning process is designed to reduce a population of 10^{12} *C. botulinum* endospores to only one. In other words, it is a 12 D process. It is virtually impossible for a food to have this high a level of initial concentration of endospores, and so the process has a wide safety margin.

Dry Heat

Dry heat is not as efficient as wet heat in killing microorganisms, requiring longer times and higher temperatures. For example, 200°C for 90 minutes of dry heat is the killing equivalent of 121°C for 15 minutes of moist heat.

Incineration oxidizes the cell components to ashes. In microbiology laboratories, for example, the wire loops continually reused to transfer bacterial cultures are sterilized by **flaming,** heating them in a flame until they are red hot. Alternatively, they can be heated to the same point in a benchtop incinerator designed for this purpose. Incineration is also used to destroy medical wastes and contaminated animal carcasses.

Temperatures achieved in hot air ovens oxidize cell components and irreversibly denature proteins. Glass Petri dishes and glass pipets are sterilized in ovens with non-circulating air at temperatures of 160°C to 170°C for 2 to 3 hours. Ovens with a fan that circulates the hot air can sterilize in a shorter time because of the more efficient transfer of heat. Powders, oils, and other anhydrous material are also sterilized in hot ovens.

MICROCHECK 5.3

Moist heat such as boiling water destroys most microorganisms and viruses. Pasteurization significantly reduces the numbers of heat-sensitive organisms. Autoclaves use pressurized steam to achieve high temperatures that kill microbes, including endospores. The commercial canning process is designed to destroy the endospores of *Clostridium botulinum*. Dry heat takes longer than moist heat to kill microbes.

- ✓ Why is it important that the commercial canning process destroys the endospores of *Clostridium botulinum*?
- ✓ What are two purposes of pasteurization?
- ✓ Would endospores be destroyed in the pasteurization process?

5.4 Using Other Physical Methods to Remove or Destroy Microbes

Focus Points

- Describe how depth filters, membrane filters, and HEPA filters are each used to remove microorganisms.
- Describe how gamma irradiation, ultraviolet irradiation, and microwaves each destroy microorganisms.

Some materials are either heat-sensitive or impractical to treat using heat. For these items, other physical methods including filtration, irradiation, and high-pressure treatment can be used to either destroy or remove microorganism.

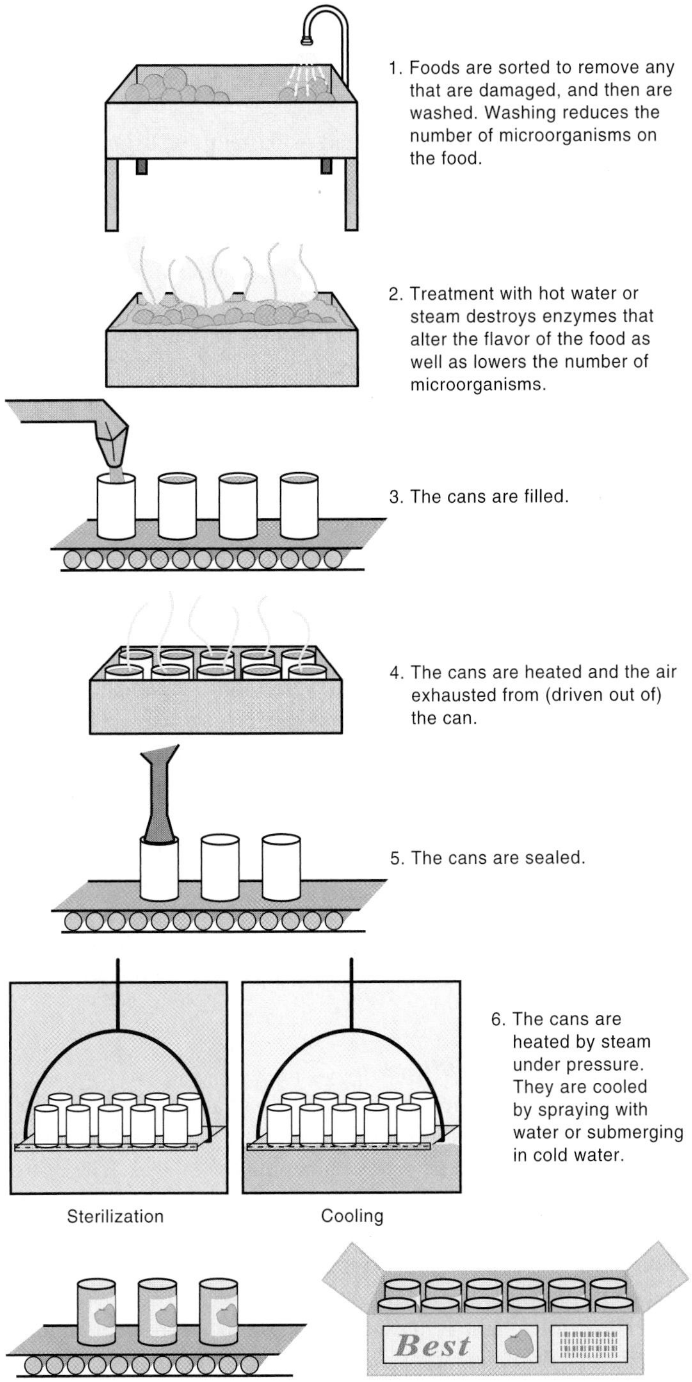

1. Foods are sorted to remove any that are damaged, and then are washed. Washing reduces the number of microorganisms on the food.
2. Treatment with hot water or steam destroys enzymes that alter the flavor of the food as well as lowers the number of microorganisms.
3. The cans are filled.
4. The cans are heated and the air exhausted from (driven out of) the can.
5. The cans are sealed.
6. The cans are heated by steam under pressure. They are cooled by spraying with water or submerging in cold water.
Sterilization
Cooling
Best
7. Cans are labeled, packaged, and shipped.

FIGURE 5.5 Steps in the Commercial Canning of Foods

Filtration

Recall that membrane filtration, which is used to determine the number of bacteria in a liquid medium, retains bacteria while allowing the fluid to pass through. That same principle can be employed to physically remove microbes from liquids or air.

■ **membrane filtration, p. 105**

Filtration of Fluids

Filtration is used extensively to remove organisms from heat-sensitive fluids. Examples include production of unpasteurized beer, sterilization of sugar solutions, and clarification of wine. Specially-designed filtration units are also used by backpackers and campers to remove *Giardia* cysts and bacteria from water.

Paper-thin **membrane filters** have microscopic pores that allow liquid to flow through while trapping particles that are too small to pass through the pores **(figure 5.6).** A vacuum is commonly used to help pull the liquid through the filter; alternatively, pressure may be applied to push the liquid through. Membrane filters are available in a variety of different pore sizes, extending below the dimensions of the smallest known viruses. Pore sizes smaller than necessary should be avoided, however, because they impede the rate of flow. Filters with a pore size of 0.2 micrometers (μm) are commonly used to remove bacteria. The filters are made of compounds such as polycarbonate or cellulose nitrate that are relatively inert chemically and absorb very little of the fluid or its biologically important constituents such as enzymes.

Depth filters trap material within thick filtration material such as cellulose fibers or diatomaceous earth. They have complex, torturous passages that retain microorganisms while letting the suspending fluid pass through the small holes. The diameter of the passages is often considerably larger than that of the microorganisms they retain, and trapping of microbes is partly a result of electrical charges on the walls of the filter passages.

Filtration of Air

Special filters called **high-efficiency particulate air (HEPA) filters** remove from air nearly all microorganisms that have a diameter greater than 0.3 μm. These filters are used for keeping microorganisms out of specialized hospital rooms in which patients who are exquisitely susceptible to infection stay. The

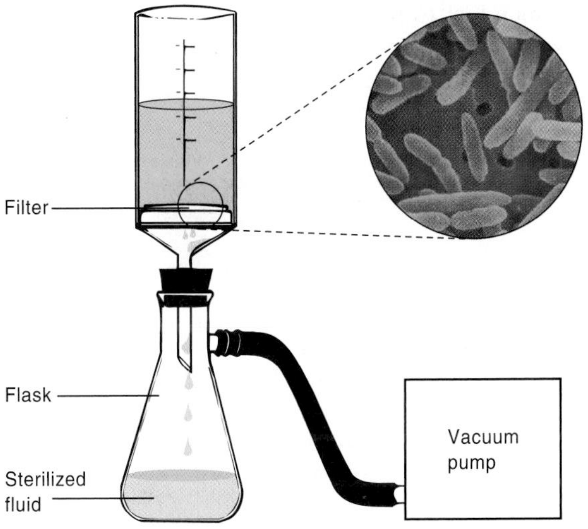

FIGURE 5.6 Filtration of Fluids Using a Membrane Filter The liquid to be sterilized flows through the filter on top of the flask in response to a vacuum produced in the flask by means of a pump. Scanning electron micrograph (5,000×) shows a membrane filter retaining cells of *Pseudomonas.*

filters are also used in biological safety cabinets, **laminar flow hoods,** in which laboratory personnel work with dangerous airborne pathogens such as *Mycobacterium tuberculosis.* A continuous flow of incoming and outgoing air is filtered through the HEPA filters to contain microorganisms within the cabinet. Biological safety cabinets are used not only to protect the worker from contamination by the sample, but also to protect the sample from environmental contamination.

Radiation

Radio waves, microwaves, visible and ultraviolet light rays, X rays, and gamma rays are all examples of a form of energy called **electromagnetic radiation.** This energy travels at the speed of light in waves and has no mass. The amount of energy in electromagnetic radiation is related to its **wavelength,** which is the distance from crest to crest (or trough to trough) of a wave, and **frequency,** which is the number of waves per second. Radiation that has short waves, and therefore high frequency, has more energy than that which has long waves and low frequency. The full range of wavelengths is called the **electromagnetic spectrum (figure 5.7).**

Electromagnetic radiation can be either ionizing, meaning it can strip electrons off of atoms, or non-ionizing. Both types can be used to destroy microbes, but the mechanisms of destruction differ.

Ionizing radiation

There are three sources of ionizing radiation: gamma rays, which are emitted from decaying radioisotopes (such as cobalt-60), X rays, and electron accelerators. The radiation causes biological harm both directly, by destroying DNA and possibly damaging cytoplasmic membranes, and indirectly, by producing reactive molecules such as superoxide and hydroxyl free radicals. The later is a highly unstable molecule because it has one unpaired electron. Bacterial endospores are among the most radiation-resistant microbial forms, whereas Gram-negative bacteria such as *Salmonella* and *Pseudomonas* species are among the most susceptible. ■ **superoxide, p. 96**

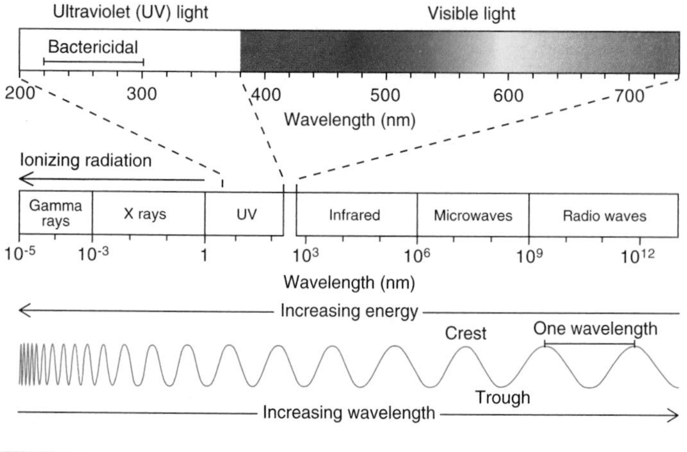

FIGURE 5.7 The Electromagnetic Spectrum Visible wavelengths include the colors of the rainbow.

Radiation is used extensively to sterilize heat-sensitive materials including medical equipment, disposable surgical supplies, and drugs such as penicillin. Radiation can even be carried out after packaging.

Foods can be either sterilized or pasteurized using radiation, depending on the doses employed. Treatments designed to sterilize food can cause undesirable flavor changes, however, which limits their usefulness. More commonly, food is irradiated as a method of pasteurization, eliminating pathogens and decreasing the numbers of spoilage organisms. For example, it can be used to kill pathogens such as *Salmonella* species in poultry with little or no change in taste of the product.

In the United States, irradiation has been used for many years to control microorganisms on spices and herbs. The Food and Drug Administration (FDA) has also approved irradiation of fruits, vegetables, and grains to control insects; pork to control the trichina parasite; and most recently, meats including poultry, beef, lamb, and pork to control pathogens such as *Salmonella* species and *E. coli* O157:H7.

Many consumers have been reluctant to accept irradiated products, even though the FDA and officials of the World Health and the United Nations Food and Agriculture Organizations have endorsed the technique. Some people erroneously believe that irradiated products are radioactive, which they are not. Others have lingering doubts about the possibility of irradiation-induced toxins or carcinogens being present in food, even though available scientific evidence indicates that consumption of irradiated food is safe. Another argument raised against irradiation is that it will cause a relaxation of other prudent food-handling practices. Irradiation, however, is intended to complement, not replace, proper food-handling procedures by producers, processors, and consumers.

Ultraviolet radiation

Ultraviolet light in wavelengths of approximately 220 to 300 nm is the only type of non-ionizing radiation that destroys microorganisms directly, and it does so by damaging their DNA. The energy of the light causes covalent bonds to form between adjacent thymine molecules in the DNA, creating thymine dimers. Actively multiplying organisms are the most easily killed, whereas bacterial endospores are the most UV-resistant. ■ **thymine dimer, p. 197**

Ultraviolet light is used extensively to destroy microbes in the air and drinking water and to disinfect surfaces. It has poor penetration power, however, so even a thin film of grease on the UV bulb or extraneous material covering microorganisms can markedly reduce its effective microbial killing. It is not useful for destroying microbes in solid substances or turbid liquids. Since most types of glass and plastic screen out ultraviolet radiation, UV light is most effective when used at close range against exposed microorganisms. Caution must be exercised in its use because UV rays can also damage the skin and eyes and promote the development of skin cancers.

Microwaves

Microwaves do not affect microorganisms directly, but they can kill microbes by the heat they generate in an item. Organisms often survive microwave cooking, however, because the food heats unevenly.

High Pressure

High pressure processing has recently been introduced as a way of pasteurizing commercial food products such as guacamole without the use of high temperatures. The process, which employs pressures of up to 130,000 psi (pounds per square inch), is thought to destroy microorganisms by denaturing proteins and altering the permeability of the cell. Products treated with high pressure processes retain the color and flavor associated with fresh foods.

MICROCHECK 5.4

Filters can be used to remove microorganisms and viruses from liquids and air. Gamma irradiation can be used to sterilize products and to decrease the number of microorganisms in foods. Ultraviolet light can be used to disinfect surfaces. Microwaves do not kill microbes directly, but by the heat they generate. Extreme pressure can kill microorganisms.

✓ What is the difference between the mechanism of a depth filter and that of a membrane filter?
✓ How does ultraviolet light kill microorganisms?
✓ Why could sterilization by gamma irradiation be carried out even after packaging?

5.5

Using Chemicals to Destroy Microorganisms and Viruses

Focus Points

- Describe the difference between sterilants, high-level disinfectants, intermediate-level disinfectants, and low-level disinfectants.
- Describe five important factors to consider when selecting an appropriate germicidal chemical.
- Compare and contrast the characteristics and use of alcohols, aldehydes, biguanides, ethylene oxide gas, halogens, metals, ozone, peroxygens, phenolic compounds, and quaternary ammonium compounds as germicidal chemicals.

Germicidal chemicals can be used to disinfect and, in some cases, sterilize. Most chemical germicides react irreversibly with vital proteins, DNA, cytoplasmic membranes or viral envelopes (**figure 5.8**). Their precise mechanisms of action, however, are often not completely understood. Although generally less reliable than heat, these chemicals are suitable for treating large surfaces and many heat-sensitive items. Some are sufficiently non-toxic to be used as antiseptics. Those that are only weakly germicidal, but have a **bacteriostatic** action, meaning that they prevent the growth of bacteria, can be used as preservatives.

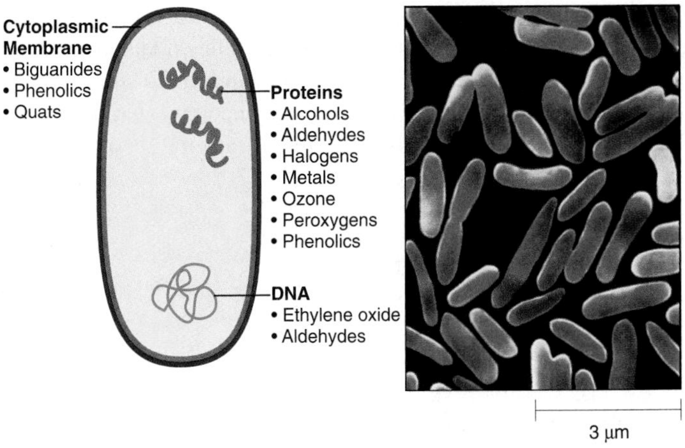

FIGURE 5.8 Sites of Action Germicidal Chemicals

Potency of Germicidal Chemical Formulations

Numerous different germicidal chemicals are marketed for medical and industrial use under a variety of trade names. Frequently, they contain more than one antimicrobial chemical as well as other chemicals such as buffers that can influence their antimicrobial activity. In the United States, the Food and Drug Administration (FDA) has the responsibility for regulating chemicals that can be used to process medical devices in order to ensure they perform as claimed. Most chemical disinfectants are considered pesticides and, as such, are regulated by the Environmental Protection Agency (EPA). To be registered with either the FDA or EPA, manufacturers of germicidal chemicals must document the potency of their products using testing procedures originally defined by the EPA. Germicides are grouped according to their potency:

- **Sterilants** can destroy all microorganisms, including their endospores, and viruses. Destruction of endospores usually requires a 6- to 10-hour treatment. Sterilants can be used to treat heat-sensitive critical instruments such as scalpels.
- **High-level disinfectants** destroy all viruses and vegetative microorganisms, but they do not reliably kill endospores. Most high-level disinfectants are simply sterilants used for time periods as short as 30 minutes, not long enough to ensure endospore destruction. They can be used to treat semicritical instruments such as gastrointestinal endoscopes.
- **Intermediate-level disinfectants** destroy all vegetative bacteria including mycobacteria, fungi, and most, but not all, viruses. They do not kill endospores even with prolonged exposure. They can be used to disinfect non-critical instruments such as stethoscopes.
- **Low-level disinfectants** destroy fungi, vegetative bacteria except mycobacteria, and enveloped viruses. They do not kill endospores, nor do they reliably destroy naked viruses. Intermediate-level and low-level disinfectants are also called **general-purpose disinfectants.**

To perform properly, germicides must be used strictly according to the manufacturer's directions, especially as they relate to dilution, temperature, and the amount of time they must be in contact with the object being treated. It is extremely important that the object be thoroughly cleaned and free of organic material before the germicidal procedure is begun.

Selecting the Appropriate Germicidal Chemical

Selecting the appropriate germicide is a complex decision. Some points to consider include:

- **Toxicity.** By nature, germicides are at least somewhat toxic to humans and the environment. Therefore, the benefit of disinfecting or sterilizing an item or surface must be weighed against the risks associated with using the germicidal procedure. For example, the risk of being exposed to a pathogenic microorganism in a hospital environment warrants using the most effective chemical germicides, even considering the potential risks of their use. The microbiological risks associated with typical household and office situations, however, may not justify the use of many of those same germicides.
- **Activity in the presence of organic matter.** Many germicidal chemicals, such as hypochlorite, are readily inactivated by organic matter and would not be appropriate to use in situations where organic material is present. Chemicals such as phenolics, however, tolerate the presence of some organic matter.
- **Compatibility with the material being treated.** Items such as electrical equipment often cannot tolerate liquid chemical germicides, and so gaseous alternatives must be employed. Likewise, corrosive germicides such as hypochlorite often damage some metals and rubber.
- **Residue.** Many chemical germicides leave a residue that is toxic or corrosive. If a germicide that leaves a residue is used to sterilize or disinfect an item, the item must be thoroughly rinsed to entirely remove the residue. Obviously, sterile items must be rinsed with sterile water.
- **Cost and availability.** Some germicides are less expensive and more readily available than others. For example, hypochlorite can easily be purchased in the form of household bleach. On the other hand, ethylene oxide gas is not only more expensive, but it must be used in a special chamber, which influences the cost and practicality of the procedure.
- **Storage and stability.** Germicides such as phenolics and iodophores are available in concentrated stock solutions, decreasing the required storage space. The stock solutions are simply diluted according to the manufacturer's instructions before use. Germicides such as glutaraldehyde and chlorine dioxide come in two-component systems that, once mixed, have a limited shelf life.
- **Environmental risk.** Germicides that retain their antimicrobial activity after use can interfere with sewage treatment systems that utilize bacteria to degrade sewage. The activity of those germicides must be neutralized before disposal.

Classes of Germicidal Chemicals

Germicides are represented in a number of chemical families. Each type has characteristics that make it more or less appropriate for specific uses **(table 5.2).**

Alcohols

Aqueous solutions of 60% to 80% ethyl or isopropyl alcohol rapidly kill vegetative bacteria and fungi. They do not, however, reliably destroy bacterial endospores and some naked viruses. Alcohol probably acts by coagulating enzymes and other essential proteins and by damaging lipid membranes. Proteins are more soluble and denature more easily in alcohol mixed with water, which is why aqueous solutions are more effective than pure alcohol.

Alcohol solutions are commonly used as antiseptics to degerm skin in preparation for procedures such as injections that break intact skin. In addition, the Centers for Disease Control recently recommended that alcohol-based hand sanitizers be used routinely by healthcare personnel as a means to protect patients. Not only have the hand sanitizers been shown to be more effective than soap and water, they are more convenient because their use does not require a sink.

Alcohol solutions are also used as disinfectants for treating instruments and surfaces. They are relatively non-toxic and inexpensive, and do not leave a residue, but they evaporate quickly which limits their effective contact time and, consequently, their germicidal effectiveness. In addition, they may damage some materials, such as rubber and some plastics.

Other antimicrobial chemicals are sometimes dissolved in alcohol. These alcohol-based solutions, called **tinctures,** can be more effective than the corresponding aqueous solutions.

Aldehydes

The aldehydes **glutaraldehyde, formaldehyde,** and **orthophthalaldehyde (OPA)** destroy microorganisms and viruses by inactivating proteins and nucleic acids. A 2% solution of alkaline glutaraldehyde is one of the most widely used liquid chemical sterilants for treating heat-sensitive medical items. Immersion in this solution for 10 to 12 hours destroys all forms of microbial life, including endospores, and viruses. Soaking times as short as 10 minutes can be used to destroy vegetative bacteria. Glutaraldehyde is toxic, however, so treated items must be thoroughly rinsed with sterile water before use. Orthophthalaldehyde is a new type of disinfectant that is being studied as an alternative to glutaraldehyde.

Formaldehyde is used as a gas or an aqueous 37% solution called **formalin.** It is an extremely effective germicide that kills most forms of microbial life within minutes. Formalin is used to kill bacteria and to inactivate viruses for use as vaccines. It has also been used to preserve biological specimens. Formaldehyde's irritating vapors and suspected carcinogenicity, however, now limit its use.

Biguanides

Chlorhexidine, the most effective of a group of chemicals called **biguanides,** is extensively used in antiseptic products. It adheres to and persists on skin and mucous membranes, is of relatively low toxicity, and destroys a wide range of microbes, including vegetative bacteria, fungi, and some enveloped viruses. Chlorhexidine is an

TABLE 5.2 Chemicals Used in Sterilization, and Disinfection, and Preservation of Non-Food Substances

Chemical (examples)	Characteristics	Uses
Alcohols (ethanol and isopropanol)	Easy to obtain and inexpensive. Rapid evaporation limits their contact time.	Aqueous solutions of alcohol are used as antiseptics to degerm skin in preparation for procedures that break intact skin, and as disinfectants for treating instruments.
Aldehydes (glutaraldehyde and formaldehyde)	Capable of destroying all forms of microbial life. Irritating to the respiratory tract, skin, and eyes.	Glutaraldehyde is widely used to sterilize medical instruments. Formalin is used in vaccine preparation.
Biguanides (chlorhexidine)	Relatively low toxicity, destroys a wide range of microbes, adheres to and persists on skin and mucous membranes.	Chlorhexidine is widely used as an antiseptic in soaps and lotions, and more recently, impregnated into catheters and surgical mesh.
Ethylene Oxide Gas	Easily penetrates hard-to-reach places and fabrics and does not damage moisture-sensitive material. It is toxic, explosive, and potentially carcinogenic.	Commonly used to sterilize medical devices.
Halogens (chlorine and iodine)	Chlorine solutions are inexpensive and readily available; however, organic compounds and other impurities neutralize the activity. Some forms of chlorine may react with organic compounds to form toxic chlorinated products. Iodine is more expensive than chlorine and does not reliably kill endospores.	Solutions of chlorine are widely used to disinfect inanimate objects, surfaces, drinking water, and wastewater. Tincture of iodine and iodophores can be used as disinfectants or antiseptics.
Metals (silver)	Most metal compounds are too toxic to be used medically.	Silver sulfadiazine is used in topical dressings to prevent infection of burns. Silver nitrate drops can be used to prevent eye infections caused by *Neisseria gonorrhoeae* in newborns. Some metal compounds are used to prevent microbial growth in industrial processes.
Ozone	This unstable form of molecular oxygen readily breaks down.	Used to disinfect drinking water and wastewater.
Peroxygens (hydrogen peroxide and peracetic acid)	Readily biodegradable and less toxic than traditional alternatives. The effectiveness of hydrogen peroxide as an antiseptic is limited because the enzyme catalase breaks it down. Peracetic acid is a more potent germicide than is hydrogen peroxide.	Hydrogen peroxide is used to sterilize containers for aseptically packaged juices and milk. Peracetic acid is widely used to disinfect and sterilize medical devices.
Phenolic Compounds (triclosan and hexachlorophene)	Wide range of activity, reasonable cost, remains effective in the presence of detergents and organic contaminants, leaves an active antimicrobial residue.	Triclosan is used in a variety of personal care products, including toothpastes, lotions, and deodorant soaps. Hexachlorophene is highly effective against *Staphylococcus aureus,* but its use is limited because it can cause neurological damage.
Quaternary Ammonium Compounds (benzalkonium chloride and cetylpyridinium chloride)	Non-toxic enough to be used on food preparation surfaces. Inactivated by anionic soaps and detergents.	Widely used to disinfect inanimate objects and to preserve non-food substances.

ingredient in a multitude of products including antiseptic skin creams, disinfectants, and mouthwashes. In the 1990s the FDA approved the use of chlorhexidine-impregnated catheters and implanted surgical mesh. Even tiny chips have been developed that can be inserted into periodontal pockets, where they slowly release chlorhexidine to treat periodontal gum disease. Adverse side effects of chlorhexidine are rare, but severe allergic reactions have been reported.

Ethylene Oxide

Ethylene oxide is an extremely useful gaseous sterilizing agent that destroys all microbes, including endospores and viruses, by reacting with proteins. As a gas, it penetrates well into fabrics, equipment, and implantable devices such as pacemakers and artificial hips. It is particularly useful for sterilizing heat- or moisture-sensitive items such as electrical equipment, pillows, and mattresses. Many disposable laboratory items, including plastic Petri dishes and pipets, are also sterilized with ethylene oxide.

A special chamber that resembles an autoclave is used to sterilize items with ethylene oxide. This allows the careful control of factors such as temperature, relative humidity, and ethylene oxide concentration, all of which influence the effectiveness of the gas. Because ethylene oxide is explosive, it is generally mixed with a non-flammable gas such as carbon dioxide. Under these carefully controlled conditions, objects can be sterilized in 3 to 12 hours. The toxic ethylene oxide must then be eliminated from the treated material using heated forced air for 8 to 12 hours. Absorbed ethylene oxide must be allowed to dissipate because of its irritating effects on tissues and its persistent antimicrobial effect, which, in the case of Petri dishes and other items used for culturing bacteria, is undesirable.

Ethylene oxide is mutagenic and therefore potentially carcinogenic. Indeed, studies have shown a slightly increased risk of malignancies in long-term users of the gas. Less toxic gaseous alternatives are currently being explored.

Halogens

Chlorine and iodine are common disinfectants that are thought to act by oxidizing proteins and other essential cell components.

Chlorine Chlorine destroys all types of microorganisms and viruses but is too irritating to skin and mucous membranes to be used as an antiseptic. Chlorine-releasing compounds such as sodium hypochlorite can be used to disinfect waste liquids, swimming pool water, instruments, and surfaces, and at much lower concentrations, to disinfect drinking water.

Chlorine solutions are inexpensive, readily available disinfectants. An effective disinfection solution can easily be made by diluting liquid household bleach (5.25% sodium hypochlorite) 1:100 in water, resulting in a solution of 500 ppm (parts per million) chlorine. This concentration is several hundred times the amount required to kill most pathogenic microorganisms and viruses, but it is usually necessary for fast, reliable killing. In situations when excessive organic material is present, a 1:10 dilution of bleach may be required. This is because chlorine also readily reacts with organic compounds and other impurities in water. These compounds consume free chlorine, reducing the germicidal activity of chlorine-releasing compounds. The use of high concentrations, however, should be avoided when possible, because chlorine is both corrosive and toxic. Diluted solutions of liquid bleach deteriorate over time; thus, fresh solutions need to be prepared regularly. More stable forms of chlorine, including sodium dichloroisocyanurate and chloramines, which are available in powders and tablets, are often used in hospitals.

Properly chlorinated drinking water contains approximately 0.5 ppm chlorine, much less than that used for disinfectant solutions. The exact amount of chlorine that must be added depends on the amount of organic material in the water. The presence of organic compounds is also a problem because chlorine can react with some organic compounds to form trihalomethanes, which are potential carcinogens. Note also that the concentrations of chlorine typically used to disinfect drinking water are not effective against *Cryptosporidium parvum* oocysts and *Giardia lamblia* cysts.

Chlorine dioxide (ClO_2) is a strong oxidizing agent that is increasingly being used as a disinfectant and sterilant. It has an advantage over chlorine-releasing compounds in that it does not react with organic compounds to form trihalomethanes or other toxic chlorinated products. Compressed chlorine dioxide gas, however, is explosive and liquid solutions decompose readily, so that it must be generated on-site. It is used to treat drinking water, wastewater, and swimming pools.

Iodine Iodine, unlike chlorine, does not reliably kill endospores, but it can be used as a disinfectant. It is used as a tincture in which the iodine is dissolved in alcohol, or more commonly as an **iodophore,** in which the iodine is linked to a carrier molecule that releases free (unbound) iodine slowly. Iodophores are not as irritating to the skin as tincture of iodine nor are they as likely to stain. Iodophores used as disinfectants contain more free iodine (30 to 50 ppm) than do those used as antiseptics (1 to 2 ppm). Stock solutions must be strictly diluted according to the manufacturer's instructions because dilution affects the amount of free iodine available.

Surprisingly, some *Pseudomonas* species survive in the concentrated stock solutions of iodophores. The reasons are unclear, but it may be due to inadequate levels of free iodine in concentrated solutions, the iodine being released from the carrier only with dilution. *Pseudomonas* species also can form biofilms, which are less permeable to chemicals. Nosocomial infections can result if a *Pseudomonas*-contaminated iodophore is unknowingly used to disinfect instruments. ■ biofilm, p. 89

Metal Compounds

Metal compounds kill microorganisms by combining with sulfhydryl groups of enzymes and other proteins, thereby interfering with their function. Unfortunately, most metals at high concentrations are too toxic to human tissue to be used medically.

Silver is one of the few metals still used as a disinfectant. Creams containing silver sulfadiazine, a combination of silver and a sulfa drug, are applied topically to prevent infection of second- and third-degree burns. Commercially available bandages with silver-containing pads have just been introduced for use on minor scalds, cuts, and scrapes. For many years, doctors were required by law to instill drops of another silver compound, 1% silver nitrate, into the eyes of newborns to prevent **ophthalmia neonatorum,** an eye infection caused by *Neisseria gonorrhoeae*, which is acquired from infected mothers during the birth process. Drops of antibiotics have now largely replaced use of silver nitrate because they are less irritating to the eye and more effective against another genitally acquired pathogen, *Chlamydia trachomatis.* ■ *Neisseria gonorrhoeae*, p. 661 ■ *Chlamydia trachomatis*, p. 663

Compounds of mercury, tin, arsenic, copper, and other metals were once widely used as preservatives in industrial products and to prevent microbial growth in recirculating cooling water. Their extensive use resulted in serious pollution of natural waters, which has prompted strict controls. The FDA is currently examining the list of antiseptics and other products that contain mercury compounds, such as thimerosal, and phenylmercuric acetate, in order to evaluate their safety.

Ozone

Ozone (O_3) is an unstable form of oxygen that is a powerful oxidizing agent. It decomposes quickly, however, so that it must be generated on-site, usually by passing air or oxygen between two electrodes. Ozone is increasingly being used as an alternative to chlorine for disinfecting drinking water and wastewater.

Peroxygens

Hydrogen peroxide and peracetic acid are powerful oxidizing agents that under controlled conditions can be used as sterilants.

PERSPECTIVE 5.1

Contamination of an Operating Room by a Bacterial Pathogen

A patient with burns infected with *Pseudomonas aeruginosa* was taken to the operating room for cleaning of the wounds and removal of dead tissue. After the procedure was completed, samples of various surfaces in the room were cultured to determine the extent of contamination. *P. aeruginosa* was recovered from all parts of the room. **Figure 1** shows how readily and extensively an operating room can become contaminated by an infected patient. Operating rooms and other patient care rooms must be thoroughly cleaned after use, in a process known as terminal cleaning.

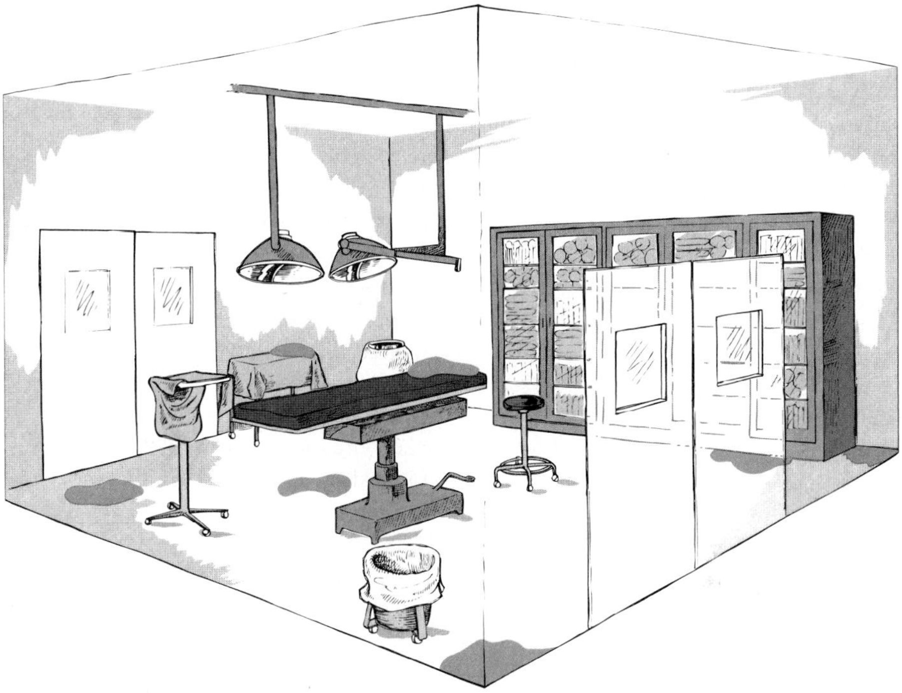

FIGURE 1 Diagram of an operating room in which dead tissue infected with *Pseudomonas aeruginosa* was removed from a patient with burns. Reddish areas indicate places where *P. aeruginosa* was recovered following the surgical procedure.

They are readily biodegradable and, in normal concentrations of use, appear to be less toxic than the traditional alternatives, ethylene oxide and glutaraldehyde.

Hydrogen Peroxide The effectiveness of hydrogen peroxide (H_2O_2) as a germicide depends in part on whether it is used on living tissue, such as a wound, or on an inanimate object. This is because all cells that use aerobic metabolism, including the body's cells, produce the enzyme catalase, which inactivates hydrogen peroxide by breaking it down to water and oxygen gas. Thus, when a solution of 3% hydrogen peroxide is applied to a wound, our cellular enzymes quickly break it down. When the same solution is used on an inanimate surface, however, it overwhelms the relatively low concentration of catalase produced by microscopic organisms. ■ catalase, p. 96

Hydrogen peroxide is particularly useful as a disinfectant because it leaves no residue and does not damage stainless steel, rubber, plastic, or glass. Hot solutions are commonly used in the food industry to yield commercially sterile containers for aseptically packaged juices and milk. Vapor-phase hydrogen peroxide is more effective than liquid solutions and can be used as a sterilant.

Peracetic Acid Peracetic acid is an even more potent germicide than hydrogen peroxide. A 0.2% solution of peracetic acid, or a combination of peracetic acid and hydrogen peroxide, can be used to sterilize items in less than 1 hour. It is effective in the presence of organic compounds, leaves no residue, and can be used on a wide range of materials. It has a sharp, pungent odor, however, and like other oxidizing agents, it is irritating to the skin and eyes.

Phenolic Compounds (Phenolics)

Phenol (carbolic acid) is important historically because it was one of the earliest disinfectants, but its use is now limited because it has an unpleasant odor and irritates the skin. A group of structurally related compounds, however, have increased germicidal activity, which enables effective use of more dilute and therefore less irritating solutions. Phenolic compounds are the active ingredients in Lysol™.

Phenolics destroy cytoplasmic membranes of microorganisms and denature proteins. They kill most vegetative bacteria and, in high concentrations (from 5% to 19%), many can kill *Mycobacterium tuberculosis*. They do not, however, reliably inactivate all groups of viruses. The major advantages of phenolic compounds include their wide range of activity, reasonable cost, and ability to remain effective in the presence of detergents and organic contaminants. They also leave an active antimicrobial residue, which in some cases is desirable.

Some phenolics, such as **triclosan** and **hexachlorophene,** are sufficiently non-toxic to be used in soaps and lotions. Triclosan is widely used as an ingredient in a variety of personal care products such as deodorant soaps, lotions, and toothpaste. Hexachlorophene has substantial activity against *Staphylococcus aureus*, the leading cause of wound infections, but high levels have been associated with symptoms of neurotoxicity. Although once widely used in over-the-counter products, antiseptic skin cleansers containing hexachlorophene are now available only with a prescription.

Quaternary Ammonium Compounds (Quats)

Quaternary ammonium compounds, also commonly called quats, are cationic (positively charged) detergents that are non-toxic enough to be used to disinfect food preparation surfaces. Like all detergents, quats have both a charged hydrophilic region and an uncharged hydrophobic region. This enables them to reduce the surface tension of liquids and help wash away dirt and organic material, facilitating the mechanical removal of microorganisms from surfaces. Unlike most common household soaps and detergents, however, which are anionic (negatively charged) and repelled by the negatively charged microbial cell surface, quats are attracted to the cell surface. They react with membranes, destroying many vegetative bacteria and enveloped viruses. They are not effective, however, against endospores, mycobacteria, or naked viruses.

Quaternary ammonium compounds are economical and effective agents that are widely used to disinfect clean inanimate objects and to preserve non-food substances. The ingredients of many personal care products include quats such as benzalkonium chloride or cetylpyridinium chloride. They also enhance the effectiveness of some other disinfectants. Cationic soaps and organic material such as gauze, however, can neutralize their effectiveness. In addition, *Pseudomonas*, a troublesome cause of nosocomial infections, resists the effects of quats and can even grow in solutions preserved with them.

MICROCHECK 5.5

Germicidal chemicals can be used to disinfect and, in some cases, sterilize, but they are less reliable than heat. They are especially useful for destroying microorganisms and viruses on heat-sensitive items and large surfaces.

- ✓ Describe four factors that must be considered when selecting a germicidal chemical.
- ✓ Explain why it is essential to dilute iodophores properly.
- ✓ Why would a heavy metal be a more serious pollutant than most organic compounds?

5.6

Preservation of Perishable Products

Focus Point

- Explain how chemical preservatives, low-temperature storage, adding salt or sugar, and drying food can all be used to preserve perishable products.

Preventing or slowing the growth of microorganisms extends the shelf life of products such as food, soaps, medicines, deodorants, cosmetics, and contact lens solutions. Preservative chemicals are often added to these products to prevent or slow the growth of microbes that are inevitably introduced from the environment. Other common methods of decreasing the growth rate of microbes include low-temperature storage such as refrigeration or freezing, and reducing available water. These methods are particularly important in preserving foods. ■ food spoilage, p. 805 ■ factors influencing the growth of microorganisms in foods, p. 796

Chemical Preservatives

Some of the germicidal chemicals previously described can be used to preserve non-food items. For example, shampoo may contain formaldehyde, mouthwash may contain a quaternary ammonium compound, nasal sprays may contain thimerosal, and leather belts may be treated with one or more phenol derivatives. Food preservatives, however, must be non-toxic for repeated safe ingestion.

Benzoic, sorbic, and propionic acids are weak organic acids that are sometimes added to foods such as bread, cheese, and juice to prevent microbial growth. In the form that predominates at a low pH, these weak acids alter cell membrane functions and interfere with energy transformation. The low pH at which they are most effective is itself sufficient to prevent the growth of most bacteria, so these preservatives are primarily added to acidic foods to prevent the growth of fungi. These organic acids also occur naturally in some foods such as cranberries and Swiss cheese.

Another preservative, nitrate, and its reduced form, nitrite, serve a dual purpose in processed meats. From a microbiological viewpoint, their most important function is to inhibit the germination of endospores and subsequent growth of *Clostridium botulinum*. Without the addition of low levels of nitrate or nitrite to cured meats such as bologna, ham, bacon, and smoked fish, *C. botulinum* may grow and produce deadly botulinum toxin. At higher concentrations than are required for preservation, nitrate and nitrite react with myoglobin in the meat to form a stable pigment that gives a desirable pink color associated with fresh meat. Nitrates and nitrites also pose a potential hazard, however, because they can be converted to nitrosamines during the frying of meats in hot oil or by the metabolic activities of intestinal bacteria. Nitrosoamines have been shown to be potent carcinogens, which has caused concern regarding the use of nitrate and nitrite as preservatives.

Low-Temperature Storage

Growth of microorganisms is temperature-dependent. At low temperatures above freezing, many enzymatic reactions are very slow or nonexistent. Thus, low temperature storage is extremely useful in preservation. Psychrotrophic and some psychrophilic organisms, however, can grow at normal refrigeration temperatures. ■ psychrophiles, p. 94

Commercially, some fruits and vegetables such as apples and potatoes are held in cold storage for many months. Products are stored at temperatures near 10°C, in the dark, and at appropriate humidity and oxygen concentration. Prior to refrigeration, foods are sometimes irradiated with UV light to reduce the number of spoilage organisms.

Freezing is also an important means of preserving foods and other products. Freezing essentially stops all microbial growth. The formation of ice crystals can irreversibly damage microbial cells, killing up to 50% of the microorganisms. The remaining organisms, however, can grow and spoil foods once they are thawed.

Reducing the Available Water

For many years, salting and drying have been used to preserve food. Both processes decrease the availability of water in food below the limits required for growth of most microorganisms. The high-solute environment causes plasmolysis, which damages cells (see figure 4.10). ■ plasmolysis, p. 97

Adding Salt or Sugar

Sugar and salt draw water out of cells, dehydrating them. High concentrations of sugars or salts are added to many foods as preservatives. For example, fruit is made into jams and jellies by adding sugar, and fish and meats are cured by soaking them in salty water, or **brine.** Some caution should be exercised when using salt as a preservative, however, because the food-poisoning bacterium *Staphylococcus aureus* can grow under quite high salt conditions. ■ *Staphylococcus aureus,* p. 806

Drying Food

Removing water, or **desiccating,** food is often supplemented by other methods, such as salting or adding high concentrations of sugar or small amounts of chemical preservatives. For example, meat jerkies usually have added salt and sometimes sugar.

Lyophilization (freeze-drying) is widely used for preserving foods such as coffee, milk, meats, and vegetables. In the process of freeze-drying, the food is first frozen and then dried in a vacuum. When water is added to the lyophilized material, it reconstitutes. The quality of the reconstituted product is often much better than that of products treated with ordinary drying methods. The light weight and stability without refrigeration of freeze-dried foods make them popular with hikers.

Although drying stops microbial growth, it does not reliably kill bacteria and fungi in or on foods. For example, numerous cases of salmonellosis have been traced to dried eggs. Eggshells and even egg yolks may be heavily contaminated with *Salmonella* species from the gastrointestinal tract of the hen. To prevent the transmission of such pathogens, some states have laws requiring dried eggs to be pasteurized before they are sold.

MICROCHECK 5.6

Preservation techniques slow or halt the growth of microorganisms to delay spoilage.

- ✓ What organism that causes food poisoning is able to grow under high-salt conditions?
- ✓ What is the risk of consuming nitrate- or nitrite-free cured meats?
- ✓ Preservation by freezing is sometimes compared to drying. Why would this be so?

FUTURE CHALLENGES

Too Much of a Good Thing?

In our complex world, the solution to one challenge may inadvertently lead to the creation of another. Scientists have long been pursuing less toxic alternatives to many traditional biocidal chemicals. For example, glutaraldehyde has now largely replaced the more toxic formaldehyde, chlorhexidine is generally used in place of hexachlorophene, and gaseous alternatives to ethylene oxide are now being sought. Meanwhile, ozone and hydrogen peroxide, which are both readily biodegradable, may eventually replace glutaraldehyde. While these less toxic alternatives are better for human health and the environment, their widespread acceptance and use may be unwittingly contributing to an additional problem—the overuse and misuse of germicidal chemicals. Many products, including soaps, toothbrushes, and even clothing and toys are marketed with the claim of containing antimicrobial ingredients. Already there are reports of bacterial resistance to some of the chemicals included in these products.

The issues surrounding the excessive use of antimicrobial chemicals are complicated. On the one hand, there is no question that some microorganisms cause disease. Even those that are not harmful to human health can be troublesome because they produce metabolic end products that ruin the quality of perishable products. Based on that information, it seems prudent to destroy or inhibit the growth of microorganisms whenever possible. The role of microorganisms in our life, however, is not that simple. Our bodies actually harbor a greater number of microbial cells than human cells, and this normal microbial flora plays an important role in maintaining our health. Excessive use of antiseptics or other antimicrobials may actually predispose a person to infection by damaging the normal flora.

An even more worrisome concern is that overuse of disinfectants and other germicidal chemicals will select for microorganisms that are more resistant to those chemicals, a situation analogous to our current problems with antibiotic resistance. By using antimicrobial chemicals indiscriminately, we may eventually make these useful tools obsolete. Excessive use of disinfectants may even be contributing to the problems of antibiotic resistance. Early indications suggest that disinfectant-resistant bacteria over-produce efflux pumps that expel otherwise damaging chemicals, including antibiotics, from the cell. Thus, by overusing disinfectants, we may be inadvertently increasing antibiotic resistance.

Another concern is over the misguided belief that "non-toxic" or "biodegradable" chemicals cause no harm, and the common notion that "if a little is good, more is even better." For example, concentrated solutions of hydrogen peroxide, though biodegradable, can cause serious damage, even death, when used improperly. Other chemicals, such as chlorhexidine, can elicit severe allergic reactions in some people.

As less toxic germicidal chemicals are developed, people must be educated on the appropriate use of these alternatives.

SUMMARY

5.1 Approaches to Control

The methods used to destroy or remove microorganisms and viruses can be **physical,** such as heat treatment, irradiation, and filtration, or **chemical.**

Principles of Control

A variety of terms are used to describe antimicrobial agents and processes.

Situational Considerations (Figure 5.1)

Situations encountered in daily life, hospitals, microbiology laboratories, food production facilities, water treatment facilities, and other industries warrant different degrees of microbial control.

5.2 Selection of an Antimicrobial Procedure

Type of Microorganism

One of the most critical considerations in selecting a method of destroying microorganisms and viruses is the type of microbial population present on or in the product.

Numbers of Microorganisms Initially Present

The amount of time it takes for heat or chemicals to kill a population of microorganisms is dictated in part by the number of cells initially present.

Microbial death generally occurs at a constant rate.

The **D value,** or **decimal reduction time,** is the time it takes to kill 90% of a population of bacteria under specific conditions. (Figure 5.2)

Environmental Conditions

Factors such as pH or presence of fats and other organic materials strongly influence microbial death rates.

Potential Risk of Infection

To guide medical biosafety personnel in their selection of germicidal procedures, instruments are categorized as **critical, semicritical,** and **non-critical** according to their potential risk of transmitting infectious agents.

Composition of the Item

Some sterilization and disinfection procedures are inappropriate for certain types of material.

5.3 Using Heat to Destroy Microorganisms and Viruses (Figure 5.1)

Moist Heat

Moist heat destroys microorganisms by causing irreversible coagulation of their proteins.

Pasteurization utilizes a brief heat treatment to destroy spoilage and disease-causing organisms.

Pressure cookers and **autoclaves** heat water in an enclosed vessel that causes the pressure in the vessel to increase beyond atmospheric pressure, increasing the temperature of steam, which kills endospores. (Figure 5.3)

The most important aspect of the commercial canning process is to ensure that endospores of *Clostridium botulinum* are destroyed. (Figure 5.5)

Dry Heat

Incineration oxidizes cell components to ashes. Temperatures achieved in hot air ovens oxidize cell components and irreversibly denature proteins.

5.4 Using Other Physical Methods to Remove or Destroy Microbes

Filtration (Figure 5.6)

Depth filters and **membrane filters** retain microorganisms while letting the suspending fluid pass through.

High-efficiency particulate air (HEPA) filters remove nearly all microorganisms.

Radiation (Figure 5.7)

Gamma rays cause biological damage by producing superoxide and hydroxyl free radicals; gamma rays can be used to sterilize heat-sensitive materials and to decrease the numbers of microorganisms in foods.

Ultraviolet light damages the structure and function of nucleic acids; it is used to disinfect surfaces.

Microwaves do not affect microorganisms directly, but kill microorganisms by the heat they generate in a product.

High Pressure

High pressure is thought to destroy microorganisms by denaturing proteins and altering the permeability of the cell.

5.5 Using Chemicals to Destroy Microorganisms and Viruses

Potency of Germicidal Chemical Formulations

Germicides are grouped according to their potency as **sterilants, high-level disinfectants, intermediate-level disinfectants,** or **low-level disinfectants.**

Selecting the Appropriate Germicidal Chemical

Factors that must be included in the selection of an appropriate germicidal chemical include toxicity, residue, activity in the presence of organic matter, compatibility with the material being treated, cost and availability, storage and stability, and ease of disposal.

Classes of Germicidal Chemicals (Table 5.2)

Solutions of 60% to 80% ethyl or isopropyl alcohol in water rapidly kill vegetative bacteria and fungi by coagulating enzymes and other essential proteins, and by damaging lipid membranes.

Glutaraldehyde and **formaldehyde** destroy microorganisms and viruses by inactivating proteins and nucleic acids.

Chlorhexidine is a **biguanide** extensively used in antiseptic products.

Ethylene oxide is a gaseous sterilizing agent that penetrates well and destroys microorganisms and viruses by reacting with proteins.

Sodium hypochlorite (liquid bleach) is one of the least expensive and most readily available forms of chlorine. **Chlorine dioxide** is used as a sterilant and disinfectant. **Iodophores** are iodine-releasing compounds used as antiseptics.

Metals interfere with protein function. Silver-containing compounds are used to prevent wound infections.

Ozone is used as an alternative to chlorine in the disinfection of drinking water and wastewater.

Peroxide and peracetic acid are both strong oxidizing agents that can be used alone or in combination as sterilants.

Phenolic compounds destroy cytoplasmic membranes and denature proteins. **Triclosan** is used in lotions and deodorant soaps.

Quaternary ammonium compounds are cationic detergents; they are non-toxic enough to be used to disinfect food preparation surfaces.

5.6 Preservation of Perishable Products

Chemical Preservatives

Benzoic, sorbic, and propionic acids are sometimes added to foods to prevent microbial growth.

Nitrate and nitrite are added to some foods to inhibit the germination and subsequent growth of *Clostridium botulinum* endospores.

Low-Temperature Storage

Low temperatures above freezing inhibit microbial growth because many enzymatic reactions are rendered slow or nonexistent.

Freezing essentially stops all microbial growth.

Reducing the Available Water

Sugar and salt draws water out of cells, preventing the growth of microorganisms.

Lyophilization is used for preserving food. The food is first frozen and then dried in a vacuum.

REVIEW QUESTIONS

Short Answer

1. What is the primary reason that milk is pasteurized?
2. What is the primary reason that wine is pasteurized?
3. What is the most chemically resistant non-spore-forming bacterial pathogen?
4. Why are low acid foods processed at higher temperatures than high acid foods?
5. Explain why it takes longer to kill a population of 10^9 cells than it does to kill a population of 10^3 cells.
6. How is an iodophore different from a tincture of iodine?
7. How does microwaving a food product kill bacteria?
8. How is preservation different from pasteurization?
9. How are heat-sensitive liquids sterilized?
10. Name two products commonly sterilized using ethylene oxide gas.

Multiple Choice

1. Unlike a disinfectant, an antiseptic
   a) sanitizes objects rather than sterilizes them.
   b) destroys all microorganisms.
   c) is nontoxic enough to be used on human tissue.
   d) requires heat to be effective.
   e) can be used in food products.
2. The D value is defined as the time it takes to kill
   a) all bacteria in a population.
   b) all pathogens in a population.
   c) 99.9% of bacteria in a population.
   d) 90% of bacteria in a population.
   e) 10% of bacteria in a population.
3. Which of the following is the most resistant to destruction by chemicals and heat?
   a) Bacterial endospores
   b) Fungal spores
   c) *Mycobacterium tuberculosis*
   d) *E. coli*
   e) HIV
4. Ultraviolet light kills bacteria by
   a) generating heat.
   b) damaging nucleic acids.
   c) inhibiting protein synthesis.
   d) damaging cell walls.
   e) damaging cytoplasmic membranes.
5. Which concentration of ethyl alcohol is the most effective germicide?
   a) 100%
   b) 75%
   c) 50%
   d) 25%
   e) 5%
6. Which of the following chemical agents can most reliably be used to sterilize objects?
   a) Alcohol
   b) Phenolic compounds
   c) Ethylene oxide gas
   d) Iodine
7. All of the following are routinely used to preserve foods, except
   a) high concentrations of sugar.
   b) high concentrations of salt.
   c) benzoic acid.
   d) freezing.
   e) ethylene oxide.
8. Aseptically boxed juices and cream containers are processed using which of the following heating methods?
   a) Canning
   b) High-temperature-short-time (HIST) method
   c) Low-temperature-long-time (LTLT) method
   d) Ultra-high-temperature (UHT) method
9. Commercial canning processes are designed to ensure destruction of which of the following?
   a) All vegetative bacteria
   b) All vegetative bacteria and their endospores
   c) Endospores of *Clostridium botulinum*
   d) *E. coli*
   e) *Mycobacterium tuberculosis*
10. Which of the following is false?
    a) A chemical that is a high-level disinfectant cannot be used as a sterilant.
    b) Critical items must be sterilized before use.
    c) Low numbers of endospores may remain on semicritical items.
    d) Standard sterilization procedures do not destroy prions.
    e) Quaternary ammonium compounds can be used to disinfect food preparation surfaces.

Applications

1. An agriculture extension agent is preparing pamphlets on preventing the spread of disease. In the pamphlet, he must explain the appropriate situations for using disinfectants around the house. What situations should the agent discuss?
2. As a microbiologist representing a food corporation, you have been asked to serve on a health food panel to debate the need for chemical preservatives in foods. Your role is to prepare a statement that compares the benefits of chemical preservatives and the risks. What points must you bring up that indicate the benefits of chemical preservatives?

Critical Thinking

1. This graph shows the time it takes to kill populations of the same microorganism under different conditions. What conditions would explain the differences in lines a, b, and c?

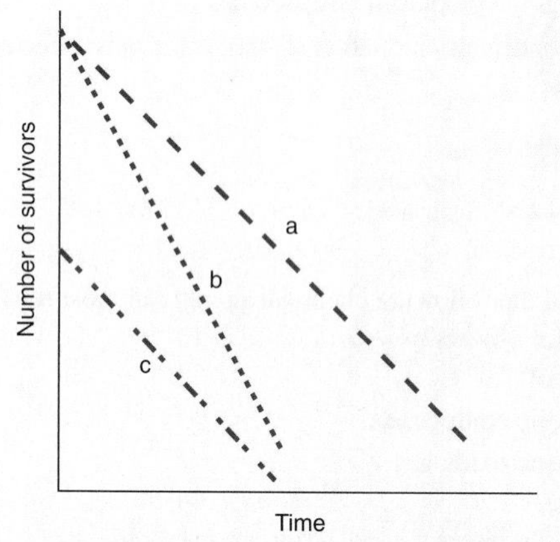

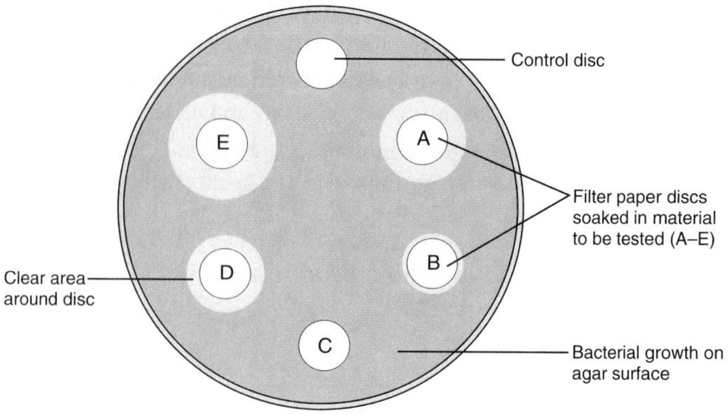

2. This diagram shows the filter paper method used to evaluate the inhibitory effect of chemical agents, heavy metals, and antibiotics on bacterial growth. A culture of test bacteria is spread uniformly over the surface of an agar plate. Small filter paper discs containing the material to be tested are then placed on the surface of the medium. A disc that has been soaked in sterile distilled water is sometimes added as a control. After incubation, a film of growth will cover the plate, but a clear zone will surround those discs that contain an inhibitory compound. The size of the zone reflects several factors, one of which is the effectiveness of the inhibitory agent. What are two other factors that might affect the size of the zone of inhibition? What is the purpose of the control disc? If a clear area were apparent around the control disc, how would you interpret the observation?

Wine—a beverage produced using microbial metabolism.

CHAPTER SIX

Metabolism: Fueling Cell Growth

A Glimpse of History

In the 1850s, Louis Pasteur, a chemist, accepted the challenge of studying how alcohol arises from grape juice. Biologists had already observed that when grape juice is held in large vats, alcohol and carbon dioxide are produced and the number of yeast cells increases. They argued that the multiplying yeast cells convert the sugar in the juice to alcohol and carbon dioxide. Pasteur agreed, but could not convince two very powerful and influential German chemists, Justus von Liebig and Friedrich Wöhler, who refused to believe that microorganisms caused the breakdown of sugar. Both men lampooned the hypothesis and tried to discredit it by publishing pictures of yeast cells looking like miniature animals taking in grape juice through one orifice and releasing carbon dioxide and alcohol through the other.

Pasteur studied the relationship between yeast and alcohol production using a strategy commonly employed by scientists today—that is, simplifying the experimental system so that relationships can be more easily identified. First, he prepared a clear solution of sugar, ammonia, mineral salts, and trace elements. He then added a few yeast cells. As the yeast grew, the sugar level decreased and the alcohol level increased, indicating that the sugar was being converted to alcohol as the cells multiplied. This strongly suggested that living cells caused the chemical transformation. Liebig, however, still would not believe the process was actually occurring inside microorganisms. To convince him, Pasteur tried to extract something from inside the yeast cells that would convert the sugar. He failed, like many others before him.

In 1897, Eduard Buchner, a German chemist, showed that crushed yeast cells could convert sugar to ethanol and CO_2. We now know that enzymes of the crushed cells carried out this transformation. For these pioneering studies, Buchner was awarded the Nobel Prize in 1907. He was the first of many investigators who received Nobel Prizes for studies on the processes by which cells degrade sugars.

To grow, all cells must accomplish two fundamental tasks. They must continually synthesize new components including cell walls, membranes, ribosomes, nucleic acids, and surface structures such as flagella. These allow the cell to enlarge and eventually divide. In addition, cells need to harvest energy and convert it to a form that is usable to power biosynthetic reactions, transport nutrients and other molecules, and in some cases, move. The sum total of chemical reactions used for biosynthetic and energy-harvesting processes is called **metabolism.**

Bacterial metabolism is important to humans for a number of reasons. Many bacterial products are commercially or medically important. For example, cheese-makers intentionally add *Lactococcus* and *Lactobacillus* species to milk because the metabolic wastes of these bacteria contribute to the flavor and texture of various cheeses. Yet those same products contribute to tooth decay when related bacteria are growing on teeth. Microbial metabolism is also important in the laboratory, because products that are characteristic of a specific group of microorganisms can be used as identifying markers. The metabolic end products of *Escherichia coli* distinguish it from related Gram-negative rods such as *Klebsiella* and *Enterobacter* species. In addition, the metabolic pathways of organisms such as *E. coli* have served as an invaluable model for studying analogous processes in eukaryotic cells, including those of humans. Metabolic processes unique to prokaryotes are potential targets for antimicrobial drugs.

6.1 Principles of Metabolism

Focus Points

- Compare and contrast catabolism and anabolism (biosynthesis).
- Describe the energy sources used by photosynthetic organisms and chemoorganoheterotrophs.

KEY TERMS

Adenosine triphosphate (ATP) The energy currency of cells. Hydrolysis of its unstable phosphate bonds can be used to power endergonic (energy-consuming) reactions.

Anabolism Processes that utilize energy stored in ATP to synthesize and assemble the subunits (building blocks) of macromolecules that make up the cell; biosynthesis.

Catabolism Processes that harvest energy released during the breakdown of compounds such as glucose, using it to synthesize ATP.

Electron transport chain Group of membrane-embedded electron carriers that pass electrons from one to another, and, in the process, move protons across the membrane to create a proton motive force.

Enzyme A protein that functions as a catalyst, speeding up a biological reaction.

Fermentation Metabolic process that stops short of oxidizing glucose or other organic compounds completely, using an organic intermediate such as pyruvate or a derivative as a terminal electron acceptor.

Oxidative phosphorylation Synthesis of ATP using the energy of a proton motive force created by harvesting chemical energy.

Photophosphorylation Synthesis of ATP using the energy of a proton motive force created by harvesting radiant energy.

Precursor metabolite Metabolic intermediates that can either be used to make the subunits of macromolecules, or be oxidized to generate ATP.

Proton motive force Form of energy generated as an electron transport chain moves protons across a membrane, creating a chemiosmotic gradient.

Respiration Process that involves transfer of electrons stripped from a chemical energy source to an electron transport chain, generating a proton motive force that is then used to synthesize ATP.

Substrate-level phosphorylation Synthesis of ATP using the energy released in an exergonic (energy-releasing) reaction.

Terminal electron acceptor Chemical such as O_2 that is ultimately reduced as a consequence of fermentation or respiration.

- Describe the components of metabolic pathways (enzymes, ATP, chemical energy source, redox reactions, electron carriers, and precursor metabolites).
- List the three central metabolic pathways.
- Distinguish between respiration and fermentation.

Metabolism can be viewed as having two components—**catabolism** and **anabolism (figure 6.1).** Catabolism encompasses processes that harvest energy released during the disassembly or breakdown of compounds such as glucose, using that energy to synthesize **ATP,** the energy currency of all cells. In contrast, anabolism, or **biosynthesis,** includes processes that utilize energy stored in ATP to synthesize and assemble subunits (building blocks) of macromolecules that make up the cell. These subunits include amino acids, nucleotides, and lipids.

Although catabolism and anabolism are often discussed separately, they are intimately linked. As mentioned, ATP generated during catabolism is used in anabolism. In addition, some of the compounds produced in steps of the catabolic processes can be diverted by the cell and used as precursors of subunits employed in anabolic processes. ■ ATP, p. 26

Harvesting Energy

Energy is defined as the capacity to do work. It can exist as **potential energy,** which is stored energy, and **kinetic energy,** which is energy of motion **(figure 6.2).** Potential energy can be stored in various forms including chemical bonds, a rock on a hill, or water behind a dam.

Energy in the universe can never be created or destroyed; however, it can be changed from one form to another. In other words, while energy cannot be created, potential energy can be converted to kinetic energy and vice versa, and one form of potential energy can be converted to another. For example, hydroelectric dams unleash the potential energy of water stored behind a dam, creating the kinetic energy of moving water; this can then be used to generate an electrical current, which can then be used to charge a battery.

Photosynthetic organisms harvest the energy of sunlight, using it to power the synthesis of organic compounds such as glucose **(figure 6.3).** In other words, they convert the kinetic energy of photons to the potential energy of chemical bonds.

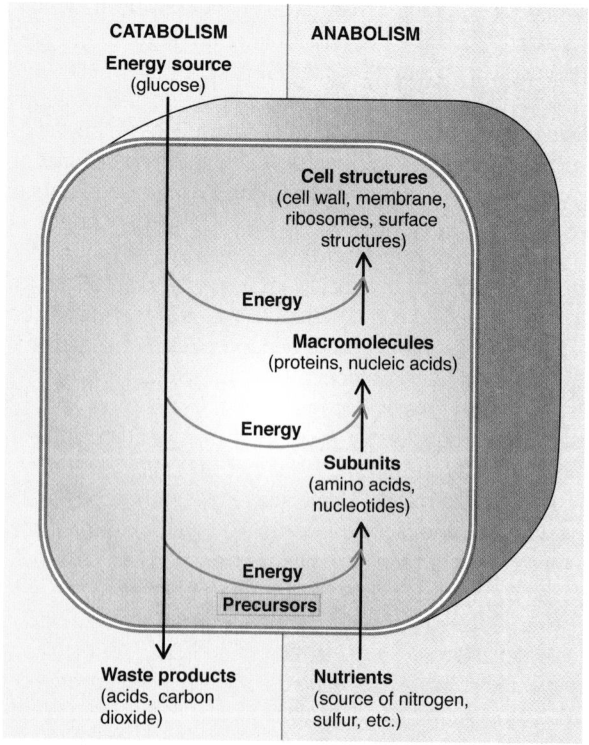

FIGURE 6.1 The Relationship Between Catabolism and Anabolism Catabolism encompasses processes that harvest energy released during disassembly of compounds, using it to synthesize ATP; it also provides precursor metabolites used in biosynthesis. Anabolism, or biosynthesis, includes processes that utilize ATP and precursor metabolites to synthesize and assemble subunits of macromolecules that make up the cell.

FIGURE 6.2 **Forms of Energy** Potential energy is stored energy, such as water held behind a dam. Kinetic energy is the energy of motion, such as movement of water from behind the dam.

Chemoorganotrophs obtain energy by degrading organic compounds such as glucose, releasing the energy of their chemical bonds. Thus, most chemoorganotrophs ultimately depend on solar energy harvested by photosynthetic organisms, because this is what is used to power the synthesis of glucose.

The amount of energy available for harvest by breaking down a compound can be explained by the concept of **free energy.** This is the energy available to do work; from a biological perspective, it is the energy that can be released when a chemical bond is broken. In a chemical reaction, some bonds are broken and others are formed. If the **reactants,** or starting compounds, have more free energy than the **products,** or final compounds, energy is released in the reaction. The reaction is said to be **exergonic.** In contrast, if the products have more free energy than the reactants, the reaction requires an input of energy and is termed **endergonic.**

The change in free energy for a given reaction is the same regardless of the number of steps involved. For example, converting glucose to carbon dioxide and water in a single step by combustion releases the same amount of energy as degrading it in a series of steps. Cells exploit this fact to slowly release free energy from compounds, harvesting the energy released at each step. A specific energy-releasing reaction is used to power an energy utilizing reaction.

Components of Metabolic Pathways

Metabolic processes often occur as a series of sequential chemical reactions, which constitute a **metabolic pathway (figure 6.4).** A series of **intermediates** are produced as the starting compound is gradually converted into the final product, or **end product.** A metabolic pathway can be linear, branched, or cyclical, and, like the flow of a river controlled by dams, its activity may be modulated

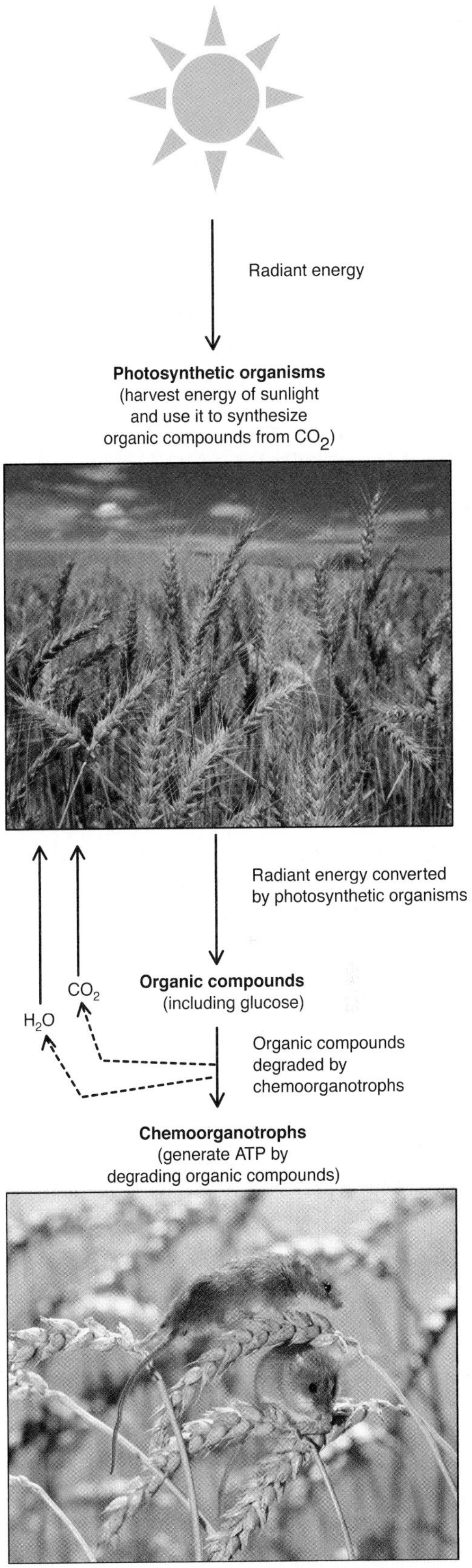

FIGURE 6.3 **Most Chemoorganotrophs Depend on the Radiant Energy Harvested by Photosynthetic Organisms** Photosynthetic organisms use the energy of sunlight to power the synthesis of organic compounds; chemoorganotrophs can then use those organic compounds as an energy source.

at certain points. In this way, a cell can regulate certain processes, ensuring that specific molecules are produced in precise quantities when needed. If a metabolic step is blocked, all products "downstream" of that blockage will be affected.

The intermediates and end products of metabolic pathways are sometimes organic acids, which are weak acids. Depending on the pH, these may exist primarily as either the undissociated form or the dissociated (ionized) form. Biologists often use the names of the two forms interchangeably, for example pyruvic acid and pyruvate. Note, however, that at the near-neutral pH inside the cell, the ionized form predominates, whereas outside of the cell, the acid may predominate. ■ pH, p. 25

To recognize what metabolic pathways accomplish, it is helpful to first understand the critical components—enzymes, ATP, the chemical energy source, electron carriers, and precursor metabolites.

The Role of Enzymes

A specific **enzyme** facilitates each step of a metabolic pathway. Enzymes are proteins that function as biological catalysts, accelerating the conversion of one substance, the **substrate,** into another, the **product.** Without enzymes, energy-yielding reactions would still occur, but at rates so slow they would be imperceptible.

An enzyme catalyzes a chemical reaction by lowering the **activation energy** of that reaction **(figure 6.5).** This is the energy it takes to initiate a chemical reaction; even exergonic chemical reactions have an activation energy. By lowering the activation energy barrier, enzymes allow chemicals to undergo rearrangements.

The Role of ATP

Adenosine triphosphate (ATP) is the energy currency of a cell, serving as the ready and immediate donor of free energy. It is composed of the sugar ribose, the nitrogenous base adenine, and three phosphate groups (see figure 2.10). Its counterpart, **adenosine diphosphate (ADP),** can be viewed as an acceptor of free energy. An input of energy is required to add an inorganic phosphate group (P_i) to ADP, forming ATP; energy is released when that group is removed from ATP, yielding ADP **(figure 6.6).**

The phosphate groups of ATP are arranged in tandem (see figure 2.10). Their negative charges repel each other, making the bonds that join them unstable. The bonds are readily hydrolyzed, releasing the phosphate group and a sufficient amount of energy

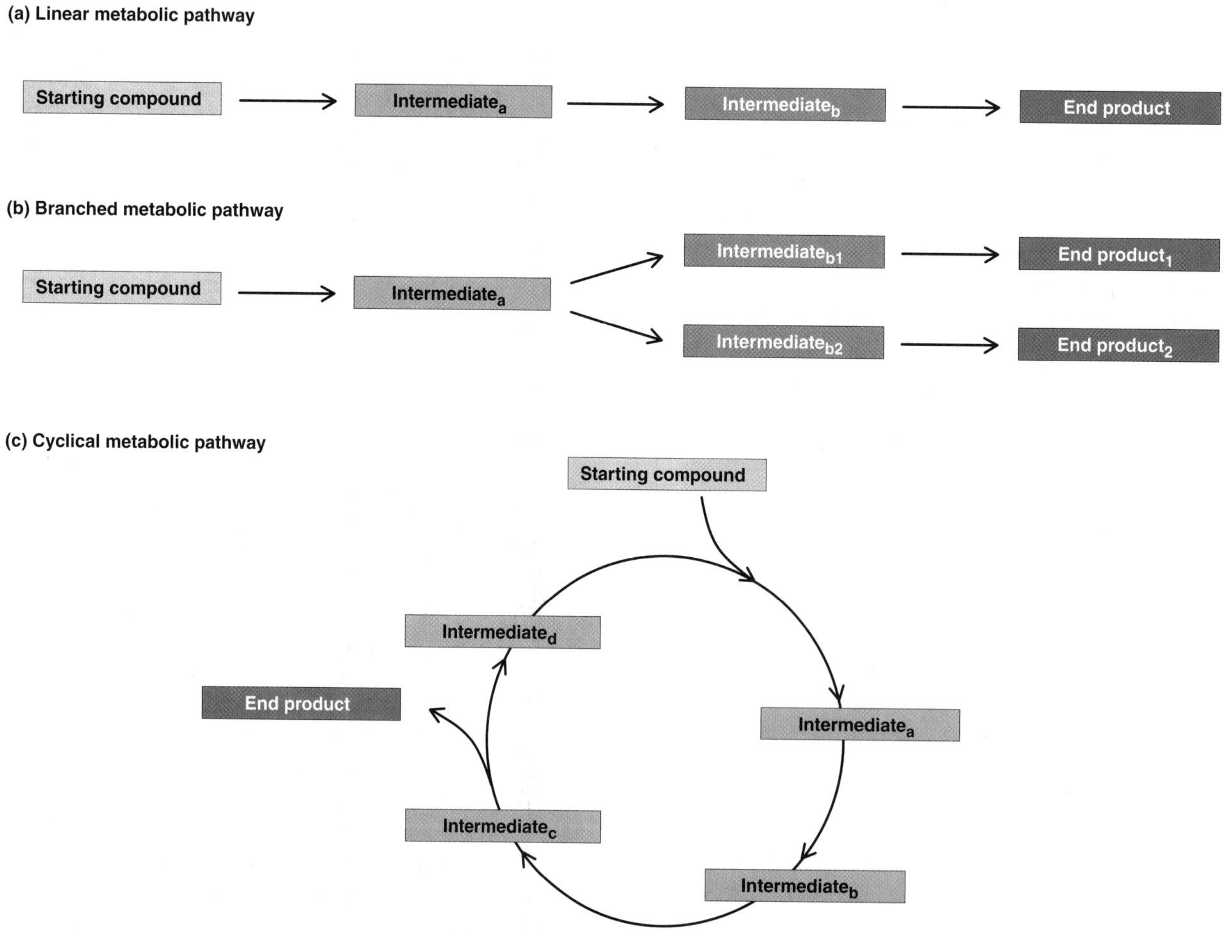

FIGURE 6.4 Metabolic Pathways Metabolic processes often occur as a series of sequential chemical reactions that convert starting compounds into intermediates and then, ultimately, into end products. A metabolic pathway can be **(a)** linear, **(b)** branched, or **(c)** cyclical.

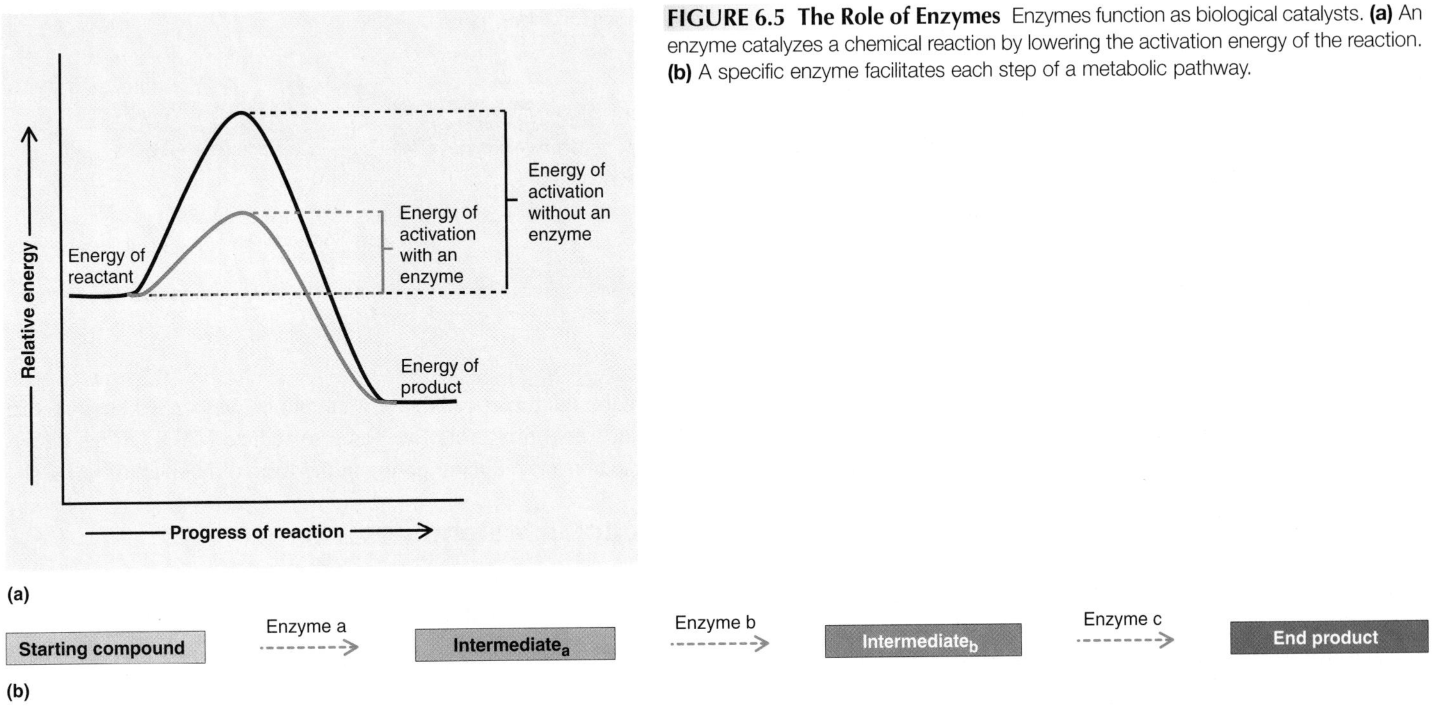

FIGURE 6.5 The Role of Enzymes Enzymes function as biological catalysts. **(a)** An enzyme catalyzes a chemical reaction by lowering the activation energy of the reaction. **(b)** A specific enzyme facilitates each step of a metabolic pathway.

to power an endergonic reaction. Because of the relatively high amount of free energy released when the bonds between the phosphate groups are hydrolyzed, they are called **high-energy phosphate bonds,** denoted by the symbol ~. ■ hydrolysis, p. 26

Cells constantly turn over ATP, powering biosynthetic reactions by hydrolyzing the high-energy phosphate bond, and then exploiting energy-releasing reactions to form it again. Two different processes are used by chemoorganotrophs to provide the energy necessary to form the high-energy phosphate bond. **Substrate-level phosphorylation** uses the chemical energy released in an exergonic reaction to add P_i to ADP; **oxidative phosphorylation** harvests the energy of proton motive force to do the same thing. Recall from chapter 3 that **proton motive force** is the form of energy that results from the electrochemical gradient

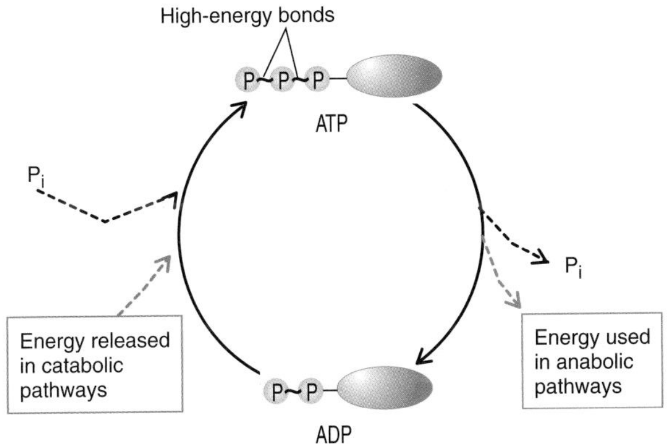

FIGURE 6.6 ATP Energy is released when unstable ("high-energy") phosphate bonds are broken; an input of energy is required to convert ADP back to ATP.

established as protons are expelled from the cell (see figure 3.26). The electron transport chain that generates this type of energy will be discussed later in this chapter. Photosynthetic organisms can generate ATP using the process of **photophosphorylation,** utilizing radiant energy of the sun to drive the formation of a proton motive force. The mechanisms they use to do this will be discussed later. ■ proton motive force, p. 58

The Role of the Chemical Energy Source

The compound broken down by a cell to release energy is called the **energy source.** As a group, prokaryotes show remarkable diversity in the variety of energy sources they can use. Many use organic compounds such as glucose. Others use inorganic compounds including hydrogen sulfide and ammonia. Harvesting energy from a compound involves a series of coupled oxidation-reduction reactions.

Oxidation-Reduction Reactions In **oxidation-reduction reactions,** or **redox reactions,** one or more electrons are transferred from one substance to another **(figure 6.7).** The molecule that loses electrons becomes **oxidized;** the one that gains those electrons becomes **reduced.** ■ electrons, p. 19

When electrons are removed from a molecule, protons (H^+) often follow. In other words, an electron-proton pair, or hydrogen atom, is often removed. Thus, the removal of a hydrogen atom is an oxidation; correspondingly, the addition of a hydrogen atom is a reduction. An oxidation reaction in which an electron and an accompanying proton are removed is called a **dehydrogenation.** A reduction reaction in which an electron and an accompanying proton are added is called a **hydrogenation.**

When electrons are removed from the energy source, or **electron donor,** they are temporarily transferred to a specific molecule that serves as an **electron carrier.** That carrier can also be viewed

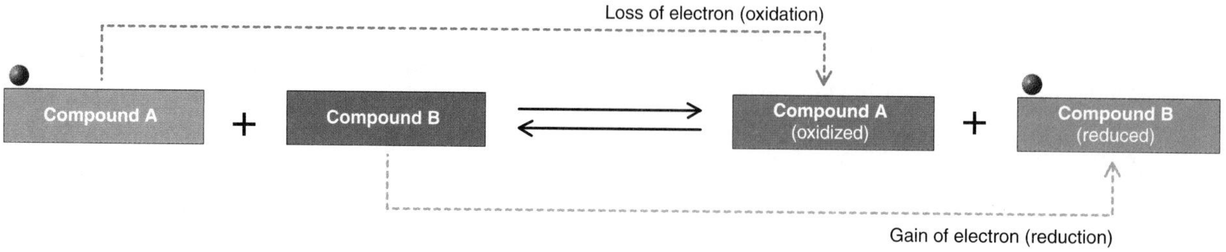

FIGURE 6.7 Oxidation-Reduction Reactions The compound that loses one or more electrons becomes oxidized; the compound that gains those electrons become reduced.

as a **hydrogen carrier** if a proton accompanies the electron. Protons, however, unlike electrons, do not require carriers when in an aqueous solution. Because of this, the whereabouts of protons in biological reactions are often ignored.

The Role of Electron Carriers

Just as cells use ATP as a carrier of free energy, they use designated molecules as carriers of electrons. Cells have several different types of electron carriers, and each of these serves a different function.

Three different types of electron carriers directly participate in reactions that oxidize the energy source **(table 6.1).** They are **NAD^+** (nicotinamide adenine dinucleotide), **FAD** (flavin adenine dinucleotide), and **$NADP^+$** (NAD phosphate). The reduced forms of these carriers are **NADH, $FADH_2$,** and **NADPH,** respectively. These electron carriers can also be considered hydrogen carriers because along with electrons, they carry protons. NAD^+ and $NADP^+$ can each carry a **hydride ion,** which consists of two electrons and one proton; $FADH_2$ carries two electrons and two protons.

Reduced electron carriers represent **reducing power** because their bonds contain a form of usable energy. The reducing power of NADH and $FADH_2$ is used to generate the proton motive force, which drives the synthesis of ATP in the process of oxidative phosphorylation. Ultimately the electrons are transferred to a compound such as O_2 that functions as a **terminal electron acceptor.** The reducing power of NADPH has an entirely different fate; it is used in biosynthetic reactions when a reduction is required. Note, however, that many microbial cells have a membrane-associated enzyme that is able to use proton motive force to reduce $NADP^+$. This allows them to convert reducing power in the form of NADH to NADPH.

Precursor Metabolites

Precursor metabolites are metabolic intermediates produced at specific steps in catabolic pathways that can be siphoned off and used in anabolic pathways. In anabolism, they serve as raw material used to make the subunits of macromolecules (see figure 6.1). For example, the precursor metabolite **pyruvate** can be converted to the amino acid alanine.

Many organisms, including *Escherichia coli,* can make all of their cell components, including proteins, lipids, carbohydrates, and nucleic acids using only a dozen or so precursor metabolites. The precursor metabolites used by *E. coli* are listed in **table 6.2.** Recall from chapter 4 that *E. coli* can grow in glucose-salts medium, which contains only glucose and a few inorganic salts. Some organisms, however, are not as versatile as *E. coli* with respect to their biosynthetic capabilities. Any essential compounds that a cell cannot synthesize from the appropriate precursor metabolite must be provided from an external source. ■ glucose-salts medium, p. 100

Scheme of Metabolism

Three key metabolic pathways, called the **central metabolic pathways,** are used to gradually oxidize glucose, the preferred

TABLE 6.1 Electron Carriers

Carrier	Oxidized Form	Reduced Form	Typical Fate of Electrons Carried
	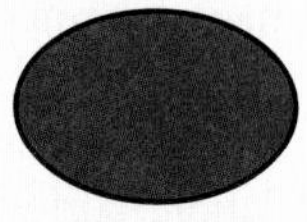	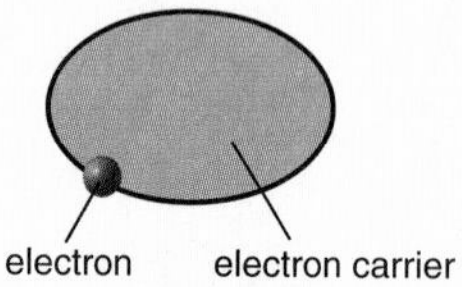	
Nicotinamide adenine dinucleotide (carries 2 electrons and 1 proton)	$NAD^+ + 2e^- + 2H^+ \rightleftharpoons$	$NADH + H^+$	Used to generate a proton motive force that can drive ATP synthesis
Flavin adenine dinucleotide (carries 2 electrons and 2 protons; i.e., 2 hydrogen atoms)	$FAD^+ + 2e^- + 2H^+ \rightleftharpoons$	$FADH_2$	Used to generate a proton motive force that can drive ATP synthesis
Nicotinamide adenine dinucleotide phosphate (carries 2 electrons and 1 proton)	$NADP^+ + 2e^- + 2H^+ \rightleftharpoons$	$NADPH + H^+$	Biosynthesis

TABLE 6.2 Precursor Metabolites, Their Source, and Their Use in Biosynthesis in *E. coli*

Precursor Metabolite	Pathway Generated	Biosynthetic Role
Glucose 6-phosphate	Glycolysis	Lipopolysaccharide
Fructose 6-phosphate	Glycolysis	Peptidoglycan
Dihydroxyacetone phosphate	Glycolysis	Lipids (glycerol component)
3-phosphoglycerate	Glycolysis	Protein (the amino acids cysteine, glycine, and serine)
Phosphoenolpyruvate	Glycolysis	Protein (the amino acids phenylalanine, tryptophan, and tyrosine)
Pyruvate	Glycolysis	Proteins (the amino acids alanine, leucine, and valine)
Ribose 5-phosphate	Pentose phosphate cycle	Nucleic acids and proteins (the amino acid histidine)
Erythrose 4-phosphate	Pentose phosphate cycle	Protein (the amino acids phenylalanine, tryptophan, and tyrosine)
Acetyl-CoA	Transition step	Lipids (fatty acids)
α-ketoglutarate	TCA cycle	Protein (the amino acids arginine, glutamate, glutamine, and proline)
Oxaloacetate	TCA cycle	Protein (the amino acids aspartate, asparagine, isoleucine, lysine, methionine, and threonine)

Some organisms use succinyl-coA as a precursor in heme biosynthesis; *E. coli* uses glutamate.

energy source of many cells, completely to carbon dioxide **(figure 6.8).** In the step-wise process, the pathways provide cells with energy in the form of ATP, reducing power, and the precursor metabolites needed to synthesize the cells' building blocks. The central metabolic pathways include:

- Glycolysis
- Pentose phosphate pathway
- Tricarboxylic acid cycle (TCA cycle)

The central metabolic pathways are catabolic, but the precursor metabolites and reducing power they generate can also be diverted for use in biosynthesis. To reflect the dual role of these pathways, they are sometimes called **amphibolic pathways** (*amphi* meaning "both kinds").

The most common pathway that initiates the breakdown of sugars is **glycolysis** (*glycos* means "sugar" and *lysis* means "dissolution"). This pathway is also called the **Embden-Meyerhof-Parnas** pathway (to honor the scientists who described it) or the **glycolytic pathway.** This multistep pathway gradually oxidizes the 6-carbon sugar glucose to form two molecules of pyruvate, a 3-carbon compound. At about midpoint in the pathway, a 6-carbon derivative of glucose is split into two 3-carbon molecules. Both of these latter molecules then undergo the same series of transformations to produce pyruvate molecules. Glycolysis provides the cell with a small amount of energy in the form of ATP, some reducing power in the form of NADH, and a number of different precursor metabolites. Some bacteria have a different pathway called the **Entner-Doudoroff pathway** (named after the scientists who described it) instead of or in addition to the glycolytic pathway; some archaea have a slightly modified version of the Entner-Doudoroff pathway. Like glycolysis, the Entner-Doudoroff pathway generates pyruvate, but it uses different enzymes, generates reducing power in the form of NADPH, and yields less ATP.

The **pentose phosphate pathway** also breaks down glucose, but its primary role in metabolism is the production of compounds used in biosynthesis, including reducing power in the form of NADPH and precursor metabolites. It operates in conjunction with other glucose-degrading pathways (glycolysis and the Entner-Doudoroff pathway). Most intermediates it generates are drawn off for use in biosynthesis, but one compound is directed to a mid-point step of glycolysis for further breakdown.

Pyruvate generated in any of the preceding pathways must be converted into a specific 2-carbon fragment to enter the Krebs cycle. This is accomplished in a complex reaction called the **transition step,** which removes CO_2, generates reducing power, and joins the resulting acetyl group to a compound called coenzyme A, forming acetyl-CoA. Note that the transition step is repeated twice for each molecule of glucose broken down.

The 2-carbon acetyl group of acetyl-CoA enters the **tricarboxylic acid cycle (TCA cycle),** also called the **Krebs cycle** (in honor of the scientist who first described it), or the **citric acid cycle.** This initiates a series of oxidations that result in the release of two molecules of CO_2. For every acetyl-CoA that enters the TCA cycle, the cyclic pathway "turns" once. Therefore, it must "turn" twice to complete the oxidation of one molecule of glucose. The TCA cycle generates precursor metabolites, a great deal of reducing power, and ATP.

Respiration uses the reducing power accumulated in glycolysis, the transition step, and the TCA cycle to generate ATP by oxidative phosphorylation **(table 6.3).** The electron carriers NADH and $FADH_2$ transfer their electrons to the electron transport chain, which ejects protons to generate a proton motive force. This transfer of electrons also serves to recycle the carriers so they can once again accept electrons during catabolic reactions. In **aerobic respiration,** electrons are ultimately passed to molecular oxygen (O_2), the terminal electron acceptor, producing water. **Anaerobic respiration** is analogous to aerobic respiration, but uses an inorganic molecule other than O_2 as a terminal electron acceptor. Organisms that use respiration, either aerobic or anaerobic, are said to **respire.**

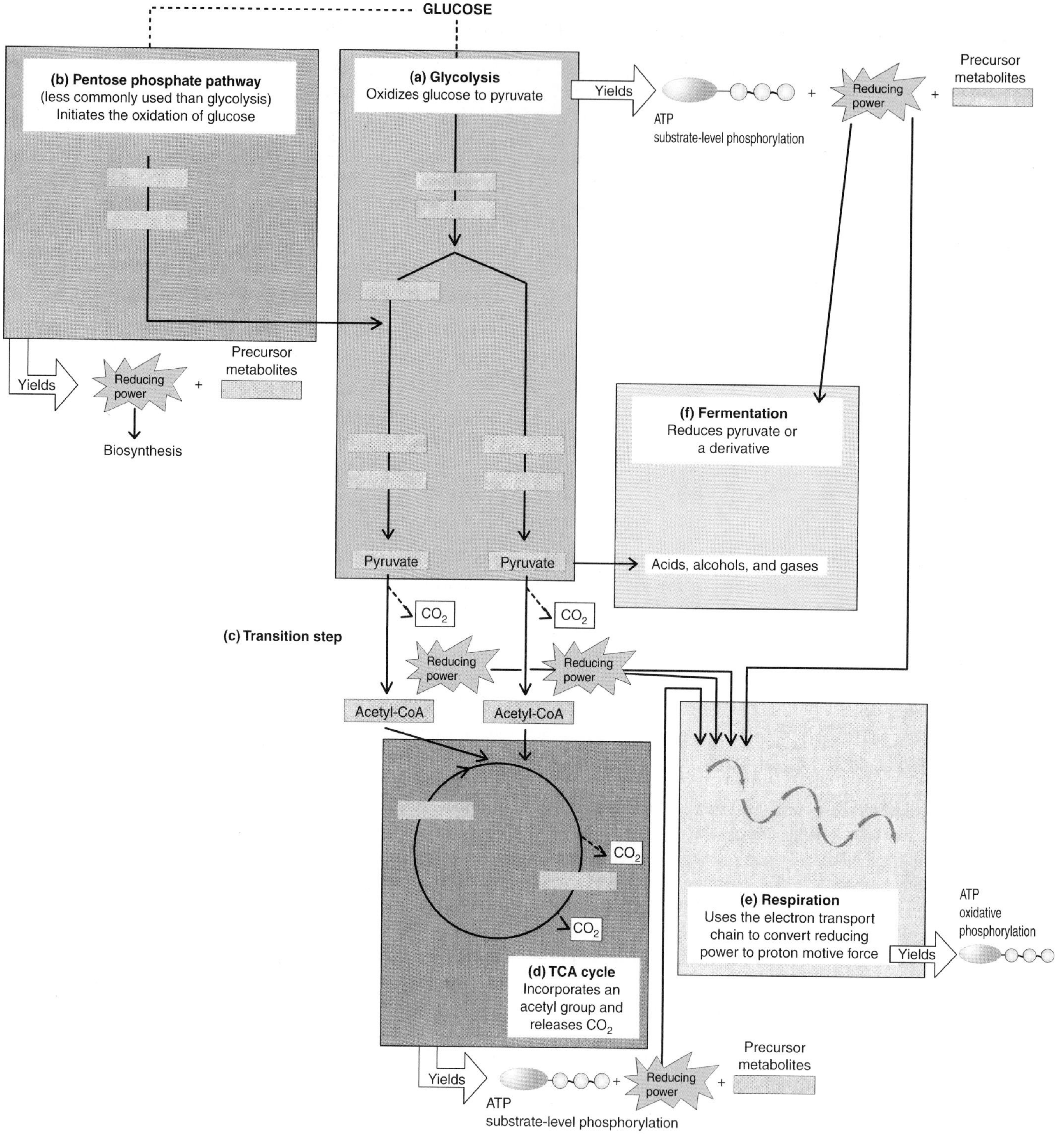

FIGURE 6.8 Scheme of Metabolism **(a)** Glycolysis, **(b)** the pentose phosphate pathway, **(c)** the transition step, and **(d)** the tricarboxylic acid cycle (TCA cycle) are used to gradually oxidize glucose completely to CO_2. Together, these pathways produce ATP, reducing power, and intermediates that function as precursor metabolites (depicted as gray bars). **(e)** Respiration uses the reducing power to generate ATP by oxidative phosphorylation, employing an inorganic molecule as a terminal electron acceptor. **(f)** Fermentation stops short of oxidizing glucose completely, and instead uses pyruvate or a derivative as an electron acceptor.

Cells that cannot respire are limited by their relative inability to recycle reduced electron carriers. A cell only has a limited number of carrier molecules; if electrons are not removed from the reduced carriers, none will be available to accept electrons. As a consequence, subsequent catabolic processes cannot occur. **Fermentation** provides a solution to this problem, but it results in only the partial oxidation of glucose. Thus, compared with respiration, fermentation produces relatively little ATP. It is used by facultative anaerobes when a suitable inorganic terminal electron acceptor is not available and by organisms that lack an electron transport chain. These cells must stop short of oxidizing glucose completely to avoid generating even more reducing power.

TABLE 6.3 ATP-Generating Processes of Prokaryotic Chemoorganoheterotrophs

Metabolic Process	Pathways Used	Terminal Electron Acceptor	ATP Generated by Substrate-Level Phosphorylation (Theoretical Maximum)	ATP Generated by Oxidative Phosphorylation (Theoretical Maximum)	Total ATP Generated (Theoretical Maximum)
Aerobic respiration	Glycolysis, TCA cycle	O_2	2 in glycolysis (net) 2 in the TCA cycle 4 total	34	38
Anaerobic respiration	Glycolysis, TCA cycle	Inorganic molecule other than O_2 such as nitrate (NO_3^-), nitrite (NO_2^-), sulfate (SO_4^{2-})	2 in glycolysis (net) 2 in the TCA cycle 4 total	Number varies; however, the ATP yield of anaerobic respiration is less than that of aerobic respiration but more than that of fermentation.	
Fermentation	Glycolysis	Organic molecule (pyruvate or a derivative)	2 in glycolysis (net) 2 total	0	2

Otherwise, they would run out of the oxidized form of the electron carriers very quickly. Instead of oxidizing pyruvate in the TCA cycle, they use pyruvate or a derivative of it as a terminal electron acceptor. By transferring the electrons carried by NADH to pyruvate or a derivative, NAD^+ is regenerated so it can once again accept electrons in the steps of glycolysis. Note that fermentation always uses an organic molecule as the terminal electron acceptor. Although fermentation does not use the TCA cycle, organisms that ferment still employ certain key steps of the cycle in order to generate the precursor molecules required for biosynthesis. ■ facultative anaerobes, p. 96

MICROCHECK 6.1

Catabolic pathways gradually oxidize an energy source so that the energy released can be harvested. A specific enzyme catalyzes each step. Substrate-level phosphorylation uses chemical energy to synthesize ATP; oxidative phosphorylation employs a proton motive force to do the same. Reducing power in the form of NADH and $FADH_2$ is used to generate the proton motive force; the reducing power of NADPH is utilized in biosynthesis. Precursor metabolites are metabolic intermediates that can be used in biosynthesis. The central metabolic pathways generate ATP, reducing power, and precursor metabolites.

- ✓ How does the fate of electrons carried by NADPH differ from those carried by NADH?
- ✓ Why are the central metabolic pathways called amphibolic pathways?
- ✓ Why does fermentation release less energy than respiration?

6.2 Enzymes

Focus Points

- Describe the active site of an enzyme and how it relates to the enzyme substrate-complex.
- Compare and contrast cofactors and coenzymes.
- List two environmental factors that influence enzyme activity.
- Describe allosteric regulation.
- Compare and contrast non-competitive enzyme inhibition and competitive enzyme inhibition.

Recall that enzymes are proteins that act as biological catalysts, facilitating the conversion of a substrate into a product (see figure 6.5). They do this with extraordinary specificity and speed, usually acting on only one, or a very limited number of, substrates. They are neither consumed nor permanently changed during a reaction, allowing a single enzyme molecule to be rapidly used over and over again. In only one second, the fastest enzymes can transform more than 10^4 substrate molecules to products. More than a thousand different enzymes exist in a cell; most are given a common name that reflects their function and ends with the suffix -ase. For example, those that degrade proteins are collectively called proteases. ■ enzymes, p. 134

Mechanisms and Consequences of Enzyme Action

An enzyme has on its surface an **active** or **catalytic site,** typically a relatively small crevice **(figure 6.9).** This is the critical site to which a substrate binds by weak forces. The binding of the substrate to the active site causes the shape of the flexible enzyme to change slightly. This mutual interaction, or **induced fit,** results in a temporary intermediate called an **enzyme-substrate complex.** The substrate is held within this complex in a specific orientation so that the activation energy for a given reaction is lowered, allowing the products to be formed. The products are then released, leaving the enzyme unchanged and free to combine with new substrate molecules. Note that enzymes may also catalyze reactions in which two substrates are joined to create one product. Theoretically, all enzyme-catalyzed reactions are reversible. The free energy change of certain reactions, however, makes them effectively non-reversible.

The interaction of the enzyme with its substrate is very specific. The substrate fitting into the active site may be likened to a hand fitting into a glove. Not only must it fit spatially, but appropriate chemical interactions such as hydrogen and ionic bonding need to occur to induce the fit. This requirement for a precise fit and interaction explains why, with minor exceptions, a different enzyme is required to catalyze every reaction in a cell. Very few molecules

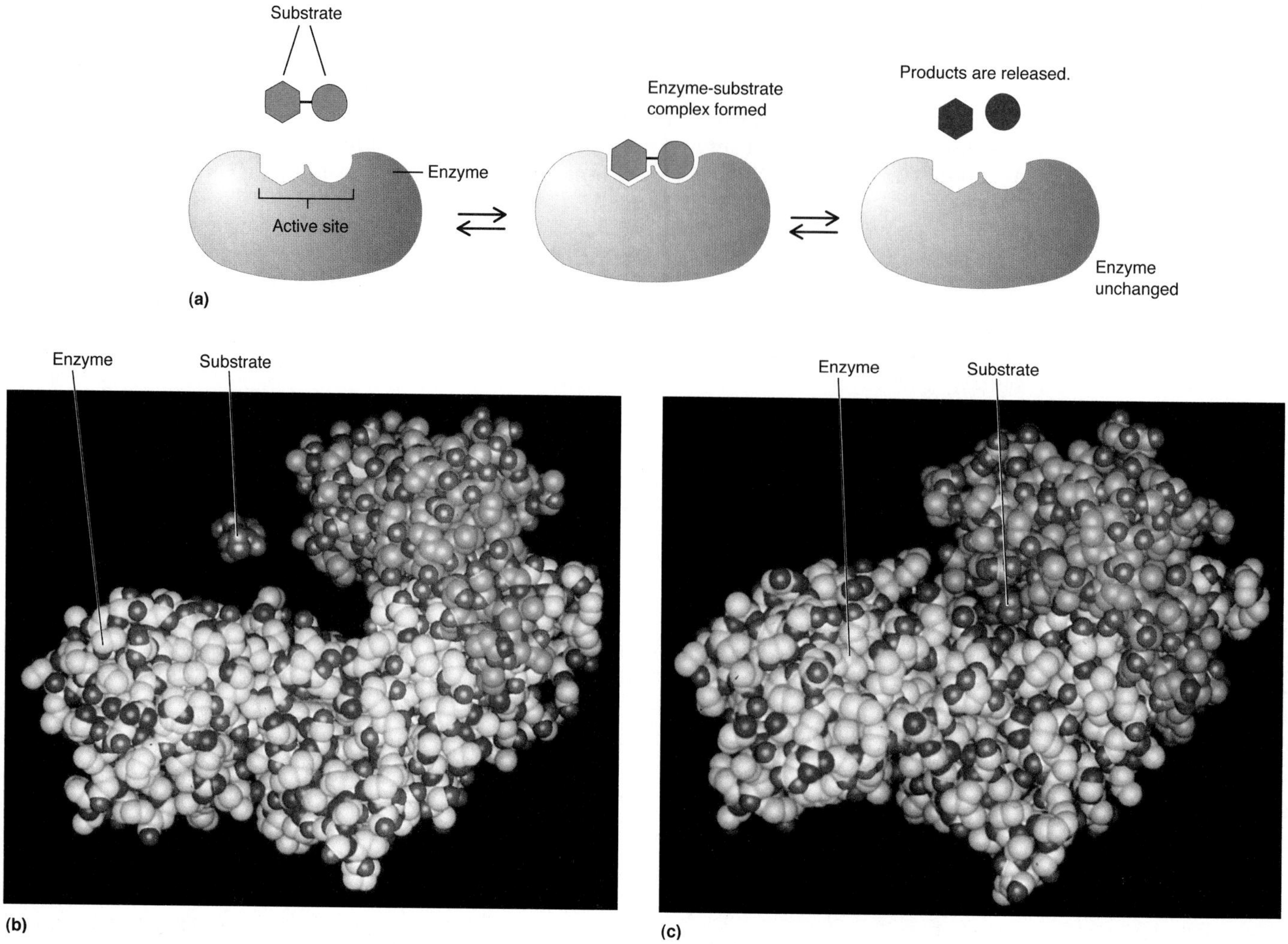

FIGURE 6.9 Mechanism of Enzyme Action **(a)** The substrate binds to the active site, forming an enzyme-substrate complex. The products are then released, leaving the enzyme unchanged and free to combine with new substrate molecules. **(b)** A model showing an enzyme and its substrate. **(c)** The binding of the substrate to the active site causes the shape of the flexible enzyme to change slightly.

of any particular enzyme are needed, however, as each is swiftly reused again and again. ■ **hydrogen bonds, p. 23** ■ **ionic bonds, p. 22**

Cofactors and Coenzymes

Some enzymes act with the assistance of a non-protein component called a **cofactor (figure 6.10). Coenzymes** are organic cofactors that act as loosely bound carriers of molecules or electrons **(table 6.4).** They include the electron carriers FAD, NAD^+, and $NADP^+$. Other cofactors attach tightly to enzymes. For example, magnesium, zinc, copper, and other trace elements required for growth often function as cofactors. ■ **trace elements, p. 98**

All coenzymes transfer substances from one compound to another, but they function in different ways. Some remain bound to the enzyme during the transfer process, whereas others separate from the enzyme, carrying the substance being transferred along with them. The same coenzyme can assist different enzymes. Because of this, far fewer different coenzymes are required than enzymes. Like enzymes, coenzymes are recycled as they function and, consequently, are needed only in minute quantities.

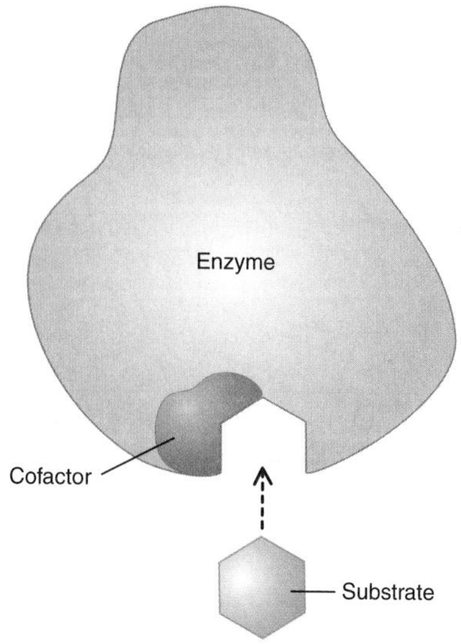

FIGURE 6.10 Enzymes Act in Conjunction with a Cofactor Cofactors are non-protein components, either coenzymes or trace elements.

TABLE 6.4 Some Coenzymes and Their Function

Coenzyme	Vitamin from Which It Is Derived	Substance Transferred	Example of Use
Nicotinamide adenine dinucleotide (NAD^+)	Niacin	Hydride ions (2 electrons and 1 proton)	Carrier of reducing power
Flavin adenine dinucleotide (FAD)	Riboflavin	Hydrogen atoms (2 electrons and 2 protons)	Carrier of reducing power
Coenzyme A	Pantothenic acid	Acyl groups	Carries the acetyl group that enters the TCA cycle
Thiamin pyrophosphate	Thiamine	Aldehydes	Facilitates the removal of CO_2 from pyruvate in the transition step
Pyridoxal phosphate	Pyridoxine	Amino groups	Transfers amino groups in amino acid synthesis
Tetrahydrofolate	Folic acid	1-carbon molecules	Used in nucleotide synthesis

Most coenzymes are synthesized from vitamins (see table 6.4). Some bacteria, such as *E. coli,* can synthesize all their required vitamins and convert them to the necessary coenzymes. In contrast, humans and other animals must be provided with vitamins from external sources. Most often they must be supplied in the diet, but in some cases vitamins synthesized by bacteria residing in the intestine can be absorbed. If an animal lacks a vitamin, the functions of all the different enzymes whose activity requires the corresponding coenzyme are impaired. Thus, a single vitamin deficiency has serious consequences.

Environmental Factors That Influence Enzyme Activity

The growth of any organism depends on the proper functioning of its enzymes. Several features of the environment influence how well enzymes function and in this way determine how rapidly bacteria multiply **(figure 6.11).** Each enzyme has a narrow range of environmental factors—including temperature, pH, and salt concentration—at which it operates optimally. A 10°C rise in temperature approximately doubles the speed of enzymatic reactions, until optimal activity is reached; this explains why bacteria tend to grow more rapidly at higher temperatures. If the temperature gets too high, however, proteins will denature and no longer function. Most enzymes operate best at low salt concentrations and at pH values slightly above 7. Not surprisingly then, most bacteria grow fastest under these same conditions. Some prokaryotes, however, particularly certain members of the *Archaea,* are found in environments where conditions are extreme. They may require high salt concentrations, grow under very acidic conditions, or be found where temperatures are near boiling. ■ **pH, p. 25** ■ **temperature and growth requirements, p. 94**

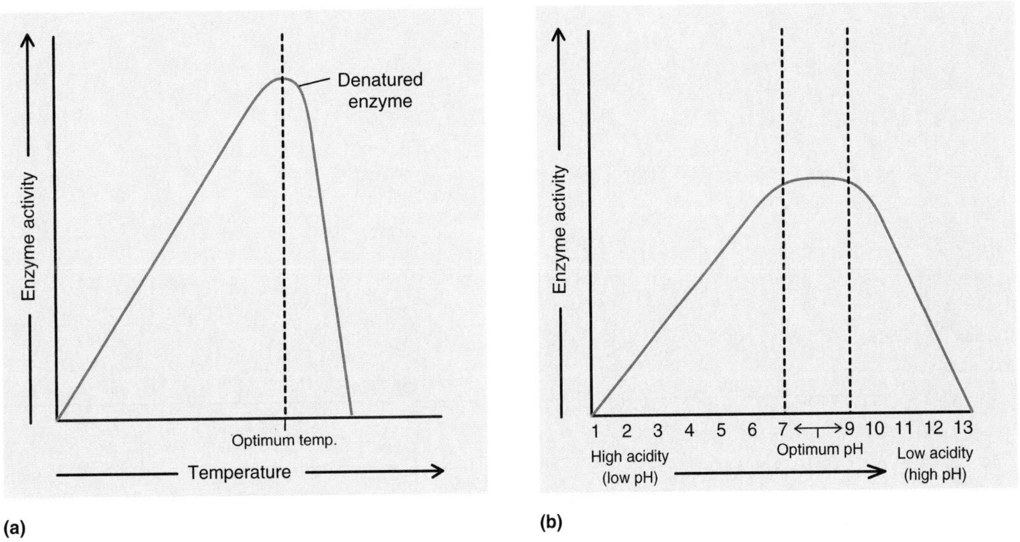

FIGURE 6.11 Enviromental Factors That Influence Enzyme Activity **(a)** A rise in temperature increases the speed of enzymatic activity until the optimum temperature is reached. If the temperature gets too high, the enzyme denatures and no longer functions. **(b)** Most enzymes function best at pH values slightly above 7.

Allosteric Regulation

Cells can rapidly fine-tune or regulate the activity of certain key enzymes using other molecules that reversibly bind to and distort them **(figure 6.12).** This has the effect of regulating the activity of metabolic pathways. These enzymes can be controlled because they are **allosteric enzymes** (*allo* means "other"), which have a binding site called an **allosteric site** that is separate from their active site. When a regulatory molecule binds to the allosteric site, the shape of the enzyme changes. This distortion alters the relative **affinity,** or chemical attraction, of the enzyme for its substrate. In some cases the binding of the regulatory molecule enhances the affinity for the substrate, but in other cases it decreases it.

Allosteric enzymes generally catalyze the step that either initiates or commits to a given pathway. Because their activity can be controlled, they provide the cell with a means to modulate the pace of metabolic processes, turning off some pathways and activating others. Cells can also control the amount of enzyme they synthesize; this control mechanism, which will be discussed in chapter 7, also involves allosteric proteins. ■ regulation, p. 182

The end product of a given biosynthetic pathway generally acts as an allosteric inhibitor of the first enzyme of that pathway—a mechanism called **feedback inhibition** (figure 6.12c). This mechanism allows the product of the pathway to modulate its own synthesis. For example, the first enzyme of the multistep pathway used to convert the amino acid threonine to isoleucine is an allosteric enzyme that is inhibited by the binding of isoleucine. This amino acid must be present at a relatively high concentration, however, to bind and inhibit the enzyme. Thus, the pathway will only be shut down when a cell accumulates sufficient isoleucine to fill its immediate needs. Because the binding of the inhibitor is reversible, the enzyme can again become active when isoleucine levels decrease.

Compounds that reflect a cell's relative energy stores often regulate allosteric enzymes of catabolic pathways, enabling cells to modulate the flow of these pathways in response to changing energy needs. High levels of ATP inhibit certain enzymes and, as a consequence, slow down catabolic processes. In contrast, high levels of ADP warn that a cell's energy stores are low, and they function to stimulate the activity of some enzymes.

Enzyme Inhibition

Enzymes can be inhibited by a variety of compounds other than the regulatory molecules normally used by the cell **(table 6.5).** These compounds can be exploited to prevent microbial growth. The site on the enzyme to which the molecules bind determines whether they function as competitive or non-competitive inhibitors.

Non-Competitive Inhibition

Non-competitive inhibition occurs when the inhibitor and the substrate act at different sites on the enzyme. Allosteric inhibition, discussed previously, is an example of non-competitive reversible inhibition and is used by the cell to modulate its processes (see figure 6.12). Non-competitive, non-reversible inhibitors damage the enzyme permanently so that it can no longer function; the inhibitor acts as an enzyme poison. For example, mercury in the antibacterial compound mercurochrome inhibits growth because it oxidizes the S—H groups of the amino acid cysteine in proteins. This converts cysteine to cystine, which cannot form the important covalent disulfide bond (S—S). As a result, the protein cannot achieve its proper shape.

Competitive Inhibition

In **competitive inhibition,** the inhibitor binds to the active site of the enzyme, obstructing access of the substrate to that site **(figure 6.13).** Generally this occurs because the inhibitor has a chemical structure similar to the normal substrate.

A good example of competitive inhibition is the action of sulfanilamide, one of the sulfa drugs used as an antimicrobial medication. Sulfa drugs inhibit an enzyme in the pathway that bacteria use to synthesize the vitamin folic acid by binding to the active

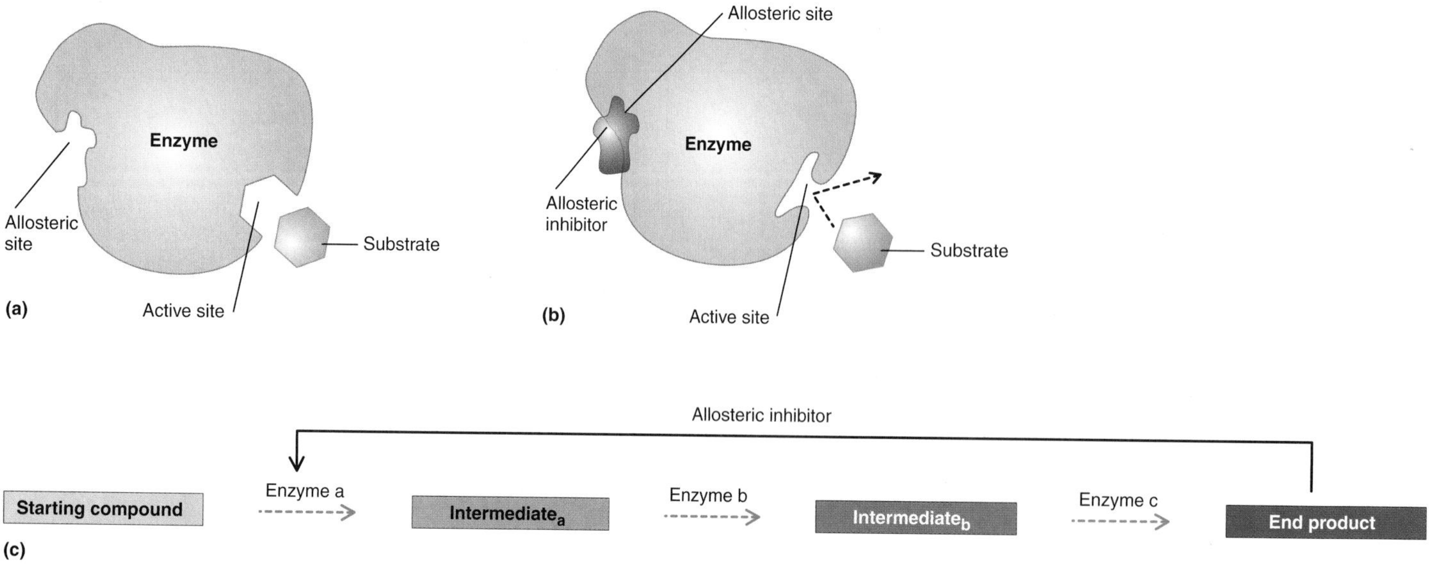

FIGURE 6.12 Regulation of Allosteric Enzymes **(a)** Allosteric enzymes have, in addition to the active site, an allosteric site. **(b)** The binding of regulatory molecule to the allosteric site causes the shape of the enzyme to change, altering the relative affinity of the enzyme for its substrate. **(c)** The end product of a given biosynthetic pathway generally acts as an allosteric inhibitor of the first enzyme of that pathway.

TABLE 6.5 Characteristics of Enzyme Inhibitors

Type	Characteristics
Non-competitive inhibition (by regulatory molecules)	Inhibitor temporarily changes the enzyme, altering the enzyme's relative affinity for the substrate. This mechanism provides cells with a means to control the activity of allosteric enzymes.
Non-competitive inhibition (by enzyme poisons)	Inhibitor permanently changes the enzyme, rendering the enzyme non-functional. Enzyme poisons such as mercury are used in certain antimicrobial compounds.
Competitive inhibition	Inhibitor binds to the active site of the enzyme, obstructing the access of the substrate. Competitive inhibitors such as sulfa drugs are used as antibacterial medications.

site of the enzyme. The drug does not affect human metabolism because humans cannot synthesize folic acid; it must be provided in the diet. Sulfa drugs have a structure similar to **para-aminobenzoic acid (PABA),** an intermediate in the bacterial pathway for folic acid synthesis. Because of this, they fit into the active site of the enzyme that normally uses PABA as a substrate, preventing the attachment of PABA. The greater the proportion of sulfa molecules relative to PABA molecules, the more likely the active site of the enzyme will be occupied by a sulfa molecule. Once the sulfa is removed, the enzyme functions normally with PABA as the substrate. ■ **sulfa drugs, p. 505**

MICROCHECK 6.2

Enzymes facilitate the conversion of a substrate into a product with extraordinary speed and specificity. They are neither consumed nor permanently changed in the reaction. Some enzymes act with the assistance of a cofactor. Environmental factors influence enzyme activity and, by doing so, determine how rapidly bacteria multiply. The activity of allosteric enzymes can be regulated. A variety of different compounds adversely affect enzyme activity.

✓ Explain why sulfa drugs inhibit the growth of bacteria without harming the human host.

✓ Explain the function of a coenzyme.

✓ Why is it important for a cell that allosteric inhibition be reversible?

6.3

The Central Metabolic Pathways

Focus Point

- List the amount of ATP and reducing power and the number of different precursor molecules generated by each of the central metabolic pathways.

The three central metabolic pathways—glycolysis, the pentose phosphate pathway, and the tricarboxylic acid cycle—modify organic molecules in a step-wise fashion to form:

- Intermediates with high-energy bonds that can be used to synthesize ATP by substrate-level phosphorylation
- Intermediates that can be oxidized to generate reducing power
- Intermediates and end products that function as precursor metabolites

Note that the precursor metabolites can be siphoned off from these pathways for use in biosynthesis. The rate at which they are removed will dramatically affect the overall energy gain of catabolism. This is generally overlooked in descriptions of the ATP-generating functions of these pathways for the sake of simplicity.

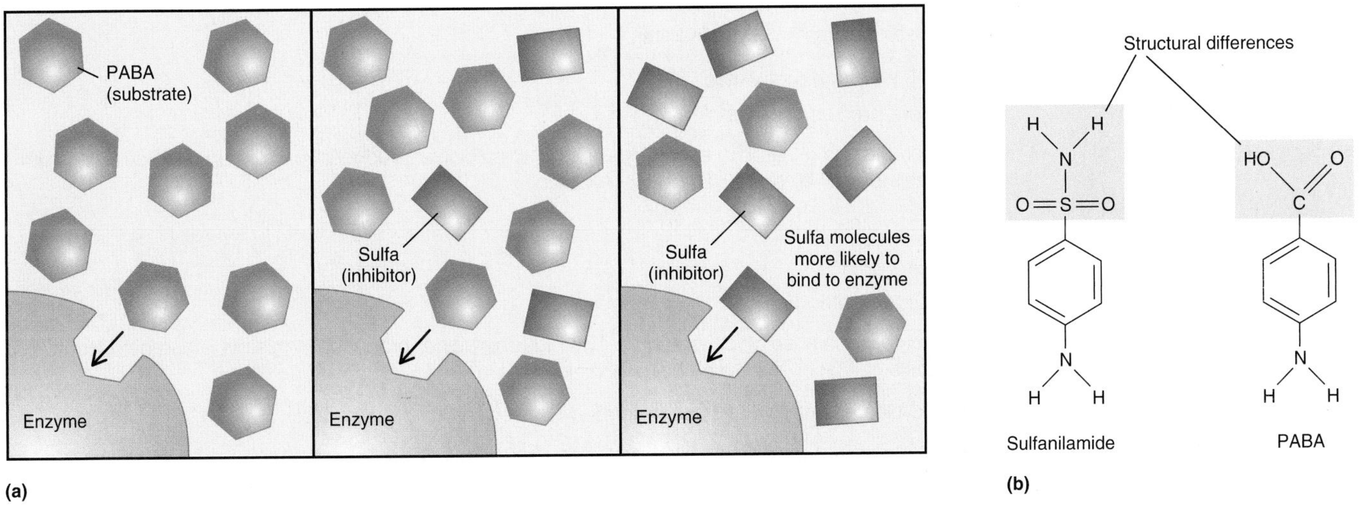

FIGURE 6.13 Competitive Inhibition of Enzymes (a) The inhibitor competes with the normal substrate for binding to the active site. The greater the proportion of inhibitor relative to substrate, the more likely the active site of the enzyme will be occupied by an inhibitor. **(b)** A competitive inhibitor generally has a chemical structure similar to the normal substrate.

Recognize, however, that because these pathways serve more than one function, the energy yields are only theoretical.

The pathways of central metabolism are compared in **table 6.6.** The entire pathways with chemical formulas and enzyme names are illustrated in Appendix IV.

Glycolysis

Glycolysis is the primary pathway used by many organisms to convert glucose to pyruvate **(figure 6.14).** In the 10-step pathway, one molecule of glucose is converted into two molecules of pyruvate. This generates a net gain of two molecules of ATP and two molecules of NADH. The overall process can be summarized as:

$$\text{glucose (6 C)} + 2\ \text{NAD}^+ + 2\ \text{ADP} + 2\ \text{P}_i \longrightarrow 2\ \text{pyruvate (3 C)} + 2\ \text{NADH} + 2\ \text{H}^+ + 2\ \text{ATP}$$

In addition to generating ATP and reducing power (NADH), the pathway produces 6 different precursor molecules needed by *E. coli* (see table 6.2).

Step 1: A high-energy bond is expended to initiate the pathway when a phosphate group from ATP is transferred to glucose, forming glucose 6-phosphate. In bacteria, the high-energy phosphate bond is expended as glucose is being transported into the cell.

Step 2: A chemical rearrangement occurs, converting glucose 6-phosphate to fructose 6-phosphate.

Step 3: A high-energy phosphate bond from ATP is expended to convert fructose 6-phosphate to fructose 1, 6-bisphosphate, priming the molecule so it can be more readily split into two molecules.

Step 4: The 6-carbon fructose 1, 6-bisphosphate is split to form two 3-carbon molecules—glyceraldehyde 3-phosphate (G3P) and dihydroxyacetone phosphate (DHP).

Step 5: DHP is converted into glyceraldehyde 3-phosphate (G3P), resulting in a total of two G3P molecules at this point in glycolysis.

Step 6: Energy released by the oxidation of G3P is used to add an inorganic phosphate group, creating 1,3-bisphosphoglycerate (BPG), which has a high-energy phosphate bond. During the oxidation, the electron carrier NAD^+ is reduced to form NADH + H^+. Note that this and subsequent steps of glycolysis each occur twice, once for each of the two G3P formed as a result of the previous step.

TABLE 6.6 Comparison of the Central Metabolic Pathways

Pathway	Characteristics
Glycolysis	Generally used in aerobic respiration, anaerobic respiration, and fermentation to obtain energy and precursor metabolites. Reducing power is also generated. In respiration, this reducing power can be used to drive the synthesis of ATP; in fermentation, it is consumed to recycle the electron carrier without an additional gain in energy. Glycolysis generates: • 2 ATP (net) by substrate-level phosphorylation • 2 NADH + 2 H^+ • 6 different precursor metabolites
Pentose phosphate cycle	Used in aerobic respiration, anaerobic respiration, and fermentation to obtain precursor metabolites and reducing power in the form of NADPH. The pentose phosphate cycle generates: • NADPH + H^+ (amount varies) • 2 different precursor metabolites
Transition step	Used in aerobic and anaerobic respiration. The reducing power produced in this step can be used to drive the synthesis of ATP by oxidative phosphorylation. The transition step, repeated twice to oxidize two molecules of pyruvate to acetyl-CoA, generates: • 2 NADH + 2 H^+ • 1 precursor metabolite
TCA cycle	Used in aerobic and anaerobic respiration. The reducing power produced in this cycle can be used to drive the synthesis of ATP by oxidative phosphorylation. The TCA cycle, repeated twice to incorporate two acetyl groups, generates: • 2 ATP by substrate-level phosphorylation (may involve conversion of GTP) • 6 NADH + 6 H^+ • 2 $FADH_2$ • 2 different precursor metabolites

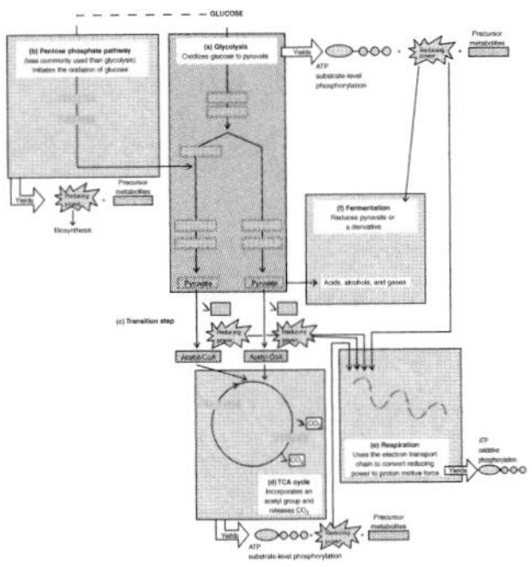

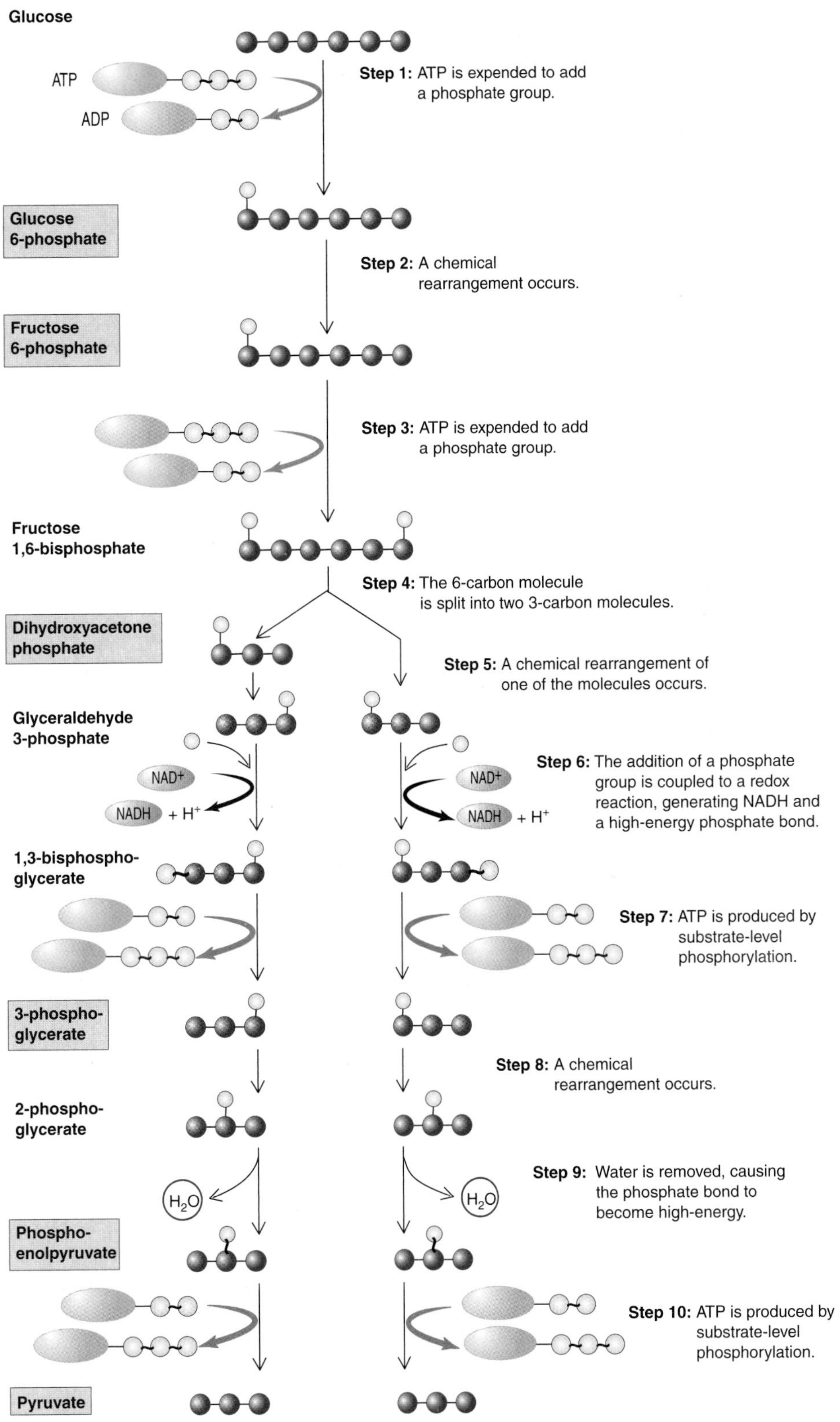
Glucose
ATP
ADP
Step 1: ATP is expended to add a phosphate group.
Glucose 6-phosphate
Step 2: A chemical rearrangement occurs.
Fructose 6-phosphate
Step 3: ATP is expended to add a phosphate group.
Fructose 1,6-bisphosphate
Step 4: The 6-carbon molecule is split into two 3-carbon molecules.
Dihydroxyacetone phosphate
Step 5: A chemical rearrangement of one of the molecules occurs.
Glyceraldehyde 3-phosphate
NAD+
NADH + H+
Step 6: The addition of a phosphate group is coupled to a redox reaction, generating NADH and a high-energy phosphate bond.
1,3-bisphospho-glycerate
Step 7: ATP is produced by substrate-level phosphorylation.
3-phospho-glycerate
Step 8: A chemical rearrangement occurs.
2-phospho-glycerate
H2O
Step 9: Water is removed, causing the phosphate bond to become high-energy.
Phospho-enolpyruvate
Step 10: ATP is produced by substrate-level phosphorylation.
Pyruvate

FIGURE 6.14 Glycolysis The glycolytic pathway oxidizes glucose to pyruvate, generating ATP by substrate-level phosphorylation, reducing power in the form of NADH, and 6 different precursor metabolites.

Step 7: Substrate-level phosphorylation occurs as the phosphate group of BPG is transferred to ADP, generating ATP and 3-phosphoglycerate (3PG). At this point in the glycolytic pathway, the net energy gain is 0, because this step simply replenishes the ATP expended in steps 1 and 2.

Step 8: 3PG is rearranged to form 2-phosphoglycerate (2PG).

Step 9: A water molecule is removed from 2PG, creating phosphoenolpyruvate (PEP), a molecule that contains a high-energy phosphate bond.

Step 10: Substrate-level phosphorylation occurs once more as the phosphate group of PEP is transferred to ADP, generating ATP and pyruvate.

Yield of Glycolysis

For every glucose molecule degraded, the steps of glycolysis produce:

- **ATP**—The maximum possible energy gain as ATP in glycolysis is:

Energy expended	2 ATP molecules (steps 1 and 3)
Energy harvested	4 ATP molecules (steps 7 and 10)
Net gain	2 ATP molecules

- **Reducing power**—A redox reaction takes place at step 6, which occurs twice, converting 2 NAD^+ to 2 NADH + 2 H^+.
- **Precursor metabolites**—Five intermediates of glycolysis as well as the end product, pyruvate, are precursor metabolites used by *E. coli*.

Pentose Phosphate Pathway

The other central metabolic pathway used by cells to break down glucose is the pentose phosphate pathway. This complex pathway generates 5- and 7-carbon sugars. In addition, glyceraldehyde 3-phosphate (G3P) is produced, and can be directed to step 6 in glycolysis for further breakdown. The greatest importance of the pentose phosphate pathway is its contribution to biosynthesis. The reducing power it generates is in the form of NADPH, which is used in biosynthetic reactions when a reduction is required. In addition, two of its intermediates, ribose 5-phosphate and erythrose 4-phosphate, are important precursor metabolites.

Yield of the Pentose Phosphate Pathway

The yield of the pentose phosphate pathway varies, depending on which of several possible alternatives are taken. It can produce:

- **Reducing power**—A variable amount of reducing power in the form of NADPH is produced.
- **Precursor metabolites**—Two intermediates of the pentose phosphate pathway are precursor metabolites.

Transition Step

The transition step links glycolysis to the TCA cycle **(figure 6.15)**. In prokaryotic cells, the entire oxidation process takes place in the cytoplasm. In eukaryotic cells, however, pyruvate must first enter the mitochondria since the enzymes of the glycolytic pathway are located in the cytoplasm of the cell, whereas those of the TCA cycle are found only within the matrix of the mitochondria. ■ mitochondria, p. 78

The transition step involves several integrated reactions catalyzed by a group of enzymes that form a large multi-enzyme complex. In the concerted series of reactions, carbon dioxide is first removed from the pyruvate, a process called decarboxylation. Then, an oxidation occurs, reducing NAD^+ to form NADH + H^+. Finally, the remaining 2-carbon acetyl group is joined to the coenzyme A to form acetyl-CoA.

Yield of the Transition Step

- **Reducing power**—The transition step, which occurs twice for every molecule of glucose that enters glycolysis, is an oxidation. This reduces 2 NAD^+ to form 2 NADH + 2 H^+.
- **Precursor metabolites**—The end product of the transition step, acetyl-CoA, is a precursor metabolite.

Tricarboxylic Acid (TCA) Cycle

The eight steps of the tricarboxylic acid (TCA) cycle complete the oxidation of glucose (see figure 6.15). The cycle incorporates the acetyl groups from the transition step, releasing CO_2 in this net reaction:

$$2 \text{ acetyl groups } (2\text{ C}) + 6\,NAD^+ + 2\,FAD + 2\,ADP + 2\,P_i \longrightarrow 4\,CO_2 + 6\,NADH + 6\,H^+ + 2\,FADH_2 + 2\,ATP$$

In addition to generating ATP and reducing power, the steps of the TCA cycle form 2 more precursor metabolites used by *E. coli* (see table 6.2).

Step 1: The cycle begins when CoA transfers its acetyl group to the 4-carbon compound oxaloacetate, thereby forming the 6-carbon compound citrate.

Step 2: Citrate is chemically rearranged to form an isomer, isocitrate. ■ isomer, p. 19

Step 3: Isocitrate is oxidized and a molecule of CO_2 is removed, forming the 5-carbon compound α-ketoglutarate. During the oxidation, NAD^+ is reduced to form NADH + H^+.

Step 4: Like the transition step that converts pyruvate to acetyl-CoA, this involves a group of reactions catalyzed by a complex of enzymes. In this step, α-ketoglutarate is oxidized, CO_2 is removed, and CoA is added, producing the 4-carbon compound succinyl-CoA. During the oxidation, NAD^+ is reduced to form NADH + H^+.

Step 5: This removes CoA from succinyl-CoA, harvesting the energy to make ATP. The reaction forms succinate. Note that some types of cells make guanosine triphosphate (GTP) rather than ATP at this step. This compound, however, can be converted to ATP.

Step 6: Succinate is oxidized to form fumarate. During the oxidation, FAD is reduced to form $FADH_2$.

Step 7: A molecule of water is added to fumarate, forming malate.

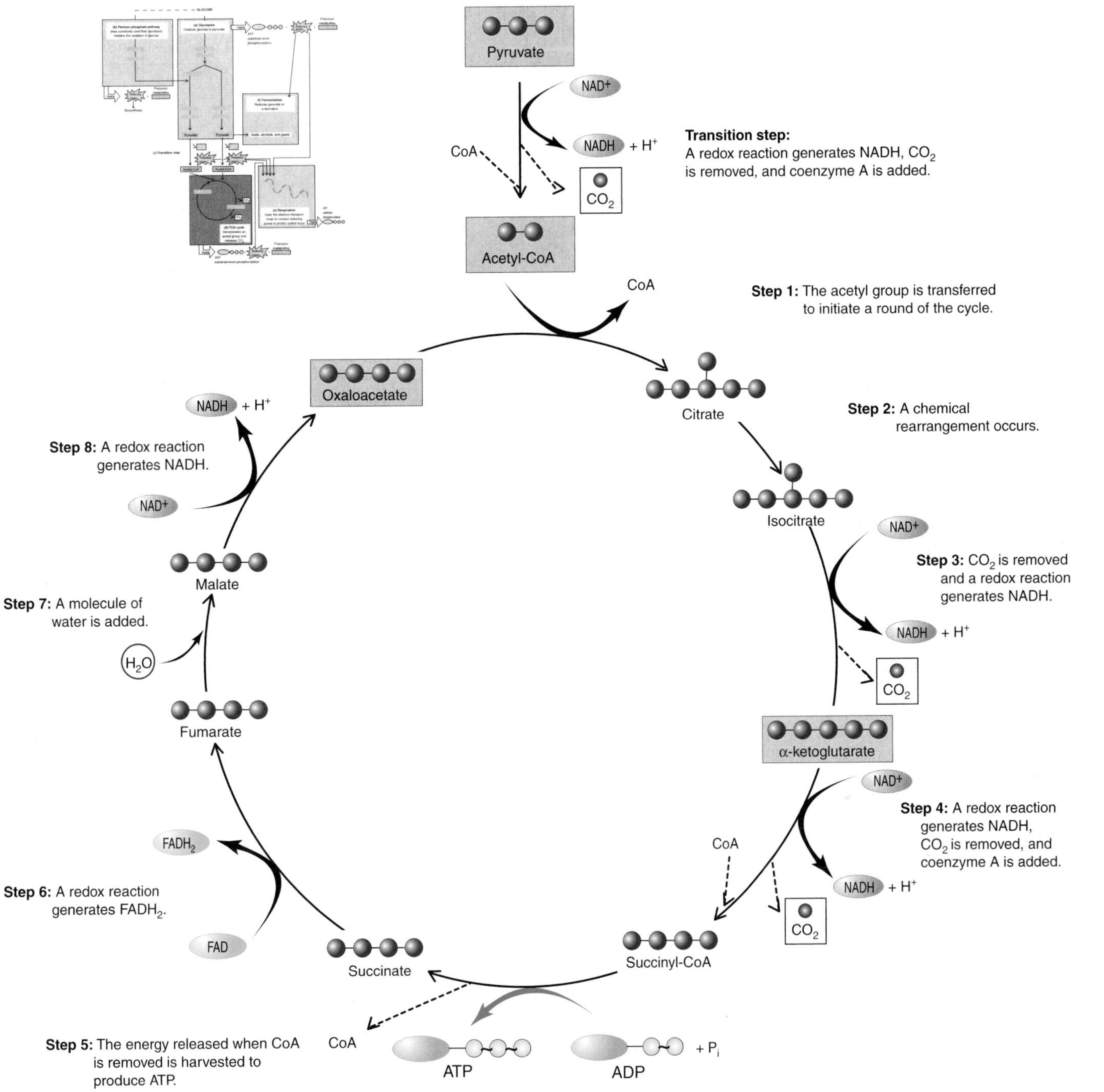
Pyruvate
NAD+
NADH + H+
CoA
CO2
Transition step:
A redox reaction generates NADH, CO2 is removed, and coenzyme A is added.
Acetyl-CoA
CoA
Step 1: The acetyl group is transferred to initiate a round of the cycle.
Oxaloacetate
Citrate
Step 2: A chemical rearrangement occurs.
NADH + H+
Step 8: A redox reaction generates NADH.
NAD+
Isocitrate
NAD+
Step 3: CO2 is removed and a redox reaction generates NADH.
Malate
Step 7: A molecule of water is added.
NADH + H+
H2O
CO2
Fumarate
α-ketoglutarate
NAD+
Step 4: A redox reaction generates NADH, CO2 is removed, and coenzyme A is added.
FADH2
CoA
Step 6: A redox reaction generates FADH2.
NADH + H+
CO2
FAD
Succinate
Succinyl-CoA
Step 5: The energy released when CoA is removed is harvested to produce ATP.
CoA
ATP
ADP
+ Pi

FIGURE 6.15 The Transition Step and the Tricarboxylic Acid Cycle The transition step links glycolysis and the TCA cycle, converting pyruvate to acetyl-CoA; it generates reducing power and 1 precursor metabolite. The TCA cycle incorporates the acetyl group of acetyl-CoA and, using a series of steps, releases CO_2; it generates ATP, reducing power in the form of both NADH and $FADH_2$, and 2 different precursor metabolites.

Step 8: Malate is oxidized to form oxaloacetate; note that oxaloacetate is the starting compound to which acetyl-CoA is added to initiate the cycle. During the oxidation, NAD^+ is reduced to form NADH + H^+.

Yield of the TCA Cycle

The tricarboxylic acid cycle "turns" once for each acetyl-CoA that enters. Because two molecules of acetyl-CoA are generated for each glucose molecule that enters glycolysis, the breakdown of one molecule of glucose causes the cycle to "turn" twice. Assuming no precursors leave the cycle, these two "turns" generate:

- **ATP**—2 ATP produced in step 5.
- **Reducing power**—6 NADH + 6 H^+ and 2 $FADH_2$. NAD^+ is reduced to NADH + H^+ during the oxidations in the TCA cycle at steps 3, 4, and 8. FAD is reduced to $FADH_2$ during the oxidation at step 6.
- **Precursor metabolites**—Two precursor metabolites used by *E. coli* are formed as a result of steps 3 and 8.

MICROCHECK 6.3

Glycolysis oxidizes glucose to pyruvate, yielding some ATP and NADH and 6 precursor metabolites. The pentose phosphate pathway initiates the breakdown of glucose; its greatest significance is its contribution of 2 precursor metabolites and NADPH for biosynthesis. The transition step and the TCA cycle, repeated twice, complete the oxidation of glucose, yielding some ATP, a great deal of reducing power, and 3 precursor metabolites.

- ✓ What is the product of the transition step?
- ✓ Explain why the TCA cycle ultimately results in a greater ATP gain than glycolysis.
- ✓ Which compound contains more free energy—pyruvate or oxaloacetate? Why?

6.4

Respiration

Focus Points

- Describe how the electron transport chain generates a proton motive force.
- Compare and contrast the electron transport chains of eukaryotes and prokaryotes.
- Describe how proton motive force is used to synthesize ATP.

Respiration uses the NADH and $FADH_2$ generated in gycolysis, the transition step, and the TCA cycle to synthesize ATP. The process, called **oxidative phosphorylation,** occurs through a combination of two mechanisms—the **electron transport chain,** which generates proton motive force, and an enzyme called **ATP synthase,** which harvests the energy of the proton motive force to drive the synthesis of ATP. In 1961, the British scientist Peter Mitchell originally proposed the **chemiosmotic theory** that describes the remarkable mechanism by which ATP synthesis is linked to electron transport, but his hypothesis was widely dismissed. Only through years of self-funded research was he finally able to convince others of its validity, and he was awarded the Nobel Prize in 1978.

The Electron Transport Chain—Generating Proton Motive Force

The **electron transport chain** is a group of membrane-embedded electron carriers that pass electrons sequentially from one to another. In prokaryotes, it is located in the cytoplasmic membrane, whereas in eukaryotic cells it is in the inner membrane of mitochondria (see figure 3.53). Because of the asymmetrical arrangement of the electron carriers, the sequential oxidation/reduction reactions result in the ejection of protons to the outside of the cell or, in the case of mitochondria, to the space between the inner and outer membranes. This expulsion of protons creates a proton gradient, or electrochemical gradient, across the membrane. Energy of this gradient, **proton motive force,** can be harvested by cells and used to fuel the synthesis of ATP. Recall from chapter 3 that prokaryotes can also use proton motive force as a source of energy to transport substances into or out of the cell, and to power the rotation of flagella.

Four types of electron carriers participate in the electron transport chain:

- **Flavoproteins** are proteins to which an organic molecule called a flavin is attached. FAD is an example of a flavin.
- **Iron-sulfur proteins** are proteins that contain iron and sulfur molecules arranged in a cluster.
- **Quinones** are lipid soluble molecules that move freely in the membrane and can therefore transfer electrons between different enzyme structures in the membrane. Several types of quinones exist, one of the most common being ubiquinone (meaning ubiquitous quinone).
- **Cytochromes** are proteins that contain heme, a chemical structure that holds an iron atom in the center. Several different cytochromes exist, each distinguished with a letter after the term, for example, cytochrome *c*.

Because of the order of the carriers in the electron transport chain, energy is gradually released as the electrons are passed from one carrier to another, much like a ball falling down a flight of stairs **(figure 6.16).** Energy release is coupled to the ejection of protons to establish a proton gradient.

General Mechanisms of Proton Ejection

An important characteristic of the electron carriers is that some accept only hydrogen atoms (proton-electron pairs), whereas others accept only electrons. The spatial arrangement of these two types of carriers in the membrane causes protons to be shuttled from the inside of the membrane to the outside. This occurs because a hydrogen carrier that receives electrons from an electron carrier must pick

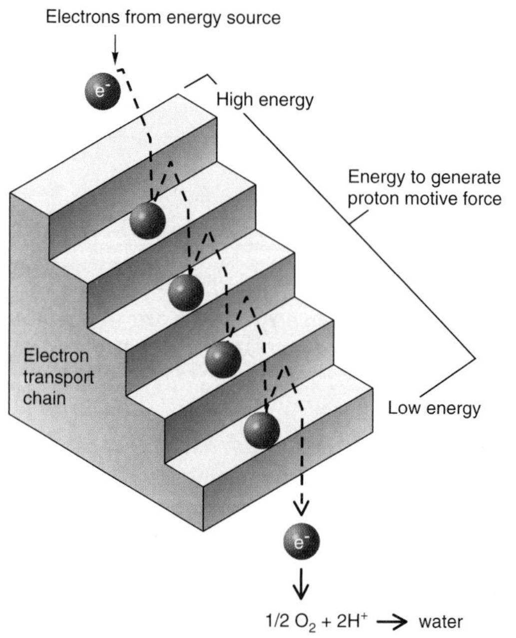

FIGURE 6.16 Electron Transport Energy released as electrons are passed along carriers of the electron transport chain is used to establish a proton gradient.

up protons; because of the hydrogen carrier's relative location in the membrane, those protons come from inside the cell (or matrix of the mitochondrion). Conversely, when a hydrogen carrier passes electrons to a carrier that accepts electrons but not protons, free protons are released to the outside of the cell (or intermembrane space of the mitochondrion). The net effect of these processes is that protons are pumped from one side of the membrane to the other, establishing the concentration gradient across the membrane.

Most carriers of the electron transport chain are grouped into several large protein complexes that function as **proton pumps;** other carriers shuttle electrons from one complex to the next.

The Electron Transport Chain of Mitochondria

Mitochondria have four different protein complexes, three of which function as proton pumps (complexes I, III, and IV). In addition, two electron carriers (coenzyme Q and cytochrome *c*) shuttle electrons between the complexes. The electron transport chain of mitochondria consists of these components **(figure 6.17):**

- **Complex I** (also called NADH dehydrogenase complex). This accepts electrons from NADH, ultimately transferring them to coenzyme Q; in the process, 4 protons are pumped across the membrane.
- **Complex II** (also called succinate dehydrogenase complex). This accepts electrons from the TCA cycle, when $FADH_2$ is formed during the oxidation of succinate (see figure 6.15, step 6). Electrons are then transferred to coenzyme Q.
- **Coenzyme Q** (also called ubiquinone). This lipid soluble carrier accepts electrons from either complex I or complex II and then shuttles them to complex III. Note that the electrons carried by $FADH_2$ have entered the electron transport chain "downstream" of those carried by NADH. Because of this, a pair of electrons carried by NAHD result in more protons being expelled than does a pair carried by $FADH_2$.
- **Complex III** (also called cytochrome bc_1 complex). This accepts electrons from coenzyme Q, ultimately transferring them to cytochrome *c;* in the process, 4 protons are pumped across the membrane.
- **Cytochrome *c*.** This accepts electrons from complex III and then shuttles them to complex IV.

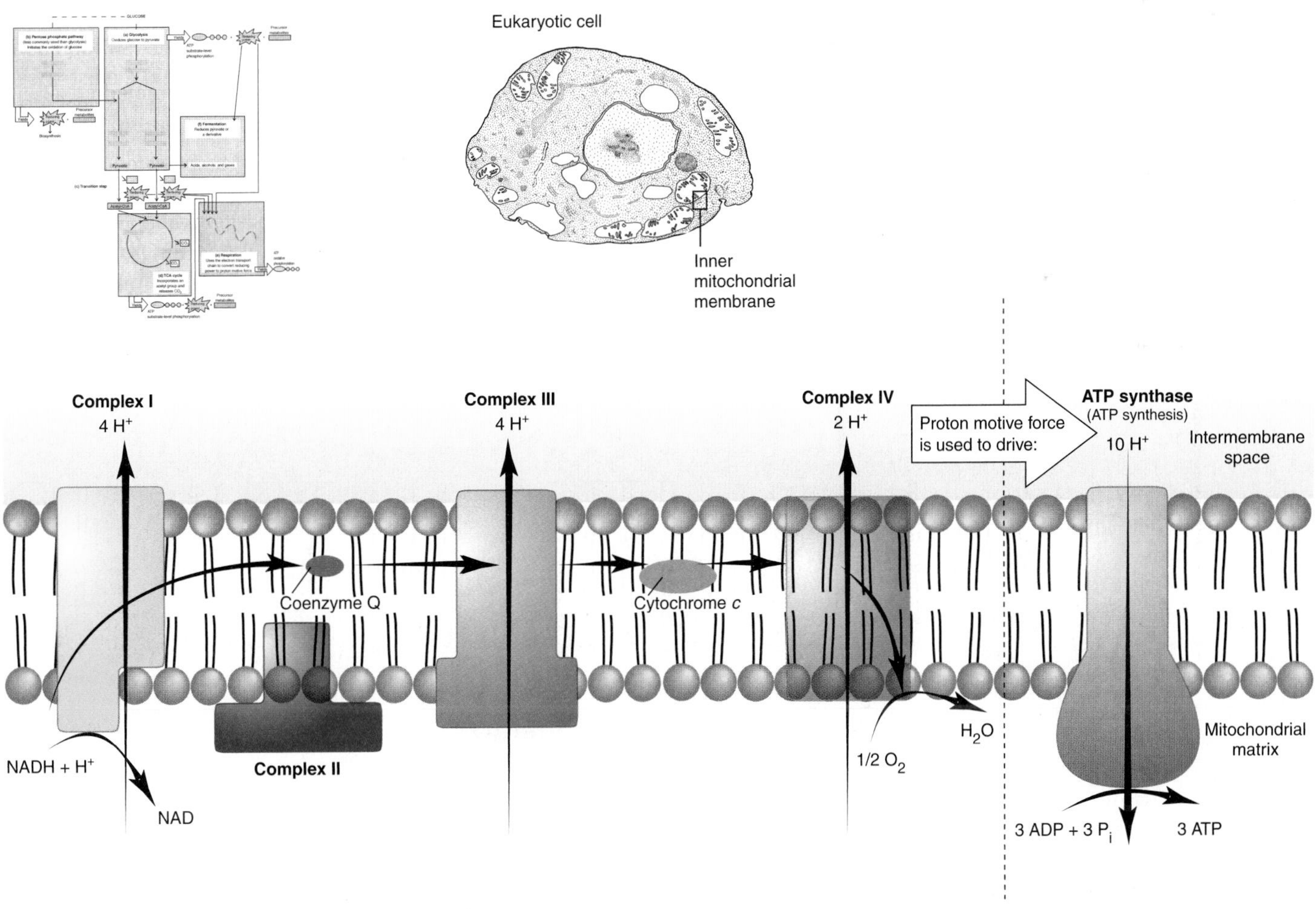

FIGURE 6.17 The Electron Transport Chain of Mitochondria The electrons carried by NADH are passed to complex I. They are then passed to coenzyme Q, which transfers them to complex III. Cytochrome *c* then transfers electrons to complex IV. From there, they are passed to O_2. Unlike the electrons carried by NADH, those carried by $FADH_2$ are passed to complex II, which then passes them to coenzyme Q; from there, the electrons follow the same path as the ones donated by NADH. Protons are shuttled from the mitochondrial matrix to the intermembrane space by complex I, III and IV, creating the proton motive force. ATP synthase allows protons to reenter the mitochondrial matrix, using the energy released to drive ATP synthesis.

- **Complex IV** (also called cytochrome *c* oxidase complex). This accepts electrons from cytochrome *c,* ultimately transferring them to oxygen (O_2), forming H_2O. In the process 2 protons are pumped across the membrane. Complex IV is a terminal oxidoreductase, meaning that it transfers the electrons to the terminal electron acceptor, which, in this case, is O_2.

The Electron Transport Chains of Prokaryotes

Considering the flexibility and diversity of prokaryotes, it is not surprising that they vary with respect to the types and arrangement of their electron transport components. In fact, a single species may have several alternative carriers so that the system as a whole can function optimally under changeable growth conditions. In the laboratory, the different electron system components provide a mechanism to distinguish between certain types of bacteria. For example, the activity of cytochrome *c* oxidase, which is found in species of *Pseudomonas, Campylobacter,* and certain other genera, is detected using the rapid biochemical test called the **oxidase test** and is important in the identification scheme of these organisms (see table 10.5).

The electron transport chain of *E. coli* provides an excellent example of the diversity found even in a single organism. This organism preferentially uses aerobic respiration, but when molecular oxygen is not available, it can switch to anaerobic respiration provided that a suitable terminal electron acceptor such as nitrate is available. The *E. coli* electron transport chain serves as a model for both aerobic and anaerobic respiration.

Aerobic Respiration When growing aerobically in a glucose-containing medium, *E. coli* can use two different NADH dehydrogenases **(figure 6.18).** One is a proton pump functionally equivalent to complex I of the mitochondrion. *E. coli* also has a succinate dehydrogenase that is functionally equivalent to complex II of the mitochondrion. In addition to these enzyme complexes, *E. coli* can produce several alternatives, enabling the organism to optimally use a variety of different energy sources, including hydrogen gas. *E. coli* does not have the equivalent of complex III or cytochrome *c;* instead quinones, including ubiquinone, shuttle the electrons directly to a terminal oxidoreductase. When O_2 is available to serve as a terminal electron acceptor, one of two variations of a terminal oxidoreductase called ubiquinone oxidase is used. One form functions optimally only in high O_2 conditions and results in the expulsion of 4 protons. The other results in the ejection of only 2 protons, but it can more effectively scavenge O_2 and thus is particularly useful when the supply of O_2 is limited.

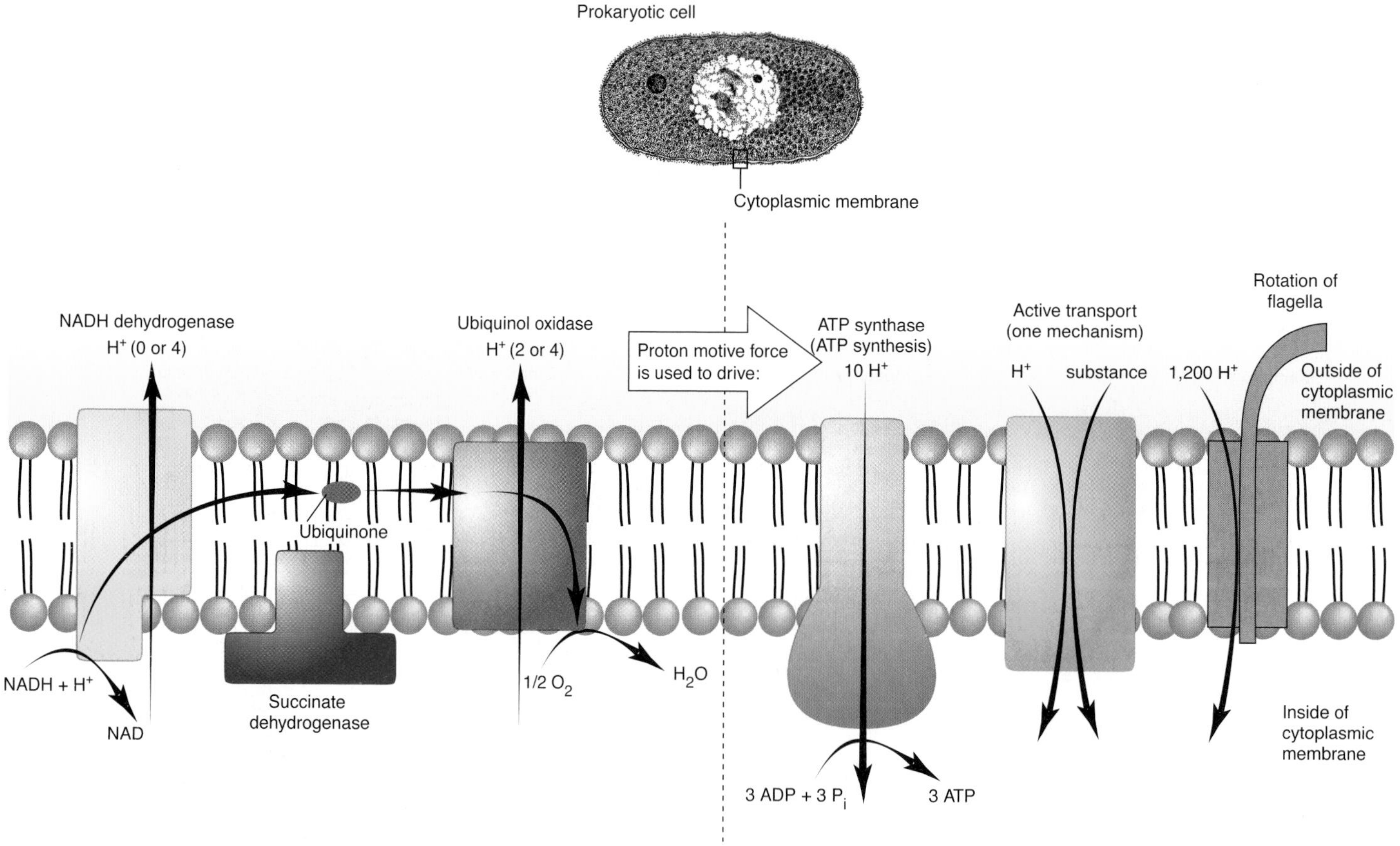

FIGURE 6.18 The Electron Transport Chain of *E. coli* Growing Aerobically in a Glucose-Containing Medium. The electrons carried by NADH are passed to one of two different NADH dehydrogenases. They are then passed to ubiquinone, which transfers them to one of two ubiquinol oxidases. From there they are passed to O_2. Unlike the electrons carried by NADH, those carried by $FADH_2$ are passed to succinate dehydrogenase, which then transfers them to ubiquinone; from there, the electrons follow the same path as the ones donated by NADH. Protons are ejected by one of the two NADH dehydrogenases and both ubiquinol oxidases, creating the proton motive force. ATP synthase allows protons to reenter the cell, using the energy released to drive ATP synthesis. The proton motive force is also used to drive one form of active transport and to power the rotation of flagella. *E. coli* has other components of the electron transport chain that function under different growth conditions.

Anaerobic Respiration Anaerobic respiration is a less efficient form of energy transformation than is aerobic respiration. This is partly due to the lesser amount of energy released in reactions that involve the reduction of inorganic chemicals other than molecular oxygen. Alternative electron carriers are used in the electron transport chain during anaerobic respiration.

When oxygen is absent and nitrate is available, *E. coli* responds by synthesizing a terminal oxidoreductase that uses nitrate as a terminal electron acceptor, producing nitrite. The organism then converts nitrite to ammonia, presumably to avoid the toxic effects of nitrite. Other bacteria can reduce nitrate further than *E. coli* can, forming compounds such as nitrous oxide (N_2O), and nitrogen gas (N_2). The quinone that bacteria use during anaerobic respiration, menaquinone, provides humans and other mammals with a source of the nutrient called vitamin K. This vitamin is required for the proper coagulation of blood, and mammals are able to obtain at least part of their requirement by absorbing menaquinone produced by bacteria growing in the intestinal tract.

A group of obligate anaerobes called the **sulfate-reducers** use sulfate (SO_4^{2-}) as a terminal electron acceptor, producing hydrogen sulfide as an end product. The diversity and ecology of the sulfate reducers will be discussed in chapter 11. ■ sulfate-reducers, p. 271

ATP Synthase—Harvesting the Proton Motive Force to Synthesize ATP

Just as energy is required to establish a concentration gradient, energy is released when a gradient is eased. The enzyme ATP synthase uses that energy to synthesize ATP. It permits protons to flow back into the bacterial cell (or matrix of the mitochondrion) in a controlled manner, harvesting the energy released to fuel the addition of a phosphate group to ADP. It appears that one molecule of ATP is formed from the entry of approximately 3 protons. The precise mechanism of how this occurs is not well understood.

Theoretical ATP Yield of Oxidative Phosphorylation

The complexity of oxidative phosphorylation makes it exceedingly difficult to determine the actual maximum yield of ATP. Unlike the yield of substrate-level phosphorylation, which can be calculated based on the stoichiometry of relatively simple chemical reactions, oxidative phosphorylation involves processes that have many variables. This is particularly true for prokaryotic cells because they use proton motive force to drive processes other than ATP synthesis, including flagella rotation and membrane transport. In addition, as a group, they use different carriers in their electron transport chain, and these may vary in the number of protons ejected per pair of electrons passed. Another complicating factor in energy yield calculations is that the number of ATP molecules generated per reduced electron carrier is not necessarily a whole number.

For each pair of electrons transferred to the electron transport chain by NADH, between 2 and 3 ATP may be generated; for each pair transferred by $FADH_2$, the yield is between 1 and 2 ATP. Although experimental studies using rat mitochondria indicate that the yield is approximately 2.5 ATP/NADH and 1.5 ATP/$FADH_2$, for simplicity we will use whole numbers (3 ATP/NADH and 2 ATP/$FADH_2$) to calculate the maximum ATP gain of oxidative phosphorylation in a prokaryotic cell. Note, however, that these numbers are only theoretical and serve primarily as a means of comparing the relative energy gains of respiration and fermentation.

The ATP gain as a result of oxidative phosphorylation will be at least slightly different in eukaryotic cells than in prokaryotic cells because of the fate of the reducing power (NADH) generated during glycolysis. Recall that in eukaryotic cells, glycolysis takes place in the cytoplasm, whereas the electron transport chain is located in the mitochondria. Consequently, the electrons carried by cytoplasmic NADH must be translocated across the mitochondrial membrane before they can enter the electron transport chain. This requires an expenditure of approximately 2 ATP.

The maximum theoretical energy yield for oxidative phosphorylation in a prokaryotic cell that uses an electron transport chain similar to that of mitochondria is:

- **From glycolysis:**
  2 NADH ⟶ 6 ATP (assuming 3 for each NADH)
- **From the transition step:**
  2 NADH ⟶ 6 ATP (assuming 3 for each NADH)
- **From the TCA cycle:**
  6 NADH ⟶ 18 ATP (assuming 3 for each NADH)
  2 $FADH_2$ ⟶ 4 ATP (assuming 2 for each $FADH_2$)

ATP Yield of Aerobic Respiration in Prokaryotes

Now that the ATP-yielding components of the central metabolic pathways have been considered, we can calculate the theoretical maximum ATP yield of aerobic respiration in prokaryotes. This yield is illustrated in **figure 6.19.**

- **Substrate-level phosphorylation:**
  2 ATP (from glycolysis; net gain)
  2 ATP (from the TCA cycle)
  4 ATP (total; substrate-level phosphorylation)
- **Oxidative phosphorylation:**
  6 ATP (from the reducing power gained in glycolysis)
  6 ATP (from the reducing power gained in the transition step)
  22 ATP (from the reducing power gained in the TCA cycle)
  34 (total; oxidative phosphorylation)
- **Total ATP gain (theoretical maximum) = 38**

MICROCHECK 6.4

Respiration uses the NADH and $FADH_2$ generated in glycolysis, the transition step, and the TCA cycle to synthesize ATP. The electron transport chain is used to convert reducing power into a proton motive force. ATP synthase then harvests that energy to synthesize ATP. The overall process is called oxidative phosphorylation. In aerobic respiration, O_2 serves as the terminal electron acceptor; anaerobic respiration employs a molecule other than O_2.

✓ Why is the overall ATP yield in aerobic respiration only a theoretical number?

✓ In bacteria, what is the role of the molecule that serves as a source of vitamin K for humans?

✓ Why could an oxidase also be called a reductase?

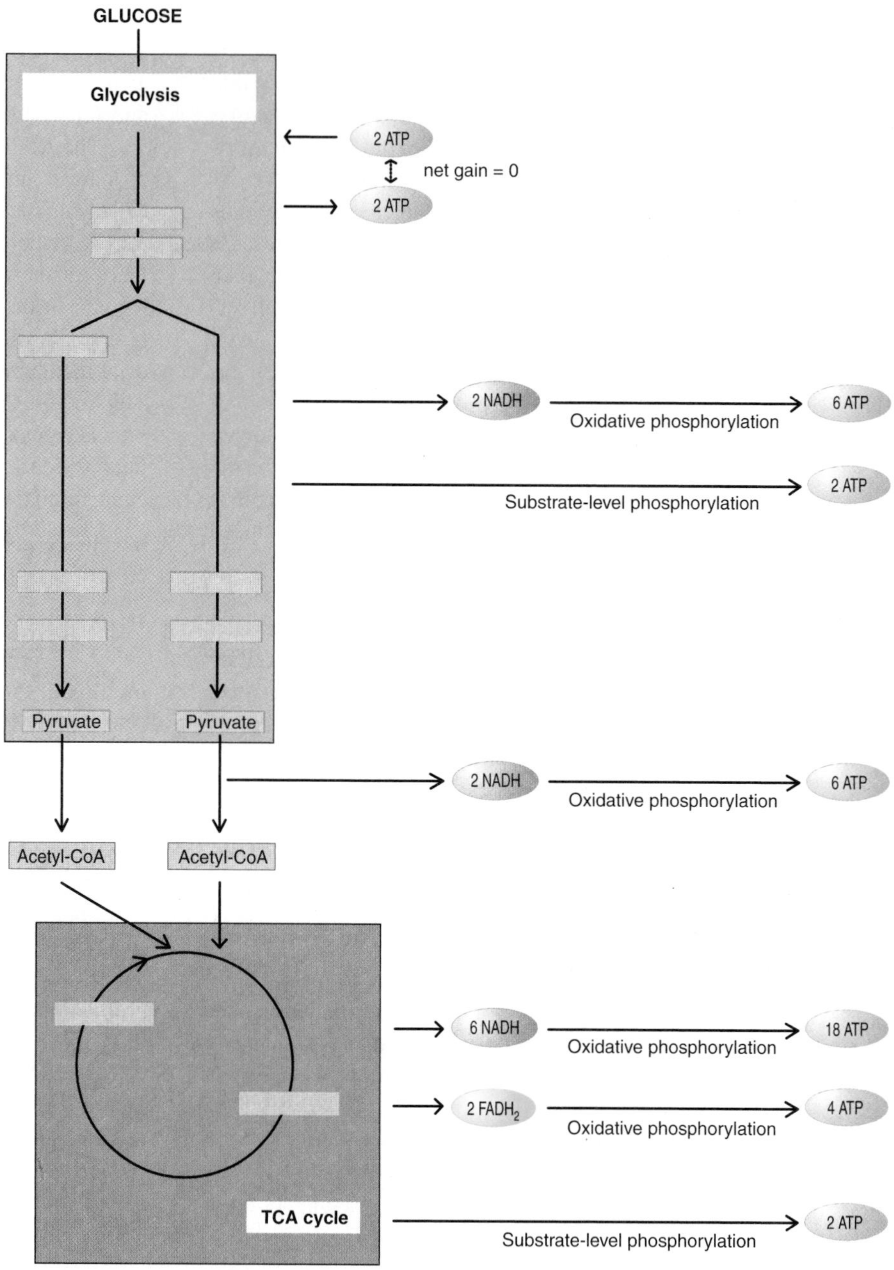

FIGURE 6.19 Maximum Theoretical Energy Yield from Aerobic Respiration in a Prokaryotic Cell This maximum energy yield calculation assumes that for every pair of electrons transferred to the electron transport chain, 3 ATP are synthesized; and for every pair of electrons donated by $FADH_2$, 2 ATP are synthesized. Note that these values are theoretical; a variety of factors, including the electron carriers employed and use of the proton motive force to drive other processes, affects the yield.

6.5 Fermentation

Focus Point

- Describe 6 common end products of fermentation, and the importance of each.

Fermentation is used by organisms that cannot respire, either because a suitable inorganic terminal electron acceptor is not available or because they lack an electron transport chain. *Escherichia coli* is a facultative anaerobe that has the ability to use any of three ATP-generating options—aerobic respiration, anaerobic respiration, and fermentation; the choice depends in part on the availability of terminal electron acceptors. In contrast, members of a group of aerotolerant anaerobes called the **lactic acid bacteria** lack the ability to respire; they only ferment, regardless of the presence of oxygen (O_2). Because they can grow in the presence of oxygen but never use it as a terminal electron acceptor, they are sometimes called **obligate fermenters.** The situation is different for obligate anaerobes that use fermentation pathways; they cannot even grow in the presence of O_2, and many are rapidly killed in its presence.

In general, the only ATP-yielding reactions of fermentation are those of glycolysis, and involve substrate-level phosphorylation. The other steps function primarily to consume excess reducing power, providing a mechanism for recycling NADH **(figure 6.20).** If this reduced carrier were not recycled, no NAD^+ would be available to accept electrons in subsequent rounds of glycolysis, blocking that ATP-generating pathway. To consume reducing power, fermentation pathways use an organic intermediate such as pyruvate or a derivative as a terminal electron acceptor.

The end products of fermentation are significant for a number of reasons. Because a given type of organism uses a charac-

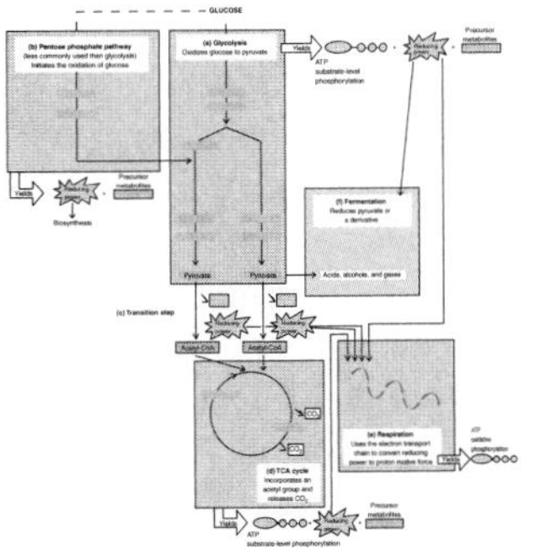

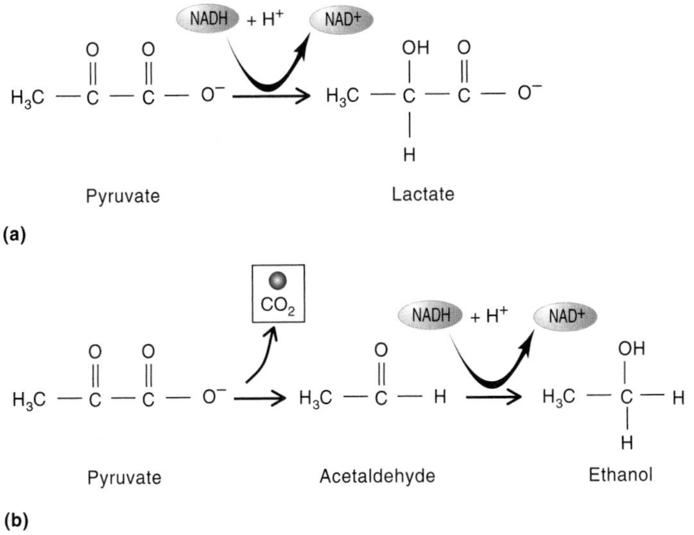

FIGURE 6.20 Fermentation Pathways Use Pyruvate or a Derivative As a Terminal Electron Acceptor (a) In lactic acid fermentation, pyruvate serves directly as a terminal electron acceptor, producing lactate. **(b)** In ethanol fermentation, pyruvate is first converted to acetaldehyde, which then serves as the terminal electron acceptor, producing ethanol.

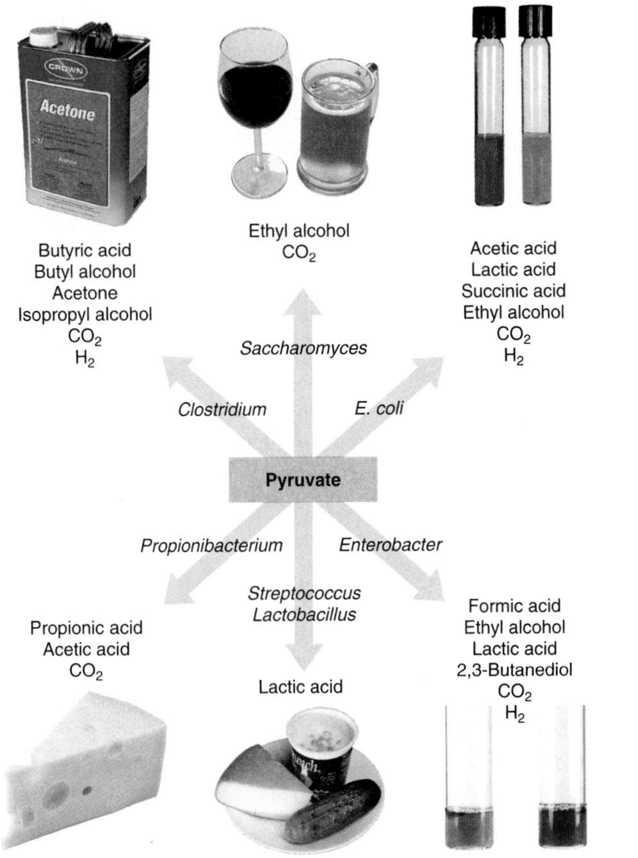

FIGURE 6.21 End Products of Fermentation Pathways Because a given type of organism uses a characteristic fermentation pathway, the end products can be used as an identifying marker. Some end products are commercially valuable.

teristic fermentation pathway, end products can sometimes be used as a marker to aid in identification. Some end products are commercially valuable. In fact, much of chapter 32 is devoted to the fermentations used to produce certain beverages and food products. Note that organic acids produced during fermentation are traditionally referred to by the name of their undissociated form. Important end products of fermentation pathways include **(figure 6.21):**

- **Lactic acid.** Lactic acid (the ionized form is lactate) is produced when pyruvate itself serves as the terminal electron acceptor. The growth of a group of Gram-positive organisms called the lactic acid bacteria is encouraged to produce fermented food products. Their end products are instrumental in creating the flavor and texture of cheese, yogurt, pickles, cured sausages, and other foods. On the other hand, lactic acid causes tooth decay and spoilage of some foods. Some animal cells use this fermentation pathway on a temporary basis when molecular oxygen is in short supply; the accumulation of lactic acid in muscle tissue causes the pain and fatigue sometimes associated with strenuous exercise. ■ **lactic acid bacteria, p. 272** ■ **cheese, yogurt and other fermented milk products, p. 798** ■ **pickled vegetables, p. 800** ■ **fermented meat products, p. 800**
- **Ethanol.** Ethanol is produced in a pathway that first removes CO_2 from pyruvate, generating acetaldehyde, which then serves as the terminal electron acceptor. The end products of these sequential reactions are ethanol and CO_2, which are used to make wine, beer, spirits, and bread (see figures 32.4, 32.5, and 32.6). Members of *Saccharomyces* (yeast) and *Zymomonas* (bacteria) use this pathway. ■ **wine, p. 800** ■ **beer, p. 802** ■ **distilled spirits, p. 802** ■ **bread, p. 804**
- **Butyric acid.** Butyric acid (the ionized form is butyrate) and a variety of other end products are produced in a complex multistep pathway used by species of *Clostridium,* which are obligate anaerobes. Under certain conditions, some species use a variation of this pathway to produce the organic solvents butanol and acetone.
- **Propionic acid.** Propionic acid (the ionized form is propionate) is generated in a multistep pathway that first removes CO_2 from pyruvate, generating a compound that then serves as a terminal electron acceptor. After NADH reduces this, it is further modified to form propionate. Members of the genus *Propionibacterium* use this pathway; their growth is encouraged in the production of Swiss cheese. The CO_2 they form makes the holes, and propionic acid gives the cheese its characteristic flavor. ■ **cheese, p. 798**
- **2, 3-Butanediol.** This is produced in a multistep pathway that uses two molecules of pyruvate to generate two molecules of CO_2 and acetoin. The latter then serves as the terminal

electron acceptor. The primary significance of this pathway is that it is used to differentiate certain members of the family *Enterobacteriaceae;* the **Voges-Proskauer test** detects acetoin, distinguishing members that use this pathway, such as *Klebsiella* and *Enterobacter,* from those that do not, such as *E. coli* (see table 10.4). ■ Voges-Proskauer test, p. 253

- **Mixed acids.** These are produced in a multistep branching pathway, generating a variety of different fermentation end products including lactic acid, succinic acid (the ionized form is succinate), ethanol, acetic acid (the ionized form is acetate), CO_2, and gases. The primary significance of this pathway is that it is used to differentiate certain members of the family *Enterobacteriaceae;* the **methyl-red test** detects end products of the pathway, distinguishing members that use this pathway, such as *E. coli,* from those that do not, such as *Klebsiella* and *Enterobacter* (see table 10.4). ■ methyl-red test, p. 253

MICROCHECK 6.5

Fermentation stops short of the TCA cycle, using pyruvate or a derivative of it as a terminal electron acceptor. Many end products of fermentation are commercially valuable.

- ✓ How do the Voges-Proskauer and methyl-red tests differentiate between certain members of the *Enterobacteriaceae?*
- ✓ Compare and contrast the fermentation pathways that generate lactic acid and propionic acid.
- ✓ Fermentation is used as a means of preserving foods. Why would it slow spoilage?

6.6 Catabolism of Organic Compounds Other Than Glucose

Focus Point

- Briefly describe how polysaccharides and disaccharides, lipids, and proteins are degraded and utilized by a cell.

Cells can use a variety of organic compounds other than glucose as energy sources, including macromolecules such as polysaccharides, lipids, and proteins. To break these down into their respective sugar, amino acid, and lipid subunits, cells synthesize **hydrolytic enzymes,** which break bonds by adding water. To use a macromolecule in the surrounding medium, a cell must secrete the appropriate hydrolytic enzyme and then transport the resulting subunits into the cell. Inside the cell, the subunits are further degraded to form appropriate precursor metabolites **(figure 6.22).** Recall that precursor metabolites can be either oxidized in one of the central metabolic pathways or used in biosynthesis. ■ hydrolysis, p. 26

Polysaccharides and Disaccharides

Starch and cellulose are both polymers of glucose, but different types of chemical bonds join their subunits. The nature of this difference profoundly affects the mechanisms by which they are degraded. Enzymes called **amylases** are produced by a wide variety of organisms to digest starches. In contrast, cellulose is digested by enzymes called **cellulases,** which are produced by relatively few organisms. Among the organisms that can degrade cellulose are bacteria that reside in the rumen of animals, and many types of fungi. Considering that cellulose is the most abundant organic compound on earth, it is not surprising that fungi are important decomposers in terrestrial habitats. The glucose subunits released when polysaccharides are hydrolyzed can then enter glycolysis to be oxidized to pyruvate. ■ polysaccharides, p. 32 ■ cellulose, p. 32 ■ rumen, p. 774

Disaccharides including lactose, maltose, and sucrose are hydrolyzed by specific **disaccharidases.** For example, the enzyme β-galactosidase breaks down lactose, forming glucose and galactose. Glucose can enter glycolysis directly, but the other monosaccharides must first be modified. ■ disaccharides, p. 32

Lipids

The most common simple lipids are fats, which are a combination of fatty acids joined to glycerol. Fats are hydrolyzed by enzymes called **lipases.** The glycerol component is then converted to the precursor metabolite dihydroxyacetone phosphate, which then enters the glycolytic pathway. The fatty acids are degraded using a series of reactions collectively called **β-oxidation.** Each sequential reaction transfers a 2-carbon unit from the end of the fatty acid to coenzyme A, forming acetyl-CoA; this can enter the TCA cycle. Each reaction is a redox reaction, generating one NADH + H^+ and one $FADH_2$. ■ simple lipids, p. 35

Proteins

Proteins are hydrolyzed by enzymes called **proteases,** which break peptide bonds that join amino acid subunits. The amino group of the resulting amino acids is removed by a reaction called a **deamination.** The remaining carbon skeletons are then converted into the appropriate precursor molecules. ■ protein, p. 27

MICROCHECK 6.6

In order for polysaccharides, lipids, and proteins to be used as energy sources, they are first hydrolyzed to release their respective subunits. These are then converted to the appropriate precursor metabolites so they can enter a central metabolic pathway.

- ✓ Why do cells secrete hydrolytic enzymes?
- ✓ Explain the process used to degrade fatty acids.
- ✓ How would cellulose-degrading bacteria in the rumen of a cow benefit the animal?

6.7 Chemolithotrophs

Focus Point

- Explain how chemolithotrophs obtain energy.

Prokaryotes as a group are unique in their ability to use reduced inorganic chemicals such as hydrogen sulfide (H_2S) and ammo-

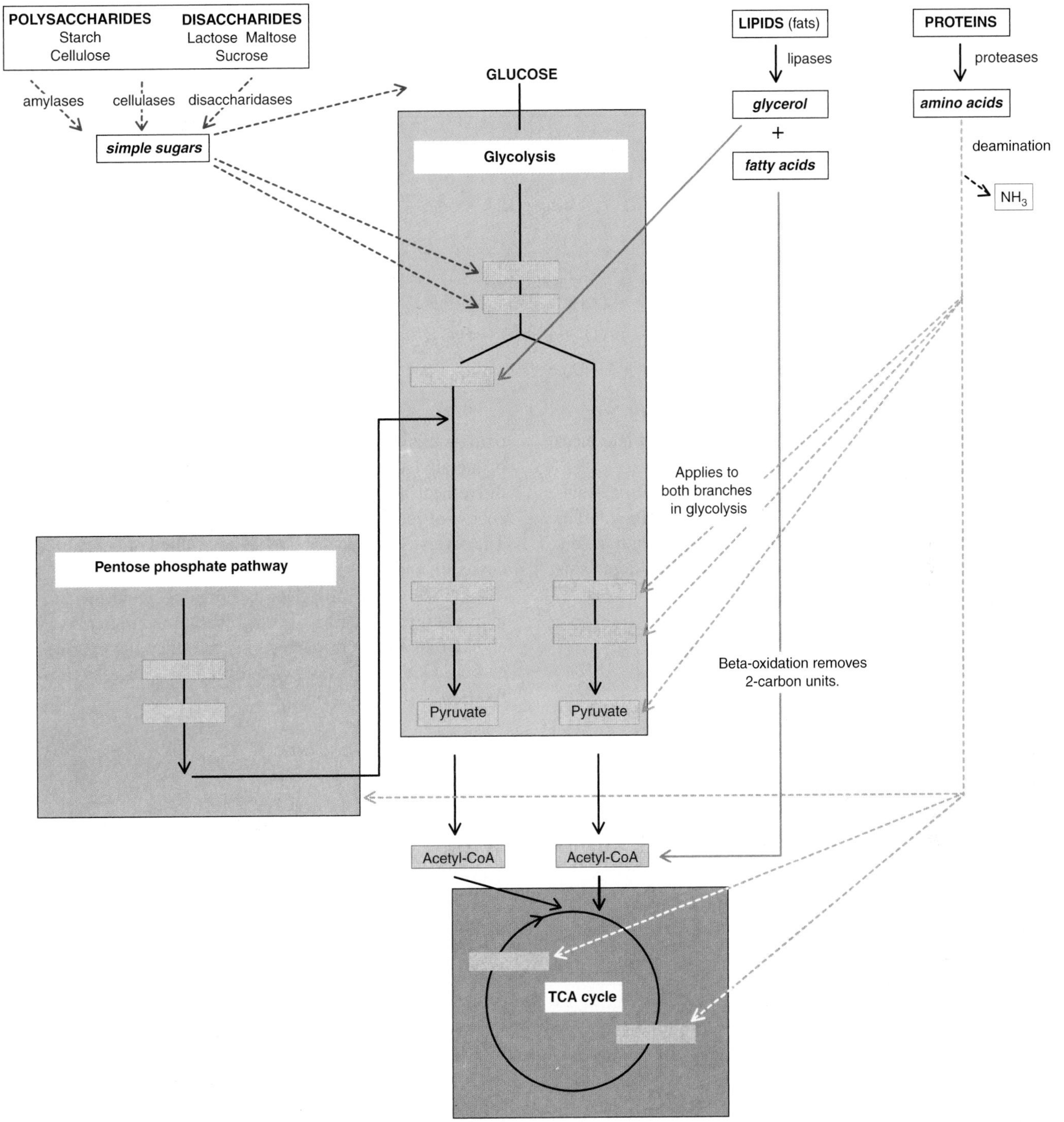

FIGURE 6.22 Catabolism of Organic Compounds Other Than Glucose The subunits of macromolecules are degraded to form the appropriate precursor metabolites. These metabolites can then either be oxidized in one of the central metabolic pathways or be used in anabolism.

nia (NH_3) as a source of energy. Note that these are the very compounds produced as a result of anaerobic respiration, when inorganic molecules such as sulfate and nitrate serve as terminal electron acceptors. This is one important example of how nutrients are cycled; the waste products of one organism serve as an energy source for another. ■ biogeochemical cycling and energy flow, p. 767

Chemolithotrophs fall into four general groups **(table 6.7):**

- **Hydrogen bacteria** oxidize hydrogen gas.
- **Sulfur bacteria** oxidize hydrogen sulfide.
- **Iron bacteria** oxidize reduced forms of iron.
- **Nitrifying bacteria** include two groups of bacteria—one oxidizes ammonia, forming nitrite, and the other oxidizes nitrite, forming nitrate.

The chemolithotrophs extract electrons from inorganic energy sources and then use the electrons to generate ATP by oxidative phosphorylation. The electrons are passed along an electron transport chain to generate a proton motive force, analogous to the processes described earlier. The amount of energy gained in

TABLE 6.7 Metabolism of Chemolithotrophs

Common Name of Organism	Source of Energy	Oxidation Reaction (Energy Yielding)	Important Features of Group	Common Genera In Group
Hydrogen bacteria	H_2 gas	$H_2 + \frac{1}{2} O_2 \longrightarrow H_2O$	Can also use simple organic compounds for energy	*Hydrogenomonas*
Sulfur bacteria (non-photosynthetic)	H_2S	$H_2S + \frac{1}{2} O_2 \longrightarrow H_2O + S$ $S + 1\frac{1}{2} O_2 + H_2O \longrightarrow H_2SO_4$	Some members of this group can live at a pH of less than 1.	*Thiobacillus* *Beggiatoa* *Thiothrix*
Iron bacteria	Reduced Iron (Fe^{2+})	$2 Fe^{2+} + \frac{1}{2} O_2 + H_2O \longrightarrow 2 Fe^{3+} + 2 OH^-$	Iron oxide present in the sheaths of these bacteria	*Sphaerotilus* *Gallionella*
Nitrifying bacteria	NH_3	$NH_3 + 1\frac{1}{2} O_2 \longrightarrow HNO_2 + H_2O$	Important in nitrogen cycle	*Nitrosomonas*
	HNO_2	$HNO_2 + 1\frac{1}{2} O_2 \longrightarrow HNO_3$	Important in nitrogen cycle	*Nitrobacter*

metabolism depends on the energy source and the terminal electron acceptor; **figure 6.23** illustrates this relationship.

Chemolithotrophs generally thrive in very specific environments where reduced inorganic compounds are found. For example, *Thiobacillus ferrooxidans* is found in certain acidic environments that are rich in sulfides. Because these organisms oxidize metal sulfides, they can be used to enhance the recovery of metals (see **Perspective 6.1**). Thermophilic chemolithotrophs thrive near hydrothermal vents of the deep ocean, harvesting the energy of reduced inorganic compounds that spew from the vents. The diversity and ecology of some of these organisms will be discussed in chapter 11.

Unlike organisms that use organic molecules to fill both their energy and carbon needs, chemolithotrophs do not require an external source of carbon. Instead, they incorporate inorganic carbon, CO_2, into an organic form. This process, called **carbon fixation,** will be described later.

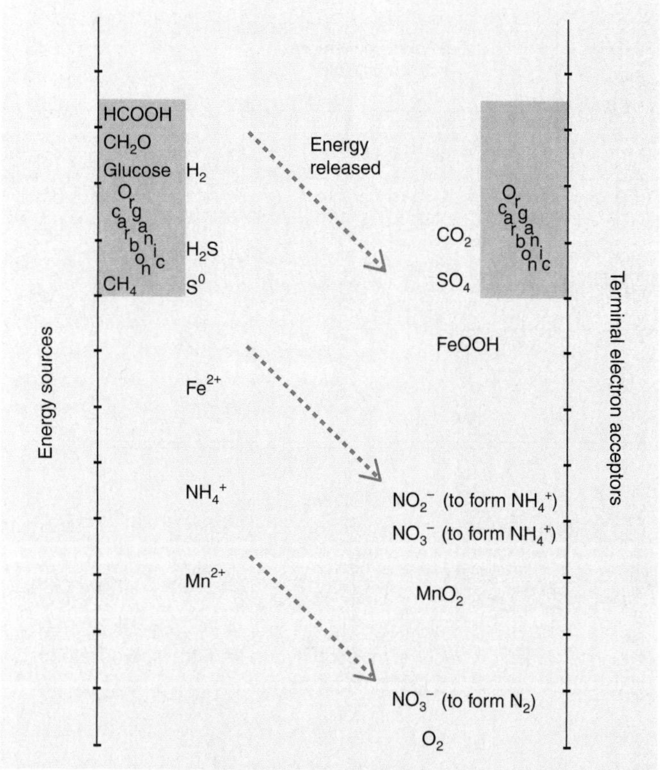

FIGURE 6.23 Relative Energy Gain of Different Types of Metabolism The left axis shows potential energy sources, ordered according to their relative tendency to give up electrons; those at the top lose electrons most easily. The right axis shows potential terminal electron acceptors, ordered according to their relative tendency to gain electrons; those at the bottom accept electrons most readily. Energy is released only when electrons are transferred from an energy source to a terminal electron acceptor that is lower on the chart; the greater the downward slope, the more energy that can be harvested to make ATP.

MICROCHECK 6.7

Chemolithotrophs use reduced inorganic compounds as an energy source. They use carbon dioxide as a carbon source.

✓ Describe the roles of hydrogen sulfide and carbon dioxide in chemolithoautotrophic metabolism.

✓ Which energy source, Fe^{2+} or H_2S, would result in the greatest energy yield when O_2 is used as a terminal electron acceptor (hint: refer to figure 6.23)?

6.8 Photosynthesis

Focus Points

- Describe the role of chlorophylls, bacteriochlorophylls, accessory pigments, reaction-center pigments, and antennae pigments in capturing radiant energy.
- Compare and contrast the tandem photosystems of cyanobacteria and photosynthetic eukaryotes with the single photosystems of purple and green bacteria.

Plants, algae, and several groups of bacteria are able to harvest the radiant energy of sunlight, and then use it to power the synthesis of organic carbon compounds from CO_2. This capture and subsequent conversion of light energy into chemical energy is called

PERSPECTIVE 6.1

Mining with Microbes

Microorganisms have been used for thousands of years in the production of bread and wine. It is only in the past several decades, however, that they are being used with increasing frequency in another area of biotechnology, the mining industry. The mining process traditionally consists of digging crude ores from the earth, crushing them, and then extracting the desired minerals from the contaminants. The extraction process of such minerals as copper and gold frequently involves harsh conditions, such as smelting, and burning off the contaminants before extracting the metal with cyanide. Such activities are expensive and deleterious to the environment. With the development of biomining, some of these problems are being solved.

In the process of biomining copper, the low grade ore is dumped outside the mine and then treated with sulfuric acid. The acid conditions encourage the growth of the acidophilic bacterium *Thiobacillus ferrooxidans,* present naturally in the ore. This organism uses CO_2 as a source of carbon and gains its energy by oxidizing sulfides of iron first to sulfur and then to sulfuric acid. The sulfuric acid dissolves the insoluble copper and gold from the ore. Currently about 25% of all copper produced in the world comes from the process of biomining. Similar processes are being applied to gold mining.

The current process of biomining employs microbes indigenous to the ore. Many improvements should be possible. For example, the oxidation of the minerals generates heat to the point that the bacteria may be killed. The use of thermophiles should overcome this problem. Further, many ores contain heavy metals, such as mercury, cadmium, and arsenic, which are toxic to the bacteria. It should be possible to isolate bacteria that are resistant to these metals. Biomining is still in its infancy.

photosynthesis. The general reaction of photosynthesis can be summarized as:

$$6\,CO_2 + 12\,H_2X \xrightarrow{\text{Light Energy}} C_6H_{12}O_6 + 12\,X + 6\,H_2O$$

Photosynthetic processes are generally considered in two distinct stages. The **light-dependent reactions,** often simply called the **light reactions,** are used to capture the energy from light and convert it to chemical energy in the form of ATP. The **light-independent reactions,** also termed the **dark reactions,** use that energy to synthesize organic carbon compounds. The process that converts carbon dioxide into organic compounds is called **carbon fixation.** We will describe the steps of carbon fixation in a separate section (see section 6.9) because a variety of prokaryotes other than photosynthetic ones use the process. Characteristics of various photosynthetic mechanisms of organisms we will describe are summarized in **table 6.8.**

Capturing Radiant Energy

Photosynthetic organisms are highly visible in their natural habitats because they possess pigments to capture light energy. These pigments vary in color because they absorb different wavelengths of light. The color we observe is due to the wavelengths that are reflected; for example, pigments that absorb only blue and red light will appear green (see figure 5.7). Multiple pigments are involved

TABLE 6.8 Comparison of the Photosynthetic Mechanisms Used by Different Organisms

	Oxygenic Photosynthesis		Anoxygenic Photosynthesis	
	Plants, Algae	**Cyanobacteria**	**Purple Photosynthetic Bacteria**	**Green Photosynthetic Bacteria**
Location of the photosystem	In membranes of thylakoids, which are within the stroma of chloroplasts	In membranes of thylakoids, located within the cell	Within the cytoplasmic membrane; extensive invaginations in that membrane effectively increase the surface area.	Primarily within the cytoplasmic membrane; chlorosomes attached to the inner surface of the membrane contain the accessory pigments.
Type of photosystem	Photosystem I and photosystem II		Similar to photosystem II	Similar to photosystem I
Primary light harvesting pigment	Chlorophyll *a*		Bacteriochlorophylls	
Mechanism for generating reducing power	Non-cyclic photophosphorylation using both photosystems		Reversed electron transport	Non-cyclic use of the photosystem
Source of electrons for reducing power	H_2O		Varies among the organisms in the group; may include H_2S, H_2, or organic compounds.	
CO_2 fixation	Calvin cycle		Calvin cycle	Reversed TCA cycle
Accessory pigments	Carotenoids	Carotenoids, phycobilins	Carotenoids	Carotenoids

in photosynthesis, increasing the range of wavelengths of light that can be absorbed by a cell. The various pigments include:

- **Chlorophylls** are found in plants, algae and a group of bacteria called cyanobacteria. The various types of chlorophylls are designated with a letter following the term, for example, chlorophyll *a*.
- **Bacteriochlorophylls** are found in two groups of bacteria, purple photosynthetic bacteria and green photosynthetic bacteria; bacteriophylls absorb wavelengths not absorbed by chlorophylls, enabling the purple and green bacteria to grow in habitats where other photosynthetic organisms cannot.
- **Accessory pigments** include carotenoids and phycobilins. They increase the efficiency of light capture by absorbing wavelengths not absorbed by chlorophylls. **Carotenoids** are found in a wide variety of photosynthetic organisms, including both prokaryotes and eukaryotes. Mammals can use one of the carotenoids, β-carotene as a source of vitamin A. **Phycobilins** are unique to cyanobacteria and red algae.

The photosynthetic pigments are located together in protein complexes called **photosystems,** which specialize in capturing and using light **(figure 6.24).** Within the photosystems, the various pigments play two very different roles:

- **Reaction-center pigments** function as electron donors in the photosynthetic process; in response to excitation by radiant energy, the pigment emits an electron, which is then passed to an electron transport chain similar to that used in respiration. The oxygenic photosynthetic organisms (plants, algae, and cyanobacteria) use chlorophyll *a* as the reaction-center pigment; the anoxygenic photosynthetic organisms (purple and green bacteria) use one of the bacteriochlorophylls.
- **Antennae pigments** make up what is called the **antenna complex,** which acts as a funnel, capturing the energy of light and then transferring it to the reaction-center pigment.

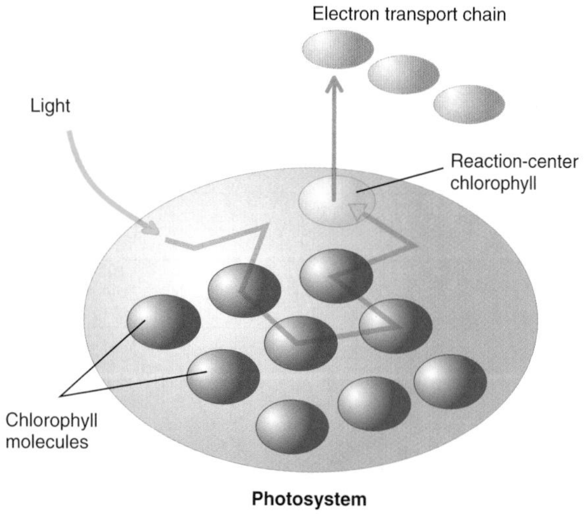

FIGURE 6.24 Photosystem Chlorophyll and other pigments capture the energy of light and then transfer it to reaction-center chlorophyll, which emits an electron that is then passed to an electron transport chain.

The photosystems of plants, algae, and cyanobacteria are located in special photosynthetic membranes. The photosystems of cyanobacteria are embedded in the membranes of stacked structures called **thylakoids** located within the cells. Plants and algae also have thylakoids, in the stroma of the chloroplast (see figure 3.54). The similarity between the structure of chloroplasts and cyanobacteria is not surprising considering that the organelle appears to have descended from an ancestor of cyanobacterium (see Perspective 3.1).

The photosystems of the purple and green bacteria are embedded in the cytoplasmic membrane. Purple bacteria have extensive invaginations in the membrane that maximize the surface area. Green bacteria have specialized structures called **chlorosomes** attached to the inner surface of the cytoplasmic membrane. These structures contain the accessory pigments.

Converting Radiant Energy into Chemical Energy

Photosynthetic organisms use the light-dependent reactions to accomplish two tasks. First, they must use radiant energy to fuel the synthesis of ATP, the process of **photophosphorylation.** They also need to generate reducing power so they can fix CO_2. Depending on the method used to fix CO_2, the type of reducing power required may be either NADPH or NADH.

Light-Dependent Reactions in Cyanobacteria and Photosynthetic Eukaryotic Cells

Cyanobacteria and chloroplasts have two distinct photosystems that work in tandem **(figure 6.25).** The sequential absorption of energy by the two photosystems allows the process to raise the energy level of electrons stripped from water high enough to be used to generate a proton motive force as well as produce reducing power. The process is **oxygenic,** that is, it generates O_2.

First we will consider the simplest situation, which occurs when the cell needs to synthesize ATP but not reducing power (NADPH). To accomplish this, only photosystem I is used. Radiant energy is absorbed by this photosystem, exciting the reaction-center chlorophylls, which causes them to emit high-energy electrons. The electrons are then passed to an electron carrier, which transports them to a proton pump; this pump is analogous to complex III in the respiratory chain of mitochondria. After being used to pump protons across the membrane, thus generating a proton motive force, the electrons are returned to photosystem I. As occurs in oxidative phosphorylation, ATP synthase harvests the energy of the proton motive force to synthesize ATP. This overall process is called **cyclic photophosphorylation** because the molecule that serves as the electron donor, reaction-center chlorophyll, also serves as the terminal electron acceptor; the electrons have followed a cyclical path.

When cells must produce both ATP and reducing power, **noncyclic photophosphorylation** is used. In this process, the electrons emitted by photosystem I are not passed to the proton pump, but instead are donated to $NADP^+$ to produce NADPH.

While this action provides reducing power, the cell must now replenish the electrons emitted by reaction center chlorophyll from another source. In addition, the cell must still generate a

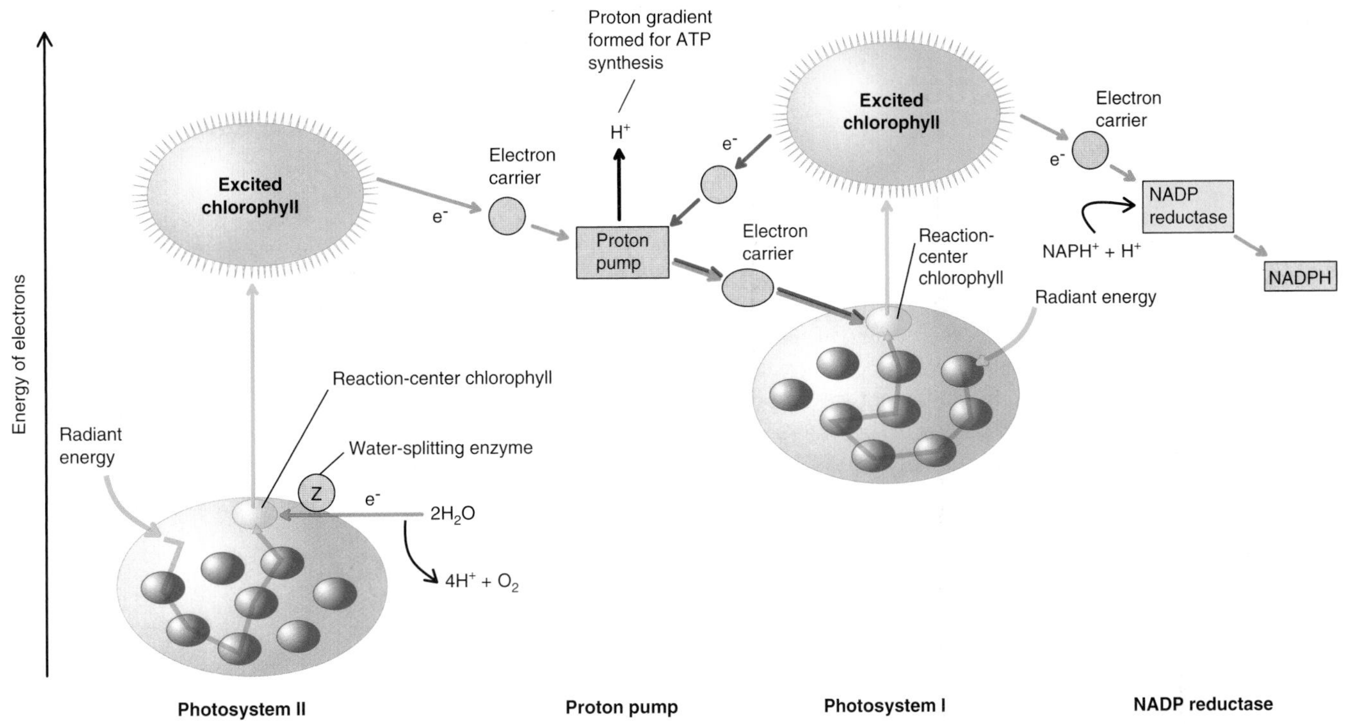

FIGURE 6.25 The Tandem Photosystems of Cyanobacteria and Chloroplasts Radiant energy captured by photosynthetic pigments excites the reaction-center chlorophyll, causing it to emit a high-energy electron, which is then passed to an electron transport chain. In cyclic photophosphorylation, electrons emitted by photosystem I are returned to that photosystem; the path of the electrons is shown in green arrows. In non-cyclic photophosphorylation, the electrons used to replenish photosystem I are donated by radiant energy-excited photosystem II; the path of these electrons is shown in orange arrows. In turn, photosystem II replenishes its own electrons by stripping them from water, producing O_2.

proton motive force in order to synthesize ATP. Photosystem II plays a pivotal role in this process. When photosystem II absorbs radiant energy, the reaction-center chlorophylls emit high-energy electrons that can be donated to photosystem I. First, however, the electrons are passed to the proton pump, which uses some of their energy to establish the proton motive force. In order to replenish the electrons emitted from photosystem II, an enzyme within that complex extracts the electrons from water, donating them to the reaction-center chlorophyll. Removal of electrons from two molecules of water generates O_2. In essence, photosystem II strips the electrons from water molecules and captures the energy of light to raise the energy of those electrons to a high enough level that they can be used to power photophosphorylation. Photosystem I then accepts those electrons, which still retain some residual energy, and again captures the energy of light to boost the energy of the electrons to an even higher level so they can be used to reduce NADPH.

Light-Dependent Reactions in Purple and Green Bacteria

Purple and green bacteria employ only a single photosystem and are unable to use water as an electron donor for reducing power. This is why they are **anoxygenic,** or do not evolve O_2. Molecules used as electron donors by purple and green bacteria include hydrogen gas (H_2), hydrogen sulfide (H_2S), and organic compounds.

Purple sulfur bacteria use a photosystem similar to the photosystem II of cyanobacteria and eukaryotes. The electrons emitted from the photosystem are passed along an electron transport chain, fueling the formation of a proton motive force, which is then used to synthesize ATP. However, the photosystem does not raise the electrons to a high enough energy level to reduce NAD^+ (or $NADP^+$), so the purple sulfur bacteria must use an alternative mechanism to generate reducing power. To do this they employ a process called reversed electron transport, which uses ATP to run the electron transport chain in the reverse direction, or "uphill."

Green bacteria employ a photosystem similar to photosystem I. The electrons emitted from this photosystem can be used to either generate a proton motive force or reduce NAD^+.

MICROCHECK 6.8

Photosynthetic organisms harvest the energy of sunlight and use it to power the synthesis of organic compounds from CO_2. Various pigments are used to capture radiant energy. These pigments are arranged in complexes called photosystems. When reaction-center chlorophyll absorbs the energy of light, a high-energy electron is emitted. This is then passed along an electron transport chain to generate a proton motive force, which is used to synthesize ATP. Plants and cyanobacteria use water as a source of electrons for reducing power, generating oxygen. Purple and green bacteria obtain electrons from a reduced compound other than water, and therefore do not evolve oxygen.

- ✓ What is the role of the antennae pigments?
- ✓ What is the advantage of having tandem photosystems?
- ✓ It requires energy to reverse the flow of the electron transport chain. Why would this be so?

6.9 Carbon Fixation

Focus Point

- Describe the three stages of the Calvin cycle.

Chemolithoautotrophs and photoautotrophs convert carbon dioxide into an organic form, the process of **carbon fixation.** In photosynthetic organisms, the process occurs in the light-independent reactions. Carbon fixation consumes a great deal of ATP and reducing power, which should not be surprising considering that the reverse process—oxidizing those same compounds to CO_2—liberates a great deal of energy. The Calvin cycle is by far the most common pathway used to fix carbon, but some prokaryotes incorporate CO_2 using other mechanisms. For example, the green sulfur bacteria and some members of the *Archaea* use a pathway that effectively reverses the steps of the TCA cycle.

Calvin Cycle

The **Calvin cycle,** or Calvin-Benson cycle, named in honor of the scientists who described much of it, is a complex cycle that can be viewed as having three essential stages—incorporation of CO_2 into an organic compound, reduction of the resulting molecule, and regeneration of the starting compound **(figure 6.26).** Because of the complexities of the cycle, it is easiest to consider the process as consisting of six "turns" of the cycle.

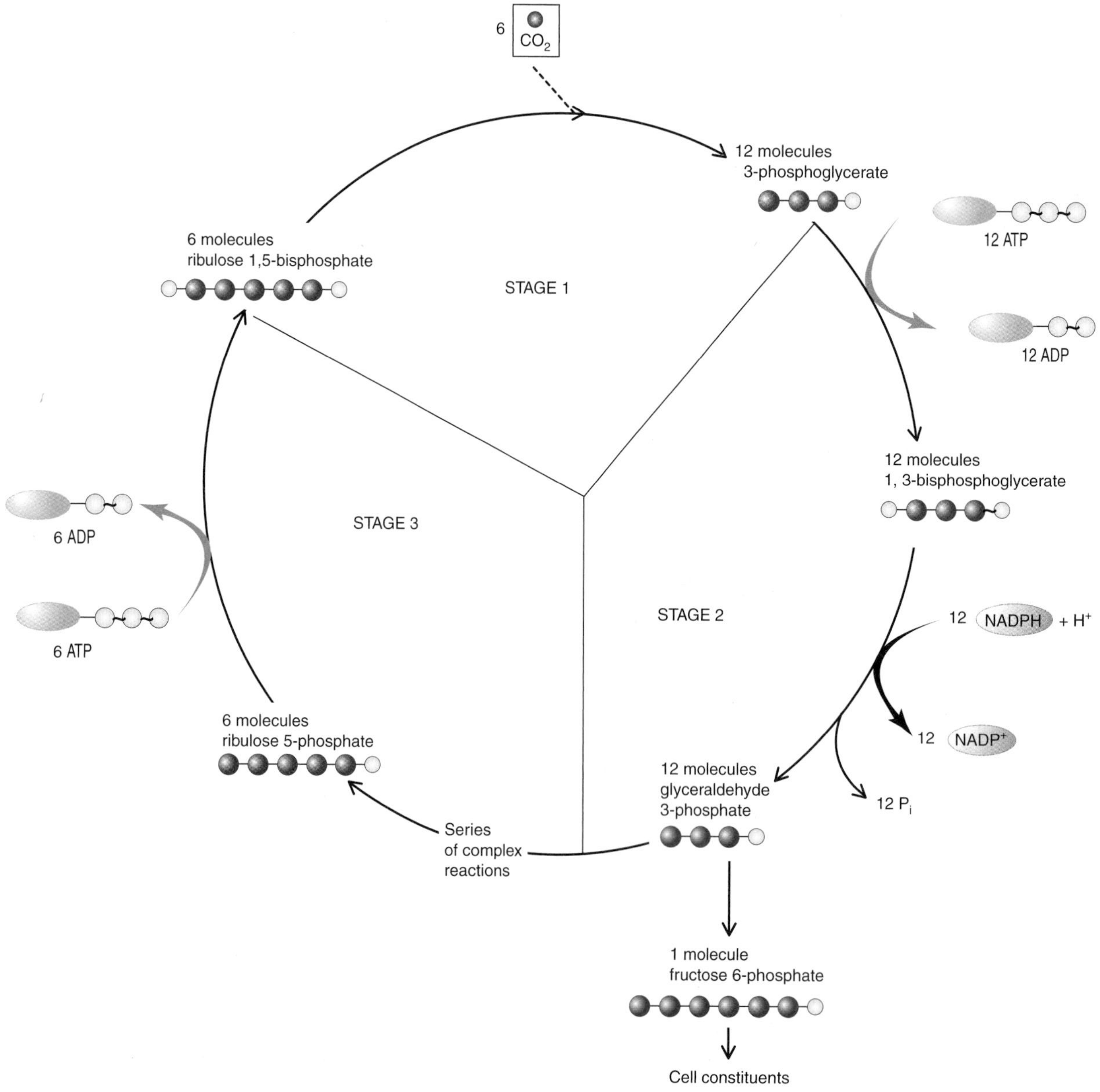

FIGURE 6.26 The Calvin Cycle The Calvin cycle has three essential stages: **(1)** incorporation of CO_2 into an organic compound; **(2)** reduction of the resulting molecule; and **(3)** regeneration of the starting compound.

Together, these six "turns" generate a net gain of two molecules of glyceraldehyde 3-phosphate, which can be converted into one molecule of fructose 6-phosphate. The Calvin cycle consists of three stages:

- **Stage 1:** Carbon dioxide enters the cycle when the enzyme ribulose bisphosphate carboxylase, commonly called **rubisco** joins it to a 5-carbon compound, ribulose 1, 5-bisphosphate. The resulting compound spontaneously hydrolyzes to produce two molecules of a 3-carbon compound, 3-phosphoglycerate (3PG). Interestingly, although rubisco is unique to autotrophs, it is thought to be the most abundant enzyme on earth.
- **Stage 2:** A sequential input of energy (ATP) and reducing power (NADPH) is used in steps that, together, convert 3PG to glyceraldehyde 3-phosphate (G3P). This compound is identical to the precursor metabolite formed as an intermediate in glycolysis. It can be converted to a number of different compounds used in biosynthesis, oxidized to make other precursor compounds, or converted to a 6-carbon sugar. A critical aspect of the pathway of CO_2 fixation, however, stems from the fact that it operates as a cycle—ribulose 1, 5-bisphosphate must be regenerated from G3P for the process to continue. Consequently, in six cycles, a maximum of 2 G3P can be converted to a 6-carbon sugar, the rest is used to regenerate ribulose 1, 5-bisphosphate.
- **Stage 3:** Many of the steps that are used to regenerate ribulose 1, 5-bisphosphate involve reactions of the pentose phosphate cycle.

Yield of the Calvin Cycle

One molecule of the 6-carbon sugar fructose can be generated for every six "turns" of the cycle. These six "turns" consume 18 ATP and 12 NADPH + H^+.

MICROCHECK 6.9

The process of carbon dioxide fixation consumes a great deal of ATP and reducing power. The Calvin cycle is the most common pathway used to incorporate inorganic carbon into an organic form.

✓ What is the role of rubisco?

✓ What would happen if ribulose 1, 5-bisphosphate were depleted in a cell?

6.10

Anabolic Pathways—Synthesizing Subunits from Precursor Molecules

Focus Point

- Describe the synthesis of lipids, amino acids, and nucleotides.

While prokaryotes as a group are highly diverse with respect to the compounds they use for energy, they are remarkably similar when comparing their biosynthetic processes. They synthesize the necessary subunits employing specific anabolic pathways that use ATP, reducing power in the form of NADPH, and the precursor metabolites formed in the central metabolic pathways **(figure 6.27). Anaplerotic reactions,** which bypass certain steps of the central metabolic pathways, can be used to replenish some of the intermediates drawn off for biosynthesis. Once the subunits are synthesized, they can be assembled to make macromolecules. Various different macromolecules can then be joined to form the structures making up the cell.

Organisms lacking one or more enzymes in a given pathway must have the end product of that pathway provided from an external source. This is why fastidious bacteria such as lactic acid bacteria require many different growth factors. ■ **fastidious, p. 98**

Lipid Synthesis

Synthesis of most lipids in microorganisms can be viewed as having two essential components—fatty acid synthesis and glycerol synthesis. Synthesis starts with transfer of the acetyl group of acetyl-CoA to a carrier protein called **acyl carrier protein (ACP).** This carrier holds the fatty acid chain as 2-carbon units are progressively added. When the newly synthesized fatty acid reaches its required length, usually 14, 16, or 18 carbons long, it is released from ACP. The glycerol component of the fat is synthesized from dihydroxyacetone phosphate.

Amino Acid Synthesis

Proteins are composed of various combinations of 20 different amino acids. Amino acids can be grouped into structurally related families that share common pathways of biosynthesis. Some are synthesized from precursor metabolites formed during glycolysis, while others are derived from compounds of the TCA cycle (see table 6.2).

Glutamate

Although all amino acids are necessary for protein synthesis, glutamate is especially important because it is used to form many other amino acids. In addition, its synthesis provides a mechanism for bacteria to incorporate nitrogen into an organic material. Recall from chapter 4 that many bacteria utilize ammonium (NH_4^+) provided in the medium as their source of nitrogen; it is primarily through the synthesis of glutamate that they do this.

Bacteria that synthesize glutamate use a single-step reaction that incorporates ammonia into the precursor metabolite α-ketoglutarate, produced in the TCA cycle **(figure 6.28a).** Once glutamate has been produced, its amino group can be transferred to other carbon compounds to produce amino acids such as aspartate (figure 6.28b). This transfer of the amino group, a **transamination,** regenerates α-ketoglutarate from glutamate. The α-ketoglutarate can then be used again to incorporate more ammonia. ■ **amino group, p. 27**

Aromatic Amino Acids

Synthesis of aromatic amino acids such as tyrosine, phenylalanine, and tryptophan requires a multistep branching pathway **(figure 6.29).**

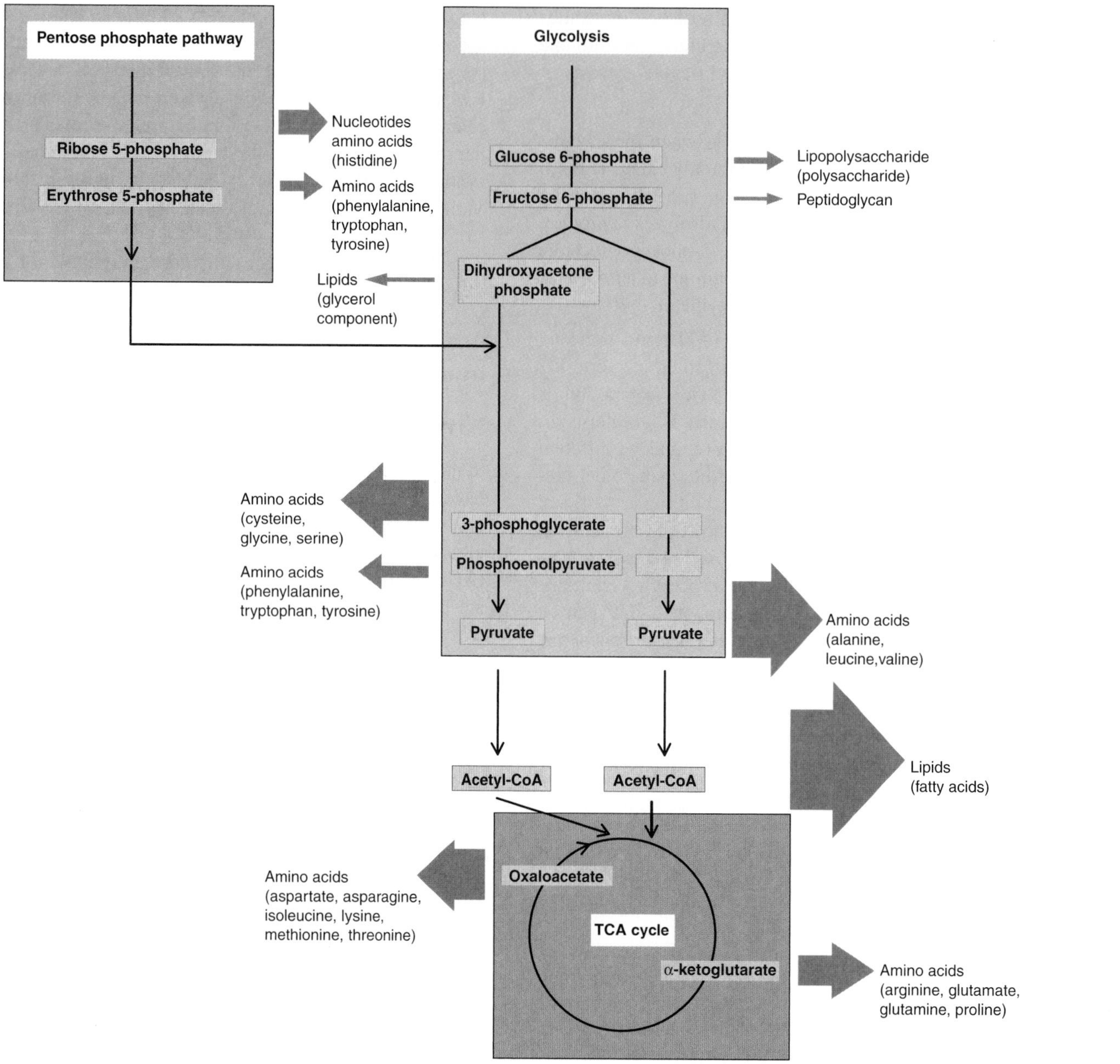

FIGURE 6.27 The Use of Precursor Metabolites in Biosynthesis The size of the arrows indicates the relative quantity of each precursor metabolite needed to produce a given weight of *E. coli* cells.

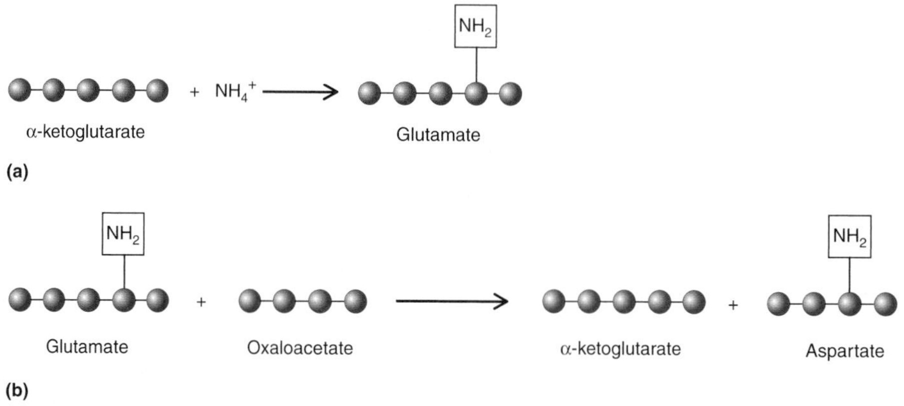

FIGURE 6.28 Glutamate (a) Glutamate is synthesized in a single-step reaction that incorporates ammonia into the precursor metabolite α-ketoglutarate. **(b)** The amino group of glutamate can be transferred to other carbon compounds in order to produce other amino acids. For example, transferring it to oxaloacetate produces aspartate.

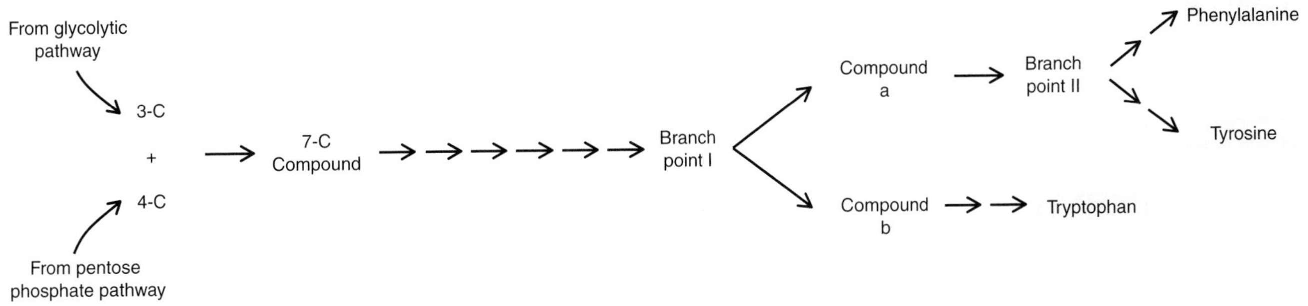

FIGURE 6.29 Synthesis of Aromatic Amino Acids A multistep branching pathway is used to synthesize aromatic amino acids. The end product of a branch inhibits the first enzyme of that branch; in addition, the end product inhibits one of the three enzymes that catalyze the first step of the pathway.

This serves as an excellent illustration of many important features of the regulation of amino acid synthesis.

The pathway begins with the formation of a 7-carbon compound, resulting from the joining of two precursor metabolites, erythrose 4-phosphate (4-carbon) and phosphoenolpyruvate (3-carbon). These precursors originate in the pentose phosphate pathway and glycolysis, respectively. The 7-carbon compound is modified through a series of steps until a branch point is reached. At this juncture, two options are possible. If synthesis proceeds in one direction, tryptophan is produced. In the other direction, another branch point is reached; from there, either tyrosine or phenylalanine can be made.

When a given amino acid is provided to a cell, it would be a waste of carbon, energy, and reducing power for that cell to continue synthesizing it. But when only one product of a branched pathway is present, how does the cell control synthesis? In the pathway for aromatic acid biosynthesis, this partly occurs by regulating the enzymes at the branch points. Tryptophan acts as a feedback inhibitor of the enzyme that directs the branch to its synthesis; this sends the pathway to the steps leading to the synthesis of the other amino acids, tyrosine and phenylalanine. Likewise, these two amino acids each inhibit the first enzyme of the branch leading to their synthesis.

In addition, the three amino acids each control the first step of the full pathway, the formation of the 7-carbon compound. Three different enzymes can catalyze this step; each has the same active site, but they have different allosteric sites. Each aromatic amino acid acts as a feedback inhibitor for one of the enzymes. If all three amino acids are present in the environment, then very little of the 7-carbon compound will be synthesized. If only one or two of those amino acids are present, then proportionally more of the compound will be synthesized.

Nucleotide Synthesis

Nucleotide subunits of DNA and RNA are composed of three units: a 5-carbon sugar, a phosphate group, and a nitrogenous base, either a purine or a pyrimidine (see figure 2.21). They are synthesized as ribonucleotides, but these can then be converted to deoxyribonucleotides by replacing the hydroxyl group on the 2′ carbon of the sugar with a hydrogen atom. ■ **purine, p. 34** ■ **pyrimidine, p. 34**

The purine nucleotides are synthesized in a distinctly different manner from the pyrimidine nucleotides. Purine nucleotides are synthesized on the sugar phosphate component in a very complex process. In fact, nearly every carbon and nitrogen of the purine ring comes from a different source **(figure 6.30).** The starting compound is ribose 5-phosphate, a precursor metabolite generated in the pentose phosphate pathway. Then, in a highly ordered sequence, atoms from the other sources are added. Once this purine is formed, it is converted to adenylic and guanylic acid, which are components of the nucleic acids. To synthesize pyrimidine nucletotides, the pyrimidine ring is made first, and then attached to ribose 5-phosphate. After one pyrimidine nucleotide is formed, the base component can be converted into one of the other pyrimidines. ■ **adenylic acid, p. 33** ■ **guanylic acid, p. 33**

MICROCHECK 6.10

Biosynthetic processes of different organisms are remarkably similar, using precursor metabolites, NADPH, and ATP to form subunits. Synthesis of the amino acid glutamate provides a mechanism for bacteria to incorporate nitrogen in the form of ammonia into organic material. Allosteric enzymes are used to regulate certain biosynthetic pathways. The purine nucleotides are synthesized in a very different manner from the pyrimidine nucleotides.

- ✓ Explain why the synthesis of glutamate is particularly important for a cell.
- ✓ What are three general requirements that the cell must fulfill in order to carry out biosynthesis?
- ✓ With a branched biochemical pathway, why would it be important for a cell to shut down the first step as well as branching steps?

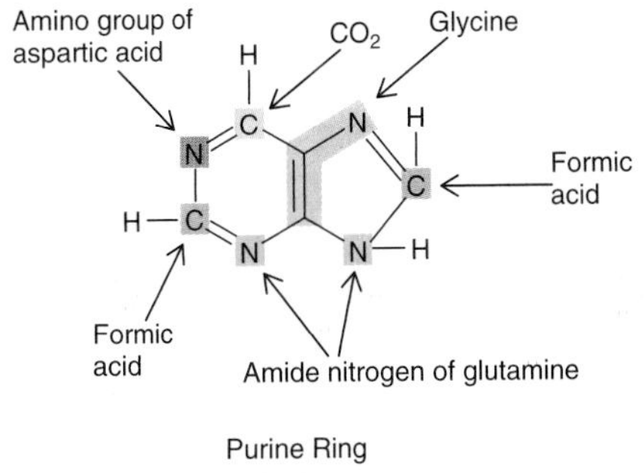

FIGURE 6.30 Source of the Carbons and Nitrogen Atoms in Purine Rings Nearly every carbon and nitrogen of the purine ring comes from a different source.

FUTURE CHALLENGES

Going to Extremes

The remarkable speed and precision of enzyme activity is already exploited in a number of different processes. For example, the enzyme glucose isomerase is used to modify corn syrup, converting some of the glucose into fructose, which is much sweeter than glucose. The resulting high-fructose corn syrup is used in the commercial production of a variety of beverages and food products. Other enzymes, including proteases, amylases, and lipases, are used in certain laundry detergents to facilitate stain removal. These enzymes break down proteins, starches, and fats, respectively, which otherwise adhere strongly to fabrics. Similar enzymes are being added to some dishwashing detergents, decreasing the reliance on chlorine bleaching agents and phosphates that can otherwise pollute the environment. Enzymes are also used by the pulp and paper industry to facilitate the bleaching process.

Even with the current successes of enzyme technology, however, only a small fraction of enzymes in nature have been characterized. Recognizing that the field is still in its infancy, some companies are actively searching diverse environments for microorganisms that produce novel enzymes, hoping that some may be commercially valuable. Among the most promising enzymes are those produced by the extremophiles, microbes that preferentially live in conditions inhospitable to other forms of life. Because these organisms live in severe environments, it is expected that their enzymes can withstand the harsh conditions that characterize certain processes. For example, the enzymes of the extreme thermophiles will likely withstand temperatures that would quickly inactivate enzymes of mesophiles.

With the aid of enzymes, many of which are still to be discovered, scientists may eventually be able to precisely control a greater variety of commercially important chemical processes. This, it is hoped, will result in fewer unwanted by-products and a decreased reliance on harsh chemicals that damage the environment.

SUMMARY

6.1 Principles of Metabolism

Catabolism encompasses processes that capture and store energy by breaking down complex molecules. **Anabolism** includes processes that use energy to synthesize and assemble the building blocks of a cell. (Figure 6.1)

Harvesting Energy

Energy is the ability to do work.

Photosynthetic organisms harvest the energy of sunlight, using it to power the synthesis of organic compounds. **Chemoorganotrophs** transform and use energy contained in organic compounds. (Figure 6.3)

Exergonic reactions release energy; **endergonic** reactions utilize energy.

Components of Metabolic Pathways

A specific **enzyme** facilitates each step of a metabolic pathway. (Figure 6.5)

ATP is the energy currency of the cell.

The **energy source** is **oxidized** to release its energy; this **oxidation-reduction** reaction **reduces** an electron carrier (Figure 6.7)

NAD^+, $NADP^+$, and **FAD** are electron carriers. (Table 6.1)

Precursor metabolites are used to make the subunits of macromolecules, and they can also be oxidized to generate energy in the form of ATP. (Table 6.2)

Scheme of Metabolism (Figure 6.8)

The **central metabolic pathways** are **glycolysis**, the **pentose phosphate pathway**, and the **tricarboxylic acid cycle (TCA cycle)**.

Respiration uses the reducing power accumulated in the central metabolic pathways to generate ATP by oxidative phosphorylation. **Aerobic respiration** uses O_2 as a terminal electron acceptor; **anaerobic respiration** uses an inorganic molecule other than O_2 as a terminal electron acceptor. (Table 6.3)

Fermentation uses pyruvate or a derivative as a terminal electron acceptor rather than oxidizing it further in the TCA cycle; this recycles the reduced electron carrier NADH.

6.2 Enzymes

Enzymes function as biological catalysts; they are neither consumed nor permanently changed during a reaction.

Mechanisms and Consequences of Enzyme Action (Figure 6.9)

The substrate binds to the **active site** or **catalytic site** to form a temporary intermediate called an **enzyme-substrate complex.**

Cofactors and Coenzymes (Figure 6.10, Table 6.4)

Enzymes sometimes act in conjunction with **cofactors** such as coenzymes and trace elements.

Environmental Factors That Influence Enzyme Activity (Figure 6.11)

The factors most important in influencing enzyme activities are temperature, pH, and salt concentration.

Allosteric Regulation (Figure 6.12)

Cells can fine-tune the activity of an **allosteric enzyme** by using a regulatory molecule that binds to the **allosteric site** of the enzyme.

Enzyme Inhibition

Non-competitive inhibition occurs when the inhibitor and the substrate act at different sites on the enzyme.

Competitive inhibition occurs when the inhibitor competes with the normal substrate for the active binding site. (Figure 6.13)

6.3 The Central Metabolic Pathways (Table 6.6)

Glycolysis (Figure 6.14)

Glycolysis converts one molecule of glucose into two molecules of pyruvate; the theoretical net yield is 2 ATP, 2 NADH + H^+, and 6 different precursor metabolites.

Pentose Phosphate Pathway

The pentose phosphate pathway forms NADPH and 2 different precursor metabolites.

Transition Step (Figure 6.15)

The transition step converts pyruvate to acetyl-CoA. Repeated twice, this produces 2 NADH + 2 H^+ and 1 precursor metabolite.

Tricarboxylic Acid (TCA) Cycle (Figure 6.15)

The TCA cycle completes the oxidation of glucose; the theoretical yield of two "turns" is 6 NADH + 6 H^+, 2 $FADH_2$, 2 ATP, and 2 different precursor metabolites.

6.4 Respiration

The Electron Transport Chain—Generating Proton Motive Force

The electron transport chain sequentially passes electrons, and, as a result, ejects protons.

The mitochondrial electron transport chain has three different complexes (complexes I, III and IV) that function as proton pumps. (Figure 6.17)

Prokaryotes vary with respect to the types and arrangements of their electron transport components. (Figure 6.18)

Some prokaryotes can use inorganic molecules other than O_2 as terminal electron acceptors. This process of anaerobic respiration harvests less energy than aerobic respiration.

ATP Synthase—Harvesting the Proton Motive Force to Synthesize ATP

ATP synthase permits protons to flow back across the membrane, harvesting the energy released to fuel the synthesis of ATP.

ATP Yield of Aerobic Respiration in Prokaryotes (Figure 6.19)

The theoretical maximum yield of ATP of aerobic respiration is 38 ATP.

6.5 Fermentation

In general, the only ATP-yielding reactions of fermentations are those of the glycolytic pathway; the other steps provide a mechanism for recycling NADH. (Figure 6.20)

Some end products of fermentation are commercially valuable. (Figure 6.21)

Because a given type of organism uses a specific fermentation pathway, the end products can be used as markers that aid in identification.

6.6 Catabolism of Organic Compounds Other Than Glucose (Figure 6.22)

Hydrolytic enzymes break down macromolecules into their respective subunits.

Polysaccharides and Disaccharides

Amylases digest starch, releasing glucose subunits, and are produced by many organisms. **Cellulases** degrade cellulose.

Sugar subunits released when polysaccharides are broken down can then enter glycolysis to be oxidized to pyruvate.

Lipids

Fats are hydrolyzed by **lipase,** releasing glycerol and fatty acids.

Glycerol is converted to dihydroxyacetone phosphate; fatty acids are degraded by a **β-oxidation,** generating reducing power and the precursor metabolite acetyl-CoA.

Proteins

Proteins are hydrolyzed by **proteases.**

Deamination removes the amino group; the remaining carbon skeleton is then converted into the appropriate precursor molecule.

6.7 Chemolithotrophs

Prokaryotes, as a group, are unique in their ability to use reduced inorganic compounds such as hydrogen sulfide (H_2S) and ammonia (NH_3) as a source of energy. (Figure 6.23)

Chemolithotrophs are autotrophs.

6.8 Photosynthesis

The **light-dependent reactions** are those used to capture energy from light and convert it to chemical energy in the form of ATP. The **light-independent reactions** use that energy to synthesize organic carbon compounds.

Capturing Radiant Energy

Various pigments such as **chlorophylls, bacteriochlorophylls, carotenoids,** and **phycobilins** are used to capture radiant energy.

Reaction center pigments function as the electron donor in the photosynthetic process; **antennae pigments** funnel radiant energy to the reaction center pigment.

Converting Radiant Energy into Chemical Energy

The high-energy electrons emitted by reaction center chlorophylls are passed to an electron transport chain, which uses them to generate a proton motive force. The energy of proton motive force is harvested by ATP synthase to fuel the synthesis of ATP. (Figure 6.24)

Photosystems I and II of cyanobacteria and chloroplasts raise the energy level of electrons stripped from water to a high enough level to be used to generate a proton motive force and produce reducing power; this process evolves oxygen. (Figure 6.25)

Purple and green bacteria employ only a single photosystem; they must obtain electrons from a reduced compound other than water and therefore do not evolve oxygen.

6.9 Carbon Fixation

Calvin Cycle (Figure 6.26)

The most common pathway used to incorporate CO_2 into an organic form is the **Calvin cycle.**

6.10 Anabolic Pathways—Synthesizing Subunits from Precursor Molecules (Figure 6.27)

Lipid Synthesis

The fatty acid components of fat are synthesized by progressively adding 2-carbon units to an acetyl group. The glycerol component is synthesized from dihydroxyacetone phosphate.

Amino Acid Synthesis

Synthesis of glutamate from α-ketoglutarate and ammonia provides a mechanism for cells to incorporate nitrogen into organic molecules. (Figure 6.28)

Synthesis of aromatic amino acids requires a multistep branching pathway. Allosteric enzymes regulate key steps of the pathway. (Figure 6.29)

Nucleotide Synthesis

Purine nucleotides are synthesized on the sugar-phosphate component; the pyrimidine ring is made first and then attached to the sugar-phosphate. (Figure 6.30)

REVIEW QUESTIONS

Short Answer

1. Explain the difference between catabolism and anabolism.
2. How does ATP serve as a carrier of free energy?
3. How do enzymes catalyze chemical reactions?
4. Explain how precursor molecules serve as junctions between catabolic and anabolic pathways.
5. How do cells regulate enzyme activity?
6. Why do the electrons carried by $FADH_2$ result in less ATP production than those carried by NADH?
7. Name three food products produced with the aid of microorganisms.
8. In photosynthesis, what is encompassed by the term light-independent reactions?
9. Unlike the oxygenic phototrophs, the anoxygenic phototrophs do not evolve oxygen (O_2). Why not?
10. What is the role of transamination in amino acid biosynthesis?

Multiple Choice

1. Which of these environmental factors does not affect general enzyme activity?
   a) Temperature
   b) Inhibitors
   c) Coenzymes
   d) Humidity
   e) pH
2. Which of the following statements is false? Enzymes
   a) bind to substrates.
   b) lower the energy of activation.
   c) convert coenzymes to products.
   d) speed up biochemical reactions.
   e) can be named after the kinds of reaction they catalyze.
3. Which of these is not a coenzyme?
   a) FAD
   b) Coenzyme A
   c) NAD^+
   d) ATP
   e) $NADP^+$
4. What is the end product of glycolysis?
   a) Glucose
   b) Citrate
   c) Oxaloacetate
   d) α-ketoglutarate
   e) Pyruvate
5. The major pathway(s) of central metabolism are
   a) glycolysis and the TCA cycle only.
   b) glycolysis, the TCA cycle, and the pentose phosphate pathway.
   c) glycolysis only.
   d) glycolysis and the pentose phosphate pathway only.
   e) the TCA cycle only.
6. Which of these pathways has the potential to produce the most ATP?
   a) TCA cycle
   b) Pentose phosphate pathway
   c) Lactic acid fermentation
   d) Glycolysis
7. In fermentation, the terminal electron acceptor is
   a) oxygen (O_2).
   b) hydrogen (H_2).
   c) carbon dioxide (CO_2).
   d) an organic compound.
8. In the process of oxidative phosphorylation, the energy of proton motive force is used to generate
   a) NADH.
   b) ADP.
   c) ethanol.
   d) ATP.
   e) glucose.
9. In the TCA cycle, the carbon atoms contained in acetate are converted into
   a) lactic acid.
   b) glucose.
   c) glycerol.
   d) CO_2.
   e) all of these.
10. Degradation of fats as an energy source involves all of the following, *except*
    a) β-oxidation.
    b) acetyl-CoA.
    c) glycerol.
    d) lipase.
    e) transamination.

Applications

1. A worker in a cheese-making facility argues that whey, a nutrient-rich by-product of cheese, should be dumped in a nearby pond where it could serve as fish food. Explain why this proposed action could actually kill the fish by depleting the oxygen in the pond.
2. Scientists working with DNA *in vitro* often store it in solutions that contain EDTA, a chelating agent that binds magnesium (Mg^{2+}). This is done to prevent enzymes called DNases from degrading the DNA. Explain why EDTA would interfere with enzyme activity.

Critical Thinking

1. A student argued that aerobic and anaerobic respiration should produce the same amount of ATP. He reasoned that they both use basically the same process; only the terminal electron acceptor is different. What is the primary error in this student's argument?
2. Chemolithotrophs near hydrothermal vents support a variety of other life forms there. Explain how their role there is analogous to that of photosynthetic organisms in terrestrial environments.

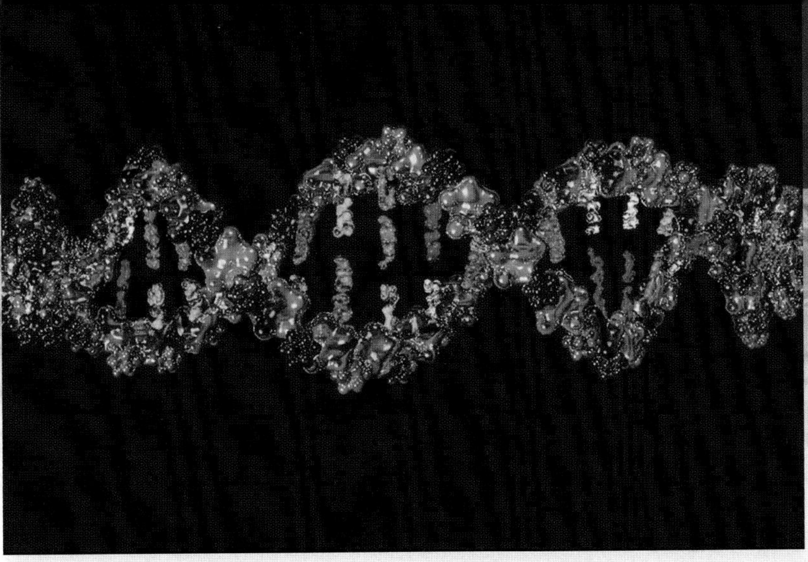

DNA double helix

CHAPTER SEVEN

The Blueprint of Life, from DNA to Protein

A Glimpse of History

In 1866, the Czech monk Gregor Mendel showed that traits are inherited by means of physical units, which we now call **genes.** It was not until 1941, however, that the precise function of genes was revealed when George Beadle, a geneticist, and Edward Tatum, a chemist, published a scientific paper reporting that genes determine the structure of enzymes. Biochemists had already shown that enzymes catalyze the conversion of one compound into another in a biochemical pathway.

Beadle and Tatum studied *Neurospora crassa,* a common bread mold that grows on a very simple medium containing sugar and simple inorganic salts. Beadle and Tatum created *N. crassa* strains with altered properties, **mutants,** by treating cells with X rays, which were known to alter genes. Some of these mutants could no longer grow on the glucose-salts medium unless growth factors such as vitamins were added to the medium. To isolate these, Beadle and Tatum had to laboriously screen thousands of progeny to find the relatively few that required the growth factors. Each mutant presumably contained a defective gene.

The next task for Beadle and Tatum was to identify the specific biochemical defect of each mutant. To do this, they added different growth factors, one at a time, to each mutant culture. The one that allowed a particular mutant to grow had presumably bypassed the function of a defective enzyme. In this manner, they were able to pinpoint in each mutant the specific step in the biochemical pathway that was defective. Then, using these same mutants, Beadle and Tatum showed that the requirement for each growth factor was inherited as a single gene, ultimately leading to their conclusion that a single gene determines the production of one enzyme. Their conclusion has been modified somewhat, because we now know that some enzymes are made up of more than one protein. A single gene determines the production of one protein. In 1958, Beadle and Tatum shared the Nobel Prize in Medicine, largely for these pioneering studies that ushered in the era of modern biology.

Consider for a moment the vast diversity of cellular life forms that exist. Our world contains a remarkable variety of microorganisms and specialized cells that make up plants and animals. Every characteristic of each of these cells, from its shape to its function, is dictated by information contained in its deoxyribonucleic acid (DNA). DNA encodes the master plan, the blueprint, for all cell structures and processes. Yet for all the complexity this would seem to require, DNA is a string composed of only four different nucleotides, each containing a particular nitrogenous base: adenine (A), thymine (T), cytosine (C), or guanine (G). ■ nucleotides, p. 33

While it might seem improbable that the vast array of life forms can be encoded by a molecule consisting of only four different units, think about how much information can be transmitted by binary code, the language of all computers, which has a base of only two. A simple series of ones and zeros can code for each letter of the alphabet. String enough of these together in the right sequence and the letters become words, and the words can become complete sentences, chapters, books, or even whole libraries.

The four nucleotides of a DNA molecule create information in a similar fashion. A set of three nucleotides encodes a specific amino acid. In turn, a string of amino acids makes up a protein, the function of which is dictated by the order of the amino acid subunits. Some proteins serve as structural components of a cell. Others, such as enzymes, mediate cellular activities including biosynthesis and energy conversion. Together, proteins synthesized by a cell are responsible for every aspect of that cell. Thus, the sequential order of nucleotide bases in a cell's DNA ultimately dictates the characteristics of that cell. ■ amino acids, p. 27 ■ protein structure, p. 29 ■ enzymes, pp. 134, 139

This chapter will focus on the processes used to replicate DNA and convert the information encoded within it into proteins, concentrating primarily on the mechanisms used by prokaryotic cells.

KEY TERMS

Codon A series of three nucleotides that code for a specific amino acid.

DNA polymerase Enzyme that synthesizes DNA, using an existing strand as a template to synthesize the complementary strand.

Gene The functional unit of the genome.

Messenger RNA (mRNA) Type of RNA molecule that is translated during the process of protein synthesis.

Primer Fragment of nucleic acid to which DNA polymerase can add nucleotides.

Promoter Nucleotide sequence to which RNA polymerase binds to initiate transcription.

Replication Duplication of DNA so that its encoded information can be passed on to future generations.

Ribosomal RNA (rRNA) Type of RNA molecule present in ribosome.

Ribosome Structure that facilitates the joining of amino acids during the process of translation; it is composed of ribosomal RNA (rRNA) and protein.

RNA polymerase Enzyme that synthesizes RNA using one strand of DNA as a template.

Transcription The process that copies the information encoded by DNA into RNA.

Transfer RNA (tRNA) Type of RNA molecule that acts as a key, interpreting the genetic code; each tRNA molecule carries a specific amino acid.

Translation The process that interprets the information carried by mRNA to synthesize the encoded protein.

The eukaryotic processes have many similarities, but are considerably more complicated and will only be discussed briefly.

7.1 Overview

Focus Points

- Compare and contrast the characteristics of DNA and RNA.
- Explain why it is important that a cell be able to regulate the expression of certain genes.

The complete set of genetic information for a cell is referred to as its **genome.** Technically, this includes plasmids as well as the chromosome; however, the term genome is often used interchangeably with chromosome. The genome of all cells is composed of DNA, but some viruses have an RNA genome. The functional unit of the genome is a **gene.** A gene encodes a product, the gene product, most commonly a protein. The study of the function and transfer of genes is called **genetics,** whereas the study and analysis of the nucleotide sequence of DNA is called **genomics.** ■ chromosome, p. 69 ■ plasmid, p. 69

All living cells must accomplish two general tasks in order to multiply. The double-stranded DNA must be duplicated before cell division so that its encoded information can be passed on to the next generation. This is the process of **DNA replication.** In addition, the information encoded by the DNA must be deciphered, or **expressed,** so that the cell can synthesize the necessary gene products at the appropriate time. Gene expression involves two interrelated processes, transcription and translation. **Transcription** copies the information encoded in DNA into a slightly different molecule, RNA. The RNA serves as a transitional, temporary form of the genetic information and is the one that is actually deciphered. **Translation** interprets information carried by RNA to synthesize the encoded protein. The chemistry and structure of DNA and RNA ensure that each of these processes can occur with great accuracy.

The flow of information from DNA to RNA to protein is often referred to as the **central dogma of molecular biology (figure 7.1).** It was once believed that information flow proceeded only in this direction. Although this direction is by far the most common, certain viruses, such as the one that causes AIDS, have an RNA genome but copy that information into the form of DNA.

Characteristics of DNA

A single strand of DNA is composed of a series of deoxyribonucleotide subunits, more commonly called nucleotides. These are joined in a chain by a covalent bond between the $5'PO_4$ (5 prime

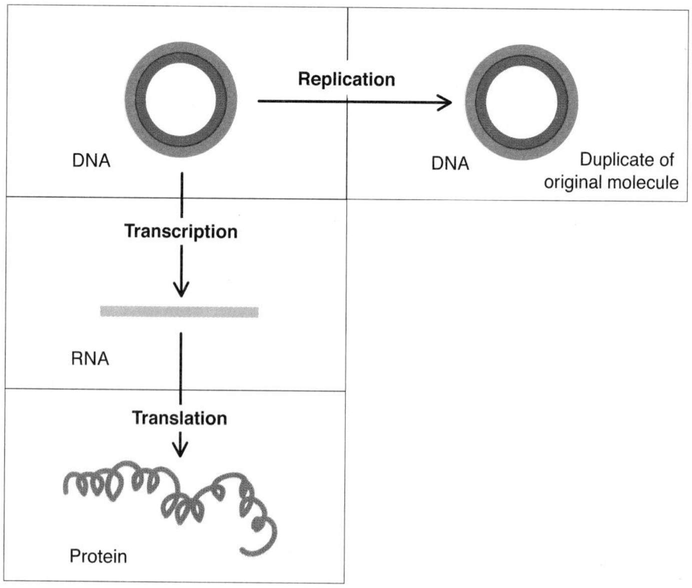

FIGURE 7.1 Overview of Replication, Transcription, and Translation DNA replication is the process that duplicates DNA so that its encoded information can be passed on to future generations. Transcription is the process that copies the genetic information into a transitional form, RNA. Translation is the process that deciphers the encoded information to synthesize a specific protein.

phosphate) of one nucleotide and the 3′OH (3 prime hydroxyl) of the next. Note that the designations 5′ and 3′ refer to the numbered carbon atoms of the pentose sugar of the nucleotide (see figure 2.21). Joining of the nucleotides in this manner creates a series of alternating sugar and phosphate moieties, called the **sugar-phosphate backbone.** Connected to each sugar is one of the nitrogenous bases, an adenine (A), thymine (T), guanine (G), or cytosine (C). Because of the chemical structure of the nucleotides and how they are joined, a single strand of DNA will always have a $5'PO_4$ at one end and a 3′OH at the other. These ends, often referred to as the **5′ end** and the **3′ end,** have important implications in DNA and RNA synthesis that will be discussed later. ■ deoxyribonucleic acid (DNA), p. 33, ■ nucleotides, p. 33

The DNA in a cell usually occurs as a double-stranded, helical structure **(figure 7.2).** The two strands are held together by weak hydrogen bonds between the nitrogenous bases of the opposing strands. While individual hydrogen bonds are readily broken, the duplex structure of double-stranded DNA is generally quite stable because of the sheer number of bonds that occurs along its length. Short fragments of DNA have correspondingly fewer hydrogen bonds, however, so they are readily separated into single-stranded pieces. Separating the two strands is called **denaturing.** ■ hydrogen bonds, p. 23

The two strands of double-stranded DNA are complementary **(figure 7.3).** Wherever an adenine is in one strand, a thymine is in the other; these opposing nucleotides are held together by two hydrogen bonds between them. Similarly, wherever a cytosine is in one strand, a guanine is in the other. These are held together by three hydrogen bonds, a slightly stronger attraction than that of an A-T pair. The characteristic bonding of A to T and G to C is called **base-pairing** and is fundamental to the remarkable functionality of DNA. Because of the rules of base-pairing, one strand can always be used as a **template** for the synthesis of the complementary opposing strand. ■ complementary, p. 34

While the two strands of DNA in the double helix are complementary, they are also **antiparallel.** That is, they are oriented in opposite directions. One strand is oriented in the 5′ to 3′ direction and its complement is oriented in the 3′ to 5′ direction. This also has important implications in the function and synthesis of nucleic acids.

Characteristics of RNA

RNA is in many ways comparable to DNA, but with some important exceptions. One difference is that RNA is made up of ribonucleotides rather than deoxynucleotides, although in both cases these are usually referred to simply as nucleotides. Another distinction is that RNA contains the nitrogenous base uracil in place of the thymine found in DNA. Like DNA, RNA consists of a sequence of nucleotides, but RNA usually exists as a single-stranded linear molecule that is much shorter than DNA. ■ ribonucleic acid (RNA), p. 33 ■ nucleotide, p. 33

A fragment of RNA, a **transcript,** is synthesized using a region of one of the two strands of DNA as a template. In making the RNA transcript, the same base-pairing rules of DNA apply except that uracil, rather than thymine, base-pairs with adenine. This base-pairing is only transient, however, and the molecule quickly leaves the DNA template. Numerous different RNA transcripts can be generated from a single chromosome using specific regions as templates. Either strand may serve as the template. In a region the size of a single gene, however, only one of the two strands is generally transcribed. As a result, two complementary strands of RNA are not normally generated.

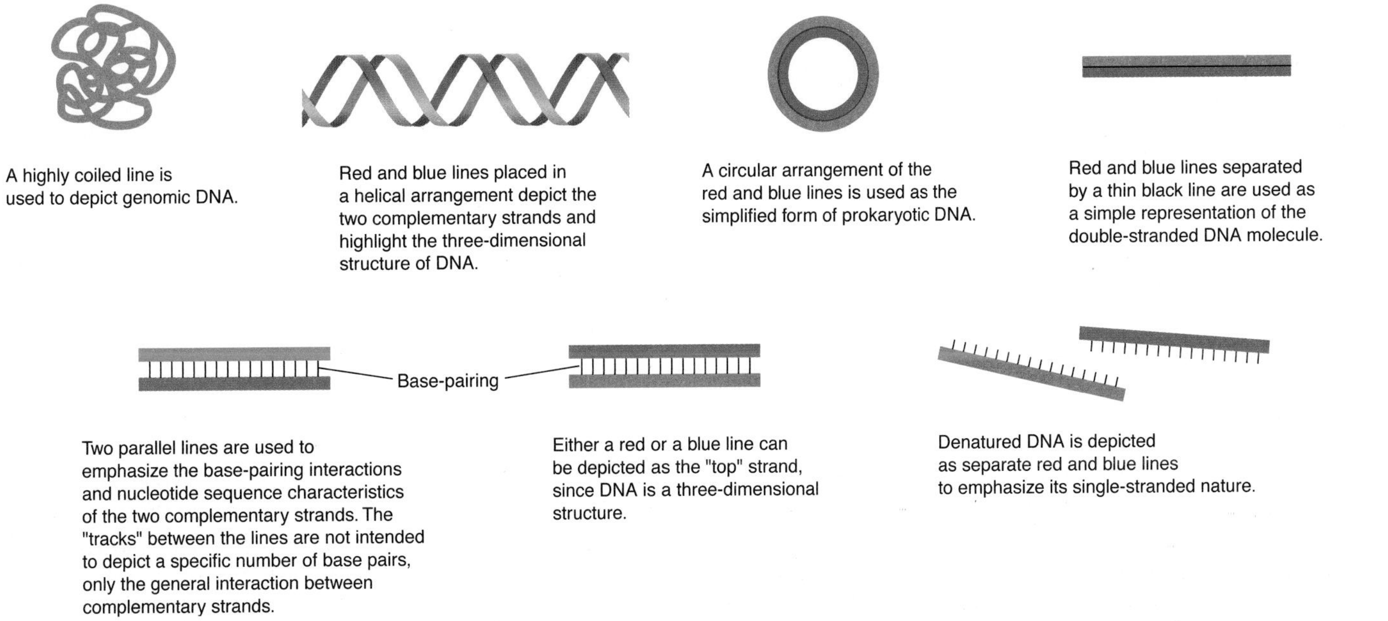

A highly coiled line is used to depict genomic DNA.
Red and blue lines placed in a helical arrangement depict the two complementary strands and highlight the three-dimensional structure of DNA.
A circular arrangement of the red and blue lines is used as the simplified form of prokaryotic DNA.
Red and blue lines separated by a thin black line are used as a simple representation of the double-stranded DNA molecule.
Base-pairing
Two parallel lines are used to emphasize the base-pairing interactions and nucleotide sequence characteristics of the two complementary strands. The "tracks" between the lines are not intended to depict a specific number of base pairs, only the general interaction between complementary strands.
Either a red or a blue line can be depicted as the "top" strand, since DNA is a three-dimensional structure.
Denatured DNA is depicted as separate red and blue lines to emphasize its single-stranded nature.

FIGURE 7.2 Diagrammatic Representations of the Structure of DNA Although DNA is a double-stranded helical structure, explanatory diagrams may depict it in a number of different ways. In chapter 7 we will use these colored coded representations.

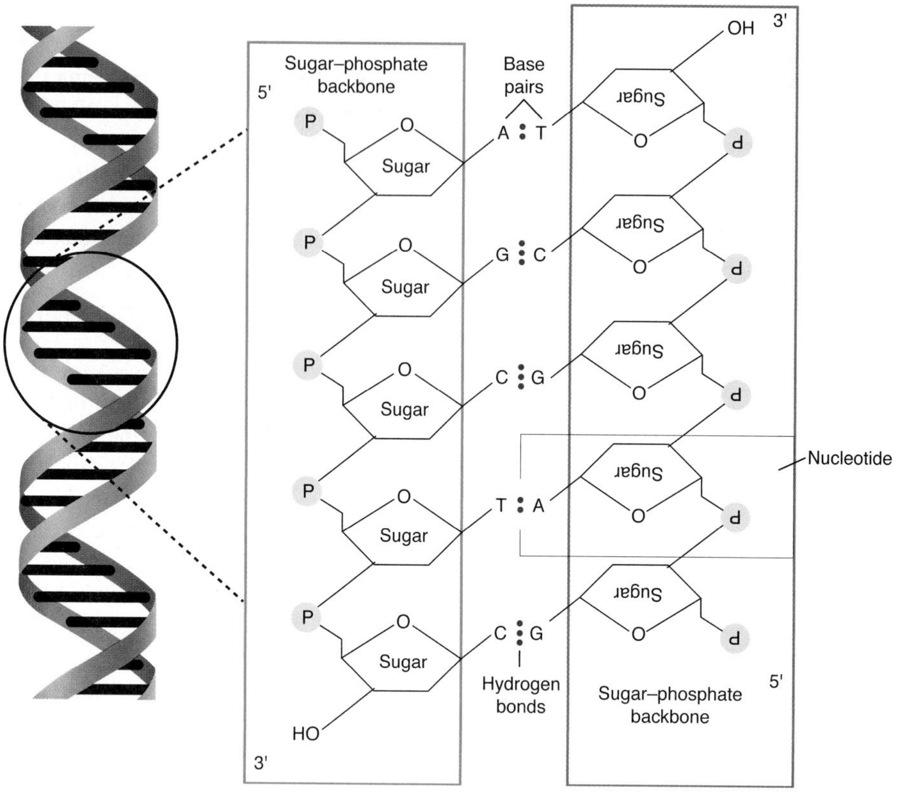

FIGURE 7.3 The Double Helix of DNA The two strands of DNA are antiparallel; one strand is oriented in the 5′ to 3′ direction, and its complement is oriented in the 3′ to 5′ direction. Hydrogen bonding occurs between the complementary base pairs; three bonds form between a G—C base pair, and two bonds form between an A—T base pair.

There are three different functional groups of RNA molecules, each transcribed from different genes. Most genes encode proteins and are transcribed into **messenger RNA (mRNA).** These molecules are translated during protein synthesis. Encrypted information in mRNA is deciphered according to the **genetic code,** which correlates each set of three nucleotides, called a **codon,** to a particular amino acid. Some genes are never translated into proteins; instead the RNAs themselves are the ultimate products. These genes encode either **ribosomal RNA (rRNA)** or **transfer RNA (tRNA),** each of which plays a different but critical role in protein synthesis.

Regulating the Expression of Genes

While the basic structure of DNA and RNA is relatively simple, the information the molecules encode is extensive and complex. The nucleotide sequence contains genes that encode the amino acid sequence of proteins, and it also codes for mechanisms to regulate expression of those genes. Not all proteins are required by a cell in the same quantity and at all times; therefore, mechanisms that determine the extent and duration of their synthesis are needed.

One of the key mechanisms a cell uses to control protein synthesis is to regulate the synthesis of mRNA molecules. Unless a gene is transcribed into mRNA, the encoded protein cannot be synthesized. The number of mRNA copies of the gene also influences the level of expression. If transcription of a gene ceases, the level of gene expression rapidly declines. This is because mRNA is short-lived, often only a few minutes, due to the activity of enzymes called **RNases** that rapidly degrade it.

MICROCHECK 7.1

Replication is the process of duplicating double-stranded DNA. Transcription is the process of copying the information encoded in DNA into RNA. Translation is the process of interpreting the information carried by messenger RNA in order to synthesize the encoded protein.

- ✓ How does the 5′ end of DNA differ from the 3′ end?
- ✓ If the nucleotide sequence of one strand of DNA is 5′ ACGTTGCA 3′, what is the sequence of the complementary strand?
- ✓ Why is a short-lived RNA important in cell control mechanisms?

7.2

DNA Replication

Focus Point

- Describe the process of replication, focusing on initiation of replication and the events that occur at the replication fork.

DNA is replicated in order to create a second DNA molecule, identical to the original. Each of the two cells generated during binary fission then receives one complete copy. ■ binary fission, p. 87

DNA replication is generally **bidirectional.** From a distinct starting point in circular DNA, replication proceeds in opposite directions, creating an ever-expanding "bubble" of two identical replicated portions of the chromosome **(figure 7.4).** Bidirectional replication allows an entire chromosome to be replicated in half the time it would take if replication were unidirectional.

Replication of double-stranded DNA is **semiconservative.** Each of the two molecules generated contains one of the original strands (the template strand) and one newly synthesized strand. Thus, the two cells produced as a result of division each have one of the original strands of DNA paired with a new complementary strand.

The process of DNA replication requires the coordinated action of many different enzymes and other proteins **(table 7.1).** The most critical of these exist together as a complex that appears to act as a fixed DNA-synthesizing factory, reeling in the DNA to be replicated. **DNA polymerases** are enzymes that synthesize DNA, using one strand as a template to generate the complementary strand. These enzymes can only add nucleotides onto a preexisting fragment of nucleic acid, either DNA or RNA. Thus, the fragment serves as a **primer** from which synthesis can continue.

DNA is synthesized one nucleotide at a time as the deoxynucleoside triphosphates (dATP, dGTP, dCTP, and dTTP) are covalently joined to the nucleotide at the 3′ end of the growing strand. Hydrolysis of a phosphate bond in the incoming molecule provides energy for the reaction. DNA polymerase always elongates the chain in the 5′ to 3′ direction. The enzyme must "read" the template strand in the 3′ to 5′ direction however, because the two DNA strands are antiparallel **(figure 7.5).** The base-pairing rules determine the specific nucleotides added.

The replication process is very accurate, resulting in only one mistake approximately every billion nucleotides. Part of the reason for this remarkable precision is the proofreading ability of some DNA polymerases. If an incorrect nucleotide is incorporated into the growing chain, the enzyme can edit the mistake by replacing that nucleotide before moving on.

It takes approximately 40 minutes for the chromosome of *E. coli* to be replicated, regardless of the environmental conditions. How, then, can *E. coli* sometimes multiply with a generation time of only 20 minutes? Under favorable growing conditions, a cell initiates replication before the preceding round of replication is completed. In this way, the two progeny resulting from cell division

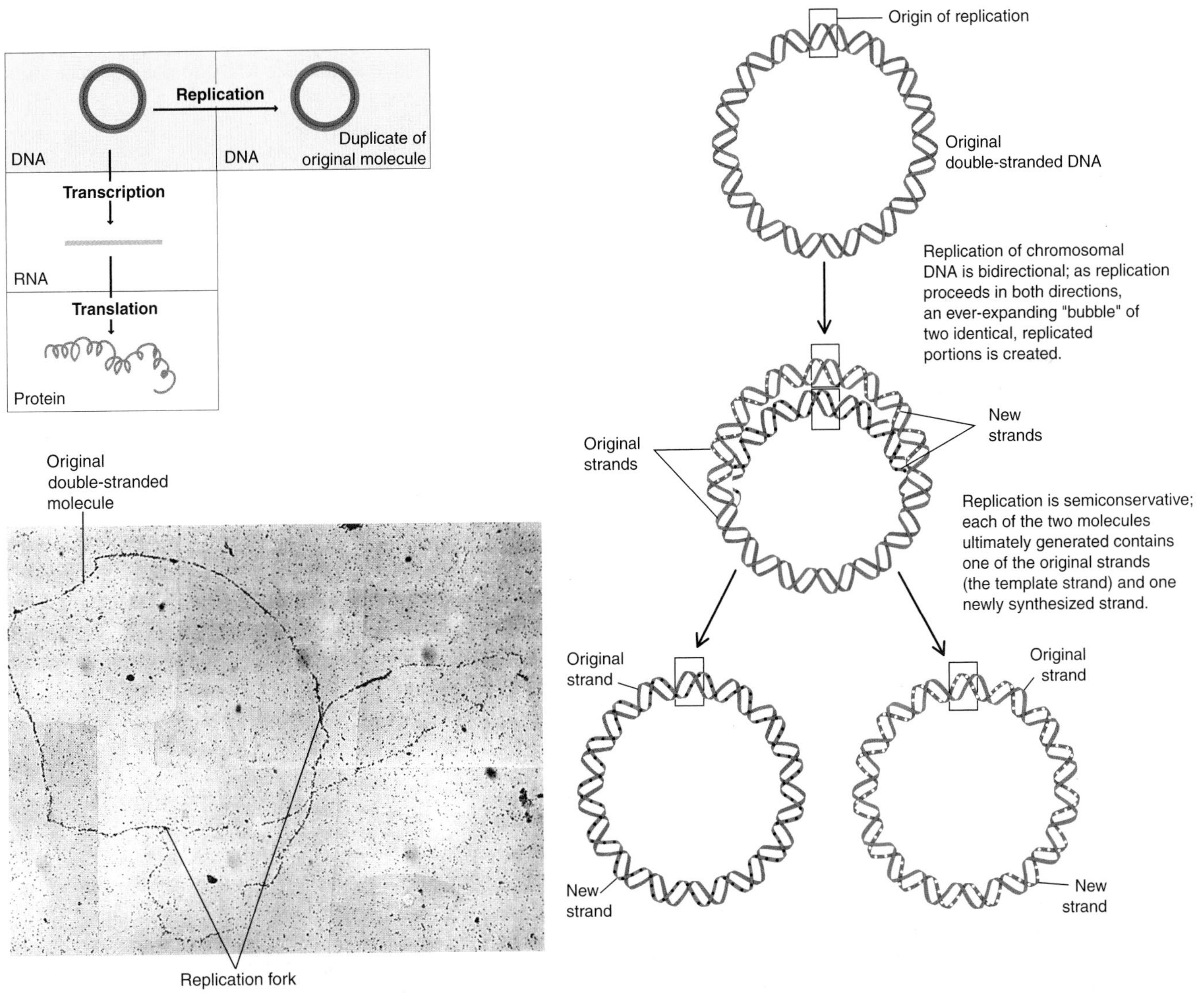

FIGURE 7.4 Replication of Chromosomal DNA of Prokaryotes

TABLE 7.1 Components of DNA Replication in Prokaryotes

Component	Comments
Primer	Fragment of nucleic acid to which DNA polymerase can add nucleotides (the enzyme can only add nucleotides to a preexisting fragment).
DNA gyrase	Enzyme that temporarily breaks the strands of DNA, relieving the tension caused by unwinding the two strands of the DNA helix; it is the target of a class of antibacterial medications called fluoroquinolones.
DNA ligase	Enzyme that joins two DNA fragments by forming a covalent bond between the sugar-phosphate residues of adjacent nucleotides.
DNA polymerases	Enzymes that synthesize DNA; they use one strand of DNA as a template to generate the complementary strand. Synthesis always occurs in the 5′ to 3′ direction.
Helicases	Enzymes that unwind the DNA helix ahead of the replication fork.
Okazaki fragment	Nucleic acid fragment generated during discontinuous replication of the lagging strand of DNA.
Origin of replication	Distinct region of a DNA molecule at which replication is initiated.
Primase	Enzyme that synthesizes small fragments of RNA to serve as primers for DNA synthesis during discontinuous replication of the lagging strand.

each will get one complete chromosome that has already started another round of replication. ■ generation time, p. 87

Initiation of DNA Replication

To begin the process of DNA replication, specific proteins must recognize and bind to a distinct region of the DNA, an **origin of replication.** All molecules of DNA, including chromosomes and plasmids, must have this region of approximately 250 nucleotides for replication to be initiated. The binding of the proteins causes localized denaturation, or **melting,** of a specific region within the origin. Using the exposed single strands as templates, small fragments of RNA are synthesized to serve as primers for DNA synthesis. The enzymes that synthesize RNA do not require a primer.

The Replication Fork

The bidirectional progression of replication around a circular DNA molecule creates two advancing Y-shaped regions where active replication is occurring. Each of these is called a **replication fork.** The

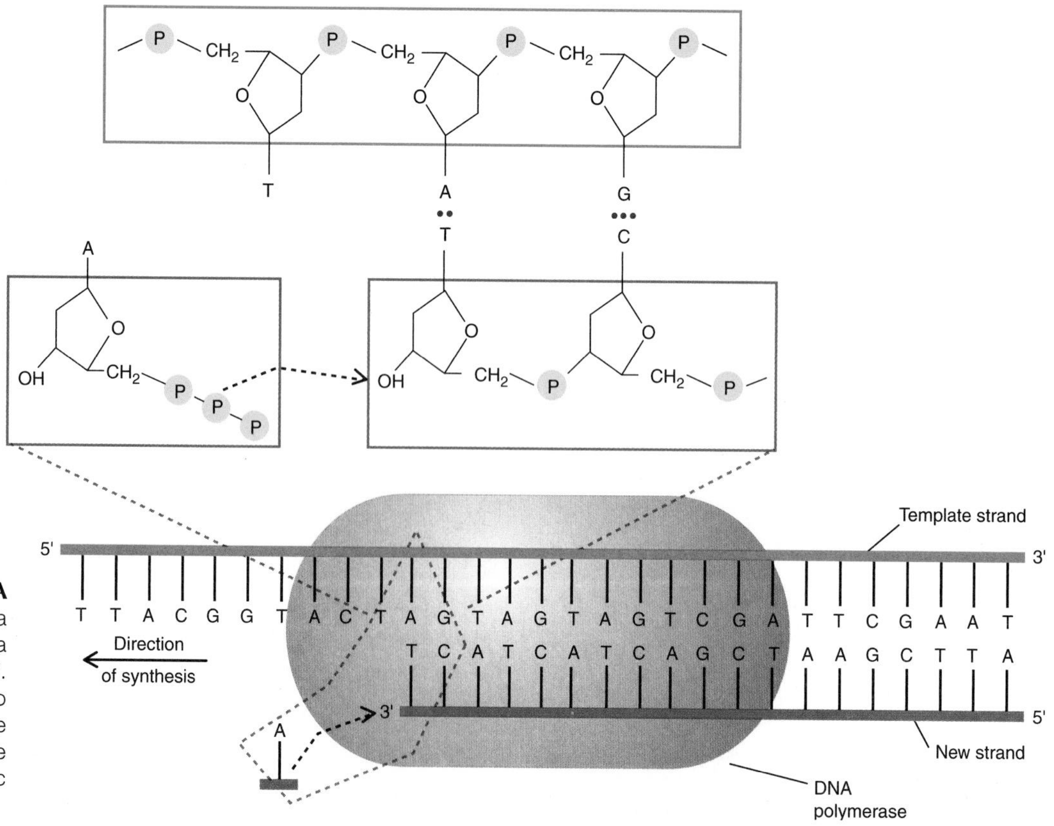

FIGURE 7.5 The Process of DNA Synthesis DNA polymerase synthesizes a new strand by adding one nucleotide at a time to the 3′ end of the elongating strand. Because DNA is synthesized in the 5′ to 3′ direction, the enzyme must "read" the template strand in the 3′ to 5′ direction. The base-pairing rules determine the specific nucleotides that are added.

template strands continue to "unzip" at each fork due to the activity of enzymes called **helicases.** Synthesis of one new strand proceeds continuously in the 5′ to 3′ direction, as fresh single-stranded template DNA is exposed **(figure 7.6).** This strand is called the **leading strand.** Synthesis of the opposing strand, the **lagging strand,** is considerably more complicated because the DNA polymerase cannot add nucleotides to the 5′ end of DNA. Instead, synthesis must be reinitiated periodically as advancement of the replication fork exposes more of the template DNA. Each initiation event must be preceded by the synthesis of an RNA primer by the enzyme **primase.** The result is the synthesis of a series of fragments, called **Okazaki fragments,** each of which begins with a short stretch of RNA. As DNA polymerase adds nucleotides to the 3′ end of an Okazaki fragment, it eventually reaches the initiating point of the previous fragment. A different type of DNA polymerase then removes those RNA primer nucleotides and simultaneously replaces them with deoxynucleotides. The enzyme **DNA ligase** seals the gaps between fragments by catalyzing the formation of a covalent bond between the adjacent nucleotides.

Several other proteins are also involved in DNA replication. Among them is **DNA gyrase,** an enzyme that temporarily breaks the strands of DNA, relieving the tension caused by the unwinding of the two strands of the DNA helix. This enzyme is one of the targets of ciprofloxacin and other members of a class of antibacterial drugs called fluoroquinolones. By inhibiting the function of gyrase, the fluoroquinolones interfere with bacterial DNA replication and prevent the growth of bacteria. ■ fluoroquinolones, p. 505

MICROCHECK 7.2

DNA polymerases synthesize DNA in the 5′ to 3′ direction, using one strand as a template to generate the complementary strand. Replication of DNA begins at a specific sequence called the origin of replication, and then proceeds bidirectionally, creating two replication forks.

- ✓ Why is a primer required for DNA synthesis?
- ✓ How does synthesis of the lagging strand differ from that of the leading strand?
- ✓ If DNA replication were shown to be "conservative," what would this mean?

7.3 Gene Expression

Focus Points

- Describe the process of transcription, focusing on the role of RNA polymerase, sigma (σ) factor, promoters, and terminators.
- Describe the process of translation, focusing on the role of mRNA, ribosomes, ribosome-binding sites, rRNAs, tRNAs, and codons.

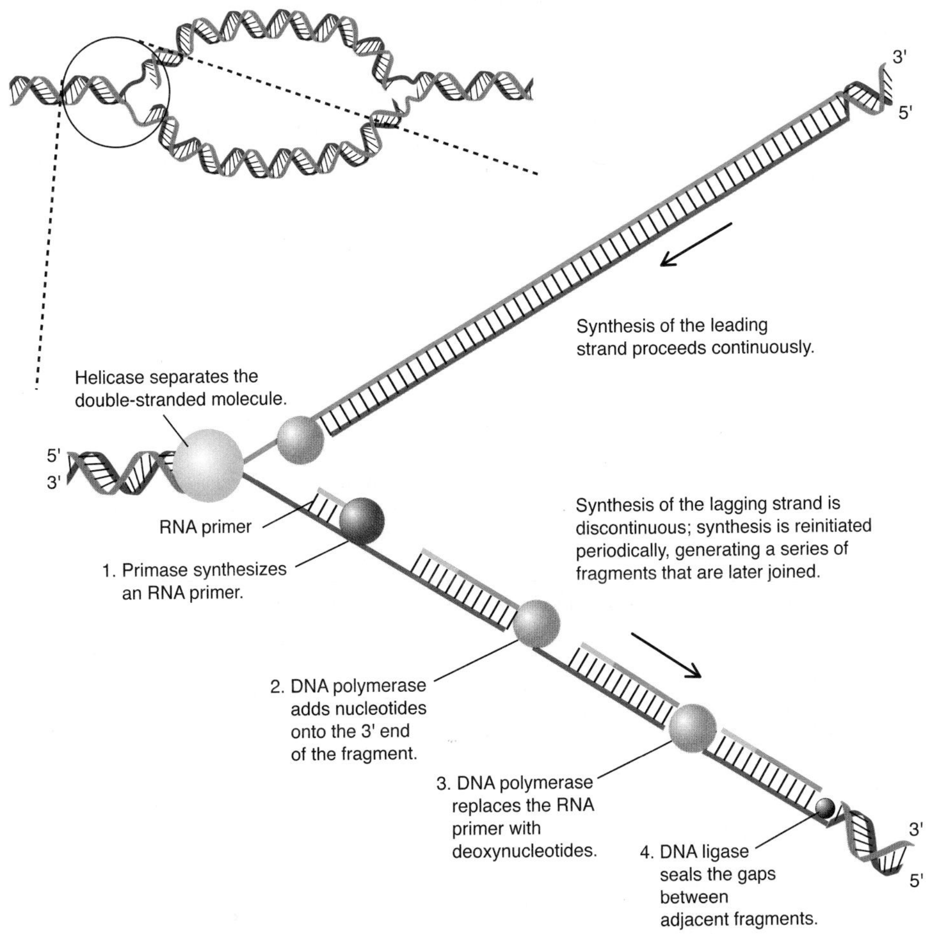
3'
5'
Synthesis of the leading strand proceeds continuously.
Helicase separates the double-stranded molecule.
5'
3'
RNA primer
1. Primase synthesizes an RNA primer.
Synthesis of the lagging strand is discontinuous; synthesis is reinitiated periodically, generating a series of fragments that are later joined.
2. DNA polymerase adds nucleotides onto the 3' end of the fragment.
3. DNA polymerase replaces the RNA primer with deoxynucleotides.
4. DNA ligase seals the gaps between adjacent fragments.
3'
5'

FIGURE 7.6 The Replication Fork This simplified diagram of the replication fork highlights the key steps in the synthesis of the lagging strand.

Gene expression involves two separate but interrelated processes, transcription and translation. Transcription is the process of synthesizing RNA from a DNA template. During translation, information encoded on an mRNA transcript is deciphered to synthesize a protein.

Transcription

The enzyme RNA polymerase catalyzes the process of transcription, producing a single-stranded RNA molecule complementary and antiparallel to the DNA template **(figure 7.7).** To describe the two strands of DNA in a region that is transcribed into RNA, the terms **minus (–) strand** and **plus (+) strand** are sometimes used **(table 7.2).** The strand that serves as the template for RNA synthesis is called the minus (–) strand, whereas its complement is called the plus (+) strand. Recall that the base-pairing rules of DNA and RNA are the same, except that RNA contains uracil in place of thymine. Therefore, because the RNA is complementary to the (–) strand, its nucleotide sequence is the same as the (+) strand, except it has uracil in place of thymine. Likewise, the RNA transcript has the same 5′ to 3′ direction, or **polarity,** as the (+) strand.

In prokaryotes, an mRNA molecule can carry the information for one or multiple genes. A transcript that carries one gene is called **monocistronic** (a cistron is synonymous with a gene). Those that carry multiple genes are called **polycistronic.** Generally, the proteins encoded on a polycistronic message are all involved in a single biochemical pathway. This enables the cell to express related genes in a coordinated manner.

Transcription begins when RNA polymerase recognizes a sequence of nucleotides on the DNA called a **promoter.** The promoter identifies the region of the DNA molecule that will be transcribed into RNA. In addition, the promoter orients the RNA polymerase in one of the two possible directions. This dictates which of the two DNA strands is used as a template **(figure 7.8).** Like DNA polymerase, RNA polymerase can only synthesize nucleic acid in the 5′ to 3′ direction and must "read" the template in the 3′ to 5′ direction. Unlike DNA polymerase, however, RNA polymerase can initiate synthesis without a primer.

The transcribed RNA molecule can be used as a reference point to describe direction on the analogous DNA. **Upstream** implies the direction toward the 5′ end of the transcribed region, whereas **downstream** implies the direction toward the 3′ end. Thus, a promoter is upstream of a gene.

Initiation of RNA Synthesis

Transcription begins after RNA polymerase recognizes and binds to a promoter on the double-stranded DNA molecule. The binding melts a short stretch of DNA, creating a region of exposed nucleotides that serves as a template for RNA synthesis.

In bacteria, a particular subunit of RNA polymerase recognizes the promoter region prior to the initiation of transcription. This subunit, **sigma (σ) factor,** dissociates from the enzyme shortly after transcription is initiated. This leaves the remaining

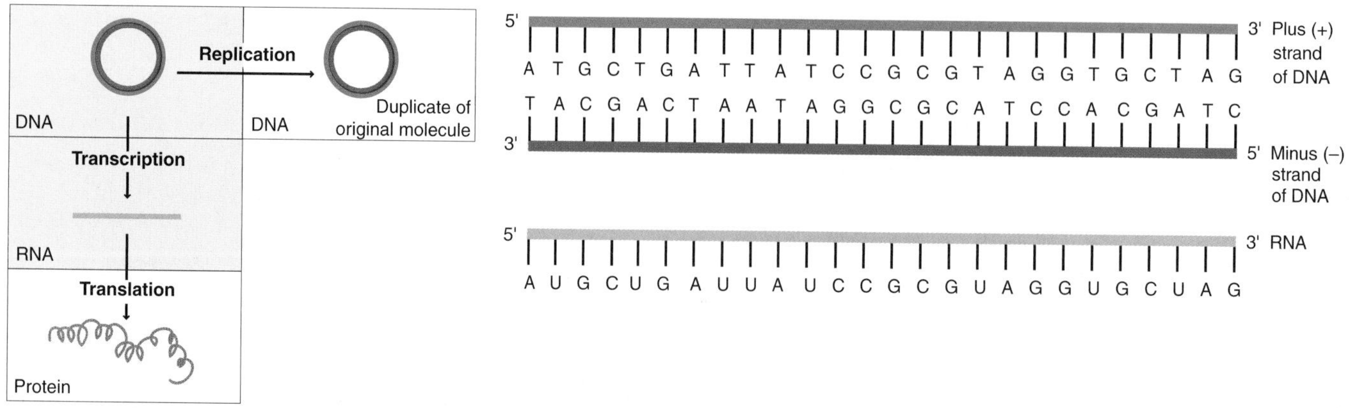

FIGURE 7.7 RNA Is Transcribed from a DNA Template The DNA strand that serves as a template for RNA synthesis is called the (–) strand of DNA. The nucleotide sequence of the transcript is analogous to that of the (+) strand, with uracil (U) occurring in place of thymine (T) in the RNA.

TABLE 7.2 Components of Transcription in Bacteria

Component	Comments
(–) strand	Strand of DNA that serves as the template for RNA synthesis; the resulting RNA molecule is complementary to this strand.
(+) strand	Strand of DNA complementary to the one that serves as the template for RNA synthesis; the sequence of the resulting RNA molecule is analogous to this strand.
Promoter	Nucleotide sequence to which RNA polymerase binds to initiate transcription.
RNA polymerase	Enzyme that synthesizes RNA using single-stranded DNA as a template; synthesis always occurs in the 5′ to 3′ direction.
Sigma (σ) factor	Component of RNA polymerase that recognizes the promoter regions. A cell may have different types of σ factors that recognize different promoters. These may be expressed at different stages of cell growth, enabling the cell to transcribe specialized sets of genes as needed.
Terminator	Sequence at which RNA synthesis stops; the RNA polymerase falls off the DNA template and releases the newly synthesized RNA.

portion of RNA polymerase, called the **core enzyme,** to complete transcription. A cell may have different types of σ factors that recognize different promoters. These may be expressed at different stages of cell growth, enabling the cell to transcribe specialized sets of genes as needed. The RNA polymerases of eukaryotic cells and archaea use **transcription factors** to recognize promoters.

Elongation

In the elongation phase, the RNA polymerase moves along the template strand of DNA, synthesizing the complementary single-stranded RNA molecule. The RNA molecule is synthesized in the 5′ to 3′ direction as the enzyme adds nucleotides to the 3′OH end of the growing chain. The core RNA polymerase advances along the DNA, melting a new stretch and allowing the previous stretch to close **(figure 7.9).** This exposes a new region of the template, permitting the elongation process to continue.

Once elongation has proceeded far enough for RNA polymerase to clear the promoter, another molecule of RNA polymerase can bind to that promoter, initiating a new round of transcription. Thus, a single gene can be transcribed multiple times in a very short time interval.

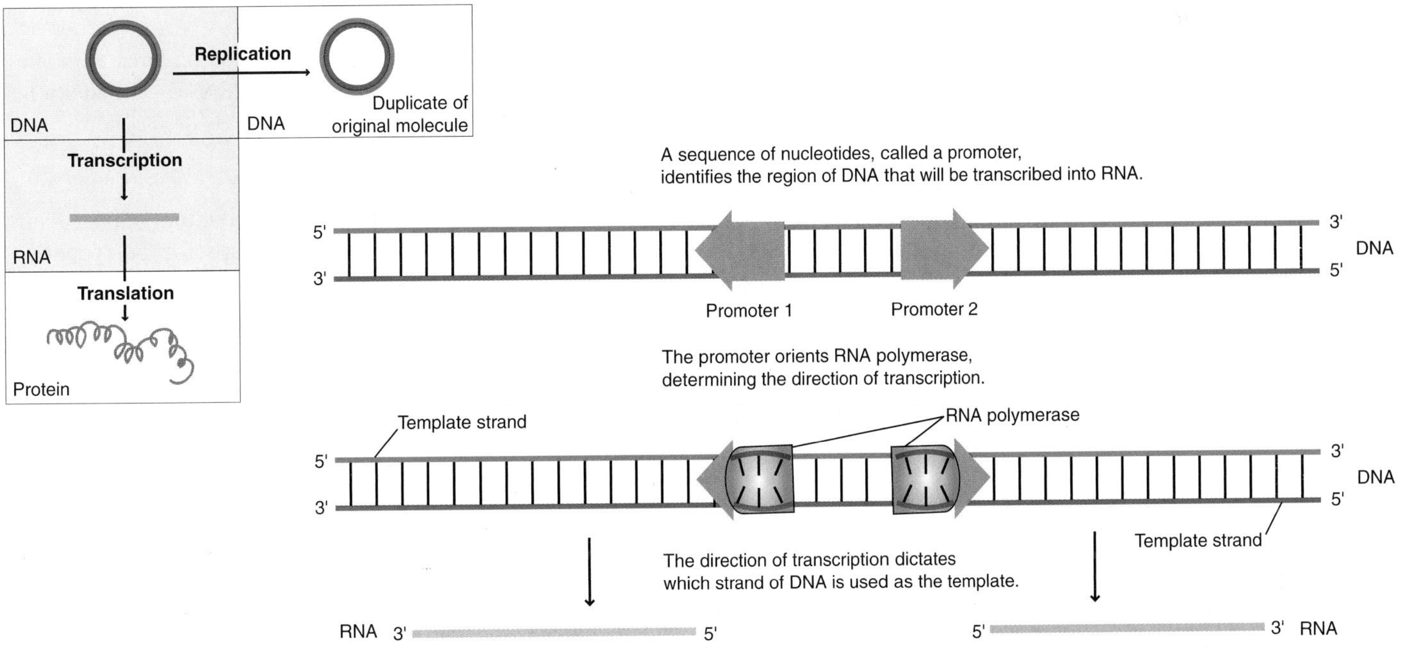

FIGURE 7.8 Promoters Direct Transcription A promoter not only identifies the region of DNA that will be transcribed into RNA, its orientation determines which strand will be used as the template. Note that the color depiction of each RNA molecule indicates which strand of DNA was used as a template. The light blue RNA was transcribed from the red DNA strand (and is therefore analogous in sequence to the blue DNA strand), whereas the pink RNA was transcribed from the blue DNA strand (and is therefore analogous in sequence to the red DNA strand).

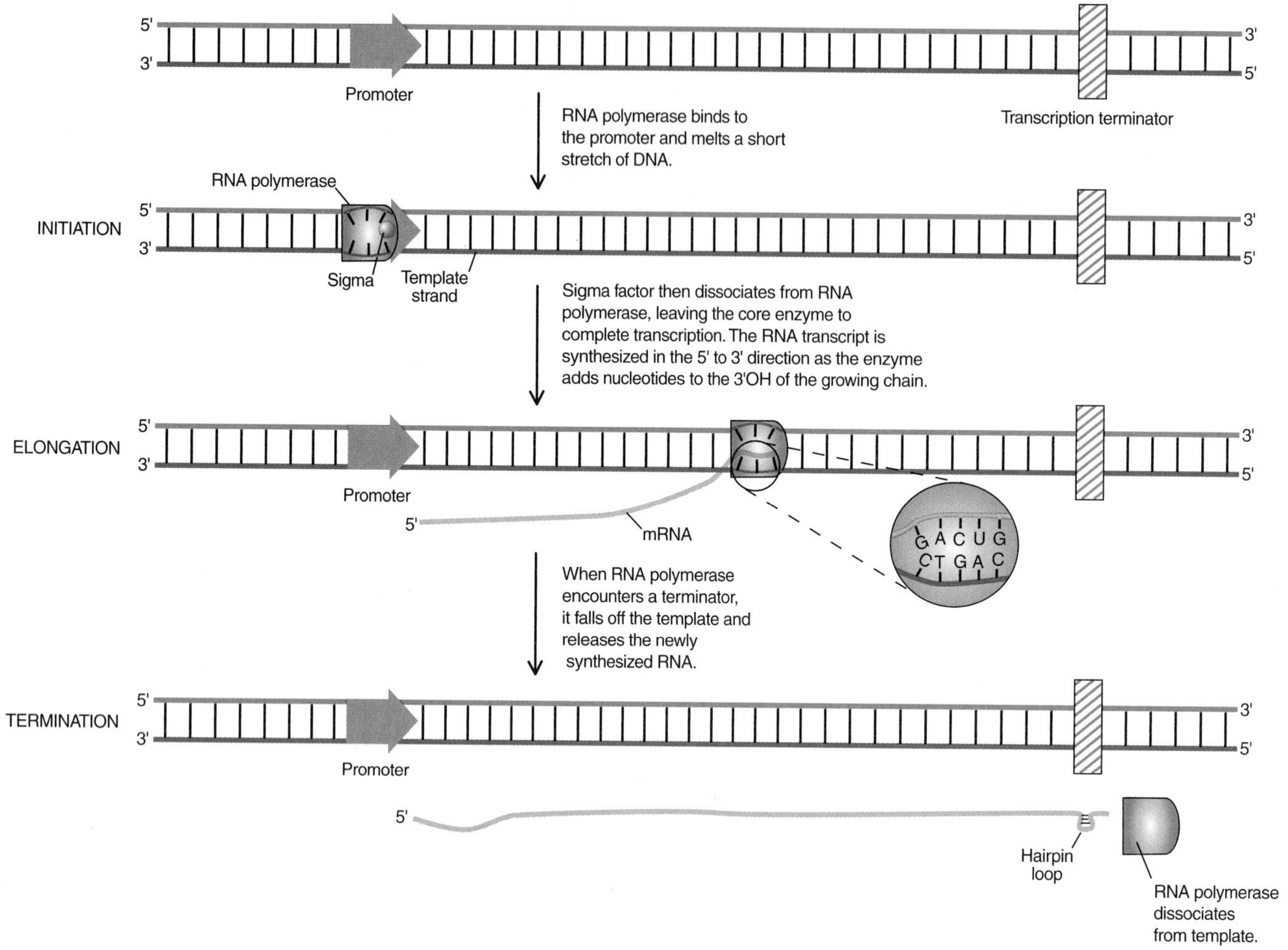

FIGURE 7.9 The Process of RNA Synthesis Bacterial RNA polymerases include a sigma subunit (as illustrated); the RNA polymerases of eukaryotic cells and archaea use transcription factors to recognize promoters.

Termination

Just as an initiation of transcription occurs at a distinct site on the DNA, so does termination. When RNA polymerase encounters a **terminator,** it falls off the DNA template and releases the newly synthesized RNA. The terminator is a sequence of nucleotides in the DNA that, when transcribed, permits two complementary regions of the resulting RNA to base-pair, forming a hairpin loop structure. For reasons that are not yet understood, this causes the RNA polymerase to stall, resulting in its dissociation from the DNA template and release of the RNA. The termination of transcription should not be confused with the termination of translation, which occurs by a totally different mechanism and will be discussed shortly.

Translation

Translation is the process of decoding the information carried on the mRNA to synthesize the specified protein. Proteins are synthesized by adding amino acid subunits sequentially to the carboxyl group at the end of an elongating polypeptide chain. Each amino acid added is specified by one codon of the mRNA, as directed by the genetic code. The process of translation requires three major components—mRNA, ribosomes, and tRNAs—in addition to various accessory proteins **(table 7.3).** ■ carboxyl group, p. 27

The Role of mRNA

The mRNA is a temporary copy of genetic information; it carries encoded instructions for synthesis of a specific polypeptide, or in the case of a polycistronic message, a specific group of polypeptides. That information is deciphered using the **genetic code,** which correlates each series of three nucleotides, a **codon,** with one amino acid **(figure 7.10).** The genetic code is practically universal, meaning that it is used in nearly its entirety by all living things.

Because a codon is a sequence of any combination of the four nucleotides, there are 64 different codons (4^3). Three of these are stop codons, which will be discussed later. The remaining 61 translate to the 20 different amino acids. This means that more than one codon can code for a specific amino acid. For example, both ACA and ACG encode the amino acid threonine. Because of this redundancy, the genetic code is said to be **degenerate.** Note, however, that two different amino acids are never coded for by the same codon.

TABLE 7.3 Components of Translation in Prokaryotes

Component	Comments
Anticodon	Sequence of three nucleotides in a tRNA molecule that is complementary to a particular codon in mRNA. The anticodon allows the tRNA to recognize and bind to the appropriate codon.
mRNA	Type of RNA molecule that contains the genetic information deciphered during translation.
Polyribosome (polysome)	Multiple ribosomes attached to a single mRNA molecule.
Reading frame	Grouping of a stretch of nucleotides into sequential triplets; an mRNA molecule has three reading frames, but only one is typically used in translation.
Ribosome	Structure that facilitates the joining of amino acids during the process of translation; composed of protein and ribosomal RNA. The prokaryotic ribosome (70S) consists of a 30S and 50S subunit; it is the target of several groups of antibacterial drugs.
Ribosome-binding site	Sequence of nucleotides in mRNA to which a ribosome binds; the first time the codon for methionine (AUG) appears after that site, translation generally begins.
rRNA	Type of RNA molecule present in ribosomes.
Start codon	Codon at which translation is initiated; it is typically the first AUG after a ribosome-binding site.
Stop codon	Codon that terminates translation, signaling the end of the protein; there are three stop codons.
tRNA	Type of RNA molecule that act as keys that interpret the genetic code; each tRNA molecule carries a specific amino acid.

An equally important aspect of mRNA is that it carries the information that indicates where the coding region actually begins. This is critical because the genetic code is read as groups of three nucleotides. Thus, any given sequence has three possible **reading frames,** or ways in which triplets can be grouped **(figure 7.11).** If translation occurs in the wrong reading frame, a very different, and generally non-functional, polypeptide would be synthesized.

The Role of Ribosomes

Ribosomes serve as the sites of translation, and their structure facilitates the joining of one amino acid to another. A ribosome brings each amino acid into a favorable position so that an enzyme can catalyze the formation of a peptide bond between them. It also helps to identify key punctuation sequences on the mRNA molecule, such as the point at which protein synthesis should be

	Middle Letter				
First Letter	U Reading frame 5' 3'	C Reading frame 5' 3'	A Reading frame 5' 3'	G Reading frame 5' 3'	Last Letter
U	UUU Phenylalanine	UCU Serine	UAU Tyrosine	UGU Cysteine	U
	UUC Phenylalanine	UCC Serine	UAC Tyrosine	UGC Cysteine	C
	UUA Leucine	UCA Serine	UAA (Stop)	UGA (Stop)	A
	UUG Leucine	UCG Serine	UAG (Stop)	UGG Tryptophan	G
C	CUU Leucine	CCU Proline	CAU Histidine	CGU Arginine	U
	CUC Leucine	CCC Proline	CAC Histidine	CGC Arginine	C
	CUA Leucine	CCA Proline	CAA Glutamine	CGA Arginine	A
	CUG Leucine	CCG Proline	CAG Glutamine	CGG Arginine	G
A	AUU Isoleucine	ACU Threonine	AAU Asparagine	AGU Serine	U
	AUC Isoleucine	ACC Threonine	AAC Asparagine	AGC Serine	C
	AUA Isoleucine	ACA Threonine	AAA Lysine	AGA Arginine	A
	AUG Methionine (Start)	ACG Threonine	AAG Lysine	AGG Arginine	G
G	GUU Valine	GCU Alanine	GAU Aspartate	GGU Glycine	U
	GUC Valine	GCC Alanine	GAC Aspartate	GGC Glycine	C
	GUA Valine	GCA Alanine	GAA Glutamate	GGA Glycine	A
	GUG Valine	GCG Alanine	GAG Glutamate	GGG Glycine	G

FIGURE 7.10 The Genetic Code The genetic code correlates each series of three nucleotides, a codon, with one amino acid. Three of the codons do not code for an amino acid and instead serve as a stop codon, terminating translation. AUG functions as a start codon.

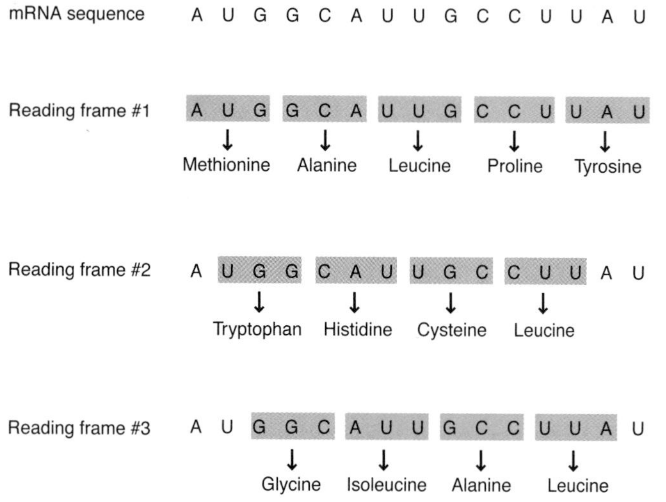

FIGURE 7.11 Reading Frames A nucleotide sequence has three potential reading frames. Because each reading frame encodes a very different order of amino acids, translation of the correct reading frame is important.

initiated. The ribosome moves along the mRNA in the 5′ to 3′ direction, "presenting" each codon in a sequential order for deciphering, while maintaining the correct reading frame.

A prokaryotic ribosome is composed of a 30S subunit and a 50S subunit, each of which is made up of protein and rRNA **(figure 7.12);** the "S" stands for Svedberg unit, which is a unit of size. Some of the ribosomal components are important in other aspects of microbiology as well. For example, comparison of the nucleotide sequences of rRNA molecules is playing an increasingly prominent role in the establishment of the genetic relatedness of various organisms. Medically, ribosomal proteins and rRNA are significant because they are the targets of several groups of antimicrobial drugs. ■ **ribosomal subunits, p. 70** ■ **rRNA sequencing, p. 255**

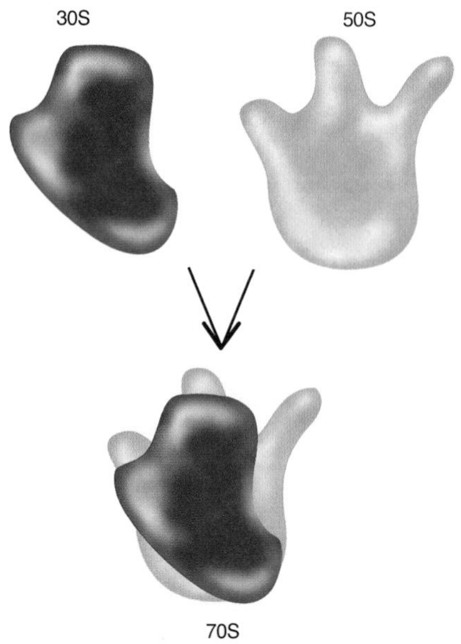

FIGURE 7.12 The Structure of the 70S Ribosome The 70S ribosome is composed of a 30S subunit and a 50S subunit.

The Role of Transfer RNA

The tRNAs are segments of RNA able to carry specific amino acids, and act as keys that interpret the genetic code. They each recognize and base-pair with a specific codon and in the process deliver the appropriate amino acid to that site. This recognition is made possible because each tRNA has an **anticodon,** three nucleotides complementary to a particular codon in the mRNA. The amino acid each tRNA carries is dictated by its anticodon and the genetic code **(figure 7.13).**

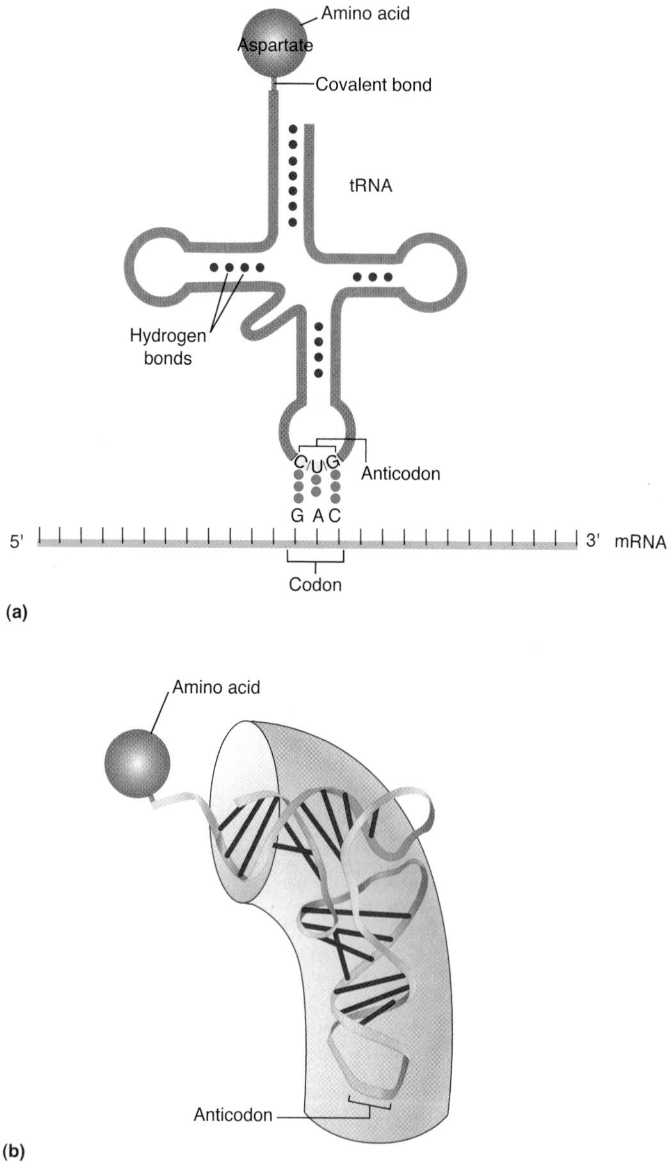

FIGURE 7.13 The Structure of Transfer RNA (tRNA) **(a)** Two dimensional illustration of tRNA. The anticodon of the tRNA base-pairs with a specific codon in the mRNA; by doing so, the appropriate amino acid is delivered to the site. The amino acid that the tRNA carries is dictated by the genetic code. The tRNA that recognizes the codon GAC carries the amino acid aspartate. **(b)** Three-dimensional illustration of tRNA.

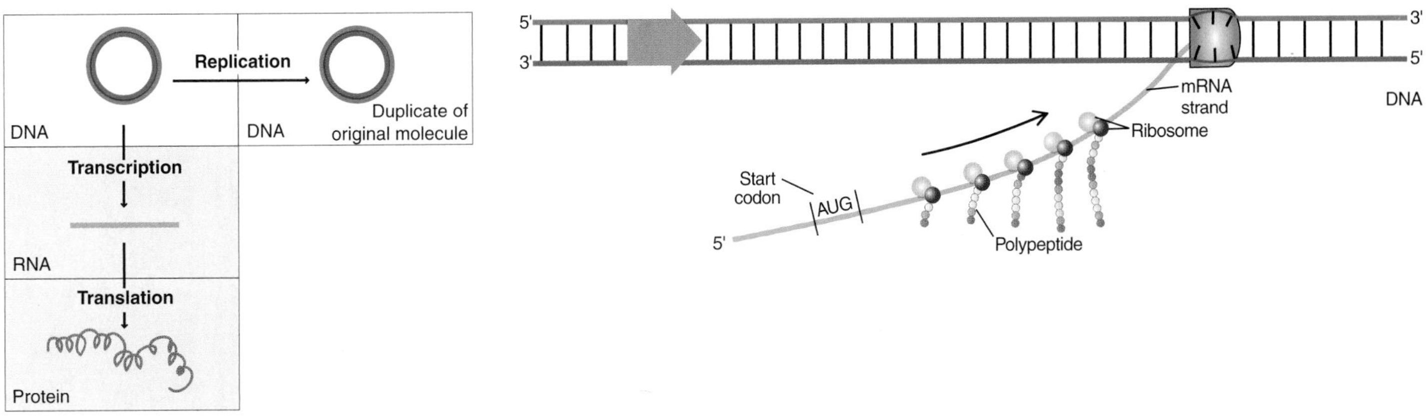

FIGURE 7.14 In Prokaryotes, Translation Begins as the mRNA Molecule Is Still Being Synthesized Ribosomes begin translating the 5′ end of the transcript even as the 3′ end is still being synthesized. More than one ribosome can be translating the same mRNA molecule.

Although there are 61 different amino acid-encoding codons, there are fewer different tRNA molecules. This is because the anticodon of some tRNA molecules can recognize more than one codon. It appears that a certain amount of "wobbling" is tolerated in the base-pairing so that recognition of the third nucleotide of the codon is not always precise. Due to the degeneracy of the genetic code, however, the correct amino acid is still incorporated into the polypeptide chain.

Initiation of Translation

In prokaryotes, translation begins as the mRNA is still being synthesized **(figure 7.14).** The 30S subunit of the ribosome binds to a sequence in mRNA called the **ribosome-binding site.** The first time the codon for methionine (AUG) appears after that site, translation generally starts. That first AUG is typically 7 nucleotides downstream of the ribosome-binding site. Note that AUG functions as a **start codon** only when preceded by a ribosome-binding site; at other sites, it simply encodes methionine. The position of the first AUG is critical, as it determines the reading frame used for translation of the remainder of that protein.

At that first AUG, the ribosome begins to assemble. An **initiation complex,** consisting of the 30S ribosomal subunit, a tRNA that carries a chemically altered form of the amino acid methionine, *N*-formylmethionine or **f-Met,** and proteins called **initiation factors,** forms. Shortly thereafter, the 50S subunit of the ribosome joins that complex and the initiation factors leave, forming the 70S ribosome. The elongation phase then begins.

Elongation

The 70S ribosome has two sites to which tRNA-carrying amino acids can bind **(figure 7.15).** One is called the **P-site** (peptidyl site), and the other is called the **A-site** (aminoacyl site, commonly referred to as the acceptor site). The initiating tRNA, carrying the f-Met, binds to the P-site. A tRNA that recognizes the next codon on the mRNA then fills the unoccupied A-site. An enzyme joins the f-Met carried by the tRNA in the P-site to the amino acid carried by the tRNA that just entered the A-site. This transfers the amino acid from the initiating tRNA to the amino acid carried by the incoming tRNA. The ribosome then advances, or **translocates,** a distance of one codon, and the tRNA that carried the f-Met is released through an adjacent site called the **E-site** (exit site). Translocation requires several different proteins, called **elongation factors.** As a result of translocation, the remaining tRNA, which now carries the two-amino-acid chain, occupies the P-site; the A-site is transiently vacant. A tRNA that recognizes the next codon then quickly fills the empty A-site, and the process repeats.

Once translation has progressed far enough for the ribosome to clear the ribosome-binding site and the first AUG, another ribosome can bind, beginning another round of synthesis of the encoded polypeptide. Thus, at any one time, multiple ribosomes can be translating a single mRNA molecule. This allows the maximal expression of protein from a single mRNA template. The assembly of multiple ribosomes attached to a single mRNA molecule is called a **polyribosome** or a **polysome.**

Termination

Elongation of the polypeptide terminates when the ribosome reaches a **stop codon,** a codon that does not code for an amino acid and is not recognized by a tRNA. At this point, enzymes called **release factors** free the newly synthesized polypeptide by breaking the covalent bond that joins it to the tRNA. The ribosome falls off the mRNA and dissociates into its two component subunits, 30S and 50S. These can then be reused to initiate translation at other sites.

Post-Translational Modification

Proteins must often be modified after they are synthesized in order to attain their functional properties. For example, some proteins must be folded into their final functional shape, a process that requires the assistance of another protein, a **chaperone.** Proteins destined for transport outside of the cytoplasmic membrane also must be modified. Such proteins have a characteristic series of hydrophobic amino acids, a **signal sequence,** at their amino terminal end, which "tags" them for transport through the membrane. The signal sequence is removed when the protein leaves the cytoplasm. ■ **chaperones, p. 30** ■ **hydrophobic amino acids, p. 28**

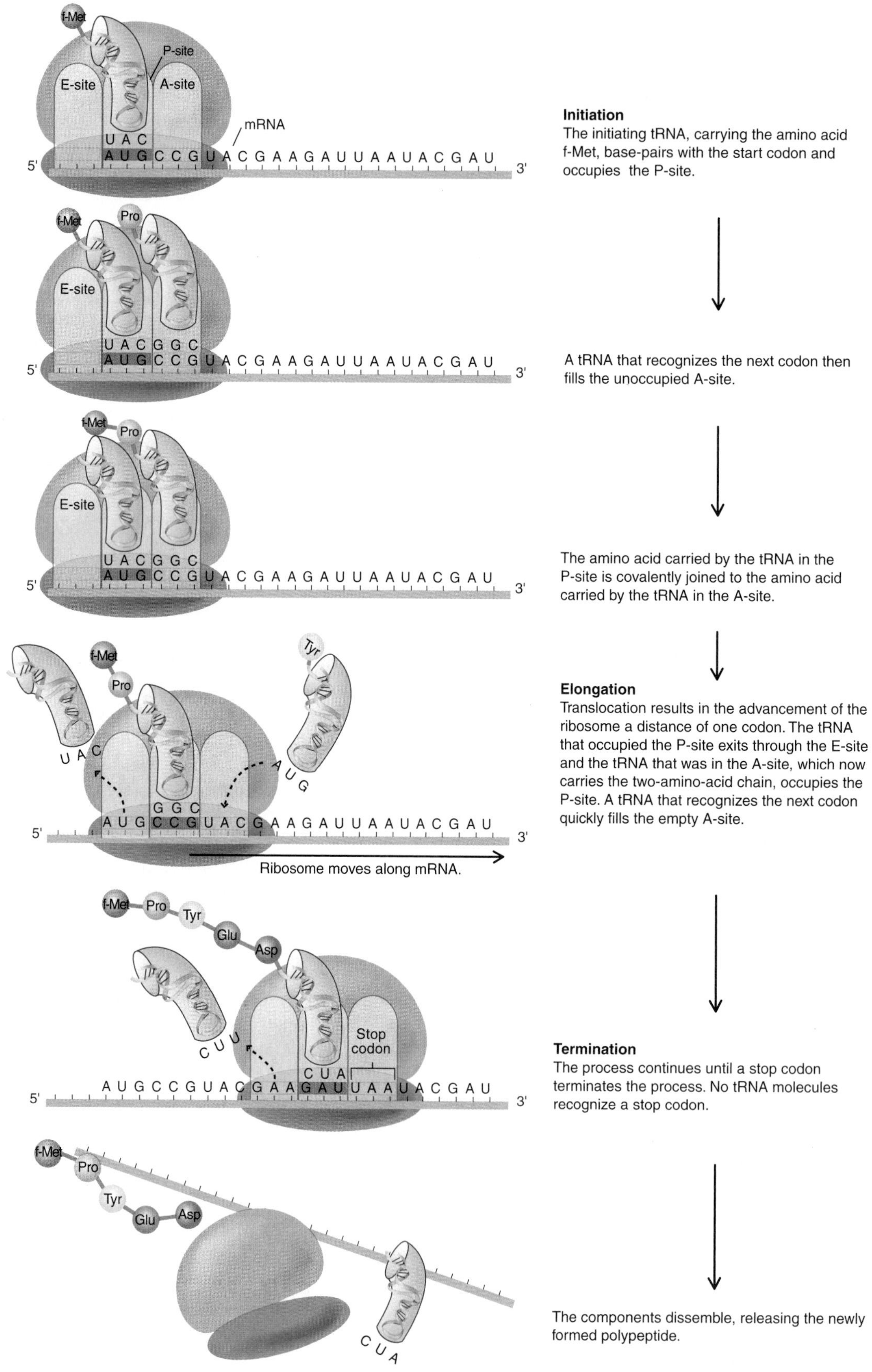

f-Met
P-site
E-site
A-site
mRNA
U A C
5'
A U G C C G U A C G A A G A U U A A U A C G A U
3'
Initiation
The initiating tRNA, carrying the amino acid f-Met, base-pairs with the start codon and occupies the P-site.
Pro
U A C G G C
A tRNA that recognizes the next codon then fills the unoccupied A-site.
The amino acid carried by the tRNA in the P-site is covalently joined to the amino acid carried by the tRNA in the A-site.
Tyr
Elongation
Translocation results in the advancement of the ribosome a distance of one codon. The tRNA that occupied the P-site exits through the E-site and the tRNA that was in the A-site, which now carries the two-amino-acid chain, occupies the P-site. A tRNA that recognizes the next codon quickly fills the empty A-site.
Ribosome moves along mRNA.
Glu
Asp
Stop codon
C U A
Termination
The process continues until a stop codon terminates the process. No tRNA molecules recognize a stop codon.
The components dissemble, releasing the newly formed polypeptide.

FIGURE 7.15 The Process of Translation For simplicity, this diagram shows a polypeptide only five amino acids long being synthesized. Note, however, that most polypeptides are over 100 amino acids long.

MICROCHECK 7.3

RNA polymerase initiates RNA synthesis after it binds to a promoter on DNA. Using one strand of DNA as a template, RNA is synthesized in the 5′ to 3′ direction. Synthesis stops when RNA polymerase encounters a terminator. Translation occurs as ribosomes move along mRNA in the 5′ to 3′ direction, with the ribosomes serving as the structure that facilitates the joining of one amino acid to another. tRNAs carry specific amino acids, thus acting to decode the genetic code.

- ✓ How does the orientation of the promoter dictate which strand is used as a template for RNA synthesis?
- ✓ Explain why it is important for the translation machinery to recognize the correct reading frame.
- ✓ Could two mRNAs have different nucleotide sequences and yet code for the same protein?

7.4

Differences Between Eukaryotic and Prokaryotic Gene Expression

Focus Point

- Describe four differences between prokaryotic and eukaryotic gene expression.

Eukaryotes differ significantly from prokaryotes in several aspects of transcription and translation **(table 7.4).** In eukaryotic cells for example, most mRNA molecules are extensively modified, or **processed,** in the nucleus during and after transcription. Shortly after transcription begins, the 5′ end of the transcript is modified, or **capped,** by the addition of a methylated guanine derivative, creating what is called a **cap.** The cap likely stabilizes the transcript and enhances translation. The 3′ end of the molecule is also modified, even before transcription has been terminated. This process, called **polyadenylation,** involves cleaving the transcript at a specific sequence of nucleotides and then adding approximately 200 adenine derivatives to the newly exposed 3′ end. This creates what is called a **poly A tail,** which is thought to stabilize the transcript as well as enhance translation. Another important modification is **splicing,** a process that removes specific segments of the transcript **(figure 7.16).** Splicing is necessary because eukaryotic genes are not always contiguous; they are often interrupted by non-coding nucleotide sequences. These intervening sequences, or **introns,** are transcribed along with the expressed regions, or **exons,** generating what is called **precursor mRNA.** The introns must be removed from precursor mRNA to form the mature mRNA that is then translated.

TABLE 7.4 Major Differences Between Prokaryotic and Eukaryotic Transcription and Translation

Prokaryotes	Eukaryotes
mRNA is not processed.	A cap is added to the 5′ end of mRNA, and a poly A tail is added to the 3′ end.
mRNA does not contain introns.	mRNA contains introns, which are removed by splicing.
Translation of mRNA begins as it is being transcribed.	The mRNA transcript is transported out of the nucleus so that it can be translated in the cytoplasm.
mRNA is often polycistronic; translation usually begins at the first AUG that follows a ribosome-binding site.	mRNA is monocistronic; translation begins at the first AUG.

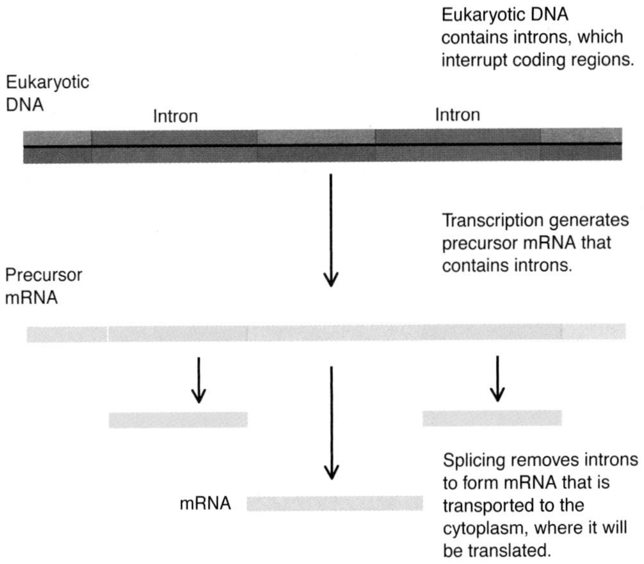

FIGURE 7.16 Splicing of Eukaryotic RNA

The mRNA in eukaryotic cells must be transported out of the nucleus before it can be translated in the cytoplasm. Thus, the same mRNA molecule cannot be transcribed and translated at the same time or even in the same cellular location. Unlike in prokaryotes, the mRNA of eukaryotes is generally monocistronic. Translation of the message generally begins at the first occurrence of AUG in the molecule.

The ribosomes of eukaryotes are different from those of prokaryotes. Whereas the prokaryotic ribosome is 70S, made up of 30S and 50S subunits, the eukaryotic ribosome is 80S, made up of 40S and 60S subunits. The differences in ribosome structure account for the ability of certain types of antibiotics to kill bacteria without causing significant harm to mammalian cells.

Some of the proteins that play essential roles in translation differ between eukaryotic and prokaryotic cells. Diphtheria toxin, which selectively kills eukaryotic but not prokaryotic cells, illustrates this difference. This toxin is produced by *Corynebacterium diphtheriae;* it binds to and inactivates one of the elongation factors of eukaryotes. Since this protein is required for translocation of the ribosome, translation ceases and the eukaryotic cell dies, resulting in the typical symptoms of diphtheria. ■ diphtheria toxin, p. 580

PERSPECTIVE 7.1

RNA: The First Macromolecule?

The 1989 Nobel Prize in Chemistry was awarded to two Americans. Sidney Altman of Yale University and Thomas Cech of the University of Colorado, who independently made the surprising and completely unexpected observation that RNA molecules can act as enzymes. Before their studies, it was believed that only proteins had enzymatic activity. The key observation was made by Cech in 1982 when he was trying to understand how introns were removed from precursor ribosomal RNA in the eukaryotic protozoan *Tetrahymena.* Since he was convinced that proteins were responsible for cutting out these introns, he added all of the protein in the cells nuclei to the RNA that still contained the introns.

As expected, the introns were cut out. As a control, Cech looked at the ribosomal RNA to which no nuclear proteins had been added, fully expecting that nothing would happen. Much to his surprise, the introns were also removed. It did not make any difference whether the protein was present—the introns were removed regardless. Thus, Cech could only conclude that the RNA acted on itself to cut out pieces of RNA.

The question remained of how widespread this phenomenon was. Did RNA have catalytic properties other than that of cutting out introns from rRNA? The studies of Altman and his colleagues, carried out simultaneously to and independently of Cech's, provided answers to these further questions. Altman's group found that RNA could convert a tRNA molecule from a precursor form to its final functional state. Additional studies have shown that enzymatic reactions in which catalytic RNAs, termed **ribozymes,** play a role are very widespread. Ribozymes have been shown to occur in the mitochondria of eukaryotic cells and to catalyze other reactions that resemble the polymerization of RNA. Whether catalytic RNA cuts out introns from mRNA in the nucleus is not known.

These observations have profound implications for evolution: which came first, proteins or nucleic acids? The answer seems to be that nucleic acids came first, specifically RNA, which acted both as a carrier of genetic information as well as an enzyme. Billions of years ago, before the present universe in which DNA, RNA, and protein are found, probably the only macromolecule that existed was RNA. Once tRNA became available, these adapters could carry amino acids present in the environment to specific nucleotide sequences on a strand of RNA. In this scenario, the RNA functions as the genes as well as the mRNA.

MICROCHECK 7.4

Eukaryotic mRNA must be processed, which involves capping, polyadenylation, and splicing. In eukaryotic cells, the mRNA must be transported out of the nucleus before it can be translated in the cytoplasm. Eukaryotic mRNA is monocistronic.

✓ What is an intron?

✓ Explain the mechanism of action of diphtheria toxin.

✓ Would a deletion of two base pairs have a greater consequence if it occurred in an intron or in an exon?

7.5 Prokaryotic Gene Regulation

Focus Points

- Give a functional example of a constitutive enzyme, an inducible enzyme, and a repressible enzyme.
- Using the *lac* operon as a model, explain the role of inducers and repressors.

To cope with changing conditions in their environment, microorganisms have evolved elaborate control mechanisms to synthesize the maximum amount of cell material from a limited supply of energy. This is critical, because generally a microorganism must reproduce more rapidly than its competitors in order to be successful.

Consider the situation of *Escherichia coli.* For over 100 million years, it has successfully inhabited the gut of mammals, where it reaches concentrations of 10^6 cells per milliliter. In this habitat, it must cope with alternating periods of feast and famine. For a limited time after a mammal eats, *E. coli* in the large intestine prosper, wallowing in the milieu of amino acids, vitamins, and other nutrients. The cells actively take up these compounds they would otherwise synthesize, expending minimal energy. Simultaneously, the cells shut down their biosynthetic pathways, channeling the conserved energy into the rapid synthesis of macromolecules, including DNA, RNA, and protein. Under these conditions, the cells divide at their most rapid rate. Famine, however, follows the feast. Between meals, which may be many days in the case of some mammals, the rich source of nutrients is depleted. Now the cells' biosynthetic pathways must be activated, using energy and markedly slowing cell division. Cells dividing several times an hour in a nutrient-rich environment may divide only once every 24 hours in a famished mammalian gut.

A cell controls its metabolic pathways by two general mechanisms. The most immediate of these is the allosteric inhibition of enzymes. The most energy-efficient strategy, however, is to control the actual synthesis of the enzymes, making only what is required. To do this, cells have the ability to control expression of certain genes. ■ allosteric regulation, p. 142

Principles of Regulation

Not all genes are subjected to the same type of regulation. Many are routinely expressed, whereas others are either turned on or off by certain conditions. Enzymes are often described according to characteristics of the regulation that governs their synthesis:

- **Constitutive enzymes** are constantly synthesized; the genes that encode these enzymes are always active. Constitutive enzymes usually play indispensable roles in the central metabolic pathways. For example, the enzymes of glycolysis are constitutive. ■ central metabolic pathways, pp. 136, 143
- **Inducible enzymes** are not regularly produced; instead, their synthesis is turned on by certain conditions. Inducible enzymes are often involved in the utilization of specific energy sources. A cell would waste precious resources if it synthesized the enzyme when the energy source is not present. An example of an inducible enzyme is **β-galactosidase,** whose sole function is to break down the disaccharide lactose into its two component monosaccharides, glucose and galac-

tose. The mechanisms by which the cell controls β-galactosidase synthesis serve as an important model for regulation and will be described shortly.

- **Repressible enzymes** are routinely synthesized, but they can be turned off by certain conditions. Repressible enzymes are generally involved in biosynthetic pathways, such as those that produce amino acids. Cells require a sufficient amount of a given amino acid to multiply; thus, the amino acid must be either synthesized or available as a component of the growth medium. If a certain amino acid is not present in the medium, then the cell must synthesize the enzymes involved in its manufacture. When the amino acid is supplied, however, synthesis of the enzymes would waste energy.

Mechanisms to Control Transcription

The mechanisms a cell uses to prevent or facilitate transcription must be readily reversible, allowing cells to effectively control the relative number of transcripts made. In some cases, the control mechanisms affect the transcription of only a limited number of genes; in other cases, a wide array of genes is coordinately controlled. For example, in *E. coli* the expression of more than 300 different genes is affected by the availability of glucose as an energy source. The simultaneous regulation of numerous genes unrelated in function is called **global control.**

Transcription of genes is often controlled by means of a regulatory region near the promoter to which a specific protein can bind, acting as a sophisticated on/off switch. When a regulatory protein binds DNA, it can either act as a repressor, which blocks transcription, or an activator, which facilitates transcription. A set of adjacent genes coordinately controlled by a regulatory protein and transcribed as a single polycistronic message is called an **operon.**

Repressors

A **repressor** is a regulatory protein that blocks transcription. It does this by binding to DNA at a region, the **operator,** located immediately downstream of a promoter. This effectively prevents RNA polymerase from progressing past that region. Regulation involving a repressor is called **negative control.**

Specific molecules may bind to the repressor and, by doing so, alter the ability of the repressor to bind DNA. This can occur because repressors are allosteric proteins, having a distinct site to which another molecule can bind. When that molecule binds, the shape of the repressor is altered. In turn, this affects the ability of the repressor to bind DNA. As shown in **figure 7.17,** there are two general mechanisms by which different repressors can function:

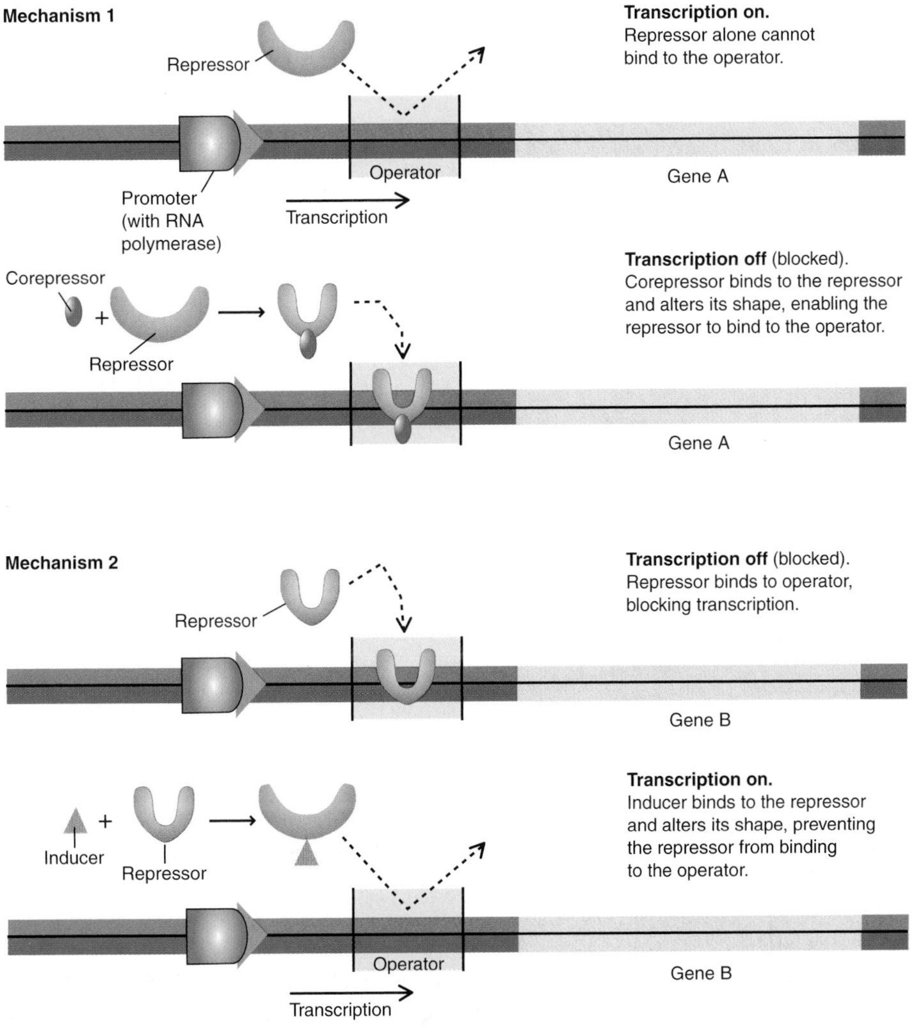
Mechanism 1
Repressor
Transcription on.
Repressor alone cannot bind to the operator.
Operator
Gene A
Promoter (with RNA polymerase)
Transcription
Corepressor
Repressor
Transcription off (blocked).
Corepressor binds to the repressor and alters its shape, enabling the repressor to bind to the operator.
Gene A
Mechanism 2
Repressor
Transcription off (blocked).
Repressor binds to operator, blocking transcription.
Gene B
Inducer
Repressor
Transcription on.
Inducer binds to the repressor and alters its shape, preventing the repressor from binding to the operator.
Operator
Gene B
Transcription

FIGURE 7.17 Transcriptional Regulation by Repressor

PERSPECTIVE 7.2

From the Junk Pile to Center Stage

For years, scientists have recognized that large regions of the eukaryotic genome do not code for proteins, often referring to these non-coding sequences as "junk DNA," implying that they have no value to the cell. Recent discoveries, however, have shed light on the essential regulatory roles of some of these non-coding regions, shattering earlier notions about the value of these sequences and ushering in the potential for promising new research tools, and perhaps even therapies.

One major discovery that altered the notion that non-coding regions are all "junk DNA" is that some RNA molecules are produced that do not take part in translation but instead silence genes, a process called **RNA interference (RNAi).** The mechanisms of RNAi are varied, but one example is a group of RNA molecules called **short interfering RNA (siRNA).** These are short RNA molecules (20 to 25 nucleotides in length) that bind complementary sequences on mRNA. The binding generates regions of double-stranded RNA, effectively tagging the mRNA molecule for destruction **(figure 1).** The siRNA is not destroyed in the process, however, so it can be reused repeatedly. This means siRNA is catalytic, providing a rapid and effective means of silencing genes that have already been transcribed.

Prokaryotic cells have fewer non-coding regions in their genomes, but researchers have found that they use regulatory RNAs as well. Certain small RNA molecules, referred to as **small RNAs (sRNAs),** for example, bind to complementary sequences on mRNA, either altering the stability of the molecule or affecting the ability of translational machinery to bind.

The study of regulatory RNA molecules is still in its early stages, but the newly discovered role of RNA is revolutionizing current views on gene regulation. In addition, it provides the promise for new mechanisms to alter gene expression. By turning off selected genes *in vitro,* scientists should be able to more precisely identify the function of those genes. An ultimate hope is that RNA interference could be used as a form of gene therapy to silence abnormal genes.

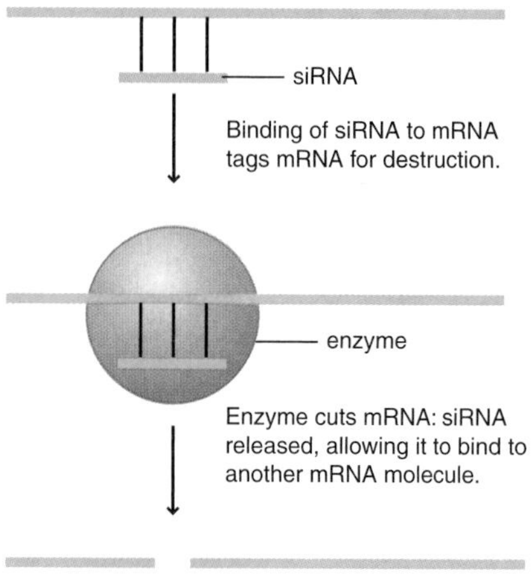
siRNA
Binding of siRNA to mRNA tags mRNA for destruction.
enzyme
Enzyme cuts mRNA: siRNA released, allowing it to bind to another mRNA molecule.

FIGURE 1 Regulatory Action of siRNA

1. The repressor is synthesized as a form that alone cannot bind to the operator. When a molecule termed a **corepressor** binds to the repressor, however, the shape of the repressor is altered so that it can bind to the operator, blocking transcription.
2. The repressor is synthesized as a form that effectively binds to the operator, blocking transcription. The binding to it of a molecule that functions as an **inducer,** alters the shape of the repressor so that it no longer binds to the operator. Consequently, the gene can be transcribed.

Activators

An **activator** is a regulatory protein that facilitates transcription. Genes controlled by an activator have an ineffective promoter that is preceded by an **activator-binding site.** The binding of the activator to the DNA enhances the ability of RNA polymerase to initiate transcription at that promoter. Regulation involving an activator is sometimes called **positive control.**

Like repressors, activators are allosteric proteins whose function can be modulated by the binding of other molecules. A molecule that binds to an activator and alters its shape so it can effectively bind to the activator-binding site functions as an inducer **(figure 7.18).** Thus, the term inducer applies to a molecule that turns on transcription, either by stimulating the function of an activator or interfering with the function of a repressor.

The *lac* Operon As a Model for Control of Metabolic Pathways

Originally elucidated in the early 1960s by Francois Jacob and Jacques Monod, the ***lac* operon** has served as an important model for understanding the control of gene expression in bacteria. The operon, which consists of three genes involved with lactose degradation, along with regulatory components, is subject to dual control by both a repressor and an activator **(figure 7.19).** The net effect is that the genes are expressed only when lactose is present but glucose is absent.

The Effect of Lactose on the Control of the Lactose Operon

The *lac* operon employs a repressor that prevents transcription of the genes when lactose is unavailable. When lactose is not present, the repressor binds to the operator, effectively blocking transcrip-

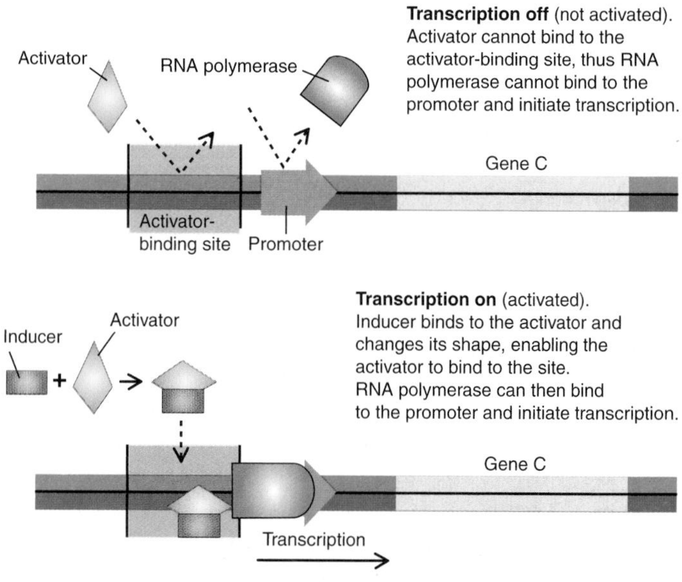
Transcription off (not activated).
Activator cannot bind to the activator-binding site, thus RNA polymerase cannot bind to the promoter and initiate transcription.
Activator
RNA polymerase
Gene C
Activator-binding site
Promoter
Transcription on (activated).
Inducer binds to the activator and changes its shape, enabling the activator to bind to the site.
RNA polymerase can then bind to the promoter and initiate transcription.
Inducer
Activator
Gene C
Transcription

FIGURE 7.18 Transcriptional Regulation by Activators

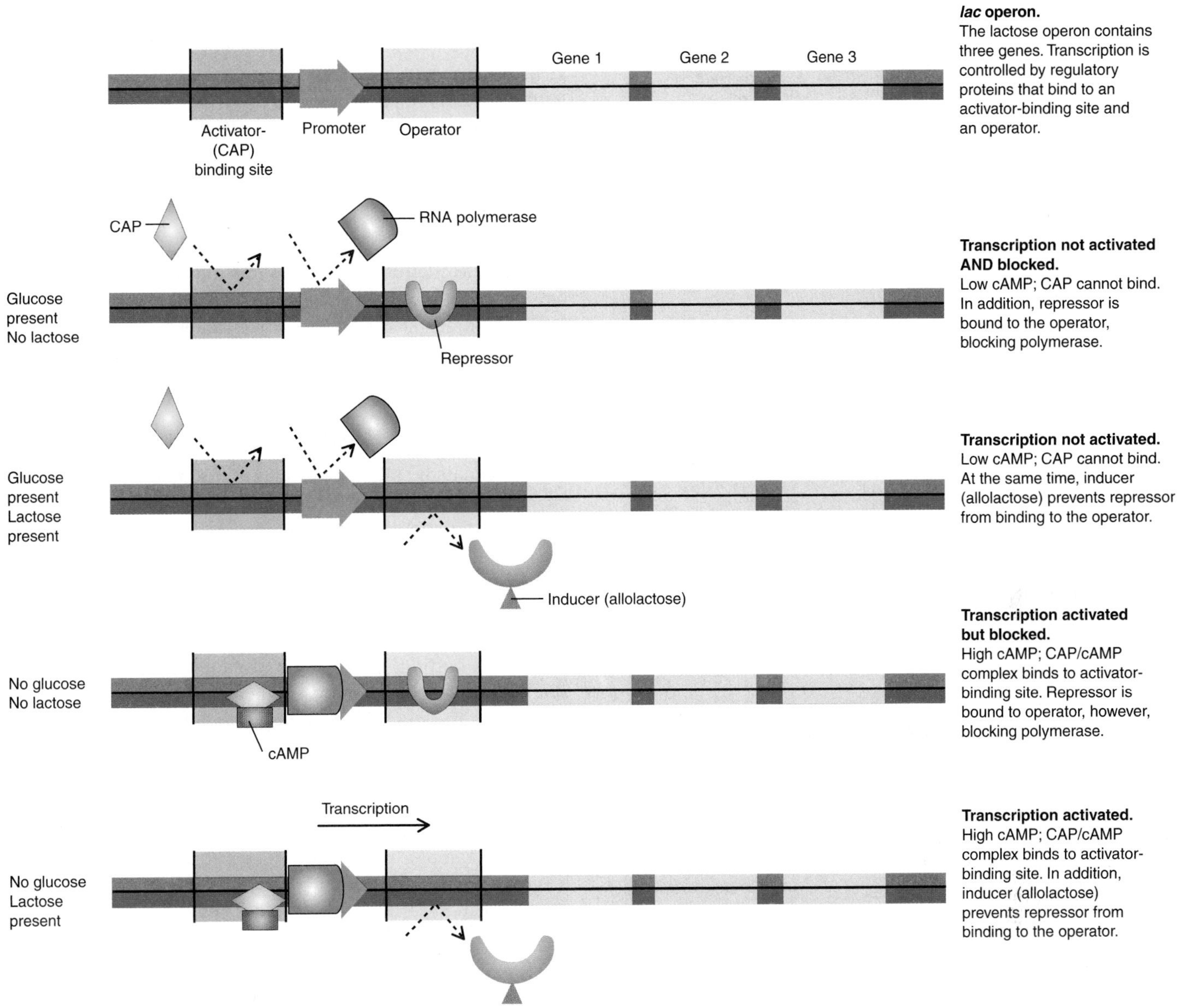

Gene 1
Gene 2
Gene 3
Activator- (CAP) binding site
Promoter
Operator
lac operon.
The lactose operon contains three genes. Transcription is controlled by regulatory proteins that bind to an activator-binding site and an operator.
CAP
RNA polymerase
Glucose present No lactose
Repressor
Transcription not activated AND blocked.
Low cAMP; CAP cannot bind. In addition, repressor is bound to the operator, blocking polymerase.
Glucose present Lactose present
Inducer (allolactose)
Transcription not activated.
Low cAMP; CAP cannot bind. At the same time, inducer (allolactose) prevents repressor from binding to the operator.
No glucose No lactose
cAMP
Transcription activated but blocked.
High cAMP; CAP/cAMP complex binds to activator-binding site. Repressor is bound to operator, however, blocking polymerase.
Transcription
No glucose Lactose present
Transcription activated.
High cAMP; CAP/cAMP complex binds to activator-binding site. In addition, inducer (allolactose) prevents repressor from binding to the operator.

FIGURE 7.19 Regulation of the *lac* Operon

tion. When lactose is present in the cell, however, some of the molecules are converted into a compound called allolactose. This compound binds to the repressor, altering its shape so that it can no longer bind to the operator. Thus, when lactose is present, the repressor no longer prevents RNA polymerase from transcribing the operon. Note, however, that the activator described in the next paragraph is needed for successful transcription.

The Effect of Glucose on the Control of the Lactose Operon

Escherichia coli preferentially uses glucose over other sugars such as lactose. This can readily be demonstrated by observing growth and sugar utilization of *E. coli* in a medium containing glucose and lactose. Cells actively grow, metabolizing only glucose until its supply is exhausted **(figure 7.20).** Growth then ceases for a short period until the cells begin utilizing lactose. At this point, the cells start multiplying again. This two-step growth response, called **diauxic growth,** represents the ability of glucose to repress the enzymes of lactose degradation—a phenomenon called **catabolite repression.**

The regulatory mechanism of catabolite repression does not directly sense glucose in a cell. Instead, it recognizes the concentration of a nucleotide derivative, cyclic AMP (cAMP), which is low when glucose is being transported into the cell and high when it is not. cAMP is an inducer of the operon; it binds to an activator that facilitates transcription of the *lac* operon. This activator, called CAP (catabolite activator protein), is only able to bind to the *lac* promoter when cAMP is bound to it. The higher the concentration of cAMP, the more likely it is to bind to CAP. Thus, when glucose concentrations in the medium are low (and therefore cAMP levels are high), the *lac* operon can be transcribed. Note, however, that even in the presence of a functional activator, the repressor prevents transcription unless lactose is present.

Catabolite repression is significant biologically because it forces cells to first use the carbon source that is most easily

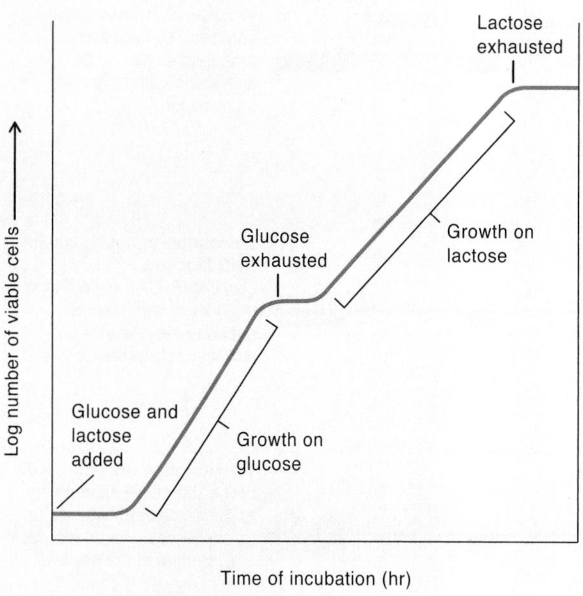

FIGURE 7.20 Diauxic Growth Curve of *E. coli* Growing in a Medium Containing Glucose and Lactose Cells preferentially use glucose. Only when the supply of glucose is exhausted do cells start metabolizing lactose. Note that the growth on lactose is slower than it is on glucose.

metabolized. Only when the supply of glucose is exhausted do cells begin degrading lactose, a carbon source that requires additional enzymatic steps to metabolize.

MICROCHECK 7.5

Enzymes can be constitutive, inducible, or repressible. A repressor blocks transcription when it binds to an operator. An activator enhances transcription when it binds to an activator-binding site. The functioning of specific activators and repressors may require or be blocked by other molecules.

- ✓ Explain the difference between a constitutive enzyme and an inducible enzyme.
- ✓ Explain the mechanism by which glucose represses the lactose operon.
- ✓ Why would it be advantageous for a cell to control the activity of an enzyme as well as its synthesis?

7.6 Sensing and Responding to Environmental Fluctuations

Focus Points

- Describe how two-component regulatory systems and quorum sensing allows cells to adapt to fluctuating environmental conditions.
- Compare and contrast antigenic variation and phase variation.

Microorganisms adapt to fluctuating conditions by altering the level of expression of certain genes. For example, certain pathogenic bacteria have mechanisms to sense when they are within the tissues of an animal; in response they can activate certain genes that facilitate their survival against the impending onslaught of host defenses.

Signal Transduction

Signal transduction is a process that transmits information from outside a cell to the inside, allowing that cell to respond to changing environmental conditions. For example, cells turn on or off certain genes in response to variations in such factors as osmotic pressure, cell concentration, and nitrogen availability.

Two-Component Regulatory Systems

One mechanism cells use to relay information about the external environment is a **two-component regulatory system.** This relies on the coordinated activities of two different proteins, a sensor and a response regulator. The **sensor** spans the cytoplasmic membrane so that the part recognizing changes in the environment is positioned outside the cell. In response to specific external variations, the sensor chemically modifies a region on its internal portion, usually by phosphorylating a specific amino acid. The phosphoryl group is then transferred to a **response regulator.** The modified response regulator can act as either an activator or a repressor, turning on or off genes, depending on the system.

Bacteria use different two-component regulatory systems to detect and respond to a wide variety of environmental cues. *E. coli,* for example, uses such systems to control the expression of genes for its alternative types of metabolism. When nitrate is present in anaerobic conditions, cells activate genes required to use nitrate as a terminal electron acceptor. Some pathogens use two-component regulatory systems to sense environmental magnesium concentrations, and then activate specific genes in response. Because the magnesium concentration within certain tissue cells is generally lower than that of extracellular sites, these pathogens are able to recognize whether or not they are within a cell. In turn, they can activate appropriate genes that help them evade the host defenses intended to protect that relative site.

Quorum Sensing

Some organisms can "sense" the density of cells within their own population—a phenomenon called **quorum sensing.** This enables them to activate genes that are only beneficial when expressed by a critical mass of cells. For example, the cooperative activities leading to biofilm formation are controlled by quorum sensing. ■ biofilms, p. 89

In the most thoroughly studied quorum sensing systems, the bacteria synthesize one or more varieties of a **homoserine lactone (HSL)** (or AHL for **acylated homoserine lactone**). These small molecules can move freely in and out of a cell. When few cells are present, the concentration of a given HSL is very low. As the cells multiply in a confined area, however, the concentration of that HSL increases proportionally. Only when it reaches a critical level does it induce the expression of specific genes.

Natural Selection

Natural selection can also play a role in the control of gene expression. The expression of some genes changes randomly, presumably enhancing the chances of survival of at least a part of a population under certain environmental conditions.

The role of natural selection is readily apparent in bacteria that undergo **antigenic variation,** an alteration in the characteristics of certain surface proteins such as flagella, pili, and outer membrane proteins. Disease-causing organisms that are able to change these proteins can stay one step ahead of the body's defenses by altering the very molecules our immune systems must learn to recognize. One of the most well characterized examples is *Neisseria gonorrhoeae,* a bacterium that successfully disguises itself from the immune system by changing several of its surface proteins. *N. gonorrhoeae* has many different genes for **pilin,** the protein subunit that makes up pili, yet most are silent. The only one that is expressed resides in a particular chromosomal location called an **expression locus.** *N. gonorrhoeae* cells have a mechanism to shuffle the pilin genes, randomly moving different ones in and out of the expression locus. In a population of 10^4 cells, at least one is expressing a different type of pilin. It appears that expression of different pilin genes is not regulated in any controlled manner but occurs randomly. Only some of the changes, however, are advantageous to a cell's survival. When the body's immune system eventually begins to respond to a specific pilin type, those cells that have already "switched" to produce a different type will survive and then multiply. Eventually, the immune system learns to recognize those, but by that time, another subpopulation will have "switched" its pilin type. Thus, natural selection serves to indirectly regulate the changes. ■ pili, p. 68 ■ *Neisseria gonorrhoeae,* p. 661

Another mechanism of randomly altering gene expression is **phase variation,** the routine switching on and off of certain genes. Presumably, phase variation helps an organism adapt to selective pressures. By altering the expression of certain critical genes, at least a part of the population is poised for change and thus able to survive and multiply. For example, phase variation of genes that encode fimbriae may allow some members of a population to attach to a surface, while permitting others to detach and colonize surfaces elsewhere. ■ fimbriae, p. 68

MICROCHECK 7.6

Signal transduction allows a cell to respond to changing conditions outside of that cell. The expression of some genes changes randomly, presumably enhancing the chances of survival of at least a subset of a population of cells under varying environmental conditions.

- ✓ Explain the mechanism by which certain bacteria can "sense" the density of cells.
- ✓ Why would it be advantageous for a bacterium to synthesize more than one type of homoserine lactone?

7.7 Genomics

Focus Point

- Explain how protein-encoding regions are found when analyzing a DNA sequence.

Increasingly rapid methods of determining the nucleotide sequence of DNA have led to exciting advancements in genomics. Fueled by the commitment to sequence the entire human genome, scientists honed the methodologies by first sequencing the genomes of select microorganisms. In 1995, the sequence of the chromosome of *Haemophilus influenzae* was published, marking the first complete genomic sequence ever determined. Since then, microbial genome sequencing has become almost commonplace, and a draft of the human genome has been competed. A table describing some of the representative prokaryotes that have been sequenced is available at the Online Learning Center (www.mmhe.com/nester5).

Although sequencing methodologies are becoming more rapid, analyzing the resulting data and extracting the pertinent information is far more complex than it might initially seem. One of the most difficult steps is to locate and characterize the potential protein-encoding regions. Imagine trying to determine the amino acid sequence of a protein encoded by a 1,000-base-pair (bp) stretch of DNA, without knowing anything about the orientation of the promoter or the reading frame of the transcribed mRNA. Since either strand of the double-stranded DNA molecule could be the template strand, two entirely different mRNA molecules could potentially code for the protein. In turn, each of those two molecules has three reading frames, for a total of six reading frames. Yet only one of these actually codes for the protein. Understandably, computers are an invaluable aid and are used extensively in deciphering the meaning of the raw sequence data. In turn, this has resulted in the emergence of a new field, **bioinformatics,** which has created the computer technology to store, retrieve, and analyze nucleotide sequence data.

Analyzing a Prokaryotic DNA Sequence

When analyzing a DNA sequence, the nucleotide sequence of the (+) strand is used to infer information contained in the corresponding RNA transcript. Because of this, terms like start codon, which actually refers to a sequence in mRNA, are used to describe sequences in DNA. For example, to locate the start codon AUG, which would be found in mRNA, one would look for the analogous sequence, ATG, in the (+) strand of DNA. In most cases it is not initially known which of the two strands is actually used as a template for RNA synthesis, so that both strands are potentially a (+) strand. Only after a promoter is located is it known which strand in a given region is actually the (+) strand.

To locate protein-encoding regions, computers are used to search for **open reading frames (ORFs),** stretches of DNA, generally longer than 300 bp, that begin with a start codon and end with a stop codon. An ORF potentially encodes a protein. Other characteristics, such as the presence of an upstream sequence that can serve as a ribosome-binding site, also indicate that an ORF encodes a protein.

The nucleotide sequence of the ORF or deduced amino acid sequence of the encoded protein can be compared with other known sequences by searching computerized databases of published sequences. Not surprisingly, as genomes of more organisms are being sequenced, information contained in these databases is growing at a remarkable rate. If the encoded protein shows certain amino acid similarities, or **homology,** to characterized proteins, a putative function can sometimes be assigned. For example, proteins that bind DNA share amino acid sequences in certain regions. Likewise, regulatory regions in DNA such as promoters can sometimes be identified based on the nucleotide homologies to known sequences.

MICROCHECK 7.7

The first genomic sequence of a microorganism was completed in 1995. The sequencing methodologies are quickly becoming more rapid, but analyzing the data and extracting the pertinent information is difficult.

- ✓ What is an open reading frame?
- ✓ Describe two things that can be learned by searching a computerized database for sequences that have homologies to a newly sequenced gene.
- ✓ There are some characteristic differences in the nucleotide sequences of the leading and lagging strands. Why might this be so?

FUTURE CHALLENGES

Gems in the Genomes?

From a medical standpoint, one of the most exciting challenges will be to capitalize on the rapidly accruing genomic information and use that knowledge to develop new drugs and therapies. The potential gains are tremendous, particularly in the face of increasing resistance to current antimicrobial drugs. For example, by studying the genomes of pathogenic microorganisms, scientists can learn more about specific genes that enable an organism to cause disease. Already we know that many of these are encoded in large segments called **pathogenicity islands** and that the genes in these segments are often coordinately regulated. By learning more about the signals and mechanisms that turn these genes on and off, scientists may be able to one day design a drug that prevents the synthesis of critical bacterial proteins. Such a drug could interfere with that pathogen's ability to survive within our body and thereby render it harmless. ■ resistance to antimicrobial drugs, p. 499

Learning more about the human genome provides another means of developing drug therapies. Already, companies are searching genomic databases, a process called **genome mining,** to locate ORFs that may encode proteins of medical value. What they generally look for are previously uncharacterized proteins that have certain sequence similarities to proteins of proven therapeutic value. Some of their discoveries are now in clinical trials to test their efficacy. For example, a protein involved in bone-building is being tested as a treatment for osteoporosis. Likewise, another protein discovered through genome mining may facilitate the healing of wounds. Genes encoding many other medically useful proteins are probably still hidden, waiting to be discovered.

SUMMARY

7.1 Overview (Figure 7.1)

Characteristics of DNA (Figure 7.3)

A single strand of DNA has a 5′ end and a 3′ end; the two strands of DNA in the double helix are **antiparallel.**

Characteristics of RNA

A single-stranded RNA fragment is transcribed from one of the two strands of DNA.

There are three different functional groups of RNA molecules: **messenger RNA (mRNA), ribosomal RNA (rRNA),** and **transfer RNA (tRNA).**

Regulating the Expression of Genes

Protein synthesis is generally controlled by regulating the synthesis of mRNA.

7.2 DNA Replication

DNA replication is generally **bidirectional** and **semiconservative.** (Figure 7.4)

The DNA chain always elongates in the 5′ to 3′ direction. (Figure 7.5)

Initiation of DNA Replication

DNA replication begins at the **origin of replication. DNA polymerase** synthesizes DNA in the 5′ to 3′ direction, using one strand as a **template** to generate the complementary strand.

The Replication Fork (Figure 7.6)

The bidirectional progression of replication around a circular DNA molecule creates two replication forks; numerous enzymes and other proteins are involved.

7.3 Gene Expression

Transcription

RNA polymerase catalyzes the process of transcription, producing a single-stranded RNA molecule that is complementary and antiparallel to the DNA template. (Figure 7.7)

Transcription begins after RNA polymerase recognizes and binds to a **promoter.** (Figure 7.8)

RNA is synthesized in the 5′ to 3′ direction. (Figure 7.9)

When **RNA polymerase** encounters a **terminator,** it falls off the DNA template and releases the newly synthesized RNA.

Translation

The information encoded by mRNA is deciphered using the genetic code. (Figure 7.10)

A nucleotide sequence has three potential **reading frames.** (Figure 7.11)

Ribosomes function as the site of translation. (Figure 7.12)

tRNAs carry specific amino acids and act as keys that interpret the genetic code. (Figure 7.13)

In prokaryotes, initiation of translation begins when the ribosome binds to the **ribosome-binding site** of the mRNA molecule. Translation starts at the first AUG downstream of that site. (Figure 7.14)

The ribosome moves along mRNA in the 5′ to 3′ direction; translation terminates when the ribosome reaches a **stop codon.** (Figure 7.15)

Proteins are often modified after they are synthesized.

7.4 Differences Between Eukaryotic and Prokaryotic Gene Expression (Table 7.4)

Eukaryotic mRNA is **processed;** a **cap** and a **poly A tail** are added.

Eukaryotic genes often contain **introns** which are removed from **precursor mRNA** by a process called **splicing.** (Figure 7.16)

In eukaryotic cells, the mRNA must be transported out of the nucleus before it can be translated in the cytoplasm.

7.5 Prokaryotic Gene Regulation

Principles of Regulation

Constitutive enzymes are constantly synthesized.

The synthesis of **inducible enzymes** can be turned on by certain conditions.

The synthesis of **repressible enzymes** can be turned off by certain conditions.

Mechanisms to Control Transcription

Repressors block transcription. (Figure 7.17)

Activators enhance transcription. (Figure 7.18)

The lac Operon As a Model for Control of Metabolic Pathways (Figure 7.19)

The *lac* operon employs a repressor that prevents transcription of the genes when lactose is not available.

Catabolite repression prevents transcription of the *lac* operon when glucose is available.

7.6 Sensing and Responding to Environmental Fluctuations

Signal Transduction

Two-component regulatory systems utilize a sensor that recognizes changes outside the cell and then transmits that information to a **response regulator.**

Bacteria that utilize **quorum sensing** synthesize a soluble compound that can move freely in and out of a cell. Only when that compound reaches a critical concentration does it activate specific genes.

Natural Selection

The expression of some genes changes randomly, enhancing the chances of survival of at least a subset of a population under varying environmental conditions.

Antigenic variation is a routine change in the expression of surface proteins.

Phase variation is the routine switching on and off of certain genes.

7.7 Genomics

Analyzing a Prokaryotic DNA Sequence

When analyzing a DNA sequence, the nucleotide sequence of the (+) strand is used to infer information carried by the corresponding RNA transcript; computers are used to search for **open reading frames (ORFs).**

REVIEW QUESTIONS

Short Answer

1. Explain what the term *semiconservative* means with respect to DNA replication.
2. How can *E. coli* have a generation time of only 20 minutes when it takes 40 minutes to replicate its chromosome?
3. What is the function of primase in DNA replication? Why is this enzyme necessary?
4. What is polycistronic mRNA?
5. Explain why knowing the orientation of a promoter is critical when determining the amino acid sequence of an encoded protein.
6. What is characteristic about the nucleotide sequence of a transcription terminator?
7. What happens to a polypeptide that has a signal sequence?
8. Compare and contrast regulation by a repressor and an activator.
9. Explain how bacteria sense the density of cells in their own population.
10. Explain why it is sometimes difficult to locate genomic regions that encode a protein.

Multiple Choice Questions

1. All of the following are involved in transcription, *except*
   a) polymerase. b) primer. c) promoter. d) sigma factor. e) uracil.
2. All of the following are involved in DNA replication, *except*
   a) elongation factors. b) gyrase. c) polymerase. d) primase. e) primer.
3. All of the following are directly involved in translation, *except*
   a) promoter. b) ribosome. c) start codon. d) stop codon. e) tRNA.
4. Using the DNA strand depicted here as a template, what will be the sequence of the RNA transcript?

   5′ GCGTTAACGTAGGC 3′

   $\longrightarrow$ promoter

   3′ CGCAATTGCATCCG 5′

   a) 5′ GCGUUAACGUAGGC 3′ b) 5′ CGGAUGCAAUUGCG 3′
   c) 5′ CGCAAUUGCAUCCG 3′ d) 5′ GCCUACGUUAACGC 3′

5. A ribosome binds to the following mRNA at the site indicated by the dark box. What are the first three amino acids that will be incorporated into the resulting polypeptide?

   5′ ■ GCCGGAAUGCUGCUGGC

   a) Alanine aspartic acid alanine
   b) Methionine threonine cysteine
   c) Methionine leucine leucine
   d) Alanine glycine methionine
6. Allolactose induces the *lac* regulon by binding to a(n)
   a) operator. b) repressor.
   c) activator. d) CAP protein.
7. Under which of the following conditions will transcription of the *lac* operon occur?
   a) Lactose present/glucose present
   b) Lactose present/glucose absent
   c) Lactose absent/glucose present
   d) Lactose absent/glucose absent
   e) A and B
8. Which of the following statements about gene expression is *false?*
   a) More than one RNA polymerase can be transcribing a specific gene at a given time.
   b) More than one ribosome can be translating a specific transcript at a given time.
   c) Translation begins at a site called a promoter.
   d) Transcription stops at a site called a terminator.
   e) Some amino acids are coded for by more than one codon.
9. Which of the following is *not* characteristic of eukaryotic gene expression?
   a) 5′ cap is added to the mRNA.
   b) A poly A tail is added to the 3′ end of mRNA.
   c) Introns must be removed to create the mRNA that is translated.
   d) The mRNA is often polycistronic.
   e) Translation begins at the first AUG.
10. Which of the following statements is *false?*
    a) A derivative of lactose serves as an inducer of the *lac* operon.
    b) Signal transduction provides a mechanism for a cell to sense the conditions of its external environment.
    c) The function of homoserine lactone is to enable a cell to sense the density of like cells.
    d) An example of a two-component regulatory system is the lactose operon, which is controlled by a repressor and an activator.
    e) An ORF is a stretch of DNA that may encode a protein.

Applications

1. A graduate student is trying to isolate the gene coding for an enzyme found in a species of *Pseudomonas* that degrades trinitrotoluene (TNT). The student is frustrated to find that the organism does not produce the enzyme when grown in nutrient broth, making it is difficult to collect the mRNA needed to help identify the gene. What could the student do to potentially increase the amount of the desired enzyme?
2. A student wants to remove the introns from a segment of DNA coding for protein X. Devise a strategy for how this could be accomplished.

Critical Thinking

1. The study of protein synthesis often uses a cell-free system where cells are ground with an abrasive to release the cell contents and then filtered to remove the abrasive. These materials are added to the system, generating the indicated results:

Materials Added	Results
Radioactive amino acids	Radioactive protein produced
Radioactive amino acids *and* RNase (an RNA-digesting enzyme)	No radioactive protein produced

   What is the best interpretation of these observations?

2. In a variation of the experiment in the previous question, the following materials were added to three separate cell-free systems, generating the indicated results:

Materials Added	Results
Radioactive amino acids	Radioactive protein produced
Radioactive amino acids *and* DNase (a DNA-digesting enzyme)	Radioactive protein produced
Several hours after grinding: Radioactive amino acids *and* DNase	No radioactive protein produced

   What is the best interpretation of these observations?

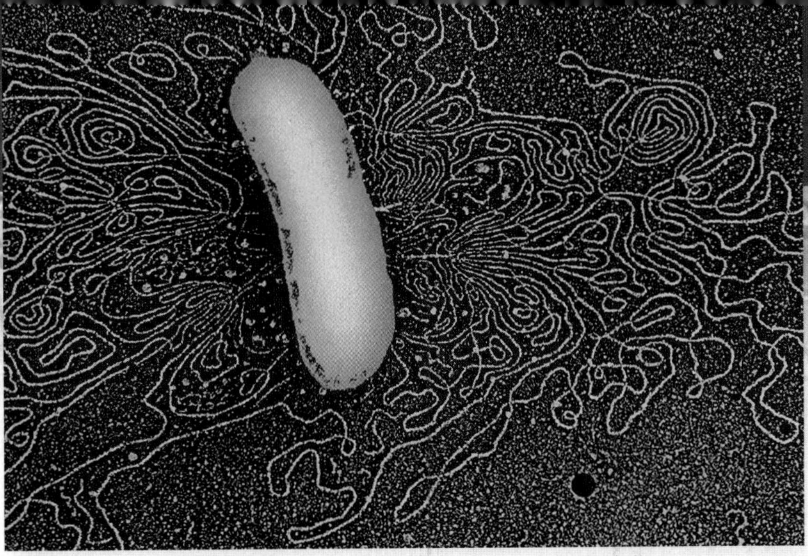

DNA bursts from this treated bacterial cell.

CHAPTER EIGHT

Bacterial Genetics

A Glimpse of History

Barbara McClintock (1902–1992) was a remarkable scientist who made several very important discoveries in genetics dealing with chromosome structure. Her studies were carried out before the age of large interdisciplinary research teams and before the sophisticated tools of molecular genetics were available. Her tools consisted of a clear mind that could make sense of confusing and revolutionary observations, and a consuming curiosity. She worked 12-hour days, 6 days a week in a small laboratory at Cold Spring Harbor on Long Island, New York.

In 1983, at age 81, McClintock received the Nobel Prize in Medicine or Physiology largely for her discovery 40 years earlier of transposable elements, or transposons, popularly called "jumping genes." Her experimental system consisted of ears of corn. She observed various colored kernels that were produced by different enzymes (see figure 8.6). If the gene coding for an enzyme responsible for color formation was inactivated, the kernel was not pigmented. If the enzyme was only partially inactivated, then the kernel was partially pigmented. Thus, by looking at kernel colors, McClintock could detect changes in gene function. She concluded that something must be moving into and out of genes to account for the differences in kernel color. What she suggested was moving were pieces of DNA. When a piece of DNA, called a transposable element, moved into a gene, the gene could no longer function. When the transposable element left a gene, it was restored to its original state, and would function normally again.

At the time McClintock published her results, most scientists believed that DNA which makes up chromosomes was very stable and unchanging. Consequently, most geneticists were very skeptical of McClintock's heretical ideas. As a result, she stopped publishing many of her observations. It was not until the late 1970s that her ideas were accepted. By that time, transposable elements had been discovered in many organisms, including bacteria. Although first discovered in plants, once transposons were found in bacteria, the field moved ahead very quickly. The techniques of molecular biology, biochemistry, and genetics made the understanding of "jumping genes" possible.

Staphylococcus aureus, the Gram-positive coccus commonly called Staph, is a frequent cause of skin infections, such as boils and pimples. Since the 1970s the usual treatment has been penicillin-like antibiotics, such as methicillin. Today, however, this approach is likely to fail. In 2003, well over 60% of the *S. aureus* strains isolated in hospitals were resistant to this antibiotic. Further, these resistant organisms were much more likely to cause various life-threatening diseases, such as infections of the skin, lungs, wounds, and bloodstream. Unfortunately, methicillin-resistant Staph are also resistant to a variety of other antibiotics. These resistant organisms now are commonly treated with a less effective antibiotic, vancomycin, often considered the antibiotic of last resort. However, in 2002 another threat arose—Staph isolated from foot ulcers on a diabetes patient in Detroit were vancomycin-resistant. This organism was also resistant to most common antibiotics, including penicillin, methicillin, and ciprofloxacin. Further, all of these resistances were transferred simultaneously to drug-susceptible strains of *S. aureus.* How did these multiple resistant strains arise and evolve? How are these resistance traits transferred so readily to other bacteria?

The answer to these and many other questions important to medical microbiology and biotechnology requires a basic understanding of bacterial genetics. This subject encompasses the study of heredity—how genes function (chapter 7), how they can change, and how they are transferred to other cells in the population. With this knowledge you will understand why antibiotics are no longer miracle drugs against infectious diseases.

KEY TERMS

Auxotroph A microorganism that requires an organic growth factor.

Conjugation Mechanism of horizontal gene transfer in which the donor cell must physically contact the recipient cell.

DNA-mediated transformation Mechanism of horizontal gene transfer between bacteria in which the bacterial DNA is transferred as "naked" DNA.

Extrachromosomal DNA which is not part of a chromosome.

Genomic islands Mobile genetic elements in the chromosome that are transferred as a unit and code for traits that can be beneficial under certain circumstances. They include pathogenicity islands and antibiotic resistance islands.

Genotype The sequence of nucleotides in the DNA of an organism.

Haploid Containing only a single set of genes.

Homologous recombination Genetic recombination between stretches of similar or identical nucleotide sequences. Involves a type of breakage and rejoining of DNA into new combinations.

Horizontal gene transfer Transmission of DNA from one bacterium to another by conjugation, DNA-mediated transformation, or transduction. Also called lateral gene transfer.

Mutation Modification in the sequence of DNA in a gene often resulting in an alteration in the protein encoded by the gene.

Phenotype The actual expression of the genotype.

Prototroph A microorganism that has no requirements for organic growth factors because it can synthesize them.

Reactive oxygen Toxic forms of oxygen that modify and damage DNA.

Replicon A piece of DNA that is capable of replicating. It contains an origin of replication.

Transduction Mechanism of horizontal gene transfer between bacteria in which the bacterial DNA is transferred inside a phage coat.

Transposable element (transposon) Genes that move from one replicon to another site on the same replicon, or to another replicon in the same cell.

8.1 Diversity in Bacteria

Focus Points

- Name the two genetic changes that can alter the properties of bacteria by which the properties of bacteria can change.
- Distinguish between the genotype and phenotype of a cell.

The study of the ways that genes which code for properties such as antibiotic resistance and the ability to cause disease can be transferred to other bacteria requires that you have some understanding of how genes and their activities can change—the subject of **diversity.**

Rapidly growing bacteria that are exposed to continually changing environments must be able to adapt quickly if they are going to successfully compete with other bacteria in the same environment. Unless they respond quickly to take advantage of the change, other organisms will crowd them out. In general, bacteria are **haploid** in that they contain only a single set of genes, so any changes in a single or many genes quickly change the bacterial cell. Further, all offspring of the cell in which the change occurs also are changed.

Bacteria can adapt to a changing environment by changing their properties by three different mechanisms, two of which involve changes in the genetic make up of bacteria. These latter changes can occur by two independent means. First, nucleotides of DNA can undergo changes in chemical structure resulting in changes in DNA which results in organisms with different properties. These alterations are called **mutations** and the changed organisms are **mutants.** All of the progeny (offspring) of the mutant are also mutant. The mutation is said to be inherited **vertically (figure 8.1a).** Second, bacteria can acquire genes from other bacteria through a process of **gene transfer,** which provides new genetic information to the cells. The transfer of genes, commonly by the transfer of a plasmid, is termed **horizontal gene transfer (figure 8.1b).** These changes in DNA, which are passed on to all progeny, are the basis for **natural selection.** If the change in genetic information allows the organism to multiply more rapidly than the original bacteria in an altered environment, then the original bacteria will be replaced in the environment. For example, if a cell becomes resistant to streptomycin either through mutation or gene

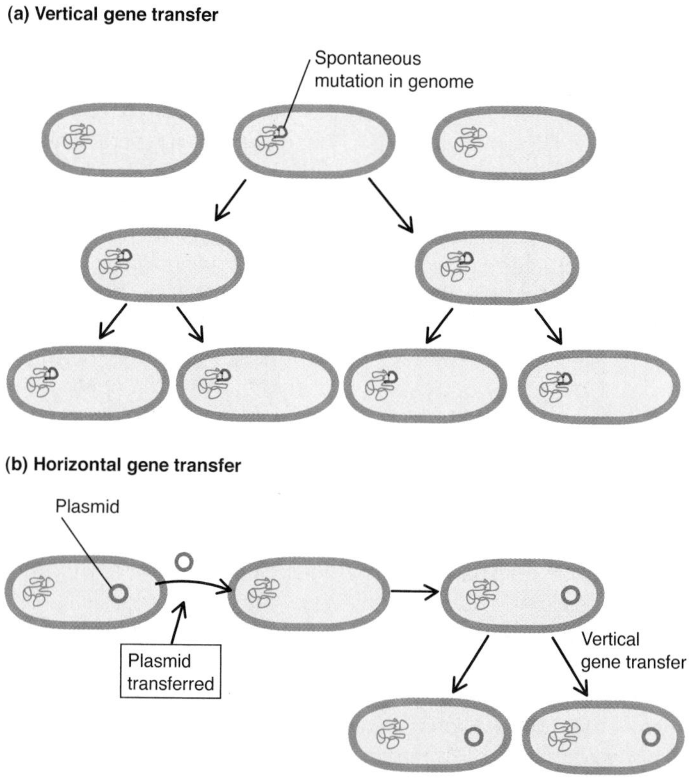

FIGURE 8.1 The Acquisition and Transfer of Genetic Information to Progeny **(a)** Spontaneous mutation. All progeny of mutant cells will be mutant. **(b)** Gene transfer or horizontal acquisition of genetic information. All progeny of the cell acquiring the plasmid will also carry the plasmid by vertical gene transfer. A copy of the plasmid remains in the cell that transfers the plasmid.

transfer in a hospital environment where streptomycin is commonly used, the resistant cells will likely replace the sensitive ones. The **genotype** of an organism is the sequence of nucleotides in the organism's DNA. If the DNA is altered, the genotype changes.

In addition to the changes in DNA that can occur, the expression of the genetic information encoded by the DNA can be regulated. Depending on the environmental conditions, some genes are turned on and others are turned off. The expression of the genotype determines the **phenotype** of an organism. The phenotype depends on the genotype of the organism as well as the environment, and therefore can change as the environment changes.

MICROCHECK 8.1

The properties of bacteria can change either through mutations, or by acquiring genetic information from other sources.

- ✓ Contrast genotype and phenotype.
- ✓ Which has a longer-lived effect on a cell, a change in the genotype, or a change in the phenotype? Explain.

GENE MUTATION AS A SOURCE OF DIVERSITY

Mutation is a change in the DNA base sequence of the **wild-type** organism. The latter is a strain whose properties are similar to the organism isolated from nature. The change in a nucleotide or nucleotide sequence may lead to an altered phenotype, or it may not lead to any observable change in which case it is called a **silent mutation.** A change in phenotype results when the protein coded by the gene does not function. The substitution of even one amino acid for another in a critical location in the protein such as in the catalytic site may cause the protein to be non-functional, thereby changing the properties of the cell. For example, if any gene of the tryptophan operon is altered so that the enzyme for which it codes no longer functions, the cells will grow only if this amino acid is in its environment. A mutant that requires a growth factor is called an **auxotroph** (*auxo* means "increase" as an increase in requirements). Cells that grow in the absence of any added growth factors are termed **prototrophs.** ■ enzymes, pp. 134, 139 ■ protein structure, p. 29 ■ operon, p. 183

By convention, the phenotype of a cell is designated by a three-letter abbreviation. A cell that requires tryptophan for growth is designated Trp^-, the superscript indicating the requirement for growth. The first letter is in caps. Each growth factor has its own three-letter designation. If a cell grows without the addition of tryptophan, then it is Trp^+. However, it is cumbersome to indicate all of the growth factors that are not required, so only the growth factors that are required are indicated. Likewise, only if a cell is resistant to an antimicrobial agent such as streptomycin is this indicated, such as Str^R. Otherwise, the cells are assumed to be sensitive, Str^S, and this is not indicated in the description of the phenotype of the cell.

Spontaneous mutations are those that occur in the natural environment. Mutations are observed infrequently and occur randomly, and each gene mutates spontaneously at a characteristic frequency. The **rate of mutation** is defined as the probability that a mutation will be observed in a given gene each time a cell divides; this rate is generally expressed in an exponential form. The mutation rate of different genes usually varies between 10^{-4} and 10^{-12} per cell division. In other words, the chances that any single gene will undergo a mutation when one cell divides into two are between one in 10,000 (10^{-4}) and one in a trillion (10^{-12}). Mutations would be observed much more frequently than they are if it were not for several different **repair mechanisms** that all cells possess. These mechanisms correct any mistakes or damage in DNA before they become established in the cell and are passed on to progeny cells. These repair mechanisms will be discussed shortly. ■ exponents, Appendix I, p. A–1

Mutations are stable, so that the progeny of streptomycin-sensitive cells that mutate to streptomycin resistance will remain streptomycin-resistant. On rare occasions, however, the nucleotide will change back to its original state, resulting in the streptomycin-resistant cells becoming streptomycin-sensitive. The change in a cell's genotype and phenotype to its original state through a change in the mutated gene is termed **reversion.** It occurs spontaneously at low frequencies.

8.2

Spontaneous Mutations

Focus Points

- Name three types of mutations that can occur spontaneously.
- Name three types of mutations that can result from base substitutions.

Base Substitution

The most common type of mutation results from a mistake during DNA synthesis, when an incorrect base is incorporated into the DNA, an event called **base substitution (figure 8.2).** If only one base pair is changed, the mutation is called a **point mutation.** This mistake in incorporation is passed on to the cell's progeny, often resulting in an incorrect amino acid being incorporated into the protein coded by the gene (see figure 8.2). A point mutation which results in the substitution of a different amino acid is termed a **missense mutation.** Frequently, the incorporation of an incorrect amino acid results in the synthesis of a protein that still partially functions. For example, a mutation in a gene of

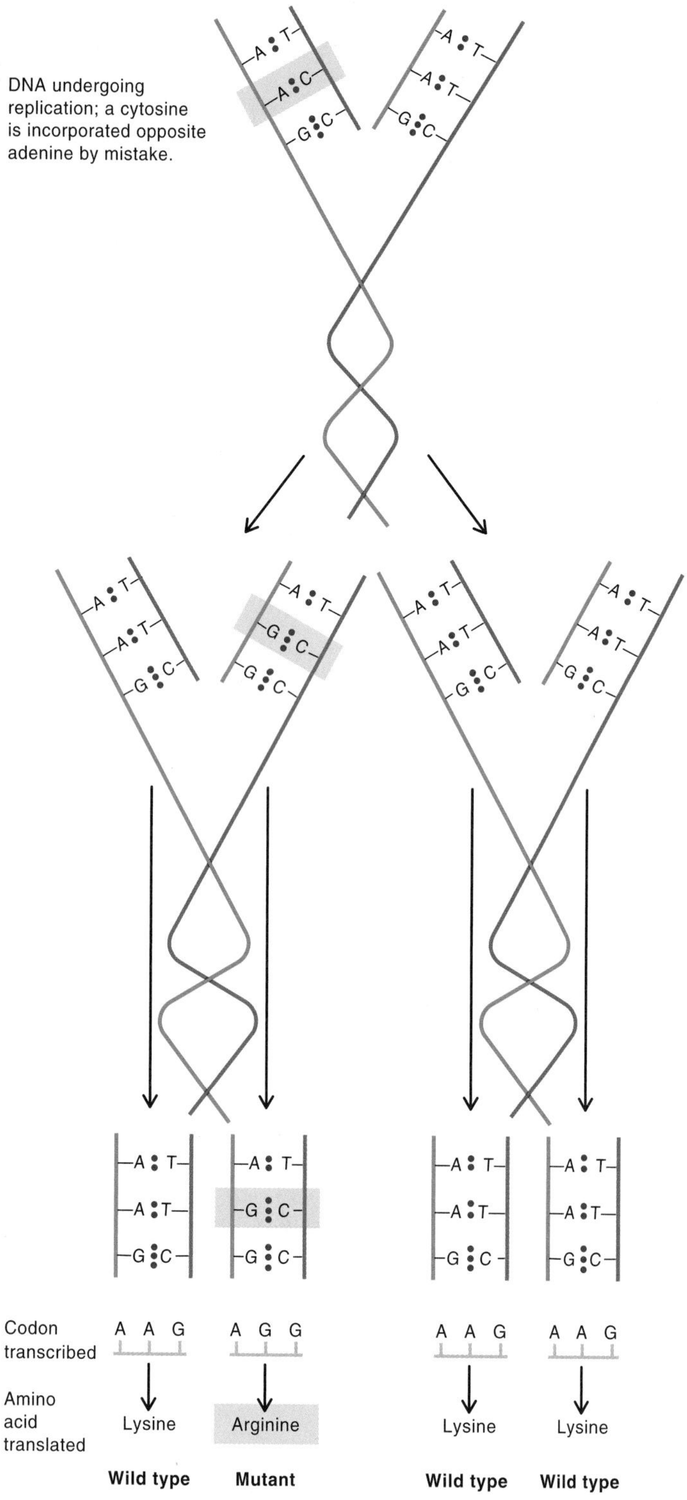

FIGURE 8.2 Base Substitution Shown here is the generation of a mutant organism as a result of the incorporation of a pyrimidine base (cytosine) in place of thymine in DNA replication. The mutation is a missense mutation.

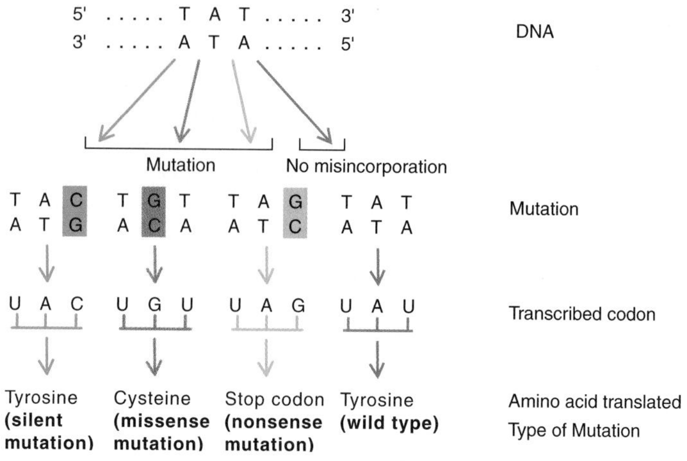

FIGURE 8.3 Types of Mutations Resulting from Base Substitutions

tryptophan biosynthesis may result in a strain that grows slowly in the absence of tryptophan. Such a mutation is termed **leaky.** A mutation that changes a codon that normally encodes an amino acid to a **stop codon** is called a **nonsense mutation.** Any mutation that totally inactivates the gene resulting in a strain that is unable to grow at all unless tryptophan is added is termed a **null** or **knockout** mutation. ■ stop codon, p. 179

Base substitutions can increase because of oxygen in the environment. As discussed in chapter 4, oxygen can be readily converted through cellular metabolism or by environmental factors into forms of oxygen that are highly toxic to cells. In part, this toxicity results from these **reactive forms of oxygen** damaging cellular DNA and causing mutations. One of the most important effects is the formation of an oxidized form of guanine after it has been incorporated into DNA. DNA polymerase often mispairs this oxidized guanine with adenine rather than cytosine, thereby resulting in a point mutation and base substitutions.

The possible outcomes of base substitutions are shown in **figure 8.3.**

Removal or Addition of Nucleotides

The deletion (removal) or addition of one or several nucleotides also changes the nucleotide sequence. Large pieces of DNA, encompassing many genes, sometimes are deleted. Because translation of a gene begins at a specific codon and proceeds one codon at a time, the deletion or addition of a nucleotide shifts the codons of the DNA when it is transcribed into mRNA (**figure 8.4**). This type of mutation is termed a **frameshift mutation.** If three nucleotides are added or removed, however, then a single amino acid usually will be added to or subtracted from the protein encoded by the DNA. ■ codon, p. 176 ■ translation, p. 176

A frameshift affects all amino acids incorporated beyond the original site at which the addition or deletion occurred. Frequently, one of the many new codons generated by the frameshift will be a **stop codon,** as in figure 8.4, so that the protein synthesized will be incomplete and non-functional. Frameshift mutations change many more codons than are changed by the substitution of a single base, and so they commonly result in a knockout mutation. The transcription and translation of downstream genes in the same operon are not affected. ■ operon, p. 183 ■ downstream genes, p. 174

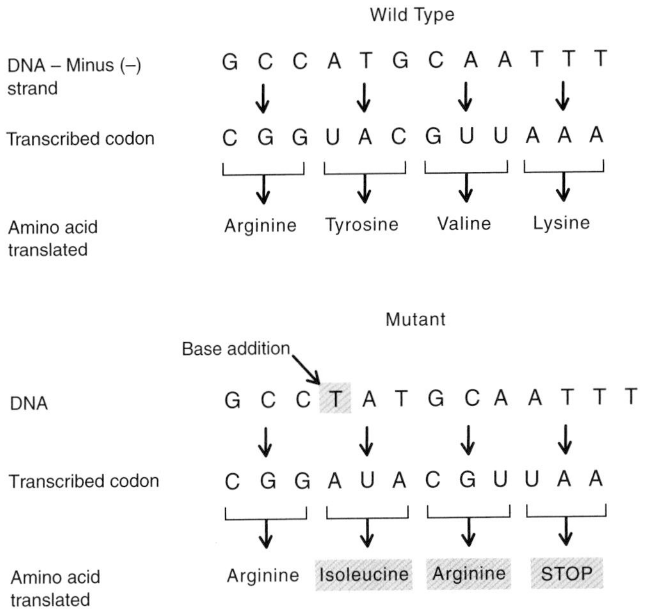

FIGURE 8.4 Frameshift Mutation As a Result of Base Addition The addition of a nucleotide (T) to the DNA results in a frameshift when the DNA is transcribed into mRNA and a new triplet code word is translated as a new amino acid. The deletion of a nucleotide would have essentially the same effect. The protein chain terminates when a stop codon appears in the DNA.

Transposable Elements (Jumping Genes)

Transposable elements, also called **transposons** or jumping genes, are special segments of DNA that can move spontaneously from one site to another in the same or different DNA molecules, a process called **transposition.** Any gene into which a transposable element inserts itself is disrupted, and no longer codes for a functional protein **(figure 8.5).** The gene usually suffers a knockout mutation in transposition. Genes downstream of the original mutation in the same operon may also be affected in transcription and translation. The structure and biology of transposons will be considered later in this chapter.

The classic studies of transposition were carried out by Dr. Barbara McClintock (see **A Glimpse of History**). She observed variation in the colors of kernels of corn as a result of transposons moving into and out of genes concerned with pigment synthesis **(figure 8.6).**

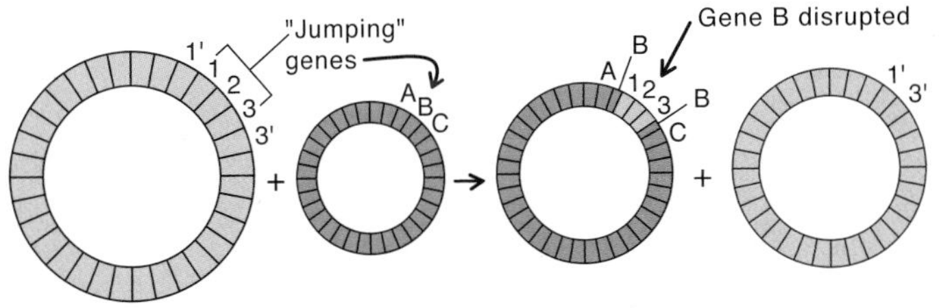

FIGURE 8.5 Transposition The transposon (genes 1, 2, 3), has the ability to "jump" from one piece of DNA to another, where it becomes integrated. In this case, the transposon has jumped into gene B, thereby mutating it.

FIGURE 8.6 Transposition Detected by Color Changes Variegation in color observed in the kernels of corn is caused by the insertion of transposable elements into genes involved in the synthesis of different pigments, thereby altering the synthesis of the pigments.

MICROCHECK 8.2

Mutations, changes in the nucleotide sequence of DNA, may result in proteins that are non-functional, thereby altering the properties of the cell. A leaky mutation results in a partially functional protein; a knockout mutation results in a non-functional protein. Mutations most commonly occur spontaneously as a result of mistakes in DNA replication, in some cases because reactive oxygen molecules have modified the guanine in DNA.

- ✓ How would the growth requirements change in a cell that has a silent mutation in a gene for histidine synthesis? How would it change if the mutation were a knockout?
- ✓ Would the addition of three bases to DNA always lead to a frameshift mutation? Explain your answer.

8.3 Induced Mutations

Focus Points

- Name four mechanisms by which mutagens act on DNA.
- Describe the effect of UV light on DNA.

Mutants are essential for studying and understanding most aspects of genetics. Consequently, geneticists spend much of their time isolating mutants. One reason why bacteria represent an excellent experimental system for genetic studies and why more is known about *E. coli* than any other organism in the world is because bacterial mutants with a broad range of properties are easier to isolate than mutants in any other system. Bacteria grow rapidly to enormous numbers in very small volumes of inexpensive media. Thus, rare mutations will be represented in a small volume of medium. Further, being haploid means that the mutation will not be obscured by a wild-type gene.

Even with these advantages, however, the frequency of spontaneous mutations is so low that investigators trying to isolate certain mutants generally resort to using **mutagens,** chemicals or radiation that can increase the frequency of mutations at least 1,000-fold. Such mutations are said to be **induced.**

Chemical Mutagens

Any chemical treatment that alters the hydrogen-bonding properties of a purine or pyrimidine base already in the DNA will increase the frequency of mutations as the DNA replicates.

Chemical Modification of Purines and Pyrimidines

One powerful mutagen that modifies purines and pyrimidines in DNA is nitrous acid (HNO_2). This chemical primarily converts amino ($^-NH_2$) to keto ($^-C{=}O$) groups—for example, converting cytosine to uracil. Uracil then pairs with adenine rather than guanine when the DNA is replicated. Nitrous acid also removes amino groups from adenine and guanine. ■ purines and pyrimidines, p. 34

The largest group of chemical mutagens consists of **alkylating agents,** highly reactive chemicals that add **alkyl groups,** short chains of carbon atoms, onto purines and pyrimidines, thereby altering their hydrogen-bonding properties. A common alkylating agent used in research laboratories is **nitrosoguanidine.** Many compounds formerly used in cancer therapy, such as nitrogen mustard, are in this group. These compounds kill rapidly dividing cancer cells, but they also damage DNA in normal cells. As a result, these agents have caused cancers which appear more than 10 years after they were used to treat the original cancer.

Base Analogs

Base analogs are compounds that resemble the purine or pyrimidine bases closely enough that they are incorporated into DNA in place of the natural bases during DNA replication **(figure 8.7).** Base analogs such as 5-bromouracil and 2-amino purine, however, do not have the same hydrogen-bonding properties as the natural bases, thymine and adenine respectively. This difference increases the probability that, once incorporated into DNA, the base analog will pair with the wrong base as the complementary strand is being synthesized. ■ DNA replication, p. 170

Intercalating Agents

A number of chemical mutagens, termed **intercalating agents,** increase the frequency of frameshift mutations. These mutagens are planar molecules of about the same size as a pair of nucleotides in DNA. These molecules do not alter hydrogen-bonding properties of the bases; rather, they insert or intercalate between adjacent base pairs in one of the strands of DNA. This pushes the nucleotides apart, producing enough space between bases that an extra nucleotide often is added in the strand being synthesized. The result is a frameshift mutation **(figure 8.8).** Less frequently, the intercalation results in a

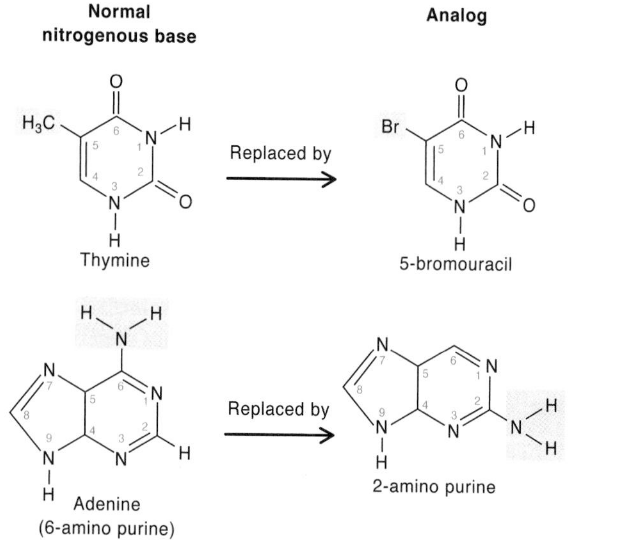

FIGURE 8.7 Common Base Analogs and the Normal Bases They Replace in DNA The important differences between the normal bases and the analogs are in boxes. Like the natural bases, they are incorporated as nucleotides into replicating DNA.

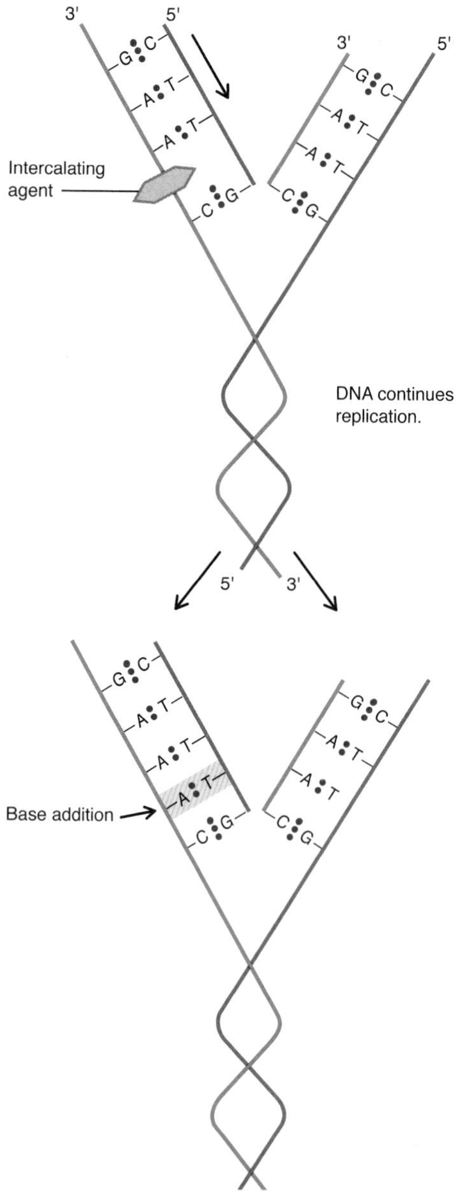

FIGURE 8.8 Base Addition in Newly Synthesized Strand of DNA Caused by An Intercalating Agent The intercalating agent pushes nucleotides apart when it intercalates in the old strand. This allows for an additional base in the newly synthesized strand.

newly synthesized strand that lacks a nucleotide. As in spontaneous frameshift mutants, the addition or subtraction of a nucleotide often results in a stop codon being generated prematurely, and a shortened protein being synthesized. An intercalating agent commonly used in the laboratory to stain DNA is **ethidium bromide.** The manufacturer now warns users that ethidium bromide should be used with great care because it likely is a **carcinogen,** a cancer-causing agent. Another intercalating agent is chloroquine, which has been used for many years to treat malaria. ■ replication fork, p. 170

Transposition

A common procedure to generate mutants in research laboratories is to introduce a transposon into a cell. The transposon, which cannot replicate on its own, must integrate into the cell's genome in order to replicate. The gene into which the transposon has inserted will usually be inactivated as a result of the **insertion.**

Radiation

Two kinds of radiation are mutagens: ultraviolet (UV) light and X rays. ■ wavelengths of radiation, p. 120

Ultraviolet Irradiation

Irradiation of cells with ultraviolet light causes covalent bond formation between adjacent thymine molecules on the same strand of DNA (intrastrand bonding), resulting in the formation of **thymine dimers (figure 8.9).** The covalent bonding distorts the DNA strand so much that the dimer cannot fit properly into the double helix, and the DNA is damaged. DNA cannot be replicated nor can genes be transcribed beyond this site of damage. As a result, the cells could die. How then can UV light be mutagenic? The major mutagenic action of UV light, results from the cell's attempt to repair the damage by a mechanism termed **SOS repair** (see the next section). ■ gene transcription, p. 174

X Rays

X rays cause several types of damage: single- and double-strand breaks in DNA, and alterations to the bases. Double-strand breaks often result in deletions that are lethal.

Table 8.1 summarizes information on the common mutagens.

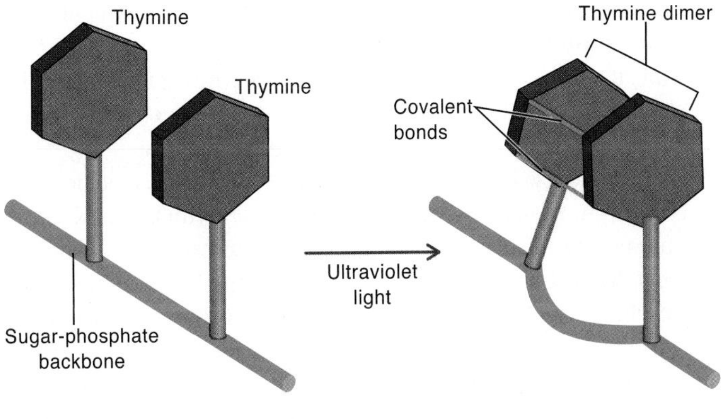

FIGURE 8.9 Thymine Dimer Formation Convalent bonds form between adjacent thymine molecules on the same strand of DNA when DNA is exposed to UV light. This distorts the shape of the DNA and prevents replication past the dimer.

TABLE 8.1 Common Mutagens

Agent	Action	Result
Chemical Agent		
Base analogs Example: 5-bromouracil	Incorporates in place of normal nucleotide in DNA	Base substitution
Intercalating agents Example: ethidium bromide	Inserts between base pairs in either the template or new strand	Addition or subtraction of base pairs
Chemical modification of bases Examples: nitrous acid	Converts amino group to keto group in adenine and cytosine	Base substitution
alkylating agents	Adds alkyl groups (CH_3 and others) to nitrogenous bases such as guanine	Base substitution
Transposons	Random insertion into any gene	Insertional inactivation
Radiation		
Ultraviolet (UV)	Intrastrand thymine dimer formation	Base substitution
X rays	Single- and double-strand breaks in DNA	Deletion of bases

MICROCHECK 8.3

The frequency of spontaneous mutations can be increased significantly by treating cells with chemicals and radiation. These treatments induce mutations. Mutations most frequently result from altering the hydrogen-bonding properties of the nitrogenous bases.

- ✓ How does UV light affect cells?
- ✓ If you wished to isolate a point mutant, what mutagen would you use? To isolate a knockout mutant?
- ✓ Do you think that mutations caused by reactive oxygen should be considered spontaneous or induced mutations? Justify your answer.

8.4 Repair of Damaged DNA

Focus Points

- Explain how DNA polymerase can correct base substitutions and prevent misincorporation of nucleotides.
- Explain the three mechanisms by which UV light damage can be repaired.
- Explain how a mutation caused by reactive oxygen is repaired.

Probably no function is more important to a cell than being able to repair damaged DNA. No molecule is more critical to the cell than its DNA. The amount of spontaneous and mutagen-induced damage to DNA that occurs in cells is enormous. Every 24 hours, the DNA in every cell in the human body is damaged spontaneously more than 10,000 times. This damage, if not repaired, can lead to cell death and, in animals, cancer. In humans, two breast cancer susceptibility genes code for enzymes that repair damaged DNA. Mutations in either one result in a high (80%) probability of breast cancer.

A major reason why mutations are so rare is that they are repaired shortly after they occur and before they can alter the properties of cells. It is not surprising that, in the course of many millions of years of evolution, all cells, both prokaryotic and eukaryotic, have developed several different mechanisms for repairing any damage that their DNA might suffer. Except for the light repair of UV dimers, the mechanisms that we will discuss operate on all types of damaged DNA.

Repair of Errors in Base Incorporation

A major cause of spontaneous mutation occurs during DNA replication—the incorporation of the wrong base by DNA polymerase. This complex enzyme selects a nucleotide with the proper base to hydrogen bond to the complementary base in the template strand. On rare occasions, however, the wrong nucleotide is selected, so that hydrogen bonding to the base in the template strand is faulty. This leads to a slight distortion in the DNA helix and, if it remains, results in a mutation. Cells have developed two ways of dealing with these errors. One is carried out by the DNA polymerase itself and is called **proofreading.** A second mechanism, called **mismatch repair,** involves several enzymes which cut and degrade single-stranded DNA. ■ DNA replication, p. 170 ■ DNA polymerase, p. 171

Proofreading by DNA Polymerase

DNA polymerase is a complex enzyme that not only is involved in the synthesis of DNA but also has a proofreading function. This enzyme can back up and excise any nucleotide that is not correctly hydrogen bonded to the base in the template strand. Following excision, the DNA polymerase then selects the proper nucleotide and incorporates it into the growing DNA strand.

Mismatch Repair

The proofreading function of DNA polymerase is very efficient. Cells, however, have a backup repair system, mismatch repair, that recognizes incorrect bases missed by the proofreading of DNA polymerase. In this process, the mismatch repair enzyme, an **endonuclease,** cuts the single-stranded DNA near the distortion. Another enzyme then degrades the single-stranded DNA and DNA polymerase synthesizes a new strand with the proper bases. PNA ligase joins this strand to the original strand which underwent excision. **(figure 8.10).** ■ DNA ligase, p. 173

If the template strand were excised, rather than the newly synthesized strand, the mutation would remain. How does the cell know which strand to excise? Certain adenine bases in DNA become methylated. However, immediately after the new strand is synthesized, these bases are not yet methylated. This difference distinguishes old and newly synthesized strands of DNA and allows the endonuclease to cleave the newly synthesized strand.

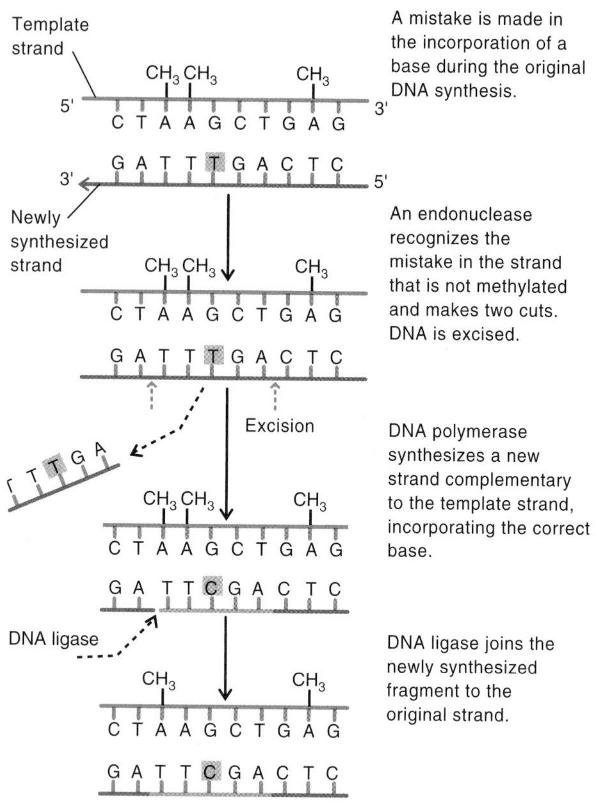
Template strand
CH_3 CH_3
CH_3
5'
3'
C T A A G C T G A G
G A T T T G A C T C
3'
5'
A mistake is made in the incorporation of a base during the original DNA synthesis.
Newly synthesized strand
An endonuclease recognizes the mistake in the strand that is not methylated and makes two cuts. DNA is excised.
Excision
DNA polymerase synthesizes a new strand complementary to the template strand, incorporating the correct base.
G A T T C G A C T C
DNA ligase
DNA ligase joins the newly synthesized fragment to the original strand.

FIGURE 8.10 Mismatch Repair The endonuclease excises a piece of DNA containing the misincorporated nucleotide in the newly synthesized strand. A new complementary strand is then synthesized and joined to the original strand by DNA ligase.

Mismatch repair also occurs in humans. Defects in this repair system lead to an increased incidence of colorectal cancers.

Repair of Thymine Dimers

Since UV light is a part of sunlight, cells are frequently exposed to this mutagenic agent in their natural environment. Many bacteria and other organisms, including people, have developed several mechanisms to combat the harmful effects of these rays which result in thymine dimer formation and a major resulting distortion of the DNA.

In one mechanism, an enzyme can break the covalent bond of thymine dimers, but only in the presence of visible light. The enzyme uses the light energy to cleave the covalent bond. This mechanism is called **light repair** or **photoreactivation** and restores the DNA to its original state **(figure 8.11a).**

Some bacteria have an endonuclease that recognizes major distortions in DNA. Major distortions are caused by thymine dimer formation but not by mismatched bases. The enzyme excises the damaged segment from a single strand of DNA and another enzyme repairs the resulting break by synthesizing a strand complementary to the undamaged strand. The repaired strand is then joined to the one end of the undamaged region by DNA ligase (figure 8.11b). This process is termed **excision repair** and corrects damage that causes a major localized distortion in DNA. Because visible light is not required for the action of these enzymes, such repair is also called **dark repair.**

This same repair mechanism is also important to the well-being of humans. People exposed to the sun, with its UV light, for long periods have a higher incidence of skin cancer than people who are not exposed. Also, people who have a defective dark repair enzyme have an increased incidence of skin cancer. This illustrates both the damage UV light can cause to DNA and the importance of repair mechanisms in overcoming the damage.

Repair of Modified Bases in DNA

The oxidized form of guanine, (G–O), resulting from reactive oxygen, is frequently found in DNA and causes a high proportion of the spontaneous base substitutions when the DNA replicates. Bacteria have several mechanisms for avoiding the mutations. In one mechanism, the bond between the oxidized guanine and deoxyribose is broken by an enzyme termed **glycosylase,** which removes the oxidized guanine. The glycosylase cuts the DNA backbone on either side of the removed base; DNA polymerase then incorporates an undamaged guanine nucleotide **(figure 8.12).** Cells have other specific glycosylases that

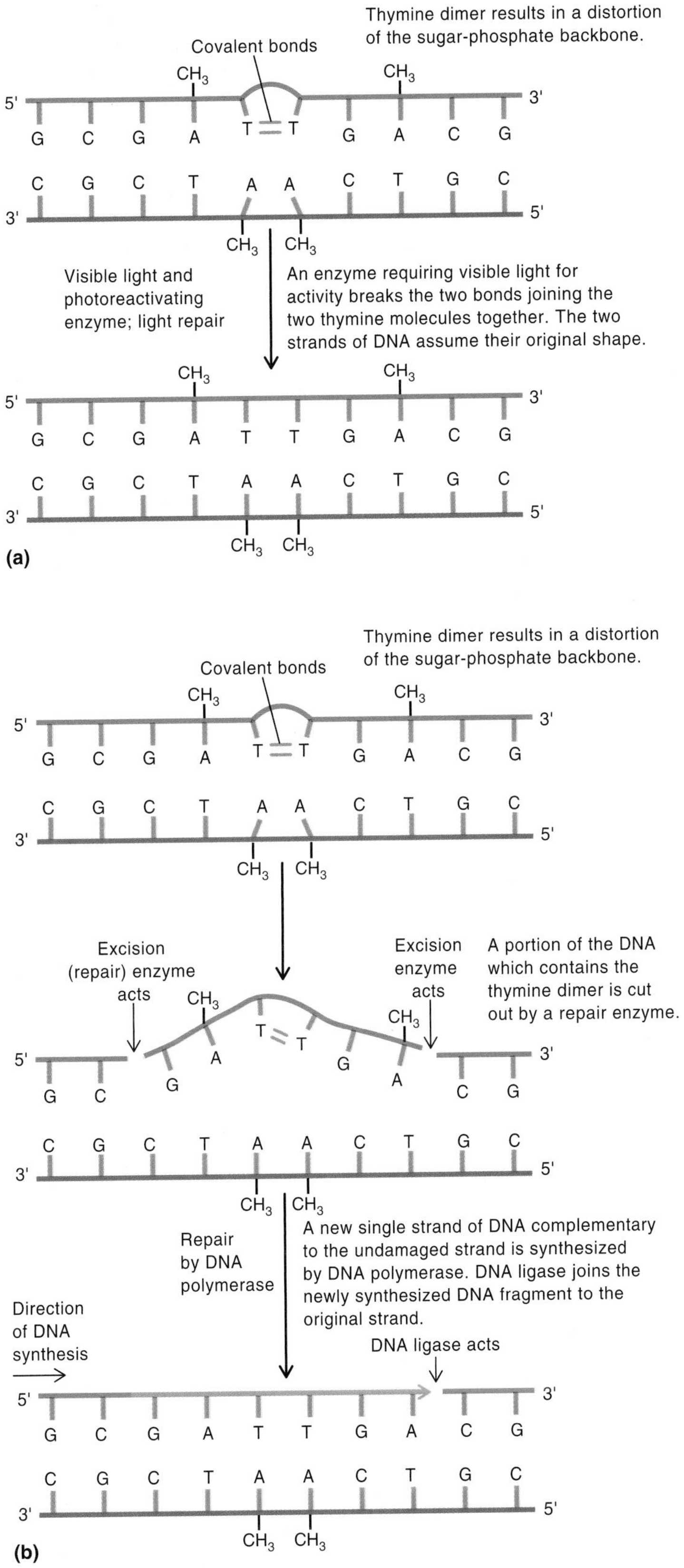

FIGURE 8.11 Repair of Thymine Dimers (a) In light repair, a light-requiring enzyme breaks the two covalent bonds (photoreactivation). **(b)** In dark, or excision, repair, the single strand of DNA containing the thymine dimer is removed and destroyed. The newly synthesized strand is joined to the end of the original strand by the enzyme DNA ligase. Light is not required, the newly synthesized strand is not methylated immediately after synthesis.

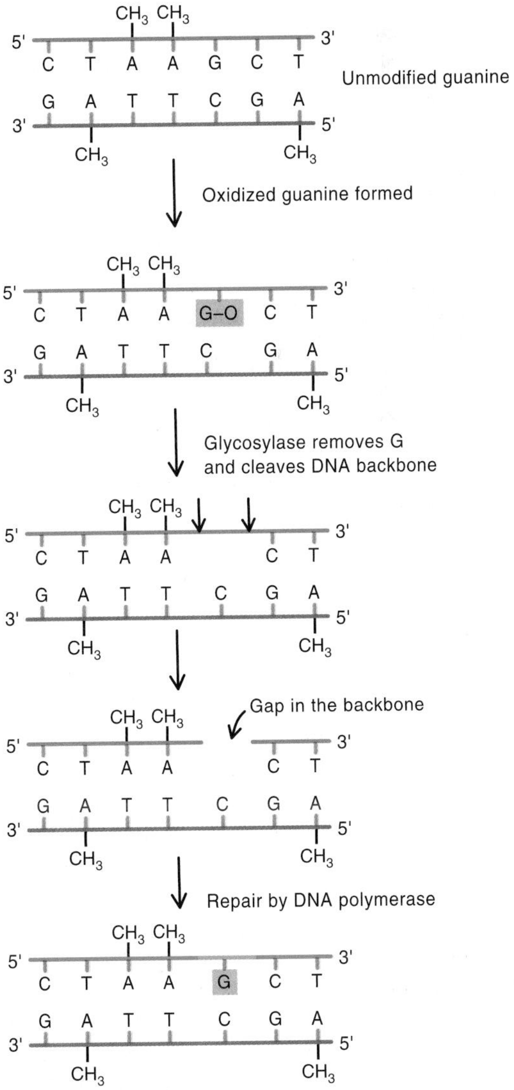

FIGURE 8.12 Repair of Oxidized Guanine in DNA In this diagram the correct base cytosine is based-paired with oxidized guanine, G–O.

remove alkylated bases. Following removal, the same repair mechanisms operate as shown in figure 8.12.

Humans have repair enzymes analogous to glycosylases in bacteria. Mutations in the genes coding for these enzymes result in an increased rate of colon cancer.

SOS Repair

If DNA is very heavily damaged by UV light such that it contains many thymine dimers, then light and excision repair may not be able to correct all of the dimers and the cells will die. Therefore, bacteria have a mechanism, termed **SOS repair,** that is a last ditch mechanism to bypass the damaged DNA and allow replication to continue. The damaged DNA induces the SOS system, which comprises over 30 genes. One of the most important activated gene products is a new DNA polymerase that is able to bypass the damaged DNA. However, unlike the standard DNA-replicating machinery which is relatively error-free, but cannot copy past the lesion, this newly activated polymerase makes many mistakes and incorporates the wrong bases in the DNA strand it is synthesizing. As a result, mutations arise.

Table 8.2 summarizes the key features of the major DNA repair systems in bacteria. Note that the cell cannot repair all types of mutations, such as insertional inactivation caused by transposition.

MICROCHECK 8.4

Bacteria can repair damaged DNA that contains errors resulting from the incorporation of wrong nucleotides by a variety of mechanisms. These include proofreading by DNA polymerase, and excising the nucleotide errors by mismatch repair. Specific glycosylases can remove modified bases. Thymine dimers can be repaired through light and dark repair mechanisms, severe damage can be overcome by the SOS repair system.

- ✓ How does UV light cause mutations?
- ✓ Distinguish between light and dark repair of thymine dimers.
- ✓ Give an example of a mutagen that causes a major distortion in DNA; a minor distortion.
- ✓ If you wish to maximize the number of mutations following UV irradiation, should you incubate the irradiated cells in the light or in the dark, or does it make any difference? Explain your answer.

8.5 Mutations and Their Consequences

Focus Point

- Explain how mutations relate to natural selection.

Because of mutations, the concept that all cells arising from a single cell are identical is not strictly true, since every large population

TABLE 8.2 Repair of Damaged DNA

	Type of Defect	Repair Mechanism	Biochemical Mechanism	Result
Spontaneous	Wrong base incorporated during DNA replication	Proofreading by DNA polymerase	Removal of mispaired base by DNA polymerase	Potential mutation eliminated
		Mismatch repair	Excision of short stretch of single-stranded DNA and synthesis of new strand by DNA polymerase	Potential mutation in non-methylated DNA eliminated
	Reactive oxygen forms oxidized guanine in DNA.	Action of glycosylase	Glycosylase removes the oxidized guanine. Short piece of DNA degraded and guanine incorporated.	Potential mutation eliminated
Mutagen—Induced				
Chemical	Wrong base incorporated during DNA replication	Same as for spontaneous mutations	Same as for spontaneous mutations	Same as for spontaneous mutations
UV light	Thymine dimer formation	Photoreactivation (light repair)	Breaking of covalent bond forming thymine molecules	Original DNA molecule restored
		Excision repair (dark repair)	Excision of a short stretch of single-stranded DNA containing thymine dimer and synthesis of a new strand by DNA polymerase	Mutation eliminated
		SOS repair	DNA synthesis by a new DNA polymerase bypasses damaged DNA.	Cell survives but numerous mutations are generated.

contains mutants. Even the cells in a single colony that contains about 1 million cells are not completely identical because of spontaneous random mutations. These mutations provide a mechanism by which organisms, with their altered characteristics, can respond to a changing environment. This is the process of **natural selection.** The environment, however, does not cause the mutation but rather selects those cells that can grow under its conditions. Thus, a spontaneous mutation to antimicrobial resistance, though rare, will result in the mutant becoming the dominant organism in a hospital environment where the antimicrobial medication is present, because only the resistant cells can survive. The antimicrobial kills the sensitive cells and thereby allows the resistant cells to take over the population.

Genes mutate independently of one another. Consequently, the chance that two given mutations will occur within the same cell is very low. Indeed, the actual occurrence is the product of the individual rates of mutation of the two genes (calculated by taking the sum of the exponents). For example, if the mutation rate to streptomycin resistance is 10^{-6} per cell division and the mutation rate to penicillin resistance is 10^{-8} per cell division, the probability that both mutations will occur within the same cell is $10^{-6} \times 10^{-8}$, or 10^{-14}. For this reason, two or more drugs may be administered simultaneously in the treatment of some diseases such as tuberculosis and AIDS. This is called **combination therapy.** Any mutant cell or virus resistant to one antimicrobial medication is likely to be sensitive to the other and therefore will be killed by the combination of the two antimicrobials. ■ combination therapy, p. 511

MICROCHECK 8.5

Mutations occur randomly—they are not caused by agents that allow mutants to grow.

✓ If the rate of mutation to streptomycin resistance is 10^{-6} and to penicillin resistance is 10^{-4}, what is the rate of mutation to simultaneous resistance to both antibiotics?

✓ Is it as effective to take two antibiotics sequentially as it is to take them simultaneously, as long as the total length of time that they are both taken is the same? Explain.

8.6

Mutant Selection

Focus Point

- Distinguish between direct and indirect selection and how mutant of each type are selected.

Even when mutagens are used, mutations that appear in the population are rare. This presents a major challenge to the investigator who wants to isolate a desired mutant. Several clever techniques have simplified this process. As discussed in chapter 4, bacteria can multiply on simple media and produce several billion cells per milliliter of medium in less than 24 hours. In such a large population, every gene should be mutant in at least one cell in the population. The major problem becomes how to find and identify the bacteria containing the desired mutation. Depending on the type of mutant being sought, one of two simple techniques can be used, direct or indirect selection.

Direct Selection

Direct selection involves inoculating cells onto a medium on which the mutant, but not the parent, can grow. For example, mutants resistant to the antibiotic streptomycin can be easily selected directly by inoculating cells onto a medium containing streptomycin. Only the rare resistant cells in the population will form a colony **(figure 8.13).** Mutants resistant to antimicrobials are usually very easy to isolate by direct selection.

Indirect Selection

Indirect selection is required to isolate an auxotrophic mutant, one that requires a growth factor, such as histidine, which the parent strain does not. On a medium that contains histidine, both the parent and the histidine auxotroph grow. On a medium lacking histidine, the histidine-requiring mutant will not grow, but the parent will. There is no medium on which the mutant will grow and the parent will not. This complicates the selection. ■ growth factor, p. 98

Replica Plating

An ingenious technique for indirect selection of auxotrophic mutants, **replica plating,** was devised by the husband-and-wife team of Joshua and Esther Lederberg in the early 1950s **(figure 8.14).** In this technique, a master plate containing isolated colonies of all

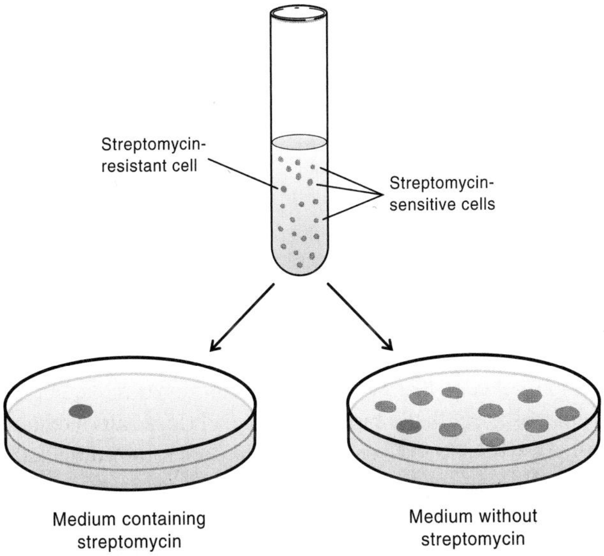

FIGURE 8.13 Direct Selection of Mutants Only the streptomycin-resistant cells will grow on the streptomycin-containing medium. All cells will grow on media without streptomycin and have the same appearance.

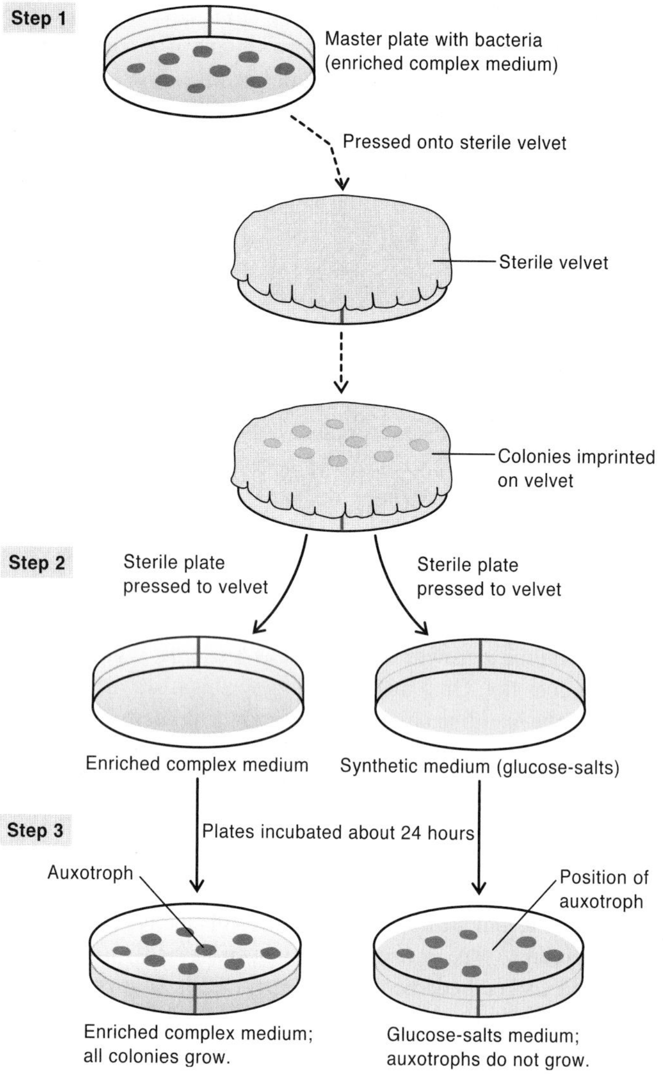

FIGURE 8.14 Indirect Selection of Mutants by Replica Plating The procedure shown is the one first used by the Lederbergs and continues to be used today in many laboratories.

cells growing on an enriched medium is pressed onto sterile velvet, a fabric with tiny threads that stand on end like tiny bristles (step 1). This operation transfers some cells of every bacterial colony onto the velvet. Next, two sterile plates, one containing a glucose-salts (minimal) medium and the second an enriched, complex medium, are pressed in succession onto the same velvet (step 2). This procedure transfers cells imprinted on the velvet from the master plate to both the glucose-salts medium and the enriched medium. Following incubation, all cells that do not have a nutritional requirement will form colonies on both the enriched and the glucose-salts medium, but auxotrophs will only form colonies on the enriched medium (step 3). ■ glucose-salts medium, p. 100

By keeping the orientation of the two plates the same as they touch the velvet, any colony on the master plate that can grow on the enriched medium but not on the glucose-salts medium can be identified. The particular growth factor required can then be determined by adding the various factors to the glucose-salts medium and determining which one promotes cell growth.

Penicillin Enrichment

Even using mutagenic agents, the frequency of mutation in a particular gene is low, ranging perhaps from less than one in 1,000 to one in 100 million cells. In cases where the parent cell is sensitive to penicillin, the proportion of auxotrophic mutants in the population can be increased by a technique called **penicillin enrichment.** Following treatment with a mutagen, the cells are grown in a glucose-salts medium containing penicillin. Since penicillin kills only growing cells, most of the cells that have no growth factor requirements will grow and so will be killed, while the non-multiplying auxotrophs will survive **(figure 8.15).** The enzyme **penicillinase** is then added to destroy the penicillin, and the cells are plated on an enriched medium. This plate can then be replica plated onto a glucose-salts medium. Any colonies that grow on the enriched medium but not on the glucose-salts medium must be auxotrophic—that is, require a growth factor. ■ action of penicillin, p. 64

Testing of Chemicals for Their Cancer-Causing Ability

Strong evidence exists that a substantial proportion of all cancers are caused by chemicals in the environment called **carcinogens.** How can the thousands of chemicals released into the environment, such as pesticides, herbicides, hair dyes, cosmetics, food additives and the by-products of manufacturing processes, be tested for their carcinogenic activity? Testing in animals takes 2 to 3 years and may cost $100,000 or more for the testing of a single compound. Today a number of much less expensive, more rapid, and simpler tests have been devised. All are based

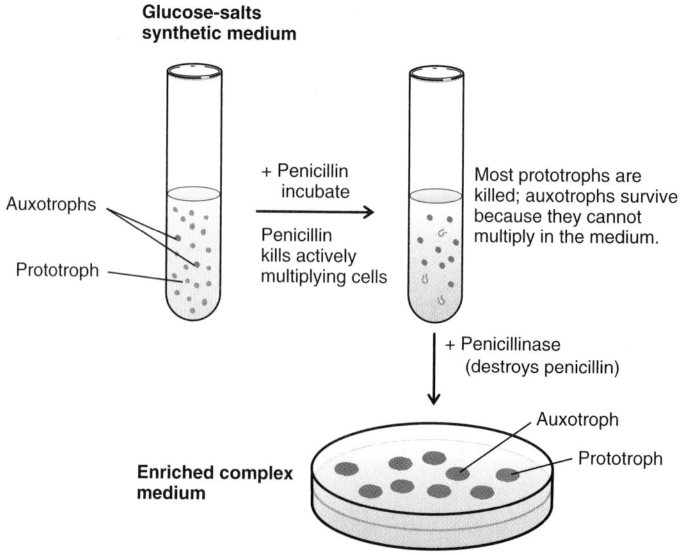

FIGURE 8.15 Penicillin Enrichment of Mutants Since auxtrophs require a growth factor to multiply, they are not killed.

on assaying the effect of the potential carcinogen on DNA in a microbiological system. The first one was devised by Bruce Ames and his colleagues in the 1960s and illustrates the concept of such tests. This test takes only a few days and is based on three facts: (1) the reversion of a mutant gene in a biosynthetic pathway, such as histidine biosynthesis, can be readily measured; (2) the frequency of reversions is increased by mutagens; and (3) most carcinogens are mutagens. Specifically, the Ames test measures the effect of a test chemical on the rate of reversion of a specific *Salmonella* strain, a histidine requiring auxotroph, to one that no longer requires histidine **(figure 8.16).** If the chemical is mutagenic, it will increase the reversion rate of the strain relative to that observed when no chemical is added (the control). The test also gives some idea about how powerful the mutagen is, and therefore how potentially hazardous the chemical is by the number of revertants that arise.

The Ames test as just discussed fails to detect many carcinogens, because some substances are not carcinogenic themselves but can be converted to active carcinogens by a metabolic reaction that occurs in animals but not in bacteria. Therefore, an extract of ground-up rat liver, which has the enzymes to carry out these conversions, is added to the Petri plates containing the suspected mutagen (carcinogen) being analyzed by the Ames test. To increase the sensitivity of the test, a mutant tester strain which lacks repair enzymes is often used. As a result reversions cannot be repaired.

Additional testing must be done on any mutagenic agent identified in the Ames test to confirm that it is actually carcinogenic in animals. Although data are not available on the percentage of mutagens that are carcinogens, it is clear that the Ames test is useful as a rapid screen test to identify those compounds that have a high probability of being carcinogenic. Thus far, no compound with a negative Ames test has been shown to be carcinogenic in animals.

MICROCHECK 8.6

Mutants can be selected using either direct techniques or indirect techniques such as replica plating. Penicillin enrichment can often help in the isolation of auxotrophic mutants by killing multiplying cells.

- ✓ Distinguish between the kinds of mutants that can be isolated by direct and indirect selection.
- ✓ When does penicillin enrichment not work?
- ✓ The Ames test measures the reversion of a mutant gene. Would it be just as good to test for the generation of a mutant gene rather than its reversion? Explain.
- ✓ How could you demonstrate by replica plating that the environment selects but does not mutate genes in bacteria?

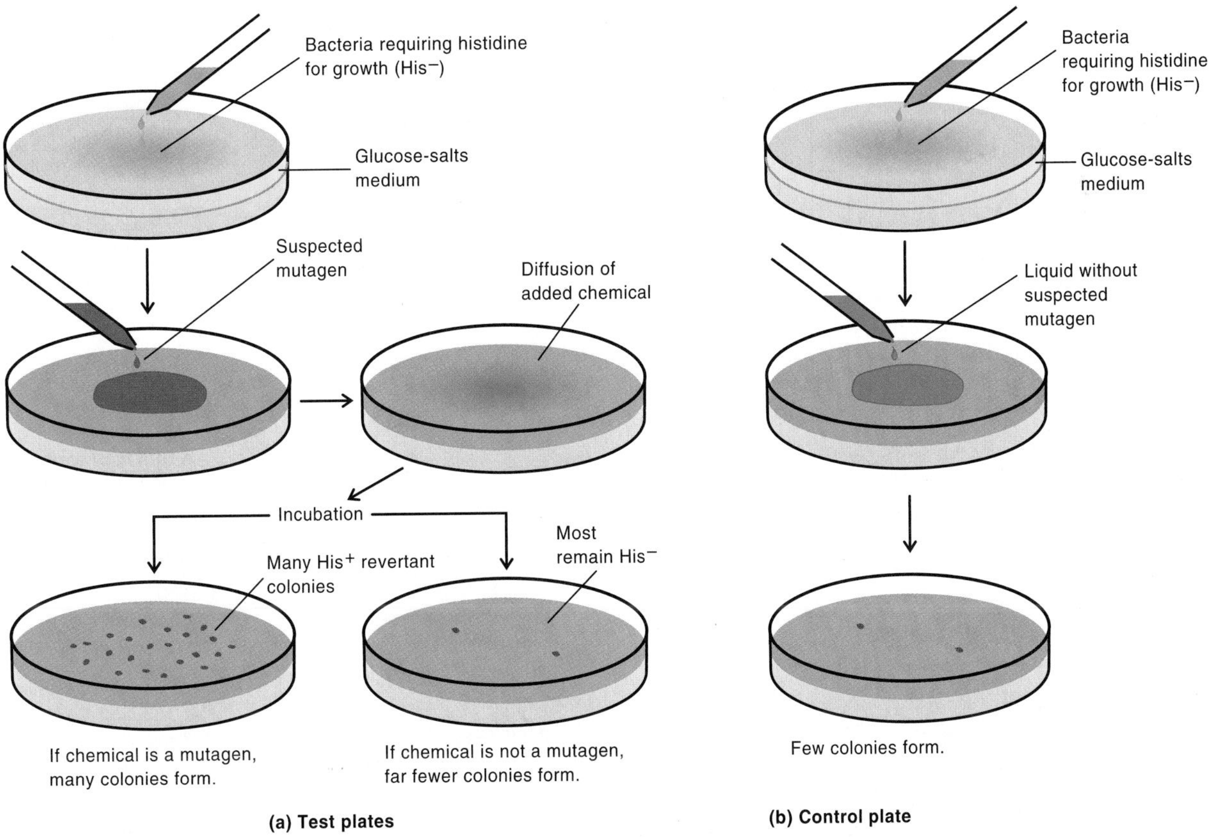

FIGURE 8.16 Ames Test to Screen for Mutagens (a) The chemical will increase the frequency of reversion of His^- to His^+ cells if it is a mutagen and, therefore, a potential carcinogen. **(b)** The control plate contains the liquid in which the suspected mutagen is dissolved.

GENE TRANSFER AS A SOURCE OF DIVERSITY

In addition to mutation, the genetic information in a cell can be altered if the cell gains genes from other cells. The movement of DNA from one cell to another, the process of **horizontal gene transfer,** accounts for the rapid spread of resistance to antimicrobial medications and heavy metals in bacterial populations, as described for *S. aureus* earlier in this chapter.

Gene transfer between bacteria can only be studied if genetic differences exist in the cells. These differences make it possible to determine whether **genetic recombination,** the combining of DNA or genes from two different cells, has occurred. Recombination in the DNA from two different bacteria mixed together can be readily recognized because the resulting cells, termed **recombinants,** have certain properties of each of the original bacteria. For example, when cells that are streptomycin resistant (Str^R) and require histidine (His^-) and tryptophan (Trp^-) to grow are mixed with cells that are killed by streptomycin (Str^S) and require leucine (Leu^-) and threonine (Thr^-), rare recombinants appear. These are resistant to streptomycin and grow on a glucose-salts medium—that is, the recombinants are His^+, Trp^+, Leu^+, Thr^+ and Str^R **(figure 8.17).** These recombinant cells contain a mixture of genes from the two original types of cells. Since the bacteria are usually haploid, such recombinants can arise only if DNA has been transferred from one cell, the **donor,** to another cell, the **recipient.** In all cases, genes must replicate if they are to be passed on to daughter cells and therefore have an origin of replication. If they do not, they must become part of a DNA molecule such as a chromosome or plasmid that can replicate. Such a molecule is termed a **replicon (figure 8.18).**
■ origin of replication, p. 172

Genes are naturally transferred between bacteria by three different mechanisms:

1. **DNA-mediated transformation,** in which DNA is transferred as "naked" DNA.

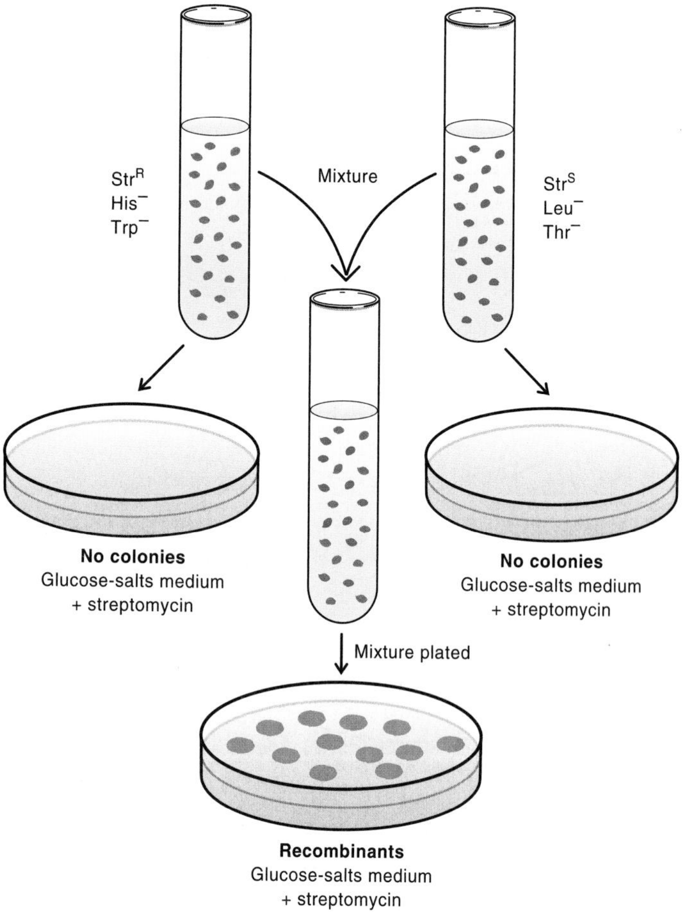

FIGURE 8.17 General Experimental Approach for Detecting Gene Transfer in Bacteria

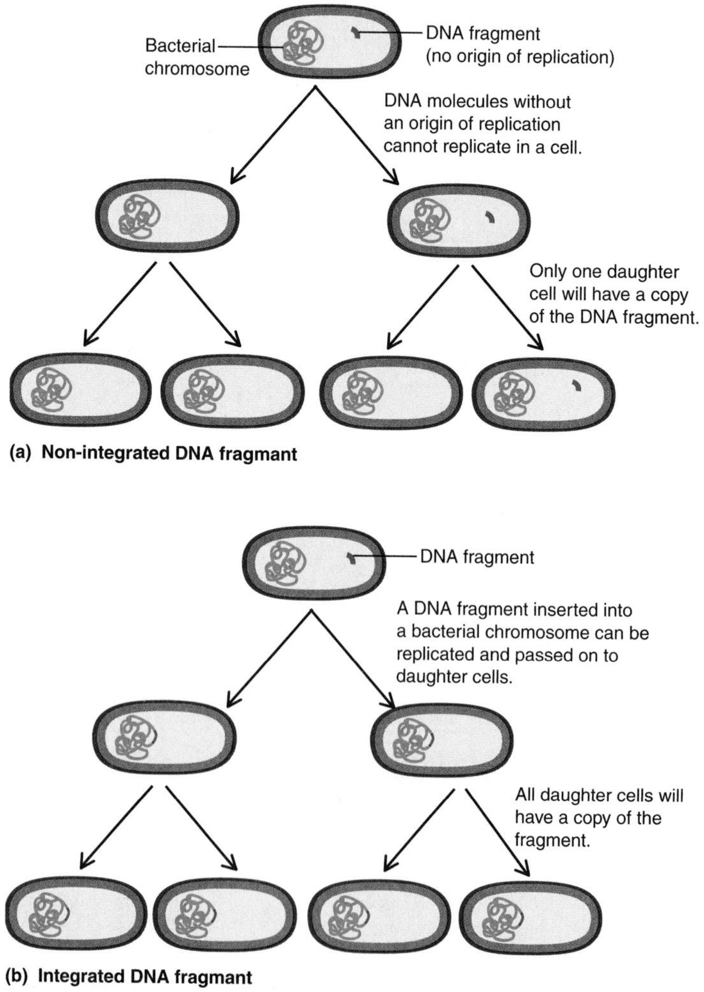

FIGURE 8.18 DNA Must Become Part of a Replicon in Order to Be Maintained in a Population of Cells The fragment of DNA will likely be destroyed by nucleases. A plasmid has an origin of replication and so can replicate.

2. **Transduction,** in which bacterial DNA is transferred by a bacterial virus.
3. **Conjugation,** in which DNA is transferred from one bacterium to another when the cells are in contact with one another.

To detect gene transfer, one can select directly for recombinant cells, by inoculating the mixture of cells on a medium on which only the recombinants will grow and form colonies. Non-recombinant bacteria are unable to grow. Since several billion bacteria can be inoculated onto the agar contained in a single Petri dish, a few recombinants in the billion cells can be detected readily.

8.7

DNA-Mediated Transformation

Focus Point

- Describe the process of DNA-mediated transformation.

DNA-mediated transformation, referred to commonly as DNA transformation, involves the transfer of "naked" DNA in the environment to recipient cells. If the cell walls of bacteria rupture, as frequently occurs in the stationary, death, and prolonged decline phases of bacterial growth, the long, circular molecules of chromosomal DNA that are tightly jammed into the bacteria break up into several hundred pieces as they explode through the broken cell walls. The pieces of DNA average about 20 genes each. Some of these DNA macromolecules pass through the cell walls and cytoplasmic membranes of the recipient cells and are then integrated into their chromosomes, replacing the homologous genes. ■ bacterial growth curve, p. 92

DNA-mediated transformation can occur naturally in a wide variety of Gram-positive and Gram-negative bacteria (see **Perspective 8.1**). In addition, the yeast *Saccharomyces cerevisiae*, a eukaryote, can be transformed.

Natural Competence

The process of DNA transformation involves recipient cells, termed **competent,** that have the unusual ability to take up and integrate donor DNA into their chromosome. The process occurs in a number of stages. First, DNA passes through the cell wall and cytoplasmic membrane. This is one of the most interesting aspects of the DNA transformation process. As discussed in chapter 3, usually only molecules whose molecular weight is no greater than a few hundred can pass through the cell envelope. It is still a mystery how DNA molecules, which are 100,000 times larger, can pass through. It is clear, however, that only under certain growth conditions can bacteria take up such large molecules of DNA. This often occurs near the end of the log phase of growth. Some bacteria take up DNA from any source; others take up only their own DNA. The mechanism by which a cell becomes competent is poorly understood, but apparently the cell undergoes a series of changes. These include modification of the cell wall and the synthesis of protein receptors on the cell surface that can bind DNA. Other **competence proteins** inside the cell are also synthesized, including those involved in the integration of donor DNA. Cells also can be made competent through artificial means in the laboratory, as will be discussed shortly. ■ log phase, p. 92

Entry of DNA

Although double-stranded DNA molecules bind to competent cells, single-stranded DNA enters. As one strand enters, nucleases at the cell surface degrade the other **(figure 8.19a,b).**

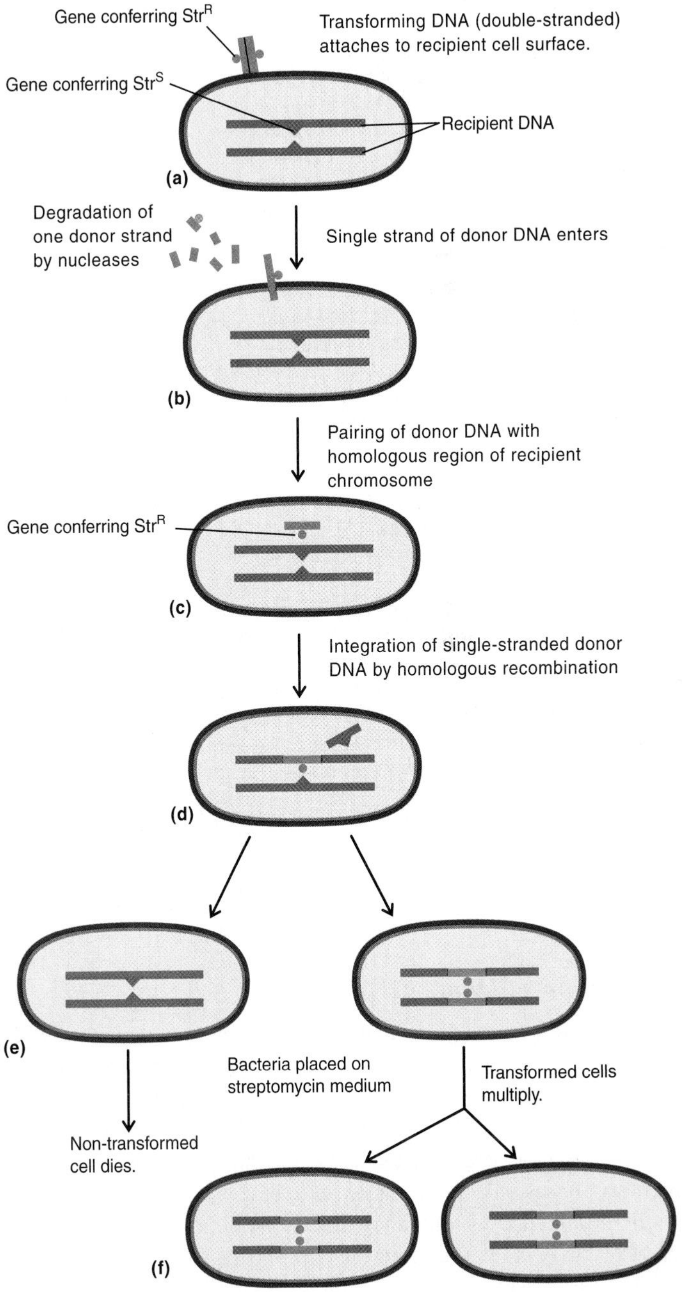

FIGURE 8.19 DNA-Mediated Transformation The donor DNA comes from a cell that is streptomycin resistant (Str^R). The recipient cell is streptomycin sensitive (Str^S).

PERSPECTIVE 8.1

The Biological Function of DNA: A Discovery Ahead of Its Time

In the 1930s, it was well known that DNA occurred in all cells, including bacteria. Its function, however, was a mystery. Since DNA consisted of only four repeating subunits, most scientists believed that it could not be a very important molecule. Its important biological role in the cell was discovered through a series of experiments conducted during a 20-year period by scientists in England and the United States.

In the 1920s, Frederick Griffith, an English bacteriologist, was studying pneumococci, the bacteria that cause pneumonia. It was known that pneumococci could cause this disease only if they made a polysaccharide capsule. In trying to understand the role of this capsule in the disease, Griffith killed encapsulated pneumococci and mixed them with living mutant pneumococci that could not synthesize a polysaccharide capsule. When he inoculated this mixture of organisms into mice, much to his surprise, they developed pneumonia and died **(figure 1).** Griffith isolated living encapsulated pneumococci from the dead mice. When he injected the killed encapsulated organisms and living non-encapsulated organisms into separate mice, they did not develop pneumonia.

Two years after Griffith reported these findings, another investigator, M. H. Dawson, lysed heat-killed encapsulated pneumococci and passed the suspension of ruptured cells through a very fine filter, through which only the cytoplasmic contents of the bacteria could pass. When he mixed the filtrate (the material passing through the filter) with living bacteria that were unable to make a capsule, some of these bacteria gained the ability to synthesize a capsule. Moreover, these bacteria passed on this ability to all of their offspring. Something in the filtrate was "transforming" the harmless; unencapsulated bacteria into bacteria with the ability to make a capsule.

What was this transforming principle? In 1944, after years of painstaking chemical analysis of lysates capsule of transforming pneumococci, three investigators from the Rockefeller Institute, Oswald T. Avery, Colin MacLeod, and Maclyn McCarty, submitted one of the most important papers ever published in biology. In it, they reported that the molecule that could change (transform) a cell's properties was DNA.

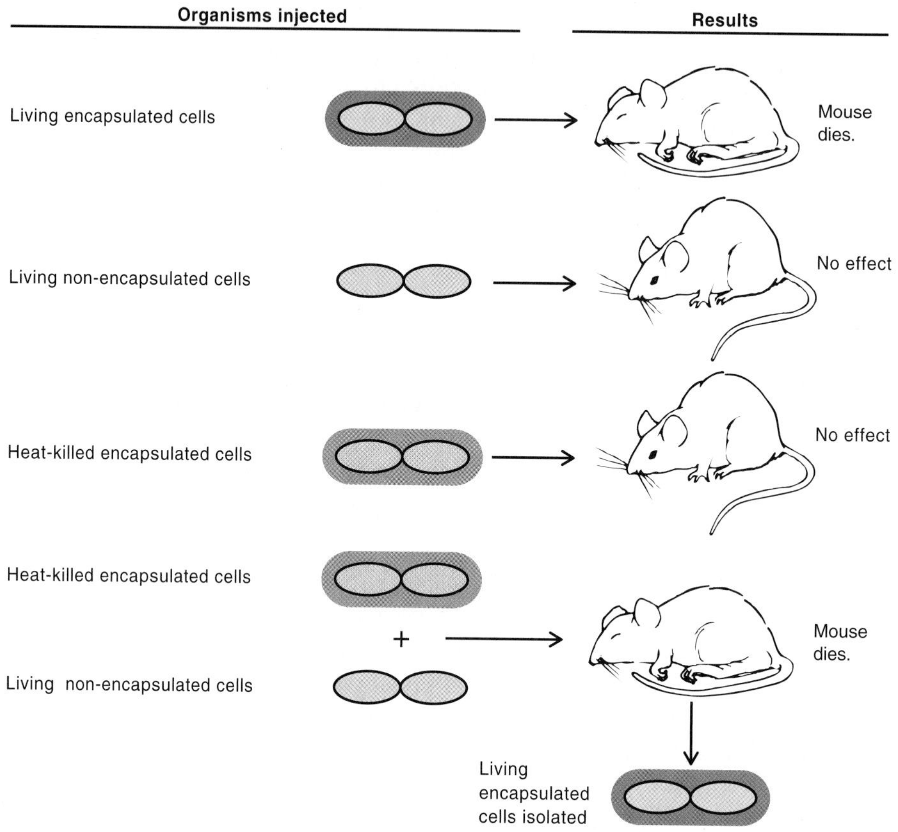

FIGURE 1 Demonstration of the Transforming Principle

The significance of their discovery was not appreciated at the time. Perhaps the discovery was premature, and scientists were slow to recognize its significance and importance. None of the three investigators received a Nobel Prize, although many scientists believe that they deserved it. Their studies pointed out that DNA is a key molecule in the scheme of life and led to James Watson and Francis Crick's determination of its structure, which they published in 1953. The understanding of the structure and function of DNA revolutionized the study of biology and ushered in the era of molecular biology. Microbial genetics serves as its foundation.

Integration of Donor DNA

Once inside the recipient cell, the single-stranded donor DNA becomes positioned, by hydrogen bonding, next to the complementary region of the recipient DNA (see figure 8.19c). The two regions are said to be **homologous.** The donor and recipient strands are held together by hydrogen bonds between complementary bases. Then, a nuclease cleaves the recipient cell's single-stranded DNA on either side of the donor DNA. This fragment of DNA is released into the cytoplasm, where it is degraded by nucleases. The donor DNA then replaces the recipient DNA precisely, by the process of **homologous recombination** (see figure 8.19d). This mechanism of recombination in which the homologous region of the recipient DNA is replaced by donor DNA is termed **breakage and reunion.** The same mechanism also accounts for the integration of donor DNA into recipient cells in both conjugation and transduction.

Multiplication of Transformed Cells

The transformed cells multiply under selective conditions in which the non-transformed cells cannot grow and form colonies (see figure 8.19f). For example, if the donor cells are Str^R and the recipient cells are Str^S, then only cells transformed to Str^R

will grow on medium that contains streptomycin. Since only one strand of the recipient cells' DNA is transformed initially to streptomycin resistance, only one half of the daughter cells will be streptomycin resistant. The other half will be streptomycin sensitive and will die on streptomycin-containing medium (see figures 8.19d and 8.19e). Although many other donor genes besides Str^R will be transferred and integrated into the chromosome of the recipient cells, these transformants will go undetected since the donor and recipient cells are identical in these other genes.

Artificial Competence

Although not all bacteria become naturally competent, double-stranded DNA can be introduced into most cells including bacteria, animals, and plants through a special treatment of the recipient cells. In one technique called **electroporation,** bacteria and DNA are mixed together and the mixture is subjected to an electric current **(figure 8.20).** The current apparently makes holes in the bacterial cell wall and cytoplasmic membrane through which the DNA enters. Once inside the cytoplasm, the DNA becomes integrated into the recipient chromosome by homologous recombination, presumably by the same mechanism as was described for DNA transformation.

MICROCHECK 8.7

Gene transfer can occur in many Gram-positive and Gram-negative bacteria by DNA-mediated transformation in which DNA is released from some cells and is taken up by other cells, termed competent. Competent cells have undergone a number of changes which allow them to bind DNA, take DNA into the cell in a single-stranded form and integrate the DNA. Artificial means such as electroporation can be used to get DNA into cells that do not become competent naturally.

- ✓ What effect would adding deoxyribonuclease to the culture have on transformation?
- ✓ If cells do not become naturally competent, can they still be made to take up DNA? Explain.
- ✓ Can you devise a test using DNA-mediated transformation that could test chemicals for their mutagenic activity?
- ✓ Explain how dead cells confer virulence on avirulent living cells.

8.8 Transduction

Focus Points

- Describe the process of bacterial gene transfer by transduction.
- Distinguish between generalized and specialized transduction.

Bacterial viruses, called **bacteriophage** or simply **phage,** can also transfer bacterial genes from one cell to another by a process called **transduction.** Phage have a protein coat that surrounds the genetic material of the virus. The phage infect bacteria by transferring only their nucleic acid into the cell. The nucleic acid replicates, and codes for the protein coat, which then encapsulates the coat prior to the phage lysing the cell. The phage are released into the environment and infect other cells in which they multiply and are then released following cell lysis. Some of the released phage may carry bacterial genes in place of phage genes inside their protein coats. These phage then infect other bacteria and thereby transfer bacterial genes from the first to the second bacterium **(figure 8.21).**

There are two types of transduction: **generalized** and **specialized.** In generalized transduction, any gene of the donor cell can be transferred. In specialized transduction, only a few specific genes can be transferred. We will briefly cover generalized transduction now and both will be discussed in more detail when the replication cycles of bacteriophage are considered in chapter 13.

In generalized transduction, after the phage infects the bacterium, the phage encoded enzyme deoxyribonuclease is expressed. This enzyme cleaves the replicated phage DNA into the proper size fragments to be enclosed in the coat protein of the phage. However, this deoxyribonuclease also cleaves the bacterial chromosome into fragments, which also can become surrounded by the phage coat, taking the place of phage DNA. Once released from the infected cell, the phage containing the bacterial DNA may infect other nearby cells and thereby transfer bacterial genes instead of phage nucleic acid. Inside the recipient cell, the bacterial DNA becomes integrated by homologous recombination, replacing genes in the recipient cell. Transduction is a common

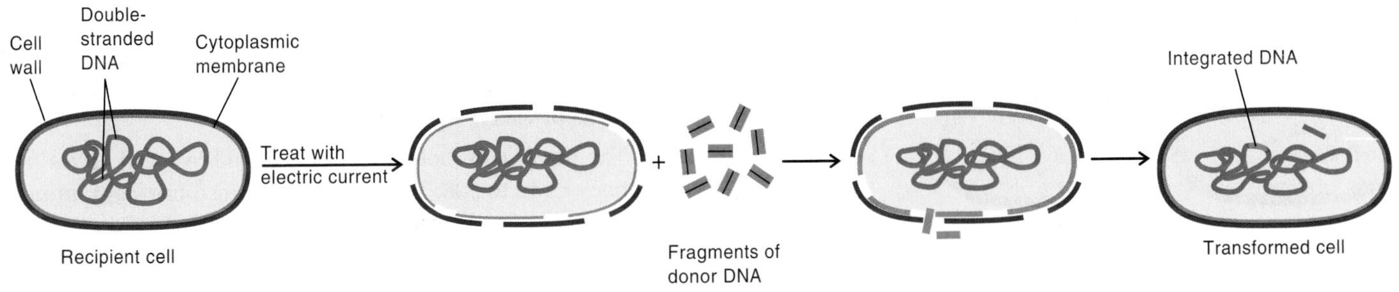

FIGURE 8.20 Electroporation The electric current makes holes in both the cell wall and the cytoplasmic membrane through which the double-stranded DNA can pass. These holes are then repaired by the cell, and the DNA becomes incorporated into the chromosome of the cell.

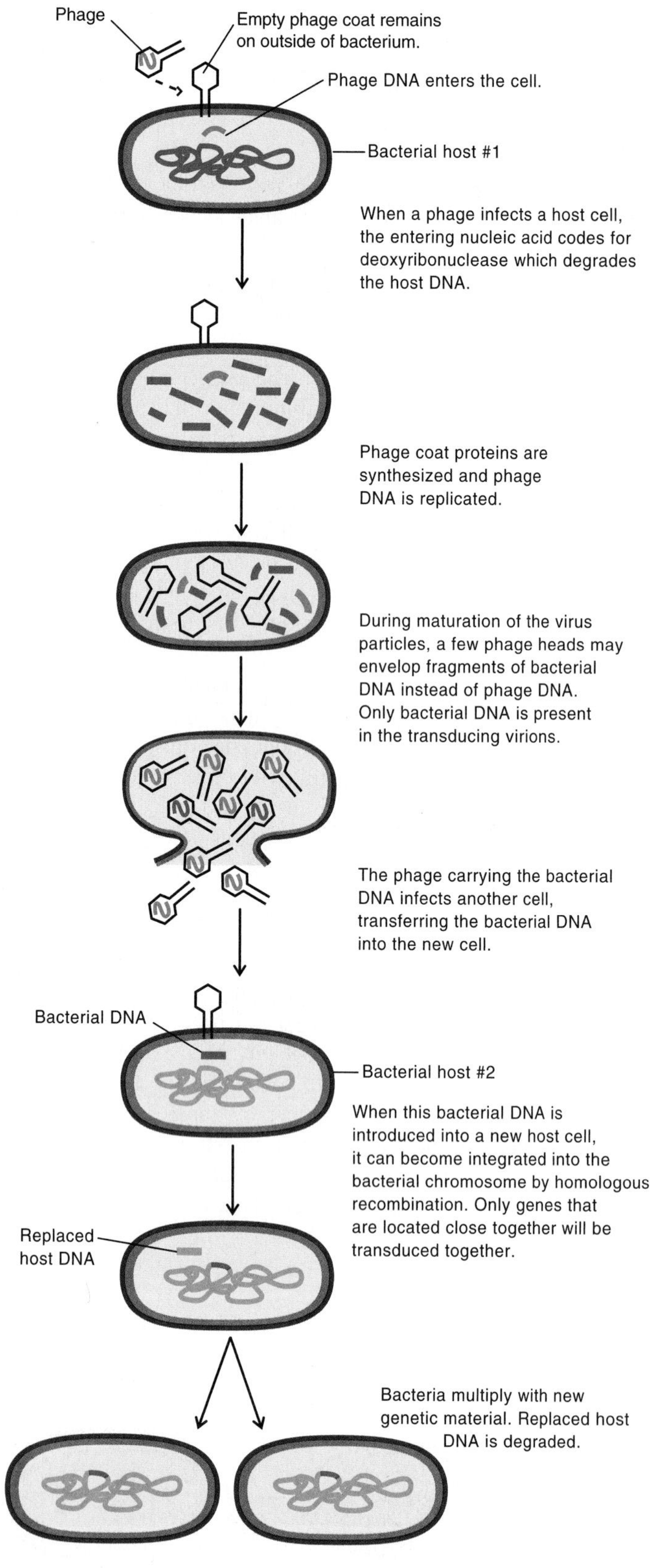

Phage
Empty phage coat remains on outside of bacterium.
Phage DNA enters the cell.
Bacterial host #1
When a phage infects a host cell, the entering nucleic acid codes for deoxyribonuclease which degrades the host DNA.
Phage coat proteins are synthesized and phage DNA is replicated.
During maturation of the virus particles, a few phage heads may envelop fragments of bacterial DNA instead of phage DNA. Only bacterial DNA is present in the transducing virions.
The phage carrying the bacterial DNA infects another cell, transferring the bacterial DNA into the new cell.
Bacterial DNA
Bacterial host #2
When this bacterial DNA is introduced into a new host cell, it can become integrated into the bacterial chromosome by homologous recombination. Only genes that are located close together will be transduced together.
Replaced host DNA
Bacteria multiply with new genetic material. Replaced host DNA is degraded.

Figure 8.21 Transduction (Generalized) Any piece of the chromosomal DNA of the donor cell can be transferred in this process. All of the DNA molecules of the bacterial virus and the bacteria are double-stranded.

mechanism of gene transfer and occurs in a wide variety of Gram-positive and Gram-negative bacteria.

MICROCHECK 8.8

Short pieces of bacterial DNA can be enclosed in a bacterial virus coat and then transferred to recipient cells when the virus invades these cells. This bacterial DNA is then integrated into the recipient cell DNA. This is the process of transduction.

✓ What effect would the addition of deoxyribonuclease to the donor cells have on this process?

✓ Two genes are transduced simultaneously. What does this suggest about the location of the two genes relative to each other? Explai9n.

8.9 Plasmids

Focus Points

- Describe the properties of resistance plasmids which make them so much of a problem in a hospital environment.
- Explain the ways in which plasmids differ from bacterial chromosomes.

Before we can discuss transfer of DNA by conjugation, we need to discuss plasmids, the form of circular DNA which is primarily transferred by this process. Plasmids are very common in the microbial world, being found in most members of the *Bacteria* and the *Archaea,* as well as in the *Eucarya.* Plasmids play key roles in the lives of these organisms—their function in the life of bacteria is especially well understood. ■ **plasmid, p. 69**

A study of a wide variety of plasmids in many different bacteria has led to the following generalizations:

- Plasmids usually are covalently closed, circular double-stranded DNA molecules.
- Plasmids vary in size from a few genes to over a thousand. They are all replicons.
- Most prokaryotes contain one or more different plasmids; their functions, however, are often unknown.
- The traits coded by plasmids generally provide the cell with useful but not essential capabilities. For example, plasmids often code for antibiotic resistance, but never for enzymes of glycolysis. Plasmids code for a wide variety of other traits, some of which are listed in **table 8.3.**
- The number of molecules of a plasmid in a cell varies from one or two to 500. The former are termed **low-copy-number plasmids;** the latter, **high-copy-number plasmids.**
- Most plasmids can multiply in only one species of bacteria. They are termed **narrow host range plasmids.** A few however, can multiply in many different species and are called **broad host range plasmids.**

TABLE 8.3 Some Plasmid-Coded Traits

Trait	Organisms in Which Trait is Found
Antibiotic resistance	*Escherichia coli, Salmonella* sp., *Neisseria* sp., *Staphylococcus* sp., *Shigella* sp., and many other organisms
Pilus synthesis	*E. coli, Pseudomonas* sp.
Tumor formation in plants	*Agrobacterium* sp. **(see Perspective 8.2)**
Nitrogen fixation (in plants)	*Rhizobium* sp.
Oil degradation	*Pseudomonas* sp.
Gas vacuole production	*Halobacterium* sp.
Insect toxin synthesis	*Bacillus thuringiensis*
Plant hormone synthesis	*Pseudomonas* sp.
Antibiotic synthesis	*Streptomyces* sp.
Increased virulence	*Yersinia enterocolitica*
Toxin production	*Bacillus anthracis*

- Plasmids replicate using the enzymes of the cell in which they are found.
- Plasmids are most readily transferred by conjugation. Some carry all of the genetic information they need for transfer. They are **self-transmissible.** Some plasmids termed **mobilizable** encode some but not all, of the information required for transfer. Both have an **origin of transfer.** A self-transmissible plasmid can help the mobilizable plasmid to transfer. Some plasmids, termed **promiscuous,** can be transferred to unrelated species. To multiply in an unrelated species requires that they also be a broad host range plasmid.

R Plasmids

A group of plasmids that has been studied extensively are the **R** or **resistance plasmids.** They are so named because they confer resistance to many different antimicrobial medications and heavy metals, such as mercury and arsenic. Like antimicrobial medications, heavy metals are found in the hospital environment, and bacteria containing R plasmids are commonly found in this environment. Many of these plasmids are composed of two parts: the **resistance** or **R genes,** which code for the resistance traits, and the **resistance transfer factor** or **RTF,** which codes for the transfer of the plasmid to other bacteria by conjugation **(figure 8.22).** In a self-transmissible plasmid, the RTF portion contains genes that code for pilus synthesis, the origin of transfer, and other mobilization genes, all of which are required for plasmid transfer.

The R genes code for resistance to widely used antimicrobial medications, which can include sulfanilamide, streptomycin, chloramphenicol, and tetracycline, and a number of different heavy metals. Certain R plasmids confer resistance to some, but not all, of these antimicrobial substances; yet others confer resistance to more than these particular ones.

Perhaps the most important feature of many R plasmids is that they can be transferred to bacteria that are sensitive to antimicrobials and heavy metals and thereby confer simultaneous resistance to several antimicrobials and heavy metals encoded by the R genes. Furthermore, many R plasmids are broad host range and can multiply in a wide variety of different Gram-negative genera. These include *Shigella, Salmonella, Escherichia, Yersinia, Klebsiella, Vibrio,* and *Pseudomonas.* If R plasmids are present in one species in a mixed population of these organisms, other cells will receive the R plasmid and thus become resistant to a variety of antimicrobial agents. This transfer of R plasmids helps explain why so many different organisms in a hospital environment are resistant to many different antimicrobials. Further, self-transmissible R plasmids can promote the transfer of plasmids in the same cell that are not self-transmissible.

■ nosocomial infections, p. 487

Not surprisingly, antimicrobial-resistant organisms are most common in locations where these medications are in greatest use. The antimicrobials kill the sensitive cells and allow the few resistant cells in the population to grow. Soon, most of the cells in this environment are antimicrobial resistant. This process explains why hospitals harbor many antimicrobial-resistant bacteria. Antimicrobial-resistant organisms are more common in certain parts of the world, particularly in developing countries. This probably results from the overuse of antimicrobials in these countries, where antimicrobials can be sold without a doctor's prescription. Also, in areas that lack proper hygiene, bacteria are more readily transferred to people through contaminated food and water. Non-disease-causing bacteria such as *E. coli* that may be carried by healthy people can serve as a reservoir for R plasmids, which then can be transferred to disease-causing organisms.

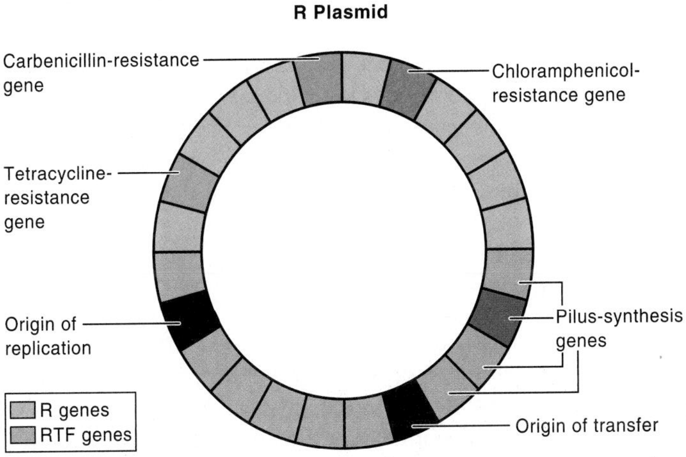

FIGURE 8.22 Two Regions of an R Plasmid The R (resistance) genes code for resistance to various antimicrobials; the RTF (resistance transfer factor) region codes for plasmid replication and the transfer of the plasmid to other bacteria.

MICROCHECK 8.9

All members of the microbial world contain plasmids, which in most cases code for unknown functions. Plasmids vary in size, copy number, host range, their genetic composition, and their ability to be transferred to other cells. One of the most important plasmids is the R plasmid, which codes for resistance to various antimicrobial medications and heavy metals.

- ✓ What single function must all plasmids encode?
- ✓ What functions must a plasmid code for in order to be self-transmissible?
- ✓ What does the phrase, "reservoir for R plasmids" mean when referring to plasmids carried by non-disease-causing bacteria?
- ✓ If a cell lost all its plasmids, would it be able to survive? Explain.

8.10 Conjugation

Focus Points

- Compare an F^+ to an F^- cell in terms of their morphology and gene content.
- Compare the state of the F plasmid in a cell that transfers only plasmids with a cell that can transfer chromosomal DNA, and with a cell that transfers both plasmid and chromosomal DNA.

An important and common mechanism of gene transfer in both Gram-positive and Gram-negative bacteria is **conjugation.** The process is quite different in the two groups but we will only consider the congugation in Gram-negative bacteria. Conjugation, in contrast to transformation and transduction, requires contact between donor and recipient cells. This requirement can be shown through the following experiment. If two different auxotrophic mutants are placed on either side of a filter through which fluids, but not bacteria, can pass, recombination does not occur. If the filter is removed, however, allowing cell-to-cell contact, recombination takes place. Some cells in the population transfer plasmids whereas other cells can transfer their chromosome. Conjugation is a complex process and many aspects are not understood even though it was first observed in *E. coli* more than 50 years ago. ■ plasmid, p. 69

Plasmid Transfer

The best studied example of conjugation is the transfer of a self-transmissible plasmid termed **F** for **fertility plasmid** between cells of *E. coli*. Populations of *E. coli* can be divided into two types of cells. The donor cell contains the F plasmid and is designated F^+. The recipient cell does not contain this plasmid and is called F^-. DNA is transferred only in one direction, from F^+ to F^- cells—that is, in a polar fashion. The F plasmid codes for the synthesis of a structure, the **sex or F pilus,** the protein appendage that attaches the donor to the recipient cell **(figure 8.23).** Donor cells can transfer their F plasmid but not their chromosome into recipient cells. ■ F pilus, p. 68

Plasmid transfer can be divided into four steps **(figure 8.24).**

Step 1 Contact between donor and recipient cells. The sex pili of the donor cells recognize and bind to specific **receptor sites** on the cell walls of the recipient cells. The sex pili likely act as grappling hooks, pulling the two cells together.

Step 2 Mobilization or activation of DNA transfer. The plasmid becomes mobilized for transfer when a plasmid-encoded enzyme cleaves one strand of the plasmid at a specific nucleotide sequence, termed the **origin of transfer.** This results in the formation of a single-stranded DNA molecule with a free end.

Step 3 Plasmid transfer. Within minutes of the F^+ cell contacting the F^- cell, a single strand of the F plasmid, beginning at the origin of transfer, enters the F^- cell. This transfer takes about 2 minutes. Despite a great deal of research, there is still no evidence that the DNA passes through the pilus. Note that a single strand of the F plasmid remains in the donor cell.

Step 4 Synthesis of a functional plasmid inside the recipient and donor cells. Once inside the recipient cell, a complementary strand to the single-stranded transferred DNA is synthesized. Likewise, a strand complementary to the single-stranded plasmid DNA remaining in the donor is synthesized. Thus, both the donor and recipient cells contain a copy of the F plasmid and are therefore F^+. Both cells can act as donors of the F plasmid. This explains why a single F^+ cell of *E. coli* mixed with a population of F^- cells can convert the entire population to

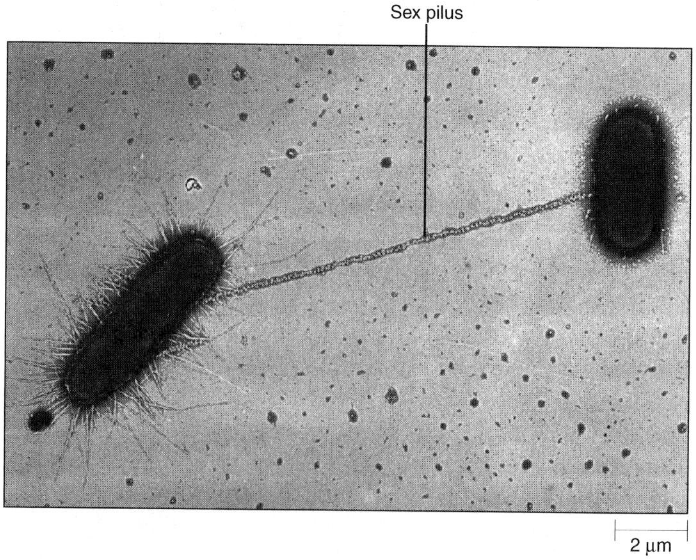

FIGURE 8.23 Sex or F Pilus Holding Together Donor and Recipient Cells of *E. coli* During DNA Transfer During the actual transfer of DNA, the pilus becomes much shorter as it pulls the cells together.

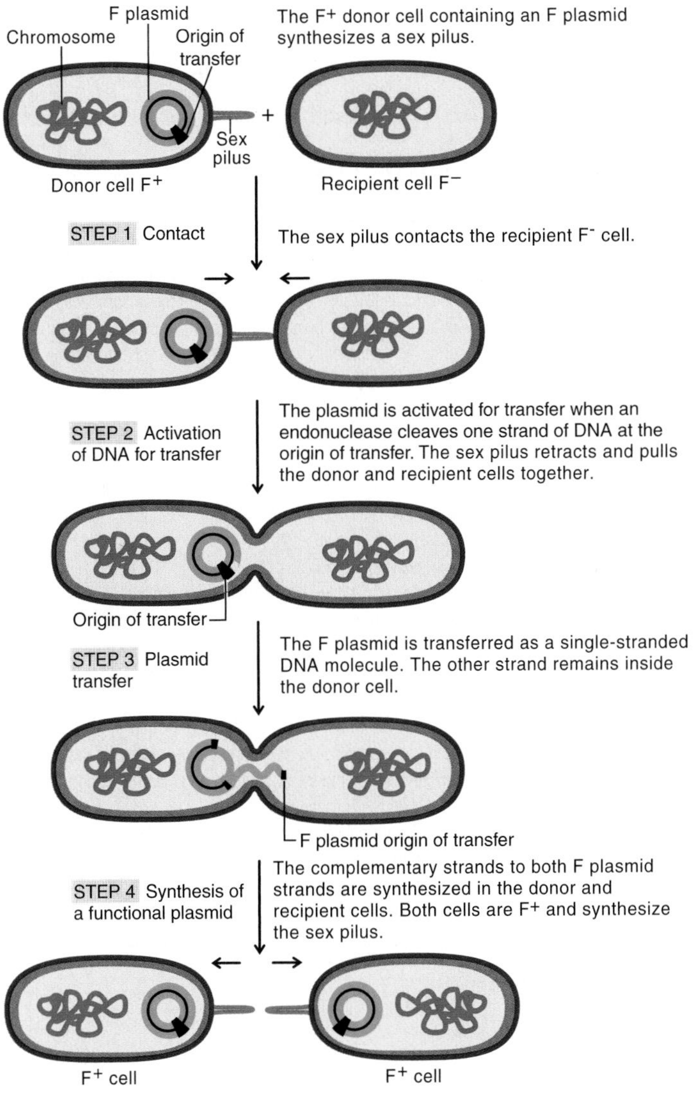

FIGURE 8.24 Conjugation—Transfer of the F Plasmid The exact process by which the donor DNA passes to the recipient cells is not known.

F+ after overnight growth of the culture. Cells can spontaneously lose their plasmids, which explains why not all cells are F+. Cells that have lost their plasmid are said to be **cured.**

Chromosome Transfer

Thus far, we have discussed only the transfer of plasmids by conjugation. However, the bacterial chromosome can be transferred if it is first mobilized by the integration of the F plasmid into the chromosome. This creates a cell termed **Hfr**—for **high frequency of recombination (figure 8.25).** The features of chromosome transfer are the same as plasmid transfer except that only a portion of the chromosome is usually transferred and the recipient cell remains F- **(figure 8.26).** Also, unlike plasmids, the piece of DNA that is transferred is not a replicon and therefore, in order to replicate, the fragment must integrate into the chromosome of the recipient cell through homologous recombination.

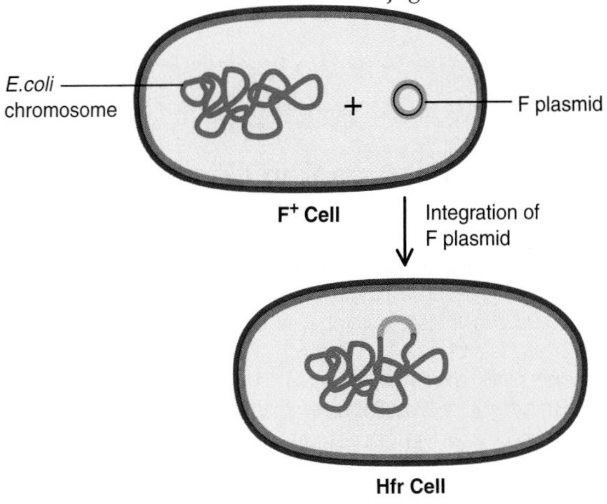

FIGURE 8.25 Hfr Formation Integration of the F plasmid into the bacterial chromosome to form Hfr. Homologous sites, termed insertion sequences, on the F plasmid and the chromosome allow the integration to occur. There is no replacement of DNA in the chromosome; the F plasmid increases the size of the chromosome. ■ **insertion sequence, p. 214**

F′ Donors

The F plasmid in the Hfr strain can be excised from the chromosome; thus, the process of F plasmid incorporation into the chromosome is reversible. In some instances in the process of excision, an error occurs and a small piece of the bacterial chromosome remains attached to the F plasmid **(figure 8.27).** This F plasmid with its piece of attached chromosome is called **F′** (F prime), and like the F plasmid it is rapidly and efficiently transferred to all F- cells in the population. Consequently, any chromosomal genes attached to the F plasmid are also transferred to all cells. The F′ plasmid usually remains **extrachromosomal**—that is, it does not become a part of the recipient cell's chromosome. On rare occasions, however, it can become incorporated into the chromosome of recipient cells, which then become Hfr since they contain the F plasmid integrated into the chromosome.

The three mechanisms of DNA transfer are compared in **table 8.4** on p. 213.

MICROCHECK 8.10

Conjugation requires contact between donor and recipient cells. Transfer is from a donor cell that synthesizes a sex pilus to one that does not. Both plasmid and chromosomal DNA can be transferred. Following transfer, plasmids replicate but chromosomal DNA must be integrated into a replicon. Groups of mobile genes form pathogenicity or genomic islands. They are transferred as a single unit and confer beneficial properties on recipient cells.

- ✓ What two transfer functions does the F plasmid encode?
- ✓ Explain why DNA is transferred in only one direction in conjugation.
- ✓ Would you expect conjugation to be more efficient if cells were plated together on solid medium (agar) or mixed together in a liquid in a shaking flask? Explain.
- ✓ Why must chromosomal (but not plasmid) DNA that is transferred be integrated into the chromosome of the recipient cell? Explain.

PERSPECTIVE 8.2

Bacteria Can Conjugate with Plants: A Natural Case of Genetic Engineering

For more than 50 years, scientists have known that DNA can be transferred between bacteria. Twenty-five years ago, it was shown that a bacterium can even transfer its genes into plant cells, such as tobacco, carrots, and cedar trees, through a process analogous to conjugation. What led to this discovery started about 100 years ago in the laboratory of a plant pathologist, Dr. Erwin Smith. He showed that the causative agent of a common plant disease, termed **crown gall,** is a bacterium, *Agrobacterium tumefaciens.* This disease is characterized by large galls or swellings that occur on the plant at the site of infection, usually near the soil line, the crown of the plant. When other investigators cultured the diseased plant tissue on agar plates containing nutrients necessary for the growth of plant tissue, it had properties that differed from normal plant tissue. Whereas normal tissue requires several plant hormones for growth, crown gall tissue grows in the absence of these added hormones. In addition, crown gall tissue synthesizes large amounts of a compound termed an **opine,** which neither normal plant tissue nor *Agrobacterium* synthesizes. The most surprising observation was that the plant cells maintained their altered nutritional requirements and the ability to synthesize opine even after the bacteria were killed by penicillin. Investigators concluded that the crown gall plant cells are permanently transformed. Although *Agrobacterium* is required to start the infection, they are not necessary to maintain the altered nutritional requirements and biosynthetic capabilities of the plant cells.

The explanation of the process by which *Agrobacterium* causes crown gall tumors and transforms plant cells was established in 1977 following a report that all strains of *Agrobacterium* capable of causing crown gall tumors contained a large plasmid termed the **tumor inducing** or **Ti plasmid.** A group of microbiologists then showed that a specific piece of the Ti plasmid, termed the **transferred DNA,** or **T-DNA,** is transferred from the bacterial cell to the plant cell, where it becomes incorporated into the plant chromosome **(figure 1).** Since no regions of DNA in the plant are similar to those of bacteria, integration occurs through **non homologous recombination.** Like conjugation between bacteria, a pilus is required for DNA transfer.

The transferred DNA acts like plant DNA because its promoters resemble those of plants rather than those of bacteria. Therefore, the genetic information in the T-DNA is expressed in plants but not in *Agrobacterium.* This DNA encodes enzymes for the synthesis of the plant hormones as well as for the opine. The expression of these genes supplies the plant cells with the plant hormones, explaining why the transformed plant cells can grow in the absence of added hormones and are able to synthesize opine. Thus, once incorporated into the plant chromosome, the DNA provides the transformed cell with additional genetic information that confers new properties on the plant cell. This is the only natural case in nature in which prokaryotic DNA is transferred and integrated into the genome of a eukaryotic cell. It seems like a good bet that other examples will follow. ■ **promoter, p. 174**

Why does *Agrobacterium* transform plants? This bacterium has the ability to use the opine as a source of carbon and energy, whereas most other bacteria in the soil, as well as plants, cannot. Therefore, *Agrobacterium* subverts the metabolism of the plant to produce food that only *Agrobacterium* can use. Thus, *Agrobacterium* is a natural genetic engineer of plants.

The *Agrobacterium*—crown gall system is of great interest for several reasons. First, it shows that DNA can be transferred from prokaryotes to eukaryotes. Many people believed that such transfer would be impossible in nature and could only occur in the laboratory. Second, this system has spawned an industry of plant biotechnology dedicated to improving the quality of higher plants. Thus, it is possible to replace the genes of hormone synthesis in the Ti plasmid with any other genes, which will then be transferred and incorporated into the plant. With this technology, genes conferring resistance to bacteria, viruses, insects, and different herbicides have been incorporated into a wide variety of plants. Rice has been transformed to synthesize high levels of β-carotene, the precursor of vitamin A. Edible vaccines are being synthesized in bananas following transformation by *Agrobacterium.*

Genetic engineering of plants became a reality once scientists learned how a common soil bacterium caused a well-recognized and serious plant disease. This system serves as a beautiful example of how solving a riddle in basic science can lead to major industrial applications.

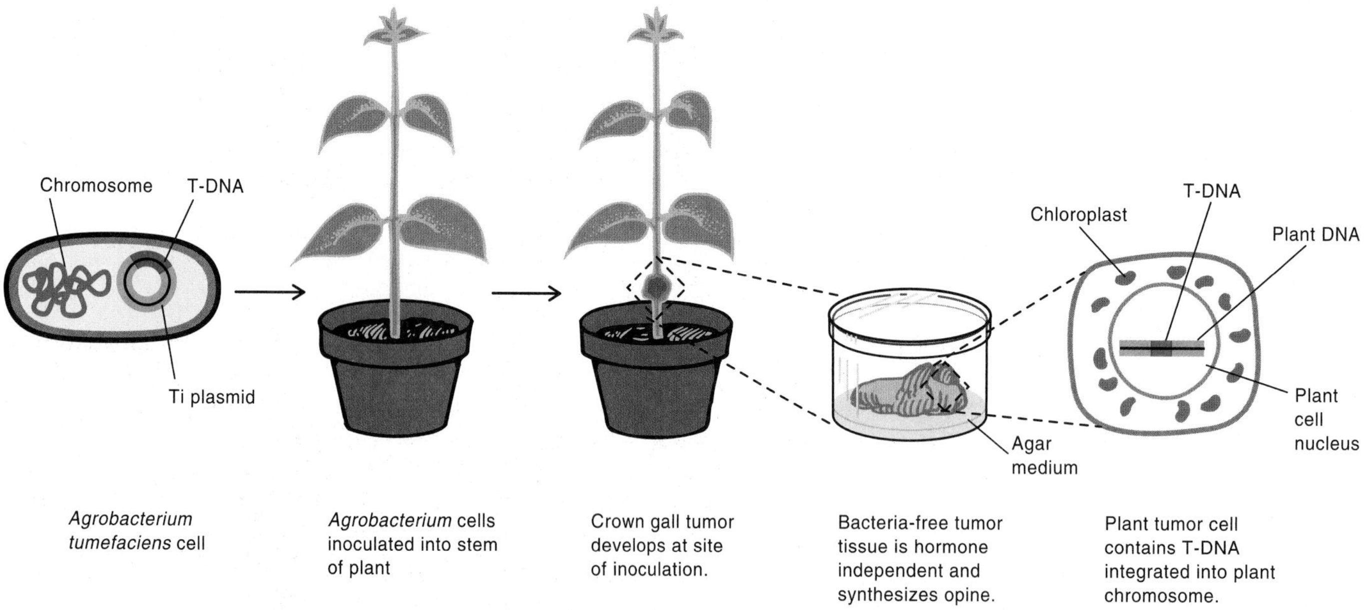
Chromosome
T-DNA
Ti plasmid
Chloroplast
T-DNA
Plant DNA
Plant cell nucleus
Agar medium
Agrobacterium tumefaciens cell
Agrobacterium cells inoculated into stem of plant
Crown gall tumor develops at site of inoculation.
Bacteria-free tumor tissue is hormone independent and synthesizes opine.
Plant tumor cell contains T-DNA integrated into plant chromosome.

FIGURE 1 ***Agrobacterium*** **sp. Causes Crown Gall and Transforms Plant Cells**

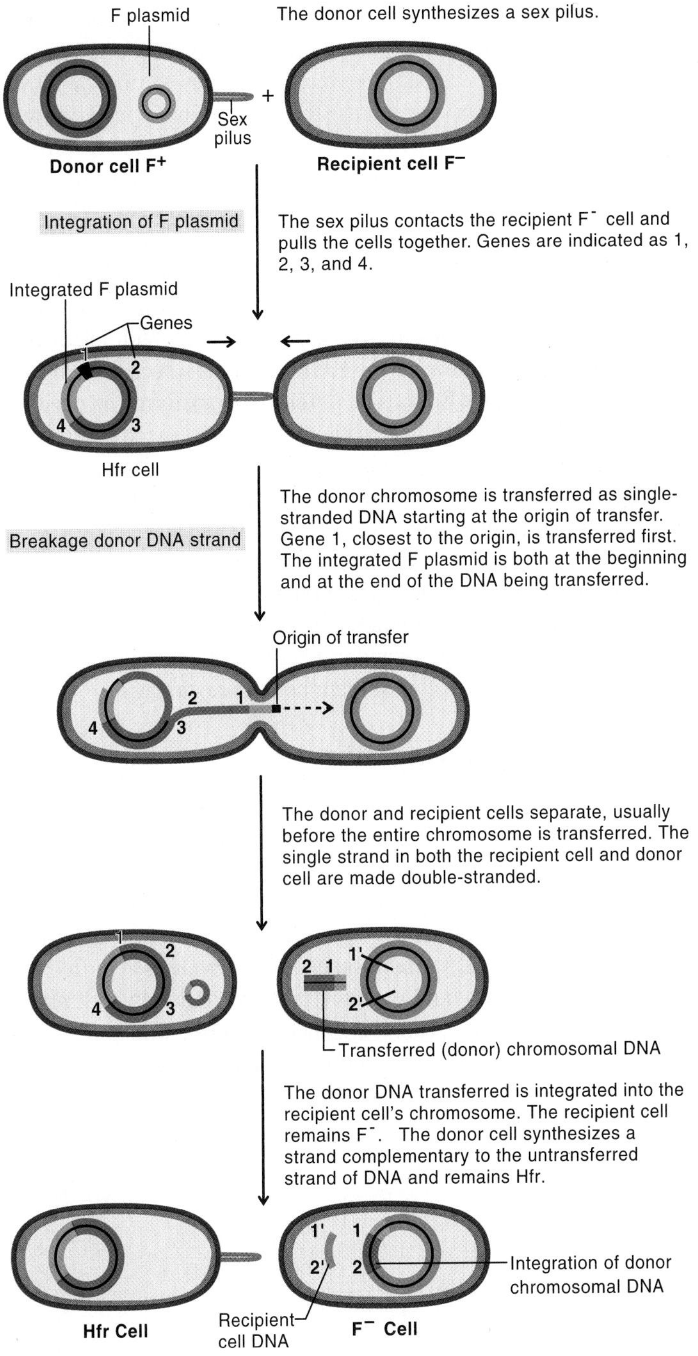

FIGURE 8.26 Conjugation-Transfer of Chromosomal DNA The DNA is transferred as a single-strangled DNA molecule. The recipient genes are designated with a prime (′). The corresponding DNA in the donor lack the prime (′).

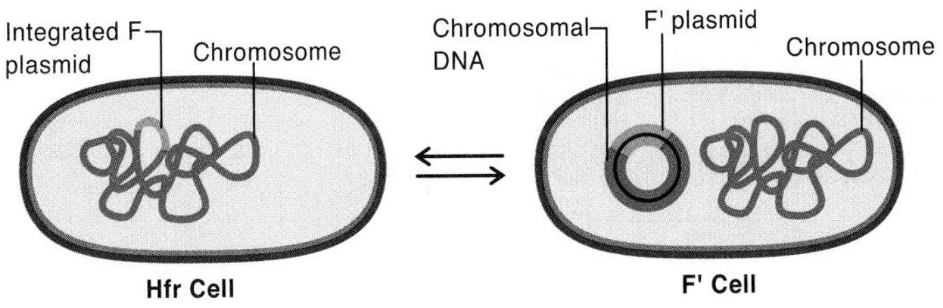

FIGURE 8.27 Formation of F′ Plasmid This F′ plasmid has the transfer properties of the F plasmid but carries chromosomal DNA. This process is reversible.

TABLE 8.4 Comparison of Mechanisms of DNA Transfer

Mechanism	Main Features	Size of DNA Transferred	Sensitivity to DNase addition
Transformation	Naked DNA transferred	About 20 genes	Yes
Transduction	DNA enclosed in a bacteriophage coat	Small fraction of the chromosome	No
Conjugation			
Plasmid transfer	Cell-to-cell contact required	Entire plasmid	No
Chromosome transfer	Cell-to-cell contact required; only certain cells can be donors (Hfr).	Variable fraction of chromosome	No

8.11 Movement of Mobile Genetic Elements—Transposons

Focus Points

- Explain how transposable elements contribute to the spread of antibiotic resistance.
- Describe the feature that is common to all transposable elements.

Many factors that confer special properties on bacteria are encoded on mobile genetic elements given the general name, **genomic islands.** These factors include genes associated with virulence, termed pathogenicity islands, antibiotic resistance loci, and genes concerned with the development of symbiosis and adaptation to environmental changes. The ability of multiple genes to move as a unit from a chromosomal location to other sites on the chromosome or to plasmids in the cell is possible because they are a part of a transposon. However, transposons can also be transferred to other cells, either related or unrelated to the donor cell, by transduction or conjugation. Integration occurs by non homologous recombination.

The introduction in this chapter presented an excellent example of how a transposon enabled a strain of *Staphylococcus aureus* to become resistant to vancomycin. More details of this phenomenon are now known. When doctors isolated the vancomycin-resistant *S. aureus* from the foot ulcer of the patient, another strain of the same organism was also present. Both strains were resistant to almost all available antibiotics. However, the strain isolated from the foot ulcer was also resistant to vancomycin, apparently the only difference between the two strains. Another vancomycin-resistant bacterium, *Enterococcus faecalis,* a Gram-positive coccus, was also isolated from the foot ulcer. Plasmids were found in all three bacteria, but the gene responsible for vancomycin resistance was only present in the *E. faecalis* and

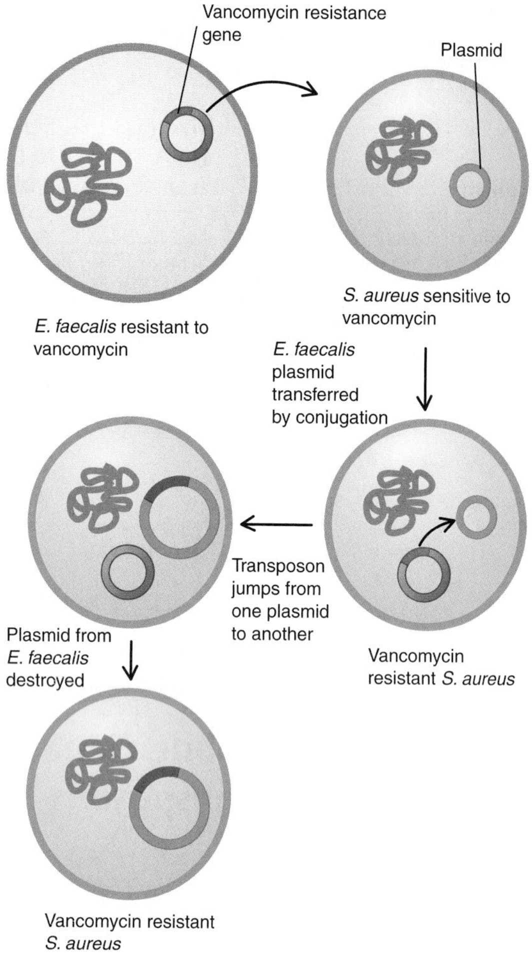

FIGURE 8.28 Transfer of Vancomycin Resistance to *S. aureus* Both *E. faecalis* and *S. aureus* are Gram + cocci but are unrelated to one another. It is quite possible that the vancomycin resistance gene was originally in the chromosome of *E. faecalis* and jumped to the plasmid. The destruction of the entering plasmid probably occurs because bacteria can destroy DNA that they recognize as foreign.

the vancomycin-resistant strain of *S. aureus*. This suggested that the vancomycin resistance gene jumped from *E. faecalis* to *S. aureus*. This idea became more credible when further analysis showed that the vancomycin resistance gene in *E. faecalis* was part of a transposon. Further, the vancomycin-resistant *S. aureus* contained a plasmid with the same transposon containing the vancomycin resistance gene as was found in *E. faecalis*. When the plasmids from the *S. aureus* sensitive and resistant strains were sequenced, they were found to be identical except in one respect. The vancomycin-resistance transposon was present in the plasmid from the resistant, but not in the sensitive strain. With all of this information, we can now surmise how *S. aureus* became resistant to vancomycin **(figure 8.28).** The *E. faecalis* transferred its plasmid containing the vancomycin resistance transposon to the sensitive *S. aureus* by conjugation. This entering plasmid was apparently destroyed by enzymes in the *S. aureus*. However, before it met its fate, the transposon jumped to the plasmid that resided in the strain, thereby creating the vancomycin-resistant *S. aureus*. This transposon is likely to jump again, perhaps to the chromosome or it may be transferred to other strains of *S. aureus*, or even to different genera or species. Is it any wonder that antibiotic resistance is such a serious problem in treating infectious diseases today?

Structure of Transposons

What is the structure of transposons, and what gives them the ability to move? Several types of transposons exist, varying in the complexity of their structure. The simplest is termed an **insertion sequence (IS).** The more complex is called a **composite transposon.** The insertion sequence (IS), consists of a gene that codes for the enzyme, **transposase.** This enzyme is required for transposition and is bound on either side by about 15 to 25 base pairs, which have the structure shown in **figure 8.29a.** The key feature of this sequence of nucleotides is that the sequence in one strand of DNA is the same as in the other strand, only going in

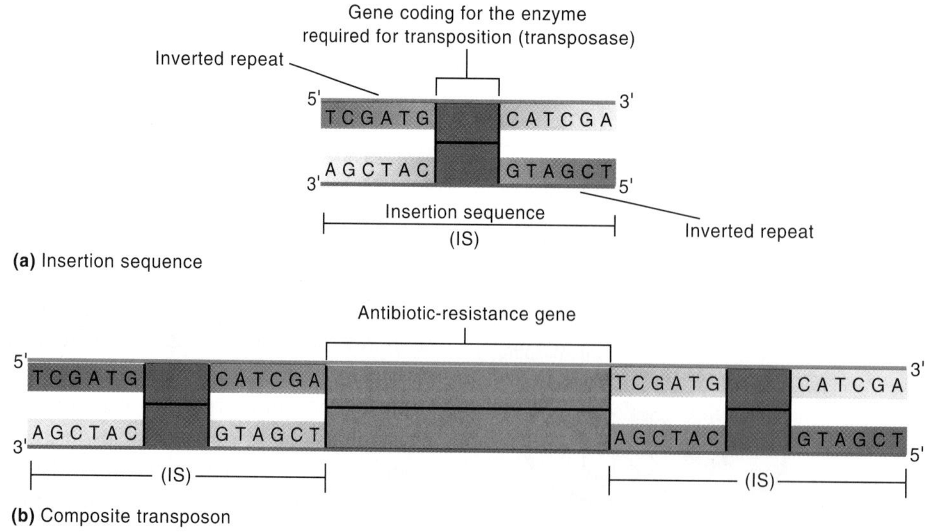

FIGURE 8.29 Transposable Elements (a) Insertion sequence. Note that the sequence of bases at the end of the IS element in one strand is the same as the sequence in the opposite strand reading the same direction (5′ to 3′). This is the inverted repeat or palindrome sequence. Only 6 of the 15 to 25 base pairs are shown. **(b)** Composite transposon. Antibiotic-resistance locus flanked by two insertion elements. The sizes of the various parts are not drawn to scale.

the opposite direction (see (a) of figure 8.29). Such a sequence is termed a palindrome or inverted repeat. The *E. coli* chromosome contains more than a dozen different ISs, labeled IS1, IS2, and so on. Several copies of each are present in the chromosome as well as on plasmids. They often are responsible for the recombination that occurs between two replicons within the same cell. This recombination accounts for the formation of an Hfr strain from an F^+ strain of *E. coli.* (see figure 8.25). ■ Hfr formation, p. 211

The composite transposon, consists of a gene whose product is easily recognized, such as a gene coding for antimicrobial resistance, flanked by ISs (figure 8.29b). The antimicrobial-resistance gene can move from one replicon to another in the cell and become integrated through non homologous recombination, and can be readily transferred to other cells. In theory, any gene or group of genes can move to another site if they are bounded by ISs.

MICROCHECK 8.11

Transposons can move from one replicon to another location in the some replicon or to other replicons. Transposition requires that the gene being transposed have inverted repeat sequences on its ends and the enzyme transposase as part of the insertion sequence.

- ✓ What are two features common to all insertion sequences?
- ✓ How does transposition promote gene transfer between bacteria?
- ✓ What would you think is the substrate for the transposase enzyme?

FUTURE CHALLENGES

Hunting for Magic Bullets

Because of the increasing resistance of microorganisms to current antimicrobial medications, the demand for new antimicrobials that will kill these resistant organisms is rapidly increasing. It is surprising and sobering to realize that only two new classes of antimicrobials have been introduced in the past 40 years. The challenge is great to develop new antimicrobial agents that strike at targets different from the few used by current antimicrobials.

With the revolution that has been occurring in biology over the past 15 years, the development of new antimicrobial agents may become easier. Promising new strategies are based on knowing the genomic sequence of microbial pathogens. More than 200 microbial genomes have now been sequenced, many of which are human pathogens. The study and analysis of the nucleotide sequence of DNA is called **genomics.** The next step is to identify genes necessary for the survival of the microorganism or required to cause disease. To gain some understanding of the function of any gene, one must compare its DNA sequence with the sequence of all other genes that have been put into a database, called GenBank. If the gene that has been sequenced is similar in sequence to any other gene, then it is assumed that the two genes have similar functions. Thus, if the function of a gene that has been sequenced in any organism is known, the function of all genes with a similar sequence should be similar. This is the science of **bioinformatics,** which involves the analysis of the nucleotide sequence of DNA in order to understand what it codes for. Genes that are required for virulence in the pathogen but are not found in the host are potential targets. In theory it should be possible to design a protein that inhibits the function of a virulence protein, thereby preventing disease.

To develop successful enzyme inhibitors requires considerable information about the enzyme, how it folds, what its three-dimensional structure is, and whether or not it interacts with other proteins.

In the past, the search for antimicrobial medications has relied on random screening. Scientists looked for growth inhibition of a pathogen by unknown organisms isolated from soil samples collected from around the world. Today, new technologies based on microbial genomics should identify new targets and provide a rational approach to developing new antimicrobials.

SUMMARY

8.1 Diversity in Bacteria

The properties of bacteria can change either through **mutations,** changes in the chemical structure of DNA, or the gain of DNA from other cells, or by changes in gene expression.

Bacteria contain only a single set of genes (haploid) so any changes in DNA are expressed rapidly.

Genes can be transferred from one organism to another, **horizontal gene transfer** (Figure 8.1b), and from parent to offspring, **vertical gene transfer.** (Figure 8.1a).

Gene Mutation As a Source of Diversity

8.2 Spontaneous Mutations

Spontaneous mutations are changes in the nucleotide sequences in DNA that occur without the addition of agents known to cause mutations.

These mutations are rare and occur at a characteristic frequency for each gene.

They are stable but on rare occasion can undergo a change back to the non-mutant form—a **reversion.**

Base Substitution (Figure 8.3)

Base substitutions usually occur during DNA replication; **point mutations** occur when only one base pair changes. (Figure 8.2)

Reactive oxygen molecules can modify guanine in DNA, leading to an increased frequency of base substitutions during DNA replication.

Removal or Addition of Nucleotides (Figure 8.4)

Frame shift mutations involve the addition or deletion of nucleotides, often resulting in the formation of a **stop codon** and the synthesis of a shortened protein.

Transposable Elements (Jumping Genes) (Figure 8.29)

Certain genes, called **transposons,** have the ability to move to any other location in the genome.

Introduction of a transposon into another gene inactivates that gene. (Figure 8.5)

8.3 Induced Mutations (Table 8.1)

Chemical Mutagens

Chemical **mutagens** frequently alter hydrogen-bonding properties of purines and pyrimidines, increasing the frequency of mutations.

Base analogs with different hydrogen-bonding properties can be incorporated into DNA in place of the usual purines and pyrimidines. (Figure 8.7)

Intercalating agents are planar molecules that insert into the double helix and push nucleotides apart, resulting in a frameshift mutation. (Figure 8.8)

Transposition

An **insertion mutation** results when a transposon integrates into a new site in the cell's genome and inactivates the gene. (Figure 8.5)

Radiation

Ultraviolet irradiation results in **thymine dimers** due to the formation of covalent bonds between adjacent thymine molecules on the same strand of DNA. (Figure 8.9)

X rays cause single-strand breaks, double-strand breaks, and alterations to the DNA bases.

8.4 Repair of Damaged DNA (Table 8.2)

Repair of Errors in Base Incorporation

DNA polymerase has a **proofreading** function.

In **mismatch repair,** an endonuclease cuts out the damaged single-stranded fragment and a new DNA strand is synthesized. (Figure 8.10)

Repair of Thymine Dimers

In **light repair,** a photoreactivating enzyme breaks the bonds of the thymine dimer, thereby restoring the original molecule. (Figure 8.11a)

In **excision** or **dark repair,** the damaged single-stranded segment is excised by an endonuclease. A new strand is synthesized by DNA polymerase. (Figure 8.11b)

Repair of Modified Bases in DNA

Specific glycosylases can remove modified bases, such as oxidized guanine and alkylated bases in DNA. (Figure 8.12)

SOS Repair

SOS repair is a last ditch repair mechanism in which about 30 enzymes are induced by damaged DNA, including a new DNA polymerase which bypasses the damaged DNA but does not proofread the DNA it synthesizes. Consequently, the synthesized DNA contains many mutations.

SOS repair accounts for the mutagenic activity of UV irradiation.

8.5 Mutations and Their Consequences

Genes mutate independently of one another, and the chance that two mutations will occur within the same cell is the product of the individual mutation rates.

Mutations provide a mechanism for altering the population of an organism to adapt to a changing environment—a process called **natural selection.**

8.6 Mutant Selection

Direct Selection

Direct selection involves inoculating cells onto a medium on which the mutant but not the parent can grow; these are the easiest kinds of mutants to isolate. (Figure 8.13)

Indirect Selection

Indirect selection is required when the desired mutant does not grow on a medium on which the parent grows.

Replica plating involves the simultaneous transfer of all the colonies on one plate to two other plates and the comparison of the growth of individual colonies on both plates. (Figure 8.14)

Penicillin enrichment increases the proportion of mutants in a population by killing growing bacteria in a medium on which only non-mutants will grow. (Figure 8.15)

Testing of Chemicals for Their Cancer-Causing Ability

The Ames test measures whether a chemical, a suspected **carcinogen,** increases the frequently of reversion; a positive test indicates the subject chemical is a mutagen and therefore a likely carcinogen. (Figure 8.16)

Gene Transfer As a Source of Diversity (Table 8.4)

8.7 DNA-Mediated Transformation

DNA-mediated transformation involves the transfer of "naked" DNA. Deoxyribonuclease addition prevents the transfer. (Figure 8.19)

Natural Competence

Natural **competence** is the ability of a cell to take up DNA.

DNA enters the cell as a single-stranded molecule and is integrated by replacing recipient cell genes via **homologous recombination.**

Artificial Competence

Cells can be made artificially competent by **electroporation;** in this process, the cells are treated with an electric current, which makes holes in the cell envelope through which DNA can pass. (Figure 8.20)

8.8 Transduction

Transduction involves the transfer of bacterial DNA by a **bacteriophage.** (Figure 8.21)

8.9 Plasmids (Table 8.3)

Plasmids are extrachromosomal replicons that code for non-essential information.

R plasmids

R plasmids code for antibiotic resistance; many are **self-transmissible** to other bacteria. (Figure 8.22)

8.10 Conjugation

Conjugation requires cell-to-cell contact. (Figure 8.23)

Plasmid Transfer

The **donor cells** synthesize a **sex pilus** encoded on an **F plasmid,** which recipient cells do not have; the F plasmid is transferred from an F^+ to an F^- cell. (Figure 8.24)

The F plasmid can often mobilize and transfer other plasmids to the recipient cell.

Many plasmids are self-transmissible and do not require the F plasmid for their transfer.

Chromosome Transfer

Chromosome transfer occurs when the F plasmid integrates into a chromosome and the resulting cell can transfer a portion of the chromosome into a recipient cell. (Figures 8.25, 8.26)

DNA must be integrated into a replicon in order to replicate. (Figure 8.18)

F′ Donors

An **F′** donor is formed when the F plasmid is excized from the chromosome and carries a piece of chromosomal DNA with it. (Figure 8.27)

8.11 Movement of Mobile Genetic Elements—Transposons

(Figure 8.28)

Transposons are genes that move as a unit from one location on DNA to another location on the same or different replicon in the cell.

Genes coding for antimicrobial resistance factors are frequently grouped together in transposons.

Transposable elements often transfer antimicrobial-resistance genes from a chromosome to a plasmid. Plasmids can be readily transferred by conjugation to unrelated bacteria.

Structure of Transposons

There are different types of transposons, which differ in complexity; all have inverted repeat sequences at their ends.

An **insertion sequence (IS)** contains a gene that codes for the enzyme **transposase.** (Figure 8.29a)

A **composite transposon** consists of one or more genes flanked by insertion sequences. (Figure 8.29b)

REVIEW QUESTIONS

Short Answer

1. What one activity must all plasmids carry out?
2. What is the term that describes a plasmid that can transfer itself from *E. coli* into *Pseudomonas,* where it can replicate?
3. What type of mutagen is most likely to result in a knockout mutation?
4. What are the two necessary features of an insertion sequence?
5. What enzyme has proofreading ability? How does it function in proofreading?
6. Give an example of gene transfer that involves homologous recombination. Give one that involves non-homologous recombination.
7. Single-strand integration of DNA has been shown to be a feature of which mechanism of DNA transfer?
8. What feature of an F′ particle is similar to chromosomal DNA? To a plasmid?
9. Name two properties of cells that are frequently encoded in transposons.
10. Name three ways in which plasmids differ from bacterial chromosomes.

Multiple Choice

1. A culture of *E. coli* is irradiated with ultraviolet (UV) light. Answer questions 1 and 2 based on this statement. The effect of the UV light is to specifically
   a) join the two strands of DNA together by covalent bonds.
   b) join the two strands of DNA together by hydrogen bonds.
   c) form covalent bonds between thymine molecules on the same strand of DNA.
   d) form covalent bonds between guanine and cytosine.
   e) delete bases.

2. The highest frequency of mutations would be obtained if, after irradiation, the cells were immediately
   a) placed in the dark.
   b) exposed to visible light.
   c) shaken vigorously.
   d) incubated at a temperature below their optimum for growth.
   e) The frequency would be the same no matter what the environmental conditions are after irradiation.
3. Penicillin enrichment of mutants works on the principle that
   a) only Gram-positive cells are killed.
   b) cells are most sensitive to antimicrobial medications during the lag phase of growth.
   c) most Gram-negative cells are resistant to penicillin.
   d) penicillin only kills growing cells.
   e) penicillin inhibits formation of the lipopolysaccharide layer.
4. Repair mechanisms that occur during DNA synthesis are
   1. mismatch repair.
   2. proofreading by DNA polymerase.
   3. light repair.
   4. SOS repair.
   5. excision repair.
   a) 1, 2 b) 2, 3 c) 3, 4 d) 4, 5 e) 1, 5
5. You are trying to isolate a mutant of wild-type *E. coli* that requires histidine for growth. This can best be done using
   1. direct selection.
   2. replica plating.
   3. penicillin enrichment.
   4. a procedure for isolating conditional mutants.
   5. reversion.
   a) 1, 2 b) 2, 3 c) 3, 4 d) 4, 5 e) 1, 5
6. The properties that all plasmids share are that they
   1. all carry genes for antimicrobial resistance.
   2. are self-transmissible to other bacteria.
   3. always occur in multiple copies in the cells.
   4. code for non-essential functions.
   5. replicate in the cells in which they are found.
   a) 1, 2 b) 2, 3 c) 3, 4 d) 4, 5 e) 1, 5
7. The addition of deoxyribonuclease to a mixture of donor and recipient cells will prevent gene transfer via
   a) DNA transformation.
   b) chromosome transfer by conjugation.
   c) plasmid transfer by conjugation.
   d) generalized transduction.
8. A sex pilus is essential for
   1. DNA transformation.
   2. chromosome transfer by conjugation.
   3. plasmid transfer by conjugation.
   4. generalized transduction.
   5. cell movement.
   a) 1, 2 b) 2, 3 c) 3, 4 d) 4, 5 e) 1, 5
9. A plasmid that can replicate in *E. coli* and *Pseudomonas* is most likely a/an
   a) broad host range plasmid.
   b) self-transmissible plasmid.
   c) high-copy-number plasmid.
   d) essential plasmid.
   e) low-copy-number plasmid.
10. The frequency of transfer of an F′ DNA molecule by conjugation is closest to the frequency of transfer of
    a) chromosomal genes by conjugation.
    b) an F plasmid by conjugation.
    c) an F plasmid by transformation.
    d) an F plasmid by transduction.
    e) an R plasmid by DNA transformation.

Applications

1. Some bacteria are more resistant to UV light than other bacteria. Discuss two reasons why this might be the case. What experiments could you do to determine whether each of the two possibilities could be correct?
2. A pharmaceutical researcher is disturbed to discover that the major ingredient of a new drug formulation causes frameshift mutations in bacteria. What other information would the researcher want before looking for a substitute chemical?

Critical Thinking

1. You have the choice of different kinds of mutants for use in the Ames test to determine the frequency of reversion by suspected carcinogens. You can choose a deletion, point mutation, or a frameshift mutation. Would it make any difference which one you chose? Explain.
2. You have isolated a strain of *E. coli* that is resistant to penicillin, streptomycin, chloramphenicol, and tetracycline. You also observe that when you mix this strain with cells of *E. coli* that are sensitive to the four antibiotics, they become resistant to streptomycin, penicillin, and chloramphenicol but remain sensitive to tetracycline. Explain what is going on.

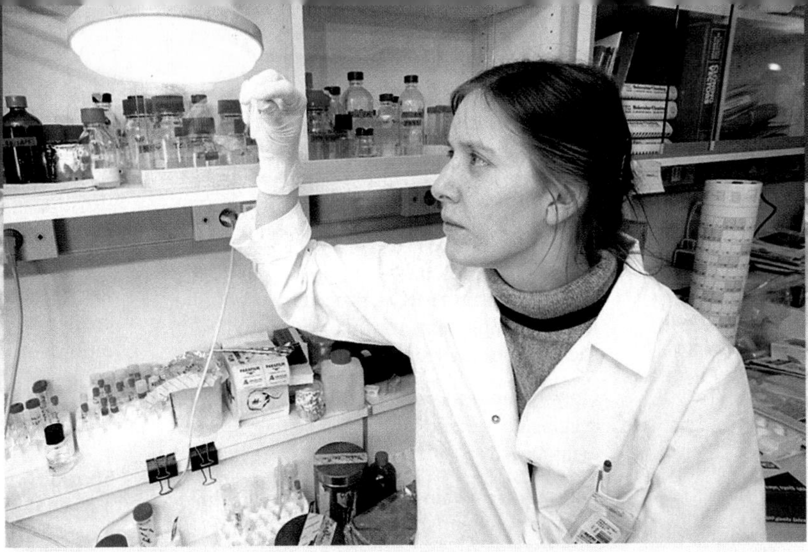

Researcher in a molecular biology laboratory

CHAPTER NINE

Biotechnology and Recombinant DNA

A Glimpse of History

In 1976, Argentinean newspapers reported a violent shootout between soldiers and the occupants of a house in suburban Buenos Aires, leaving the five extremists inside dead. Conspicuously absent from those reports was the identity of the "extremists"—a young couple and their three children, ages six years, five years, and six months. Over the next seven years, similar scenarios recurred as the military junta that ruled Argentina eliminated thousands of its citizens perceived as threats. This "Dirty War," as it came to be known, finally ended in 1983 with the collapse of the military junta and the election of a democratic government. The new leaders opened previously sealed records, which confirmed what many had already suspected—that more than 200 children survived the carnage and had in fact been kidnapped and placed with families in favor with the junta.

Dr. Mary-Claire King was at the University of California at Berkeley when her help was enlisted in the effort to return the children to the surviving members of their biological families. Dr. King and others recognized that DNA technology could be used for this important humanitarian cause. By analyzing certain DNA sequences, blood and tissue samples from one individual can be distinguished from those of another. These same principles can also be used to show that a particular child is the progeny of a given set of parents. Because a person has two copies of each chromosome—one inherited from each parent—one half of a child's DNA will represent maternal sequences and the other half will represent paternal traits. The case of the Argentinean children presented a great challenge, however, as most of the parents were dead or missing. Often, the only surviving relatives were aunts and grandmothers, and it is difficult to use chromosomal DNA to show genetic relatedness between a child and such relatives. Dr. King decided to investigate mitochondrial DNA (mtDNA). This organelle DNA, unlike chromosomal DNA, is inherited only from the mother. A child will have the same nucleotide sequence of mtDNA as his or her siblings, the mother and her siblings, as well as the maternal grandmother.

By comparing the nucleotide sequences of mtDNA in different individuals, Dr. King was able to locate key positions that varied extensively among unrelated people, but were similar in maternal relatives. Dr. King's technique, born out of a desire to help reunite families victimized by war, has now found many uses. Today her lab, which is now at the University of Washington, remains very active using molecular biology techniques for humanitarian efforts, identifying the remains of victims of atrocities around the world.

A revolution has occurred in molecular biology over the past several decades—the science has been transformed from a descriptive study of what cells are, to an intricate study of how cells function. A driving force in that revolution was the development of simple methods to extract and manipulate DNA, the blueprint of life.

Biotechnology is the use of microbiological and biochemical techniques to solve practical problems and produce more useful products. In the past, this usually meant laboriously searching for naturally occurring mutants that produced maximal product or expressed other desirable characteristics. Today, the rapid developments in **recombinant DNA techniques,** the methods scientists use to study and manipulate DNA, have made it possible to genetically alter organisms to give them more useful traits. Researchers can isolate genes from one organism, manipulate the purified DNA *in vitro,* and then transfer the genes into another organism, a process called **gene cloning.** In fact, biotechnology is now nearly synonymous with **genetic engineering,** the process of deliberately altering an organism's genetic information using *in vitro* techniques.

KEY TERMS

Colony blotting Technique used to determine which colonies on an agar plate contain a given nucleotide sequence.

DNA microarray Technique used to screen a single sample for a vast range of different nucleotide sequences simultaneously; it is often used to study gene expression.

DNA probe Single-stranded piece of DNA tagged with a detectable marker and used to detect its complement.

DNA sequencing Technique used to determine the sequence of nucleotides in a DNA molecule.

Fluorescence *in situ* hybridization Technique used to detect a given nucleotide sequence within intact cells affixed to a microscope slide.

Gel electrophoresis A procedure used to separate DNA fragments (or other macromolecules) according to their size.

Genetic engineering Deliberately altering an organism's genetic information using *in vitro* techniques.

Polymerase chain reaction (PCR) Technique used to exponentially amplify specific regions of a DNA molecule.

Primer Fragment of nucleic acid to which DNA polymerase can add nucleotides; used by researchers to choose the site where *in vitro* DNA synthesis will initiate.

Recombinant DNA molecule DNA molecule created by joining DNA fragments from two different sources.

Restriction enzyme Type of enzyme that recognizes and cleaves a specific sequence of DNA.

Southern blotting Technique used to detect a given nucleotide sequence in DNA fragments that have been separated according to size.

Vector DNA molecule, often a plasmid, that acts as a carrier of cloned DNA.

Since the advent of gene cloning, a virtual toolbox of DNA technologies has been developed. These have generated information and innovations that are impacting society in innumerable ways—from agricultural practices and medical diagnoses to evidence used in the courtroom.

9.1

Fundamental Tools Used in Biotechnology

Focus Point

- Describe the function of restriction enzymes, gel electrophoresis, nucleic acid probes, and primers.

Before exploring the applications of biotechnology, it is helpful to understand some of the basic components of a molecular biologist's "tool kit." These include restriction enzymes, gel electrophoresis, DNA probes, and primers. They allow scientists to cut DNA into fragments, separate DNA fragments according to size, locate certain nucleotide sequences, and initiate *in vitro* DNA synthesis at specific locations.

As we describe the various tools, it is important to remember that descriptions and diagrams focus on only one or a few DNA molecules in a solution to illustrate what is happening at a molecular level. In reality, scientists are generally working with cultures containing over a million cells, DNA isolated from those millions of cells, or millions of copies of chemically synthesized DNA molecules.

Restriction Enzymes

Restriction enzymes are naturally occurring enzymes that allow scientists to easily cut DNA into fragments in a predictable and controllable manner. Each enzyme recognizes a specific nucleotide sequence, usually a 4 or 6 base-pair palindrome, and then cuts both strands of the molecule within or near that sequence **(table 9.1).** This action digests the DNA, generating a series of pieces called **restriction fragments (figure 9.1a).** Each restriction enzyme has been given a seemingly peculiar name, but the name simply represents the bacterium from which the enzyme was first isolated. The first letter represents the first letter of the genus name, and the next two letters are derived from the species name. Any other numbers or letters designate the strain and order of discovery. For example, a restriction enzyme from *E. coli* strain RY13 is called *Eco*RI. ■ restriction enzymes, p. 332

Researchers use restriction enzymes not only to cut DNA, but also to generate fragments that can easily be joined to fragments from an entirely different source. This is possible because many restriction enzymes produce a staggered cut in the recognition sequence, generating ends with a short overhang of usually 4

TABLE 9.1 Examples of Common Restriction Enzymes

Enzyme	Microbial Source	Recognition Sequence (arrows indicate cleavage sites)
AluI	*Arthrobacter luteus*	↓ (between G and C) 5′ A G C T 3′ 3′ T C G A 5′ ↑ (between C and G)
BamHI	*Bacillus amyloliquefaciens* H	↓ (between G and G) 5′ G G A T C C 3′ 3′ C C T A G G 5′ ↑ (between G and G)
EcoRI	*Escherichia coli* RY13	↓ (between G and A) 5′ G A A T T C 3′ 3′ C T T A A G 5′ ↑ (between A and G)

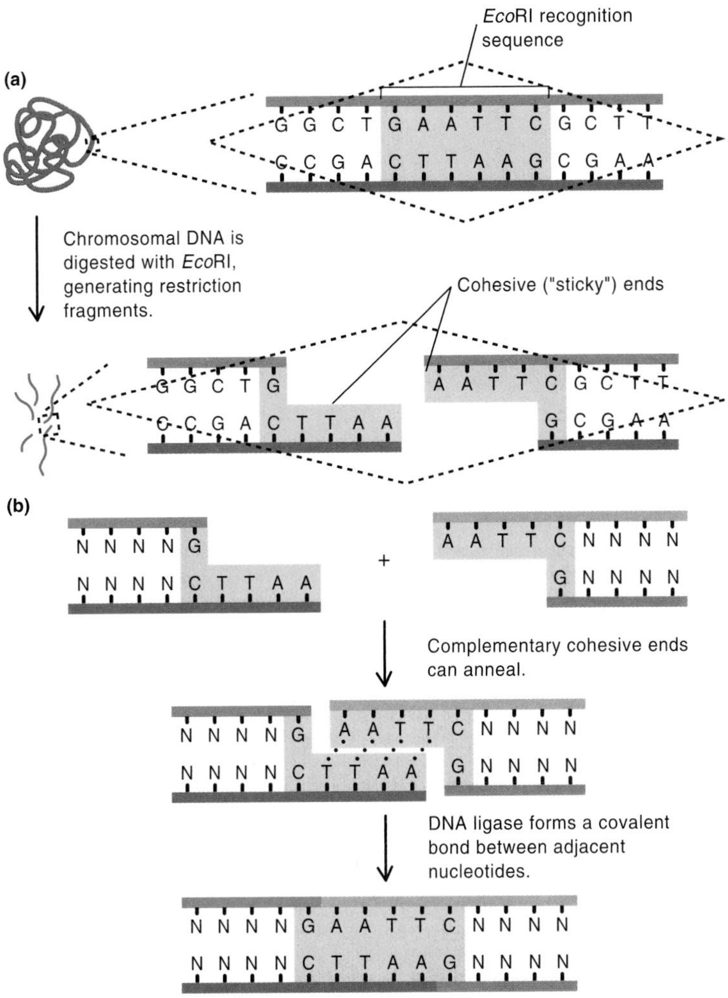

FIGURE 9.1 Action of Restriction Enzymes **(a)** Digesting DNA with a restriction enzyme generates restriction fragments. **(b)** Fragments that have complementary cohesive ends can anneal, regardless of their original source (N = nucleotide, meaning that it could be any of the 4 bases as long as base-pairing rules are followed).

bases (see figure 9.1b). The overhangs are called **sticky ends** or **cohesive ends** because they will form base pairs, or **anneal,** with one another. Any two complementary cohesive ends can anneal, even those from two different organisms. The relatively weak hydrogen bonds that hold the strands together are only temporary, however. The enzyme **DNA ligase** forms a covalent bond between the sugar-phosphate residues of adjacent nucleotides, joining the two molecules. Thus, if restriction enzymes are viewed as scissors that cut DNA into fragments, then DNA ligase is the glue that pastes the fragments together. The combined actions of restriction enzymes and DNA ligase enable researchers to join fragments of DNA from diverse sources, creating **recombinant DNA molecules.** ■ DNA ligase, p. 173

Gel Electrophoresis

Gel electrophoresis is used to separate DNA fragments according to size **(figure 9.2).** The technique uses a slab of gel that has the consistency of a very firm gelatin and is made of either agarose, a highly purified form of agar, or polyacrylamide. A DNA sample is put into a well in the gel; there are generally numerous wells in a gel so that multiple samples can be analyzed simultaneously. As a means to eventually determine the size of the various DNA fragments in the samples, a **size standard** is routinely put into a well of the same gel. This is simply a series of DNA fragments of known sizes that can be used as a basis for later comparison.

The gel is then subjected to an electrical current. DNA is negatively charged, so the fragments migrate toward the positively-charged electrode. As the DNA moves through the gel, however, not all fragments progress at the same rate. This is because the gel acts as a sieve, impeding the long fragments while allowing the shorter ones to pass through more quickly. Because of the sieve-like effect of the gel, the restriction fragments are separated according to their size.

The DNA is not visible in the gel unless it is stained. To do this, the gel containing the separated DNA fragments is immersed in a solution containing the **ethidium bromide.** This dye binds DNA and fluoresces when viewed with UV light (see figure 9.2b). Each fluorescent band represents millions of molecules of a specific-sized fragment of DNA.

Gel electrophoresis can also be used to separate other macromolecules, specifically RNA and proteins, according to their size. The basic principles are similar to that illustrated for separating DNA, but the gel compositions differ.

DNA Probes

DNA probes are used to locate specific nucleotide sequences in DNA or RNA samples that have been affixed to a solid surface **(figure 9.3).**

(a)

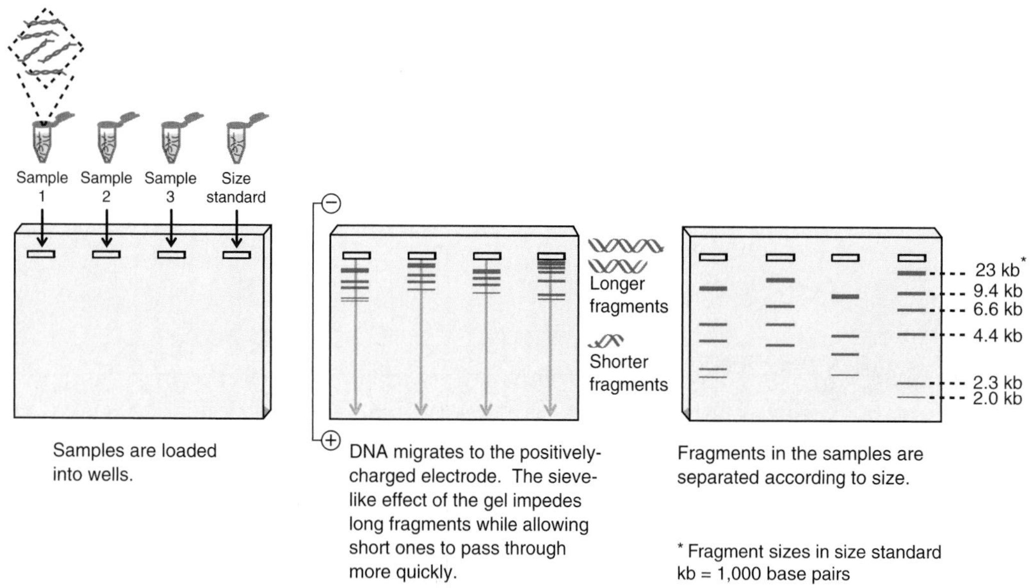

(b)

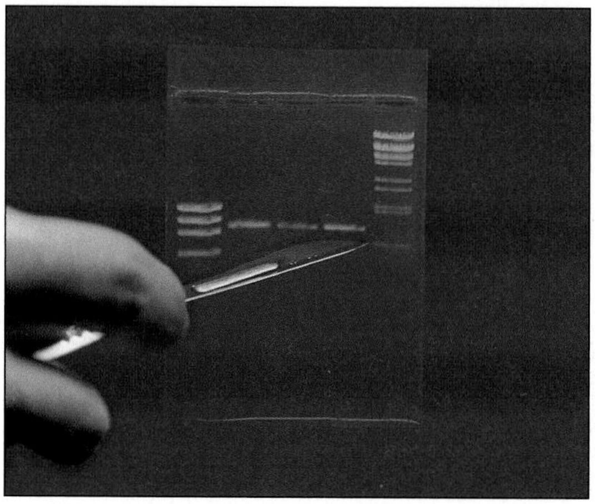

FIGURE 9.2 Gel Electrophoresis **(a)** Gel electrophoresis separates DNA fragments according to size. **(b)** DNA on the gel is visible when stained with ethidium bromide and viewed with UV light; each fluorescent band represents millions of molecules of a specific-sized fragment.

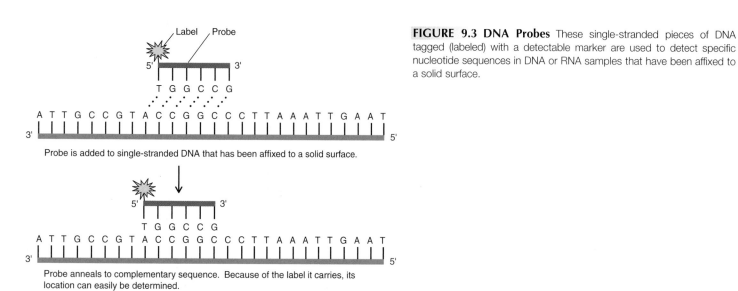

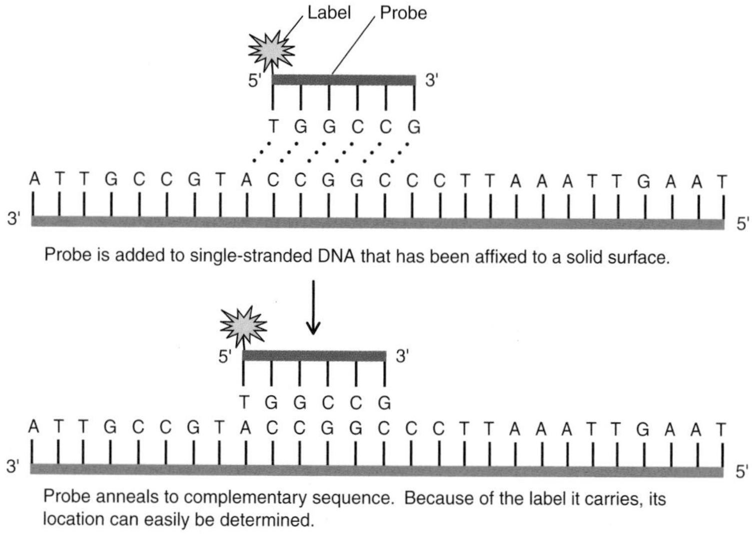

FIGURE 9.3 DNA Probes These single-stranded pieces of DNA tagged (labeled) with a detectable marker are used to detect specific nucleotide sequences in DNA or RNA samples that have been affixed to a solid surface.

The probe is a single-stranded piece of DNA that has been tagged, or labeled, with a detectable marker such as a radioactive isotope or a fluorescent dye. Because of the label the probe carries, its location can easily be determined. Obviously, unbound probe must be washed off before the detection step.

To understand how a probe functions, you must recognize that double-stranded DNA, when exposed to a high temperature or a high pH solution, will **denature,** or separate into two single strands. When the temperature is lowered and the pH is neutral, the two strands will anneal because of the base-pairing interactions of the complementary strands. Two complementary strands from different sources will also anneal, but the process is then called **hybridization** to reflect the fact that each strand originated from a different source to create a hybrid molecule. Thus, a probe will hybridize to its complement, essentially "finding" the sequence of interest in a sample and making it detectable.

Primers

Primers, like DNA probes, are single-stranded DNA fragments that bind to complementary DNA sequences. Primers, however, do not carry a detectable label. Instead, they are used as a component of *in vitro* DNA synthesis reactions, serving as the nucleic acid fragment to which DNA polymerase can add additional nucleotides **(figure 9.4).** Through appropriate primer selection, a researcher can choose the site where DNA synthesis will initiate.

MICROCHECK 9.1

Restriction enzymes recognize specific nucleotide sequences, and then cut the DNA, generating restriction fragments. Gel electrophoresis is used to separate DNA fragments according to their size. DNA probes detect specific nucleotide sequences in a sample. Primers are used to control the site where *in vitro* DNA synthesis will initiate.

- ✓ How does gel electrophoresis separate different-sized DNA fragments?
- ✓ What is the significance of cohesive ends?
- ✓ Based on the protocol for naming restriction enzymes, what is the name of one isolated from *Staphylococcus aureus* strain 3A?

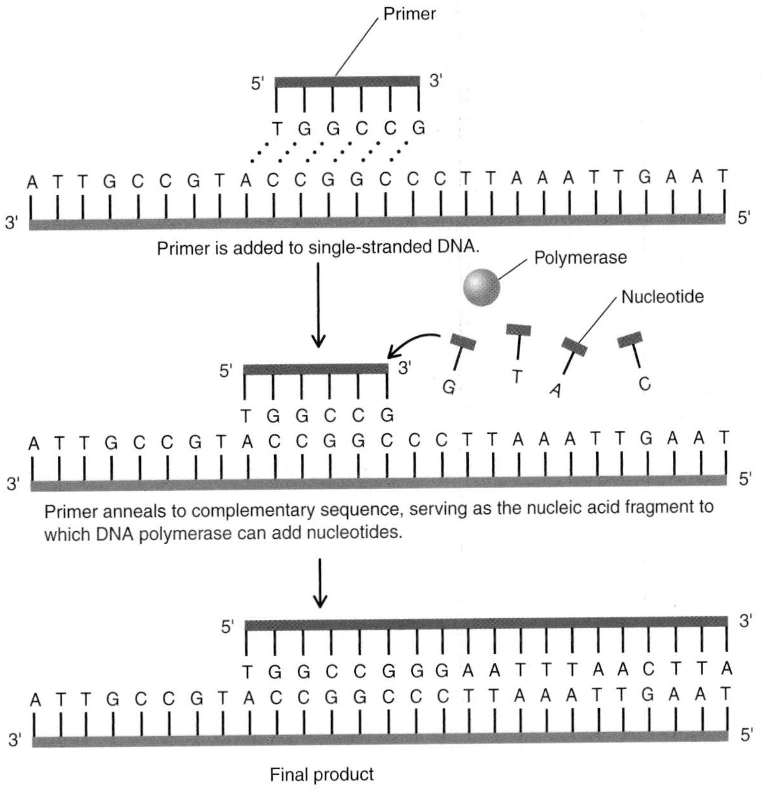

FIGURE 9.4 Primers Through appropriate primer selection, a researcher can choose the site where *in vitro* DNA synthesis will initiate.

APPLICATIONS OF BIOTECHNOLOGY

In this section we will explore some of the many applications of biotechnology, including genetic engineering, DNA probe technologies, polymerase chain reaction, and DNA sequencing. The second portion of the chapter will cover the fundamentals of the techniques.

9.2

Applications of Genetic Engineering

Focus Point

- Describe three general applications of genetically engineered bacteria, and four general applications of genetically engineered plants.

Genetic engineering brought biotechnology into a new era by providing a powerful tool for manipulating *E. coli* and other microorganisms for medical, industrial, and research uses **(table 9.2).** More recently, techniques that permit the genetic engineering of plants and animals have been developed.

Genetically Engineered Bacteria

Genetic engineering relies on **DNA cloning,** a process that involves isolating DNA from one organism, using restriction enzymes to cut the DNA into fragments, and then introducing those fragments into cells of another organism, most commonly *E. coli.* As part of the process, the cloned DNA must replicate in the recipient in order for it to be passed to daughter cells, generating a population of cells that each harbor a copy of the DNA fragment (see figure 8.18). Most DNA fragments, however, are unlikely to contain an origin of replication and therefore will not replicate independently in a cell, nor will they integrate into the chromosome. To overcome this problem, each fragment being cloned must be inserted into a plasmid or other independently replicating DNA molecule to form a **recombinant molecule.** The DNA molecule used as a carrier of the cloned DNA is called a **cloning vector,** or, more simply, a **vector.** The DNA that has been incorporated into the vector is called an **insert.** ■ origin of replication, p. 172

An approach frequently used to clone a specific gene is to clone a set of restriction fragments that together make up the entire genome of the organism being studied into a population of *E. coli* cells **(figure 9.5).** While each cell in the resulting population contains only one fragment of the genome, the entire genome is represented in the population as a whole. Because each cloned molecule can be viewed as one "book" of the total genetic information, the collection of clones is called a **DNA library.** Once a DNA library has been prepared, colony blots (which will be described later) can be used to determine which cells contain the gene of interest.

Genetically engineered bacteria have a variety of uses, including protein production, DNA production, and research. In fact, a great deal of the information described in this textbook has been revealed through research involving genetically engineered bacteria.

Protein Production

Bacteria can be engineered to produce commercially important proteins more efficiently. A gene coding for a valuable protein can be inserted into a high-copy-number vector and then introduced into the same or a different organism. The organism will then make increased amounts of the protein, because each gene copy can be transcribed and translated **(figure 9.6).** Not only can bacteria be engineered to make increased amounts of commercially valuable microbial products, such as various enzymes, they can also be engineered to synthesize proteins normally produced only by animal cells (see table 9.2). ■ high-copy-number plasmid, p. 208

Pharmaceutical Proteins A variety of proteins can be used to treat people suffering from certain diseases. In the past, these proteins were extracted from live animal or cadaver tissues, which made them expensive and limited in supply. Human insulin, used in treating diabetics, was one of the first important pharmaceutical proteins to be produced through genetic engineering. The original commercial product, extracted from pancreatic glands of cattle and pigs, caused allergic reactions in approximately 1 in 20 patients. Once the gene for human insulin was cloned into bacteria, microorganisms became the major source of insulin sold in the United States. A 2,000-liter culture of *E. coli* that contains the insulin gene yields 100 grams of purified insulin, an amount that would require 1,600 pounds of pancreatic glands! The microbial production of insulin is safer and more economical than extracting it from animal tissues.

Vaccines Vaccines protect against disease by harmlessly exposing a person's immune system to a killed or weakened form of the pathogen, or to a part of the pathogen. Although a vaccine is generally composed of whole bacterial cells or viral particles, only specific proteins, or parts of the proteins, are actually necessary to induce protection, or immunize, against the disease. The genes coding for these proteins can be cloned in yeast or bacteria so that a large amount of the pure immunizing proteins can be produced. This type of vaccine is currently used to prevent hepatitis B in humans and foot-and-mouth disease of domestic animals. ■ vaccines, p. 415

Other Commercially Valuable Proteins One of the most widely used proteins made by genetically engineered organisms is chymosin, a proteolytic enzyme used in cheese production. It is a natural component of rennin, a preparation from the stomach of calves. Chymosin causes milk to coagulate and produces desir-

TABLE 9.2 Some Applications of Genetic Engineering

Example	Use
PROTEIN PRODUCTION	
Pharmaceutical proteins	
Alpha interferon	Treating cancer and viral infections
Erythropoietin	Treating some types of anemia
Beta interferon	Treating multiple sclerosis
Deoxyribonuclease	Treating cystic fibrosis
Factor VIII	Treating hemophilia
Gamma interferon	Treating cancer
Glucocerebrosidase	Treating Gaucher disease
Growth hormone	Treating dwarfism
Insulin	Treating diabetes
Platelet derived growth factor	Treating foot ulcers in diabetics
Streptokinase	Dissolving blood clots
Tissue plasminogen activator	Dissolving blood clots
Vaccines	
Hepatitis B	Preventing hepatitis
Foot-and-mouth disease	Preventing foot-and-mouth disease in animals
Other proteins	
Bovine somatotropin	Increasing milk production in cows
Chymosin	Cheese-making
Restriction enzymes	Cutting DNA into fragments
DNA PRODUCTION	
DNA for study	Determining nucleotide sequences; obtaining DNA probes
DNA for vaccines	Studying the potential of using DNA-based vaccines to prevent certain diseases
RESEARCHING GENE FUNCTION AND REGULATION	
Creating gene fusions	Studying the conditions that affect gene activity
TRANSGENIC PLANTS	
Pest-resistant plants	Insect-resistant corn, cotton, and potatoes
Herbicide-resistant plants	Biodegradable herbicide can be used to kill weeds without killing engineered plants (soybean, cotton, corn)
Plants with improved nutritional value	Rice that produces vitamin A and iron
Plants that function as edible vaccines	Enables researchers to study foods as vehicles for edible vaccines

able changes in the characteristics of cheeses as they ripen. Using genetically engineered bacteria to produce chymosin is preferable to isolating rennin from calves because the microbial product is less expensive and more reliably available. Other proteins produced by genetically engineered microbes include various restriction enzymes and bovine somatotropin, a growth hormone used to increase milk production in dairy cows.

DNA Production

In many cases, a researcher is interested in obtaining readily available supplies of certain DNA fragments. By cloning a segment of DNA into a well-characterized bacterium such as *E. coli,* an easy source of that sequence is available for study and further manipulation. This has been used to further our understanding in a broad range of areas, from the impact of bacteria on human health to the role of environmental bacteria in various ecological processes.

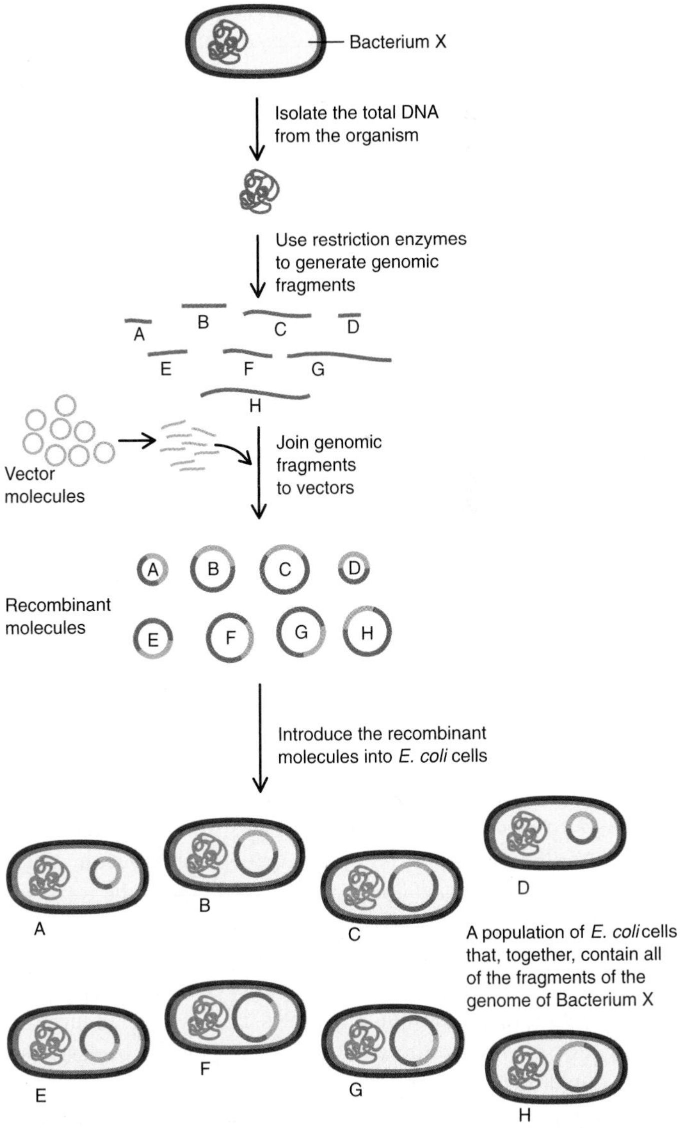

FIGURE 9.5 A DNA Library Each cell contains one fragment of a given organism's genome.

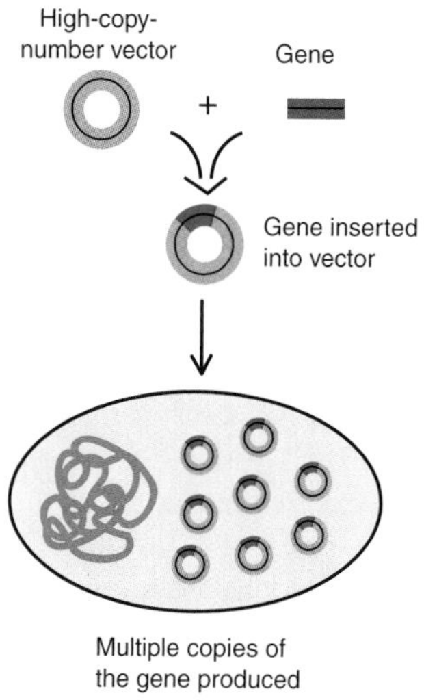

FIGURE 9.6 Cloning into a High-Copy-Number Vector When a gene is inserted into a high-copy-number vector, multiple copies of that gene will be present in a single cell, resulting in the synthesis of many more molecules of the encoded protein.

DNA for Study Genetic engineering can be used to study genomic characteristics of some of the 99% of bacteria that have not been grown in culture. This was exemplified in recent research that led to the discovery of a mechanism of energy capture in marine bacteria which had previously been described only in certain members of the *Archaea.* Researchers isolated random DNA fragments from ocean samples and then cloned them into *E. coli.* Using some of the techniques that will be discussed later, the researchers were then able to determine the nucleotide sequences of various cloned bacterial DNA molecules. One of these was found to encode a novel gene for bacterial rhodopsin, a light-sensitive pigment that can be used to harvest energy from sunlight. The pigment provides the bacterium with a mechanism for phototrophy that does not require chlorophyll. Further studies showed that variations of the bacterial rhodopsin gene are widespread among marine bacteria, suggesting it might be an important mechanism for energy accumulation in ocean environments. All of this was discovered without ever growing the marine microbes in culture!

Human genes are often cloned into bacteria to make them easier to study. A human cell contains an estimated 25,000 genes, whereas *E. coli* contains only 4,500 genes; thus, a human gene cloned into the bacterium on a high-copy-number vector represents a much higher percentage of the total DNA in the recipient cell than in the original cell. This makes it easier to isolate the DNA as well as the gene product. In addition, since bacteria are much smaller than human cells and grow considerably faster, many more cells can be quickly grown in the same volume of growth medium. Also, the conditions for growing bacteria are much simpler than for growing human cells.

DNA for Vaccines Researchers have found that when plasmid DNA is injected into a person's tissues, the encoded proteins are expressed for a short time. This gives rise to the possibility that certain vaccines may someday be administered by injecting DNA that encodes proteins from disease-causing organisms. DNA-based vaccines are still in the experimental stage, but promising results have been obtained in animal studies.

Researching Gene Function and Regulation

Gene function and regulation can more easily be studied in *E. coli* because systems for manipulating its DNA have been developed. For example, regulation of gene expression can be studied by creating a **gene fusion,** joining the gene being studied and a **reporter gene (figure 9.7).** The reporter gene encodes a readily observable phenotype such as fluorescence, making it possible to directly observe the expression of the gene. This, in turn, makes it possible to determine the conditions that affect gene activity. One widely used reporter gene encodes a protein called green fluorescent protein (GFP).

Genetically Engineered Eukaryotes

Yeast can be genetically engineered to perform many of the functions described for bacteria. They serve as an important model for gene function and regulation in eukaryotic cells.

A plant or animal into which a cloned gene has been introduced is called a **transgenic organism.** Transgenic plants are of particular interest to microbiologists because their development was spawned as a result of basic research studying *Agrobacterium tumefaciens,* a plant pathogen (see Perspective 8.2). This organism is a natural genetic engineer; it transfers a distinct portion of its Ti (tumor-inducing) plasmid to the chromosome of a plant cell. Researchers genetically modified the Ti plasmid, removing the tumor-inducing genes, so it could be used as a vector to deliver desirable genes to plant cells. Examples of genetically modified plants include:

- **Pest-resistant plants** Corn, cotton, and potatoes have been engineered to produce a biological insecticide, a protein crystal called Bt-toxin. This toxin is naturally produced by the bacterium *Bacillus thuringiensis* as it forms endospores. Unlike many chemically synthesized toxins, Bt-toxin is toxic only to insects, including their larvae. Crystal/spore preparations have been applied to a variety of plants around the world for over 30 years without any apparent harm to the environment. ■ endospore, p. 71
- **Herbicide-resistant plants** Soybeans, cotton, and corn have been engineered to resist the effects of the herbicide glyphosate (Roundup™). This enables growers to apply this readily biodegradable herbicide, which kills weeds and other non-engineered plants, in place of more persistent alternatives. Also, because the herbicide can be applied throughout the growing season, the soil can be tilled less frequently, preventing erosion.
- **Plants with improved nutrient value** Researchers around the world are attempting to employ genetic engineering to improve the nutritional value of plants used as food. A recent example is the introduction of the genes that code for the synthesis of β-carotene, a precursor of vitamin A, into rice. The rice was also engineered to provide more dietary iron. Since

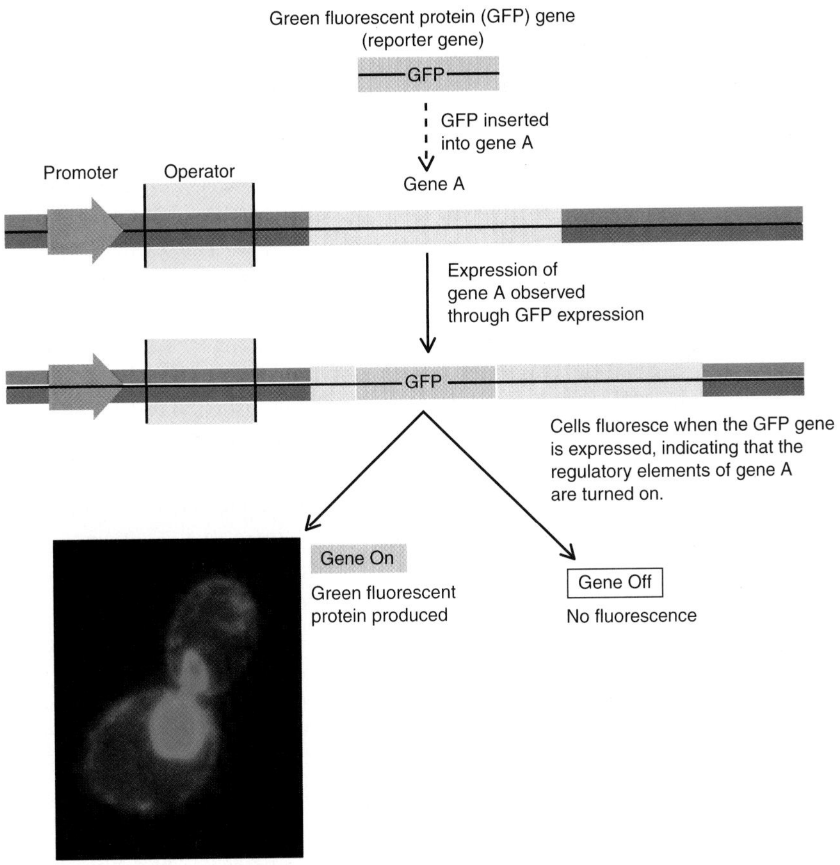

FIGURE 9.7 The Function of a Reporter Gene Expression of a reporter gene can be readily detected, making it useful in the study of gene regulation.

the diet of a significant proportion of the world's population is deficient in these essential nutrients, advances such as this could have a profound impact on world health.

- **Plants that function as edible vaccines** Bananas or other foods could someday be used as vehicles for edible vaccines. Researchers have successfully genetically engineered potatoes to produce certain proteins from pathogens and have shown that the immune system responds to these proteins, raising hopes for the development of an edible vaccine. Whether the immune response is strong enough to protect against the disease remains to be determined.

MICROCHECK 9.2

Genetically engineered bacteria can be used to produce a variety of products including medically important proteins, vaccines, commercially important proteins, and DNA for study. They are also used as research tools. Genetic engineering of plants can be used to develop pest-resistant plants, herbicide-resistant plants and plants with improved nutritional value. Through genetic engineering, edible vaccines might one day be possible.

✓ Name two diseases that are treated using proteins produced by genetically engineered microorganisms.

✓ Describe the attributes of two different types of transgenic plants.

✓ Potatoes are relatively easy to genetically engineer, which is why they are being used in the edible vaccine studies. Why will edible vaccines eventually require the engineering of a food product that is routinely consumed raw?

9.3

Applications of Probe Technologies

Focus Point

- Compare and contrast the applications of colony blotting, Southern blotting, FISH, and DNA microarray technologies.

A variety of technologies employ DNA probes to locate specific nucleotide sequences. They include colony blotting, Southern blotting, fluorescence *in situ* hybridization (FISH), and DNA microarray technologies.

Colony Blotting

Colony blotting uses probes to detect specific DNA sequences in colonies grown on agar plates **(figure 9.8).** The term "blot" in the name reflects the fact that the colonies are transferred in place ("blotted") onto a nylon membrane, creating a pattern of colonies identical to that of the original plate. The membrane serves as a durable permanent support for the cells and their DNA. After the transfer, the membrane is soaked in an alkaline solution to simultaneously lyse the cells and denature their DNA, generating single-stranded DNA molecules to which the probe can bind. Colony blots are commonly used to determine which cells in a collection of clones contain the DNA of interest.

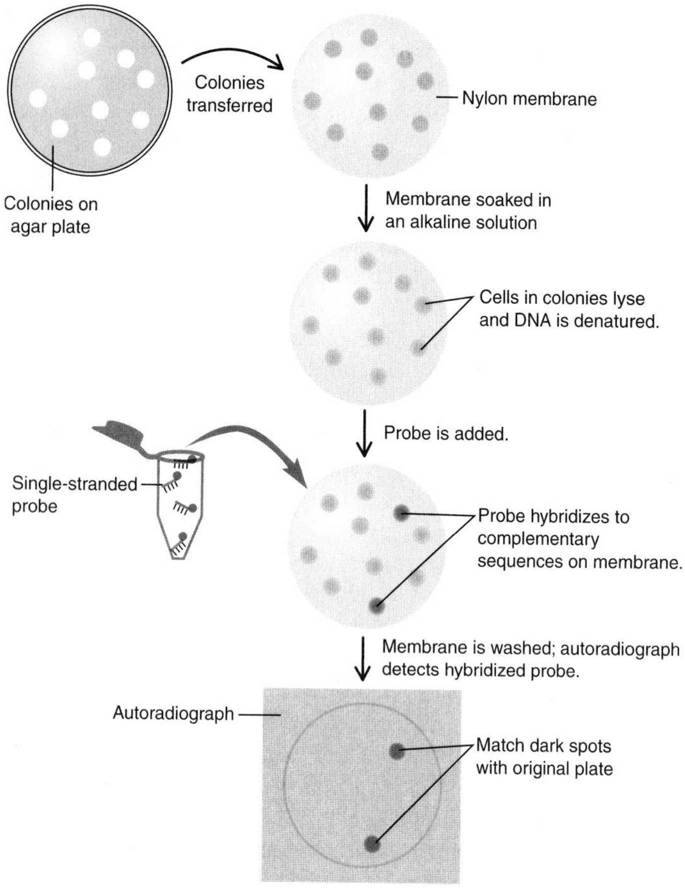

FIGURE 9.8 Colony Blotting This technique is used to determine which colonies on an agar plate contain a given DNA sequence. In this example, the probe is labeled with a radioactive isotope, which can be detected using autoradiography.

Southern Blotting

Southern blotting uses probes to detect given DNA sequences in restriction fragments that have been separated by size using gel electrophoresis **(figure 9.9).** Like the procedure for colony blotting, the DNA is transferred in-place ("blotted") to a nylon membrane and the probe then added. Before the transfer, however, the gel is soaked in an alkaline solution to denature the DNA.

Southern blotting is named after the scientist who developed the procedure, E. M. Southern. Analogous techniques involving separation of macromolecules and probing for certain sequences or motifs have now been developed to study RNA and protein. To reflect the relationship of these techniques to Southern blotting, they are referred to as Northern blotting and Western blotting, respectively.

The most obvious application of Southern blotting is to locate DNA sequences that have similar sequences to the one being studied, which is how many functionally related genes have been discovered and characterized. In this case, one strand of the gene being studied is used as a probe. This information can also be used to simplify a cloning experiment. For example, if the gene of interest is shown to be encoded on a restriction fragment 6,000 base pairs in length, then fragments of that size can be separated from the rest and cloned.

A less apparent but equally important use of the Southern blot is to distinguish different strains of a given species by detecting subtle variations in their nucleotide sequences. Certain mutations will create, others will destroy, restriction enzymes recognition sequences at particular sites in the genome. Thus, when genomic DNA of different strains is digested with the same restriction enzyme, each will give rise to a slightly different assortment of restriction fragment sizes **(figure 9.10).** Each variation is called a **restriction fragment length polymorphism (RFLP).** Southern blot hybridization is used to selectively visualize restriction fragments that often vary in size. The probe employed is one that has already been shown by trial and error to hybridize to fragments that demonstrate maximal differences among various strains.

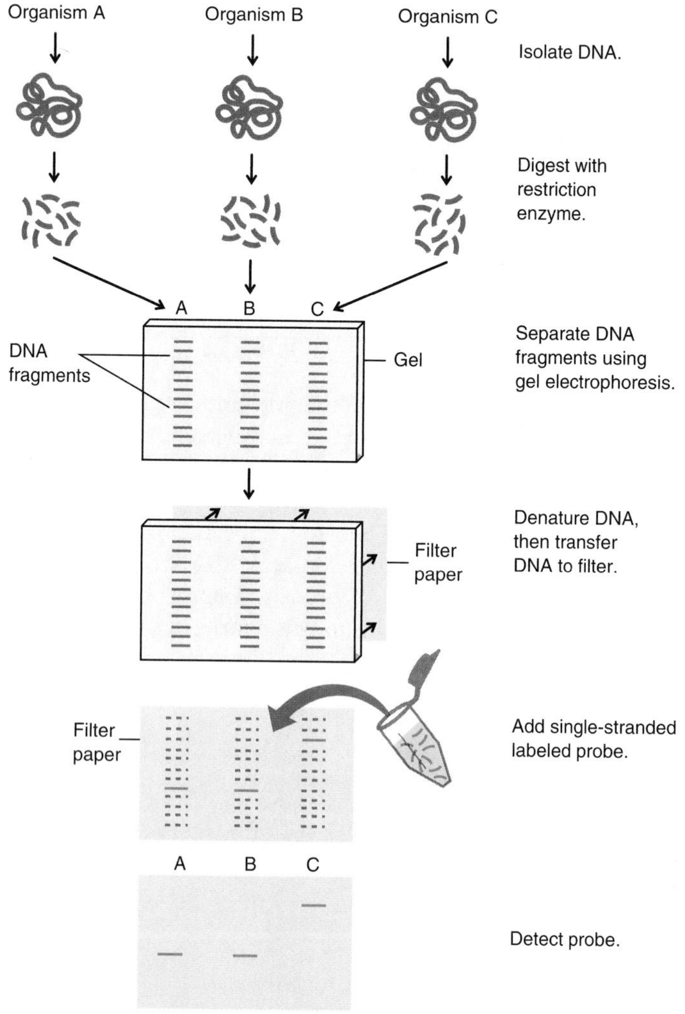

FIGURE 9.9 Southern Blotting This technique is used to verify the presence or absence of a given nucleotide sequence and determine the size of any restriction enzyme fragments that contain the sequence.

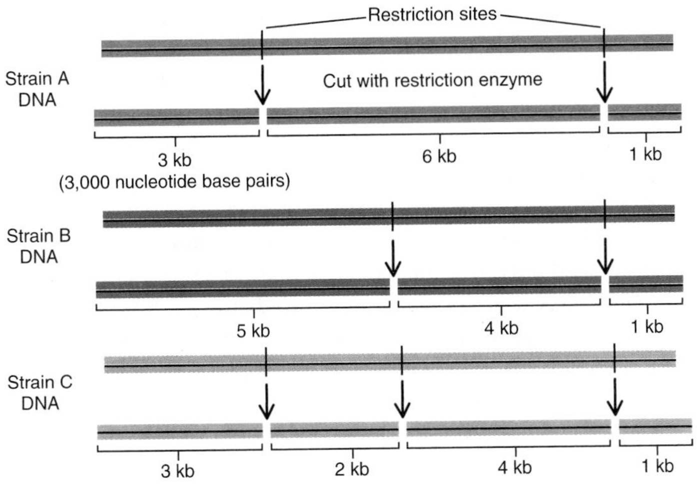

FIGURE 9.10 Restriction Fragment Length Polymorphism (RFLP) Different strains of a species may have subtle variations in nucleotide sequences that give rise to a slightly different assortment of restriction fragment sizes.

Fluorescence *in situ* Hybridization (FISH)

Fluorescence *in situ* hybridization (FISH) uses fluorescently-labeled probes to detect specific nucleotide sequences within intact cells affixed to a microscope slide. Cells within which the probe hybridized can then be viewed using a fluorescence microscope. To study prokaryotes, a probe that binds to ribosomal RNA (rRNA) is generally used. Because actively growing cells can have thousands of copies of rRNA, this increases the sensitivity of the technique. Other characteristics of rRNA that make it useful for identifying prokaryotes are discussed in chapter 10. ■ **fluorescence microscope, p. 46** ■ **using genotypic characteristics to identify prokaryotes, p. 255**

FISH is revolutionizing the study of microbial ecology and holds great promise in clinical laboratories. It provides a means of rapid identification of microorganisms directly in a specimen, bypassing the need to grow organisms in culture. FISH can be used to observe either a specific species or a group of related organisms, depending on the nucleotide sequence of the probe employed. For example, FISH can be used to determine the relative proportion of two different groups of prokaryotes in the same specimen. This is done by using two separate probes, one specific for each group, labeled with different colored fluorescent markers **(figure 9.11)**. Another use is to identify and enumerate *Mycobacterium tuberculosis* cells in a sputum specimen. ■ **studying microbial ecology, p. 763**

DNA Microarray Technologies

DNA arrays are solid supports that have fixed patterns of numerous different single-stranded DNA fragments of known sequences attached to them. One of the most sophisticated types is a **DNA microarray,** a solid support of less than an inch in diameter that carries an arrangement of tens or hundreds of thousands of **oligonucleotides,** short DNA fragments **(figure 9.12).** The power of these arrays is that each DNA fragment functions in a manner analogous to a probe, enabling a researcher to screen a single sample for a vast range of different sequences simultaneously. Unlike typical probes, however, the arrays do not carry a detectable label. Instead, the label must be attached to the nucleic acid of interest—for example, genomic DNA from a bacterium. That DNA is digested into small fragments, labeled with a fluorescent marker, denatured, and then added to the array, where it will hybridize to complementary sequences. After washing the array to remove unhybridized DNA, the locations of the labeled DNA molecules are detected using a computerized scanner. Because the sequence of each of the fragments that make up the array is known, the location of the label can be used to determine the presence of specific sequences in the DNA of interest.

DNA microarrays can also be used to study gene expression in those organisms whose genome has been sequenced. Using the information gleaned from the DNA sequence, a microarray can be constructed to contain an oligonucleotide specific for each gene of that particular organism. mRNA isolated from a culture grown under a particular set of conditions and then labeled with a fluorescent marker is allowed to hybridize to the array. The location of the hybridized mRNA reveals the genes that are transcribed under those particular conditions. By repeating the experiment using a culture grown under a different set of conditions, perhaps an environment that mimics what a pathogen would encounter in the body, differences in gene expression can be demonstrated.

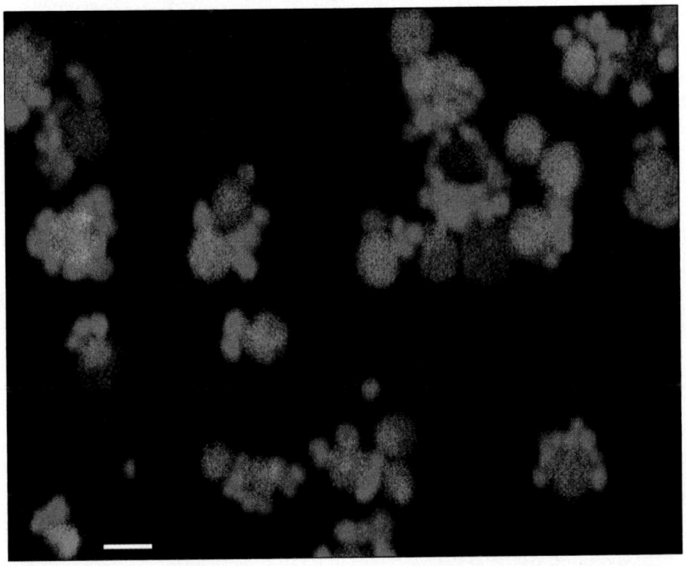

FIGURE 9.11 Fluorescence *in situ* Hybridization (FISH) Two different probes have been used to stain the cells. The probe that hybridizes to *Ignicoccus* rRNA fluoresces green; the one that hybridizes to *Nanoarchaeum* rRNA fluoresces red. Size bar = 1 μm.

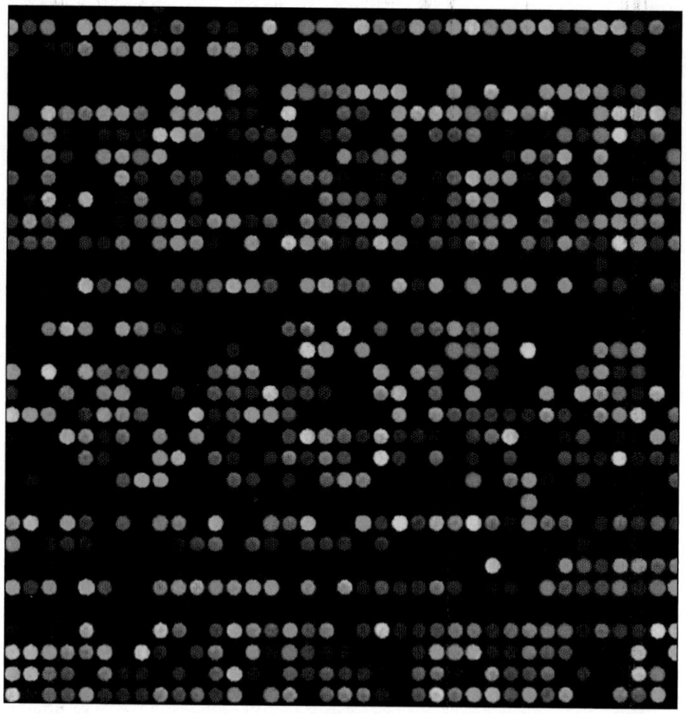

FIGURE 9.12 A DNA Microarray Two different nucleic acid samples (one labeled with a red fluorescent marker and the other with a green fluorescent marker) were simultaneously hybridized to the microarray. Red dots indicate the positions to which one sample hybridized, and green dots indicate the positions of the other. Yellow dots indicate that both samples hybridized. The arrays, read with the aid of computerized scanners, are often used to study gene expression.

MICROCHECK 9.3

Colony blotting uses probes to identify colonies that contain a given sequence of DNA. Southern blotting uses probes to determine the size of the restriction fragments that contain a sequence of interest and to detect subtle variations in nucleotide sequences that occur in different strains of a given species. Fluorescence *in situ* hybridization is used to observe individual cells that contain a given sequence. DNA microarray technologies enable researchers to screen a sample for a vast range of different sequences simultaneously.

- ✓ What role does colony blotting play in cloning?
- ✓ What is an RFLP?
- ✓ Why would a pathogen express different genes when inside the body?

9.4 Applications of DNA Sequencing

Focus Point

- Describe two applications of DNA sequencing.

The **Human Genome Project,** the recently completed undertaking to determine the sequence of the human genome, has resulted in highly automated and efficient DNA sequencing techniques. This has enabled scientists to more readily determine the genomic sequence of other organisms, including both prokaryotes and eukaryotes, fueling the rapidly growing field of genomics. ■ genomics, p. 187

Genomic approaches are leading to many exciting advances, such as the discovery mentioned earlier of the bacterial rhodopsin gene in a marine bacterium that has never been cultivated. Cloning techniques contributed to the study, but DNA sequencing and subsequent analysis of predicted protein-encoding regions were also integral to the finding. Previous genomic studies of other organisms enabled the researchers to learn that the amino acid sequence of one predicted protein was similar to that of bacteriorhodopsin, a light-driven proton pump of a *Halobacterium* species, a member of the *Archaea.* ■ analyzing a prokaryotic DNA sequence, p. 187

Knowing the typical DNA sequence of a human gene helps scientists identify genetic alterations that result in certain diseases. For example, sickle cell anemia is due to a single base-pair change in the gene that encodes a part of the hemoglobin protein. This alteration results in a distorted protein that does not function properly. Likewise, the genetic disease cystic fibrosis is most often caused by a three-base-pair deletion in a protein involved with chloride transport in and out of cells. ■ protein structure, p. 29

DNA sequence analysis is also used to study evolutionary relatedness of organisms. Those with extensive sequence homology are likely to be closely related. Conversely, those with vastly different sequences are probably only distantly related. Comparing DNA sequences of ribosomal RNA genes has proven particularly valuable for determining relatedness. ■ 16S rDNA sequence analysis, p. 261

MICROCHECK 9.4

By determining the nucleotide sequence of a gene, scientists can learn about the protein it encodes and identify genetic alterations that result in certain diseases. DNA sequence analysis can also be used to study evolutionary relatedness.

- ✓ What is the Human Genome Project?
- ✓ Name two diseases that are due to genetic alterations.
- ✓ Why would the sequence of ribosomal RNA genes remain relatively stable over time?

9.5 Applications of the Polymerase Chain Reaction (PCR)

Focus Point

- Describe one application of PCR.

Development of the **polymerase chain reaction (PCR)** revolutionized research by making it possible to create millions of copies of a given region of DNA in only a matter of hours. The technique exploits the specificity of primers to selectively replicate only chosen regions, referred to as **target DNA.** As a result, starting with only a few DNA molecules, millions of molecules of target DNA are synthesized. In fact, target DNA can be generated in sufficient concentration to be visible when fragments in the sample are separated by gel electrophoresis, stained with ethidium bromide, and viewed with UV light

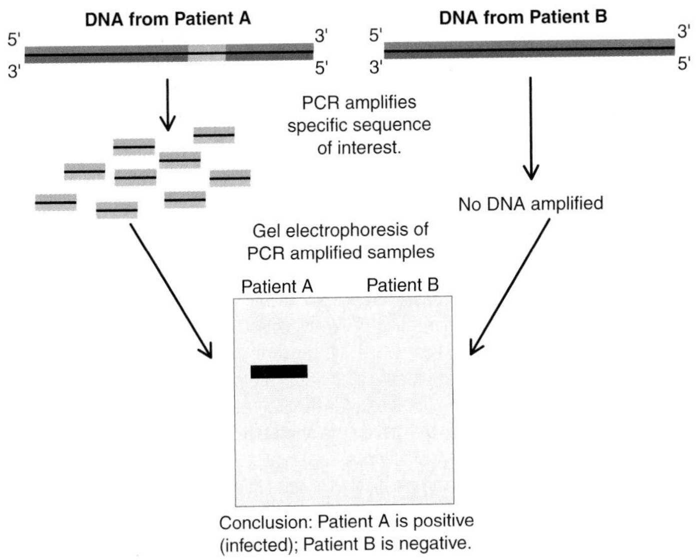

FIGURE 9.13 PCR Amplifies Selected Sequences By amplifying a chosen sequence that is unique to a given organism, it is possible to detect the presence of even minute numbers of that organism in a sample.

(figure 9.13). Other DNA in the sample will also be stained, but only amplified molecules will fluoresce brightly enough to be seen.

By choosing primers that anneal to sequences unique to a given organism, it is possible to detect that organism, even in samples that contain a wide assortment of different microbes. For example, if a nucleotide sequence found only in *Neisseria gonorrhoeae* can be amplified from a vaginal secretion, then *N. gonorrhoeae* must be present in that specimen, indicating that the patient has the sexually transmitted disease gonorrhea. Likewise, PCR can be used to detect HIV nucleotide sequences in a sample of blood cells, diagnosing HIV infection. The exquisite sensitivity of PCR, however, is also its greatest drawback. Great care must be taken not to contaminate a sample with an external source of the target DNA. In the example of HIV detection, inadvertently contaminating a specimen with even a minute amount of HIV nucleic acid from another source would result in a false-positive test.

MICROCHECK 9.5

The polymerase chain reaction is used to amplify target DNA, even in impure samples.

✓ How can PCR be used to diagnose gonorrhea?

9.6 Concerns Regarding DNA Technologies

Focus Point

- Describe some of the concerns regarding DNA technologies.

Advent of any new technology should bring scrutiny over the safety and efficacy of the procedures. When recombinant DNA technologies first allowed the cloning of genes over two decades ago, controversies swirled about their use and possible abuse. Even the scientists who developed the technologies were concerned about potential dangers of gene cloning. In response, the National Institutes of Health (NIH) formed the Recombinant DNA Advisory Committee (RAC) to develop a set of guidelines for conducting research that involved recombinant DNA techniques and gene cloning. Today, we are enjoying the fruits of many of those technologies, as evidenced by the list of commercially available products in table 9.2. Despite the fact that the technologies can be used to produce life-saving products, however, there can never be a guarantee that the same techniques will not be used for malicious purposes. Today, the idea that "superbugs" are being created for the purpose of bioterrorism is a disturbing possibility.

Recent advances in genomics have generated new cause for concern, primarily involving ethical issues regarding the appropriateness and confidentiality of information gained by analyzing a person's DNA. For example, will it be in an individual's best interest to be told of a genetic life-terminating disease? Could such information be used to deny an individual certain rights and privileges? Ongoing discussions about these complex issues must continue as the technologies advance.

Genetically modified (GM) organisms hold many promises, but the debate over their use is fraught with concerns, some logical and others not. For example, some people have expressed fear over the fact that GM foods "contain DNA"; considering that DNA is consumed routinely as we eat plants and animals, this is obviously an irrational concern. More reasonable fears include the worry that unanticipated allergens could be introduced into a food product, posing a threat to the health of some people. To address this issue, the FDA has implemented strict guidelines, including the requirement for producers to demonstrate that GM products intended for human consumption do not elicit allergic reactions. Mistakes, however, such as the inadvertent use of GM corn that had not been approved for human consumption as an ingredient in tortilla chips, continue to fuel apprehension about the regulatory control over GM products. Another concern about GM products is their possible unintended effects on the environment. For example, some laboratory studies have shown that pollen from plants that have been genetically modified to produce Bt toxin have inadvertently killed monarch butterflies; other studies, however, have refuted the evidence. In addition, there are indications that herbicide-resistance genes can be transferred to other plants, decreasing the usefulness of the herbicide. As with any new technology, the impact of GM organisms should continue to be carefully scrutinized to hopefully avoid any negative consequences.

MICROCHECK 9.6

Concerns about genetic engineering are varied, including ethical and moral issues associated with genomics, and potentially adverse impacts of genetically modified organisms on human health and the environment.

✓ Describe two concerns regarding information that can be gained by analyzing a person's DNA.

✓ Describe two concerns regarding the use of genetically modified organisms.

PERSPECTIVE 9.1

Science Takes the Witness Stand

After serving more than 10 years on a rape charge, a wrongfully convicted young man was released from prison when a new DNA typing technique exonerated him. The new technique, which used polymerase chain reaction (PCR) to amplify specific sequences, showed that the semen sample taken from the rape victim did not contain the man's DNA. Indeed, a database indicated a DNA match with a man currently in prison for an unrelated rape charge.

Stories abound about the growing power of DNA evidence for obtaining convictions and also clearing the wrongly accused, but how is DNA used in forensics? It is not feasible to compare the entire nucleotide sequence of two people; instead, specific regions that vary significantly between individuals are analyzed. In the past, forensics labs commonly looked at restriction fragment length polymorphisms, employing Southern blot hybridization to detect the differences (see figures 9.9 and 9.10). This provides valuable information but cannot be used on small or degraded samples and is quite time-consuming. Most forensics labs have now switched to using a PCR-based method because results can be obtained in less than 5 hours from a sample as small as a drop of blood the size of a pinhead. In fact, the FBI now catalogs PCR-based DNA profiles from unsolved crimes and convicted violent offenders, making it easier to track or link the crimes of serial offenders. The national database is called CODIS (**Co**mbined **D**NA **I**ndex **S**ystem).

PCR-based DNA typing amplifies certain chromosomal regions that contain **short tandem repeats (STRs)**. These consist of a core sequence of 2 to 6 base pairs that repeat a variable number of times in different people. On chromosome 2, for example, in an intron within the thyroid peroxidase gene, the sequence AATG is repeated sequentially between 5 to 14 times. In one individual, there may be 9 of these STRs in one copy of that chromosome and 7 in the other, whereas another individual may have 11 and 5 **(figure 1).** This variation, or polymorphism, makes tandem repeats a useful genetic marker for distinguishing individuals. With PCR, using primers that bind regions flanking the repeating sequences, the number of repeats can be determined. A fragment that contains 9 repeats, for example, will be longer than one that contains only 7. The PCR-amplified fragments can be quickly separated using a rapid type of gel electrophoresis called capillary electrophoresis. Their size can then be determined by comparing their positions as they move out of the gel to those of known standards.

The FBI's CODIS database catalogs the amplification pattern of 13 different STR loci (chromosomal locations). Commercially available kits contain fluorescently-labeled primers that allow simultaneous amplification and subsequent recognition of each of the 13 loci. A laser detects the color of each amplified fragment as it moves out of the capillary gel, and computer analysis generates a pattern of peaks that reflect the STR profile of the DNA sample.

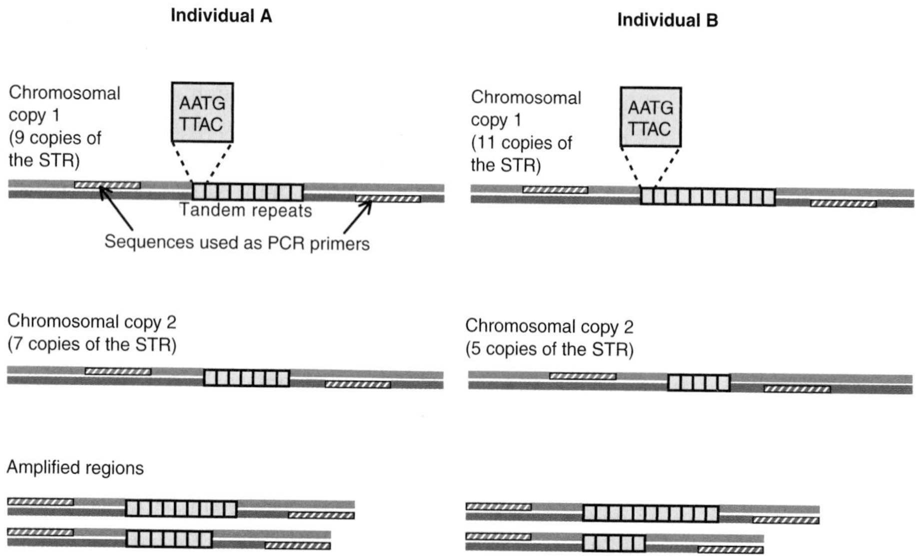

FIGURE 1 Using PCR to Type ("Fingerprint") DNA PCR is used to amplify chromosomal regions containing short tandem repeats (STRs). The number of copies of a given STR vary among people, resulting in corresponding differences in the length of the amplified fragments. Typically, at least 13 different STR locations are analyzed.

RECOMBINANT DNA TECHNIQUES

9.7

Techniques Used in Genetic Engineering

Focus Points

- Explain how introns are removed from eukaryotic genes.
- Describe the characteristics of a typical vector.
- Explain how cells that harbor recombinant molecules are obtained.

This section will describe methods used to clone DNA in bacterial cells **(figure 9.14).** For specific information regarding the engineering of eukaryotic organisms, see Perspective 8.2 and visit the Online Learning Center (www.mmhe.com/nester5).

Obtaining DNA

The first step of a cloning experiment is to obtain the DNA that will be cloned. To do this, cells in a broth culture are lysed by adding a detergent. As the cells burst open, the relatively fragile DNA is inevitably sheared into many pieces of varying lengths.

When cloning eukaryotic genes into bacteria, the introns must first be removed if the goal is protein production. To do this, mRNA from which the eukaryotic cell has already removed the introns is first isolated from the appropriate eukaryotic tissue. Then, a strand of DNA complementary to the mRNA is synthe-

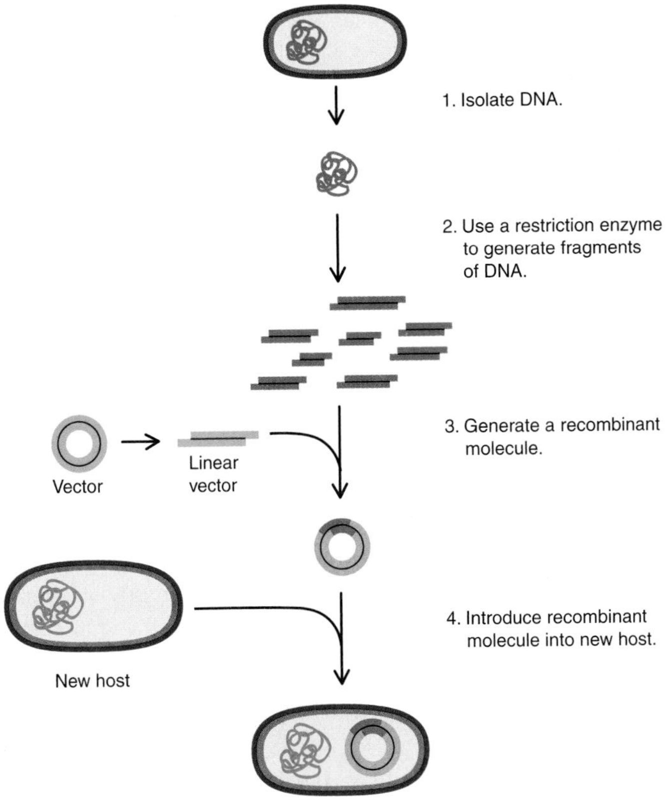
1. Isolate DNA.
2. Use a restriction enzyme to generate fragments of DNA.
3. Generate a recombinant molecule.
Vector
Linear vector
4. Introduce recombinant molecule into new host.
New host

FIGURE 9.14 The Steps of a Cloning Experiment

sized *in vitro* using **reverse transcriptase,** an enzyme encoded by retroviruses. That strand of DNA is then used as a template for synthesis of its complement, creating double-stranded DNA. The resulting copy of DNA, or **cDNA,** encodes the same protein as the original DNA, but lacks the introns **(figure 9.15).** ■ introns, p. 181 ■ retrovirus, p. 349

Generating a Recombinant DNA Molecule

As described earlier restriction enzymes and DNA ligase are used to create a recombinant molecule consisting of a vector and insert. The vector, usually a modified plasmid or bacteriophage, has an origin of replication and functions as a carrier of the cloned DNA **(figure 9.16).** Vectors also must have at least one restriction enzyme recognition site. This allows the circular vector to be cut, forming a linear molecule to which the insert can be joined. Many vectors have been engineered to contain a short sequence called a **multiple-cloning site** that has the recognition sequences of several different restriction enzymes. The value of a multiple-cloning site is its versatility; a fragment obtained by digesting with any of a number of different restriction enzymes can be inserted into the site.

Vectors typically encode some type of **selectable marker,** a gene whose product allows cells to grow in conditions that would otherwise be inhibitory or lethal. A common selectable marker is a gene that codes for resistance to ampicillin or another antibiotic; cells that harbor a vector or recombinant molecule

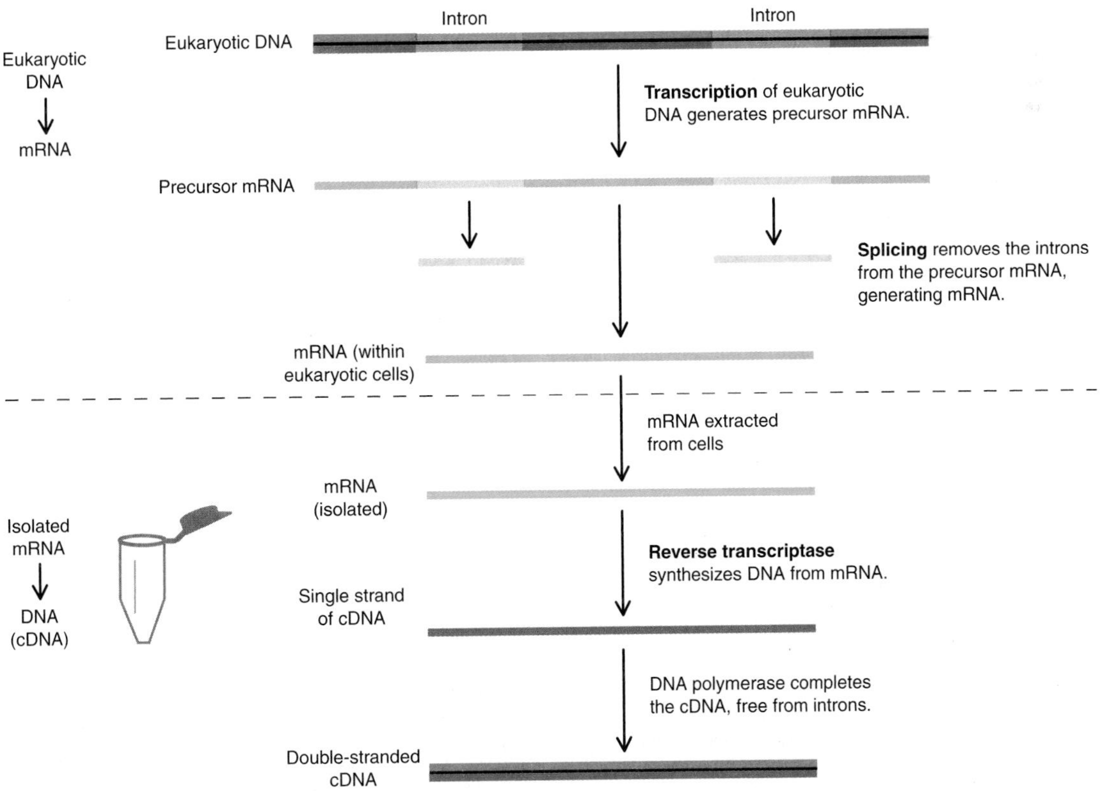
Eukaryotic DNA
mRNA
Eukaryotic DNA
Intron
Intron
Transcription of eukaryotic DNA generates precursor mRNA.
Precursor mRNA
Splicing removes the introns from the precursor mRNA, generating mRNA.
mRNA (within eukaryotic cells)
mRNA extracted from cells
mRNA (isolated)
Isolated mRNA
DNA (cDNA)
Reverse transcriptase synthesizes DNA from mRNA.
Single strand of cDNA
DNA polymerase completes the cDNA, free from introns.
Double-stranded cDNA

FIGURE 9.15 Making cDNA from Eukaryotic mRNA In order for eukaryotic genes to be expressed by a prokaryotic cell, a copy of DNA without introns must be cloned. The cDNA encodes the same protein as the original DNA but lacks introns.

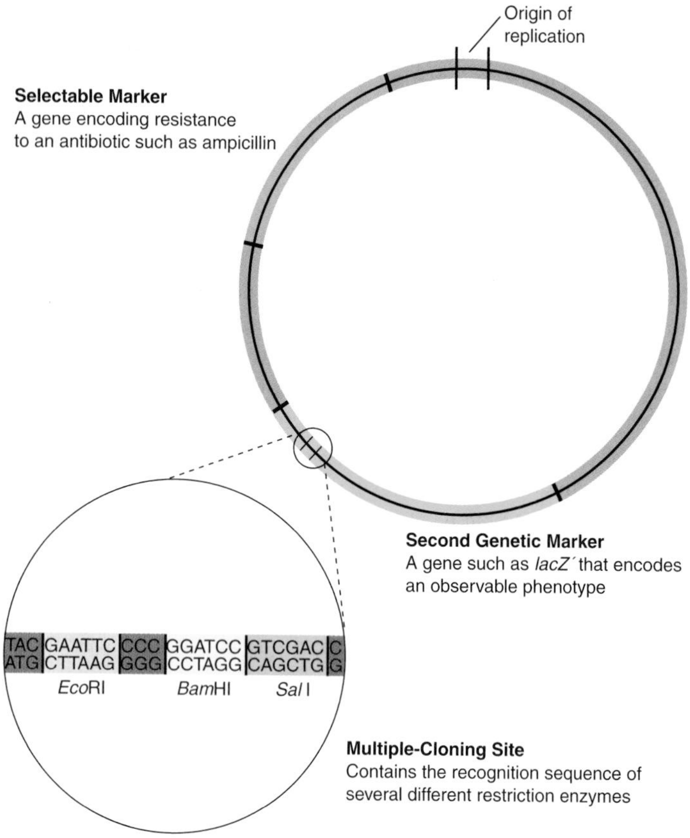
Origin of replication
Selectable Marker
A gene encoding resistance to an antibiotic such as ampicillin
Second Genetic Marker
A gene such as lacZ′ that encodes an observable phenotype
TAC GAATTC CCC GGATCC GTCGAC C
ATG CTTAAG GGG CCTAGG CAGCTG G
EcoRI
BamHI
SalI
Multiple-Cloning Site
Contains the recognition sequence of several different restriction enzymes

FIGURE 9.16 Typical Properties of an Ideal Vector Most vectors have an origin of replication, a selectable marker, and a multiple-cloning site. A second genetic marker, used to differentiate cells containing recombinant plasmids from those that contain intact vector, spans the multiple-cloning site.

are able to grow on the antibiotic-containing medium. This is important because when DNA is added to a host, most cells do not take up that DNA. The selectable marker is used to eliminate cells that have not taken up vector sequences. ■ **antibiotic, p. 496** ■ **ampicillin, p. 502**

Most vectors have a second genetic marker, in addition to the selectable marker, used to distinguish cells that contain recombinant plasmids from those containing intact vector. This is significant because when the vector and insert DNA are both cut with the same restriction enzyme and the fragments mixed together, not all molecules will join to form the desired recombinant molecules. For example, the two ends of the vector can anneal to each other, regenerating the circular vector, which can replicate when introduced into a cell. The second genetic marker is situated so that it is insertionally inactivated when the DNA to be cloned is successfully ligated into the multiple-cloning site of the vector. A good illustration of the utility of the second genetic marker is provided by the common vector, pUC18 (**figure 9.17**). The second genetic marker of pUC18 is a gene called ***lacZ′***. The product of *lacZ′* enables cells to cleave a colorless chemical, x-gal, to form a blue compound. Because the multiple-cloning site of pUC18 is within the gene, creation of a vector-insert hybrid results in a nonfunctional gene product. Thus, colonies of cells that harbor intact vector have a functional *lacZ′* gene and are blue, whereas those that contain a recombinant molecule are white. ■ **insertional inactivation, p. 197** ■ **phenotype, p. 193**

The type of vector used to clone eukaryotic DNA into a bacterial cell depends largely on the ultimate purpose of the procedure. If the goal of cloning is to produce the protein encoded by the DNA, then a vector designed to optimize transcription and translation of the insert DNA is used. To create a DNA library of a human or other eukaryotic genome, however, a vector that can carry a large insert is generally used. Information about these vectors can be obtained by visiting the Online Learning Center (www.mhhe.com/nester5).

Introducing the Recombinant DNA into a New Host

Once recombinant plasmids are generated, they must be transferred into a suitable host where the molecules can replicate. For routine cloning experiments, one of the many well-characterized laboratory strains of *E. coli* is generally used. These strains are desirable hosts because they are easy to grow and much is known about their genetics and biochemistry. They also have known phenotypic characteristics such as sensitivity to specific antibiotics. ■ **antibiotics, p. 496**

A common method of introducing DNA into a bacterial host is DNA-mediated transformation. In this process, cells in a physiological state called **competence** take up naked DNA from their surrounding environment. While some bacteria are naturally competent, *E. coli* cells must be specially treated in a dilute calcium chloride solution to induce them to take up DNA. Even though this method is used routinely by a multitude of laboratories, the exact mechanism by which it enables cells to become competent is not clear. An alternative technique is to introduce the DNA by **electroporation,** a procedure that sub-

GENETIC ENGINEERING LAB
YOU'VE GOT MAIL.
I CROSSED A CARRIER PIGEON WITH A PARROT.
THAVES 5-3
©2003 Thaves / Dist. by NEA, Inc.
E-mail:BobThaves@aol.com

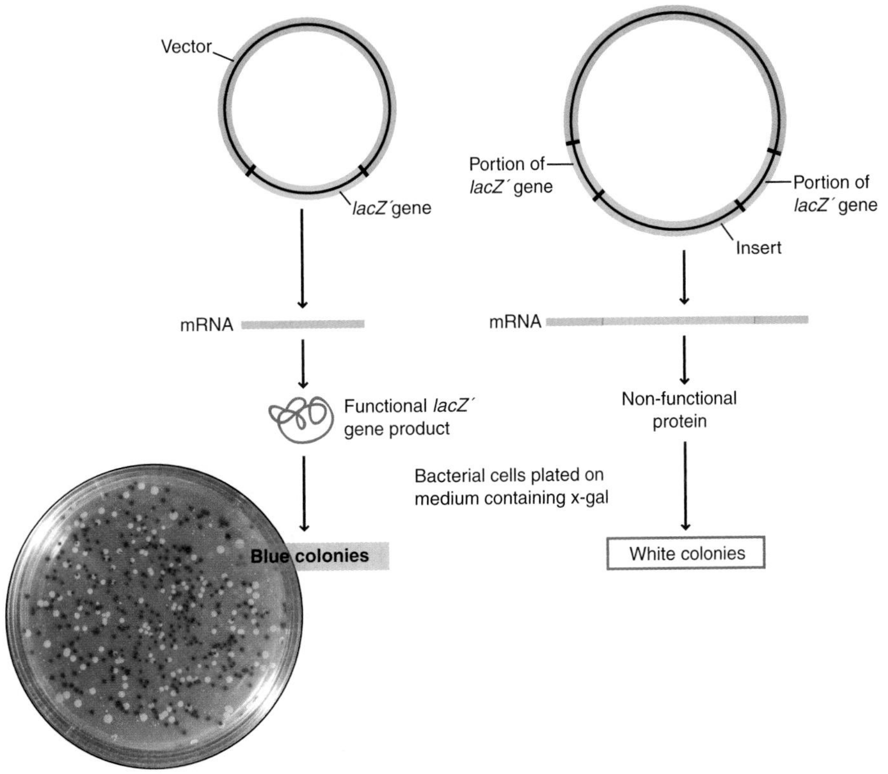

FIGURE 9.17 The Function of the *lacZ′* Gene in a Vector The *lacZ′* gene is used to differentiate cells that contain recombinant plasmid from those that contain vector alone. A functional *lacZ′* gene results in blue colonies when bacteria harboring intact vector are plated on a medium containing x-gal. Because disruption of the gene by an insert generates a non-functional product, cells harboring recombinant plasmids form white colonies.

jects the cells to an electric current. ■ DNA-mediated transformation, p. 205 ■ electroporation, p. 207

After the DNA is introduced into the new host, the transformed bacteria are cultivated on a medium that both selects for cells containing vector sequences and differentiates those carrying recombinant plasmids. The medium exploits the selective marker encoded on the vector to permit growth of only those cells that have taken up either a recombinant molecule or an intact vector. If, for example, the vector encodes resistance to the antibiotic ampicillin, then the transformed cells are grown on ampicillin-containing medium. To differentiate the cells that took up a recombinant plasmid from those that took up intact vector, the medium exploits the second genetic marker. If that marker is the *lacZ′* gene, the chemical x-gal is added to the medium. Colonies that are white (rather than blue) likely harbor a vector carrying an insert; these colonies are then further characterized to determine if they harbor the gene of interest (see figure 9.17). ■ ampicillin, p. 502

MICROCHECK 9.7

Introns must first be removed if eukaryotic DNA is to be expressed in a prokaryotic cell. Vectors typically have an origin of replication, a selectable marker, a multiple-cloning site, and a second genetic marker.

- ✓ Explain the role of reverse transcriptase in the procedure to clone eukaryotic DNA.
- ✓ Explain how the *lacZ′* gene is used to distinguish colonies that harbor a recombinant plasmid.
- ✓ What would happen if a competent cell took up a molecule of circular insert DNA?

9.8 Techniques Used in Probe Technologies

Focus Points

- Describe two methods used to obtain a probe.
- Compare and contrast the essential steps of colony and Southern blotting, FISH, and DNA microarray technologies.

Probe technology exploits the specificity of base-pairing between two strands of nucleic acid to detect certain nucleotide sequences. Methods that use probes include colony blotting, Southern blotting, fluorescence *in situ* hybridization (FISH), and DNA microarray technologies.

Obtaining a Probe

A DNA probe can be obtained in a number of ways. In some cases, a similar gene from another organism has already been cloned, and this cloned DNA can be used as a probe. For example, DNA encoding the Shiga toxin gene of *Shigella dysenteriae* can be used as a probe to look for similar toxin genes, such as the one encoded by *E. coli* O157:H7. The double-stranded DNA is labeled with a detectable marker and then denatured to create the single-stranded probe. Because the probe originated from a double-stranded DNA molecule, it contains each of the two strands of complementary DNA. These two probe strands can potentially anneal to each other, but the concentration of probe molecules ensures that sufficient numbers will remain single-stranded until they can hybridize to the DNA of interest. ■ Shiga toxin, p. 626 ■ *E. coli* O157:H7, p. 627

Another way to obtain a probe is to synthesize a short sequence of nucleotides, an **oligonucleotide.** Rapid and efficient DNA synthesis machines now make this a relatively simple task. Synthesizing the appropriate probe, however, requires at least some advance knowledge about the sequence of nucleotides to be located.

Techniques Used in Colony Blotting and Southern Blotting

Colony blotting is used to locate specific sequences in colonies growing on an agar plate (see figure 9.8), whereas Southern blotting is used to locate specific sequences in restriction fragments that have been separated by gel electrophoresis (see figure 9.9). In both cases, a blotting step transfers the sample in-place to a nylon membrane that serves as a solid support, and procedures are incorporated to denature the double-stranded DNA. A solution containing the probe is then added to the membrane and incubated under conditions that allow the probe to hybridize to complementary sequences on the filter. Any probe that has not bound is then washed off. If the probe was labeled with a radioactive isotope, a process called autoradiography is used to locate the positions of the hybridized probe. In this procedure, X-ray film is placed on the filter containing the probe-bound DNA and incubated. After the film is developed, visible black grains can be seen at the sites where probe was located. Different methods are used to detect probes that have been labeled with other markers.

Techniques Used in Fluorescence *in situ* Hybridization

Sample preparation is a critical aspect of fluorescence *in situ* hybridization (FISH). The sample must first be treated with chemicals to preserve the shape of the cells, inactivate enzymes that might otherwise degrade the nucleic acid, and make the cells more permeable so that the labeled probe molecules can readily enter. The methods used depend largely on the type of organisms being detected. The specimen is then applied to a glass slide that has been coated with material that facilitates attachment of the cells.

Once the specimen has been prepared, a solution containing the fluorescently-labeled probe is applied and incubated under conditions that allow hybridization to occur. Then, unbound probe is washed off. Finally, the specimen is viewed using a fluorescence microscope (see figure 9.11).

Techniques Used in DNA Microarray Technologies

Sophisticated techniques are used to construct DNA microarrays. One method employs a robotic device to deliver microscopic droplets, each containing a different DNA sequence, onto exact positions of a solid support. Another synthesizes oligonucleotides, one nucleotide at a time, directly on the solid support.

The sample of nucleic acid to be analyzed is first labeled with a fluorescent marker. Then, the labeled DNA (denatured) or RNA is added to the microarray and incubated using conditions that facilitate hybridization. Unbound material is then washed off and the location of the fluorescent label detected. Note that separate samples can be analyzed simultaneously by using different fluorescent labels (see figure 9.12).

MICROCHECK 9.8

A probe can be labeled single-stranded DNA of a gene similar to the one being detected, or a labeled oligonucleotide. Colony blotting and Southern blotting both require a blotting step and a procedure to denature the double-stranded DNA. Sample preparation is a critical aspect of FISH. Sophisticated techniques are used to construct DNA microarrays.

✓ Describe the differences between colony blotting and Southern blotting.

✓ Why is sample preparation a critical aspect of FISH?

9.9

Techniques Used in DNA Sequencing

Focus Point

- Describe the traditional dideoxy chain termination method used to sequence DNA, and how it has been modified for automated DNA sequencing.

The most widely used technique for determining the nucleotide sequence of DNA is the dideoxy chain termination method. Newer developments in DNA sequencing techniques make the process more automated and consequently more rapid.

Dideoxy Chain Termination Method

The fundamental element of the **dideoxy chain termination method** is an *in vitro* DNA synthesis reaction. Like any DNA synthesis reaction, a sequencing reaction requires:

- A single-stranded piece of DNA, the **template,** from which a complementary copy is synthesized. ■ template, p. 169
- A primer that anneals to the single-stranded template. Often, the DNA being sequenced has been cloned into a vector. Because the nucleotide sequences of vectors are known, a primer that anneals to a portion of the vector adjacent to the DNA to be sequenced can be readily obtained. ■ primer, p. 223
- DNA polymerase, the enzyme that catalyzes DNA synthesis. ■ DNA polymerase, p. 171
- Each of the four deoxynucleotides that are used in DNA synthesis—dATP, dGTP, dCTP, and dTTP. One of these is labeled with a detectable marker such as a radioisotope to facilitate detection of the newly synthesized DNA. ■ nucleotide, p. 33

If these were the only ingredients in the reaction, then a full-length molecule complementary to the template DNA would be synthesized. A key additional ingredient is added, however, that can terminate DNA synthesis before a full-length complement is made. This key ingredient is a **dideoxynucleotide (ddNTP).** Dideoxynucleotides are identical to their deoxynucleotide (dNTP) counterparts except they lack the 3′OH group, the portion of a nucleotide required for the addition of subsequent nucleotides during DNA synthesis **(figure 9.18).** Because they

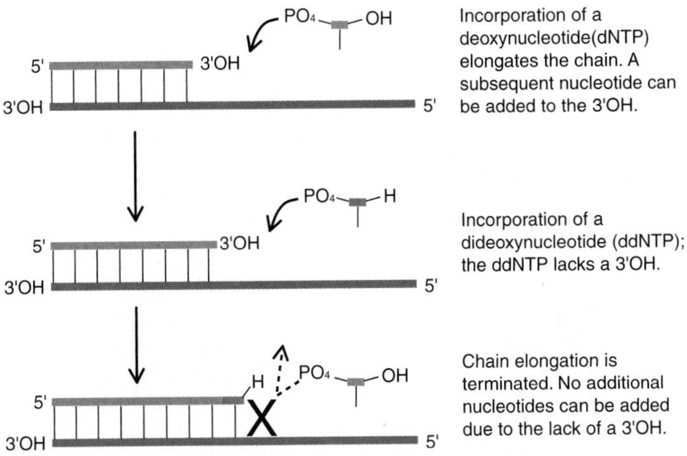

FIGURE 9.18 Chain Termination by a Dideoxynucleotide Once a dideoxynucleotide is incorporated into a growing strand, subsequent nucleotides cannot be added due to the lack of a 3′OH.

lack the 3′OH group, dideoxynucleotides are **chain terminators.** When one of these is incorporated into a growing strand of DNA, no additional nucleotides can be added, and elongation of that strand ceases.

To perform a sequencing reaction, DNA polymerase, template DNA, primer, and each of the four deoxynucleotides are mixed together and then apportioned equally into four separate tubes **(figure 9.19).** Each tube then receives a very small amount of a different dideoxynucleotide (ddATP, ddGTP, ddCTP, or ddTTP). In other words, ddATP is added to one tube, ddGTP to the next, and so on. When the reaction is incubated at an appropriate temperature, each primer anneals to a template molecule and DNA synthesis begins. In each case, chain elongation proceeds until a dideoxynucleotide (ddNTP) is incorporated, terminating synthesis at that point. Termination, however, is an infrequent event because of the numerous template molecules and the small amount of the ddNTP relative to its dNTP counterpart. The result

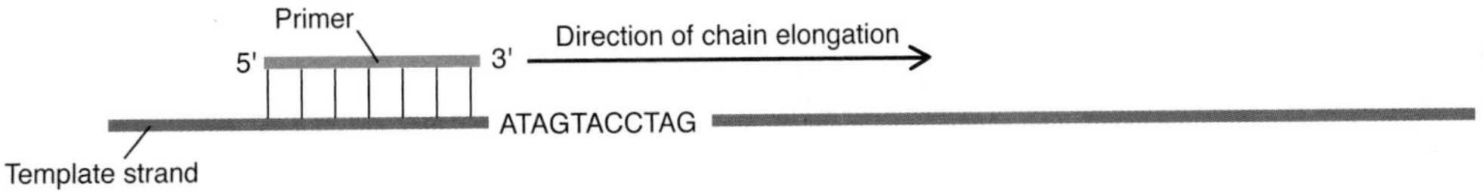

Dideoxynucleotide added to tube	ddATP	ddTTP	ddGTP	ddCTP
Sequencing reaction products in the tube (bold indicates the terminating dideoxynucleotide)	-T**A** -ATAGTACCTAG- -TATC**A** -ATAGTACCTAG- -TATCATGG**A** -ATAGTACCTAG-	-**T** -ATAGTACCTAG- -TA**T** -ATAGTACCTAG- -TATCA**T** -ATAGTACCTAG- -TATCATGGA**T** -ATAGTACCTAG-	-TATCAT**G** -ATAGTACCTAG- -TATCATG**G** -ATAGTACCTAG-	-TAT**C** -ATAGTACCTAG- -TATCATGGAT**C** -ATAGTACCTAG-
Length of newly synthesized fragments (number of nucleotides, not including primer)	2 5 9	1 3 6 10	7 8	4 11

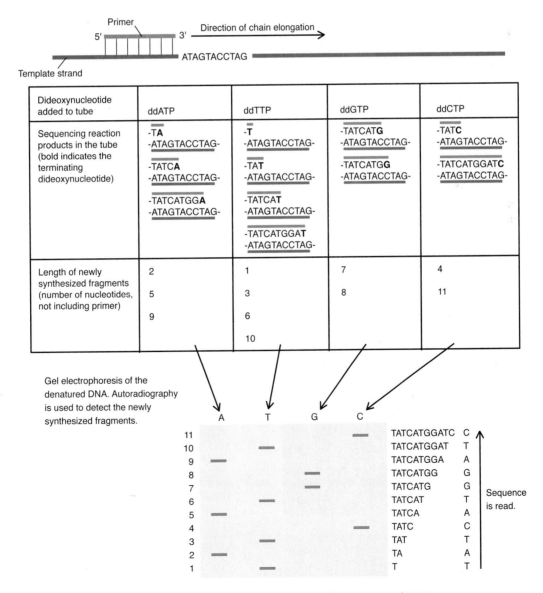

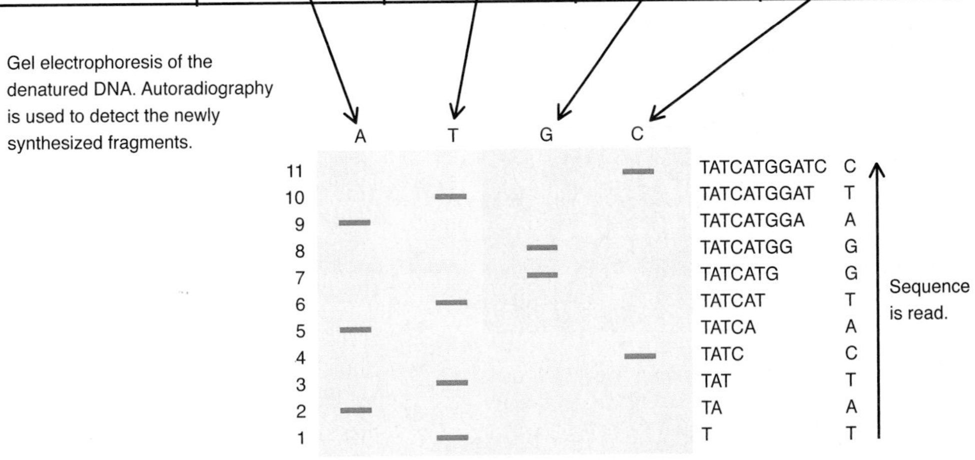

FIGURE 9.19 Dideoxy Chain Termination Method for Determining the Nucleotide Sequence of DNA

is that a tube will contain a set of newly synthesized DNA strands of various lengths. Each strand will have been terminated at the point that the specific ddNTP was incorporated into the chain. For example, in the tube that contained ddATP, numerous fragments of different lengths will be obtained, but each fragment will have been terminated at a position that called for the incorporation of the nucleotide base adenine. The sizes of the fragments in a tube indicate the positions of a specific nucleotide base in the synthesized DNA strand.

A special type of gel electrophoresis is used to separate the DNA fragments and determine their relative size. The contents of the four tubes from the sequencing reaction are placed in separate wells. The gel conditions (pH, temperature, and gel concentration) denature the DNA and enable separation of fragments that differ by only one nucleotide in length. Autoradiography is then used to detect the relative positions of the newly synthesized fragments. The order that the terminating nucleotides were incorporated can then be determined by "reading" the gel from the bottom up **(figure 9.20).**

Automated DNA Sequencing

Most automated techniques do not use a radioactive label to detect the newly synthesized DNA, but instead use a fluorescent dye attached directly to the ddNTP. Different dye colors are used for each of the four ddNTPs. By having each different ddNTP labeled with a distinct color, the reaction can be done in a single tube and run in one lane of the gel. Again, gel electrophoresis is used to separate the bands. A laser is used to detect the colors of fluorescent bands as they run off the gel, recording their intensity as a peak. The order of the colored peaks reflects the nucleotide sequence of the DNA **(figure 9.21).**

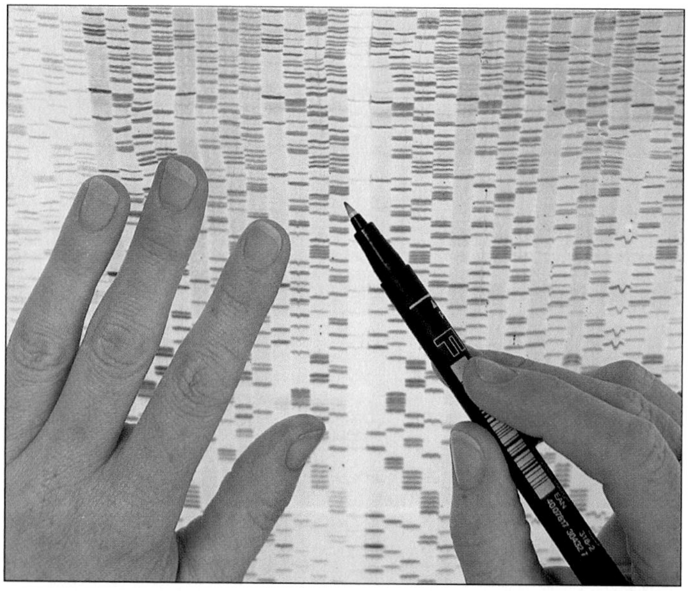

FIGURE 9.20 An Autoradiograph of a Sequencing Gel Each dark band represents a specific-sized fragment. The sequence of the newly synthesized strand can be determined by "reading" the gel from the bottom up.

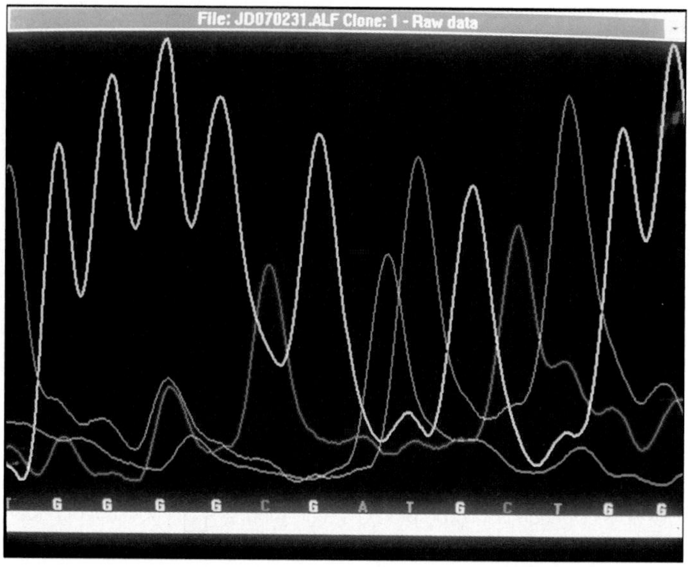

FIGURE 9.21 Results of Automated DNA Sequencing The order of the colored peaks reflects the nucleotide sequence of the DNA.

MICROCHECK 9.9

The dideoxy chain termination method is a widely used sequencing technique.

- ✓ Describe the chemical difference between a ddNTP and a dNTP.
- ✓ How does a ddNTP terminate DNA synthesis?
- ✓ What would happen in the sequencing reaction if the relative concentration of a dideoxynucleotide were increased?

9.10 Techniques Used in the Polymerase Chain Reaction (PCR)

Focus Point

- Explain how PCR can be used to exponentially amplify a select region of DNA.

The polymerase chain reaction (PCR) starts with a double-stranded DNA molecule, from which millions of identical copies of a select region can be produced. The process involves a series of DNA synthesis reactions and the following key ingredients:

- Double-stranded DNA containing the region to be amplified, the **target DNA.**
- A heat-stable DNA polymerase, ***Taq*** polymerase, which is from the thermophile *Thermus aquaticus.*
- Each of the four nucleotides (dATP, dGTP, dCTP, dTTP).
- Short single-stranded segments of DNA, generally about 20 nucleotides in length, to serve as primers. The selection of these primers will be discussed shortly.

The Three-Step Amplification Cycle

PCR requires a repeating cycle consisting of three steps **(figure 9.22).** In the first step, the double-stranded DNA is denatured by heating the sample to approximately 95°C. In the second step, the temperature is lowered to approximately 50°C; within seconds, the primers anneal to their complementary sequences on the denatured target DNA. In the third step, DNA synthesis occurs when the temperature is raised to the optimal temperature for *Taq* DNA polymerase, approximately 70°C. The DNA polymerase adds nucleotides to the 3′ end of the DNA primer using the opposing strand as a template. The net result is the synthesis of two new strands of DNA, each complementary to the other. In other words, the three-step cycle results in the duplication of the original target DNA. Since each of the newly synthesized strands can then serve as a template strand for the next cycle, the DNA is amplified exponentially. After a single cycle of the three-step reaction, there will be two double-stranded DNA molecules for every original double-stranded target; after the next cycle, there will be four; after the next cycle there will be eight, and so on.

A critical factor in PCR is the heat-stable DNA polymerase of a thermophile, *Thermus aquaticus. Taq* polymerase, unlike the DNA polymerase of *E. coli,* is not destroyed at the high temperature used to denature the DNA in the first step of each amplification cycle. If a heat-stable polymerase were not used, fresh polymerase would need to be added for every cycle of the reaction. Thus, the discovery and characterization of *T. aquaticus* through basic research was instrumental in developing this widely used and commercially valuable method. ■ **thermophile, p. 95**

Generating a Discrete-Sized Fragment

While the preceding description explains how PCR amplifies the target DNA exponentially, it does not clarify how a discrete-length fragment, referred to as the **PCR product,** becomes the predominant product. The generation of fragments of a particular size is important, because it enables a researcher to use PCR coupled with gel electrophoresis to readily detect the presence of target DNA in a sample. After PCR, the amplified target (PCR product) can be viewed as a single band on the ethidium bromide-treated gel.

To understand how discrete-sized fragments of target DNA are generated, you must consider the exact sites to which the primers anneal, and visualize at least three cycles of replication **(figure 9.23).** In the first cycle, two new fragments are generated. Note, however, that these fragments are shorter than the original full-length template molecules but longer than the target DNA. Their 5′ end is primer DNA. These mid-length products will be

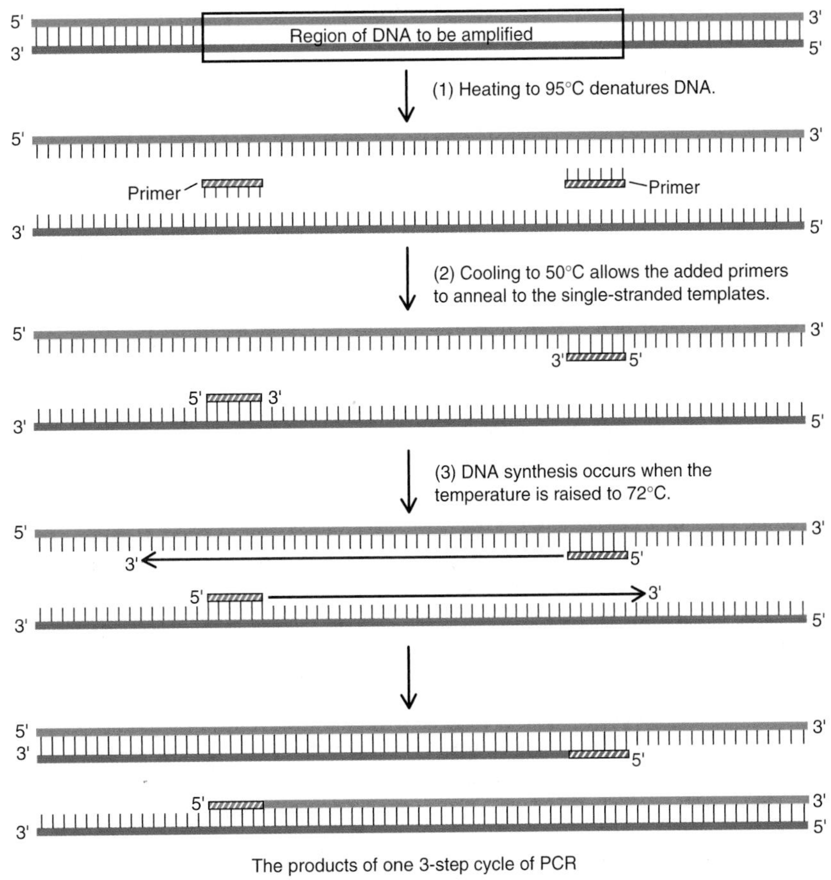

FIGURE 9.22 Steps of a Single Cycle of PCR

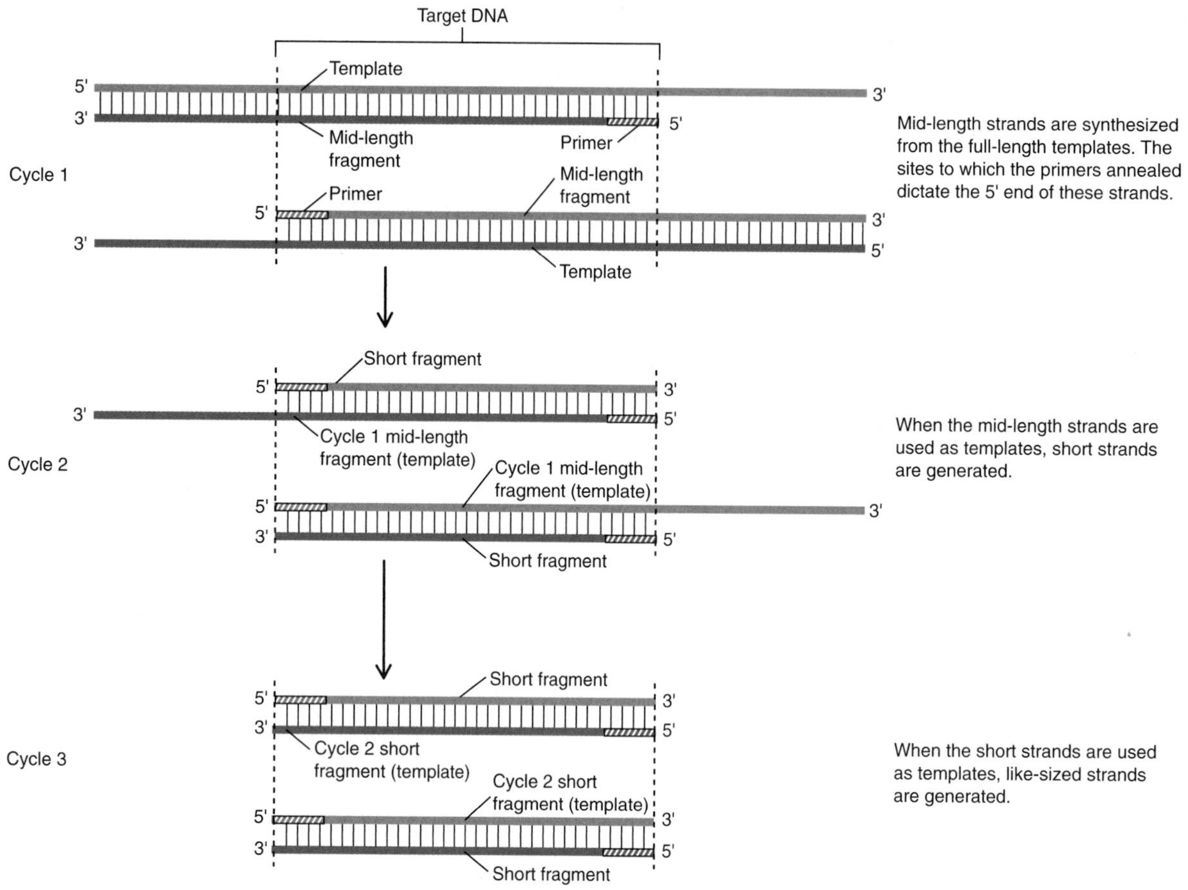

FIGURE 9.23 The PCR Product Is a Fragment of Discrete Size The positions to which the primers anneal to the original template molecule dictate the size and sequence of the fragment that is amplified exponentially.

generated whenever the original full-length molecule is used as a template, which is one time each replication cycle.

In the next cycle, the full-length molecules will again be used as templates, repeating the process just described. More importantly, the mid-length fragments created during the first cycle will be used as templates for DNA synthesis. As before, the primers will anneal to these fragments and then nucleotides will be added to the 3′ end. Elongation, however, will stop at the 5′ end of the template molecule, because DNA synthesis requires a template. Recall that the 5′ end of the template is primer DNA. Thus, whenever a mid-length fragment is used as a template, a short fragment is generated. The 5′ and 3′ ends of this fragment are determined by the sites to which the primers initially annealed.

In the third round of replication, the full-length and the mid-length fragments again will be used as templates, repeating the processes just described. The short fragments generated in the preceding round will also be used as templates, however, generating short double-stranded molecules. Continuing to follow the events in further rounds of replication will reveal that it is this fragment that is exponentially amplified **(figure 9.24).** Ultimately, enough of these short fragments are generated to be detectable using gel electrophoresis followed by ethidium bromide staining.

Selecting Primer Pairs

The nucleotide sequences of the two primers are critical because the primers dictate which portion of the DNA is amplified. Each must be complementary to a sequence on the appropriate strand, flanking the region to be synthesized. The synthesis reaction will then add nucleotides onto the primers, elongating the DNA chain so that the DNA between those primers is copied. Thus, if a researcher wants to amplify a DNA sequence that encodes a specific protein, then the researcher must first determine the nucleotide sequences flanking the gene that encodes the protein and then synthesize the appropriate pair of oligonucleotides to serve as primers.

MICROCHECK 9.10

The polymerase chain reaction (PCR) is used to rapidly increase the amount of either a specific segment or total DNA in a sample.

- ✓ What happens during each of the three temperature steps of PCR (95°C, 50°C, and 70°C)?
- ✓ Explain why it is important to use a polymerase from a thermophile in the PCR reaction.
- ✓ Sequencing reactions can be done using PCR. In this case would two primers be necessary?

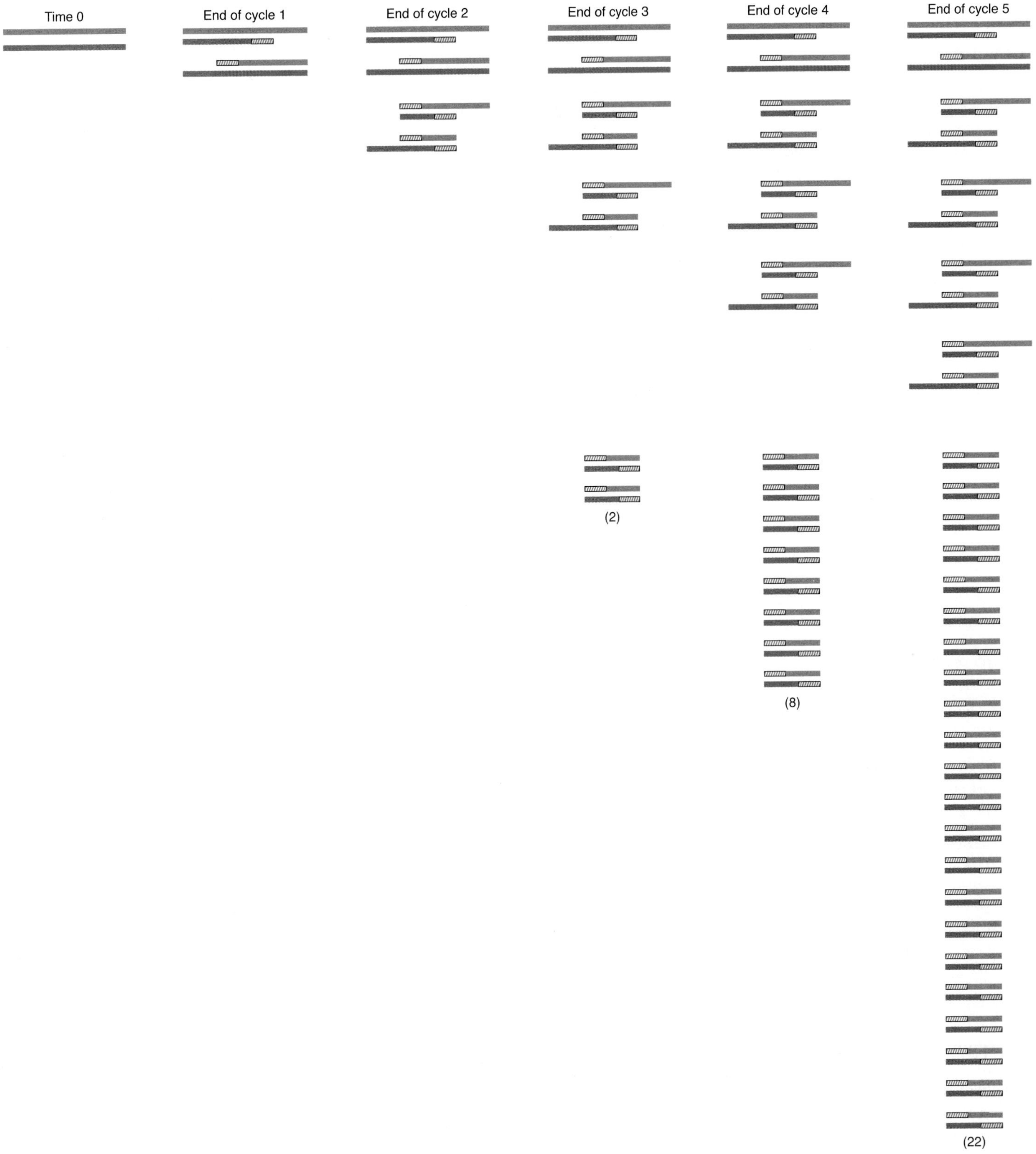

FIGURE 9.24 Exponential Amplification of Target DNA During PCR, mid-length fragments are amplified linearly (arithmetically), whereas the discrete-sized target DNA, referred to as PCR product, is amplified exponentially. After 30 cycles of PCR, over a billion molecules of PCR product will have been synthesized.

FUTURE CHALLENGES

Beyond Genomics

Now that the genome of certain organisms has been revealed, some scientists are turning their attention to questions posed as a result of the information, spawning the emergence of new scientific disciplines. For example, scientists are now working to characterize all the proteins, the "master parts list," encoded by the genetic blueprint. Researchers are particularly interested in determining how various proteins interact to direct the activities within a cell, or even neighboring cells.

Proteomics is the study of the **proteome,** the inventory of proteins encoded by a genome. One important aspect of proteomics is to discover which of the many proteins in a cell interact with each other. A powerful tool for studying protein-protein interactions is the **yeast two-hybrid system.** This ingenious technique relies on two yeast proteins that work in concert to activate a reporter gene; one binds to a specific sequence of DNA and the other activates the gene. The two proteins can do this, however, only when they are physically linked. The yeast two-hybrid system involves two separate preparations. First, a specialized cDNA library of the organism of interest is created, giving rise to fusions between the DNA-binding protein of the yeast two-hybrid system and the various proteins encoded by the cloned genes. Then, another recombinant molecule is made; this one creates a fusion between the activating protein of the yeast two-hybrid system and the protein of interest. This second recombinant molecule will function as a "lure" that can be used to "fish" for proteins in the cDNA library that interact with the protein of interest. When the "lure" is transferred into cells that harbor the cDNA library, the reporter gene will be activated in those cells that express a protein that interacts with the protein of interest. The interactions of various proteins in the yeast *Saccharomyces cerevisiae* have already been characterized using the yeast two-hybrid system. Currently, researchers are attempting to map the protein-protein interactions of the entire human proteome. The fact that cells modify many proteins after they are made makes this project much more challenging than it might seem.

SUMMARY

9.1 Fundamental Tools Used in Biotechnology

Restriction Enzymes (Figure 9.1)

Restriction enzymes are used to cut DNA into fragments.

Cohesive ends will **anneal** with one another, making it possible to join DNA from two different organisms.

Gel Electrophoresis (Figure 9.2)

Gel electrophoresis is used to separate DNA fragments according to their size.

DNA Probes (Figure 9.3)

DNA probes are used to locate specific nucleotide sequences.

Primers (Figure 9.4)

Primers are used to choose the sites where *in vitro* DNA synthesis will initiate.

Applications of Biotechnology

9.2 Applications of Genetic Engineering (Table 9.2)

Genetically Engineered Bacteria (Figures 9.5, 9.6)

Bacteria can be engineered to produce pharmaceutical proteins, vaccines, and other proteins more efficiently.

By **cloning** a segment of DNA into *E. coli,* an easy source of that sequence is available for study and further manipulation.

Gene function and regulation can more easily be studied in *E. coli* because systems for manipulating its DNA have been developed.

Genetically Engineered Eukaryotes

Transgenic plants have been engineered to resist pests and herbicides, have improved nutritional value, and function as edible vaccines.

9.3 Applications of Probe Technologies

Colony Blotting

Colony blotting uses a **probe** to identify colonies that contain a given sequence of DNA. (Figure 9.8)

Southern Blotting

Southern blotting uses a **probe** to determine the size of the restriction fragments that contain a sequence of interest. (Figure 9.9)

Fluorescence in situ Hybridization (FISH)

Fluorescence *in situ* hybridization (FISH) uses a fluorescently-labeled probe to detect specific nucleotide sequences within intact cells affixed to a microscope slide. (Figure 9.11)

DNA Microarray Technologies

DNA microarrays contain tens or hundreds of thousands of oligonucleotides that each function in a manner analogous to a probe. (Figure 9.12)

9.4 Applications of DNA Sequencing

Nucleotide sequences can be used to identify genetic alterations that result in certain diseases, and to study evolutionary relatedness.

9.5 Applications of the Polymerase Chain Reaction (PCR)

PCR is used to rapidly increase the amount of a specific DNA segment in a sample. (Figure 9.13)

9.6 Concerns Regarding DNA Technologies

Advances in **genomics** raise ethical issues and concerns about confidentiality.

Genetically modified organisms hold many promises, but concerns exist about the introduction of allergens into a food product and adverse effects on the environment.

Recombinant DNA Techniques

9.7 Techniques Used in Genetic Engineering (Figure 9.14)

Obtaining DNA

To isolate DNA, cells are lysed by adding a detergent. In order to obtain eukaryotic DNA without introns, reverse transcriptase is used to make a copy of DNA from an mRNA template. (Figure 9.15)

Generating a Recombinant DNA Molecule

DNA ligase is used to join the **vector** and the **insert.** (Figures 9.16, 9.17)

Introducing the Recombinant DNA into a New Host

The recombinant molecule is introduced into the new host, usually *E. coli,* using transformation or electroporation.

The transformed cells are cultivated on medium that both selects for cells containing vector sequences and differentiates those that carry recombinant molecules.

9.8 Techniques Used in Probe Technologies

Obtaining a Probe

Cloned DNA encoding a gene of interest can be labeled and denatured, and then used as a probe to look for similar genes.

A labeled oligonucleotide can be used as a probe.

Techniques Used in Colony Blotting and Southern Blotting

To do a colony blot, colonies are replica-plated onto a nylon membrane; after lysing the cells and denaturing the DNA, a DNA probe is used to identify colonies that contain the sequence of interest.

A Southern blot involves several steps. Gel electrophoresis is used to separate DNA fragments according to size, the separated and then denatured DNA is transferred in-place to a nylon membrane, and then a DNA probe is added to the membrane to locate specific nucleotide sequences. (Figure 9.16)

Techniques Used in Fluorescence in situ Hybridization

Samples must be treated to preserve the shape of the cells, inactivate enzymes, and make the cells permeable before adding the probe.

Techniques Used in DNA Microarray Technologies

Sophisticated techniques are used to construct microarrays. The DNA to be analyzed is labeled and added to the microarray.

9.9 Techniques Used in DNA Sequencing

Dideoxy Chain Termination Method

A key ingredient in a sequencing reaction is a dideoxynucleotide, a nucleotide that lacks the 3′OH and therefore functions as a chain terminator. (Figure 9.18)

The sizes of fragments in a sequencing reaction indicate the positions of the terminating nucleotide base in the synthesized DNA strands. (Figures 9.19, 9.20)

Automated DNA Sequencing

Each different ddNTP is labeled with a different fluorescent dye; the reactions can be done in one tube and run in one lane of a gel; a laser detects the color of the band as it runs off the gel. (Figure 9.21)

9.10 Techniques Used in the Polymerase Chain Reaction (PCR)

The Three-Step Amplification Cycle (Figure 9.22)

Double-stranded DNA is denatured, primers **anneal** to their complementary sequences, and then DNA is synthesized, amplifying the target sequence.

Generating a Discrete-Sized Fragment (Figures 9.23, 9.24)

A discrete-sized fragment that is amplified exponentially is obtained after three cycles of replication.

Selecting Primer Pairs

The primers selected dictate which portion of the DNA is amplified.

REVIEW QUESTIONS

Short Answer

1. Why are restriction enzymes useful in biotechnology?
2. Describe three general uses of genetically engineered bacteria.
3. Describe the function of a reporter gene.
4. Describe four uses of genetically engineered plants.
5. What information can you determine from a Southern blot that cannot be determined from a colony blot?
6. Explain how DNA microarray technology can be used to study gene expression.
7. What is cDNA? Why is it used when cloning eukaryotic genes?
8. Explain how gel electrophoresis separates DNA fragments.
9. How many different temperatures are used in each cycle of the polymerase chain reaction?
10. Explain how PCR eventually generates a discrete-sized fragment from a much longer piece of DNA.

Multiple Choice

1. What is the function of a vector?
   a) Destroys cells that do not contain cloned DNA
   b) Allows cells to take up foreign DNA
   c) Carries cloned DNA, enabling it to replicate in cells
   d) Encodes herbicide resistance
   e) Encodes Bt-toxin
2. The Ti plasmid of *Agrobacterium tumefaciens* is used to genetically engineer which of the following cell types?
   a) Animals b) Bacteria c) Plants
   d) Yeast e) All of these
3. RFLPs are distinguished using which technique?
   a) Cloning
   b) Colony blotting

c) Polymerase chain reaction
d) Sequencing
e) Southern blotting

4. An ideal vector has all of the following, *except*
   a) an origin of replication.
   b) a gene encoding a restriction enzyme.
   c) a gene encoding resistance to an antibiotic.
   d) a multiple-cloning site.
   e) the *lacZ′* gene.
5. Which of the following describes the function of the *lacZ′* gene in a cloning vector?
   a) Means of selecting for cells that contain vector sequences
   b) Means of distinguishing cells that have taken up recombinant molecules
   c) Site required for the vector to replicate
   d) Mechanism by which cells take up the DNA
   e) Gene for a critical nutrient required by transformed cells
6. Southern blots, but not colony blots, require which of the following?
   a) Autoradiography
   b) DNA hybridization
   c) Gel electrophoresis
   d) Labeled probe
   e) Membrane filter
7. Which of the following does a dideoxynucleotide lack?
   a) $5'PO_4$ b) $3'OH$ c) $5'OH$
   d) $3'PO_4$ e) C and D
8. In a sequencing reaction, the dATP was left out of the tube to which ddATP was added. What would be the result of this error?
   a) No synthesis would occur.
   b) Synthesis would always stop at the position that the first A was incorporated.
   c) Synthesis would not stop until the end of the template.
   d) Synthesis would terminate randomly, regardless of the nucleotide incorporated.
   e) The error would have no effect.
9. The polymerase chain reaction uses *Taq* polymerase rather than a DNA polymerase from *E. coli,* because *Taq* polymerase
   a) introduces fewer errors during DNA synthesis.
   b) is heat-stable.
   c) can initiate DNA synthesis at a wider variety of sequences.
   d) can denature a double-stranded DNA template.
   e) is easier to obtain.
10. The polymerase chain reaction generates a fragment of a distinct size even when an intact chromosome is used as a template. What determines the boundaries of the amplified fragment?
    a) The concentration of one particular deoxynucleotide in the reaction.
    b) The duration of the elongation step in each cycle.
    c) The position of a termination sequence, which causes the *Taq* polymerase to fall off the template.
    d) The sites to which the primers anneal.
    e) The temperature of the elongation step in each cycle.

Applications

1. Two students in a microbiology class are arguing about the origins of biotechnology. One student argued that biotechnology started with the advent of genetic engineering. The other student disagreed, saying that biotechnology was as old as ancient civilization. What was the rationale for the argument by the second student?
2. A student wants to clone Gene X. On both sides of the DNA encoding Gene X are the recognition sequences for *Alu*I and *Bam*HI. Which enzyme would be easier to use for the cloning experiment and why?

Critical Thinking

1. Discuss some potential issues regarding gene therapy, the use of genetic engineering to correct genetic defects.
2. An effective DNA probe can sometimes be developed by knowing the amino acid sequence of the protein encoded by the gene. A student argued that this process is too time-consuming since it is necessary to determine the complete amino acid sequence in order to create the probe. Does the student have a valid argument? Why or why not?

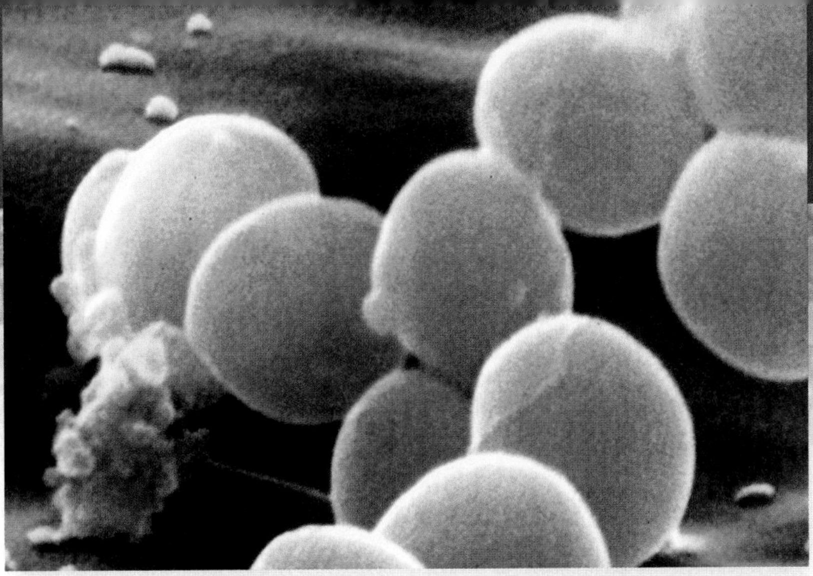

Bacterial cells

CHAPTER TEN

Identification and Classification of Prokaryotes

A Glimpse of History

In the early 1870s, the German botanist Ferdinand Cohn published several papers on bacterial classification, grouping microorganisms according to shape: spherical, short rods, elongated rods, and spirals. He recognized, however, that classification based solely on shapes was not adequate for categorizing all of the different bacteria. There were too many kinds and too few shapes.

The second major attempt at bacterial classification was initiated by Sigurd Orla-Jensen. His early training in Copenhagen was in chemical engineering, but he soon became interested in microbiology. In 1908, he proposed that bacteria be classified according to their physiological properties rather than morphology.

A quarter of a century later, two Dutch microbiologists, Albert Kluyver and C. B. van Niel, proposed classification systems based on presumed evolutionary relationships. They recognized a very serious problem, however: There was no way to distinguish between "resemblance" and "relatedness." The fact that two prokaryotes look alike does not mean they are genetically related.

In 1970, Roger Stanier, a microbiologist at the University of California, Berkeley, pointed out that relationships could be determined by comparing either gene products, such as proteins and cell walls, or nucleotide sequences. At that time, most microbiologists, including Stanier, assumed that all prokaryotes are basically similar. When the chemical compositions of a wide variety of prokaryotes were examined in detail, however, it was found that many had features that differed from those of *Escherichia coli,* considered a "typical" bacterium. These "unusual" features pertained to the chemical nature of the cell wall, cytoplasmic membrane, and ribosomal RNA.

In the late 1970s, Carl Woese and his colleagues at the University of Illinois determined the nucleotide sequence of ribosomal RNA in a wide variety of organisms. Based on the data, they recognized that prokaryotes could be divided into two major groups that differ from one another as much as they differ from eukaryotic cells. This led to a system of classification that separates prokaryotes into two domains—the *Archaea* and the *Bacteria.* Each of these is on the same level as the *Eucarya,* which includes the animals, plants, and fungi (all eukaryotes).

Information that is logically organized is easier to both retrieve and understand. Newspapers, for instance, do not scatter various subjects throughout the paper; rather they are divided into sections such as local news, sports, and entertainment. A large library would be extremely difficult to use if the multitude of books were not split into sections by subject matter. Likewise, scientists have divided living organisms into different groups, the better to understand the relationships among the species.

Take a moment and think about how you would group bacteria if you were to arrange a classification system. Would you group them according to shape? Or would it make more sense to group them according to their motility? Perhaps you would group them according to their medical significance. But then, how would you classify two similar bacteria that differ in their disease-causing potential? And how would you classify a newly identified organism of unknown medical significance?

10.1 Principles of Taxonomy

Focus Point

- Describe how prokaryotes are identified, classified, and assigned names.

Taxonomy is the science that studies organisms in order to arrange them into groups (taxa), those organisms with similar

KEY TERMS

Classification The process of arranging organisms into similar or related groups (taxa), primarily to provide easy identification and study.

Dichotomous key Flowchart of tests used for identifying organisms.

Domain A collection of similar kingdoms; there are three domains—*Bacteria, Archaea,* and *Eucarya.*

Genus A collection of related species.

Identification The process of characterizing an isolate in order to determine the group (taxon) to which it belongs.

Lateral (horizontal) gene transfer Transfer of DNA from one organism to another through conjugation, DNA-mediated transformation, or transduction.

Nomenclature The system of assigning names to organisms.

Phylogeny Evolutionary relatedness of organisms.

Signature sequence Characteristic sequences in the ribosomal RNA genes, or their products, that can be used to classify or identify certain organisms.

Species A group of related isolates or strains.

Strain An isolate.

Taxonomy The science that studies organisms in order to arrange them into groups (taxa); involves three interrelated areas—identification, classification, and nomenclature.

properties are grouped together and separated from ones that are different. Taxonomy can be viewed as three separate but interrelated areas:

- **Identification**—the process of characterizing an isolate in order to determine the group (taxon) to which it belongs.
- **Classification**—the process of arranging organisms into similar or related groups, primarily to provide easy identification and study.
- **Nomenclature**—the system of assigning names to organisms.

Strategies Used to Identify Prokaryotes

In practical terms, identifying the genus and species of a prokaryote may be more important than understanding its genetic relationship to other microbes. For example, a food manufacturer is most interested in detecting the presence of microbial contaminants that can spoil a food product. In a clinical laboratory, it is critical to quickly identify a pathogen isolated from a patient so the best possible treatment can be given.

To characterize and identify microorganisms, a wide assortment of technologies may be used including microscopic examination, culture characteristics, biochemical tests, and nucleic acid analysis. In a clinical laboratory, the patient's disease symptoms play an important role in identifying the infectious agent. For example, pneumonia in an otherwise healthy adult is typically caused by *Streptococcus pneumoniae,* an organism that is easily differentiated from others using a few specific tests. In contrast, diagnosing the cause of a wound infection is often more difficult, because many different microorganisms could be involved. Often, however, it is only necessary to rule out the presence of organisms known to cause a particular disease, rather than to conclusively identify each and every organism in the specimen. For instance, a fecal specimen from a patient complaining of a diarrhea and fever would generally only be tested for the presence of specific organisms that cause those symptoms. ■ *Streptococcus pneumoniae,* p. 588

The various methods used to identify prokaryotes will be discussed in detail later in the chapter.

Strategies Used to Classify Prokaryotes

Understanding the evolutionary relatedness, or **phylogeny,** of prokaryotes is important in constructing a classification scheme that reflects the actual evolution and biology of these organisms. Such a scheme is more useful than one that simply groups organisms by arbitrary characteristics, because it is less prone to the bias of human perceptions. It also makes it easier to classify newly recognized organisms and allows scientists to make predictions, such as which genes are likely to be transferred between organisms.

Unfortunately, determining genetic relatedness among prokaryotes is more difficult than it is for plants and animals. Not only do prokaryotes have few differences in size and shape, they do not undergo sexual reproduction. In higher organisms such as plants and animals, the basic taxonomic unit, a **species,** is generally considered to be a group of morphologically similar organisms that are capable of interbreeding to produce fertile offspring. Obviously, it is not possible to apply these same criteria to prokaryotes, thus making classification problematic.

Historically, taxonomists have relied heavily on phenotypic attributes to classify prokaryotes. The development and application of molecular techniques such as nucleotide sequencing, however, is finally making it possible to determine the genetic relatedness of microorganisms. ■ genotype, p. 193 ■ phenotype, p. 193

Taxonomic Hierarchies

Taxonomic classification categories are arranged in a hierarchical order, with the species being the basic unit. The species designation gives a formal taxonomic status to a group of related isolates or **strains,** which, in turn, permits their identification. Without classification, scientists and others would not be able to communicate about organisms with any degree of accuracy. Taxonomic categories include:

- **Species**—a group of related isolates or strains. Note that members of a species are not all identical; individual strains may vary in minor properties. The difficulty for the taxonomist is to decide how different two isolates must be in order to be classified as separate species rather than strains of the same species.
- **Genus**—a collection of related species.
- **Family**—a collection of similar genera. In prokaryotic nomenclature, the name of the family ends in the suffix *-aceae.*
- **Order**—a collection of similar families. In prokaryotic nomenclature, the name of the order ends in the suffix *-ales.*
- **Class**—a collection of similar orders.
- **Phylum** or **Division**—a collection of similar classes.
- **Kingdom**—a collection of similar phyla or divisions.
- **Domain**—a collection of similar kingdoms. The domain is a relatively new taxonomic category that reflects the characteristics of the cells that make up the organism.

Note, however, that microbiologists often group prokaryotes into informal categories rather than utilizing the higher taxonomic ranks such as order, class, and phylum. Examples of such informal groupings include the lactic acid bacteria, the anoxygenic phototrophs, the endospore-formers and the sulfate reducers. Organisms within these groupings share similar phenotypic and physiological characteristics, but may not be genetically related. ■ lactic acid bacteria, p. 272 ■ anoxygenic phototrophs, p. 273 ■ sulfate reducers, p. 271

An example of how a particular bacterial species is classified is shown in **table 10.1.** Note that the table intentionally omits the taxonomic category of kingdom. This is because the use of kingdoms within the *Bacteria* is still in a state of flux.

Classification Systems

Taxonomy is still an evolving discipline, with systems of classification that change over the years as new information is discovered. There is no such thing as an "official" classification system, and, as new ones are introduced, others fall into disfavor. The classification scheme currently favored by most microbiologists is the three-domain system. This designates all organisms as belonging to one of the three domains—*Bacteria, Archaea,* and *Eucarya* **(figure 10.1).** The system is based on the work of Carl Woese and colleagues who compared the sequences of nucleotide bases in ribosomal RNA from a wide variety of organisms. They showed that prokaryotes could be divided into two major groups that differ from one another as much as they do from the eukaryotic cell. The ribosomal RNA data are consistent with other observed differences between the *Archaea* and *Bacteria,* including the chemical compositions of their cell wall and cytoplasmic membrane **(table 10.2).** ■ *Bacteria,* p. 10 ■ *Archaea,* p. 10 ■ *Eucarya,* p. 10

Before the three-domain classification system was introduced, the most widely accepted scheme was the five-kingdom system, proposed by R. H. Whittaker in 1969. The five kingdoms in this system are Plantae, Animalia, Fungi, Protista (mostly single-celled eukaryotes), and Prokaryotae. While the five-kingdom system recognizes the obvious morphological differences between plants and animals, it does not reflect the recent genetic insights of the ribosomal RNA data, which indicates that plants and animals are more closely related to each other than *Archaea* are to *Bacteria.*

Bergey's Manual of Systematic Bacteriology While there is no "official" classification of prokaryotes, microbiologists generally rely on the reference text *Bergey's Manual of Systematic Bacteriology* as a guide. All known species are described there, including those that have not yet been cultivated. If the properties of a newly isolated organism do not agree with any description in *Bergey's Manual,* then presumably a new organism has been isolated. The newest edition of this comprehensive manual is being published in five volumes and classifies prokaryotes according to the most recent information on their genetic relatedness **(table 10.3).** In some cases, this classification differs substantially from that of the previous edition, which grouped organisms according to their phenotypic characteristics.

In addition to containing descriptions of organisms, all volumes contain information on the ecology, methods of enrichment, culture, and isolation of the organisms as well as methods for their maintenance and preservation. However, the heart of the work is a description of all characterized prokaryotes and their groupings.

TABLE 10.1 Taxonomic Ranks of the Bacterium *Escherichia coli*

Formal Rank	Example
Domain	*Bacteria*
Phylum	*Proteobacteria*
Class	*Gammaproteobacteria*
Order	*Enterobacteriales*
Family	*Enterobacteriaceae*
Genus	*Escherichia*
Species	*coli*

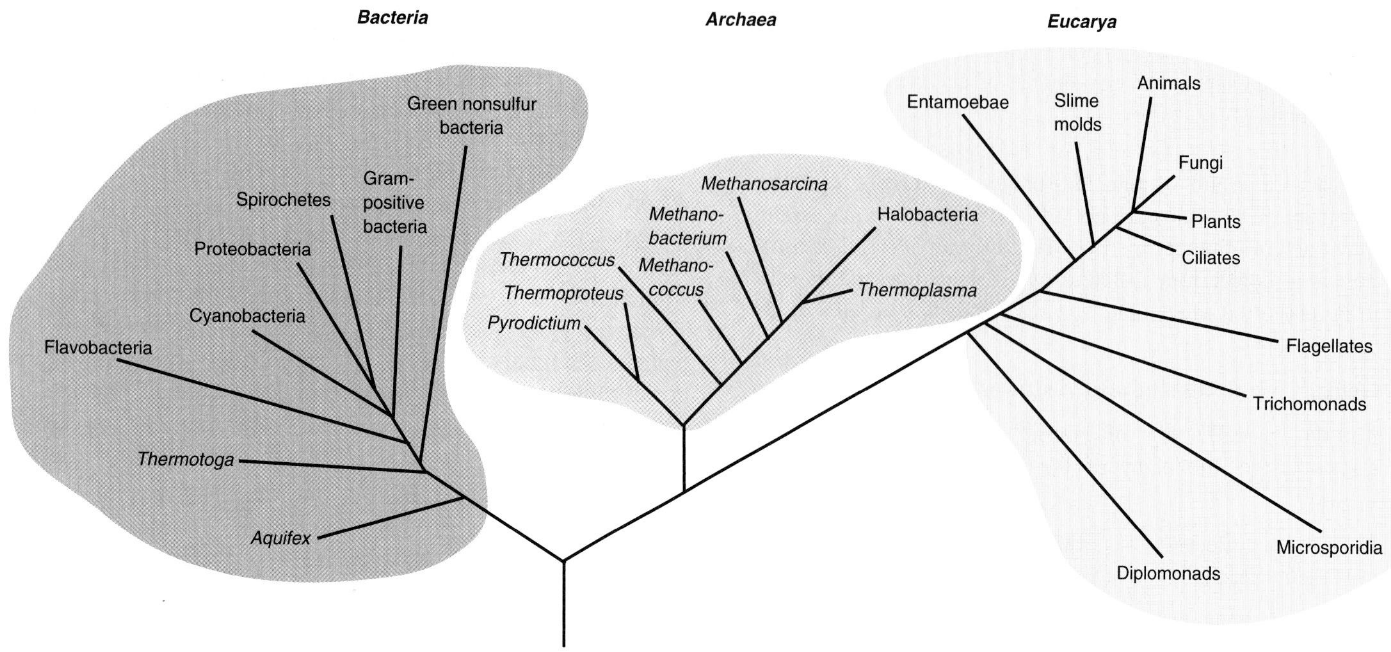

FIGURE 10.1 The Three-Domain System of Classification This classification system separates prokaryotic organisms into two domains—*Bacteria* and *Archaea*. The third domain, *Eucarya*, contains all organisms composed of eukaryotic cells. This system of classification is based on ribosomal RNA sequence data.

Nomenclature

Bacteria are given names according to an official set of internationally recognized rules, the *International Code for the Nomenclature of Bacteria.* Bacterial names may originate from any language, but they must be given a Latin suffix. In some cases the name reflects a characteristic of an organism such as its habitat, but often bacteria are named in honor of a prominent researcher.

Just as classification is always in a state of flux, so is the assignment of names. While revision of names is desirable from a scientific perspective, it is often a great source of confusion from a practical standpoint, particularly when the names of medically important bacteria are changed. To ease the transition of nomenclature changes, the former name is sometimes included in parentheses. For example, *Lactococcus lactis,* a bacterium that until recently was included in the genus *Streptococcus,* is often indicated as *Lactococcus (Streptococcus) lactis.*

MICROCHECK 10.1

Taxonomy consists of three interrelated areas: identification, classification, and nomenclature. In clinical laboratories, identifying the genus and species of an organism is more important than understanding its evolutionary relationship to other organisms.

- ✓ Why is it generally easier to determine the cause of pneumonia than it is to determine the cause of a wound infection?
- ✓ Why do microbiologists prefer the three-domain system of classification?
- ✓ Some biologists have been reluctant to accept the three-domain system. Why might this be?

TABLE 10.2 A Comparison of Some Properties of the Three Domains—*Archaea, Bacteria,* and *Eucarya*

Cell Feature	*Archaea*	*Bacteria*	*Eucarya*
Peptidoglycan Cell Wall	No	Yes	No
Cytoplasmic Membrane Lipids	Hydrocarbons (not fatty acids) linked to glycerol by ether linkage	Fatty acids linked to glycerol by ester linkage	Fatty acids linked to glycerol by ester linkage
Ribosomes	70S	70S	80S
Presence of Introns	Sometimes	No	Yes
Membrane-Bound Nucleus	No	No	Yes

TABLE 10.3 Taxonomic Outline of *Bergey's Manual of Systematic Bacteriology,* 2nd edition

	Representative Genera
Volume 1: The *Archaea* and the Deeply Branching Phototrophic Bacteria	
Domain *Archaea*	
Phylum *Crenarchaeota*	*Pyrodictium, Ignicoccus*
Phylum *Euryarchaeota*	*Halobacterium, Methanococcus, Natronococcus, Picrophilus*
Domain *Bacteria*	
Phylum *Aquificae*	*Aquifex*
Phylum *Thermotogae*	*Thermotoga*
Phylum *Thermodesulfobacteria*	*Thermodesulfobacterium*
Phylum *Deinococcus–Thermus*	*Deinococcus, Thermus*
Phylum *Chrysiogenetes*	*Chrysiogenes*
Phylum *Chloroflexi*	*Chloroflexus*
Phylum *Thermomicrobia*	*Thermomicrobium*
Phylum *Nitrospira*	*Nitrospira*
Phylum *Deferribacteres*	*Deferribacter*
Phylum *Cyanobacteria*	*Anabaena, Spirulina, Synechococcus*
Phylum *Chlorobi*	*Chlorobium, Pelodictyon*
Volume 2: The *Proteobacteria*	
Phylum *Proteobacteria*	
Class *Alphaproteobacteria*	*Agrobacterium, Caulobacter, Ehrlichia, Nitrobacter, Rhodospirillum, Rickettsia, Rhizobium*
Class *Betaproteobacteria*	*Neisseria, Nitrosomonas, Thiobacillus*
Class *Gammaproteobacteria*	*Azotobacter, Chromatium, Escherichia, Legionella, Nitrosococcus, Pseudomonas, Vibrio*
Class *Deltaproteobacteria*	*Bdellovibrio, Myxococcus*
Class *Epsilonproteobacteria*	*Campylobacter, Helicobacter*
Volume 3: The Low G + C Gram-Positive Bacteria	
Phylum *Firmicutes*	
Class I. *Clostridia*	*Clostridium, Heliobacterium*
Class II. *Mollicutes*	*Mycoplasma*
Class III. *Bacilli*	*Bacillus, Streptococcus, Listeria, Staphylococcus*
Volume 4: The High G + C Gram-Positive Bacteria	
Phylum *Actinobacteria*	*Corynebacterium, Bifidobacterium, Micrococcus, Mycobacterium, Streptomyces*
Volume 5: The *Planctomycetes, Spirochaetes, Fibrobacteres, Bacteroides, Fusobacteria*	
Phylum *Planctomycetes*	*Planctomyces*
Phylum *Chlamydiae*	*Chlamydia*
Phylum *Spirochaetes*	*Borrelia, Treponema*
Phylum *Fibrobacteres*	*Fibrobacter*
Phylum *Acidobacteria*	*Acidobacterium*
Phylum *Bacteroidetes*	*Bacteroides*
Phylum *Fusobacteria*	*Fusobacterium*
Phylum *Verrucomicrobia*	*Verrucomicrobium*
Phylum *Dictyoglyomi*	*Dictyoglomus*
Phylum *Gemmatimonadetes*	*Gemmatinonas*

10.2

Using Phenotypic Characteristics to Identify Prokaryotes

Focus Point

- Describe how phenotypic characteristics including microscopic morphology, metabolic capabilities, serology, and fatty acid analysis can be used to identify prokaryotes.

Phenotypic characteristics such as cell morphology, colony morphology, biochemical traits, and the presence of specific proteins can all be used in the process of identifying microorganisms. Most of these methods do not require sophisticated equipment and can easily be done anywhere in the world. Methods used to identify prokaryotes are summarized in **table 10.4.**

Microscopic Morphology

An important initial step in identifying a microorganism is to determine its size, shape, and staining characteristics. Microscopic examination gives information very quickly and is sometimes enough to make a presumptive identification.

Size and Shape

The size and shape of a microorganism can readily be determined by microscopically examining a wet mount. Based only on the size and shape, one can readily decide whether the organism in question is a prokaryote, fungus, or protozoan. In a clinical lab, this can sometimes provide all the information needed for diagnosis of certain eukaryotic infections. For example, a wet mount of vaginal secretions is routinely used to diagnose infections caused by yeast or by the protozoan *Trichomonas* **(figure 10.2).** A wet mount of stool is examined for the eggs of parasites when certain roundworms are suspected. The size, shape, and special features of the eggs are often sufficient to allow identification of the intestinal parasite. ■ wet mount, p. 51

Gram Stain

The Gram stain distinguishes between Gram-positive and Gram-negative bacteria (see figure 3.14). This relatively rapid test narrows the list of possible identities of an organism by excluding numerous others and provides suggestive information that can be helpful in the identification process. ■ Gram stain, p. 50

In a clinical lab, the Gram stain of a specimen by itself is generally not sensitive or specific enough to diagnose the cause of most infections, but it is still an extremely useful tool. The clinician can see the Gram reaction, the shape and arrangement of the bacteria, and whether the organisms appear to be growing as a pure culture or with other bacteria and/or cells of the host. However, most medically important bacteria do not have distinctive shapes or staining characteristics and usually cannot be identified by Gram stain alone. For example, *Streptococcus pyogenes,* which causes strep throat, cannot be distinguished microscopically from the other streptococci that are part of the normal flora of the throat. A Gram stain of a stool specimen cannot distinguish *Salmonella* species from *E. coli.* These organisms generally must be isolated in pure culture and tested for their biochemical attributes to provide precise identification. ■ strep throat, p. 577

In certain cases, the Gram stain gives enough information to start appropriate antimicrobial therapy while awaiting more accurate identification. For example, a Gram stain of sputum showing numerous white blood cells and Gram-positive encapsulated diplococci is highly suggestive of *Streptococcus pneumoniae,* an organism that causes pneumonia **(figure 10.3a).** In certain other cases, the result of a Gram stain is enough for accurate diagnosis. For instance, the presence of Gram-negative diplococci clustered

TABLE 10.4 Methods Used to Identify Prokaryotes

Method	Comments
Phenotypic Characteristics	Most of these methods do not require sophisticated equipment and can easily be done anywhere in the world.
Microscopic morphology	Size, shape, and staining characteristics such as Gram stain can give suggestive information as to the identity of the organism. Further testing, however, is needed to confirm the identification.
Metabolic capabilities	Culture characteristics can give suggestive information. A battery of biochemical tests can be used to confirm the identification.
Serology	Proteins and polysaccharides that make up a prokaryote are sometimes characteristic enough to be considered identifying markers. These can be detected using specific antibodies.
Fatty acid analysis	Cellular fatty acid composition can be used as an identifying marker and is analyzed by gas chromatography.
Genotypic Characteristics	These methods are increasingly being used to identify microorganisms.
Nucleic acid probes to detect specific nucleotide sequences	Probes can be used to identify prokaryotes grown in culture. In some cases, the method is sensitive enough to detect the organism directly in a specimen.
Amplifying specific DNA sequences using PCR	Even an organism that occurs in very low numbers in a mixed culture can be identified.
Sequencing rRNA genes	This method requires amplifying and then sequencing rRNA genes, but it can be used to identify organisms that have not yet been grown in culture.

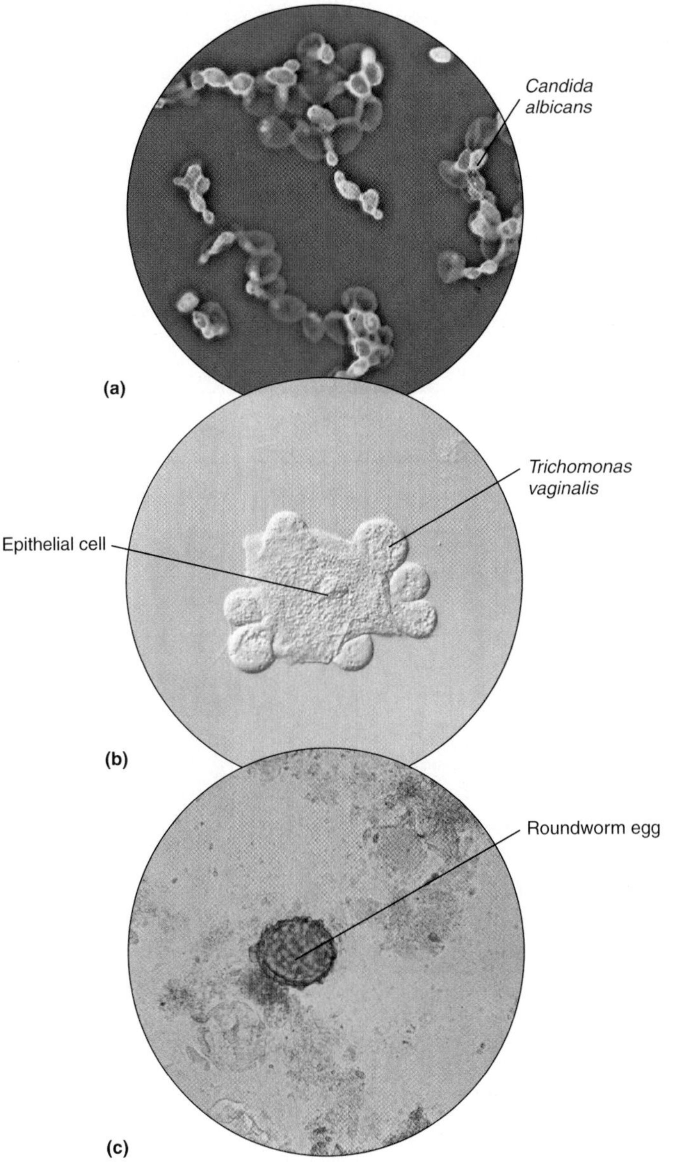

FIGURE 10.2 Wet Mounts of Clinical Specimens (a) Vaginal secretions containing yeast (*Candida albicans*, 410×); **(b)** *Trichomonas vaginalis* attached to squamous epithelium, as viewed through a Nomarski microscope (400×); and **(c)** roundworm (*Ascaris*) eggs in a stool (400×).

in white blood cells in a sample of a urethral secretion from a male is considered diagnostic for gonorrhea, the sexually transmitted disease caused by *Neisseria gonorrhoeae* (figure 10.3b). This diagnosis can be made because *N. gonorrhoeae* is the only Gram-negative diplococcus found inhabiting the normally sterile urethra of a male. ■ pneumonia, p. 588 ■ gonorrhea, p. 661

Special Stains

Certain microorganisms have unique characteristics that can be detected with special staining procedures. As an example, members of the genus *Mycobacterium* are some of the few microorganisms that are acid-fast (see figure 3.15). If a patient has symptoms of tuberculosis, then an acid-fast stain will be done on a sample of their sputum to determine whether *Mycobacterium tuberculosis* can be detected. ■ acid-fast stain, p. 51

Metabolic Capabilities

The identification of most prokaryotes relies on analyzing their metabolic capabilities such as the types of sugars utilized or the end products produced. In some cases these characteristics are revealed by the growth and colony morphology on cultivation media, but most often they are demonstrated using biochemical tests. ■ growth of colonies, p. 93

Culture Characteristics

Microorganisms that can be grown in pure culture are the easiest to identify, because it is possible to obtain high numbers of a single type of microorganism. Even the colony morphology can give initial clues to the identity of the organism. For example, colonies of streptococci are generally fairly small relative to many other bacteria such as staphylococci. Colonies of *Serratia marcescens* are often red when incubated at 22°C due to the production of a pigment. *Pseudomonas aeruginosa* often produces a soluble greenish pigment, which discolors the growth medium (see figure 11.12). In addition, cultures of *P. aeruginosa* have a distinct fruity odor.

In a clinical lab, where rapid but accurate diagnosis is essential, specimens are plated onto media specially designed to provide important clues as to the identity of the disease-causing organism. For instance, a specimen taken by swabbing the throat of a patient complaining of a sore throat is inoculated onto blood agar. This allows detection of the characteristic β-hemolytic colonies typical of *Streptococcus pyogenes* (see figure 4.11). Urine collected from a patient suspected of having a urinary tract infection is plated

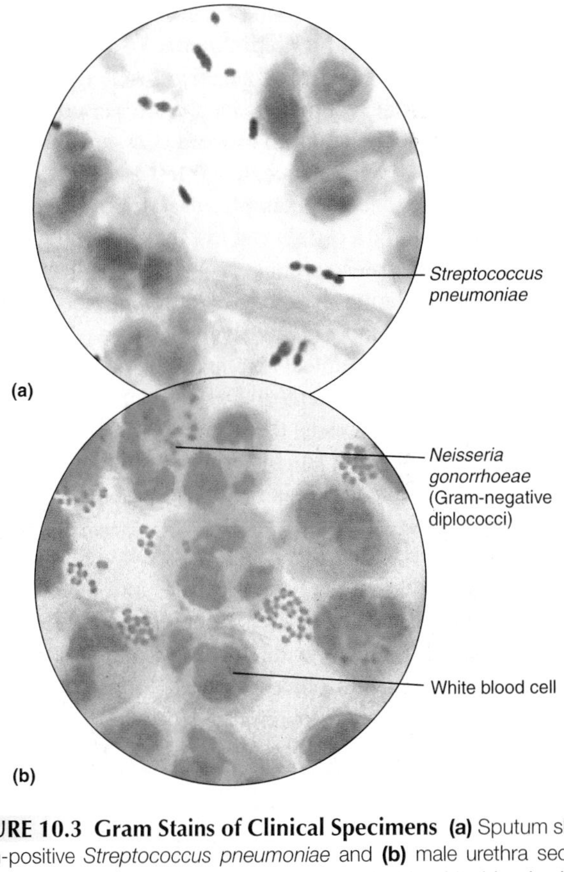

FIGURE 10.3 Gram Stains of Clinical Specimens (a) Sputum showing Gram-positive *Streptococcus pneumoniae* and **(b)** male urethra secretions showing Gram-negative *Neisseria gonorrhoeae* inside white blood cells.

onto MacConkey agar. *E. coli,* the most common cause of urinary tract infections, forms characteristic pink colonies on MacConkey agar due to its ability to ferment lactose (see figure 4.12). Some other bacteria can also grow and ferment lactose on this medium, however, so colony appearance alone is not enough to conclusively identify *E. coli.* ■ blood agar, p. 100 ■ MacConkey agar, p. 101

Biochemical Tests

Growth characteristics on culture media can give clues as to the identity of an organism, but biochemical tests are generally necessary for a more conclusive identification. One of the simplest of these is an assay for the enzyme catalase **(figure 10.4a).** Nearly all bacteria that grow in the presence of oxygen are catalase positive. Important exceptions are the lactic acid bacteria, which include members of the genus *Streptococcus.* Thus, if a throat culture yields β-hemolytic colonies but further testing reveals they are all catalase positive, then *Streptococcus pyogenes* has been ruled out. ■ catalase, p. 96 ■ *Streptococcus pyogenes,* p. 577

Most biochemical tests rely on a pH indicator or chemical reaction that results in a color change when a compound is degraded. To test for the ability of an organism to ferment a given sugar, a broth medium containing that sugar and a certain pH indicator is employed. Fermentation of the sugar results in acid production, which lowers the pH, resulting in a color change from pink to yellow; an inverted tube traps any gas produced (figure 10.4b). A medium designed to detect **urease,** an enzyme that degrades urea to produce carbon dioxide and ammonia, utilizes a pH indicator that turns bright pink in alkaline conditions (figure 10.4c). The characteristics of these and other important biochemical tests are summarized in **table 10.5.**

The basic strategy for identifying bacteria based on biochemical tests relies on the use of a **dichotomous key,** a flowchart of tests that give either a positive or negative result **(figure 10.5).** Because each test often requires an incubation period, however, it would be too time-consuming to proceed one step at a time. In addition, relying on a single biochemical test at each step could lead to misidentification. For example, if a strain that normally gives a positive result for a certain test lost the ability to produce a key enzyme, it would instead produce a negative result. Therefore, simultaneously inoculating a battery of different tests identifies the organism faster and more conclusively.

In certain cases, biochemical testing can be done without culturing the organism. *Helicobacter pylori,* the cause of most stomach ulcers, can be detected using the **breath test,** which assays for the presence of urease. The patient drinks a solution containing urea that has been labeled with an isotope of carbon. If *H. pylori* is present, its urease breaks down the urea, releasing labeled carbon dioxide, which escapes through the airway. Several hours after drinking the solution, the patient exhales into a balloon. The expired air is then tested for labeled carbon dioxide. This test is less invasive and, consequently, much cheaper and faster than the stomach biopsy that would otherwise need to be performed to culture the organism. ■ *Helicobacter pylori,* p. 617 ■ isotope, p. 27

Commercial Modifications of Traditional Biochemical Tests

Several less labor-intensive commercial modifications of traditional biochemical tests are available **(figure 10.6).** The API™

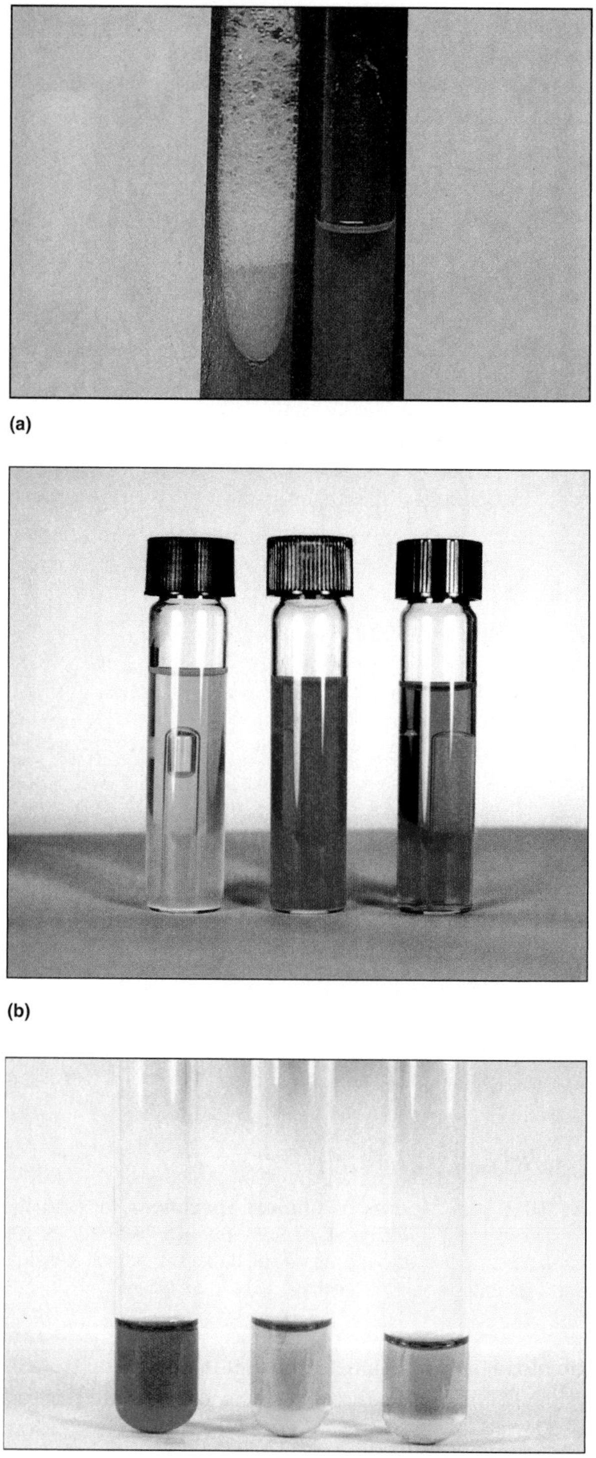

(a)

(b)

(c)

FIGURE 10.4 Biochemical Tests (a) Catalase production. Bacteria that produce catalase break down hydrogen peroxide to release oxygen gas ($2\ H_2O_2 \rightarrow 2\ H_2O + O_2$), which causes the bubbling shown in the left tube. A negative catalase test is shown in the right tube. **(b)** Sugar fermentation. The tube on the left shows acid (yellow color) and gas, indicating that the sugar was fermented and gas was produced during the process. The center tube shows no color change, indicating that the sugar was not utilized. The tube on the right is an uninoculated control. **(c)** Urease production. Breakdown of urea releases ammonia, which turns the pH indicator pink, as shown in the left tube. The tube in the center shows no color change, indicating that urease was not produced. The tube on the right is an uninoculated control.

system utilizes a strip holding a series of cupules that contain dehydrated media. A liquid suspension of the test bacterium is inoculated into each of the compartments, thus rehydrating the media. Because the formulations of the media are similar in composition to those used in traditional tests, the positive results give rise to similar color changes. After a 16-hour incubation of the inoculated test strip, the results are read manually. The pattern of results is converted to a numerical score, which can then be entered into a computer to identify the organism. A similar system is the Enterotube™, a tube with small compartments each containing a different type of medium. One end of a metal rod that runs through the tube is used to touch a bacterial colony. When the rod is withdrawn it inoculates each of the compartments. A system by Biolog uses a **microtiter plate,** a small tray containing 96 wells, to assay simultaneously an organism's ability to use a wide variety of carbon sources. Modifications of these plates enable researchers to characterize the metabolic capabilities of microbial communities, such as those in soil, water, or wastewater.

Highly automated systems also are available. The Vitek™ system uses a miniature card that contains multiple wells with different formulations of dehydrated media. A computer then reads the growth pattern in the wells after a relatively short incubation period.

Serology

The proteins and polysaccharides that make up a bacterium are sometimes characteristic enough to be considered identifying markers. The most useful of these are the molecules that make up surface structures including the cell wall, capsule, flagella, and pili. For example, some species of *Streptococcus* contain a unique carbohydrate molecule as part of their cell wall that can be used to distinguish them from other species. These carbohydrates, as well as any distinct proteins or polysaccharides, can be detected using techniques that rely on the specificity of interaction between antibodies and antigens. Methods that exploit these interactions are called serology and will be discussed in more detail in later chapters. Some serological tests, such as those used to confirm the identity of *S. pyogenes,* are quite simple and rapid. ■ **antibodies, p. 392** ■ **antigens, p. 391** ■ **serology, p. 421**

Fatty Acid Analysis (FAME)

Bacteria differ in the type and relative quantity of fatty acids that make up their membranes; thus, the cellular fatty acid composition can be used as an identifying marker. In the case of Gram-negative bacteria,

TABLE 10.5 Characteristics of Some Important Biochemical Tests

Biochemical Test	Principle of the Test	Positive Reaction
Catalase	Detects the activity of the enzyme catalase, which causes the breakdown of hydrogen peroxide to produce O_2 and water.	Bubbles.
Citrate	Determines whether or not citrate can be used as a sole carbon source.	Growth, which is usually accompanied by the color change of a pH indicator.
Gelatinase	Detects enzymatic breakdown of gelatin to polypeptides.	The solid gelatin is converted to liquid.
Hydrogen Sulfide Production	Detects H_2S liberated as a result of the degradation of sulfur-containing amino acids.	A black precipitate forms due to the reaction of H_2S with iron salts in the medium.
Indole	Detects the enzymatic removal of the amino group from tryptophan.	The product, indole, reacts with a chemical reagent that is added, turning the reagent a deep red color.
Lysine Decarboxylase	Detects the enzymatic removal of the carboxyl group from lysine.	The medium becomes more alkaline, causing a pH indicator to change color.
Methyl Red	Detects mixed acids, the characteristic end products of a particular fermentation pathway. ■ **mixed acids, p. 154**	The medium becomes acidic ($pH < 4.5$); a red color develops upon the addition of a pH indicator.
Oxidase	Detects the activity of cytochrome *c* oxidase, a component of the electron transport chain of specific organisms. ■ **cytochrome *c*, p. 149**	A dark color develops upon the addition of a specific reagent.
Phenylalanine Deaminase	Detects the enzymatic removal of the amino group from phenylalanine.	The product of the reaction, phenylpyruvic acid, reacts with ferric chloride to give the medium a green color.
Sugar Fermentation	Detects the acidity resulting from fermentation of the sugar incorporated into the medium. Also detects gas production.	The color of a pH indicator incorporated into the medium changes if acid if produced. An inverted tube traps any gas that is made.
Urease	Detects the enzymatic degradation of urea to carbon dioxide and ammonia.	The medium becomes alkaline, causing a pH indicator to change color.
Voges-Proskauer	Detects acetoin, an intermediate of the fermentation pathway that leads to the production of a 2, 3-butanediol. ■ **2, 3-butanediol, p. 153**	A red color develops upon addition of chemicals that detect acetoin.

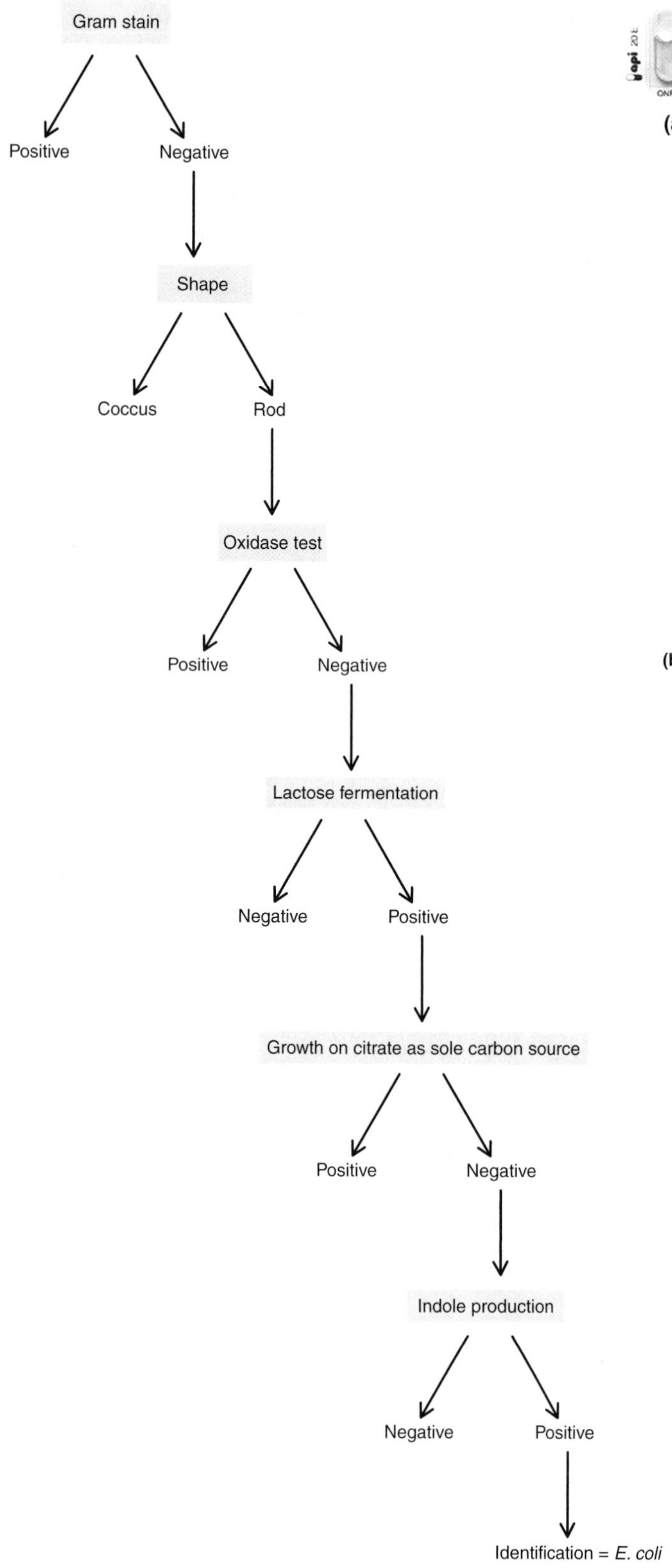

FIGURE 10.5 An Example of a Dichotomous Key Leading to the Identification of *E. coli* The biochemical tests are usually initiated simultaneously to speed identification.

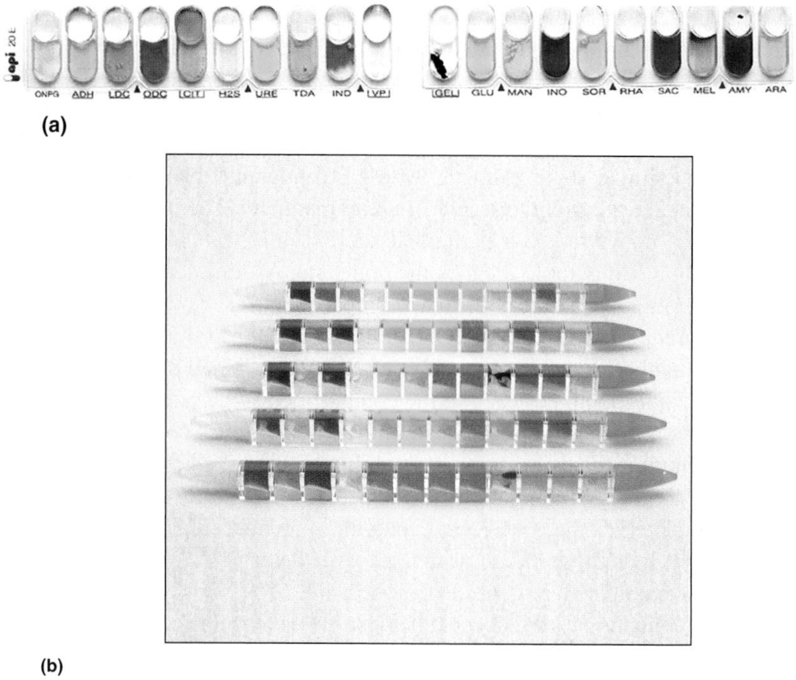

FIGURE 10.6 Commercial Modifications of Traditional Biochemical Tests These methods are less labor-intensive than traditional tests. **(a)** An API™ test strip. Each of the cupules contains a dehydrated medium similar in formulation to the traditional tests. A liquid suspension of the isolated test bacterium is added to each compartment; after incubation, the results are read manually. **(b)** An Enterotube™. Each compartment contains a different type of medium. One end of a metal rod that runs through the tube is used to touch a bacterial colony. When the rod is withdrawn it inoculates each of the compartments. After incubation, the results are read manually.

the fatty acids are contained in both the cytoplasmic and outer membranes. Gram-positive bacteria, however, lack an outer membrane; the cytoplasmic membrane is the source of their fatty acids. To analyze their fatty acid composition, bacterial cells are grown under standardized conditions. The cells are then chemically treated with sodium hydroxide and methanol to release the fatty acids and to convert those acids to their more volatile methyl ester form (FAME stands for fatty acid methyl ester). The resulting fatty acid methylated esters can then be separated and analyzed using gas chromatography. By comparing the pattern of peaks, or **chromatogram,** to those of known species, an isolate can be identified **(figure 10.7).**

MICROCHECK 10.2

The size, shape, and staining characteristics of a microorganism, all of which can be viewed using a microscope, yield important clues to its identity. Conclusive identification generally requires a battery of biochemical tests that assay for compounds indicating the presence of specific biochemical pathways. The proteins and polysaccharides that make up a bacterium are sometimes unique enough to be considered identifying markers. Cellular fatty acid composition can be used as an identifying characteristic.

- ✓ How does MacConkey agar help to identify the cause of a urinary tract infection?
- ✓ Describe two methods that can be used to test for the enzyme urease.
- ✓ Why must a sample contain many microorganisms for any to be viewed by microscopic examination?

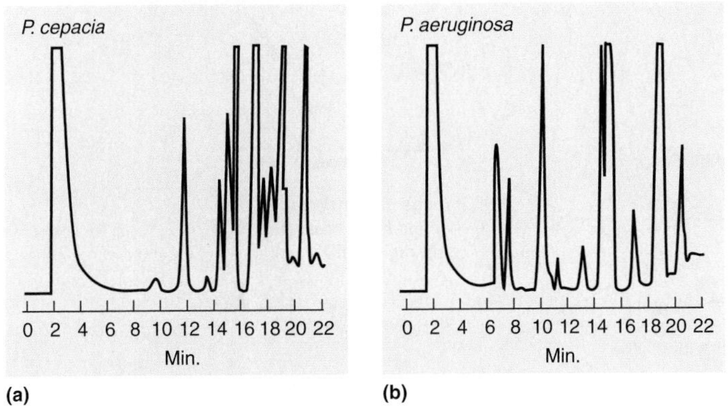

FIGURE 10.7 Chromatogram of the Fatty Acid Profiles Each peak represents a different fatty acid; the size of the peak correlates with the relative amount of that particular molecule. **(a)** A chromatogram of the fatty acids of *Pseudomonas cepacia* and **(b)** a chromatogram of the fatty acids of a closely related species, *Pseudomonas aeruginosa*.

10.3

Using Genotypic Characteristics to Identify Prokaryotes

Focus Point

- Describe how nucleic acid probes, PCR, and DNA sequencing of 16S rDNA can be used to identify prokaryotes.

Many of the technologies discussed in chapter 9 are being used to identify microorganisms based on their genotype. For example, both DNA probes and polymerase chain reaction (PCR) can be used to detect nucleotide sequences unique to a given species. A significant limitation, however, is that detection of specific sequence can only determine whether a given organism or group of related organisms is present or not. Thus, if the isolate could be one of five different possibilities, then five different probes would be required, each either used in separate reactions or labeled with different detectable markers. A distinct advantage of these methods, though, is that they make it possible to identify organisms that cannot yet be grown in culture. ■ DNA probe, p. 221 ■ polymerase chain reaction, pp. 230, 238

Nucleic Acid Probes to Detect Specific Nucleotide Sequences

A nucleic acid probe can be used to locate a unique nucleotide sequence that characterizes a particular species **(figure 10.8).** The probe is a single-stranded piece of nucleic acid, usually DNA, that has been labeled with a detectable tag, such as a radioisotope or a fluoresent dye. It is complementary to the sequence of interest.

Methods that employ nucleic acid probes to detect DNA sequences generally rely on some type of an amplification step. For example, in some cases the bacteria in the specimen must first be cultured on an agar plate so that each cell can multiply to form a colony containing well over a million cells. In other cases, a preliminary *in vitro* DNA amplification step is required.

Unlike most methods that use nucleic acid probes, fluorescence *in situ* hybridization (FISH) often employs probes that bind 16S ribosomal RNA (rRNA). The technique does not require an amplification step because numerous copies of rRNA are naturally present in a cell. Various different probes that bind rRNA are available, each specific for a given **signature sequence** found in rRNA. A signature sequence characterizes either a certain species or a group of related organisms (see figure 9.11). Clinical and environmental applications of FISH, as well as the techniques involved, were discussed in chapter 9. ■ fluorescence *in situ* hybridization, p. 229

Amplifying Specific DNA Sequences Using the Polymerase Chain Reaction

The polymerase chain reaction (PCR) can be used to amplify target sequences of DNA, allowing researchers to detect specific sequences in samples such as body fluids, soil, food, and water (see figure 9.13). The technique can be used to detect organisms that are present in extremely small numbers as well as those that cannot yet be grown in culture.

To use PCR to detect a microbe of interest, a sample is first treated to release and denature the DNA. Specific primers and other ingredients are then added to the denatured DNA, forming the components of the PCR reaction (see figure 9.22). Some information about the nucleotide sequence of the organism must be known in order to select the appropriate primers. After approximately 30 cycles of PCR, the DNA region flanked by the primers will have been amplified approximately a billion-fold (see figure 9.24). In most cases, this results in a sufficient quantity for the amplified fragment to be readily visible as a discrete band on an ethidium bromide-stained agarose gel. Alternatively, a DNA probe can be used to detect the amplified DNA. ■ ethidium bromide, p. 221 ■ gel electrophoresis, p. 221

Sequencing Ribosomal RNA Genes

The nucleotide sequence of ribosomal RNA (rRNA) can be used to identify prokaryotes, particularly those that are difficult or currently impossible to grow in culture. The prokaryotic 70S ribosome, which plays an indispensable role in protein synthesis, is composed of protein and three different rRNAs (5S, 16S, and 23S) **(figure 10.9).** Because of their highly constrained and essential function, the nucleotide sequence changes that can occur in the rRNAs, yet still allow the ribosome to operate, are limited. This is why they have proved so useful in microbial classification and, more recently, identification. While earlier methods relied on determining the sequence of the rRNA molecule itself, newer techniques sequence the DNA that encodes rRNA, which is called rDNA.

Of the different rRNAs, the 16S molecule has proved most useful in taxonomy because of its moderate size (approximately 1,500 nucleotides). That molecule, as well as its eukaryotic counterpart (18S RNA), is sometimes referred to as **small subunit (SS or SSU)**

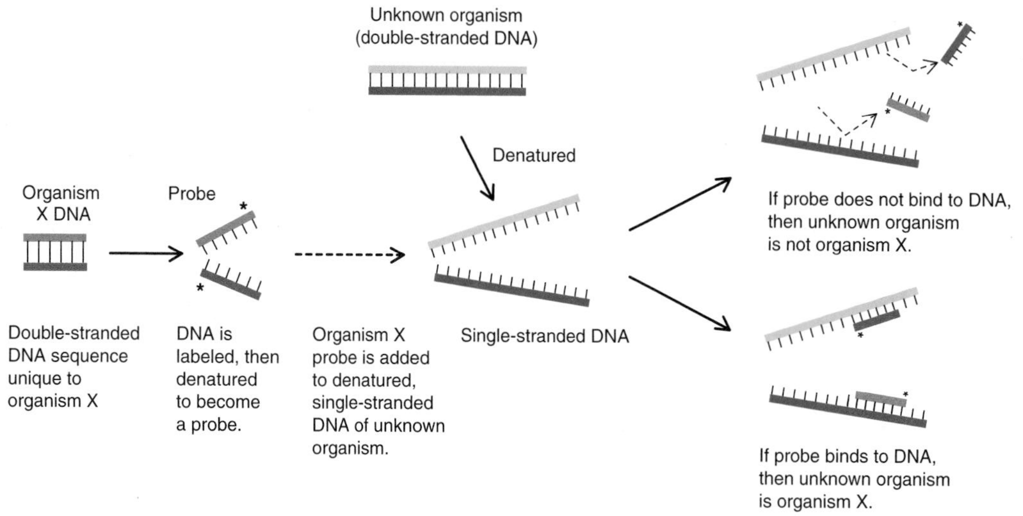

FIGURE 10.8 Nucleic Acid Probes to Detect Specific DNA Sequences The probe, which is a single-stranded piece of nucleic acid that has been labeled with a detectable marker, is used to locate a unique nucleotide sequence that identifies a particular known species of microorganism.

rRNA, reflecting the fact that it is part of the small subunit of the ribosome (see figure 10.9). Once the nucleotide sequence of SSU RNA in an unknown organism has been determined, it can be compared with sequences of known organisms by searching extensive computerized databases.

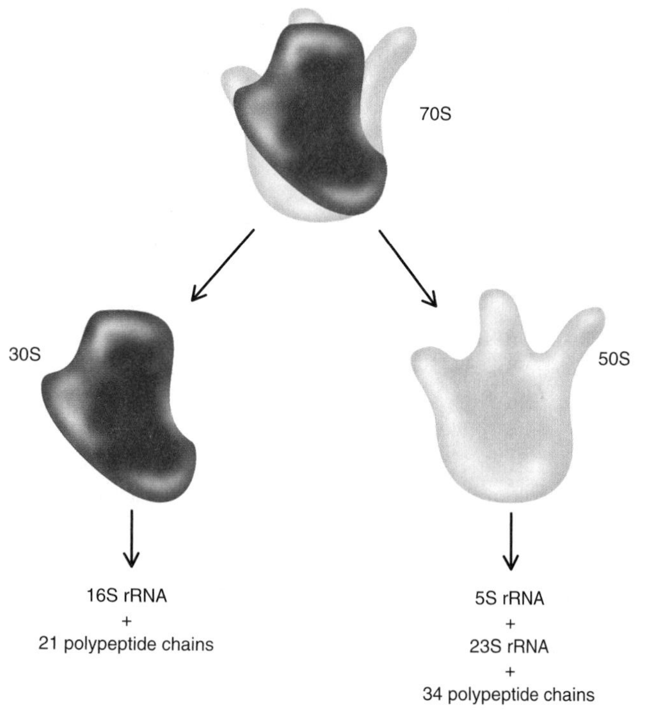

FIGURE 10.9 Ribosomal RNA The 70S ribosome of prokaryotes has three types of rRNA: 5S, 16S, and 23S.

Using rDNA to Identify Currently Unculturable Organisms

In any environment, including soil, water, and the human body, a multitude of organisms exist that cannot yet be grown in culture. Some scientists estimate that every gram of fertile soil contains more than 4,000 different species of prokaryotes, the vast majority of which have not been identified. With current technologies that enable amplification of specific portions of DNA, followed by the cloning and then sequencing of those fragments, it is possible not only to detect such organisms, but also to obtain information about their identity.

One of the first examples of using molecular biology to identify an organism that had not been cultured was the characterization of the causative agent of a rare illness called Whipple's disease. This was done by using PCR to amplify bacterial 16S rDNA from intestinal tissue of patients who had symptoms of Whipple's disease. That DNA was then cloned and sequenced. The nucleotide sequence suggested that the causative agent was an actinomycete unrelated to any of those previously identified. It was given the name *Tropheryma whippelii.* Even though it had never been grown in culture, a specific probe was then developed that can detect it in intestinal tissue. Since that time it has been successfully cultured.

MICROCHECK 10.3

A microorganism can be identified by using a probe or PCR to detect a nucleotide sequence that is unique to that particular organism. Ribosomal RNA genes can be sequenced to identify an organism that cannot be grown in culture.

- ✓ When using a probe to identify an organism, why is it necessary to have some idea as to the organism's identity?
- ✓ How can ribosomal DNA be used to identify bacteria that cannot be grown in culture?
- ✓ Why are molecular methods especially useful when bacteria are difficult to cultivate?

10.4

Characterizing Strain Differences

Focus Point

- Describe five distinct methods by which different strains can be distinguished.

In some situations, it is helpful to distinguish different strains of a given species. In 2004, for example, an initial cluster of five salmonellosis cases in the United States were found to involve a specific strain of *Salmonella enterica* serotype Enteritidis. The patients all reported consuming raw almonds prior to their illness, leading to a widespread recall of approximately 13 million pounds of the product. Linking a mere five cases amid the thousands of salmonellosis cases that occur nationwide each year would not have been possible without methods to determine strain differences and then catalog those results, making it feasible to match cases from around the country.

Characterizing strain differences is not limited to investigations of foodborne illness. It also plays an instrumental role in forensic investigations of bioterrorism and other biocrimes, and in identifying cause of disease when only certain strains are pathogenic. The methods used to characterize different strains are summarized in **table 10.6.**

Biochemical Typing

Biochemical tests are used to identify various species of bacteria, but they can also be used to distinguish strains. If the biochemical variation is uncommon, it can be used for tracing the source of certain disease outbreaks. Strains that have a characteristic biochemical pattern are called a **biovar** or a **biotype.** A biochemical variant of *Vibrio cholerae* called Eltor is increasingly being implicated in outbreaks of cholera around the world. Because this biovar can be readily distinguished, its spread can be traced. ■ *Vibrio cholerae,* p. 624

Serological Typing

Proteins and carbohydrates that vary among strains can be used to differentiate strains. For example, *E. coli* and other Gram-negative bacteria vary in the antigenic structure of certain parts of the lipopolysaccharide portion of the cell wall, the **O antigen** (see figure 11.14). The composition of the flagella, the **H antigen,** can also vary. The "O157:H7" designation of *E. coli* O157:H7 refers to the structure of its lipopolysaccharide and flagella. Strains that differ serologically from other strains are called a **serovar** or a **serotype.** ■ lipopolysaccharide, p. 62 ■ *E. coli* O157:H7, p. 627

Genomic Typing

Subtle differences in DNA sequences can be used to distinguish among strains that are phenotypically identical. These genomic variations are used to trace epidemics of foodborne illness in which a single source of contaminated food is shipped to several states. The ability to link geographically distant cases can enable public health officials to determine the source of the epidemic, leading to the recall of the implicated product and preventing further cases of disease. One method of doing this is to compare the patterns of fragment sizes produced when the same restriction enzyme is used to digest DNA from each organism. When the lengths of the restriction fragments vary among organisms, the fragments are said to be polymorphic (see figure 9.10). The different patterns of fragment sizes obtained by digesting DNA with restriction enzymes are called **restriction fragment length polymorphisms (RFLPs) (figure 10.10).** Two isolates of the same species that have different RFLPs are considered different strains. Two isolates that have identical RFLPs may be the same strain. It cannot be concluded with absolute certainty, however, that they are indeed the same strain. ■ restriction enzymes, p. 220 ■ restriction fragment length polymorphisms, p. 228

To facilitate the tracking of foodborne disease outbreaks, the Centers for Disease Control recently established the **National**

TABLE 10.6 Summary of Methods Used to Characterize Different Strains

Method	Characteristics
Biochemical Typing	Biochemical tests are most commonly used to identify various species of bacteria, but in some cases they can be used to distinguish different strains. Strains that have a characteristic biochemical pattern are called a biovar or a biotype.
Serological Typing	Proteins and carbohydrates that vary among strains can be used to differentiate strains. Strains that have a characteristic serological type are called a serovar or a serotype.
Genomic Typing	Molecular methods such as pulsed-field gel electrophoresis can be used to detect restriction fragment length polymorphisms (RFLPs).
Phage Typing	Strains of a given species sometimes differ in their susceptibility to various types of bacteriophage.
Antibiograms	Antibiotic susceptibility patterns can be used to characterize strains.

PERSPECTIVE 10.1

Tracing the Source of an Outbreak of Foodborne Disease

In October 1996, physicians at the Children's Hospital and Medical Center in Seattle, Washington, noticed a slight increase in cases of children with severe bloody diarrhea. They quickly recognized that the children were infected with *Escherichia coli* O157:H7, a strain that can cause a fatal disease. Within days, the source of the outbreak was traced to contaminated unpasteurized apple juice, prompting the manufacturer to immediately recall that and related products from all stores in their seven-state distribution area. The prompt action by physicians, health officials, and the juice manufacturer ended the outbreak and averted a potential widespread tragedy. ■ ***E. coli* O157:H7, p. 628**

While the sequence of events that led to the recognition and cessation of the *E. coli* O157:H7 outbreak may sound quite simple, they are actually very complex. For one thing, most strains of *E. coli* are normal inhabitants of the intestine and can be found in nearly any stool sample. How was this particular strain separated and distinguished from the hundreds of *E. coli* strains that do not cause diarrheal disease? It is also true that sporadic cases of *E. coli* O157:H7 infections occur regularly, originating from unrelated sources. How was it recognized that these cases were connected?

To identify *E. coli* O157:H7 in a stool specimen, the sample is plated onto a special agar medium designed to distinguish it from strains that typically inhabit the large intestine. One such medium is sorbitol-MacConkey, a modified version of MacConkey agar in which the lactose is replaced with the carbohydrate sorbitol. On this medium most *E. coli* O157:H7 isolates are colorless because they do not ferment sorbitol. In contrast, common strains of *E. coli* ferment the carbohydrate, giving rise to pink colonies. Serology is then used to determine if the colorless *E. coli* colonies are serotype O157; those that test positive are then generally tested to confirm they are serotype H7.

The next task is to determine whether or not two isolates of *E. coli* O157:H7 originated from the same source. DNA is extracted and purified from each isolate and is then digested with restriction enzymes. Pulsed-field gel electrophoresis is generally used to compare the resulting restriction fragment length polymorphism (RFLP) patterns of the isolates (see figure 10.10). Those that have identical patterns are presumed to have originated from the same source. The patients from whom those isolates originated can then be questioned to determine their likely point of contact with the disease-causing organism. Culture methods are then used to try to isolate the organism from the suspected source. If that attempt is successful, the RFLP pattern of that isolate is then compared with those of the related cases.

Molecular Subtyping Network for Foodborne Disease Surveillance (PulseNet), which catalogs the RFLPs of certain foodborne bacterial pathogens. Laboratories from around the country can submit RFLP patterns to a computer database and quickly receive information about other isolates showing the same patterns. Using this database, multistate foodborne disease outbreaks can more readily be recognized and traced. This is how the salmonellosis cases that led to the almond recall were found to be related.

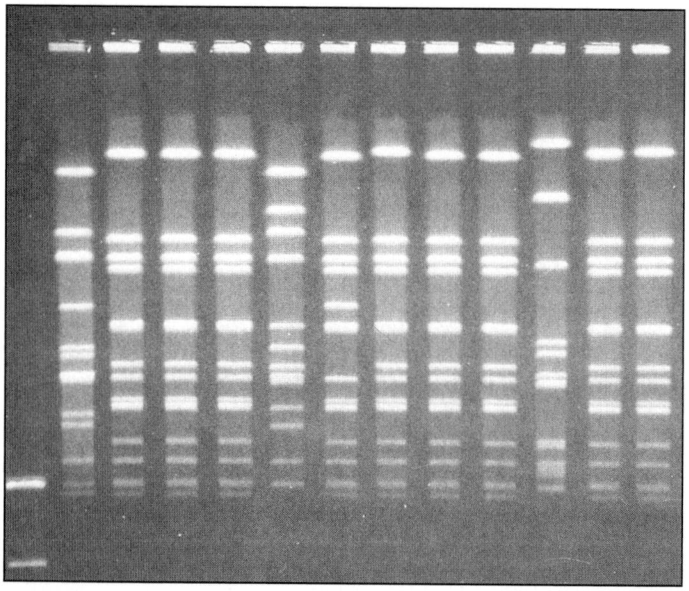

FIGURE 10.10 Restriction Fragment Length Polymorphisms (RFLPs) In the method shown, genomic DNA is digested with a restriction enzyme that cuts infrequently; the resulting fragments are separated by pulsed-field gel electrophoresis and then stained with ethidium bromide.

Phage Typing

Strains of a given species sometimes differ in their susceptibility to various types of **bacteriophages.** A bacteriophage, or **phage,** is a virus that infects and multiplies within bacteria and usually lyses the infected cells; each type of phage has a limited host range. Lysis of the infected cell releases more phage, which in turn infect neighboring cells. The susceptibility of an organism to a particular type of phage can be readily demonstrated in the laboratory. First, a culture of the test organism is inoculated into melted, cooled nutrient agar and poured onto the surface of an agar plate, thus creating a uniform layer of cells. Then drops of different types of bacteriophage are carefully placed on the surface of the agar. During incubation, the bacteria multiply, forming a visible haze of cells. A clear area will form at each spot where bacteriophage was added, if the organism is susceptible to the type of phage. The patterns of clearing indicate the susceptibility of the test organism to different phages and it is these patterns that are compared to determine strain differences **(figure 10.11).** Bacteriophage typing has now largely been replaced by molecular methods that detect genomic differences, but it is still a useful tool for laboratories that lack sophisticated equipment. ■ **bacteriophage, p. 319** ■ **host range, p. 331**

Antibiograms

Antibiotic susceptibility patterns, or **antibiograms,** can be used to distinguish among different strains. As with phage

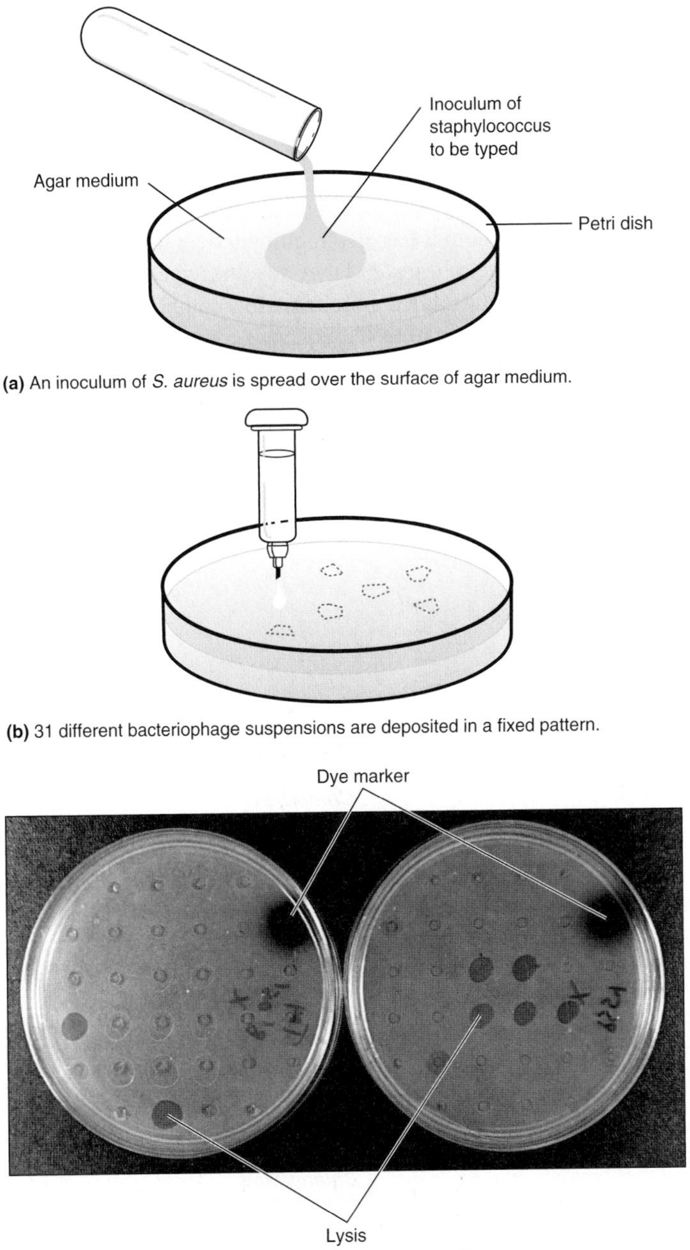

(a) An inoculum of *S. aureus* is spread over the surface of agar medium.

(b) 31 different bacteriophage suspensions are deposited in a fixed pattern.

(c) After incubation, different patterns of lysis are seen with different strains of *S. aureus*.

FIGURE 10.11 Phage Typing

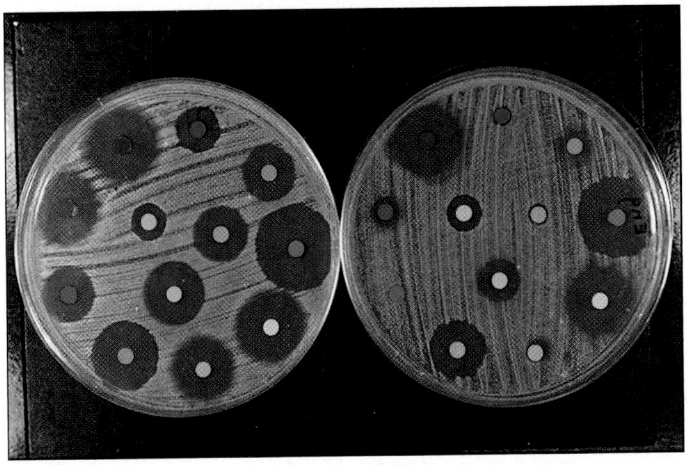

FIGURE 10.12 An Antibiogram In this example, 12 different antimicrobial drugs incorporated in paper discs have been placed on two plates containing different cultures of *Staphylococcus aureus*. Clear areas represent zones of inhibited growth. The different patterns of clearing indicate that these are two different strains of *S. aureus*.

typing, this method has now largely been replaced by molecular techniques. To determine the antibiogram, a culture is uniformly inoculated onto the surface of a nutritional agar medium. Paper discs, each of which has been impregnated with a given antibiotic, are then placed on the surface of the agar. During incubation, the organism will multiply to form a visible film of cells. A clear area, indicating lack of growth, will form around each antibiotic disc that inhibits the organism. Different strains will have different patterns of clearing **(figure 10.12).**

■ **antibiotic, p. 496**

MICROCHECK 10.4

Strains of a given species may differ in phenotypic attributes such as biochemical capabilities, protein and polysaccharide components, susceptibility to bacteriophages, and sensitivity to antimicrobial drugs. Molecular techniques can be used to detect subtle genomic differences between strains that are phenotypically identical.

✓ Explain the difference between a biotype and serotype.

✓ Describe the significance of RFLPs.

10.5 Classifying Prokaryotes

Focus Point

- Describe how 16S rRNA sequences, DNA hybridization, and DNA base ratios are used to classify prokaryotes.

As mentioned earlier in the chapter, the goal of phylogenetic classification is to categorize organisms according to their evolutionary relatedness. Unfortunately, this is difficult when trying to place the diverse types of prokaryotes in their proper position with respect to the evolution of living beings. Fossilized **stromatolites,** coral-like mats of filamentous microorganisms, are available for study, but because of the relatively few sizes and shapes of prokaryotes, these remains do little to help identify or understand these ancient organisms.

Prokaryotic classification has historically relied on phenotypic attributes such as size and shape, staining characteristics, and metabolic capabilities to group organisms. Using this system, a species can loosely be defined as a group of organisms that share many properties and differ significantly from other groups. While this is a convenient approach to prokaryotic taxonomy, there are several drawbacks. For instance, observable differences may be due to only a few gene products, and a single mutation resulting in a non-functional enzyme can dramatically alter that phenotypic property. In addition, organisms that are phenotypically similar may, in fact, be only distantly related. Conversely, those that appear dissimilar may be closely related.

Newer molecular techniques such as DNA sequencing circumvent some of the problems associated with phenotypic classification while also giving greater insights into the evolutionary relatedness of microorganisms. DNA sequences are viewed as **evolutionary chronometers,** meaning that sequence differences appear to provide a relative measure of the time elapsed since the organisms diverged from a common ancestor. This is because random mutations cause sequences to change over time. Thus, the more time that has elapsed since two organisms diverged, the greater the differences in the sequences of their DNA.

DNA sequencing enables one to more accurately construct a **phylogenetic tree.** These trees are somewhat like a family tree, tracing the evolutionary heritage of organisms. Each line, or **branch,** of the tree represents the evolutionary distance between two species **(figure 10.13).** Individual species are represented as **nodes.** Ancient prokaryotes, those that branch at an early point in evolution, are sometimes called **deeply branching** to reflect their position in the phylogenetic tree.

While sequencing data has solved some difficulties in prokaryotic classification, it has also highlighted an important obstacle. Prokaryotic cells transfer DNA to other species, a process called **horizontal** or **lateral gene transfer,** complicating insights provided by some types of DNA sequence comparison. The bacterium *Thermotoga maritima,* for example, appears to have acquired one-fourth of its genes from a hyperthermophilic archaeal species. Observations such as this have prompted some scientists to suggest that the tree of life (see figure 10.1) is more appropriately depicted as a shrub with interwoven branches **(figure 10.14).**

Table 10.7 summarizes some of the methods used to classify prokaryotes.

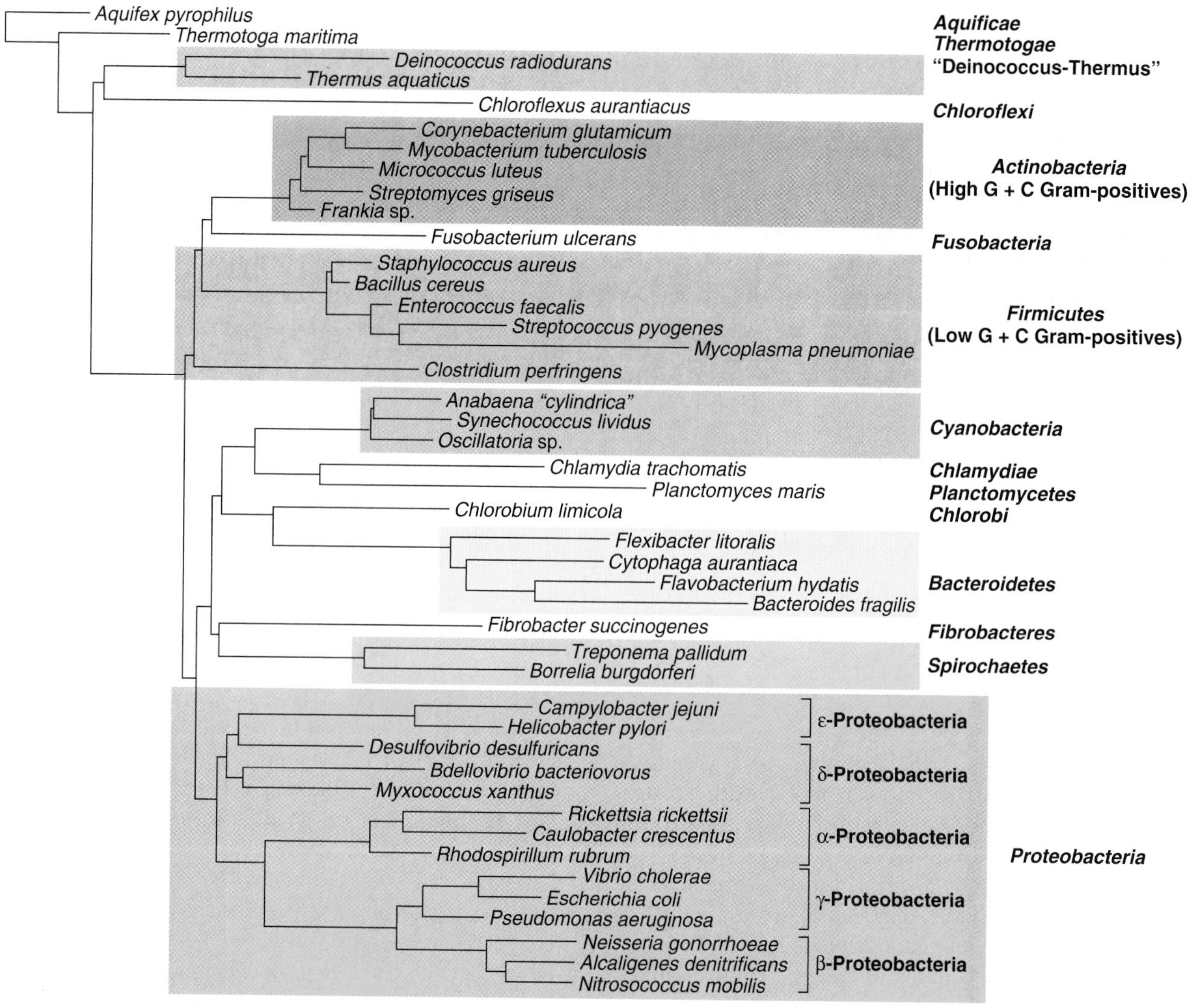

FIGURE 10.13 Phylogenetic Tree of the *Bacteria* Each branch represents the evolutionary distance between two species.
Source: The Ribosomal Database Project

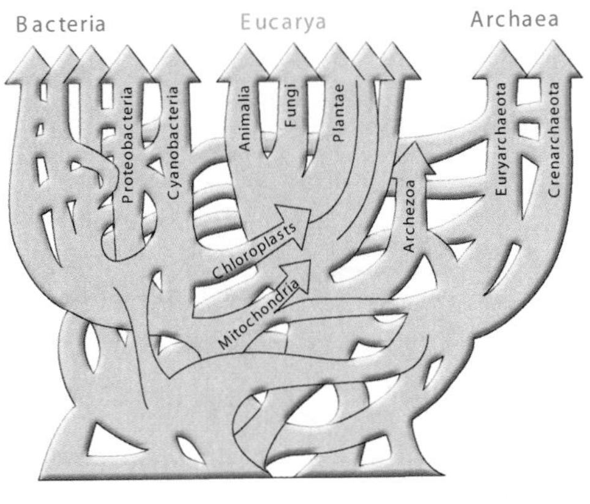

FIGURE 10.14 "Shrub" of Life

16S rDNA Sequence Analysis

Analyzing and comparing the nucleotide sequences of 16S ribosomal RNA (rRNA) and, more recently, the genes that encode rRNA (16S rDNA) has revolutionized the classification of organisms (see **Glimpse of History**). This is because rRNA, which is present in all organisms, performs a critical and functionally constant task, limiting the number of mutations that can happen in certain regions without affecting the viability of an organism. Long after organisms have diverged, the nucleotide sequences of portions of their 16S rDNA are still similar. Changes in these highly conserved regions occur very slowly over time and are thus useful for determining even distant relationships of diverse organisms. At the same time, certain regions are relatively variable. Comparing these sequences can be used to determine more recent divergence. In addition, horizontal gene transfer is unlikely to complicate the analysis because rDNA transfer appears to be rare.

Even the phylogeny of the multitude of prokaryotes that have not yet been grown in culture can be tentatively determined by 16S rDNA sequence analysis. DNA can be extracted from environmental samples such as soil and water, and the 16S rDNA then amplified, cloned, and sequenced using techniques similar to those employed to identify currently unculturable organisms. The resulting sequences can be compared to databases containing 16S rDNA sequences of known organisms to assess the relatedness. The results obtained from such procedures have uncovered a variety of prokaryotes quite distinct from those already described. In fact, while most characterized archaeal genera are extremophiles, 16S rDNA sequences from soil and water samples indicate that members of this domain are common in non-extreme environments as well. Clearly, the prokaryotic world is more diverse than most people recognize. ■ Using rDNA to identify currently unculturable organisms, p. 256

While 16S rDNA sequence analysis has been instrumental in determining the phylogeny of distantly related organisms, it sometimes does not resolve differences at the species level. This is because closely related prokaryotes can have identical 16S rDNA sequences, even though the organisms are phenotypically distinct. In these cases, DNA hybridization (discussed next) is a better tool to assess relatedness.

DNA Hybridization

The extent of nucleotide sequence similarity between two organisms can be determined by measuring how completely single strands of their DNA will hybridize to one another. Just as the complementary strands of DNA from one organism will anneal (base-pair), so will homologous DNA of a different organism. The extent of hybridization reflects the degree of sequence similarity. Two strains that show at least 70% similarity are often considered to be members of the same species. Surprisingly, DNA hybridization studies have shown that members of the genera *Shigella* and *Escherichia,* which are quite different based on biochemical tests, should actually be grouped in the same species. Note that human and chimpanzee DNA have approximately 99% similarity by DNA hybridization studies. Therefore, by the criteria used to classify prokaryotes, humans and chimpanzees would be members of the same species! ■ DNA hybridization, p. 223

DNA Base Ratio (G + C Content)

One way to roughly compare the genomes of different bacteria is to determine their DNA base ratio, which is the relative portion of adenine (A), thymine (T), guanine (G), and cytosine (C). Because of base-pairing rules, the number of molecules of G in double-

TABLE 10.7 Methods Used to Determine the Relatedness of Different Prokaryotes for Purposes of Classification

Methods	Comments
Genotypic Characteristics	Differences in DNA sequences can be used to determine the point in time at which two organisms diverged from a common ancestor.
Comparing the sequences of 16S rDNA	This technique has revolutionized classification. Certain regions of the 16S rDNA can be used to determine distant relatedness of diverse organisms; other regions can be used to determine more recent divergence.
DNA hybridization	The extent of nucleotide sequence similarity between two isolates can be determined by measuring how completely single strands of their DNA will hybridize to one another.
DNA base composition	Determining the G + C content offers a crude comparison of genomes. Organisms with identical G + C contents can be entirely unrelated, however.
Phenotypic Characteristics	Traditionally, relatedness of different bacteria has been decided by comparing properties such as ability to degrade lactose and the presence of flagella. These characteristics, however, do not necessarily reflect the evolutionary relatedness of organisms.

stranded DNA always equals the number of molecules of C. Likewise, the number of molecules of T equals that of A. The base ratio of an organism is usually expressed as the percent of guanine plus cytosine, termed the **G + C content,** or more commonly, the GC content. If the GC content of two organisms differs by more than a small percent, they cannot be closely related. A similarity of base compositions, however, does not necessarily mean that the organisms are related, however, since the nucleotide sequences and genome sizes could differ greatly.

The GC content is often measured by determining the temperature at which the double-stranded DNA denatures, or **melts.** DNA that has a high GC content melts at a higher temperature because G-C base pairs are held together by three hydrogen bonds, whereas A-T pairs are held together by only two hydrogen bonds. The temperature at which double-stranded DNA melts can readily be determined by monitoring the absorbance of UV light by a solution of DNA as it is heated. The absorbance rapidly increases as the DNA denatures **(figure 10.15).**

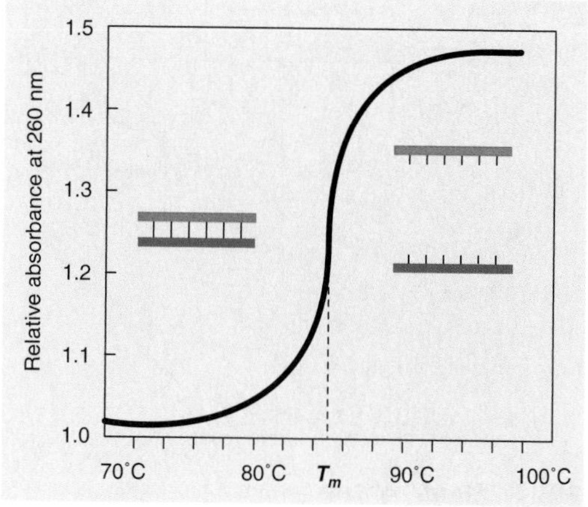

FIGURE 10.15 A DNA Melting Curve The absorbance (relative absorbance at 260 nm) rapidly increases as double-stranded DNA denatures, or melts. The T_m is the temperature at which 50% of the DNA has melted; it reflects the GC content.

Phenotypic Methods

While 16S ribosomal nucleic acid sequences are playing an increasingly prominent role in prokaryotic classification, phenotypic methods are still important, particularly because they provide a foundation for prokaryotic identification. In addition, some taxonomists believe classification should be based on more than just genotypic traits.

Numerical taxonomy uses a quantitative approach to phenotypic classification, comparing a battery of characteristics. Information about this method can be obtained by visiting the Online Learning Center (www.mmhe.com/nester5).

MICROCHECK 10.5

Analyzing and comparing the sequences of ribosomal RNA genes has revolutionized the classification of organisms. Other characteristics used to classify prokaryotes include DNA hybridization, GC ratio, and phenotypic properties.

✓ Explain why 16S rDNA has proved so useful in determining evolutionary relatedness.

✓ Explain the role of DNA hybridization in classification.

✓ Why would it be easier to sequence rDNA than rRNA?

FUTURE CHALLENGES

Tangled Branches in the Phylogenetic Tree

While 16S rDNA sequencing has given remarkable new insight into the evolutionary relatedness of organisms, total genome sequencing promises to reveal myriad additional information. In some cases this will serve to clarify the evolutionary picture, providing solid evidence that two organisms are, in fact, closely related. Genomic sequencing, however, can also give information that conflicts with that of rDNA data, creating an uncomfortable confusion. Already, examples exist that challenge the current rDNA phylogenetic tree. For example, sequences of some genes for highly conserved proteins show a closer relationship between some members of the *Archaea* and *Bacteria* than their rDNA sequences suggest. This conflicting data might be accounted for by evidence suggesting that horizontal DNA transfer has occurred even between distantly related organisms. Due to gene transfer, an organism from one domain may contain genes acquired from an organism in a different domain. As a result, some suggest that the phylogenetic tree may be closer to a shrub, with lateral gene transfer giving rise to intertwining branches.

The vast amount of genetic knowledge being obtained is affecting bacterial nomenclature. As more genomes are sequenced, the evolutionary relatedness among organisms will become apparent. Nomenclature is bound to change as a result of the new insights. Already, some species of what were formerly included in the genus *Streptococcus* have been removed to create two relatively new genera, *Enterococcus* and *Lactococcus*. The genera *Pseudomonas* and *Bacillus* will likely be similarly subdivided. Meanwhile, other bacteria will be moved from one existing genus to another. All of these changes will create a potential source of confusion for the scientist and layperson alike.

SUMMARY

10.1 Principles of Taxonomy

Taxonomy consists of three interrelated areas: **identification, classification,** and **nomenclature.**

Strategies Used to Identify Prokaryotes

To characterize and identify microorganisms, a wide assortment of technologies is used, including microscopic examination, cultural characteristics, biochemical tests, and nucleic acid analysis.

Strategies Used to Classify Prokaryotes

Taxonomic classification categories are arranged in a hierarchical order, with the **species** being the basic unit.

Taxonomic categories include **species, genus, order, class, phylum** (or division), **kingdom,** and **domain.** Individual **strains** within a species vary in minor properties. (Table 10.1)

Nomenclature

Prokaryotes are assigned names governed by official rules.

10.2 Using Phenotypic Characteristics to Identify Prokaryotes (Table 10.4)

Microscopic Morphology

The size, shape, and staining characteristics of a microorganism yield important clues as to its identity. (Figures 10.2, 10.3)

Metabolic Capabilities

The use of selective and differential media in the isolation process can provide information that helps identify an organism.

Most biochemical tests rely on a pH indicator or chemical reaction that shows a color change when a compound is degraded. The basic strategy for identification using biochemical tests relies on the use of a **dichotomous key.** (Figures 10.4, 10.5, Table 10.5)

Serology

Proteins and polysaccharides that make up a prokaryote's surface are sometimes characteristic enough to be identifying markers.

Fatty Acid Analysis (FAME)

Cellular fatty acid composition can be used as an identifying marker. (Figure 10.7)

10.3 Using Genotypic Characteristics to Identify Prokaryotes

Nucleic Acid Probes to Detect Specific Nucleotide Sequences

By selecting a probe that is complementary to a sequence unique to a given microbe, researchers can use nucleic acid hybridization to detect specific organisms. (Figure 10.8)

Amplifying Specific DNA Sequences Using the Polymerase Chain Reaction

By selecting primers that can be used to amplify a nucleotide sequence unique to a microbe of interest, researchers can apply PCR to determine if a particular agent is present.

Sequencing Ribosomal RNA Genes

The nucleotide sequence of ribosomal RNA (rRNA) can be used to identify prokaryotes. Newer techniques simply sequence rDNA, the DNA that encodes rRNA. (Figure 10.9)

Organisms that cannot yet be cultured can be identified by amplifying, cloning, and then sequencing specific regions of rDNA.

10.4 Characterizing Strain Differences (Table 10.6)

Biochemical Typing

Strains that have a characteristic biochemical variation are called a **biovar** or a **biotype.**

Serological Typing

Strains that differ serologically from other strains are called a **serovar** or a **serotype.**

Genomic Typing

Two isolates of the same species that have different **restriction fragment length polymorphisms (RFLPs)** are considered different strains. (Figure 10.10)

Phage Typing

The susceptibility to various types of bacteriophages can be used to demonstrate strain differences. (Figure 10.11)

Antibiograms

Antibiotic susceptibility patterns can be used to distinguish strains. (Figure 10.12)

10.5 Classifying Prokaryotes (Table 10.7)

DNA sequencing enables one to more accurately construct a **phylogenetic tree.** (Figure 10.13)

Horizontal (lateral) gene transfer can complicate insights provided by some types of DNA sequence comparison. (Figure 10.14)

16S rDNA Sequence Analysis

Analyzing and comparing the sequences of rRNA and more recently, rDNA, has revolutionized the classification of organisms.

DNA Hybridization

The extent of nucleotide sequence similarity between two organisms can be determined by measuring how completely single strands of their DNA will anneal to one another.

DNA Base Ratio (G + C Content)

The **G + C content** can be measured by determining the temperature at which double-stranded DNA melts. (Figure 10.15)

Phenotypic Methods

Some taxonomists believe that classification should be based on more than just genotypic traits.

REVIEW QUESTIONS

Short Answer

1. Name and describe each of the areas of taxonomy.
2. Compare and contrast the five-kingdom and three-domain systems of classification.
3. Describe how a dichotomous key is used in the identification of bacteria.
4. Describe the difference between using a probe and using PCR to detect a specific sequence.
5. Explain how signature sequences are used in bacterial identification.
6. Describe the function of PulseNet.
7. Describe how the GC content of DNA can be measured.
8. Explain why DNA sequences are viewed as evolutionary chronometers.
9. What is a phylogenetic tree?
10. Why is it preferable for a classification scheme to reflect the phylogeny of organisms?

Multiple Choice

1. Which of the following is the newest taxonomic unit?
   a) Strain b) Family c) Order
   d) Species e) Domain
2. An acid-fast stain can be used to detect which of the following organisms?
   a) *Cryptococcus neoformans* b) *Mycobacterium tuberculosis*
   c) *Neisseria gonorrhoeae* d) *Streptococcus pneumoniae*
   e) *Streptococcus pyogenes*
3. The "breath test" for *Helicobacter pylori* infection assays for the presence of which of the following?
   a) Antigens b) Catalase c) Hemolysis
   d) Lactose fermentation e) Urease
4. The "O" of *E. coli* O157:H7 refers to the
   a) biotype. b) serotype. c) phage type.
   d) ribotype. e) antibiogram.
5. PulseNet catalogs which of the following?
   a) Biotype b) Serotype c) Phage type
   d) RFLP e) Antibiogram
6. Which of the following is an example of an evolutionary chronometer?
   a) Ability to form endospores b) 16S ribosomal RNA sequence
   c) Sugar degradation d) Motility
7. If the GC content of two organisms is 70%, which of the following is true?
   a) The organisms are definitely related.
   b) The organisms are definitely not related.
   c) The AT content is 30%.
   d) The organisms likely have extensive DNA homology.
   e) The organisms likely have many characteristics in common.
8. Which of the molecular methods of assessing similarity gives the crudest approximation of relatedness?
   a) DNA hybridization b) PCR
   c) 16S rDNA sequencing d) DNA base composition
9. The sequence of which ribosomal genes are most commonly used for establishing phylogenetic relatedness?
   a) 5S b) 16S
   c) 23S d) All of these are commonly used.
10. Which of the following statements is false?
    a) *Tropheryma whippelii* could be identified before it had been grown in culture.
    b) The GC content of DNA can be measured by determining the temperature at which double-stranded DNA melts.
    c) Sequence differences between organisms can be used to assess their relatedness.
    d) Based on DNA homology studies, members of the genus *Shigella* should be in the same species as *Escherichia coli.*
    e) Pulsed-field gel electrophoresis is used to determine the serotype of an organism.

Applications

1. Microbiologists debate the use of biochemical similarities and cell features as a way of determining the taxonomic relationships among prokaryotes. Explain why some microbiologists believe these similarities and differences are a powerful taxonomic indicator while others think they are not very useful for that purpose.
2. The mitochondria of eukaryotic cells are theorized to have bacterial origins. A researcher interested in investigating the relationship of mitochondria to bacteria must now decide on the best method to make this determination. What advice would you give the researcher?

Critical Thinking

1. In figure 10.15, how would the curve appear if the GC content of the DNA sample were increased? How would the curve appear if the AT content were increased?
2. When DNA probes are used to detect specific sequence similarities in bacterial DNA, the probe is heated and the two strands of DNA are separated. Why must the probe DNA be treated in this way before detection is possible?

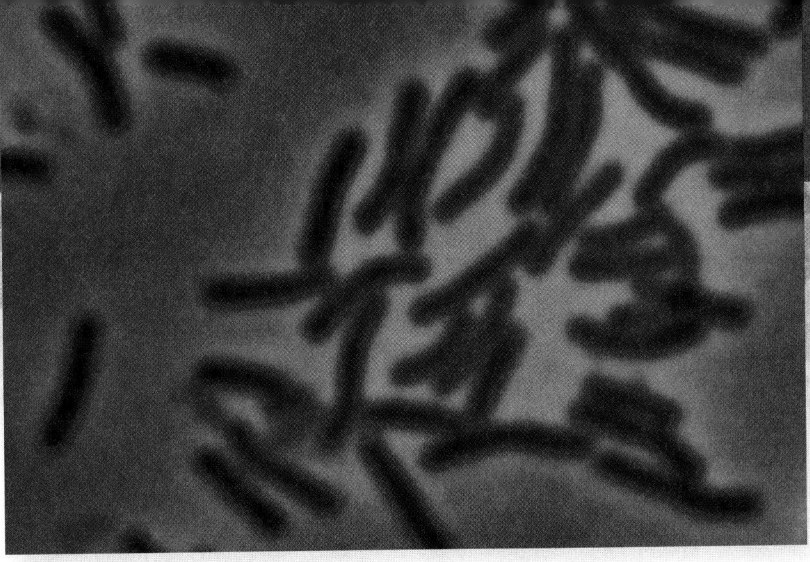

Bacterial cells

CHAPTER ELEVEN

The Diversity of Prokaryotic Organisms

A Glimpse of History

Cornelis B. van Niel (1897–1985) earned his Ph.D. from the Technological University in Delft, the home of an approach to the study of microbiology now commonly referred to as "the Delft School." The outstanding program there was chaired in succession by two prominent microbiologists—Martinus Beijerinck and Albert Kluyver.

As Kluyver's student, van Niel was heavily influenced by his mentor's belief that biochemical processes were fundamentally the same in all cells and that microorganisms could be important research tools, serving as a model to study biochemical process. Thirty years later, Kluyver and van Niel presented lectures that would be published in a book entitled *The Microbe's Contribution to Biology.*

Shortly after completing his dissertation in 1928, van Niel accepted a position at the Hopkins Marine Station in California. There, he continued work he started under Kluyver's direction on the photosynthetic activities of the vividly colored purple bacteria. He conclusively demonstrated that these organisms require light for growth, yet, unlike plants and algae, do not evolve O_2. He also showed that in order to fix CO_2, the purple bacteria oxidize hydrogen sulfide. Furthermore, van Niel noted that the stoichiometry of the photosynthetic reactions in all these organisms was remarkably similar, except that the purple bacteria use hydrogen sulfide in place of water, and produce oxidized sulfur compounds instead of O_2. This finding raised the possibility that O_2 generated by plants and algae did not come from carbon dioxide, as was believed at the time, but rather from water.

In addition to his scientific contributions, van Niel was an outstanding teacher. During the summers at Hopkins Marine Station, he taught a bacteriology course, inspiring many microbiologists with his enthusiasm for the diversity of microorganisms and their importance in nature. His keen memory and knowledge of the literature, along with his appreciation for the remarkable abilities of microorganisms, enabled him to successfully impart the awe and wonder of the microbial world to his students.

Scientists are only beginning to understand the vast diversity of microbial life. Although a million species of prokaryotes are thought to exist, only approximately 6,000 of these, grouped into over 950 genera, have been actually described and classified. Traditional culture and isolation techniques have not supported the growth, and subsequent study, of the vast majority. Not surprisingly, most effort has been put into the study of microbes intimately associated with the human population, especially those causing disease, and these have been most extensively described. This situation is changing as new molecular techniques aid in the discovery and characterization of previously unrecognized species. The sheer volume of the rapidly accruing information made possible by this modern technology, however, can be daunting for scientists and students alike.

This chapter covers a wide spectrum of prokaryotes, focusing primarily on their extraordinary diversity rather than concentrating on the phylogenetic relationships discussed in chapter 10. To highlight the remarkable abilities of prokaryotes and convey a sense of appreciation for the environments they inhabit and the essential roles they play in our biosphere, groups of microorganisms are described according to their metabolic characteristics and other physiological traits. Note, however, that no single chapter could describe all known prokaryotes and, consequently, only a relatively small selection is presented.

Table 11.1 serves as an outline of the chapter and summarizes the characteristics of the genera covered. It also lists the phylum of each to highlight the evolutionary relationships of these prokaryotes (illustrated in figure 10.13). To learn more about the taxonomy of these organisms, visit the Online Learning Center (www.mmhe.com/nester5) to see the classification of prokaryotes used in *Bergey's Manual of Systematic Bacteriology,* 2nd edition. **Table 11.2** indicates the medical importance of select species.

■ phylum, p. 247

KEY TERMS

Anoxygenic phototroph Phototrophic organism that does not produce O_2.

Chemolithotroph An organism that harvests energy by oxidizing inorganic chemicals.

Chemoorganotroph An organism that harvests energy by oxidizing organic chemicals.

Chemotroph An organism that harvests energy by oxidizing chemicals.

Extremophile An organism that grows best in extreme environments.

Photoautotroph An organism that harvests energy from sunlight and obtains carbon from CO_2.

Photoheterotroph An organism that harvests energy from sunlight and obtains carbon from organic compounds.

Phototroph An organism that harvests energy from sunlight.

TABLE 11.1 Prokaryotes Notable for Their Environmental Significance

Group/Genera	Characteristics	Phylum
METABOLIC DIVERSITY		
Anaerobic Chemolithotrophs		
Methanogens – *Methanospirillum, Methanosarcina*	Members of the *Archaea* that oxidize hydrogen gas, using CO_2 as a terminal electron acceptor to generate methane.	*Euryarchaeota*
Anaerobic Chemoorganotrophs—Anaerobic Respiration		
Sulfur- and sulfate-reducing bacteria – *Desulfovibrio*	Use sulfate as a terminal electron acceptor, generating hydrogen sulfide. Found in anaerobic muds that are rich in organic material. Gram-negative.	*Proteobacteria*
Anaerobic Chemoorganotrophs—Fermentation		
Clostridium	Endospore-forming obligate anaerobes. Common inhabitants of soil. Gram-positive.	*Firmicutes*
Lactic acid bacteria – *Streptococcus, Enterococcus, Lactococcus, Lactobacillus, Leuconostoc*	Produce lactic acid as the major end product of their fermentative metabolism. Aerotolerant anaerobes. Several genera are exploited by the food industry. Gram-positive.	*Firmicutes*
Propionibacterium	Obligate anaerobes that produce propionic acid as their primary fermentation end product. Used in the production of Swiss cheese. Gram-positive.	*Actinobacteria*
Anoxygenic Phototrophs		
Purple sulfur bacteria – *Chromatium, Thiospirillum, Thiodictyon*	Grow in colored masses in sulfur springs and other sulfur-rich habitats, using sulfur compounds as a source of electrons when making reducing power. Gram-negative.	*Proteobacteria*
Purple non-sulfur bacteria – *Rhodobacter, Rhodopseudomonas*	Grow in a wide variety of aquatic habitats, preferentially using organic compounds as a source of electrons for reducing power. Many are metabolically versatile. Gram-negative.	*Proteobacteria*
Green sulfur bacteria – *Chlorobium, Pelodictyon*	Found in habitats similar to those preferred by the purple sulfur bacteria. Gram-negative.	*Chlorobi*
Green non-sulfur bacteria – *Chloroflexus*	Characterized by their filamentous growth. Metabolically similar to the purple non-sulfur bacteria. Gram-negative.	*Chloroflexi*
Others – *Heliobacterium*	Have not been studied extensively.	*Firmicutes*
Oxygenic Phototrophs—Cyanobacteria		
Anabaena, Synechococcus, Trichodesmium	Photosynthetic bacteria once thought to be algae. Important primary producers. Those that fix N_2 support the growth of unrelated organisms in environments that would otherwise be nitrogen-deficient. Gram-negative.	*Cyanobacteria*
Aerobic Chemolithotrophs		
Filamentous sulfur oxidizers – *Beggiatoa, Thiothrix*	Oxidize sulfur compounds as an energy source. Found in sulfur springs, sewage-polluted waters, and on the surface of marine and freshwater sediments. Gram-negative.	*Proteobacteria*

TABLE 11.1 Prokaryotes Notable for Their Environmental Significance *(continued)*

Group/Genera	Characteristics	Phylum
Unicellular sulfur oxidizers – *Thiobacillus*	Oxidize sulfur compounds as an energy source. Some species can produce enough acid to lower the pH to 1.0. Oxidation of metal sulfides causes bioleaching. Gram-negative.	*Proteobacteria*
Nitrifiers – *Nitrosomonas, Nitrosococcus, Nitrobacter, Nitrococcus*	Oxidize ammonia or nitrate as an energy source. In so doing, they convert certain fertilizers to a form that is readily leached from soils, and deplete O_2 in waters polluted with ammonia containing wastes. Genera that oxidize nitrite prevent the toxic buildup of this compound in soils. Gram-negative.	*Proteobacteria*
Hydrogen-oxidizing bacteria – *Aquifex, Hydrogenobacter*	Thermophilic bacteria that oxidize hydrogen gas as an energy source. According to 16S rRNA studies, they were one of the earliest bacterial forms to exist on earth.	*Aquifacae*
Aerobic Chemoorganotrophs—Obligate Aerobes		
Micrococcus	Widely distributed; common contaminants on bacteriological media. Gram-positive.	*Actinobacteria*
Mycobacterium	Waxy cell wall resists staining; acid-fast.	*Actinobacteria*
Pseudomonas	Common environmental bacteria that, as a group, can degrade a wide variety of compounds. Gram-negative.	*Proteobacteria*
Thermus	*Thermus aquaticus* is the source of *Taq* polymerase, the heat-resistant polymerase used in PCR. Stains Gram-negative, but has an unusual cell wall.	*Deinococcus-Thermus*
Deinococcus	Extraordinarily resistant to the damaging effects of gamma radiation. Stains Gram-positive, but unusual cell wall has multiple layers.	*Deinococcus-Thermus*
Aerobic Chemoorganotrophs—Facultative Anaerobes		
Corynebacterium	Widespread in nature. Gram-positive.	*Actinobacteria*
The *Enterobacteriaceae* – *Escherichia, Enterobacter, Klebsiella, Proteus, Salmonella, Shigella, Yersinia*	Most reside in the intestinal tract. Those that ferment lactose are coliforms; their presence in water serves as an indicator of fecal pollution. Gram-negative.	*Proteobacteria*
ECOPHYSIOLOGY		
Thriving in Terrestrial Environments		
Endospore-formers – *Bacillus, Clostridium*	Endospores are the most resistant life form known. *Bacillus* species include both obligate aerobes and facultative anaerobes; *Clostridium* species are obligate anaerobes. Gram-positive.	*Firmicutes*
Azotobacter	Form a resting stage called a cyst. Notable for their ability to fix nitrogen in aerobic conditions. Gram-negative.	*Proteobacteria*
Myxobacteria – *Chondromyces, Myxococcus, Stigmatella*	Congregate to form a fruiting body; cells within this differentiate to form dormant microcysts. Gram-negative.	*Proteobacteria*
Streptomyces	Resemble fungi in their pattern of growth, forming dormant conidia. Naturally produce a wide array of medically useful antibiotics. Gram-positive.	*Actinobacteria*
Agrobacterium	Cause plant tumors. Scientists use their plasmid to introduce desired genes into plant cells. Gram-negative.	*Proteobacteria*
Rhizobia – *Rhizobium, Sinorhizobium, Bradyrhizobium, Mesorhizobium, Azorhizobium*	Fix nitrogen; form a symbiotic relationship with legumes. Gram-negative.	*Proteobacteria*
Thriving in Aquatic Environments		
Sheathed bacteria – *Sphaerotilus, Leptothrix*	Form chains of cells enclosed within a protective sheath. Swarmer cells move to new locations. Gram-negative.	*Proteobacteria*
Prosthecate bacteria – *Caulobacter, Hyphomicrobium*	Appendages increase their surface area. Gram-negative.	*Proteobacteria*
Bdellovibrio	Predator of *E. coli* and other bacteria, multiplying within the periplasm of the prey. Gram-negative.	*Proteobacteria*

(continued)

TABLE 11.1 Prokaryotes Notable for Their Environmental Significance *(continued)*

Group/Genera	Characteristics	Phylum
Bioluminescent bacteria – *Photobacterium, Vibrio fischeri*	Some bioluminescent species form a symbolic relationship with specific types of squid and fish. Gram-negative.	*Proteobacteria*
Legionella	Often reside within protozoa. Gram-negative.	*Proteobacteria*
Free-living spirochetes – *Spirochaeta, Leptospira* (some species)	Long spiral-shaped bacteria that move by means of an axial filament. Gram-negative.	*Spirochaetes*
Magnetospirillum	Contain a string of magnetic crystals that enable them to move up or down in water and sediments. Gram-negative.	*Proteobacteria*
Spirillum	Spiral-shaped, microaerophilic bacteria; some species form metachromatic granules. Gram-negative.	*Proteobacteria*
Sulfur-oxidizing, nitrate-reducing marine bacteria – *Thioploca, Thiomargarita*	Use novel mechanisms to compensate for the fact that their energy source (reduced sulfur compounds) and terminal electron acceptor (nitrate) do not coexist.	*Proteobacteria*
Animals as Habitats – See table11.2		
ARCHAEA		
Methanogens – *Methanospirillum, Methanosarcina*	Generate methane when they oxidize hydrogen gas as an energy source, using CO_2 as a terminal electron acceptor.	*Euryarchaeota*
Extreme halophiles – *Halobacterium, Halorubrum, Natronobacterium, Natronococcus*	Found in salt lakes, soda lakes, and brines.	*Euryarchaeota*
Extreme Thermophiles – *Methanothermus, Pyrodictium, Pyrolobus, Sulfolobus, Thermophilus, Picrophilus, Nanoarchaeum*	Found near hydrothermal vents and in hot springs; some grow at temperatures above 100°C. Includes examples of methane-generating, sulfur-reducing, and sulfur-oxidizing archaea, as well as extreme acidophiles.	*Crenarchaeota, Euryarchaeota, and Nanoarchaeota*

TABLE 11.2 Medically Important Chemoorganotrophs

Organism	Medical Significance	Phylum
Gram-Negative Rods		
Bacteroides species	Obligate anaerobes that commonly inhabit the mouth, intestinal tract, and genital tract. Cause abscesses and bloodstream infections.	*Bacteroidetes*
Enterobacteriaceae		*Proteobacteria*
Enterobacter species	Normal flora of the intestinal tract.	
Escherichia coli	Normal flora of the intestinal tract. Some strains cause urinary tract infections; some strains cause specific types of intestinal disease. Causes meningitis in newborns.	
Klebsiella pneumoniae	Normal flora of the intestinal tract. Causes pneumonia.	
Proteus species	Normal flora of the intestinal tract. Cause urinary tract infections.	
Salmonella Enteritidis	Causes gastroenteritis. Grows in the intestinal tract of infected animals; acquired by consuming contaminated food.	
Salmonella Typhi	Causes typhoid fever. Grows in the intestinal tract of infected humans; transmitted in feces.	
Shigella species	Cause dysentery. Grow in the intestinal tract of infected humans; transmitted in feces.	
Yersinia pestis	Causes bubonic plague, which is transmitted by fleas, and pneumonic plague, which is transmitted in respiratory droplets of infected individuals.	

TABLE 11.2 Medically Important Chemoorganotrophs *(continued)*

Organism	Medical Significance	Phylum
Haemophilus influenzae	Causes ear infections, respiratory infections, and meningitis in children.	*Proteobacteria*
Haemophilus ducreyi	Causes chancroid, a sexually transmitted disease.	*Proteobacteria*
Legionella pneumophila	Causes Legionnaires' disease, a lung infection. Grows within protozoa; acquired by inhaling contaminated water droplets.	*Proteobacteria*
Pseudomonas aeruginosa	Causes burns, urinary tract, and bloodstream infections. Ubiquitous in the environment. Grows in nutrient-poor aqueous solutions and is resistant to many disinfectants and antimicrobial medications.	*Proteobacteria*
Gram-Negative Rods—Obligate Intracellular Parasites		
Chlamydia pneumoniae	Causes atypical pneumonia, or "walking pneumonia." Acquired from an infected person.	*Chlamydiae*
Chlamydia psittaci	Causes psittacosis, a form of pneumonia. Transmitted by birds.	*Chlamydiae*
Chlamydia trachomatis	Causes a sexually transmitted disease that mimics the symptoms of gonorrhea. Also causes trachoma, a serious eye infection, and conjunctivitis in newborns.	*Chlamydiae*
Coxiella burnetii	Causes Q fever. Acquired by inhaling organisms shed by infected animals.	*Proteobacteria*
Ehrlichia chaffeenis	Causes human ehrlichiosis. Transmitted by ticks.	*Proteobacteria*
Orientia tsutsugamushi	Causes scrub typhus. Transmitted by mites.	*Proteobacteria*
Rickettsia prowazekii	Causes epidemic typhus. Transmitted by lice.	*Proteobacteria*
Rickettsia rickettsii	Causes Rocky Mountain spotted fever. Transmitted by ticks.	*Proteobacteria*
Gram-Negative Curved Rods		
Campylobacter jejuni	Causes gastroenteritis. Grows in the intestinal tract of infected animals; acquired by consuming contaminated food.	*Proteobacteria*
Helicobacter pylori	Causes stomach and duodenal ulcers. Neutralizes stomach acid by producing urease, resulting in the breakdown of urea to form ammonia.	*Proteobacteria*
Vibrio cholerae	Causes cholera, a severe diarrheal disease. Grows in the intestinal tract of infected humans; acquired by drinking contaminated water.	*Proteobacteria*
Vibrio parahaemolyticus	Causes gastroenteritis. Acquired by consuming contaminated seafood.	*Proteobacteria*
Gram-Negative Cocci		
Neisseria meningitidis	Causes meningitis.	*Proteobacteria*
Neisseria gonorrhoeae	Causes gonorrhea, a sexually transmitted disease.	*Proteobacteria*
Gram-Positive Rods		
Bacillus anthracis	Causes anthrax. Acquired by inhaling endospores in soil, animal hides, and wool. Bioterrorism agent.	*Firmicutes*
Bifidobacterium species	Predominant member of the intestinal tract in breast-fed infants. Thought to play a protective role in the intestinal tract of infants by excluding pathogens.	*Actinobacteria*
Clostridium botulinum	Causes botulism. Disease results from ingesting toxin-contaminated foods, typically canned foods that have been improperly processed.	*Firmicutes*
Clostridium perfringens	Causes gas gangrene. Acquired when soil-borne endospores contaminate a wound.	*Firmicutes*
Clostridium tetani	Causes tetanus. Acquired when soil-borne endospores are inoculated into deep tissue.	*Firmicutes*
Corynebacterium diphtheriae	Toxin-producing strains cause diphtheria, a frequently fatal throat infection.	*Actinobacteria*
Gram-Positive Cocci		
Enterococcus species	Normal intestinal flora. Cause urinary tract infections.	*Firmicutes*
Micrococcus species	Found on skin as well as in a variety of other environments; often contaminate bacteriological media.	*Actinobacteria*
Staphylococcus aureus	Leading cause of wound infections. Causes food poisoning and toxic shock syndrome.	*Firmicutes*

(continued)

TABLE 11.2 Medically Important Chemoorganotrophs *(continued)*

Organism	Medical Significance	Phylum
Staphylococcus epidermidis	Normal flora of the skin.	*Firmicutes*
Staphylococcus saprophyticus	Causes urinary tract infections.	*Firmicutes*
Streptococcus pneumoniae	Causes pneumonia and meningitis.	*Firmicutes*
Streptococcus pyogenes	Causes pharyngitis (strep throat), rheumatic fever, wound infections, glomerulonephritis, and streptococcal toxic shock.	*Firmicutes*
Acid-Fast Rods		
Mycobacterium tuberculosis	Causes tuberculosis.	*Actinobacteria*
Mycobacterium leprae	Causes Hansen's disease (leprosy); peripheral nerve invasion is characteristic.	*Actinobacteria*
Spirochetes		
Treponema pallidum	Causes syphilis, a sexually transmitted disease. The organism has never been grown in culture.	*Spirochaetes*
Borrelia burgdorferi	Causes Lyme disease, a tick-borne disease.	*Spirochaetes*
Borrelia recurrentis and *B. hermsii*	Causes relapsing fever. Transmitted by arthropods.	*Spirochaetes*
Leptospira interrogans	Causes leptospirosis, a waterborne disease. Excreted in urine of infected animals.	*Spirochaetes*
Cell Wall-less		
Mycoplasma pneumoniae	Causes atypical pneumonia ("walking pneumonia"). Not susceptible to penicillin because it lacks a cell wall.	*Firmicutes*

METABOLIC DIVERSITY

11.1 Anaerobic Chemotrophs

Focus Point

- Compare and contrast the metabolism and habitats of methanogens, sulfur- and sulfate-reducing bacteria, *Clostridium* species, lactic acid bacteria, and *Propionibacterium* species.

For approximately the first 1.5 billion years that prokaryotes inhabited earth, the atmosphere was **anoxic,** or devoid of O_2. In that anaerobic environment, some early chemotrophs probably used a pathway of anaerobic respiration, employing terminal electron acceptors such as carbon dioxide or elemental sulfur, which were plentiful in the environment. Others may have used fermentation, passing the electrons to an organic molecule such as pyruvate. ■ chemotrophs, p. 98 ■ anaerobic respiration, pp. 137, 151 ■ terminal electron acceptor, p. 136 ■ fermentation, p. 152

Today, anaerobic habitats still abound. Mud and tightly packed soil limit the diffusion of gases, and any O_2 that does penetrate is rapidly consumed by aerobically respiring chemotrophs. This creates anaerobic conditions just below the surface. Aquatic environments may also become anaerobic if they contain nutrients that foster the rapid growth of O_2-consuming microbes. This is evident in polluted lakes, where fish may die because of a lack of dissolved O_2. The bodies of humans and other animals also provide numerous anaerobic environments. It is estimated that 99% of the bacteria that inhabit the intestinal tract are obligate anaerobes. Even the skin and the oral cavity, which are routinely exposed to O_2, have anaerobic microenvironments. These are created via the localized depletion of O_2 by aerobes. ■ obligate anaerobes, p. 96

Anaerobic Chemolithotrophs

Chemolithotrophs oxidize reduced inorganic chemicals such as hydrogen gas (H_2) to obtain energy. Those that grow anaerobically obviously cannot use O_2 as a terminal electron acceptor and instead must use an alternative such as carbon dioxide or sulfur. Relatively few anaerobic chemolithotrophs have been discovered, and most are members of the Domain *Archaea.* Some bacterial examples that inhabit aquatic environments will be discussed later.

The Methanogens

The **methanogens** are a group of archaea that generate ATP by oxidizing hydrogen gas, using CO_2 as a terminal electron acceptor. This process generates methane (CH_4), a colorless, odorless, flammable gas:

$$4\,H_2 + CO_2 \longrightarrow CH_4 + H_2O$$

Many methanogens can also use alternative energy sources such as formate; some can use methanol or acetate as well. Representative genera of methanogens include *Methanospirillum* and *Methanosarcina* **(figure 11.1).**

Methanogens are found in anaerobic environments where hydrogen gas and carbon dioxide are available. Because these gases are generated by chemoorganotrophs during the fermentation of organic material, methanogens often grow in association with these microorganisms. Methanogens, however, are generally not found in environments that contain high levels of sulfate, nitrate, or other inorganic electron acceptors. This is because microorganisms that oxidize hydrogen gas using these electron acceptors have a competitive advantage; the use of CO_2 as an electron acceptor releases comparatively little energy (see figure 6.23). Environments from which methanogens are commonly isolated include sewage, swamps, marine sediments, rice paddies, and the digestive tracts of humans and other animals. The methane produced can present itself as bubbles rising in swamp waters or the 10 cubic feet of gas discharged from a cow's digestive system each day. As a by-product of sewage treatment plants, methane gas can be collected and used for heating, cooking, and even the generation of electricity (see Perspective 31.1). ■ chemoorganotrophs, p. 99

The study of methanogens is quite challenging because they are exquisitely sensitive to O_2, as are many of their enzymes. Special techniques, including anaerobe jars and anaerobic chambers, are used for their cultivation. ■ culturing anaerobes, p. 102

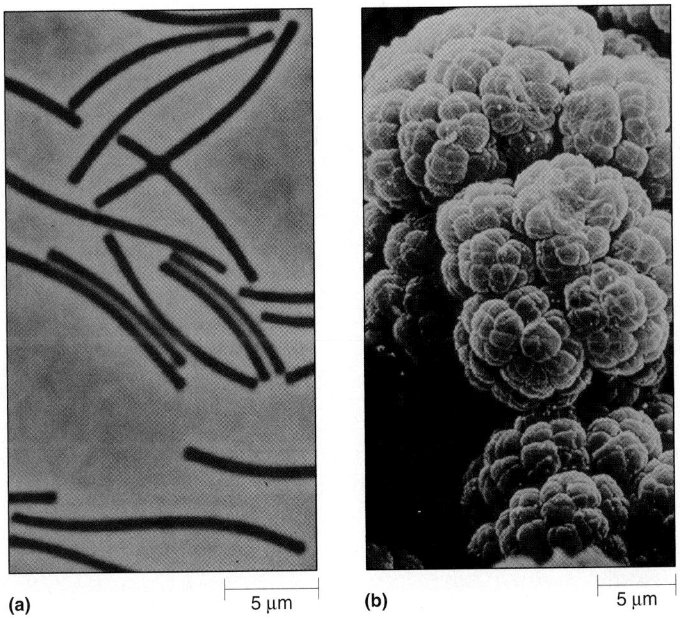

FIGURE 11.1 Methanogens (a) Phase-contrast micrograph of a *Methanospirillum* species. **(b)** Scanning electron micrograph of a *Methanosarcina* species.

Anaerobic Chemoorganotrophs—Anaerobic Respiration

Chemoorganotrophs oxidize organic compounds such as glucose to obtain energy. Like the chemolithotrophs, chemoorganotrophs that grow anaerobically employ terminal electron acceptors other than O_2. Sulfur and sulfate are common inorganic compounds used as terminal electron acceptors by these organisms.

Sulfur- and Sulfate-Reducing Bacteria

When sulfur compounds are used as terminal electron acceptors, they become reduced to form hydrogen sulfide, the compound responsible for the rotten-egg smell of many anaerobic environments. In addition to the unpleasant odor, the H_2S is a problem to industry because it reacts with metals, corroding pipes and other structures. Ecologically, however, prokaryotes that reduce sulfur compounds are an indispensable component of the sulfur cycle. ■ sulfur cycle, p. 770

Sulfate- and sulfur-reducing bacteria generally live in mud rich in organic material and oxidized sulfur compounds. The H_2S they produce causes mud and water to turn black when it reacts with iron molecules. At least a dozen genera are recognized in this group, the most extensively studied of which are species of *Desulfovibrio*. These are Gram-negative curved rods.

Some representatives of the *Archaea* also use sulfur compounds as terminal electron acceptors, but the characterized examples generally do not inhabit the same environments as their bacterial counterparts. While most of the sulfur-reducing bacteria are mesophiles or thermophiles, the known sulfur-reducing archaea are hyperthermophiles, inhabiting extreme environments such as hydrothermal vents. They will be discussed later in the chapter. ■ thermophiles, p. 95 ■ hyperthermophiles, p. 95

Anaerobic Chemoorganotrophs: Fermentation

Numerous types of anaerobic bacteria obtain energy using the process of fermentation, producing ATP only by substrate-level phosphorylation.

The Genus Clostridium

Members of the genus *Clostridium* are Gram-positive rods that can form endospores (see figure 3.45). They are common inhabitants of soil, where the vegetative cells live in the anaerobic microenvironments created when aerobic organisms consume available O_2. Their endospores, a dormant form, are indifferent to O_2 and can survive for long periods by withstanding measures of heat, desiccation, chemicals, and irradiation that would kill all vegetative bacteria. When the appropriate conditions are renewed, these endospores germinate, and the resulting vegetative bacteria may once again multiply. Vegetative cells that arise from soil-borne endospores are responsible for a variety of diseases, including tetanus (caused by *C. tetani*), gas gangrene (caused by *C. perfringens*), and botulism (caused by *C. botulinum*). Some species of *Clostridium* are normal inhabitants of the intestinal tract of humans and other animals. ■ endospores, p. 71 ■ tetanus, p. 557 ■ gas gangrene, p. 559 ■ botulism, p. 690

As a group, *Clostridium* species ferment a wide variety of compounds, including sugars, cellulose, and ethanol. Some of the

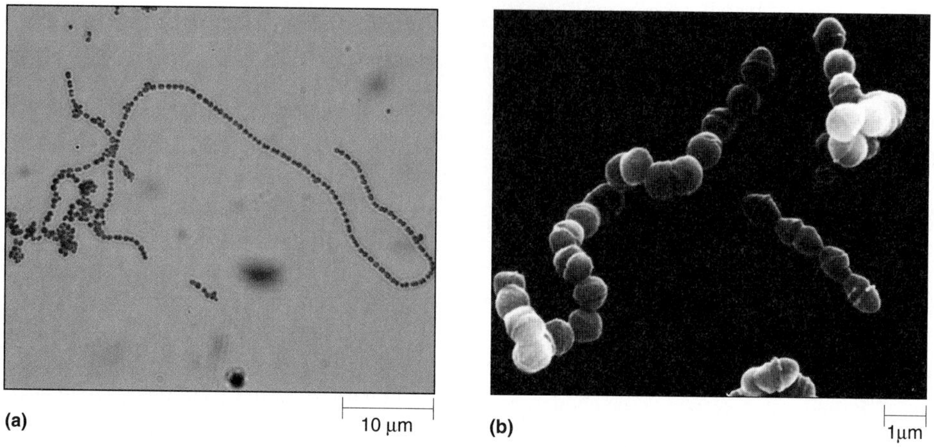

FIGURE 11.2 ***Streptococcus*** **Species** **(a)** Gram stain. **(b)** Scanning electron micrograph.

end products are commercially valuable; for example, *C. acetobutylicum* produces acetone and butanol. Some species can ferment amino acids by an unusual process that oxidizes one amino acid, using another as a terminal electron acceptor. This generates a variety of foul-smelling end products associated with putrefaction.

The Lactic Acid Bacteria

Gram-positive bacteria that produce lactic acid as a major end product of their fermentative metabolism make up a group called the **lactic acid bacteria.** They include members of the genera *Streptococcus, Enterococcus, Lactococcus, Lactobacillus,* and *Leuconostoc.* Most can grow in aerobic environments, but all are obligate fermenters and thus derive no benefit from O_2. They can be readily distinguished from other bacteria that grow in the presence of O_2 because they lack the enzyme catalase (see figure 10.4). ■ obligate fermenters, pp. 96, 152 ■ catalase, p. 96

Streptococcus species are cocci that typically grow in chains of varying lengths **(figure 11.2).** They inhabit the oral cavity, generally as normal flora. Some, however, are notable for their adverse effect on human health. One of the most important is *S. pyogenes* (Group A strep), which causes pharyngitis (strep throat) and other diseases. Unlike the streptococci that typically inhabit the throat, *S. pyogenes* is β-hemolytic, an important characteristic used in its identification (see figure 4.11). ■ *Streptococcus pyogenes,* p. 577 ■ hemolysis, p. 101

Species of *Lactococcus* and *Enterococcus* were at one time included in the genus *Streptococcus.* The genus *Lactococcus* now includes those species used by the dairy industry to produce fermented milk products such as cheese and yogurt. *Enterococcus* species typically inhabit the intestinal tract of humans and other animals. ■ fermentation of dairy products, p. 798

Members of the genus *Lactobacillus* are rod-shaped organisms that grow as single cells or loosely associated chains. They are common among the microflora of the mouth and the healthy human vagina during child-bearing years. In the vagina, they metabolize glycogen, which has been deposited in the vaginal lining in response to the female sex hormone, estrogen. The low pH that results helps the vagina resist infection. Lactobacilli are also often present in decomposing plant material, milk, and other dairy products. Like the lactococci, they are important in the production of fermented foods **(figure 11.3).**

The Genus Propionibacterium

Propionibacterium species are Gram-positive pleomorphic (irregular shaped) rods that produce propionic acid as their primary fermentation end product. Significantly, they can also ferment lactic acid. Thus, *Propionibacterium* species can extract residual energy from a waste product of another group of bacteria.

Propionibacterium species are important to the dairy industry because their fermentation end products play an indispensable role in the production of Swiss cheese. The propionic acid is responsible for the typical nutty flavor of Swiss cheese. The CO_2, also a product of the fermentation, creates the signature holes in the cheese. *Propionibacterium* species are also found growing in the intestinal tract and in anaerobic microenvironments on the skin. ■ Swiss cheese production, p. 799

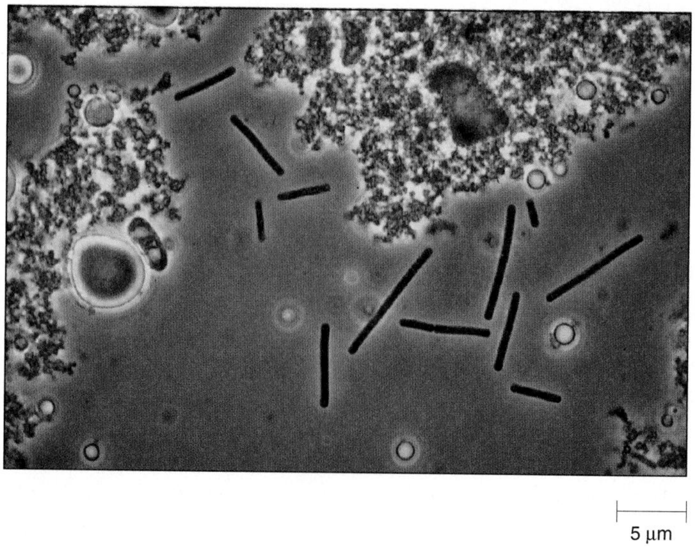

FIGURE 11.3 ***Lactobacillus*** **Species from Yogurt**

MICROCHECK 11.1

Methanogens are archaea that oxidize hydrogen gas, using CO_2 as a terminal electron acceptor to generate methane. The sulfur and sulfate-reducing bacteria oxidize organic compounds, with sulfur compounds serving as terminal electron acceptors to generate hydrogen sulfide. *Clostridium* species, the lactic acid bacteria, and *Propionibacterium* species oxidize organic compounds, with an organic compound serving as a terminal electron acceptor.

✓ What metabolic process creates the rotten-egg smell characteristic of many anaerobic environments?

✓ Describe two beneficial contributions of the lactic acid bacteria.

✓ Relatively little is known about many obligate anaerobes. Why would this be so?

11.2

Anoxygenic Phototrophs

Focus Point

- Compare and contrast the metabolism and habitats of the purple bacteria and the green bacteria.

The earliest photosynthesizing organisms were likely **anoxygenic phototrophs.** These use hydrogen sulfide or organic compounds rather than water as a source of electrons when making reducing power in the form of NADPH, and therefore do not generate O_2. Modern anoxygenic phototrophs are a phylogenetically diverse group of bacteria that inhabit a restricted ecological niche that provides adequate light penetration yet little or no O_2; most often, they are found in aquatic habitats such as bogs, lakes, and the upper layer of muds. ■ reducing power, p. 136

As discussed in chapter 6, the photosynthetic systems of the anoxygenic phototrophs are fundamentally different from those of plants, algae, and cyanobacteria. They have a unique type of chlorophyll called **bacteriochlorophyll.** This and their other light-harvesting pigments absorb wavelengths of light that penetrate to greater depths and are not used by other photosynthetic organisms. ■ photosynthetic pigments, p. 158

The Purple Bacteria

The **purple bacteria** are Gram-negative organisms that appear red, orange, or purple due to their light-harvesting pigments. Unlike other anoxygenic phototrophs, the components of their photosynthetic apparatus are all contained within the cytoplasmic membrane. Invaginations in this membrane effectively increase the surface area available for the photosynthetic processes.

Purple Sulfur Bacteria

Purple sulfur bacteria can sometimes be seen growing as colored masses in sulfur-rich habitats such as sulfur springs **(figure 11.4a).** The cells are relatively large, sometimes in excess of 5 μm in diameter, and some are motile by flagella. They may also have gas vesicles, enabling them to move up or down to their preferred level in the water column. Most accumulate sulfur in granules that are readily visible microscopically and appear to be contained within the cell (figure 11.4b).

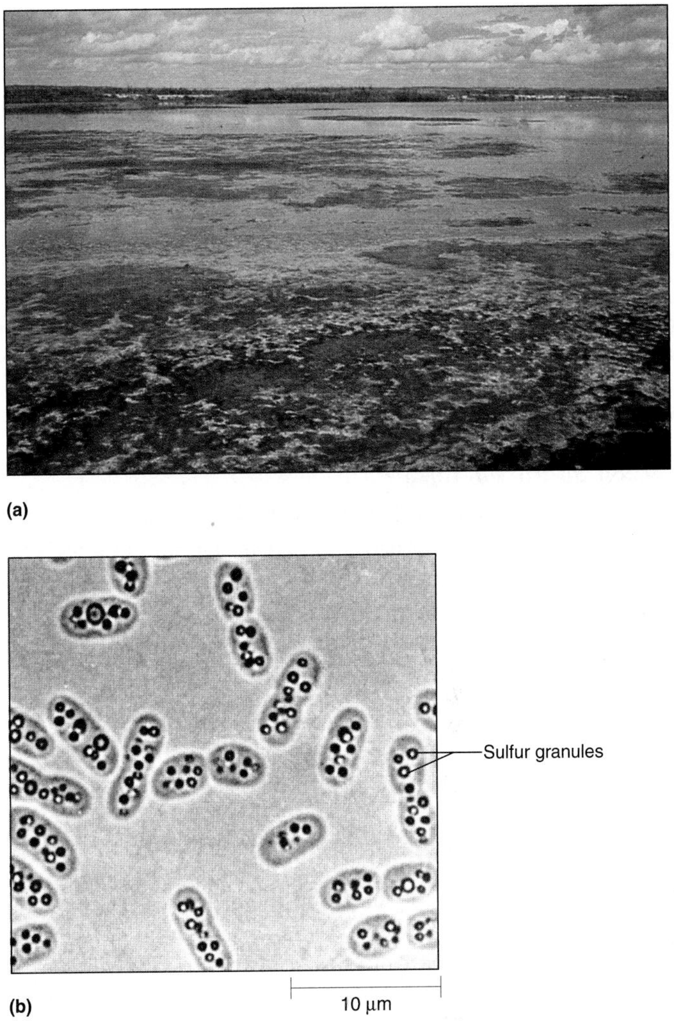

FIGURE 11.4 Purple Sulfur Bacteria (a) Photograph of bacteria growing in a bog. **(b)** Photomicrograph showing intracellular sulfur granules.

The purple sulfur bacteria preferentially use hydrogen sulfide to generate reducing power, although some species can use other inorganic molecules, such as H_2, or organic compounds, such as pyruvate. Many are strict anaerobes and phototrophs, but some can grow in absence of light aerobically, oxidizing reduced inorganic or organic compounds as a source of energy. Representative genera of purple sulfur bacteria include *Chromatium, Thiospirillum,* and *Thiodictyon.*

Purple Non-Sulfur Bacteria

The purple non-sulfur bacteria are found in a wide variety of aquatic habitats, including moist soils, bogs, and paddy fields. One important characteristic that distinguishes them from the purple sulfur bacteria is that they preferentially use a variety of organic molecules rather than hydrogen sulfide as a source of electrons for reducing power. In addition, they lack gas vesicles. If sulfur does accumulate, the granules form outside of the cell.

Purple non-sulfur bacteria are remarkably versatile metabolically. Not only do they grow as phototrophs using organic molecules to generate reducing power, but many can use a metabolism similar to the purple sulfur bacteria, employing hydrogen gas or hydrogen sulfide as an electron source. In addition, most can grow aerobically in the absence of light using chemotrophic metabolism. Representative genera of purple sulfur bacteria include *Rhodobacter* and *Rhodopseudomonas.*

The Green Bacteria

The **green bacteria** are Gram-negative organisms that are typically green or brownish in color. Unlike the purple bacteria, their accessory pigments are located in structures called **chlorosomes** and their cytoplasmic membranes do not have extensive invaginations. ■ accessory pigments, p. 158

Green Sulfur Bacteria

Green sulfur bacteria are found in habitats similar to those preferred by the purple sulfur bacteria. Like the purple sulfur bacteria, they use hydrogen sulfide as a source of electrons for reducing power and they form sulfur granules. The granules, however, form outside of the cell **(figure 11.5).** Green sulfur bacteria lack flagella, but many have gas vesicles. All are strict anaerobes, and none can use a chemotrophic metabolism. Representative genera include *Chlorobium* and *Pelodictyon.*

Green Non-Sulfur Bacteria

Green non-sulfur bacteria are characterized by their filamentous growth. Metabolically, they resemble the purple non-sulfur bacteria, preferentially using organic compounds to generate reducing power. As an alternative, they can use hydrogen gas or hydrogen sulfide. In addition, they can grow in the dark aerobically using chemotrophic metabolism. *Chloroflexus* is the only genus in this group that has been grown in pure culture.

Other Anoxygenic Phototrophs

While the green and purple bacteria have been studied most extensively, other types of anoxygenic phototrophs have recently been discovered. Among these are members of the genus *Heliobacterium,* Gram-positive endospore-forming rods related to members of the genus *Clostridium.*

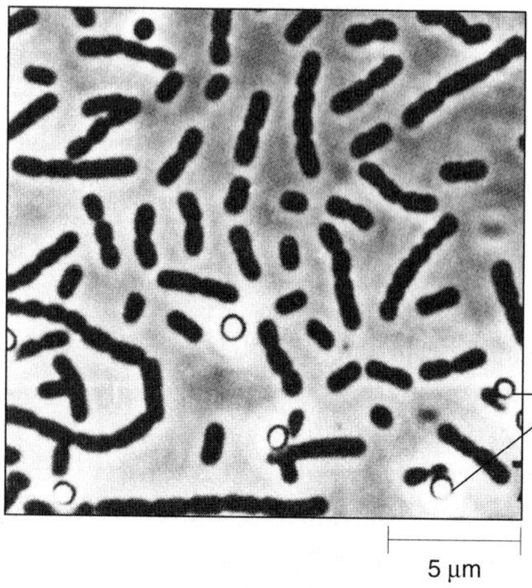

FIGURE 11.5 Green Sulfur Bacteria Note that the sulfur granules are extracellular.

MICROCHECK 11.2

Anoxygenic phototrophs harvest the energy of sunlight, but do not generate O_2. The purple sulfur bacteria and the green sulfur bacteria use hydrogen sulfide as a source of electrons to generate reducing power; the purple non-sulfur and green non-sulfur bacteria preferentially use organic compounds.

- ✓ Describe a structural characteristic that distinguishes the purple sulfur bacteria from the green sulfur bacteria.
- ✓ What is the function of gas vesicles?
- ✓ Why is it beneficial to the anoxygenic phototrophs to have light-harvesting pigments that absorb wavelengths of light that penetrate to greater depths?

11.3 Oxygenic Phototrophs

Focus Point

- Describe the cyanobacteria, including how nitrogen-fixing species protect their nitrogenase enzyme from O_2.

Nearly 3 billion years ago, the earth's atmosphere began changing as O_2 was gradually introduced to the previously anoxic environment. This change was probably due to the evolution of the cyanobacteria, thought to be the earliest **oxygenic phototrophs.** These are photosynthetic organisms that use water as a source of electrons for reducing power, liberating O_2.

$$6\,CO_2 + 6\,H_2O \longrightarrow C_6H_{12}O_6 + 6\,O_2$$

Today, cyanobacteria still play an essential role in the biosphere. As **primary producers,** they harvest the energy of sunlight, using it to convert CO_2 into organic compounds. They were initially thought to be a form of algae and were called blue-green algae until electron microscopy revealed their prokaryotic structure. Unfortunately, this early misunderstanding generated long-lasting confusion in their classification and nomenclature. ■ primary producers, p. 760

The Cyanobacteria

The cyanobacteria are a diverse group of more than 60 genera of Gram-negative bacteria. They inhabit a wide range of environments, including freshwater and marine habitats, soils, and the surfaces of rocks. In addition to being photosynthetic, many are able to convert nitrogen gas (N_2) to ammonia, which can then be incorporated into cell material. This process, called **nitrogen fixation,** is an exclusive ability of prokaryotes. ■ nitrogen fixation, p. 769

General Characteristics of Cyanobacteria

Cyanobacteria are morphologically diverse. Some genera are unicellular, with typical prokaryotic shapes such as cocci, rods, and spirals. Others form filamentous multicellular associations called **trichomes** that may or may not be enclosed within a sheath, a tube that holds and surrounds a chain of cells **(figure 11.6).** Motile trichomes glide as a unit. Cyanobacteria that inhabit aquatic environments often have gas vesicles, enabling them to move vertically within the water column. When large numbers of buoyant cyanobacteria accumulate in stagnant lakes or other freshwater habitats, they may form mats on the surface. In the bright, hot conditions of summer, these cells lyse and decay, creating an odoriferous scum called a **nuisance bloom (figure 11.7).** The ecological effects of these blooms on aquatic habitats are discussed in chapter 30. ■ aquatic habitats, p. 763

The photosynthetic systems of the cyanobacteria are like those contained within the chloroplasts of algae and plants. This is not surprising in light of the genetic evidence indicating chloroplasts evolved from a species of cyanobacteria that once resided as endosymbionts within eukaryotic cells (see Perspective 3.1). In addition to light-harvesting chlorophyll pigments, cyanobacteria have **phycobiliproteins.** These pigments absorb energy from wavelengths of light not well absorbed by chlorophyll. They contribute to the blue-green, or sometimes reddish, color of the cyanobacteria.

Nitrogen-Fixing Cyanobacteria

Nitrogen-fixing cyanobacteria are critically important ecologically. Because they can incorporate both N_2 and CO_2 into organic material, they generate a form of these nutrients that can then be used by other organisms. Thus, their activities can ultimately support the growth of a wide range of organisms in environments that would otherwise be devoid of usable nitrogen and carbon. As an example, nitrogen-fixing cyanobacteria that inhabit the oceans are essential primary producers that support other sea life. Also, like all cyanobacteria, they help control atmospheric carbon dioxide buildup by utilizing the gas as a carbon source.

Nitrogenase, the enzyme complex that mediates the process of nitrogen fixation, is destroyed by O_2; therefore, nitrogen-fixing cyanobacteria must protect the enzyme from the O_2 they generate. Species of *Anabaena,* which are filamentous, isolate nitrogenase by confining the process of nitrogen fixation to a specialized thick-walled cell called a **heterocyst (figure 11.8).** Heterocysts lack photosystem II and consequently, do not generate O_2. The heterocysts of some species form at very regular intervals within the filament, reflecting the ability of cells within a trichome to communicate. One species of *Anabaena, A. azollae,* forms an intimate relationship with the water fern *Azolla.* The bacterium grows and fixes nitrogen within the protected environment of a special sac in the fern, providing *Azolla* with a source of available nitrogen. *Synechococcus* species, which are unicellular, fix nitrogen only in the dark. Consequently, nitrogen fixation and photosynthesis are temporally separated. Remarkably, members of the genus *Trichodesmium* fix nitrogen even while they are photosynthesizing. How they protect their nitrogenase enzyme from O_2 is still not understood. ■ photosystem II, p. 159

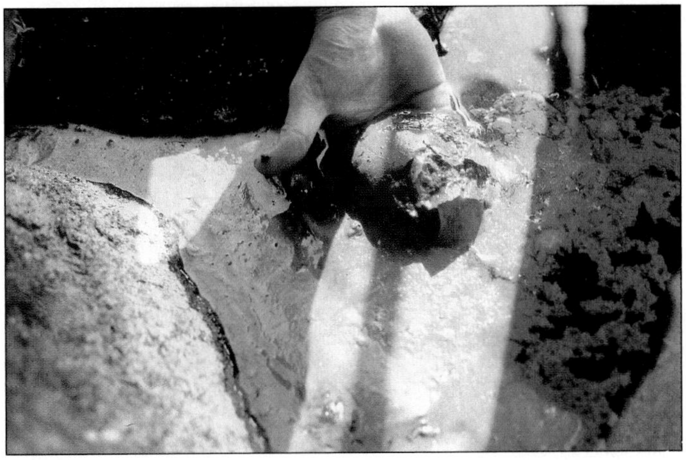

FIGURE 11.7 Nuisance Bloom Excessive growth of cyanobacteria causes buoyant masses of cells to rise to the surface.

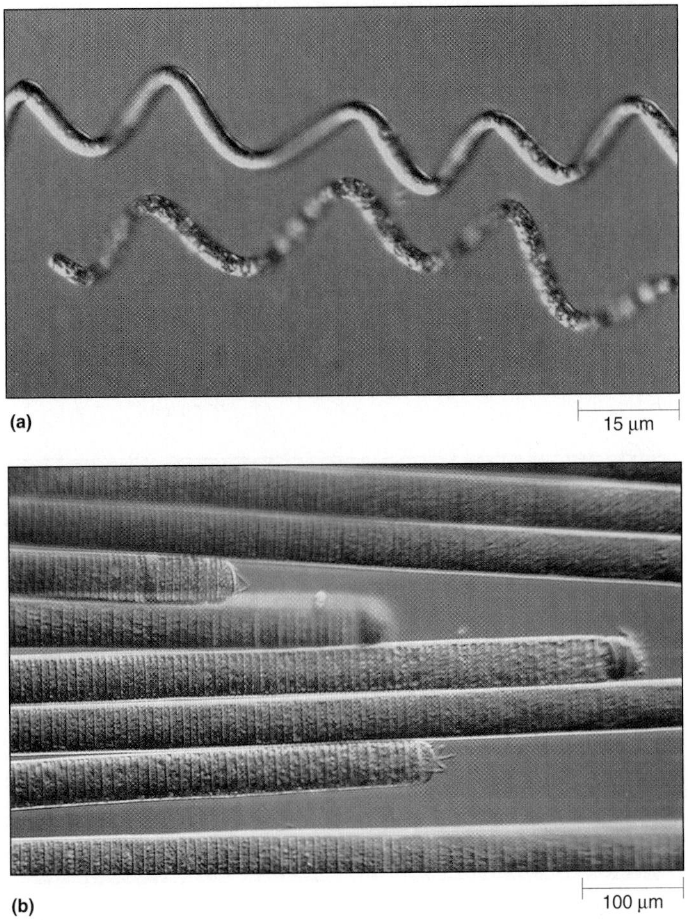

(a) 15 μm

(b) 100 μm

FIGURE 11.6 Cyanobacteria (a) The spiral trichome of *Spirulina* species. **(b)** Differential interference contrast photomicrograph of a species of *Oscillatoria.* Note the arrangement of the individual cells in the trichome.

Other Notable Characteristics of Cyanobacteria

Cyanobacteria have various other notable characteristics—some beneficial, others damaging. Filamentous cyanobacteria appear to be responsible for maintaining the structure and productivity of soils in cold desert areas such as the Colorado Plateau. Their sheaths persist in soil, creating a sticky fibrous network that prevents erosion. In addition, these bacteria provide an important source of nitrogen and organic carbon in otherwise nutrient-poor soils. Cyanobacteria growing in freshwater lakes and reservoirs used as a source of drinking water can impart an undesirable taste

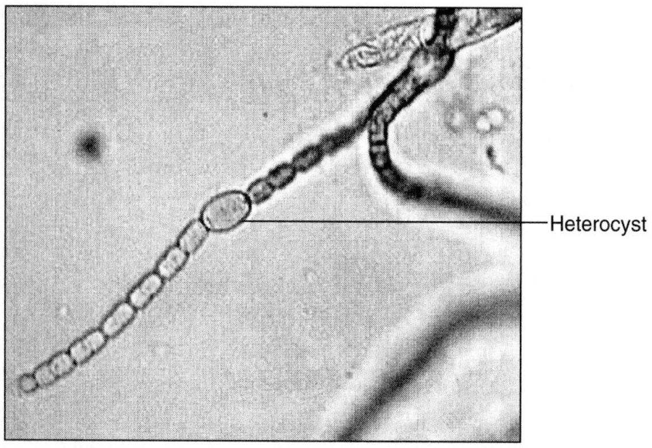

FIGURE 11.8 Heterocyst of an *Anabaena* Species Nitrogen fixation occurs within these specialized cells.

to the water. This is due to their production of a compound called **geosmin,** which has a distinctive "earthy" odor. Finally, some aquatic species such as *Microcystis aeruginosa* can produce toxins. These can be deadly to animals that consume them.

MICROCHECK 11.3

The photosynthetic systems of cyanobacteria generate O_2 and are similar to those of algae and plants. Many cyanobacteria species can fix nitrogen.

- ✓ What is the function of a heterocyst?
- ✓ How do cyanobacteria prevent erosion in cold desert regions?
- ✓ How could heavily fertilized lawns foster the development of nuisance blooms?

11.4 Aerobic Chemolithotrophs

Focus Point

- Compare and contrast the metabolism and habitats of sulfur-oxidizing bacteria, nitrifiers, and hydrogen-oxidizing bacteria.

Aerobic chemolithotrophs obtain energy by oxidizing reduced inorganic chemicals, using O_2 as a terminal electron acceptor.

The Sulfur-Oxidizing Bacteria

The sulfur-oxidizing bacteria are Gram-negative rods or spirals, which sometimes grow in filaments. They obtain energy by oxidizing elemental sulfur and reduced sulfur compounds, including hydrogen sulfide and thiosulfate. Molecular oxygen serves as a terminal electron acceptor, generating sulfuric acid. These bacteria play an important role in the sulfur cycle. ■ sulfur cycle, p. 770

Filamentous Sulfur Oxidizers

Species of the filamentous sulfur oxidizers *Beggiatoa* and *Thiothrix* live in sulfur springs, in sewage-polluted waters, and on the surface of marine and freshwater sediments. They accumulate sulfur, depositing it as intracellular granules. Members of the genera *Beggiatoa* and *Thiothrix* differ in the nature of their filamentous growth **(figure 11.9).** The filaments of *Beggiatoa* species move by gliding motility, the mechanism of which is poorly understood. The filaments may flex or twist to form a tuft. In contrast, the filaments of *Thiothrix* species are immobile; they fasten at one end to rocks or other solid surfaces. Often they attach to other cells, causing the filaments to form a characteristic rosette arrangement. Progeny cells detach from the ends of these filaments and use gliding motility to disperse to new locations, where they form new filaments. Overgrowth of these filamentous organisms in sewage at treatment facilities causes a problem called **bulking.** Because the masses of filamentous organisms do not settle easily, bulking interferes with the separation of the solid sludge from the liquid effluent. ■ sewage treatment, p. 780

Unicellular Sulfur Oxidizers

Thiobacillus species are found in both terrestrial and aquatic habitats, where their ability to oxidize metal sulfides is responsible for a process called **bioleaching.** In this process, insoluble metal sulfides are oxidized, producing sulfuric acid while converting the

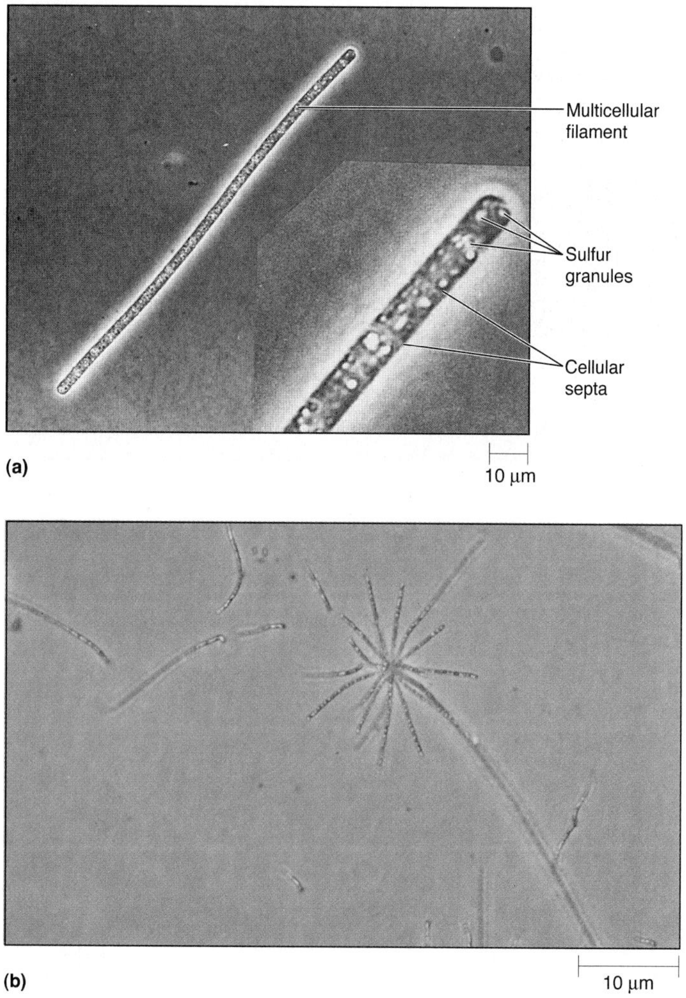

FIGURE 11.9 Filamentous Sulfur Bacteria Phase-contrast photomicrographs. **(a)** Multicellular filament of a *Beggiatoa* species. **(b)** Multicellular filaments of a *Thiothrix* species, forming a rosette arrangement.

metal to a soluble form; some species can produce enough acid to lower the pH to 1.0. Bioleaching can cause severe environmental problems. For example, the strip mining of coal exposes metal sulfides, which can then be oxidized by *Thiobacillus* species to produce sulfuric acid. The resulting runoff can acidify nearby streams, killing trees, fish, and other wildlife **(figure 11.10).** The runoff may also contain toxic metals made soluble by the bacteria. Under controlled conditions, however, bioleaching can enhance the recovery of metals. For example, gold can be extracted from deposits of gold sulfide. The metabolic activities of *Thiobacillus* species can also be used to prevent acid rain, which results from the burning of sulfur-containing coals and oils. After allowing the bacteria to oxidize the sulfur to sulfate, the latter can be extracted from the fuel. One species of *Thiobacillus, T. ferrooxidans,* can oxidize iron as well as sulfur.

The Nitrifiers

Nitrifiers are a diverse group of Gram-negative bacteria that obtain energy by oxidizing inorganic nitrogen compounds such as ammonia or nitrite. These bacteria are of particular interest to farmers who fertilize their crops with ammonium nitrogen, a form of nitrogen that is retained by soils because its positive charge enables it to adhere to negatively charged soil particles. The potency and longevity of the fertilizer are affected by nitrifying bacteria converting the ammonia to nitrate. While plants use this form of nitrogen more readily, it is rapidly leached from soils. Nitrifying bacteria are also an important consideration in disposal of sewage or other wastes with a high ammonia concentration. As nitrifying bacteria oxidize nitrogen compounds, they consume O_2. Because of this, waters polluted with nitrogen-containing wastes can quickly become hypoxic (low in dissolved O_2).

The nitrifiers encompass two metabolically distinct groups of bacteria that typically grow in close association. Together, they can oxidize ammonia to form nitrate. The **ammonia oxidizers,** which include the genera *Nitrosomonas* and *Nitrosococcus,* convert ammonia to nitrite. The **nitrite oxidizers,** which include the genera *Nitrobacter* and *Nitrococcus,* then convert nitrite to nitrate. The latter group is particularly important in preventing the buildup of nitrite in soils, which is toxic and can leach into groundwater. The oxidation of ammonia to nitrate is called **nitrification** and is an important part of the nitrogen cycle. ■ nitrogen cycle, p. 769

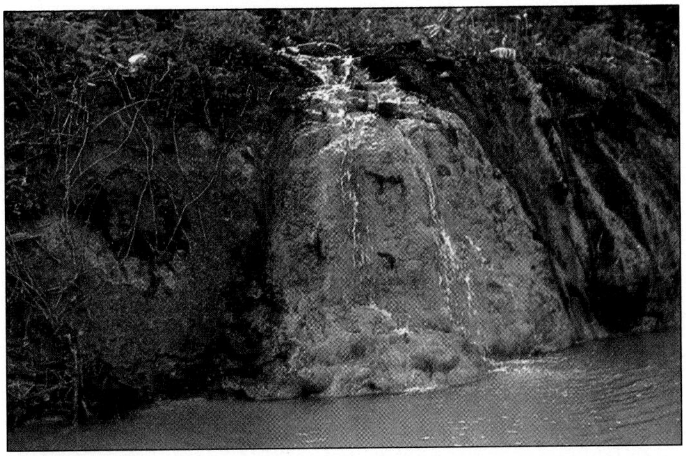

FIGURE 11.10 Acid Drainage from a Mine Sulfur-oxidizing bacteria oxidize exposed metal sulfides, generating sulfuric acid. The yellow-red color is due to insoluble iron oxides.

The Hydrogen-Oxidizing Bacteria

Members of the Gram-negative genera *Aquifex* and *Hydrogenobacter* are among the few hydrogen-oxidizing bacteria that are obligate chemolithotrophs. These related organisms are thermophilic and typically inhabit hot springs. Some *Aquifex* species have a maximum growth temperature of 95°C, the highest of any members of the Domain *Bacteria.* The hydrogen-oxidizing bacteria are deeply branching in the phylogenetic tree, meaning that according to 16S rRNA studies, they were one of the earliest bacterial forms to exist on earth. The fact that they require O_2 seems contradictory to their evolutionary position, but in fact, the low amount they require might have been available early on in certain niches due to photochemical processes that split water.

A wide range of aerobic chemoorganotrophs can also oxidize hydrogen gas. These organisms switch between energy sources as conditions dictate.

MICROCHECK 11.4

Sulfur oxidizers use sulfur compounds as an energy source, generating sulfuric acid. The nitrifiers oxidize nitrogen compounds such as ammonium or nitrite.

- ✓ How does the growth of *Thiobacillus* species cause bioleaching?
- ✓ Why would farmers be concerned about nitrifying bacteria?
- ✓ Why would sulfur-oxidizing bacteria accumulate sulfur?

11.5 Aerobic Chemoorganotrophs

Focus Points

- Compare and contrast the metabolism and habitats of two obligate aerobes and one facultative anaerobe.
- Describe members of the family *Enterobacteriaceae,* and what distinguishes coliforms from other members of this family.

Aerobic chemoorganotrophs oxidize organic compounds to obtain energy, using O_2 as a terminal electron acceptor. They include a tremendous variety of bacteria, ranging from those that inhabit very specific environments to those that are ubiquitous. This section will profile only representative genera that are found in a variety of different environments. Later sections will describe other chemoorganotrophs, emphasizing those adapted to live in specific habitats.

Obligate Aerobes

Obligate aerobes obtain energy using respiration exclusively; none can use fermentation as an alternative.

The Genus Micrococcus

Members of the genus *Micrococcus* are Gram-positive cocci found in soil and on dust particles, inanimate objects, and skin. Because they are often airborne, they easily contaminate bacteriological media. There, they typically form pigmented colonies, a characteristic that aids in their identification. The colonies of *M. luteus,* for example, are generally yellow **(figure 11.11).** Like members of the genus *Staphylococcus,* which will be discussed later, they tolerate arid conditions and can grow in 7.5% NaCl.

The Genus Mycobacterium

Mycobacterium species are widespread in nature and include harmless **saprophytes,** which live on dead and decaying matter, as well as organisms that produce disease in humans and domestic animals. Although they have a Gram-positive type of cell wall, these bacteria stain poorly because of a waxy lipid in their cell wall. Special procedures can be used to enhance the penetration of the stain. Once stained, they resist destaining, even when acidic decolorizing solutions are used. Because of this, *Mycobacterium* species are called **acid-fast,** and the acid-fast staining procedure is an important step in their identification (see figure 3.15). *Nocardia* species, a related group of bacteria that commonly reside in the soil, are also acid-fast. ■ acid-fast, p. 51

Mycobacterium species are generally pleomorphic rods; they often occur in chains that sometimes branch, or bunch together to form cordlike groups. Two species are notable for their effect on human health—*M. tuberculosis,* as the name implies, causes tuberculosis, and *M. leprae* causes Hansen's disease (leprosy). *Mycobacterium* species are more resistant to disinfectants than most other vegetative bacteria. In addition, they differ from other bacteria in their susceptibility to antimicrobial drugs.

The Genus Pseudomonas

Pseudomonas species are Gram-negative rods that are motile by polar flagella and often produce pigments **(figure 11.12).** Although most are strict aerobes, some can grow anaerobically if nitrate is available as a terminal electron acceptor. The fact that they do not ferment and are oxidase positive serve, in the laboratory, as important characteristics that distinguish them from members of the family *Enterobacteriaceae,* which will be discussed in a later section. ■ oxidase, p. 150

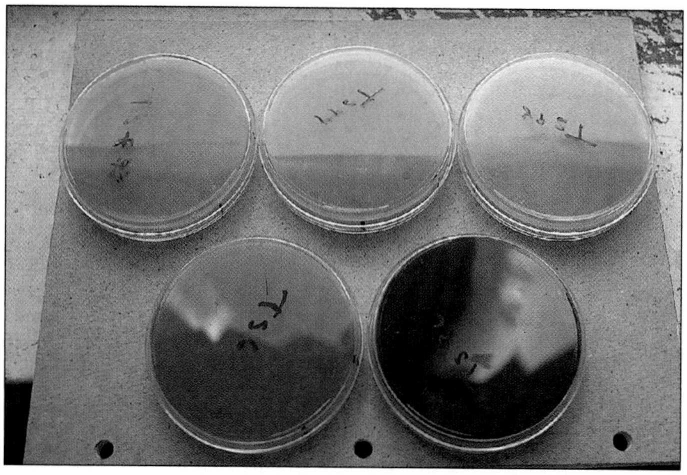

FIGURE 11.12 Pigments of *Pseudomonas* Species Cultures of different strains of *Pseudomonas aeruginosa*. Note the different colors of the water-soluble pigments.

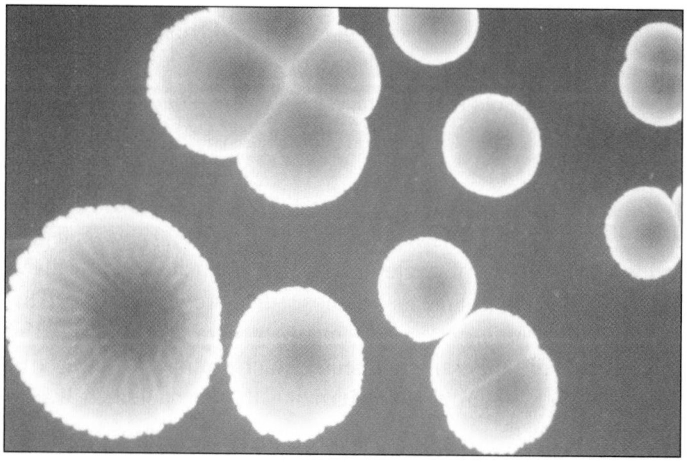

FIGURE 11.11 *Micrococcus luteus* Colonies

As a group, *Pseudomonas* species have extremely diverse biochemical capabilities. Some can use more than 80 different substrates, including unusual sugars, amino acids, and compounds containing aromatic rings. Because of this, *Pseudomonas* species play an important role in the degradation of many synthetic and natural compounds that resist breakdown by most other microorganisms. The ability to carry out some of these degradations is encoded by plasmids.

Pseudomonas species are widespread, typically inhabiting soil and water. While most are harmless, some cause disease in plants and animals. Medically, the most significant species is *P. aeruginosa.* It is a common **opportunistic pathogen,** meaning that it primarily infects people who have underlying medical conditions. Unfortunately, it can grow in nutrient-poor environments, such as water used in respirators, and it is resistant to many disinfectants and antimicrobial medications. Because of this, hospitals must be diligent to prevent its spread among patients. Many species that were formerly classified as *Pseudomonas* have recently been removed and placed in one of several new genera. This revision was prompted in part by ribosomal RNA studies. ■ *Pseudomonas aeruginosa*, p. 555 ■ opportunistic pathogen, p. 454

The Genera Thermus and Deinococcus

Thermus and *Deinococcus* are related genera that have scientifically and commercially noteworthy characteristics. *Thermus* species are thermophilic, as their name implies. This trait has proven to be extremely valuable because of their heat-stable enzymes, including DNA polymerase. An integral part of the polymerase chain reaction (PCR) is ***Taq* polymerase,** the DNA polymerase of *T. aquaticus.* Although the organisms have an unusual cell wall, they stain Gram-negative. *Deinococcus* species are unique in their

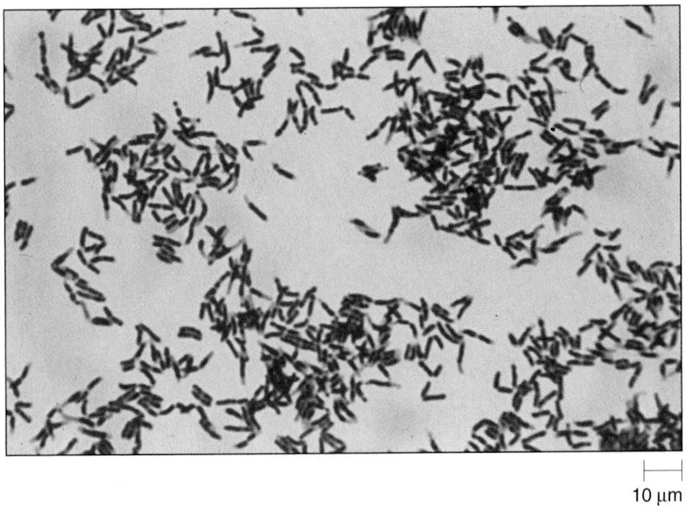

FIGURE 11.13 ***Corynebacterium*** The Gram-positive pleomorphic rods are often arranged to form V shapes or palisades.

extraordinary resistance to the damaging effects of gamma radiation. For example, *D. radiodurans* can survive exposure to a dose several thousand times that lethal to a human being. The dose literally shatters the organism's genome into many fragments, yet enzymes are able to repair the extensive damage. Scientists anticipate that through genetic engineering, *Deinococcus* species may eventually help clean up the soil and water contaminated by the 10 million cubic yards of radioactive waste that have accumulated in the United States. Although their unusual cell wall has multiple layers, they stain Gram-positive. ■ PCR, pp. 230, 238

Facultative Anaerobes

Facultative anaerobes preferentially use aerobic respiration if O_2 is available. As an alternative, however, they can use fermentative metabolism.

The Genus Corynebacterium

Members of the genus *Corynebacterium* commonly inhabit soil, water, and the surface of plants. They are Gram-positive pleomorphic rods that are often club-shaped and arranged to form V shapes or palisades (*koryne* is Greek for "club") **(figure 11.13).** Bacteria that exhibit this characteristic microscopic morphology are sometimes referred to as **coryneforms** or **diphtheroids.** *Corynebacterium* species are generally facultative anaerobes, although some are strict aerobes. Many species of *Corynebacterium* reside harmlessly in the throat, but toxin-producing strains of *C. diphtheriae* can cause the disease diphtheria. ■ diphtheria, p. 579

The Family Enterobacteriaceae

Members of the family *Enterobacteriaceae,* frequently referred to as **enterics** or **enterobacteria,** are Gram-negative rods. Their name reflects the fact that most reside in the intestinal tract of humans and other animals (Greek *enteron* means "intestine"), although some thrive in rich soil. Enterics that are part of the normal flora of the intestine include *Enterobacter, Klebsiella,* and *Proteus* species as well as most strains of *E. coli.* Those that cause diarrheal disease include *Shigella* species, *Salmonella* Enteritidis, and some strains of *E. coli.* Life-threatening systemic diseases include typhoid fever, caused by *Salmonella* Typhi, and both the bubonic and pneumonic forms of plague, caused by *Yersinia pestis.* ■ diarrheal disease, p. 622 ■ typhoid fever, p. 628 ■ plague, p. 717

Members of the family *Enterobacteriaceae* are facultative anaerobes that ferment glucose and, if motile, have peritrichous flagella. The family includes about 40 recognized genera that can be distinguished using biochemical tests. Within a given species, many different strains have been described. These are often distinguished using serological tests that detect differences in their cell walls, flagella, and capsules **(figure 11.14).** ■ peritrichous flagella, p. 67

Enterics that ferment lactose are included in a group called **coliforms.** This is an informal grouping of certain common intestinal inhabitants such as *E. coli* that are easy to detect in food and water; they are used by regulatory agencies as an indicator of fecal pollution. Their presence indicates a potential health risk because fecal-borne pathogens might also be present. ■ coliform, p. 787

MICROCHECK 11.5

Members of the genera *Micrococcus, Mycobacterium, Pseudomonas, Thermus,* and *Deinococcus* are obligate aerobes that generate ATP by degrading organic compounds, using O_2 as a terminal electron acceptor. Most *Corynebacterium* species and all members of the family *Enterobacteriaceae* are facultative anaerobes.

✓ What is the significance of coliforms being present in drinking water?

✓ What unique characteristic makes members of the genus *Deinococcus* noteworthy?

✓ Why would it be an advantage for a *Pseudomonas* species to encode enzymes for degrading certain compounds on a plasmid rather than the chromosome?

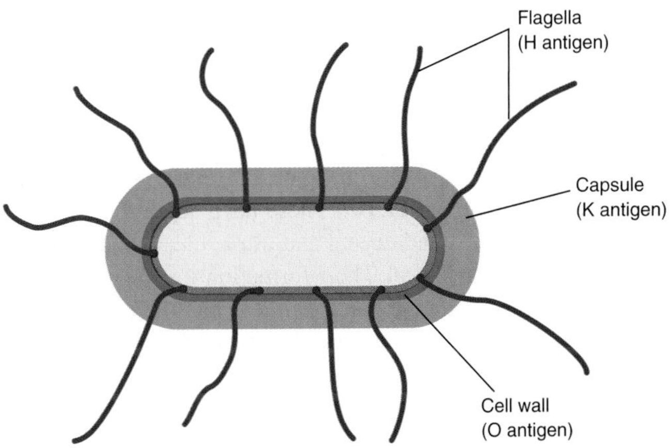

FIGURE 11.14 Schematic Drawing of a Member of the Family *Enterobacteriaceae* The cell structures used to distinguish different strains are shown.

ECOPHYSIOLOGY

11.6

Thriving in Terrestrial Environments

Focus Point

- Describe two mechanisms that terrestrial bacteria use to thrive in the ever-changing environment of soil, and list two genera that use each mechanism.

Microorganisms that inhabit soil must endure a variety of conditions. Daily and seasonally, soil is an environment that can routinely alternate between wet and dry as well as warm and cold. The availability of nutrients can also cycle from abundant to sparse. To thrive in this ever-changing environment, microbes have evolved mechanisms to cope with adverse conditions and to exploit unique sources of nutrients.

Bacteria That Form a Resting Stage

Several genera that inhabit the soil can form a resting stage that enables them to survive the dry periods typical in many soils. Of these various types of dormant cells, endospores are by far the most resistant to environmental extremes.

Endospore-Formers

Bacillus and *Clostridium* species are common Gram-positive rod-shaped bacteria that form endospores; the position of the spore in the cell can be used as an aid in identification **(figure 11.15).** *Clostridium* species, which are obligate anaerobes, were discussed earlier. *Bacillus* species include both obligate aerobes and facultative anaerobes, and some are medically important. *Bacillus anthracis* causes the disease anthrax, which can be acquired from contacting its endospores in soil or in animal hides or wool. Unfortunately, the spores can also be used as an agent in bioterrorism. ■ anthrax, p. 490

The Genus Azotobacter

Azotobacter species are Gram-negative pleomorphic, rod-shaped bacteria that live in alkaline soil. They can form a type of resting cell called a **cyst (figure 11.16).** These have negligible metabolic activity and can withstand drying and ultraviolet radiation but are not highly resistant to heat. Their formation involves changes in the cell wall of a vegetative bacterium, causing the cell to shorten and the wall to thicken; the enzyme content of the cyst is similar to that of the cell from which it arises. Cysts differ from endospores in both their manner of formation and their lesser degree of resistance to harmful agents.

Azotobacter species are also notable for their ability to fix nitrogen in aerobic conditions; recall that the enzyme nitrogenase is inactivated by O_2. Apparently, the exceedingly high respiratory rate of *Azotobacter* species consumes O_2 so rapidly that a low O_2 environment is maintained inside the cell.

Myxobacteria

The myxobacteria are a group of aerobic Gram-negative rods that have a unique developmental cycle as well as a resting stage. When conditions are favorable, cells secrete a slime layer that other cells then follow, creating a **swarm** of cells. But then, when nutrients are exhausted, the behavior of the group changes. The cells begin to move toward each other and congregate. They then pile up to form a complex structure called a **fruiting body,** which is often brightly colored **(figure 11.17).** In some species the fruiting body is quite elaborate, consisting of a mass of cells elevated and supported by a stalk made of a hardened slime. The cells within the fruiting body differentiate to become spherical, dormant forms called **microcysts.** These are considerably more resistant to heat, drying, and radiation than are the vegetative cells of myxobacteria, but are much less resistant than bacterial endospores.

Myxobacteria are important in nature as degraders of complex organic substances; they can digest bacteria and certain algae and fungi. Scientifically, even though the mechanisms the cells use for group communication are still poorly understood, these bacteria serve as an important model for developmental biology. Included in the myxobacteria are members of the genera *Chondromyces, Myxococcus,* and *Stigmatella.*

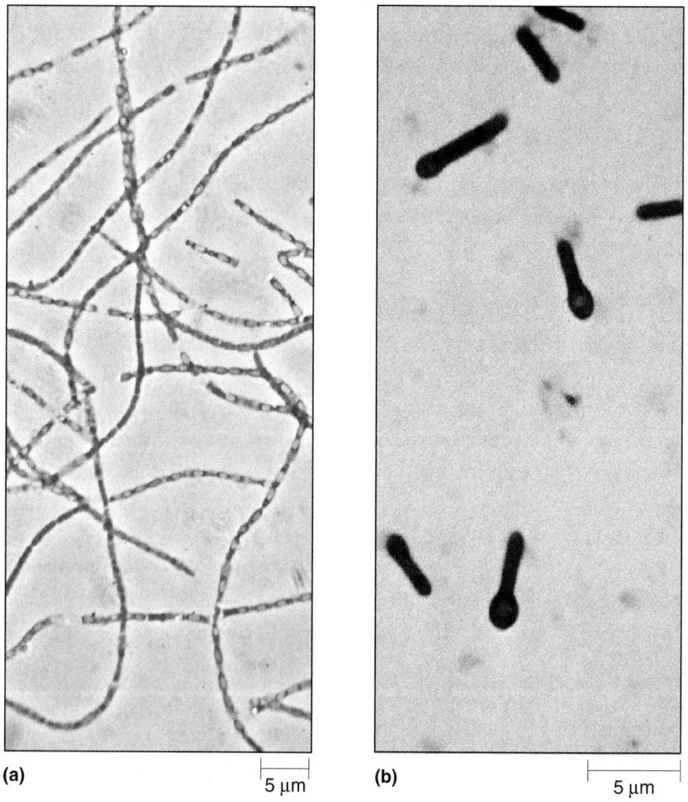

FIGURE 11.15 Endospore-Formers (a) Endospores forming in the mid-portion of the cells of *Bacillus anthracis*. **(b)** Endospores forming at the ends of the cells in *Clostridium tetani*. Both of these species can cause fatal disease, but many other species of endospore-formers are harmless.

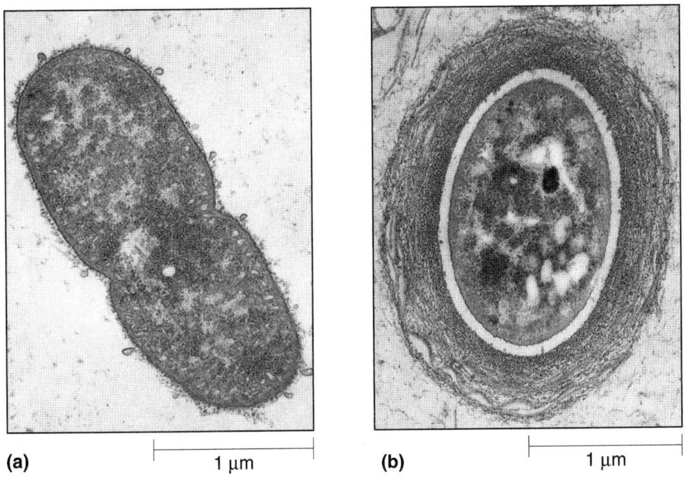

FIGURE 11.16 ***Azotobacter*** **(a)** Vegetative cells; **(b)** cyst.

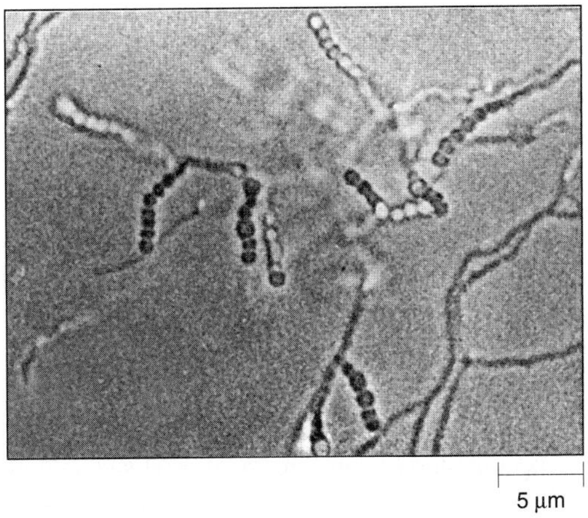

FIGURE 11.18 ***Streptomyces*** A photomicrograph showing the spherical conidia at the ends of the filamentous hyphae.

The Genus Streptomyces

The genus *Streptomyces* encompasses more than 500 species of Gram-positive bacteria that resemble fungi in their pattern of growth. Like the fungi, they form a **mycelium,** which is a visible mass of branching filaments. The filaments are called **hyphae.** At the tips of the hyphae, chains form of characteristic spores called **conidia (figure 11.18).** These dormant spores are resistant to drying and are readily dispersed in air currents to potentially more favorable locations. Note that while this pattern of growth resembles fungi, which are eukaryotes, *Streptomyces* species are much smaller and are prokaryotes.

Streptomyces species are obligate aerobes that produce a variety of extracellular enzymes, which enables them to degrade a variety of organic compounds. They are also responsible for the characteristic "earthy" odor of soil; like the cyanobacteria, they produce geosmin. One species of *Streptomyces, S. somaliensis,* can cause an infection of subcutaneous tissue called an actinomycetoma.

Streptomyces species naturally produce a wide array of medically useful antibiotics, including streptomycin, tetracycline, and erythromycin. The role that these antimicrobial compounds play in the life cycle of *Streptomyces* has not been proven, but it is quite possible that they provide the organism a competitive advantage.

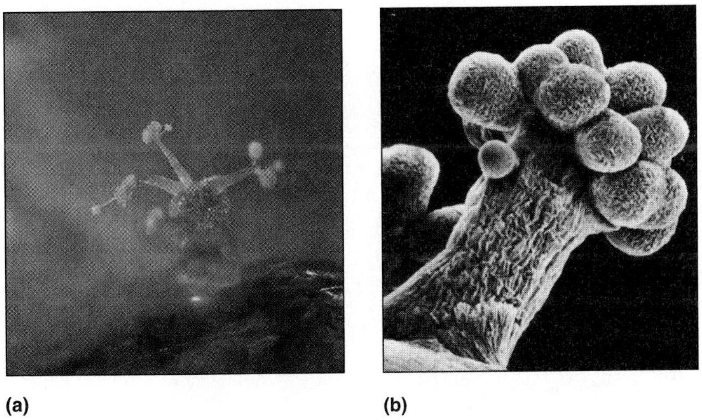

FIGURE 11.17 Fruiting Bodies of Myxobacteria These are the elaborate fruiting bodies of a species of *Chondromyces*: **(a)** photograph; **(b)** scanning electron micrograph.

Bacteria That Associate with Plants

Members of two related genera use very different means to obtain the nutrients needed for growth from plants. *Agrobacterium* species are plant pathogens that cause tumorlike growths, whereas *Rhizobium* species form a mutually beneficial relationship with certain types of plants.

The Genus Agrobacterium

Agrobacterium species have an unusual mechanism of gaining a competitive advantage in soil. They cause plant tumors, a manifestation of their ability to genetically alter a plant for their own benefit **(figure 11.19).** These Gram-negative rod-shaped bacteria enter the plant via a wound, and then transfer to the plant a portion of a plasmid; in *Agrobacterium tumefaciens* that plasmid is called the **Ti plasmid** (for "tumor-inducing"). The transferred DNA encodes the ability to synthesize a specific plant growth hormone, causing

FIGURE 11.19 Plant Tumor Caused by ***Agrobacterium tumefaciens***

uncontrolled growth of the plant tissue and resulting in a tumor. The transferred DNA also encodes enzymes that direct the synthesis of an **opine,** an unusual amino acid derivative; *Agrobacterium* can then use this compound as a nutrient source (see Perspective 8.2).

Scientists have now modified the Ti plasmid, turning it into a commercially valuable tool. By removing those genes that cause tumor formation, the plasmid can be used as a vector to introduce DNA into plant cells. ■ vector, p. 224

Rhizobia

Rhizobia are a group of Gram-negative rod-shaped bacteria that fix nitrogen and form intimate relationships with **legumes,** plants that bear seeds in pods. This group of bacteria includes members of the genera *Rhizobium, Sinorhizobium, Bradyrhizobium, Mesorhizobium,* and *Azorhizobium.* The bacteria live within cells in nodules formed on the root of the plant **(figure 11.20).** The plant synthesizes the protein **leghemoglobin,** which binds and controls the levels of O_2 (see figure 30.14). Within the resulting microaerobic confines of the nodule, the bacteria are able to fix nitrogen. Rhizobia residing within plant cells are examples of **endosymbionts**, organisms that provide a benefit to the cells they reside within. ■ symbiotic nitrogen fixers, p. 773

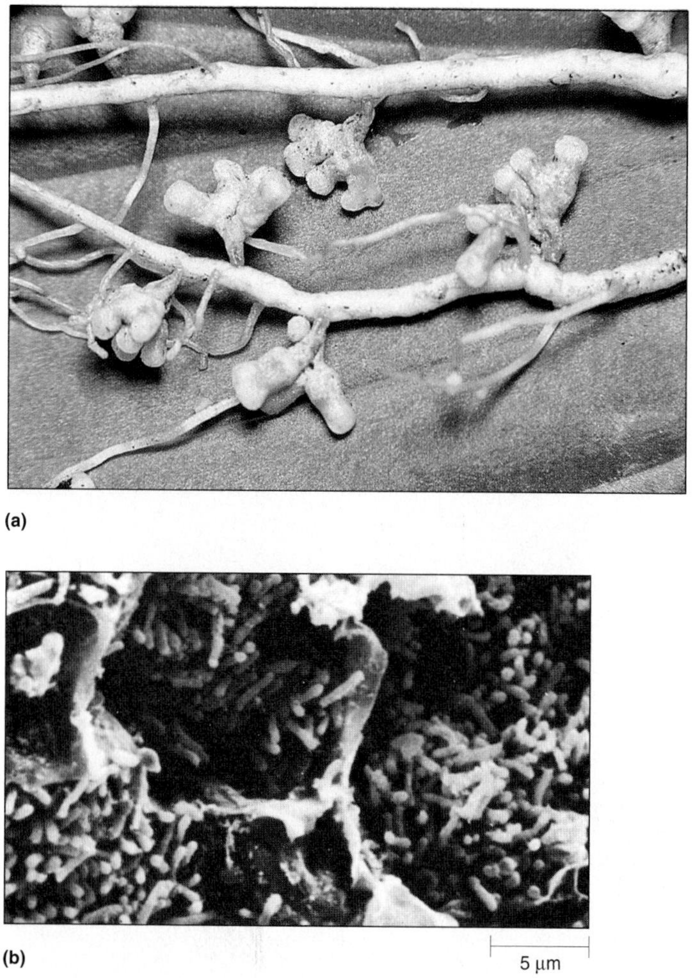

FIGURE 11.20 Symbiotic Relationship Between *Rhizobia* and Certain Plants **(a)** Root nodules. **(b)** Scanning electron micrograph of bacterial cells within a nodule.

MICROCHECK 11.6

Bacillus and *Clostridium* species produce endospores, the most resistant life form known. *Azotobacter* species, myxobacteria, and *Streptomyces* species all produce dormant forms that tolerate some adverse conditions but are less resistant than endospores. *Agrobacterium* species and rhizobia derive nutrients from plants, although the former are plant pathogens and the latter benefit the plant.

- ✓ How does an endospore differ from a cyst of *Azotobacter?*
- ✓ How does *Agrobacterium* derive a benefit from inducing a plant tumor?
- ✓ If you wanted to determine the number of endospores in a sample of soil, what could you do before plating it?

11.7 Thriving in Aquatic Environments

Focus Point

- Describe four mechanisms by which aquatic bacteria are able to maximize nutrient acquisition and retention, and list one genus that uses each mechanism.

Most aquatic environments lack a steady supply of nutrients. To thrive in these habitats, bacteria have evolved various mechanisms to maximize nutrient acquisition and retention. This can mean clustering within a sheath that can attach to solid objects in favorable locations, producing extensions called prosthecae that maximize the absorptive surface area, exploiting nutrients provided by other organisms, efficiently moving to more favorable locations, or forming storage granules. ■ storage granules, p. 70

Sheathed Bacteria

Sheathed bacteria form chains of cells encased within a tube, or **sheath (figure 11.21).** This is thought to provide a protective func-

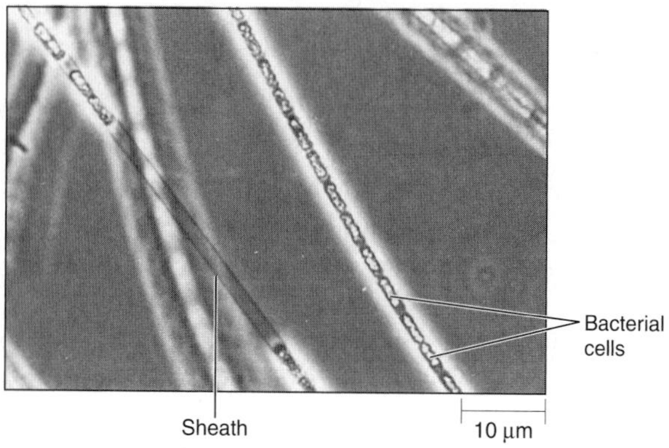

FIGURE 11.21 Sheathed Bacteria Phase-contrast photomicrograph of a *Sphaerotilus* species.

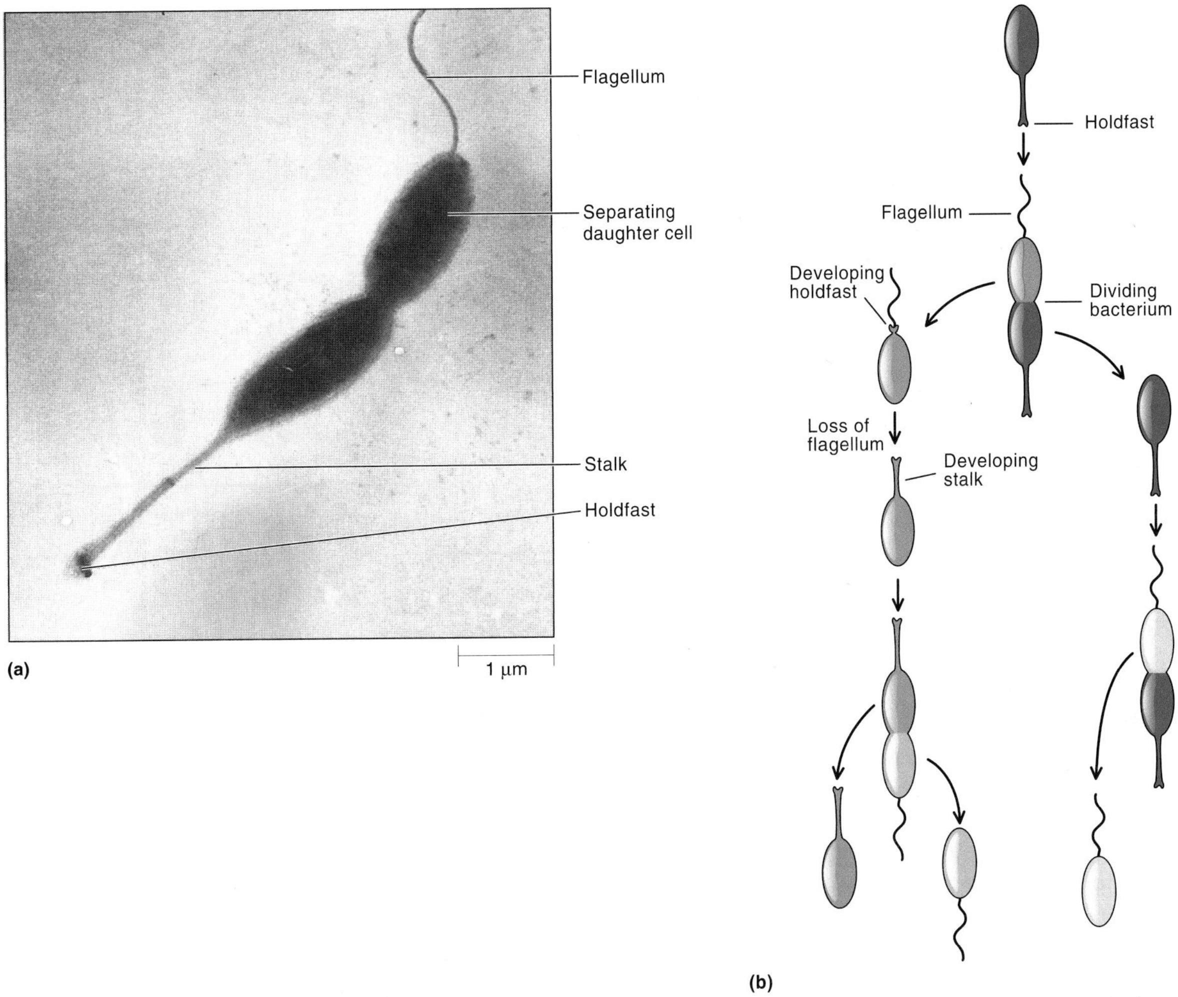

FIGURE 11.22 ***Caulobacter*** **(a)** Photomicrograph; **(b)** life cycle.

tion, helping the bacteria attach to solid objects located in favorable habitats while sheltering them from attack by predators. Masses of these filamentous sheaths can often be seen streaming from rocks or wood in flowing water polluted by nutrient-rich effluents. They often interfere with sewage treatment and other industrial processes by clogging pipes. Sheathed bacteria include species of *Sphaerotilus* and *Leptothrix,* which are Gram-negative rods.

Sheathed bacteria disperse themselves by forming **swarmer cells,** which have polar flagella and exit through the unattached end of the sheath. These motile cells move to a new solid surface, where they attach. If enough nutrients are present, they can multiply and form a new sheath, which elongates as the chain of cells grows.

Prosthecate Bacteria

A diverse group of Gram-negative bacteria possess projections called **prosthecae,** which are extensions of the cytoplasm and cell wall. These extensions are thought to provide increased surface area to facilitate absorption of nutrients. Some prosthecae enable the organisms to attach to a solid surface.

The Genus Caulobacter

Because of their remarkable life cycle, *Caulobacter* species have served as a model for the research of cellular differentiation. Entirely different events occur in an orderly fashion at opposite ends of the cell. *Caulobacter* cells have a single polar prostheca, commonly called a **stalk (figure 11.22).** At the tip of the stalk is an adhesive **holdfast,** which provides a mechanism for attachment. To multiply, the cell elongates and divides by binary fission at the end opposite its stalk, producing a motile swarmer cell. This swarmer cell has a single polar flagellum, located at the pole opposite the site of division. The cell detaches and moves to a new location, where it adheres via a holdfast near the base of its flagellum. It then loses its flagellum, replacing it with a stalk. Only then can the daughter cell replicate its DNA and repeat the process. In favorable conditions, a single cell can divide and produce daughter cells many times. With each division, a ring remains at the site of division, enabling a researcher to count the number of progeny.

The Genus Hyphomicrobium

Hyphomicrobium species are in many ways similar to *Caulobacter* species, except they have a distinct method of reproduction. The

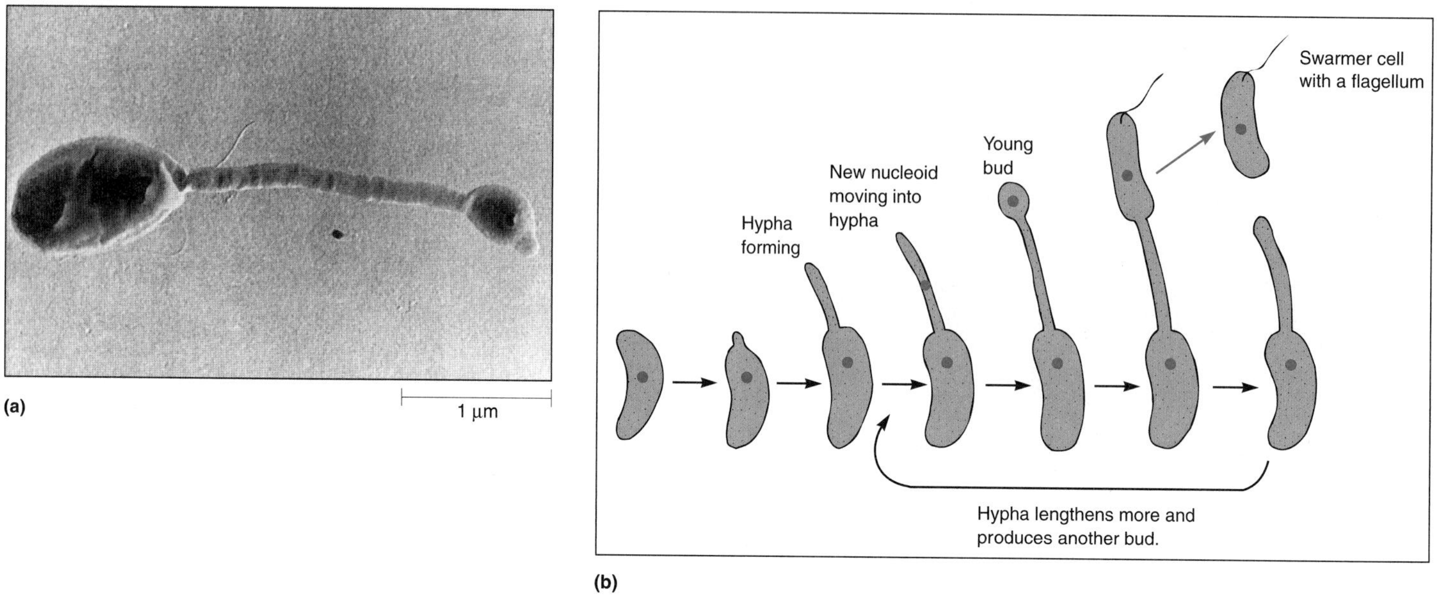

FIGURE 11.23 ***Hyphomicrobium*** **(a)** Photomicrograph. Note the bud forming at the tip of the polar prostheca. **(b)** Life cycle.

single polar prostheca of the parent cell enlarges at the tip to form a bud **(figure 11.23).** This continues enlarging and develops a flagellum, eventually giving rise to a motile daughter cell. The daughter cell then detaches and moves to a new location, eventually losing its flagellum and forming a polar prostheca at the opposite end to repeat the cycle. As with *Caulobacter* species, a single cell can sequentially produce multiple daughter cells.

Bacteria That Derive Nutrients from Other Organisms

Some bacteria obtain nutrients directly from other organisms. *Bdellovibrio* species do this by preying on other bacteria, attacking them and digesting their contents, eventually killing them. Bioluminescent bacteria use another tactic; they have established relationships with fish and squid in which the animal provides nutrients and protection while the bacterium provides a source of luminescence. *Legionella* species can live intracellularly within the protected confines of protozoa.

The Genus Bdellovibrio

Bdellovibrio species (*bdello,* from the Greek word for "leech") are highly motile Gram-negative bacteria that prey on *E. coli* and other Gram-negative bacteria **(figure 11.24).** They are small, curved rods, approximately 0.25 μm wide and 1 μm long, with a polar flagellum. When a *Bdellovibrio* cell attacks, it strikes its prey with such a high velocity that it actually propels the prey a short distance. The parasite then attaches to its host and rotates with a spinning motion. At the same time, it synthesizes digestive enzymes that break down lipids and peptidoglycan. Within 10 minutes, a hole in the cell wall of the prey is formed. This allows the parasitic bacterium to penetrate, lodging in the periplasm between the cytoplasmic membrane and the peptidoglycan layer. There, over a period of several hours, *Bdellovibrio* degrades and utilizes the prey's cellular contents. It derives energy by aerobically oxidizing amino acids and acetate. The parasite increases in length as it resides in the periplasm, ultimately dividing to form several motile daughter cells. When the host cell lyses, the *Bdellovibrio* progeny are released to find new hosts, repeating the growth and reproduction cycle.

Bioluminescent Bacteria

Some species of *Photobacterium* and *Vibrio* can emit light **(figure 11.25).** This phenomenon, called **bioluminescence,** plays an important role in the symbiotic relationship between some of these bacteria and specific types of fish and squid. For example, certain types of squid have a specialized organ within their ink sac that is colonized by *Vibrio fischeri.* The light produced in the organ is thought to serve as a type of camouflage, obscuring the squid's contrast against the light from above and any shadow it might otherwise cast. It appears that the squid provides nutrients to the symbiotic bacteria, facilitating their growth. Another example is the flashlight fish, which has a light organ in a specialized pouch below its eye that harbors bioluminescent bacteria. By opening and closing a lid that covers the pouch, the fish can control the amount of light released, which is believed to confuse predators and prey.

Luminescence is catalyzed by the enzyme **luciferase.** Studies of the regulation of its synthesis revealed that the genes encoding it are only expressed when the density of the bacterial population reaches a critical point. This phenomenon of **quorum sensing** is now recognized as an important mechanism used by a variety of different bacteria to regulate the expression of certain genes. ■ quorum sensing, p. 186

Members of the genera *Photobacterium* and *Vibrio* are Gram-negative rods (the rods of *Vibrio* species are curved) with polar flagella. They are facultative anaerobes and typically inhabit aqueous environments. Those species that require sodium for growth

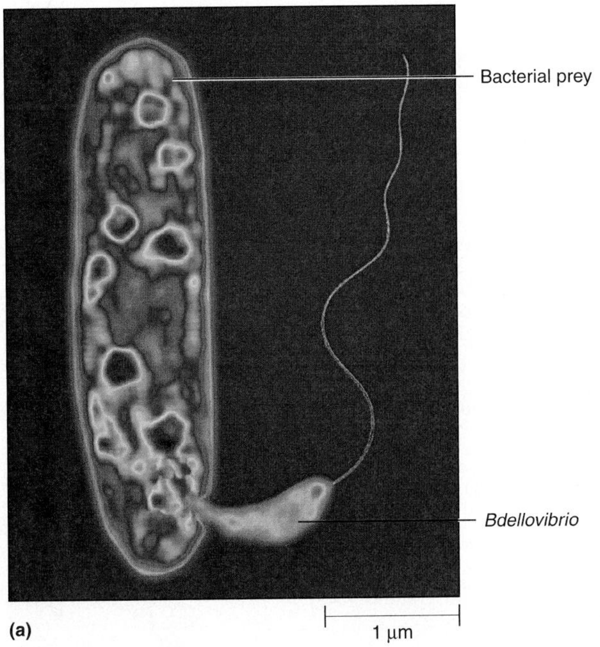

(a)

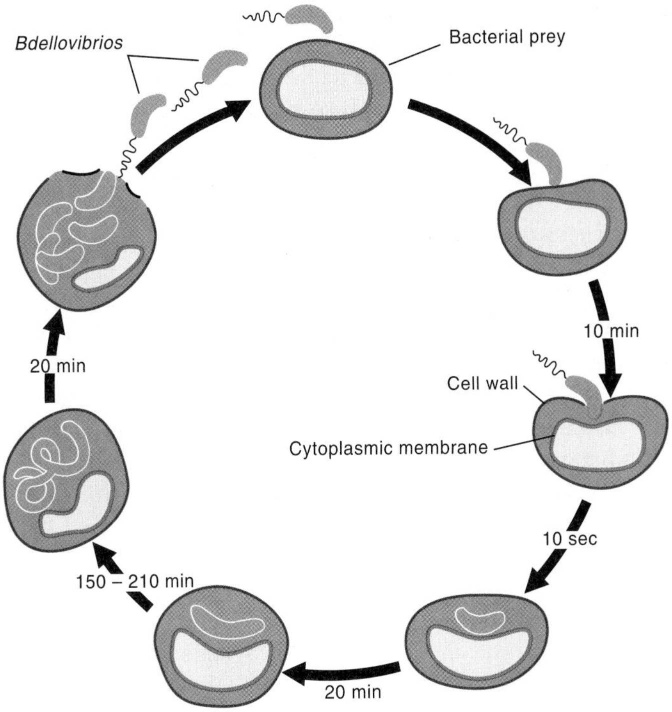

(b)

FIGURE 11.24 *Bdellovibrio* **(a)** Color-enhanced transmission micrograph of *Bdellovibrio bacteriovorus* attacking its prey. **(b)** Life cycle of *B. bacteriovorus*. Note that the diagram exaggerates the size of the space in which *B. bacteriovorus* multiplies.

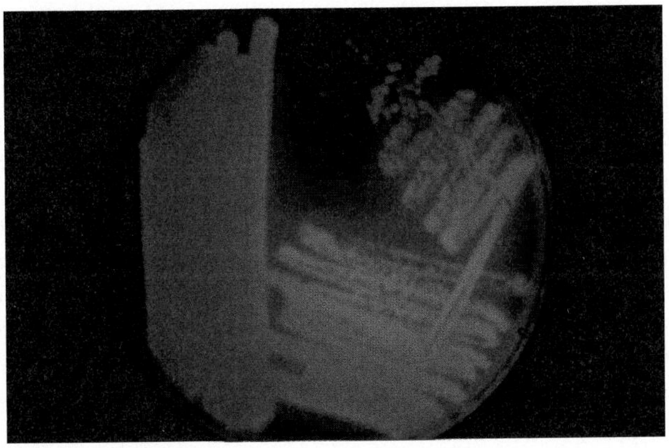

(a)

(b)

FIGURE 11.25 Luminescent Bacteria **(a)** Plate culture of bioluminescent bacteria. **(b)** Photograph of a flashlight fish; under the eye is a light organ colonized with bioluminescent bacteria.

are usually found in marine environments. Not all are luminescent, and some species of *Vibrio* cause human disease. Medically important species include *V. cholerae,* which causes cholera, and *V. parahaemolyticus,* which causes gastrointestinal disease; neither of these are bioluminescent.

The Genus Legionella

Legionella species are commonly found in aquatic environments, where they often reside within protozoa. They have even been isolated from water in air conditioners and produce misters. They are Gram-negative obligate aerobes that utilize amino acids but not carbohydrates as a source of carbon and energy. *Legionella pneumophila* can cause respiratory disease when it is inhaled in aerosolized droplets.

Bacteria That Move by Unusual Mechanisms

Some bacteria have unique mechanisms of motility that enable them to easily move to desirable locations. These organisms include the spirochetes and the magnetotactic bacteria.

Spirochetes

The **spirochetes** (Greek *spira* for "coil" and *chaete* for "hair") are a group of Gram-negative bacteria with a unique motility mechanism that enables them to move through thick, viscous environments such as mud. Distinguishing characteristics include their spiral shape, flexible cell wall, and motility by means of an **axial filament.** The axial filament is composed of sets of flagella that originate from both poles of the cell; unlike typical flagella, these are contained within the periplasm. The opposing sets of flagella extend toward each other, overlapping in the mid-region of the cell. Rotation of the flagella within the confines of the periplasm causes the cell to move like a corkscrew, sometimes deviating into flexing motions. Many spirochetes are very slender and can only be seen using special methods such as dark-field microscopy **(figure 11.26).** Many are also difficult or impossible to cultivate, and their classification is based largely on their morphology and ability to cause disease. ■ periplasm, p. 63

Spirochetes include free-living bacteria that inhabit aquatic environments, as well as species that reside on or in animals. Members of the genus *Spirochaeta* are anaerobes or facultative anaerobes that thrive in muds and anaerobic waters. *Leptospira* species are aerobic; some species are free-living in aquatic environments, whereas others thrive within animals. *Leptospira interrogans* causes the disease leptospirosis, which can be transmitted in the urine of infected animals. Spirochetes that are adapted to reside in body fluids of humans and other animals will be discussed later. ■ leptospirosis, p. 653

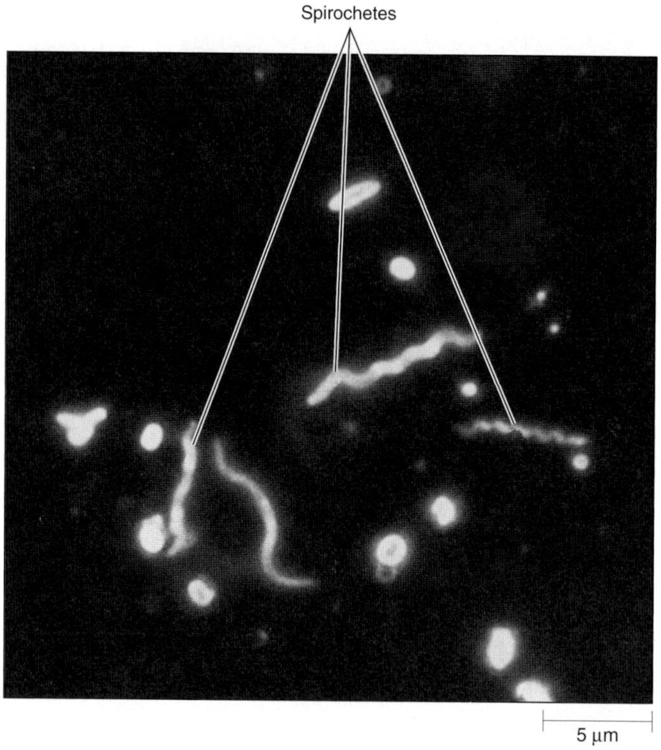

FIGURE 11.26 Spirochetes Dark-field photomicrograph of spirochetes.

Magnetotactic Bacteria

Magnetotactic bacteria such as *Magnetospirillum (Aquaspirillum) magnetotacticum* contain a string of magnetic crystals that align them with the earth's magnetism (see figure 3.40). This enables them to efficiently move up or down in the water or sediments. It is thought that this unique type of movement enables them to locate the microaerophilic habitats they require. *Magnetospirillum* species are Gram-negative spiral-shaped organisms. ■ magnetotaxis, p. 68

Bacteria That Form Storage Granules

A number of aquatic bacteria form granules that serve to store nutrients. Recall that anoxygenic phototrophs often store sulfur granules, which can later be used as a source of electrons for reducing power. Some bacteria store phosphate, and others store compounds that can be used to generate ATP.

The Genus Spirillum

Members of the genus *Spirillum* are Gram-negative spiral-shaped, microaerophilic bacteria. *Spirillum volutans* forms volutin granules, which are storage forms of phosphate. These are sometimes called **metachromatic granules** to reflect their characteristic staining with the dye methylene blue. The cells of *S. volutans* are typically large, over 20 μm in length. In wet mounts, *Spirillum* species may be seen moving to a narrow zone near the edge of the coverslip, where O_2 is available in the optimum amount. ■ volutin, p. 70

Sulfur-Oxidizing, Nitrate-Reducing Marine Bacteria

Some marine bacteria store both sulfur, which can be oxidized as an energy source, and nitrate, which can serve as an electron acceptor. This provides an advantage to the bacteria, because anaerobic marine sediments are often abundant in reduced sulfur compounds but deficient in suitable terminal electron acceptors. In contrast, waters above those sediments lack reduced sulfur compounds but provide a source of nitrate. In other words, the energy source and terminal electron acceptor do not coexist. *Thioploca* species respond by forming long sheaths within which filamentous cells shuttle between the sulfur-rich sediments and nitrate-rich waters, storing reserves of sulfur and nitrate in order to obtain energy.

Scientists recently discovered a huge bacterium in the ocean sediments off the coast of the African country of Namibia that they named *Thiomargarita namibiensis*, "sulfur pearl of Namibia" (see Perspective 1.1). The cells are a pearly white color due to globules of sulfur in their cytoplasm. The cells each contain a large nitrate storage vacuole. It is thought that these organisms, which may reach a diameter of ¾ mm, can store a 3-month supply of sulfur and nitrate. The cells are not motile and instead appear to rely on occasional disturbances such as storms to bring them into contact with the nitrate-rich water.

MICROCHECK 11.7

Sheathed bacteria cluster within a tube that can attach to solid objects in favorable locations. Prosthecate bacteria produce extensions that maximize the absorptive surface area. *Bdellovibrio* species, bioluminescent bacteria, and *Legionella* species exploit nutrients provided by other organisms. Spirochetes and magnetotactic bacteria move by unusual mechanisms to more favorable locations. Some organisms form storage granules.

- ✓ What characteristic of *Caulobacter* species makes them an important model for research?
- ✓ How do squid benefit from having a light organ colonized by luminescent bacteria?
- ✓ The genomes of free-living spirochetes are larger than those of ones that live within an animal host. Why would this be so?

11.8

Animals As Habitats

Focus Point

- Describe one genus that inhabits the skin, three genera that inhabit mucous membranes, and two that are obligate intracellular parasites.

The bodies of animals, including humans, provide a wide variety of ecological habitats in which prokaryotes reside—from arid, O_2-rich surfaces to moist, anaerobic recesses.

Bacteria That Inhabit the Skin

The skin is typically dry and salty, providing an environment inhospitable to many microorganisms. Members of the genus *Staphylococcus,* however, thrive under these conditions. The propionic acid bacteria, which were discussed earlier, inhabit anaerobic microenvironments of the skin.

The Genus *Staphylococcus*

Staphylococcus species are Gram-positive cocci that are facultative anaerobes. Most, such as *S. epidermidis,* reside harmlessly as a component of the normal flora of the skin. Like most bacteria that aerobically respire, *Staphylococcus* species are catalase positive. This distinguishes them from *Streptococcus, Enterococcus,* and *Lactococcus* species, which are also Gram-positive cocci but lack the enzyme catalase. Several species of *Staphylococcus* are notable for their medical significance. *Staphylococcus aureus* causes a variety of diseases, including skin and wound infections, as well as food poisoning. *Staphylococcus saprophyticus* causes urinary tract infections.

Bacteria That Inhabit Mucous Membranes

Mucous membranes of the respiratory, genitourinary, and intestinal tracts provide a habitat for numerous kinds of bacteria, many of which have already been discussed. For example, *Streptococcus* and *Corynebacterium* species reside in the respiratory tract, *Lactobacillus* species inhabit the vagina, and *Clostridium* species and members of the family *Enterobacteriaceae* thrive in the intestinal tract. Some of the other genera are discussed next.

The Genus *Bacteroides*

Members of the genus *Bacteroides* are small, strictly anaerobic Gram-negative rods and coccobacilli. They inhabit the mouth, intestinal tract, and genital tract of humans and other animals. *Bacteroides fragilis* and related species constitute about 30% of the bacteria in human feces and are often responsible for abscesses and bloodstream infections that follow appendicitis and abdominal surgery. Since many are killed even by brief exposure to O_2, they are difficult to study.

The Genus *Bifidobacterium*

Bifidobacterium species are irregular Gram-positive rod-shaped anaerobes that reside primarily in the intestinal tract of humans and other animals. They are the predominant members of the intestinal flora of breast-fed infants and are thought to provide a protective function by excluding disease-causing bacteria. Formula-fed infants are also colonized with members of this genus, but generally the concentrations are lower.

The Genera *Campylobacter* and *Helicobacter*

Members of the genera *Campylobacter* and *Helicobacter* are genetically related curved Gram-negative rods that include species of major medical importance. As microaerophiles, they require specific atmospheric conditions to be successfully cultivated. *Campylobacter jejuni* causes diarrheal disease in humans. It typically resides in the intestinal tract of domestic animals, particularly poultry. *Helicobacter pylori* inhabits the stomach, where it can cause stomach and duodenal ulcers. It has also been implicated in the development of stomach cancer. An important factor in its ability to survive in the stomach is its production of the enzyme **urease.** This enzyme breaks down urea to produce ammonia, which neutralizes the acid in the immediate surroundings. ■ stomach ulcers, p. 617

The Genus *Haemophilus*

Members of the genus *Haemophilus* are tiny Gram-negative coccobacilli that, as their name reflects, are "blood loving." They require one or more compounds found in blood, such as hematin and NAD. Many species are common flora of the respiratory tract, but *H. influenzae* can also cause ear infections, respiratory infections, and meningitis, primarily in children. *Haemophilus ducreyi* causes the sexually transmitted disease chancroid. ■ ear infections, p. 583 ■ meningitis, p. 684 ■ chancroid, p. 667

The Genus *Neisseria*

Neisseria species are Gram-negative kidney-bean-shaped cocci that typically occur in pairs. They are common inhabitants of animals including humans, growing on mucous membranes. *Neisseria* species are obligate aerobes, and many are nutritionally fastidious. Those noted for their medical significance include *N. gonorrhoeae,* which causes the sexually transmitted disease gonorrhea, and *N. meningitidis,* which causes meningitis. ■ fastidious, p. 98 ■ gonorrhea, p. 661 ■ meningitis, p. 665

The Genus *Mycoplasma*

Members of the genus *Mycoplasma* lack a cell wall, making them pliable and able to pass through the pores of filters that retain other bacteria. Most have sterols in their membrane, providing added strength and rigidity, thereby protecting the cells from osmotic lysis. They are among the smallest forms of life, and their genomes are thought to be the minimum size for encoding the essential functions for a free-living organism; the genome of *Mycoplasma genitalium* is only 5.8×10^5 base pairs, which is approximately one-eighth the size of the *E. coli* genome.

Medically, the most significant member of this group is *M. pneumoniae,* which, as its name implies, causes a form of pneumonia. This type of pneumonia cannot be treated with penicillin and other antimicrobial drugs that interfere with peptidoglycan synthesis, because these organisms lack a cell wall. Colonies of

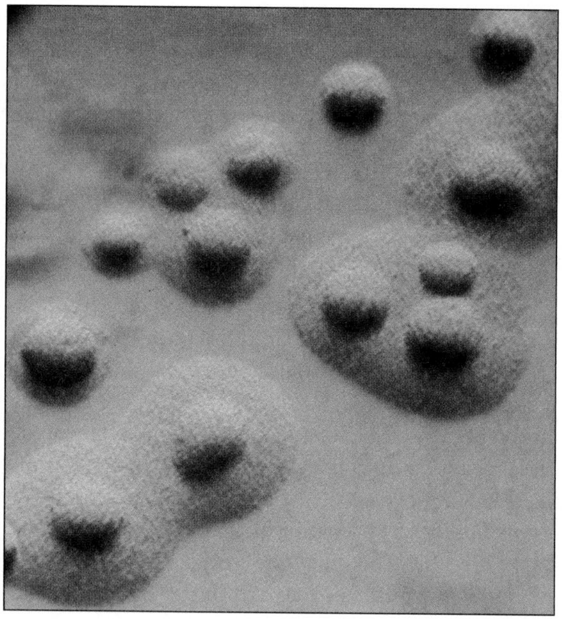

FIGURE 11.27 ***Mycoplasma pneumoniae* Colonies** Note the dense central portion of the colony, giving it the typical "fried egg" appearance.

Mycoplasma species growing on solid media produce a characteristic "fried egg" appearance **(figure 11.27).**

The Genera *Treponema* and *Borrelia*

Members of the genera *Treponema* and *Borrelia* are spirochetes that typically inhabit body fluids and mucous membranes of humans and other animals. Recall that spirochetes are characterized by their corkscrew shape and axial filaments. Although they have a Gram-negative cell wall, they are often too thin to be viewed by conventional microscopy.

Treponema species are obligate anaerobes or microaerophiles that often inhabit the mouth and genital tract. Study of the species that causes syphilis, *T. pallidum,* is difficult because it has never been grown in culture. Its genome has been sequenced, however, providing evidence that it is a microaerophile with a metabolism that is highly dependent on its host. It lacks critical enzymes of the TCA cycle and a variety of other pathways.

Three species of *Borrelia* are medically significant microaerophiles that are transmitted by arthropods such as ticks and lice. *B. recurrentis* and *B. hermsii* both cause relapsing fever; *Borrelia burgdorferi* causes Lyme disease. A striking feature of *Borrelia* species is their genome, which is composed of a linear chromosome and many linear and circular plasmids.

Obligate Intracellular Parasites

Obligate intracellular parasites are unable to reproduce outside a host cell. By living within these host cells, the parasites are supplied with a readily available source of compounds they would otherwise need to synthesize for themselves. As a result, most intracellular parasites have lost the ability to synthesize substances needed for extracellular growth. Bacterial examples include members of the genera *Rickettsia, Orientia, Ehrlichia, Coxiella,* and *Chlamydia,* which are all tiny Gram-negative rods or coccobacilli.

The Genera *Rickettsia, Orientia,* and *Ehrlichia*

Species of *Rickettsia, Orientia,* and *Ehrlichia* are responsible for several serious human diseases that are spread when a blood-sucking arthropod such as a tick or louse that has fed on an infected animal transfers bacteria to a human from whom it takes another blood meal. *Rickettsia rickettsii* causes Rocky Mountain spotted fever, *R. prowazekii* causes epidemic typhus, *O. tsutsugamushi* causes scrub typhus, and *E. chaffeenis* causes human ehrlichiosis.

The Genus *Coxiella*

The only species of *Coxiella, C. burnetii,* is an obligate intracellular bacterium that survives well outside the host cell and is transmissible from animal to animal without necessarily involving a blood-sucking parasite. During its intracellular growth, *C. burnetii* forms sporelike structures that later allow it to survive in the environment. The structures, however, lack the extreme resistance to heat and disinfectants characteristic of most endospores **(figure 11.28).** *Coxiella burnetii* causes Q fever of humans, a disease most often acquired by inhaling bacteria shed from infected animals.

The Genus *Chlamydia*

Chlamydia species are quite different from the other obligate intracellular parasites. They are transmitted directly from person to person rather than through the bite of a blood-sucking arthropod, and they have a unique growth cycle **(figure 11.29).** Inside the host cell, they initially exist as fragile non-infectious forms called **reticulate bodies** that reproduce by binary fission. Later in the infection, the bacteria differentiate into smaller, dense-appearing infectious forms called **elementary bodies** that are released upon death and rupture of the host cell. The cell wall of *Chlamydia* species is highly unusual among the *Bacteria* in that it lacks peptidoglycan, although

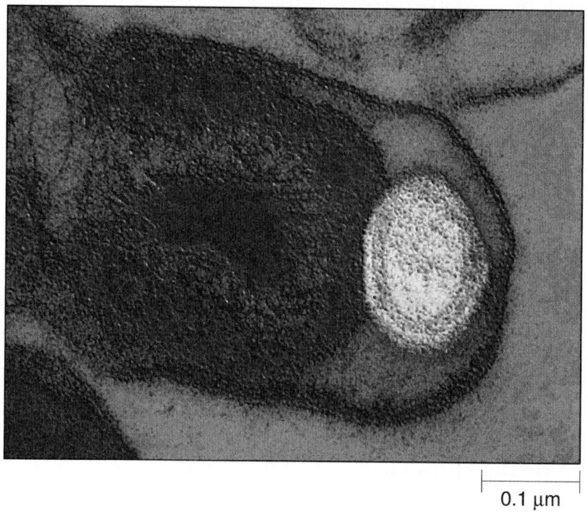

FIGURE 11.28 ***Coxiella*** Color-enhanced transmission electromicrograph of *C. burnetii*. The oval copper-colored object is the sporelike structure.

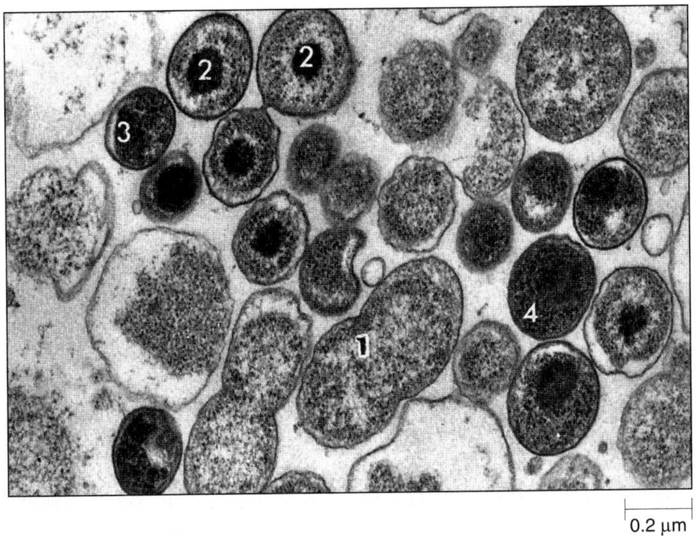

FIGURE 11.29 ***Chlamydia* Growing in Tissue Cell Culture** The numbers indicate the development from the dividing reticulate body to an infectious elementary body.

it has the general appearance of a Gram-negative type of cell wall. *Chlamydia trachomatis* causes eye infections and a sexually transmitted disease that mimics gonorrhea, *C. pneumoniae* causes atypical pneumonia, and *C. psittaci* causes psittacosis, a form of pneumonia. ■ *Chlamydia trachomatis,* p. 663

MICROCHECK 11.8

Staphylococcus species are able to thrive in the dry, salty conditions of the skin. *Bacteroides* and *Bifidobacterium* species reside in the gastrointestinal tract; *Campylobacter* and *Helicobacter* species can cause disease when they reside there. *Neisseria* species, mycoplasma, and spirochetes inhabit other mucous membranes. Obligate intracellular parasites including *Rickettsia, Orientia, Ehrlichia, Coxiella,* and *Chlamydia* species are unable to reproduce outside of a host cell.

- ✓ What characteristic of *Mycoplasma* species separates them from other bacteria?
- ✓ How is *Helicobacter pylori* able to withstand the acidity of the stomach?
- ✓ Why would breast feeding affect the composition of a baby's intestinal flora?

11.9

Archaea That Thrive in Extreme Conditions

Focus Point

- Describe the habitats of the extreme halophiles and extreme thermophiles.

Members of the *Archaea* that have been characterized typically thrive in extreme environments that are otherwise devoid of life. These include conditions of high heat, acidity, alkalinity, and salinity. An exception to this attribute is the methanogens, which inhabit anaerobic niches shared with members of the *Bacteria.* Because of their intimate association with bacteria, the methanogens were discussed earlier in the chapter. In addition to the characterized archaea, many others have been detected in a variety of non-extreme environments by using DNA probes that bind to ribosomal RNA (rRNA) genes. ■ DNA probes, p. 221

Extreme Halophiles

The extreme halophiles are found in very high numbers in high-salt environments such as salt lakes, soda lakes, and brines used for curing fish. Most can grow well in a saturated salt solution (32% NaCl), and they require a minimum of about 9% NaCl. Because they produce pigments, their growth can be seen as red patches on salted fish and pink blooms in concentrated salt water ponds **(figure 11.30).**

Extreme halophiles are aerobic or facultatively anaerobic chemoheterotrophs, but some also can obtain additional energy from light. These organisms have the light-sensitive pigment **bacteriorhodopsin,** which absorbs energy from sunlight and uses it to expel protons from the cell. This creates a proton gradient that can be used to drive flagella or synthesize ATP.

Extreme halophiles come in a variety of shapes, including rods, cocci, discs, and triangles. They include genera such as *Halobacterium, Halorubrum, Natronobacterium,* and *Natronococcus;* members of these latter two genera are extremely alkaliphilic as well as halophilic.

Extreme Thermophiles

The extreme thermophiles (hyperthermophiles) are found in regions of volcanic vents and fissures that exude sulfurous gases and other hot vapors. Because these regions are thought to closely mimic the environment of early earth, scientists are particularly interested

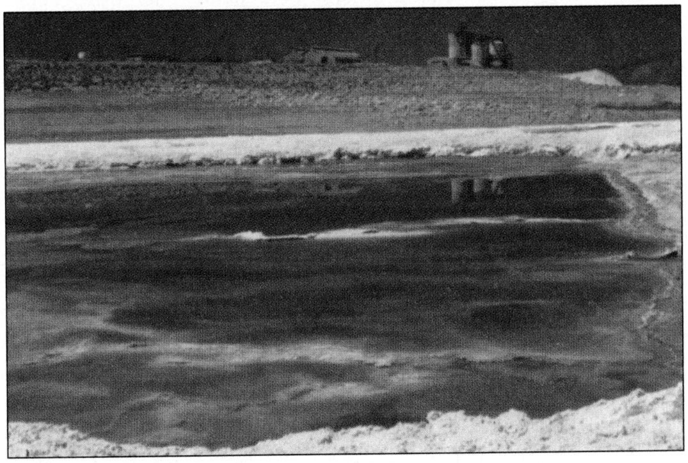

FIGURE 11.30 Typical Habitat of Extreme Halophiles The red color in these solar evaporation ponds is due to the pigments of extreme halophiles such as *Halobacterium* species.

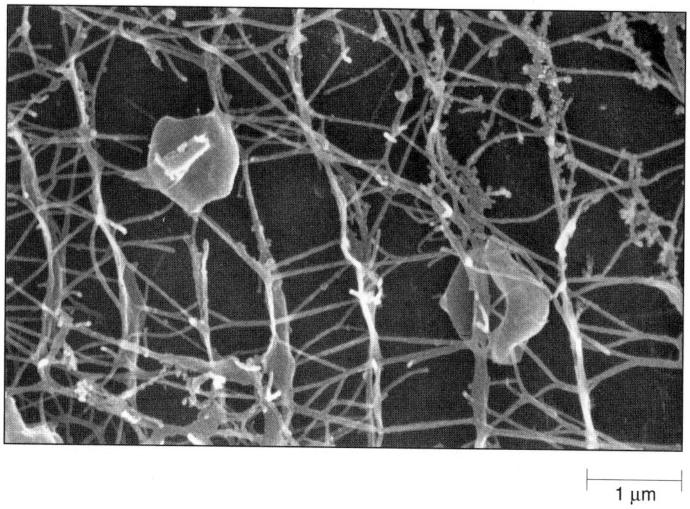

FIGURE 11.31 ***Pyrodictium*** The disc-shaped cells are connected by hollow tubes. Scanning electron micrograph.

FIGURE 11.32 Typical Habitat of *Sulfolobus* Sulfur hot spring in Yellowstone National Park.

in studying the prokaryotes that thrive there. Others are found in hydrothermal vents in the deep sea and hot springs. ■ hyperthermophiles, p. 95

Methane-Generating Hyperthermophiles

Recall that methanogens are archaea, but they live in anaerobic environments inhabited by a diverse assortment of bacteria. Some methanogens, however, are extreme thermophiles. Like the mesophilic methanogens, these organisms oxidize H_2, using CO_2 as a terminal electron acceptor to yield methane. For example, *Methanothermus* species, which can grow in temperatures as high as 97°C, grow optimally at approximately 84°C.

Sulfur-Reducing Hyperthermophiles

The sulfur-reducing hyperthermophiles are obligate anaerobes that use sulfur as a terminal electron acceptor, generating H_2S. They harvest energy by oxidizing organic compounds and/or H_2. These archaea can be isolated from hot sulfur-containing environments such as sulfur hot springs and hydrothermal vents. They include some of the most thermophilic organisms known, a few even growing above 100°C. One notable example, *Pyrolobus fumarii,* was isolated from a "black smoker" 3,650 m (about 12,000 feet) deep in the Atlantic Ocean and grows between 90°C and 113°C. Another hydrothermal vent isolate, *Pyrodictium occultum,* has an optimum temperature of approximately 105°C, and cannot grow below 82°C. Its disc-shaped cells are connected by hollow tubes, forming a weblike network **(figure 11.31).** The record-holder for the highest maximum growth temperature, currently dubbed "strain 121" to reflect that it grows at 121°C, appears to be most closely related to *Pyrodictium* species, but it uses iron as an electron acceptor.

Nanoarchaea

The discovery of an archaeum so unique that it represents an entirely new phylum, *Nanoarcheota* ("dwarf archaea"), was made possible by the earlier discovery of a new genus of sulfur-reducing hyperthermophiles, *Ignicoccus* ("the fire sphere"). *Nanoarchaeum equitans* ("rides the fire sphere") grows as 400 nm spheres attached to the surface of—presumably parasitizing—*Ignicoccus* species (see figure 9.11).

Sulfur Oxidizers

Sulfolobus species are found at the surface of acidic sulfur-containing hot springs such as many of those found in Yellowstone National Park **(figure 11.32).** They are obligate aerobes that oxidize sulfur compounds, using O_2 as a terminal electron acceptor to generate sulfuric acid. In addition, they are thermoacidophilic, only growing above 50°C and at a pH between 1 and 6.

Thermophilic Extreme Acidophiles

Members of two genera, *Thermoplasma* and *Picrophilus,* are notable for their preference of growing in extremely acidic, hot environments. *Thermoplasma* species grow optimally at pH 2; in fact, *T. acidophilum* lyses at neutral pH. It was originally isolated from coal refuse piles. *Picrophilus* species tolerate conditions that are even more acidic, growing optimally at a pH below 1. Two species have been isolated in Japan from acidic areas in regions that exude sulfurous gases.

MICROCHECK 11.9

Many *Archaea* that have been characterized typically inhabit extreme environments that are otherwise devoid of life. These include conditions of high salinity, heat, acidity, and alkalinity.

- ✓ Why do seawater ponds sometimes turn pink as the water evaporates?
- ✓ At which relative depth in a sulfur hot spring would a sulfur reducer likely be found? How about a sulfur oxidizer?
- ✓ What characteristic of the methanogens makes it logical to discuss them with the *Bacteria* rather than the other *Archaea*?

FUTURE CHALLENGES

Astrobiology: The Search for Life on Other Planets

If life as we know it exists on other planets, one form it will likely take will be microbial. The task, then, is to figure out how to find and detect such extraterrestrial microorganisms.

Considering that we still know relatively little about the microbial life on our own planet, coupled with the extreme difficulty of obtaining or testing extraterrestrial samples, this is a daunting challenge with many as yet unanswered questions. For example, what is the most likely source of life on other planets? What is the best way to preserve specimens for study on earth? What will be the culture requirements to grow such organisms? **Astrobiology,** the study of life in the universe, is a new field that is bringing together scientists from a wide range of disciplines, including microbiology, geology, astronomy, biology, and chemistry, to begin answering some of these questions. The goal is to determine the origin, evolution, distribution, and destiny of life in the universe. These astrobiologists are also given the task of developing lightweight, dependable, and meaningful testing devices to be used in future space missions.

Astrobiologists believe that within our solar system, life would most likely be found either on Europa, a moon of Jupiter, or on Mars. This is because Europa and Mars appear to have, or have had, water, which is crucial for all known forms of life. Europa has an icy crust, beneath which may be liquid water or even a liquid ocean. Mars is the planet that is closest to earth, and it has the most similar environment. Images and data from the recent Mars missions indicate that flowing water once existed there.

To prepare for researching life on other planets, microbiologists have turned to some of the most extreme environments here on earth. These include glaciers and ice shelves, hot springs, deserts, volcanoes, deep ocean hydrothermal vents, and subterranean features such as caves. Because select microorganisms can survive in these environs, which are analogous to conditions expected on other planets, they are good testing grounds for the technology to be used on future missions.

SUMMARY

Metabolic Diversity (Table 11.3)

11.1 Anaerobic Chemotrophs

Anaerobic Chemolithotrophs

The **methanogens** are a group of archaea that generate energy by oxidizing hydrogen gas (H_2), using CO_2 as a terminal electron acceptor. (Figure 11.1)

Anaerobic Chemoorganotrophs—Anaerobic Respiration

Desulfovibrio reduces sulfur compounds to form hydrogen sulfide.

Anaerobic Chemoorganotrophs—Fermentation

Clostridium species form endospores.

The **lactic acid bacteria** produce lactic acid as their primary fermentation end product. (Figures 11.2, 11.3)

Propionibacterium species produce propionic acid as their primary fermentation end product.

11.2 Anoxygenic Phototrophs

The Purple Bacteria

The **purple bacteria** appear red, orange, or purple; the components of their photosynthetic apparatus are all contained within the cytoplasmic membrane, which has extensive invaginations.

The Green Bacteria

The **green bacteria** are typically green or brownish in color. Their accessory pigments are located in structures called **chlorosomes,** and their cytoplasmic membranes do not have extensive invaginations.

Other Anoxygenic Phototrophs

Other anoxygenic phototrophs have been discovered, including some that form endospores.

11.3 Oxygenic Phototrophs

The Cyanobacteria (Figures 11.6, 11.7)

Genetic evidence indicates that chloroplasts of plants and algae evolved from a species of cyanobacteria.

Nitrogen-fixing cyanobacteria are critically important ecologically, because they provide an available source of both carbon and nitrogen. Filamentous species may maintain the structure and productivity of some soils.

Some species of cyanobacteria produce toxins that can be deadly to animals that ingest heavily contaminated water.

11.4 Aerobic Chemolithotrophs

The Sulfur-Oxidizing Bacteria (Figure 11.10)

The filamentous sulfur oxidizers *Beggiatoa* and *Thiothrix* live in sulfur springs, in sewage-polluted waters, and on the surface of marine and freshwater sediments. (Figure 11.9)

Thiobacillus species are found in both terrestrial and aquatic habitats.

The Nitrifiers

Ammonia oxidizers convert ammonia to nitrite and include *Nitrosomonas* and *Nitrosococcus;* nitrite oxidizers oxidize nitrite to nitrate and include *Nitrobacter* and *Nitrococcus.*

The Hydrogen-Oxidizing Bacteria

Aquifex and *Hydrogenobacter* species are thermophilic bacteria that are thought to be among the earliest bacterial forms to exist on earth.

11.5 Aerobic Chemoorganotrophs

Obligate Aerobes

Micrococcus species are found in soil and on dust particles, inanimate objects, and skin. (Figure 11.11)

Mycobacterium species are widespread in nature. They are **acid-fast.**

Pseudomonas species are widespread in nature and have extremely diverse metabolic capabilities. (Figure 11.12)

Thermus aquaticus is the source of *Taq* polymerase, which is an essential component in the polymerase chain reaction.

Deinococcus radiodurans can survive exposure to a dose of gamma radiation several thousand times that lethal to a human being.

Facultative Anaerobes

Corynebacterium species commonly inhabit soil, water, and the surface of plants. (Figure 11.13)

Members of the family *Enterobacteriaceae* typically inhabit the intestinal tract of animals, although some reside in rich soil. Enterics that ferment lactose are included in the group **coliforms** and are used as indicators of fecal pollution. (Figure 11.14)

Ecophysiology

11.6 Thriving in Terrestrial Environments

Bacteria That Form a Resting Stage

Of the various types of dormant cells produced by soil organisms, endospores are by far the most resistant to environmental extremes. Endospore-forming genera include *Bacillus* and *Clostridium* (Figure 11.15)

Azotobacter species form a resting cell called a **cyst** and they are notable for their ability to fix nitrogen in aerobic conditions. (Figure 11.16)

Myxobacteria aggregate to form a **fruiting body** when nutrients are exhausted; within the fruiting body, cells differentiate to form dormant microcysts. (Figure 11.17)

Streptomyces species resemble fungi in their pattern of growth; they form chains of **conidia** at the end of **hyphae.** Many species naturally produce antibiotics. (Figure 11.18)

Bacteria That Associate with Plants

Agrobacterium species cause plant tumors. They transfer a portion of the Ti plasmid to plant cells, genetically engineering the plant cells to produce opines and plant growth hormones.

Rhizobia reside as **endosymbionts** in nodules formed on the roots of **legumes.** In these protected confines, they fix nitrogen. (Figure 11.20)

11.7 Thriving in Aquatic Environments

Sheathed Bacteria

Sheathed bacteria form chains of cells encased in a **sheath,** which enables cells to attach to solid objects in favorable habitats while sheltering them from attack by predators. (Figure 11.21)

Prosthecate Bacteria

Caulobacter species have a single polar prostheca called a **stalk;** at the tip of the stalk is a **holdfast.** The cells divide by binary fission. (Figure 11.22)

Hyphomicrobium species divide by forming a bud at the tip of their single polar prostheca. (Figure 11.23)

Bacteria That Derive Nutrients from Other Organisms

Bdellovibrio species prey on other bacteria. (Figure 11.24)

Certain species of bioluminescent bacteria establish symbiotic relationships with specific types of squid and fish. (Figure 11.25)

Legionella species often reside within protozoa and can cause respiratory disease when inhaled in aerosolized droplets.

Bacteria That Move by Unusual Mechanisms

Spirochetes move by means of an axial filament. (Figure 11.26)

Magnetotactic bacteria contain a string of magnetic crystals that enable them to move up or down in water or sediments to the microaerophilic niches they require.

Bacteria That Form Storage Granules

Spirillum volutans forms polyphosphate granules.

Thiomargarita namibiensis is the largest bacterium known; it stores granules of sulfur and has a nitrate-containing vacuole.

11.8 Animals As Habitats (Table 11.2)

Bacteria That Inhabit the Skin

Staphylococcus species are facultative anaerobes.

Bacteria That Inhabit Mucous Membranes

Bacteroides species inhabit the mouth, intestinal tract, and genital tract of humans and other animals.

Bifidobacterium species reside primarily in the intestinal tract of animals, including humans, particularly breast-fed infants.

Campylobacter and *Helicobacter* species are microaerophilic.

Haemophilus species require compounds found in blood for growth.

Neisseria species are nutritionally fastidious, obligate aerobes that grow in the oral cavity and genital tract.

Mycoplasma species lack a cell wall; they often have sterols in their membrane that provide strength and rigidity. (Figure 11.27)

Treponema and *Borrelia* species are spirochetes that typically inhabit mucous membranes and body fluids of humans and other animals.

Obligate Intracellular Parasites

Species of *Rickettsia, Orientia,* and *Ehrlichia* are spread when a blood-sucking arthropod transfers bacteria during a blood meal.

Coxiella burnetii survives well outside the host due to the production of sporelike structures. (Figure 11.28)

Chlamydia species are transmitted directly from person to person. (Figure 11.29)

11.9 Archaea That Thrive in Extreme Conditions

Extreme Halophiles

Extreme halophiles are found in salt lakes, soda lakes, and brines used for curing fish; they can grow well in saturated salt solutions. (Figure 11.30)

Extreme Thermophiles

Methanothermus species are hyperthermophiles that generate methane.

Sulfur-reducing hyperthermophiles are obligate anaerobes that use sulfur as a terminal electron acceptor.

Nanoarchaea grow as spheres attached to *Ignicoccus* species.

Sulfur-oxidizing hyperthermophiles oxidize sulfur compounds, using O_2 as a terminal electron acceptor, to generate sulfuric acid.

Thermophilic extreme acidophiles have an optimum pH of 2 or below.

REVIEW QUESTIONS

Short Answer

1. What kind of bacteria might compose the subsurface scum of polluted ponds?
2. What kind of bacterium might be responsible for plugging the pipes in a sewage treatment facility?
3. Give three examples of energy sources used by chemolithotrophs.
4. Name two genera of endospore-forming bacteria. How do they differ?
5. Serological tests involving which structures help distinguish the different enterobacteria from each other?
6. What unique motility structure characterizes the spirochetes?
7. In what way does the metabolism of *Streptococcus* species differ from that of *Staphylococcus* species?
8. How have species of *Streptomyces* contributed to the treatment of infectious diseases?
9. What characteristic of *Azotobacter* species protects their nitrogenase enzyme from inactivation by O_2?
10. Compare and contrast the relationships of *Agrobacterium* and *Rhizobium* species with plants.

Multiple Choice

1. A catalase-negative colony growing on a plate that was incubated aerobically could be which of these genera?
   a) *Bacillus* b) *Escherichia* c) *Micrococcus*
   d) *Staphylococcus* e) *Streptococcus*
2. All of the following genera are spirochetes, *except*
   a) *Borrelia* b) *Caulobacter* c) *Leptospira*
   d) *Spirochaeta* e) *Treponema*
3. Which of the following genera would you most likely find growing in acidic runoff from a coal mine?
   a) *Clostridium* b) *Escherichia* c) Lactic acid bacteria
   d) *Thermus* e) *Thiobacillus*
4. The dormant forms of which of the following genera are the most resistant to environmental extremes?
   1. *Azotobacter* 2. *Bacillus* 3. *Clostridium*
   4. *Myxobacteria* 5. *Streptomyces*
   a) 1, 2 b) 2, 3 c) 3, 4
   d) 4, 5 e) 1, 5
5. Members of which of the following genera are coliforms?
   a) *Bacteroides* b) *Bifidobacterium* c) *Clostridium*
   d) *Escherichia* e) *Streptococcus*
6. Which of the following genera preys on other bacteria?
   a) *Bdellovibrio* b) *Caulobacter* c) *Hyphomicrobium*
   d) *Photobacterium* e) *Sphaerotilus*
7. All of the following genera are obligate intracellular parasites, *except*
   a) *Chlamydia* b) *Coxiella* c) *Ehrlichia*
   d) *Mycoplasma* e) *Rickettsia*
8. Which of the following genera fix nitrogen?
   1. *Anabaena* 2. *Azotobacter* 3. *Deinococcus*
   4. *Mycoplasma* 5. *Rhizobium*
   a) 1, 3, 4 b) 1, 2, 5 c) 2, 3, 5
   d) 2, 4, 5 e) 3, 4, 5
9. Which of the following archaea would most likely be found coexisting with bacteria?
   a) *Nanoarchaeum* b) *Halobacterium* c) *Methanococcus*
   d) *Picrophilus* e) *Sulfolobus*
10. *Thermoplasma* and *Picrophilus* grow best in which of the following extreme conditions?
   a) Low pH b) High salt c) High temperature
   d) a and c e) b and c

Applications

1. A student argues that it makes no sense to be concerned about coliforms in drinking water because coliforms are harmless members of our normal intestinal flora. Explain why regulatory agencies are concerned about coliforms.
2. A friend who has lakefront property and cherishes her lush green lawn complains of the green odoriferous scum on the lake each summer. Explain how her lawn might be contributing to the problem.

Critical Thinking

1. Soil often goes through periods of extreme dryness and extreme wetness. What characteristics of *Clostridium* species make them well suited for these conditions?
2. Some organisms use sulfur as an electron donor (a source of energy), whereas others use sulfur as an electron acceptor. How can this be if there must be a difference between the electron affinity of electron donors and acceptors for an organism to obtain energy?

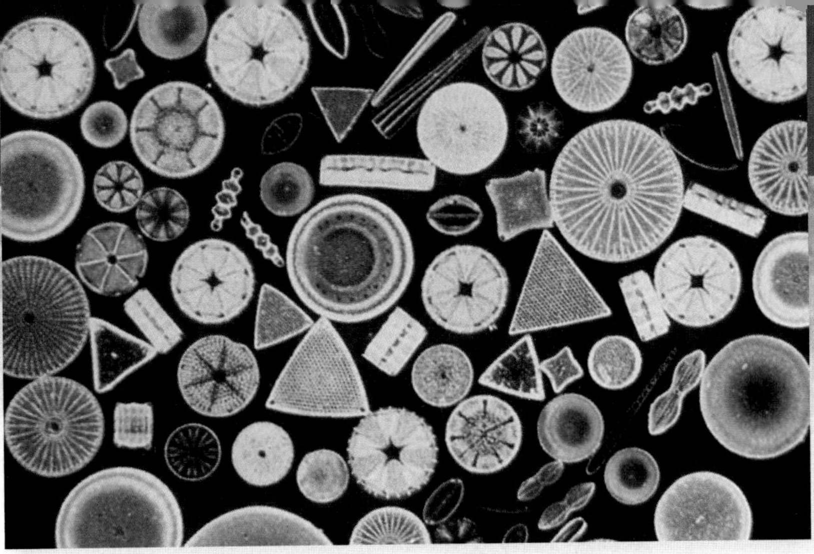

Diatoms, a type of algae, have complex cell walls.

CHAPTER TWELVE

The Eukaryotic Members of the Microbial World

A Glimpse of History

How is it possible that the funguslike organism *Phytophthora infestans,* which causes late blight in potatoes, could have had such an impact on the history of the United States?

In the year 1845 almost half of the potato crop in Ireland was affected by late blight and by 1847 nearly the entire population of Ireland was facing starvation. As a result 1.5 million Irish people died and more than 1 million emigrated to other countries—primarily the United States and Canada. In fact, during the nineteenth century about 5 million emigrated from Ireland to the United States.

Potatoes and the associated late blight disease of the potato have been growing in the Andes mountains of South America for thousands of years. Potatoes are an indigenous plant in South America; there are hundreds of varieties of potato, in all sizes, shapes, colors, and ability to grow in widely diverse climates.

However, the story of the potato and its importance in European and American history begins in 1537 when the first Spaniards explored South America and found the Incas growing "papas" (potatoes). Explorers took the potato back to Spain—along with *Phytophthora infestans.* Potato cultivation spread throughout Europe; however, potatoes were not a major food source for most of Europe during the sixteenth, seventeenth, and eighteenth centuries. Wheat and other grains such as barley and rye were more important.

When the potato arrived in Ireland, however, it was found that the climate was particularly suited for potatoes, and large acreage was devoted to its cultivation. Further, with the advent of the Industrial Revolution and the move of people from the farm to the cities to work in the factories, the potatoes became a convenient and very good food source. One acre of potatoes grows three times more food calories than the same acreage growing grain and one acre can support a family for an entire year, as well as some livestock. Potatoes have all of the vitamins and enough protein to support human life. Potatoes are easy to grow because they are grown as clones. Thus, once a farmer has sown his field with potatoes he only needs to save a few potatoes or leave some in the ground and he is able to grow a new crop of potatoes. Also, potatoes generally store very well in a cool place for months.

However, dependency on a single crop such as the potato resulted in disaster for the Irish people. *Phytophthora infestans,* the cause of late blight, affects every part of the plant including the leaves, the stems, and the tubers. Once a field is infected it is very difficult to rid it of the infection, which can occur rapidly and is not always visible until it has destroyed the entire plant. The infection is spread both by the asexual and sexual spores, and the spores, which can last for years in the soil, are spread by wind as well as by handling the potatoes.

Because late blight of the potato was so intensely studied due to its economic importance in the 1870s, plant pathology as a field of study became important and also contributed to the acceptance of the germ theory of disease that Koch and Pasteur were promoting at this time. Plant breeders in the twentieth century developed resistant strains of potatoes and fungicides were also used to control the disease as well. However, in the 1980s at first in Europe, the Middle East and Far East, and then spreading to North America in the late 1980s and 1990s, *Phytophthora infestans* infections again became a problem. Organisms resistant to the fungicides spread, affecting many acres of potatoes. Once again the study of this organism is important.

As noted at the beginning of this book, when the ribosomal RNA (rRNA) sequences of organisms are compared, the living world can be divided into three divisions: *Bacteria, Archaea,* and *Eucarya.* In this chapter we will consider the ***Eucarya.*** These organisms, which include the algae, fungi, protozoa, multicellular parasites, and insect vectors, have one feature in common: they are all eukaryotic organisms. Recall from chapter 3 that the basic cell structure of the *Eucarya* is distinctly different from that of the *Bacteria* and *Archaea.* They are included in a

KEY TERMS

Alga (pl., algae) A primitive photosynthetic eukaryotic organism.

Arthropod Taxonomic grouping of invertebrate animals that includes insects, ticks, lice, and mites.

Convergent evolution Process of evolution when two genetically different organisms develop similar environmental adaptations.

Eucarya Name of the domain comprising eukaryotic organisms.

Fungus (pl., fungi) A non-photosynthetic eukaryotic organism.

Helminth A parasitic worm.

Nematode Roundworm.

Neurotoxin Toxin that damages the nervous system.

Phytoplankton Floating and swimming algae and photosynthetic prokaryotic organisms of lakes and oceans.

Polymorphic Having different distinct forms.

Protozoa Group of single-celled eukaryotic organisms.

Toxin Poisonous chemical substance.

Trematodes Flatworms known also as flukes.

Yeasts Unicellular fungi.

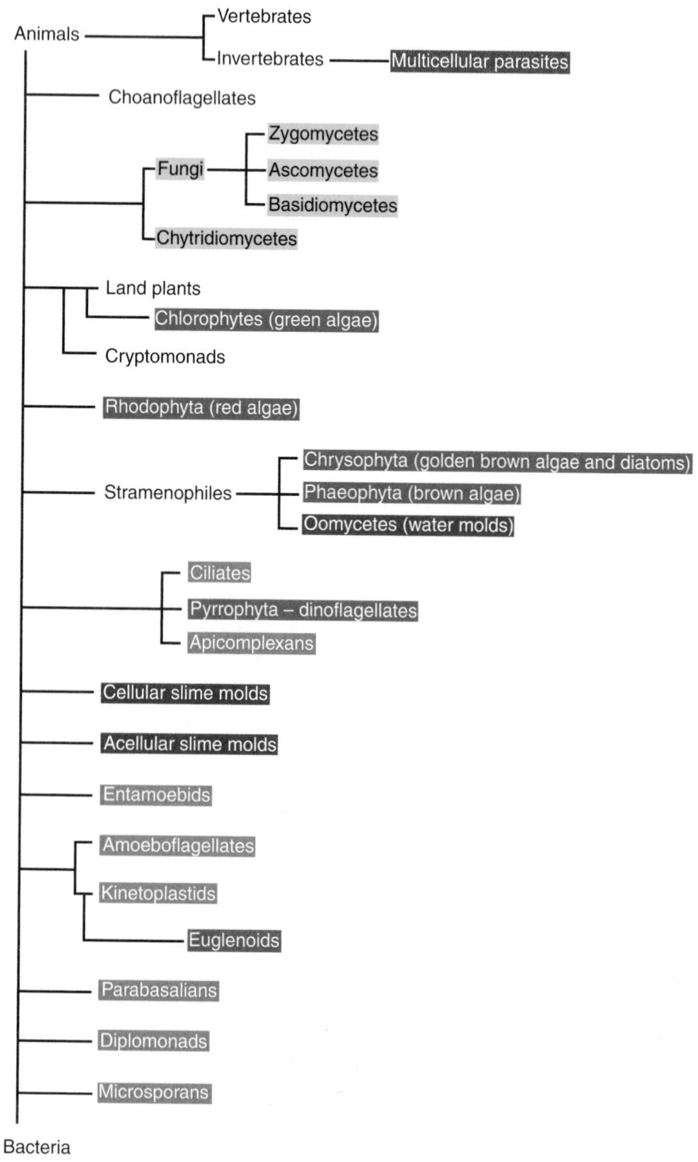

FIGURE 12.1 A Phylogeny of the Eukaryote Based on Ribosomal RNA Sequence Comparison. Algae are green; fungi are yellow; protozoa are red; slime molds are blue; multicellular parasites are brown.

textbook of microbiology because many members of these groups are microscopic and are studied with techniques that are similar to those used to study bacteria and archaea. In addition, many of these organisms cause disease in humans as well as plants and animals. ■ *Eucarya,* p. 10

Classification using gross anatomical characteristics of algae, fungi, protozoa, and even some multicellular parasites has always been problematic. Now, however, with modern techniques that examine these organisms at the molecular and ultrastructural levels, it has been discovered that some of the organisms that were traditionally grouped together are more dissimilar than similar. Instead, they arose at various times along a continuum of evolution. Therefore, in classification schemes that describe an accurate evolutionary history of organisms and are based on molecular and ultrastructure examination, the words *algae, fungi,* and *protozoa* are no longer really accurate. For the purposes of this book, however, we will use the term algae to describe the photosynthetic members and fungi and protozoa to describe the non-photosynthetic members that are discussed in this chapter. In addition, a discussion of arthropods and helminths is included because these eukaryotes are also implicated in human disease. **Figure 12.1** shows a phylogeny based on the ribosomal RNA sequences of the eukaryotic organisms. We will refer to this phylogeny throughout this chapter, indicating where the organisms fit on this evolutionary scale.

12.1 Algae

Focus Points

- Explain how algae differ from the other members of eukaryotic microbial world.
- Describe how algae can affect human health.

The algae are a diverse group of eukaryotic organisms that share some fundamental characteristics but are not related on the phylogenetic tree. These organisms are studied by **algologists** in a field known as **algology.** Algae are organisms that use light energy to convert CO_2 and H_2O to carbohydrates and other cellular products with the release of oxygen. Algae contain chlorophyll *a,* which is necessary for photosynthesis. In addition, many algae contain other pigments that extend the range of light waves that can be used by these organisms for photosynthesis. Algae include both microscopic unicellular members and macroscopic multicellular organisms **(figure 12.2).** Algae, however, differ from other eukaryotic photosynthetic organisms such as land plants in their lack of an organized vascular system and their relatively simple reproductive structures. ■ photosynthesis, p. 156

Algae do not directly infect humans, but some produce toxins that cause paralytic shellfish poisoning. Some of these toxins do not cause illness in the shellfish that feed on the algae but accumulate in their tissues. When the shellfish are eaten by humans the toxins cause nerve damage. ■ paralytic shellfish poisoning, p. 299

As one of the primary producers of carbohydrates and other cellular products, the algae are essential in the food chains of the world. In addition, they produce a large proportion of the oxygen in the atmosphere.

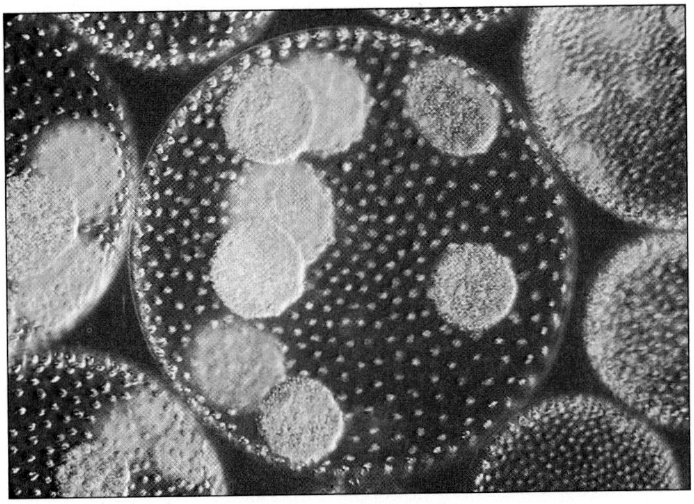

(a)

(b)

FIGURE 12.2 Algae (a) *Volvox* sp. a colony of cells formed into a hollow sphere (125x). The yellow-green circles are reproductive cells that will eventually become new colonies. **(b)** *Corallina gracilis,* red coral algae.

Classification of Algae

As just noted, *algae* is not a strict classification term; nevertheless, organisms considered under the general heading of algae are grouped for identification by a number of properties. These include the principal photosynthetic pigments of each group, cell wall structure, type of storage products, mechanisms of motility, and mode of reproduction. The names of the different algal groups are derived from the major color displayed by most of the algae in that group. Note that the different algal groups lie in different places along the evolutionary tree (see figure 12.1—green).

Some of the general characteristics of the algal groups are summarized in **table 12.1,** on page 298.

Algal Habitats

Algae are found in both fresh and salt water, as well as in soil. Since the oceans cover more than 70% of the earth's surface, aquatic algae are major producers of oxygen as well as important users of carbon dioxide. Unicellular algae make up a significant part of the **phytoplankton** (*phyto* means "plant" and *plankton* means "drifting"), the free-floating, photosynthetic organisms that are found in marine environments. More oxygen is produced by the phytoplankton than by all forests combined.

Phytoplankton is a major food source for many animals, both large and small. Microscopic animals in the **zooplankton** (*zoo* means "animal") graze on this phytoplankton, and then both the zooplankton and phytoplankton, for example, become food for the benthic whales, some of the world's largest mammals, as well as other animals in the sea. The unicellular algae of the phytoplankton are well adapted to this aquatic environment. As single cells, they have large, adsorptive surfaces relative to their volume and can move freely about, thus effectively using the dilute nutrients available.

Because one or more algal species can grow in almost any environment, algae often grow where other forms of life cannot thrive. Frequently, algae are among the first organisms to become established in barren environments, where they synthesize the organic materials necessary for the subsequent invasion and survival of other organisms. They are often found on rocks, preparing the surface for the growth of more complex members of the biological community.

Structure of Algae

Algae can be both microscopic and macroscopic. Microscopic algae can be single-celled organisms floating free or propelled by flagella, or they can grow in long chains or filaments. Some microscopic algae such as *Volvox* form colonies of 500 to 60,000 biflagellated cells, which can be visible to the naked eye (see figure 12.2a).

Macroscopic algae are multicellular organisms with a variety of specialized structures that serve specific functions **(figure 12.3).** Some possess a structure called a **holdfast,** which looks like a root system but primarily serves to anchor the organism to

TABLE 12.1 Characteristics of Major Groups of Algae

Group and Representative Member(s)	Usual Habitat	Principal Pigments (in addition to chlorophyll *a*)	Storage Products	Cell Walls	Mode of Motility (if present)	Mode of Reproduction
Chlorophyta						
Green algae	Fresh water; salt water; soil; tree bark; lichens	Chlorophyll *b;* carotenes; xanthophylls	Starch	Cellulose and pectin	Mostly non-motile except one order, but some reproductive elements are flagellated	Asexual by multiple fission; spores or sexual
Phaeophyta						
Brown algae	Salt water	Xanthophylls, especially fucoxanthin	Starchlike carbohydrates; mannitol; fats	Cellulose and pectin; alginic acid	Two unequal, lateral flagella	Asexual, motile zoospores; sexual, motile gametes
Rhodophyta						
Red algae, corallines	Mostly salt water, several genera in fresh water	Phycobilins including phycoerythrin and phycocyanin; carotenes; xanthophylls	Starchlike carbohydrates	Cellulose and pectin; agar; carrageenan	Non-motile	Asexual spores; sexual gametes
Chrysophyta						
Diatoms, golden brown algae	Fresh water; salt water; soil; higher plants	Carotenes	Starchlike carbohydrates	Pectin, often impregnated with silica or calcium	Unique diatom motility; one, two, or more unequal flagella	Asexual or sexual
Pyrrophyta						
Dinoflagellates	Mostly salt water but common in fresh water	Carotenes; xanthophylls	Starch; oils	Cellulose and pectin	Two unequal, lateral flagella in different planes	Asexual; rarely sexual
Euglenophyta						
Euglena	Fresh water	Chlorophyll *b;* carotenes; xanthophylls	Fats; starchlike carbohydrates	Lacking, but elastic pellicle present	One to three anterior flagella	Asexual only by binary fission

a rock or some other firm substrate. Unlike a root, it is not used to obtain water and nutrients for the organism. Nutrients and water surround the organism and do not need to be drawn up from the soil. The stalk of an alga, known as the **stipe,** usually has leaflike structures or **blades** attached to it. The blades are the principal photosynthetic portion of an alga, and some also bear the reproductive structures. Many large algae have gas-containing **bladders** or floats that help them maintain their blades in a position suitable for obtaining maximum sunlight.

Cell Walls

Algal cell walls are rigid and for the most part composed of cellulose, often associated with pectin. Some multicellular species of algae such as some red algae contain large amounts of other compounds in their cell walls. Compounds such as carrageenan and agar are harvested commercially and commonly used in foods as stabilizing compounds. As described earlier, agar is also used to solidify growth media in the laboratory. It is useful because although it melts at 100°C, it stays in a liquid state at relatively low temperatures (45°C to 50°C) so that nutrients can be added, and yet is solid at room temperatures to act as a growing surface in a Petri dish. ■ agar, p. 90 ■ Petri dish, p. 90

Diatoms are algae that have silicon dioxide incorporated into their cell walls. When these organisms die, their shells sink to the bottom of the ocean, and the silicon-containing material does not decompose. Deposits of diatoms that formed millions of years ago are mined for a substance known as diatomaceous earth, used for filtering systems, abrasives in polishes, insulation, and many other purposes.

Eukaryotic Cell Structures

As is true in all eukaryotes, algae have a membrane-bound **nucleus.** The genetic information is contained in a number of chromosomes that are tight packages of DNA with their associated basic protein. These chromosomes are enclosed in a nuclear membrane. ■ nucleus, p. 78

In addition, algae have other organelles in their cytoplasm such as **chloroplasts** and **mitochondria.** Chloroplasts contain chlorophyll as well as other light-trapping pigments such as carot-

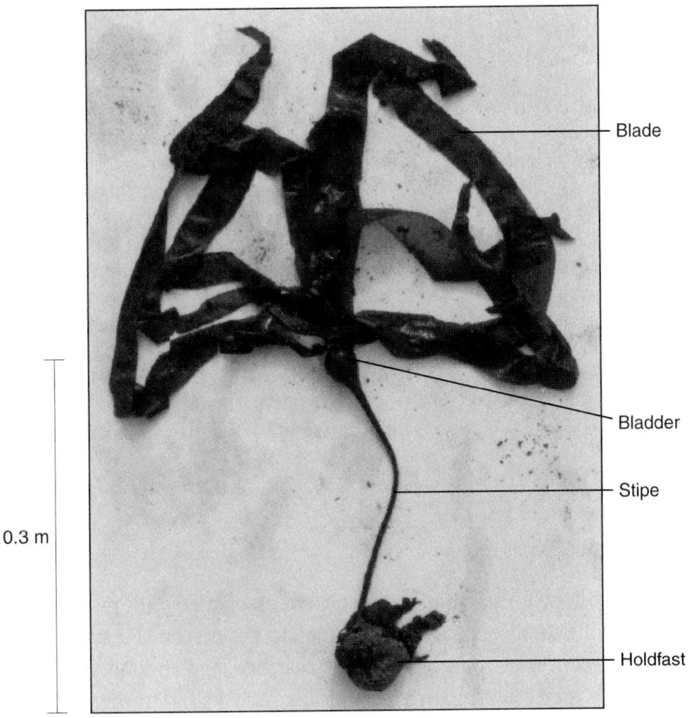

FIGURE 12.3 A Young *Nereocystis luetkeana,* the Bladder Kelp The alga has a large bladder filled with gas. This bladder keeps the blades floating on the surface of the water to maximize exposure to sunlight. The blades are the most active sites for photosynthesis. The holdfast anchors the kelp to rocks or other surfaces. In a single season, kelp can grow to lengths of 5 to 15 m.

enoids and phycocyanin. Photosynthesis occurs in the chloroplast. Respiration and oxidative phosphorylation occur in the mitochondria. ■ chloroplasts, p. 79 ■ mitochondria, p. 78

Algal Reproduction

Most single-celled algae reproduce asexually by binary fission, as do most bacteria **(figure 12.4).** The major difference between prokaryotic and eukaryotic fission involves events that take place with the genetic material within the cell. Recall from chapter 3 that in prokaryotic fission, the circular DNA replicates and each daughter cell receives half the original double strand of DNA plus a newly replicated strand. In eukaryotic organisms with multiple chromosomes, after the DNA is replicated, the chromosomes go through a nuclear division process called **mitosis.** This process ensures that the daughter cells receive the same number of chromosomes as the original parent.

Some algae, especially multicellular filamentous species, reproduce asexually by fragmentation. In this type of reproduction, portions of the parent organisms break off to form new organisms (see figure 12.4), and the parent organism survives.

Sexual reproduction also regularly occurs in most algae. During the process known as **meiosis, haploid** cells with half the chromosome content are formed. These cells are called **gametes** and when they fuse together they form a **diploid** cell with a full complement of chromosomes known as a **zygote.** Gametes are often flagellated and highly motile. Many algae alternate between a haploid generation and a diploid generation. Sometimes, as is the case with *Ulva* (sea lettuce), the generations look physically similar and can only be told apart by microscopic examination. In other cases, the two forms look quite different.

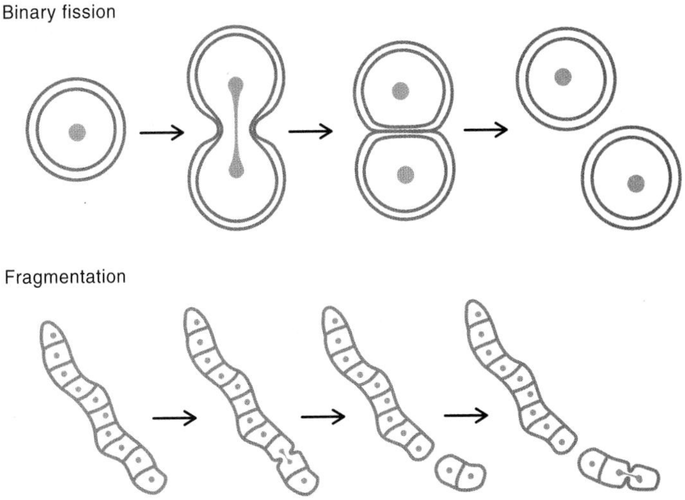

FIGURE 12.4 Binary Fission Is an Asexual Reproduction Process in Which a Single Cell Divides into Two Independent Daughter Cells Fragmentation is a form of asexual reproduction in which a filament composed of a string of cells breaks into pieces to form new organisms.

Paralytic Shellfish Poisoning

Although algae do not directly cause disease in humans, they do so indirectly. A number of algae produce toxins that are poisonous to humans and other animals. Several dinoflagellates of the group Pyrrophyta cause red tides, or algal blooms in the ocean. Red tides were reported in the Bible along the Nile and today seem to be spreading worldwide. In the warm waters of Florida and Mexico, red tides result from an abundance of *Gymnodinium breve* **(figure 12.5).** This dinoflagellate discolors the water about 17 to 75 km from shore and produces **brevetoxin,** which kills the fish that feed on the phytoplankton. It is unclear why algae suddenly grow in

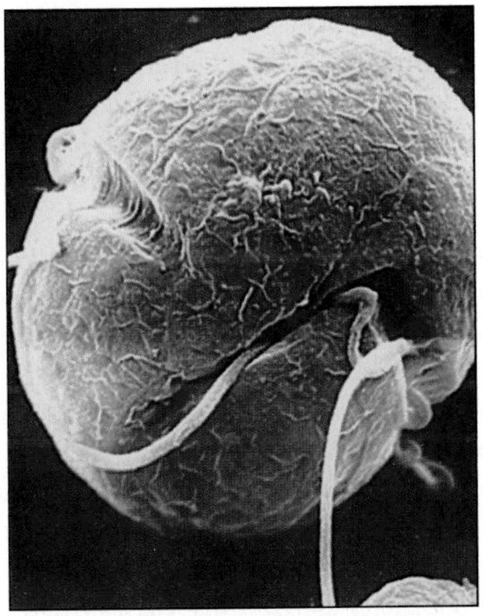

FIGURE 12.5 The Dinoflagellate *Gymnodinium* Scanning Electron Micrograph (4000×)

PERSPECTIVE 12.1

How Marine Phytoplankton Help Combat Global Warming

It has only been in recent times that the scientific community has come to realize that the small single-celled organisms that constitute the phytoplankton of the oceans and other waterways have such an influence on the climate of the world. These single-celled organisms are able to draw significant amounts of carbon dioxide (CO_2) out of the atmosphere and store it deep in the sea. Researchers in the last few years have been able to use satellite images to make these observations.

Previously it was thought that the land plants were the primary users of the CO_2 in the atmosphere. That perception changed in 1997 when NASA launched the Sea Wide Field Sensor, the first satellite capable of observing the entire planet's phytoplankton population in a single week. From their observations the scientists concluded that every year phytoplankton incorporate 45 to 50 billion metric tons of inorganic carbon into their cells, nearly double the amount previously estimated. What also surprised scientists was that the new satellite analysis showed that land plants assimilated only about 52 billion tons of carbon, half the amount earlier estimated. Thus the phytoplankton can draw out just as much CO_2 from the atmosphere as all the land plants put together.

Some scientists have suggested that it might be possible to add nutrients such as fertilizer and iron to seawater to increase the growth of the phytoplankton and thus increase the amount of CO_2 used up. This might allow for additional burning of fossil fuels and other human activities that have added CO_2 to the atmosphere, one of the causes of global warming. However, other scientists have cautioned that this might actually add more CO_2 to the atmosphere as these organisms die. Thus much more study of the impact of this increase in phytoplankton as it affects the ecosystems of the ocean is required before such projects are carried out on any large scale.

such large numbers, but it is thought that sudden changes in conditions of the water are responsible. The runoff of fertilizers along the waterways and coastlines may also be the cause of red tides. In addition, an upwelling of the water often brings more nutrients as well as the cysts that are resting, resistant stages of the *G. breve* from the ocean bottom to the surface. When these cysts encounter warmer waters and additional nutrients, they are released from their resting state and begin to multiply rapidly. Persons eating fish that have ingested *G. breve* and thus contain brevetoxin may suffer a tingling sensation in their mouths and fingers, a reversal of hot and cold perceptions, reduced pulse rate, and diarrhea. The symptoms may be unpleasant but are rarely deadly, and people recover in 2 to 3 days.

Red tides caused by the dinoflagellate of the genus *Gonyaulax* are much more serious. *Gonyaulax* species produce **neurotoxins** such as **saxitoxin** and **gonyautoxins,** some of the most potent non-protein poisons known. Shellfish such as clams, mussels, scallops, and oysters feed on these dinoflagellates without apparent harm and, in the process, accumulate the neurotoxin in their tissues. Then when humans eat the shellfish, they suffer symptoms of paralytic shellfish poisoning including general numbness, dizziness, general muscle weakness, and impaired respiration. Death can result from respiratory failure. *Gonyaulax* species are found in both the North Atlantic and the North Pacific. They have seriously affected the shellfish industry on both coasts over the years. At least 200 manatees died along the coast of Florida in the spring of 1996 as a result of red tide poisoning.

Another dinoflagellate, *Pfiesteria piscida,* usually is found as a non-toxic cyst or ameba in marine sediments. This organism changes when a school of fish approaches. The fish secrete a chemical cue that alerts the *Pfiesteria* to transform into a flagellated zoospore. It then releases two toxins. One stuns the fish and the other causes its skin to slough away. The *Pfiesteria* then enjoys a meal on the fish's red blood cells and sexually reproduces. The toxins are so potent that researchers working with them in a laboratory were seriously affected. This organism now must be studied using the same precautions that are used to study the virus that causes AIDS.

Another algal toxin found in some species of diatoms has more recently been recognized to cause paralytic shellfish poisoning. This poison is domoic acid and is most often associated with mussels and other shellfish and crabs that accumulate the poison. Persons eating the shellfish suffer nausea, vomiting, diarrhea, and abdominal cramps as well as some neurological symptoms such as loss of memory.

State agencies constantly monitor for algal toxins, and it is wise to check with the local health department before harvesting shellfish for human consumption. Algal toxins may be present even when the water is not obviously discolored. Cooking the shellfish does not destroy these toxins.

MICROCHECK 12.1

Algae are a diverse group of eukaryotic organisms that all contain chlorophyll *a* and carry out photosynthesis. Algae are found in both fresh and salt water and are a significant part of the phytoplankton. Algae do not cause disease directly, but they can produce toxins that are harmful when ingested by humans.

- ✓ What are the primary characteristics used to distinguish algae from other organisms?
- ✓ What harmful effect can algae have on humans?
- ✓ Why should single cells have a large absorptive surface relative to their surface area?
- ✓ Would organisms that reproduce by binary fission necessarily be genetically identical? Why or why not?

12.2 Protozoa

Focus Points

- Explain how protozoa are different from other members of eukaryotic microbial world.
- Describe some of the diseases of humans that are caused by protozoa.

Along with the algae, the protozoa constitute another group of eukaryotic organisms that traditionally have been considered part of the microbial world. Protozoa are microscopic, unicellular organisms that lack photosynthetic capability, usually are motile at least at some stage in their life cycle, and reproduce most often by asexual fission.

Classification of Protozoa

As with algae, classification of protozoa according to rRNA and ultrastructure shows that they are not a unified group, but appear along the evolutionary continuum (see figure 12.1—red). The primary reason that they are lumped together in a field known as **protozoology** is because they are all single-celled eukaryotic organisms that lack chlorophyll. Some members of this group cause disease. We will concentrate on these organisms.

Protozoa have traditionally been divided into groups primarily based on their mode of locomotion. **Table 12.2** and figure 12.1 show where each group fits in these schemes.

The phylum **Sarcomastigophora** includes two subphyla in which most of the human disease-causing protozoa are found. The subphylum **Mastigophora** includes the flagellated protozoa. They are mostly unicellular and have one or more flagella at some time in their life cycle. These flagella are used for locomotion and food gathering as well as sensory receptors. The most important disease-causing Mastigophora are *Giardia lamblia, Leishmania* species, *Trichomonas vaginalis, Trypanosoma brucei rhodesiense,* and *Trypanosoma brucei gambiense* (see table 12.2). Each of these diseases will be discussed later in this book. ■ flagella, p. 66

Members of the subphylum **Sarcodina** move by means of pseudopodia. The Sarcodina change shape as they move. *Entamoeba histolytica* infects humans, causing diarrhea ranging from mild asymptomatic disease to severe dysentery. ■ diarrhea, p. 622

The phylum **Ciliophora,** or the **ciliates,** includes organisms that have cilia. The cilia are similar in construction to the flagella and usually completely cover the surface of an organism. Most often, they are arranged in distinct rows and are connected to one another by fibrils known as kinetodesma. Cilia beat in a coordinated fashion in waves across the body of the protozoan. A beat of one cilium affects the cilia immediately around it, but there is no evidence that the connecting fibrils aid in this coordination. The cilia found near the oral cavity propel food into the opening. Paramecia are members of the Ciliophora. *Balantidium coli* is the only known ciliate to cause human disease. It produces ulcers in the large intestines, and pigs are its major reservoir.

Organisms in the phylum **Apicomplexa,** also referred to as **sporozoa,** cause some of the most serious protozoan diseases of humans. Malaria is caused by any of four *Plasmodium* species. It is transmitted by the female *Anopheles* mosquito. Cats are the primary host for *Toxoplasma gondii,* with humans serving as secondary hosts. Another Apicomplexa is *Cryptosporidium parvum,* which causes the diarrheal disease cryptosporidiosis. ■ malaria, p. 725 ■ toxoplasmosis, p. 749 ■ cryptosporidiosis, p. 639

The phylum **Microspora** includes the intracellular protozoa that infect immunocompromised humans, especially persons with AIDS. There are other protozoan phyla such as Labyrinthomorpha, Ascetospora, and Myxozoa, but they are not implicated in human disease and so we will not consider them here. They are most often found in marine habitats and are parasitic on fish and other sea life.

Protozoan Habitats

A majority of protozoa are free-living and found in marine, freshwater, or terrestrial environments. They are essential as decomposers in many ecosystems. Some species, however, are parasitic, living on or in other host organisms. The hosts for protozoan parasites range from simple organisms, such as algae, to complex

TABLE 12.2 Protozoa of Medical Importance

Traditional Classification	18s rRNA Classification	Genus of Disease-Causing Protozoa	Disease Caused by Protozoa	Mode of Motility	Mode of Asexual Reproduction	Page for Additional Information
Phylum: Sarcomastigophora						
Subphylum:						
Mastigophora	Kinetoplastid	*Trypanosoma*	African sleeping sickness	Flagella	Longitudinal fission	p. 701
	Diplomonad	*Giardia*	Giardiasis			p. 638
	Parabasalian	*Trichomonas*	Trichomoniasis			p. 657
	Kinetoplastic	*Leishmania*	Leishmaniasis			
Sarcodina	Entamoebids	*Entamoeba*	Amebiasis (diarrhea)	Pseudopodia	Binary fission	p. 641
Phylum: Ciliophora	Ciliates	*Balantidium*	Dysentery	Cilia	Transverse fission	
Phylum: Apicomplexa	Apicomplexans	*Plasmodium*	Malaria	Flagella	Multiple fission	p. 725
		Toxoplasma	Toxoplasmosis			p. 749
		Cryptosporidium	Cryptosporidiosis			p. 640
Phylum: Microspora	Microsporans	*Microsporidium*	Diarrhea	Polar filament	?	

vertebrates, including humans. All protozoa require large amounts of moisture, no matter what their habitat.

In marine environments, protozoa make up part of the zooplankton, where they feed on the algae of the phytoplankton and are an important part of the aquatic food chains. On land, protozoa are abundant in soil as well as in or on plants and animals. Specialized protozoan habitats include the guts of termites, roaches, and ruminants such as cattle.

Protozoa are an important part of the food chain. They eat bacteria and algae and, in turn, serve as food for larger species. The protozoa help maintain an ecological balance in the soil by devouring vast numbers of bacteria and algae. For example, a single paramecium can ingest as many as 5 million bacteria in one day. Protozoa are important in sewage disposal because most of the nutrients they consume are metabolized to carbon dioxide and water, resulting in a large decrease in total sewage solids. ■ sewage treatment, p. 780

Structure of Protozoa

Cell Wall

Protozoa lack the rigid cellulose cell wall found in algae. Most protozoa do, however, have a specific shape determined by the rigidity or flexibility of the material lying just beneath the plasma membrane. **Foraminifera** have distinct hard shells composed of silicon or calcium compounds **(figure 12.6).** The foraminiferans, which secrete a calcium shell, have through the course of millions of years formed limestone deposits such as the white cliffs of Dover on England's southern coast.

Eukaryotic Cell Structures

Protozoa are eukaryotic organisms and as such have a membrane-bound nucleus as well as other membrane-bound organelles such as mitochondria. Protozoa are not photosynthetic and thus lack chloroplasts. ■ eukaryotic organelles, p. 78

Protozoa have specialized structures for movement such as **cilia, flagella,** or **pseudopodia.** As described in chapter 3, eukaryotic flagella and cilia are distinctly different in construction from prokaryotic flagella (see figures 3.40 and 3.54). Protozoa are grouped by their mode of locomotion. For example, the Mastigophora have flagella, and Ciliophora have cilia during at least some part of their life cycle, and Sarcodina use pseudopodia for movement (see table 12.2). ■ flagella, p. 66

FIGURE 12.6 A Group of Protozoa with Hard Silicon Shells

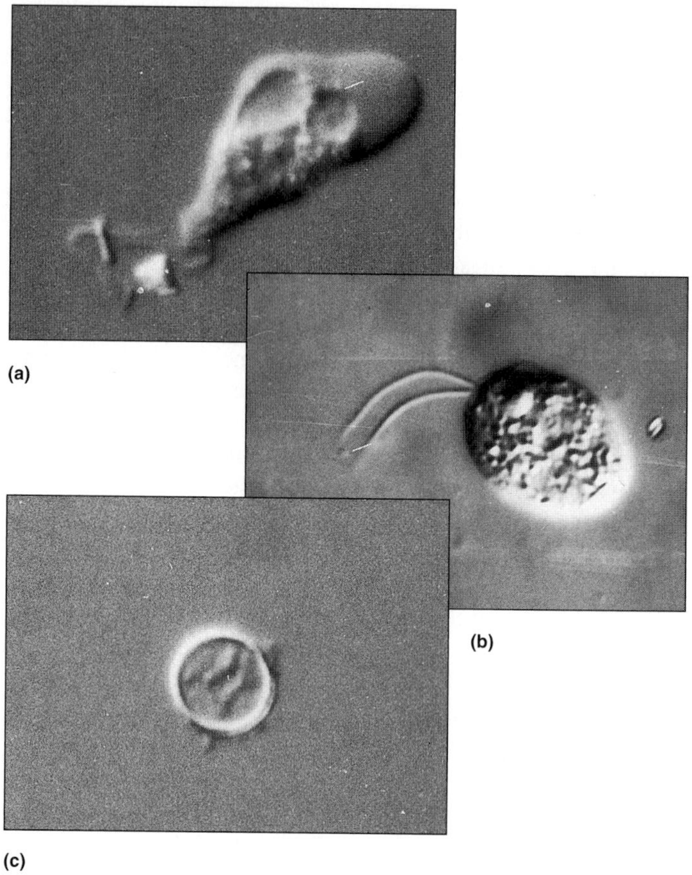

FIGURE 12.7 Polymorphism in a Protozoan The species of *Naegleria* may infect humans. **(a)** In human tissues, the organism exists in the form of an ameba (10–11 μm at its widest diameter). **(b)** After a few minutes in water, the flagellate form appears. **(c)** Under adverse conditions, a cyst is formed.

Feeding in Protozoa

Since protozoa live in an aquatic environment, water, oxygen, and other small molecules readily diffuse through the cell membrane. In addition, as described in chapter 3, protozoa use either pinocytosis or phagocytosis to obtain food and water (see figure 3.50).

Protozoan Reproduction

The life cycles of protozoa are sometimes complex, involving more than one habitat or host. Morphologically distinct forms of a single protozoan species can be found at different stages of the life cycle. Such organisms are said to be **polymorphic (figure 12.7).** This polymorphism is comparable in some respects to the differentiation of various cell types that form plant and animal tissues.

The ability to exist in either a **trophozoite** (vegetative or feeding form) or **cyst** (resting form) is characteristic of many protozoa. Certain environmental conditions, such as the lack of nutrients, moisture, oxygen, low temperature, or the presence of toxic chemicals may trigger the development of a protective cyst wall within which the cytoplasm becomes dormant. Cysts provide a means for the dis-

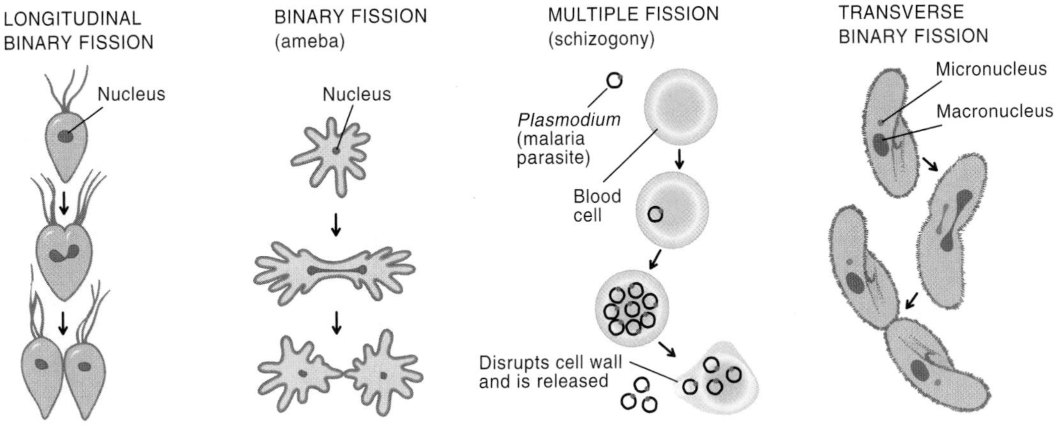

FIGURE 12.8 Various Forms of Asexual Reproduction in Protozoa

persal and survival of protozoa under adverse conditions and can be compared to the bacterial endospore. Protozoan cysts, however, are not as resistant to heat and other adverse conditions as are bacterial endospores. When the cyst encounters a favorable environment, the trophozoite emerges. Thus, a number of parasitic protozoa are disseminated to new hosts during their cyst stage. ■ endospores, p. 71

Both asexual and sexual reproduction are common in protozoa and may alternate during the complicated life cycle of some organisms. Binary fission takes place in many groups of protozoa **(figure 12.8).** In the flagellates, it usually occurs longitudinally, and in the ciliates, it occurs transversely. Since some protozoa possess both cilia and flagella, their method of asexual reproduction determines in which group they are classified.

Some protozoa divide by multiple fissions, or **schizogony,** in which the nucleus divides a number of times and then the cell produces many small single-celled organisms, each one capable of infection. Multiple fission of the asexual forms in the human host results in large numbers of parasites released into the host's circulation at regular intervals, producing the characteristic cyclic symptoms of malaria. A more detailed account of this process is described in chapter 28.

Protozoa and Human Disease

The major threat posed by protozoa results from their ability to parasitize and often kill a wide variety of animal hosts. Human infections with the protozoans *Toxoplasma gondii,* which causes toxoplasmosis, *Plasmodium* species, which are responsible for malaria, *Trypanosoma* species, which cause sleeping sickness, and *Trichomonas vaginalis,* which causes vaginitis, are common in many parts of the world. Malaria has been one of the greatest killers of humans through the ages. At least 300 million people in the world contract malaria each year, and 1 million die of it. Protozoan infections of animals are so common that it is difficult to estimate their extent or overestimate their economic importance. Some parts of tropical Africa are uninhabitable, due in large part to the presence of the tsetse fly, the carrier of the trypanosomes that cause African sleeping sickness. Humans have no natural defense mechanisms against this infection. Some animals, including cows and horses, are reservoirs for these organisms.

Some diseases caused by protozoa are given in table 12.2.

MICROCHECK 12.2

Protozoa are microscopic, single-celled, non-photosynthetic, motile organisms. Most are free-living, but some can cause serious human disease. Protozoa are a very important part of the food chain.

✓ What are the primary characteristics that distinguish protozoa from other eukaryotic organisms?

✓ What are some important diseases caused by protozoa?

✓ Why would all protozoa be expected to require large amounts of water?

12.3 Fungi

Focus Points

- Explain how fungi are different from other members of eukaryotic microbial world.
- Describe the economic importance of fungi.
- Describe some of the diseases of humans caused by fungi.

The term fungi describes a taxonomic classification of organisms but no longer includes organisms such as slime molds and water molds that had traditionally been considered to be fungi (see figure 12.1—yellow). The slime molds and water molds once thought to be related to the fungi now appear to have evolved much earlier and will be considered separately in this chapter.

Fungi require organic compounds for energy and as a carbon source, often from dead organisms. Most fungi are aerobic or facultatively anaerobic. Only a few fungi are anaerobic. ■ aerobic, p. 95 ■ facultatively anaerobic, p. 96 ■ anaerobic, p. 95

A large number of fungi cause disease in plants. Fortunately, only a few species cause disease in animals and humans. As modern medicine has advanced to treat once-fatal diseases, however, it has left many individuals with impaired immune systems. It is these immunocompromised individuals who are most vulnerable to the fungal diseases.

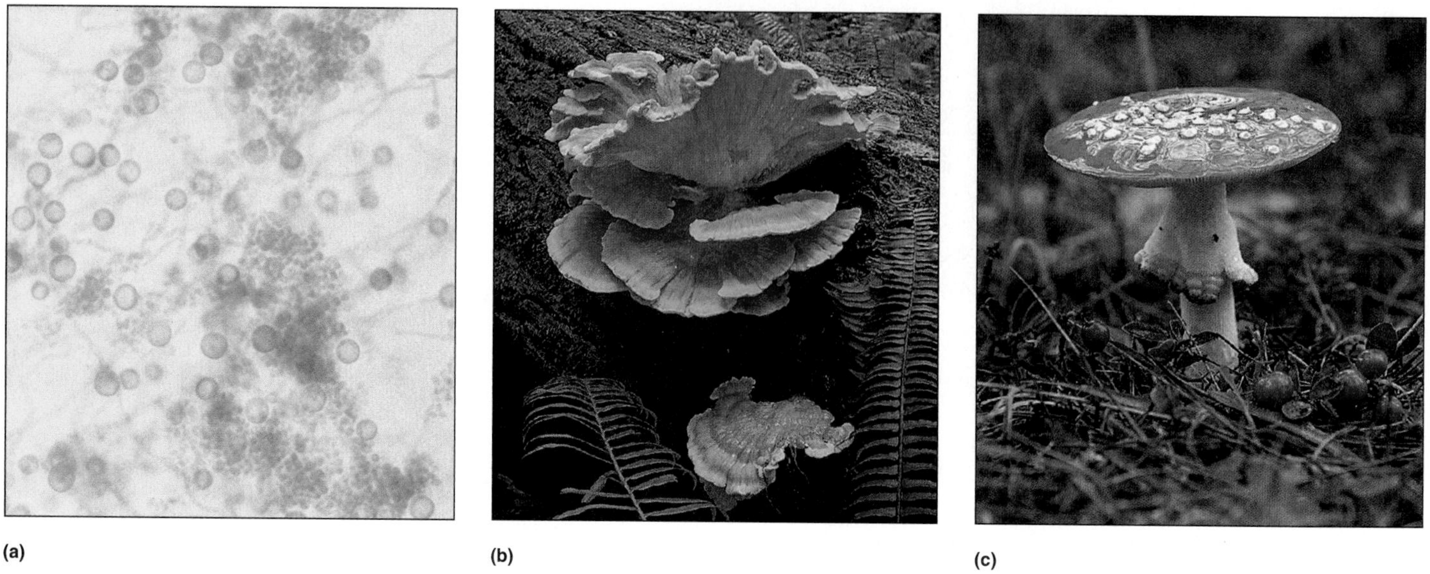

FIGURE 12.9 Fungi Range in Size from Microscopic to Macroscopic Forms **(a)** Microscopic *Candida albicans,* showing the chlamydospores (large, round circles) that are an asexual reproductive spore. **(b)** *Polyporus sulphureus* (chicken of the woods), a shelflike fungus growing on a tree. **(c)** *Amanita muscaria,* a highly poisonous mushroom, growing in a cranberry bog on the Oregon coast.

The study of fungi is known as **mycology,** and a person who studies fungi is known as a **mycologist.** Along with bacteria, fungi are the principal decomposers of carbon compounds on earth. This decomposition releases carbon dioxide into the atmosphere and nitrogen compounds into the soil, which are then taken up by plants and converted into organic compounds. Without this breakdown of organic material, the world would quickly be overrun with organic waste.

Classification of Fungi

Many fungi are microscopic and can be examined using basic microbiological techniques; others are macroscopic **(figure 12.9).** All fungi have chitin in their cell walls and no flagellated cells at any time during their life cycle. There are four groups of true fungi, the **Zygomycetes, Basidiomycetes, Ascomycetes,** and **Deuteromycetes** or **Fungi Imperfecti.** The classification of the first three groups is based on their method of sexual reproduction. For the fourth group, the Deuteromycetes, sexual reproduction has not been observed, and so these fungi have traditionally been lumped together. With additional rRNA analysis, however, most Deuteromycetes can now be placed in one of the other three fungal groups. Most are either Ascomycetes or Basidiomycetes who have lost the sexual part of their life cycle **(table 12.3).**

The Zygomycetes include the common bread mold (*Rhizopus*) and other food spoilage organisms. The Ascomycetes include fungi that cause Dutch elm disease and rye smut. Smuts got this common name because the black spores that are produced give the

TABLE 12.3 Characteristics of Major Groups of Fungi

Group and Representative Member	Usual Habitat	Some Distinguishing Characteristics	Asexual Reproduction	Sexual Reproduction
Zygomycetes *Rhizopus stolonifer* (black bread mold)	Terrestrial	Multicellular, coenocytic mycelia (with many haploid nuclei)	Asexual spores develop in sporangia on the tips of aerial hyphae	Sexual spores known as zygospores can remain dormant in adverse environment
Basidiomycetes *Agaricus campestris* (meadow mushroom) *Cryptococcus neoformans*	Terrestrial	Multicellular, uninucleated mycella. Group includes mushrooms, smuts, rusts that affect the food supply	Commonly absent	Produce basidiophores that are borne on club-shaped structures at the tips of the hyphae
Ascomycetes *Neurospora, Saccharomyces cerevisiae* (baker's yeast)	Terrestrial, on fruit and other organic materials	Unicellular and multicellular with septated mycelia	Is common by budding; conidiospores	Involves the formation of an ascus (sac) on specialized hyphae
Deuteromycetes (Fungi Imperfecti) *Penicillium, Aspergillus*	Terrestrial	A number of these are human pathogens	Budding	Absent or unknown

appearance of soot. The Basidiomycetes include the common mushrooms and puffballs. Many medically and economically important species of fungus, including the one that produces penicillin, belong to the Deuteromycetes. In addition to these four groups of fungi, the **Chytridiomycetes** are a close relative on the evolutionary scale. They have flagellated sexual spores and more variable life cycles, however, than the fungi. Most of these organisms live in water or soil, and a few are parasitic. Black wart disease of potatoes is caused by a chytridiomycete.

Common Groupings of Fungal Forms

When people talk about fungi, they frequently use terms such as yeast, mold, and mushroom. These terms have nothing to do with the classification of fungi but instead indicate their morphological forms.

Yeasts are single-celled fungi **(figure 12.10).** Yeasts can be spherical, oval, or cylindrical and are usually 3 to 5 μm in diameter. Some yeasts reproduce by binary fission, whereas others reproduce by budding, in which a small outgrowth on the cell produces a new cell **(figure 12.11).**

Molds are filamentous fungi. A single filament is known as a **hypha** (plural, **hyphae**), and a collection of hyphae growing in one place is known as a **mycelium.** Hyphae develop from fungal spores. A fungal reproductive spore is typically a single cell about 3 to 30 μm in diameter, depending on the species. When a fungal spore lands on a suitable substrate, it germinates and sends out a projection called a **germ tube (figure 12.12).** This tube grows at the tip and develops into a hypha. The cells divide and form new cells. In some fungi, the cell wall does not completely close off one cell from another. In that case the cells become multinucleated. The white mass seen inside the potato or on moldy bread **(figure 12.13)** is an example of a mycelium. Only a small portion of the mycelium is actually visible on the surface of the bread; the rest is buried deep within. Some mycelia appear above the surface of the substrate as a mushroom, or puffball **(figure 12.14).** These macroscopic structures produce reproductive spores. Some large mushrooms are edible.

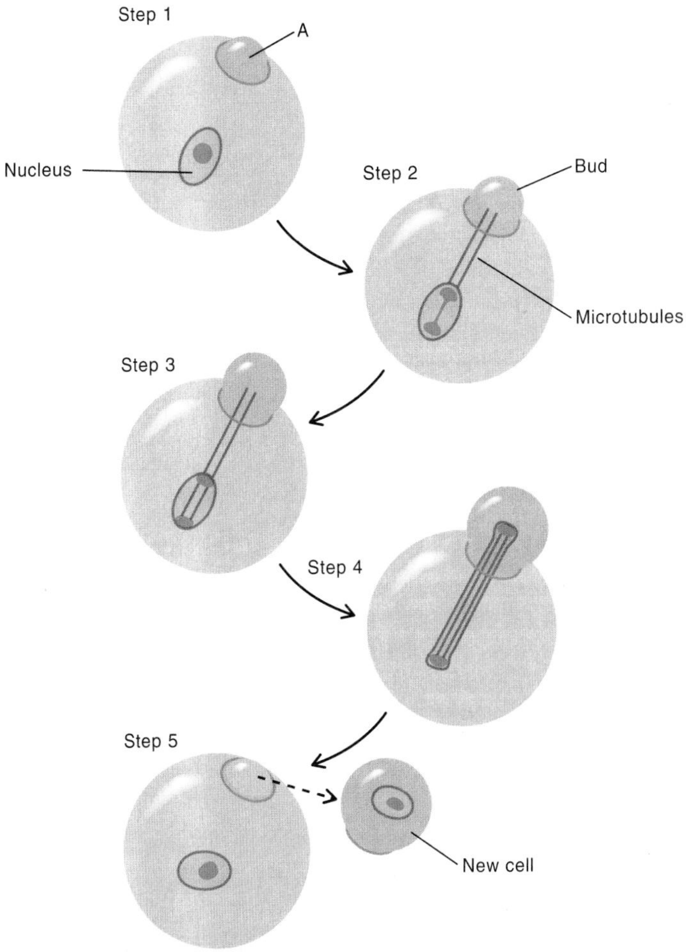

FIGURE 12.11 Budding in Yeast **(1)** Cell wall softens at point A, allowing the cytoplasm to bulge out. **(2, 3)** Nucleus divides by mitosis, and **(4)** one of the nuclei migrates into the bud. **(5)** Cell wall grows together and the bud breaks off, forming a new cell.

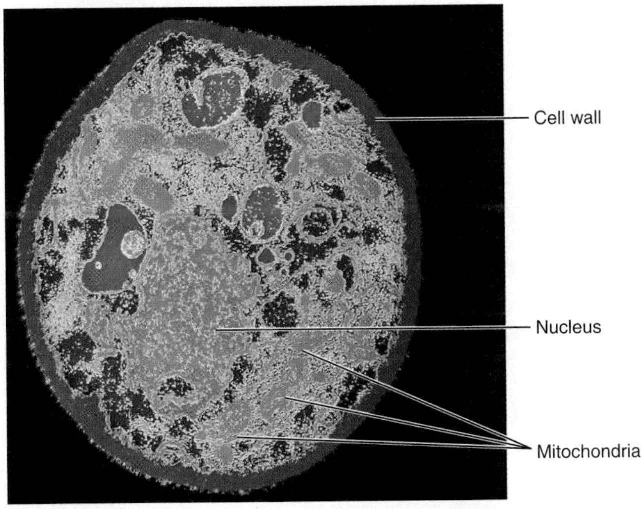

FIGURE 12.10 Morphology of a Yeast Cell As Seen with an Electron Microscope

Hyphae are well adapted to absorb nutrients. They are narrow and threadlike. With their high surface-to-volume ratio, they can absorb large amounts of nutrients. Hyphae release enzymes that break down the material into readily absorbed smaller organic compounds. In addition, these enzymes act to repel the growth of other hyphae near each other. As a result, hyphae spread throughout the food source, ensuring that each hypha will have access to adequate nutrients.

Parasitic fungi have specialized hyphae called **haustoria,** which can penetrate animal or plant cell walls to gain nutrients. Saprophytic fungi sometimes have specialized hyphae called **rhizoids,** which anchor them to the substrate.

Dimorphic Fungi

Dimorphic fungi are capable of growing either as yeastlike cells or as mycelia, depending on the environmental conditions. Many of the fungi that cause disease in humans are dimorphic. Certain fungi such as *Coccidioides immitis* grow in the soil as molds. When their spores, which are readily carried in the air, are inhaled into the warm, moist environment of the lungs, they develop into the yeast form of the organism and cause disease.

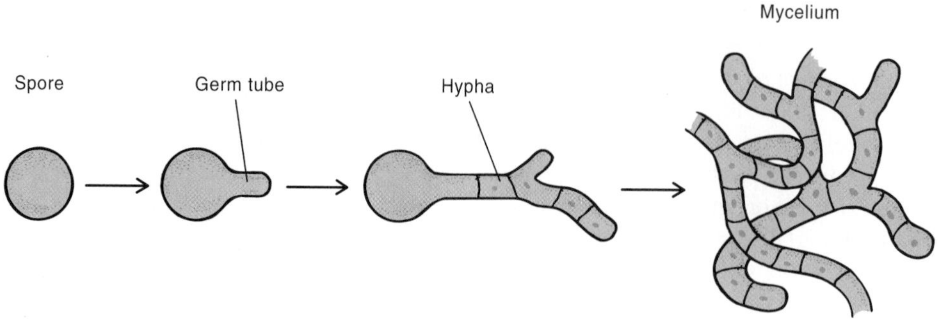

FIGURE 12.12 Formation of Hyphae and Mycelium Spores of fungi germinate to form a projection from the side of the cell called a germ tube, which elongates to form hyphae. As the hyphae continue to grow, they form a tangled mass called a mycelium.

Fungal Habitats

Fungi are found in virtually every habitat on the earth where organic materials exist. Whereas algae and protozoa grow primarily in aquatic environments, the fungi are mainly terrestrial organisms. Some species occur only on a particular strain of one genus of plants, whereas others are extremely versatile in what they can attack and use as a source of carbon and energy. Materials such as leather, cork, hair, wax, ink, jet fuel, and even some synthetic plastics like the polyvinyls can be attacked by fungi. Some species can grow in concentrations of salts, sugars, or acids strong enough to kill most bacteria. Thus, fungi are often responsible for spoiling pickles, fruit preserves, and other foods. Some fungi are resistant to pasteurization and others can grow at temperatures below the freezing point of water, rotting bulbs and destroying grass in frozen ground. Fungi are found in the thermal pools at Yellowstone National Park, in volcanic craters, and in lakes with very high salt content, such as the Great Salt Lake and the Dead Sea. ■ food spoilage, p. 805

Fungal reproductive cells, or spores, are found throughout the earth. They also occur in tremendous numbers in the air near the earth's surface as well as at altitudes of more than 7 miles. Although not as resistant as bacterial endospores, fungal spores are generally resistant to the ultraviolet rays of sunlight. Sunlight will, however, sometimes kill fungal vegetative cells. Fungal spores are a major cause of asthma. ■ asthma, p. 436

Growth Requirements of Fungi

Most fungi prefer a slightly moist environment with a relative humidity of 70% or more, and various species can grow at temperatures ranging from −6°C to 50°C. The optimal temperature for the majority of fungi is in the range of 20°C to 35°C.

The pH at which different fungi can grow varies widely, ranging from as low as 2.2 to as high as 9.6, but fungi usually grow well at an acid pH of 5.0 or lower. This explains why fungi grow well on fruits and many vegetables that tend to be acidic.

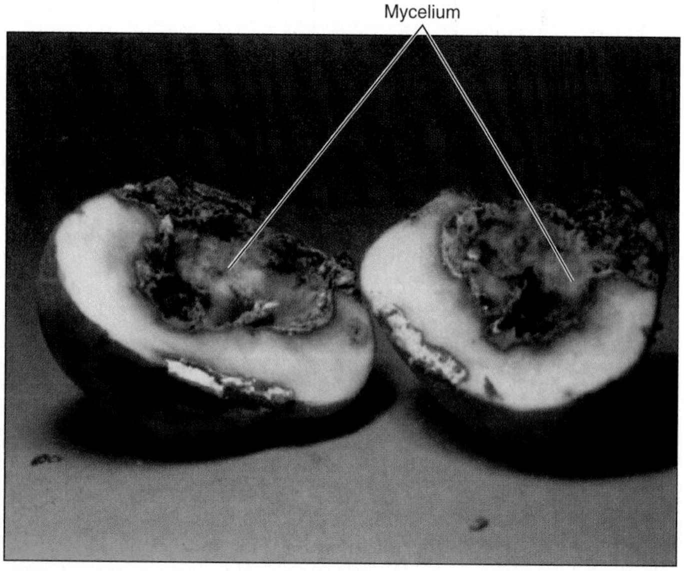

(a)

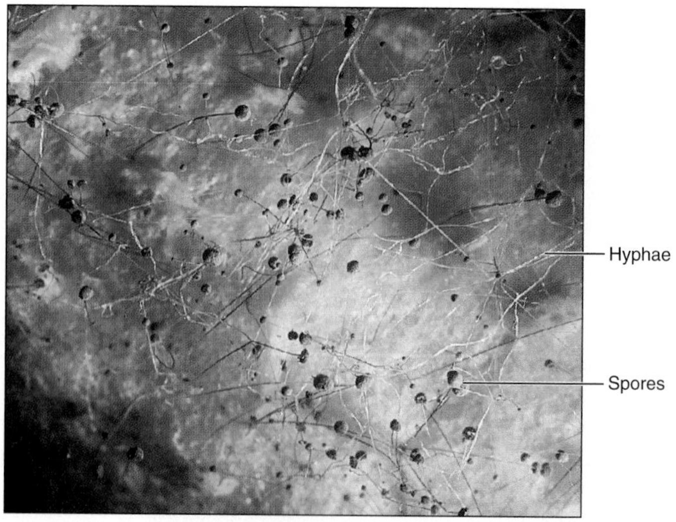

(b)

FIGURE 12.13 Examples of a Mycelium on Various Foods **(a)** The cottony white mass inside the potato is an example of a mycelium. **(b)** Magnified hyphae of *Rhizopus stolonifer*, black bread mold, showing the hyphae and the spores.

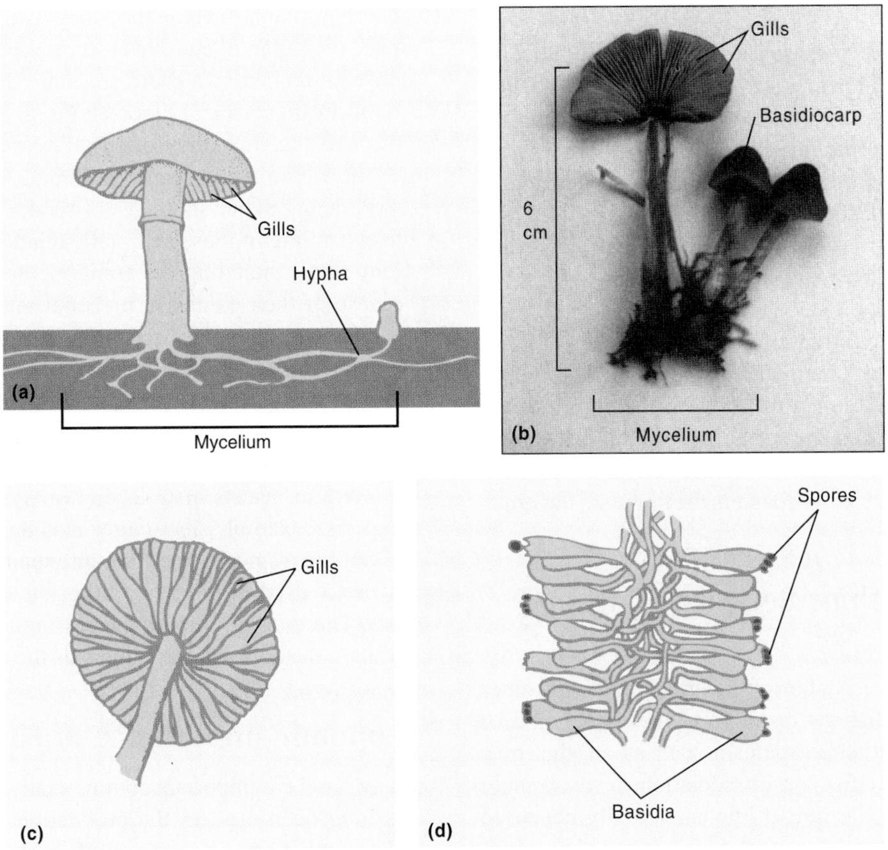

FIGURE 12.14 A Meadow Mushroom, *Agaricus campestri* **(a)** A drawing shows the extensive underground mycelium with a fruiting body emerging as a small button. **(b)** A photograph of *Lepiota rachodes,* a similar mushroom, showing the fruiting bodies and gills. **(c)** The underside of the cap is composed of radiating gills. **(d)** Magnified view of the surface of the gill showing a mass of basidia, bearing spores.

As heterotrophs, fungi secrete a wide variety of enzymes that degrade organic materials, especially complex carbohydrates, into small molecules that can be readily absorbed. Most fungi are aerobic, but some of the yeasts are facultative anaerobes and carry out alcoholic fermentation. Facultatively anaerobic fungi live in the intestines of certain species of fish and help degrade algae. Some fungi living in the rumen of cows and sheep are known to be obligately anaerobic. They are important in the digestion of the plant material that these animals ingest.

Fungal Disease in Humans

Fungi cause disease in humans in one of four ways. First, a person may develop an allergic reaction to fungal spores or vegetative cells. Second, a person may react to the toxins produced by fungi. Third, the fungi may actually grow on or in the human body, causing disease or **mycoses.** Fourth, fungi can destroy the human food supply, causing starvation and death.

Allergic Reactions in Humans

Medical mycologists study fungi that affect humans, including fungi that cause allergic reactions. Allergic diseases such as hay fever and asthma can result from inhaling fungi or their spores if exposed humans have become sensitized. Sometimes, severe, long-term allergic lung disease results from these allergic reactions. ■ hay fever, p. 435 ■ asthma, p. 436

Effect of Fungal Toxins

For their hallucinogenic properties, certain mushrooms have long been used as part of religious ceremonies in some cultures. The lethal effects of many mushrooms have also been known for centuries. The poisonous effects of a rye smut called **ergot** were known during the Middle Ages, but only recently has the active chemical been purified from this fungus to yield the drug ergotamine, which is now used to control uterine bleeding, relieve migraine headaches, and assist in childbirth.

Some fungi produce toxins that are carcinogenic. The most thoroughly studied of these carcinogenic toxins, produced by species of *Aspergillus,* are called **aflatoxins.** Ingestion of aflatoxins in moldy foods, such as grains and peanuts, has been implicated in the development of liver cancer (hepatoma) and thyroid cancer in hatchery fish. Governmental agencies monitor levels of aflatoxins in foods such as peanuts, and if a certain level is exceeded, the food cannot be sold. ■ aflatoxin, p. 805

Mycoses

Fungal diseases are called **mycoses.** The names of the individual diseases often begin with the names of the causative fungi. Thus, **histoplasmosis,** a disease seen worldwide, is a mycosis caused by the fungus *Histoplasma capsulatum.* Similarly, **coccidioidomycosis** is a mycosis caused by *Coccidioides immitis,* a fungus unique to certain arid regions of the Western Hemisphere. Diseases caused by the yeast *Candida albicans* are called **candidiasis** and are among the most common mycoses. ■ histoplasmosis, p. 603 ■ coccidioidomycosis, p. 602 ■ candidiasis, p. 657

Infections can also be referred to by the parts of the body that they affect. **Superficial mycoses** affect only the hair, skin, or nails. **Intermediate mycoses** are limited to the respiratory tract or the skin and subcutaneous tissues. **Systemic mycoses** affect tissues deep within the body. Some diseases caused by fungi are given in **table 12.4** and are discussed in the chapters dealing with the organ systems that are affected.

Symbiotic Relationships Between Fungi and Other Organisms

Fungi form several types of symbiotic relationships with other organisms. For example, lichens result from the association of a fungus with a photosynthetic organism such as an alga or a cyanobacterium **(figure 12.15).** These associations are extremely close and, in some cases, the fungal hyphae actually penetrate the cell wall of the photosynthetic partner. The fungus provides the protection and growing platform for the pair. In addition, the fungus absorbs water and minerals for the association. The photosynthetic member supplies the fungus with organic nutrients. It is possible to grow each partner of the lichen association separately. Usually the algal partner is able to grow well when separated, but the fungal partner does not. Because of this association, lichens can grow in extreme ecosystems where neither could survive on its own. Lichens are often a good indicator of air quality since they are very sensitive to sulfur dioxide, ozone, and toxic metals. You will not find very many lichens in cities with air pollution.

Mycorrhizae, fungal symbioses of particular importance, are formed by the intimate association between fungi and the roots of certain plants such as the Douglas fir. It is estimated that 80% of the vascular plants have some type of mycorrhizal association with their roots. There are more than 5,000 species of fungi that form mycorrhizal associations. By increasing the absorptive power of the root, they often allow their plant partners to grow in soils where these plants could not otherwise survive. With the world facing major shortages of food and forest products, a better understanding of these symbiotic relationships is urgently needed. Many trees, including the conifers, are able to live in sandy soil because of their extensive mycelial mycorrhizas. In Puerto Rico, for example, the pine tree industry almost perished before the proper fungi were introduced to form mycorrhizal relationships with the trees. Now the industry is flourishing. Similarly, orchids cannot grow without mycorrhizal association of a fungus that helps provide nutrients to the young plant. ■ mycorrhizae, p. 772

Certain insects also depend on symbiotic relationships with fungi. For example, leaf cutter ants are estimated to bring about 15% of the tropical vegetation into their nests to use for food. The leaves are used as food by a fungus that the ants cultivate in their nests. The fungus removes the poison from the leaves of the plant, and then the ants use the fungus as their food source.

Economic Importance of Fungi

Many fungi are important commercially. The yeast *Saccharomyces* has long been used in the production of wine, beer, and bread. Other fungal species are useful in making the large variety of cheeses that are found throughout the world. Penicillin, griseofulvin, and other antimicrobial medicines are synthesized by fungi.

Ironically, fungi are also among the greatest spoilers of food products, and large amounts of food are thrown away each year because they have been made inedible by species of *Penicillium, Rhizopus,* and others.

Fungi also cause many diseases of plants. Dutch elm disease caused by *Ceratocystis ulmi* is transmitted by beetles. It has destroyed the American elm trees that once shaded the streets in many cities. The wheat rust (*Puccinia graminis*) destroys tons of wheat yearly. Rust-resistant varieties have been bred to reduce the losses, but mutations in the rusts have made these advantages short-lived.

TABLE 12.4 Some Medically Important Fungal Diseases

Disease	Causative Agent	Page for More Information
Candidial skin infection	*Candida albicans*	p. 545
Coccidioidomycosis	*Coccidioides immitis*	p. 602
Cryptococcal meningoencephalitis	*Cryptococcus neoformans*	p. 700
Histoplasmosis	*Histoplasma capsulatum*	p. 603
Pneumocytosis	*Pneumocystis carinii*	p. 749
Sporotrichosis	*Sporothrix schenckii*	p. 568
Vulvovaginal candidiasis	*Candida albicans*	p. 657

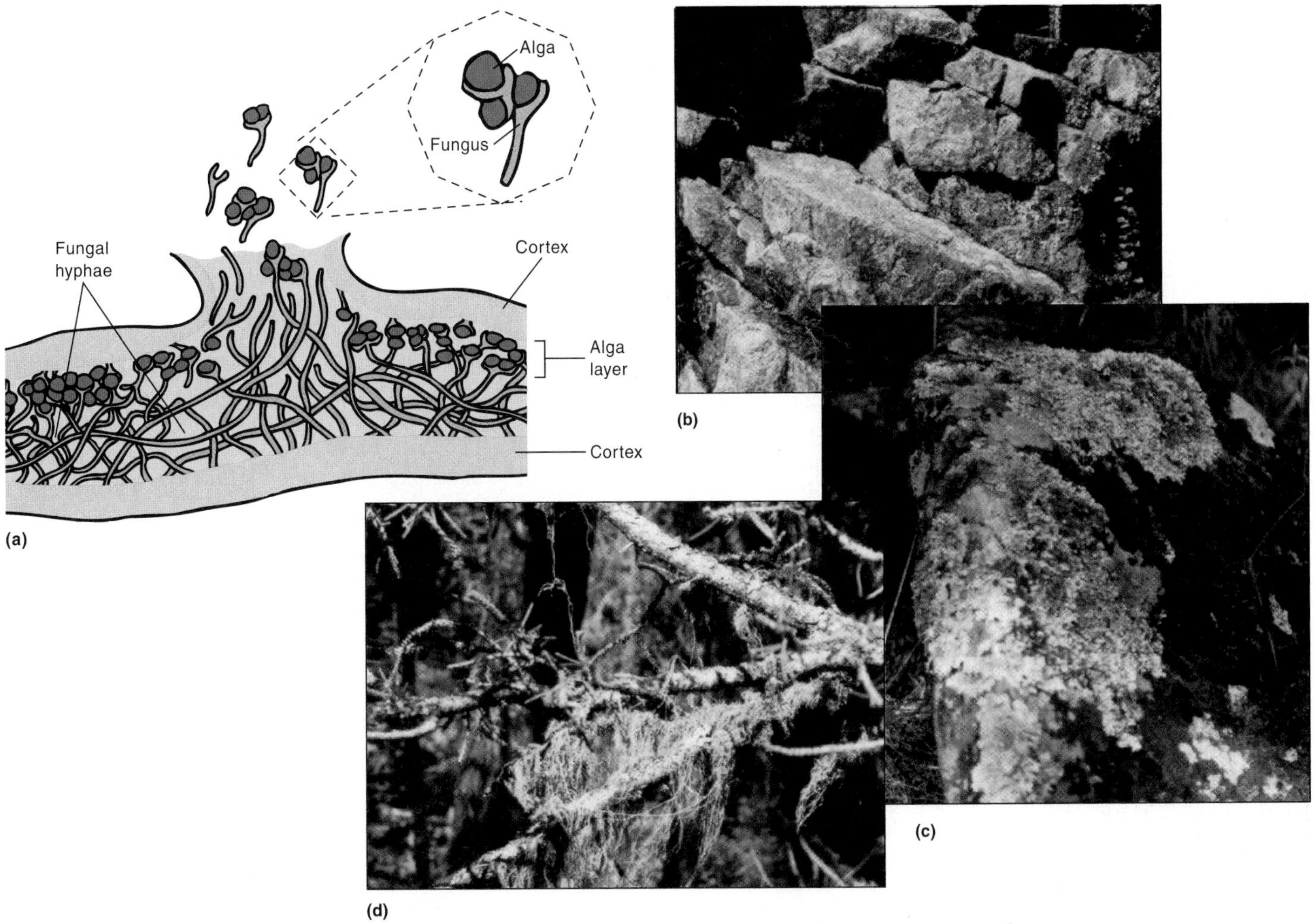

FIGURE 12.15 Lichens (a) Diagram of a lichen, consisting of cells of a phototroph, either an alga or a cyanobacterium, entwined within the hyphae of the fungal partner. **(b–d)** Photographs of lichens on rocks and trees.

Fungi have been very useful tools for genetic and biochemical studies. *Neurospora crassa,* a common mold, has been widely used for investigating biochemical reactions. *Aspergillus nidulans* is a model for genetic studies. More recently, yeasts have been genetically engineered to produce human insulin and the human growth hormone somatostatin, as well as a vaccine against hepatitis B. ■ **biotechnology, p. 219**

MICROCHECK 12.3

True fungi are organisms that have chitin in their cell walls and reproduce by both asexual and sexual methods. They are saprophytes and do not have motile cells during any stage in their life cycle. They are a source of food as well as a source of disease in plants and animals including humans.

- ✓ What are the primary characteristics that distinguish true fungi from other eukaryotic organisms?
- ✓ What are some ways that fungi cause disease in humans?
- ✓ What kind of symbiotic relationships do fungi form with other organisms? How are these relationships beneficial to each partner?
- ✓ How would the narrow, threadlike structure of hyphae indicate that they have a high surface-to-volume ratio?

12.4 Slime Molds and Water Molds

Focus Points

- Explain how slime molds and water molds are examples of convergent evolution.
- Explain why slime molds and water molds were once considered fungi.

The slime molds and water molds used to be considered types of fungus. They are, however, completely unrelated to the true fungi and are good examples of **convergent evolution.** Convergent evolution occurs when two organisms develop similar characteristics because of adaptations to similar environments and yet are not related on a molecular level (see figure 12.1—blue).

Acellular and Cellular Slime Molds

There are two groups of slime molds, the **acellular slime molds** and the **cellular slime molds.** The slime molds are terrestrial organisms living on soil, leaf litter, or the surfaces of decaying leaves or wood. They are non-motile, and reproduction depends on the formation of spores that can dispersed. Acellular slime molds are widespread and readily visible in their natural environment. Following sporulation and germination of the spores, ameboid cells fuse to form a myxameba. The nucleus of this ameba divides repeatedly, forming a multinucleated stage called a **plasmodium.** The plasmodium oozes like slime over the surface of decaying wood and leaves. As it moves, it ingests microorganisms, spores of other fungi, and any other organic material with which it comes in contact. Eventually the plasmodium is stimulated to form a spore-bearing fruiting body, and the process begins again **(figure 12.16a).**

The cellular slime mold has a vegetative form composed of single, ameba-like cells. When cellular slime molds run out of food, the single cells congregate into a mass of cells called a slug that then forms a fruiting body and spores. These fruiting bodies and spores look very much like fungal fruiting bodies and spores (figure 12.16b).

Slime molds are important links in the food chain in the soil. They ingest bacteria, algae, and other organisms and, in turn, serve as food for larger predators. Slime molds have been valuable as unique models for studying cellular differentiation during their aggregation and formation of their fruiting bodies.

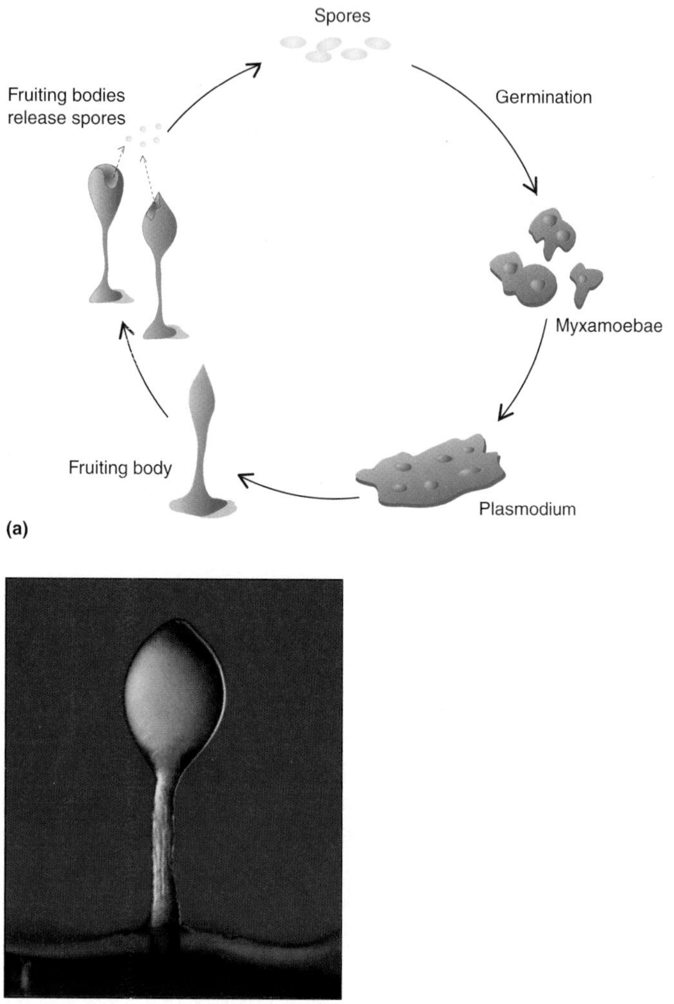

FIGURE 12.16 Slime Molds **(a)** Life cycle of an acellular slime mold. **(b)** Fruiting body of a cellular slime mold.

Oomycetes (Water Molds)

The **oomycetes,** or **water molds,** are members of a group of organisms known as **heterokonts.** The oomycetes do not have chlorophyll, whereas other heterokonts, which include the grass green algae, diatoms, and brown algae, have chlorophyll and other photosynthetic pigments. Oomycetes were once considered fungi because they look like fungi. They form masses of white threads on decaying material. They have flagellated reproductive cells known as **zoospores.** Oomycetes cause some serious diseases of food crops. The late blight of potato (*Phytophthora infestans*) and downy mildew of grapes are included in this group. The late blight of potato was the cause of the potato famine in Ireland in the 1840s that sent waves of immigrants to the United States (see **A Glimpse of History**).

MICROCHECK 12.4

There are three other types of fungilike organisms, the acellular slime molds, the cellular slime molds, and the water molds. They are examples of convergent evolution.

- ✓ Why were the slime molds and water molds once considered to be fungi?
- ✓ When cellular slime molds run out of food, they form a fruiting body. What would be the advantage of this reproductive strategy?

12.5

Multicellular Parasites: Arthropods and Helminths

Focus Points

- Explain the differences between arthropods and helminths.
- Explain how each group causes disease in humans.

A number of disease-causing multicellular organisms are also studied using the same microscopic and immunological techniques that are used to study microorganisms and viruses. As a result, they are included here. Most of the medically important multicellular parasites fall into one of two groups of invertebrates (see figure 12.1—brown): **arthropods** and **helminths.** The arthropods are more highly advanced on the evolutionary scale and include the insects, ticks, lice, and mites. Their main medical importance is that they serve as **vectors** that may transmit microorganisms and viruses to humans. The helminths, which include the **nematodes** (roundworms), **cestodes** (tapeworms), and the **trematodes** (flukes), are more primitive animals. In only a few instances do they transmit microbial infections to their host animal. Instead, they cause disease by invading the host's tissues or robbing it of nutrients.

Most multicellular parasites have been well controlled in the industrialized nations, but they still cause death and misery to many millions in the economically underdeveloped areas of the world. Our need to know about these problems has come about because more people are traveling farther, more people are moving from one place to another, and more goods are being exchanged worldwide. A clear example of this occurred in New York City in the summer of 1999 when West Nile fever was contracted by a number of people. At least 61 persons suffered serious disease and seven people died. A significant number of crows died at the same time and were found to be carrying the disease. In addition to birds and people, horses, cats, and dogs were also found to carry the virus. It is not clear how the virus arrived in New York City, but it perhaps could have been carried by a traveler from Africa, West Asia, or the Middle East, where it is commonly found. It could possibly have been brought by an imported bird from the same areas. Worldwide travel makes us more vulnerable to diseases from other parts of the world. ■ West Nile fever, p. 693

In addition, worldwide climatic conditions are changing and bringing increases in certain insect populations to areas that were previously free of them. As a result, more cases of multi-cellular parasitic infections are being seen by physicians in the United States than previously.

Arthropods

The arthropods include insects, ticks, fleas, and mites. Arthropods act as vectors for transmitting diseases. In some instances, an arthropod such as a fly simply picks up a pathogen on its feet from some contaminated material such as feces and then lands on food that is then eaten by humans, thus transmitting the pathogen. In this case, the fly acts as a **mechanical vector.** In other cases, such as with *Plasmodium* sp., the cause of malaria, the vector, a mosquito, is a host for the organism before it transfers that organism to a human through a bite on the skin. In this case, the vector acts as an essential part of the life cycle of the organism and is known as a **biological vector.** The pathogen actually multiplies in number within the vector. ■ mechanical vector, p. 480 ■ biological vector, p. 480

Examples of some important arthropods, the agents they transmit, and the resulting diseases are shown in **table 12.5.**

Mosquitoes

The female mosquito needs the blood of a warm-blooded animal for the proper development of her eggs. To get this, she needs to bite such an animal. The mosquito can take in as much as twice its body weight in blood, thus giving it a relatively good chance of picking up infectious agents such as malarial parasites circulating within the host's capillaries. The anatomy of a mosquito is particularly adapted to transmit disease **(figure 12.17).** The mouthparts of the female mosquito consist of sharp stylets that are forced through the host's skin to the subcutaneous capillaries. One of these needlelike stylets is hollow, and the mosquito's saliva is pumped through it. The saliva increases blood flow and prevents clotting as the victim's blood is sucked into a tube formed by the other mouthparts of the insect. The saliva can also cause allergic reactions (the itch of a mosquito bite). After the mosquito has taken more than one blood meal, she can transmit disease from one animal to the next. Viruses found in the blood of the first animal are then transmitted to the next, and so on.

Mosquitoes in an area of arthropod-borne disease can be trapped and identified microscopically, and the blood they have ingested can be tested to see on which kinds of animals the different species are feeding. Precise identification of species and subspecies of these genera is important because different species of mosquitoes differ greatly in their breeding areas, time of feeding, and choice of host. Identification depends largely on microscopic examination of antennae, wings, claws, mating apparatus, and other features. Correct identification is often essential in designing specific control measures. ■ epidemiology, p. 475

Fleas

Fleas are wingless insects that depend on powerful hind legs to jump from place to place. Points of importance in identifying fleas include the spines (combs) about the head and thorax, the muscular pharynx, the long esophagus, and the spiny valve composed of rows of teethlike cells. Fleas are generally more of a nuisance than a health hazard, but they can transmit the bacterium *Yersinia pestis,* which causes plague, and a rickettsial disease, murine typhus, to humans. Larval fleas have a chewing type of mouth for feeding on organic matter. They ingest eggs of the common dog and cat tapeworm, *Dipylidium caninum,* serving as its intermediate host. Children acquire this tapeworm when they accidentally swallow fleas. Fleas can live in vacant buildings in a dormant stage for

TABLE 12.5 Some Arthropods That Transmit Infectious Agents

Arthropod	Infectious Agent	Disease and Characteristic Features	Page for More Information
Insects			
Mosquito (*Anopheles* species)	*Plasmodium* species	Malaria—chills, bouts of recurring fever	p. 725
Mosquito (*Culex* species)	Togavirus	Equine encephalitis—fever, nausea, convulsions, coma	p. 693
Mosquito (*Aedes aegypti*)	Flavivirus	Yellow fever—fever, vomiting, jaundice, bleeding	p. 724
Flea (*Xenopsylla cheopis*)	*Yersinia pestis*	Plague—fever, headache, confusion, enlarged lymph nodes, skin hemorrhage	p. 717
Louse (*Pediculus humanus*)	*Rickettsia prowazekii*	Typhus—fever, hemorrhage, rash, confusion	p. 521
Arachnids			
Tick (*Dermacentor* species)	*Rickettsia rickettsii*	Rocky Mountain spotted fever—fever, hemorrhagic rash, confusion	p. 529
Tick (*Ixodes* species)	*Borrelia burgdorferi*	Lyme disease—fever, rash, joint pain, nervous system impairment	p. 532

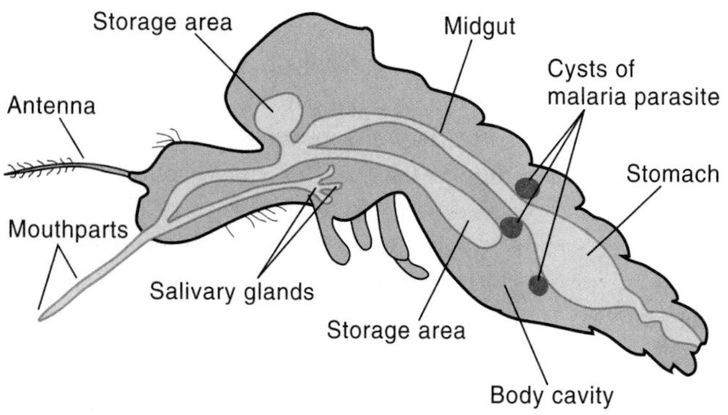

FIGURE 12.17 Internal Anatomy of a Mosquito Note the storage areas that allow ingestion of large amounts of blood and the salivary glands that discharge pathogens into the host.

many months. When the building becomes inhabited, the fleas quickly mature and hungrily greet the new hosts. ■ plague, p. 717

Lice

Like fleas, lice are small, wingless insects that prey on warm-blooded animals by piercing their skin and sucking blood. The legs and claws of lice, however, are adapted for holding onto body surfaces and clothing rather than for jumping. Human lice generally survive only a few days away from their hosts.

Pediculus humanus, the most notorious of the lice, is 1 to 4 mm long, with a characteristically small head and thorax, and a large abdomen **(figure 12.18).** This louse has a membrane-like lip with tiny teeth that anchor it firmly to the skin of the host. Within the floor of the mouth is a piercing apparatus somewhat similar to that of fleas and mosquitoes. *Pediculus humanus* has only one host—humans—but easily spreads from one person to another by direct contact or by contact with personal items, especially in areas of crowding and poor sanitation.

There are two subspecies, popularly termed head lice and body lice. Body lice can transmit trench fever, which is caused by the bacterium *Bartonella quintana;* epidemic typhus, which is caused by the bacterium *Rickettsia prowazekii;* and relapsing fever, caused by the bacterium *Borrelia recurrentis.* Trench fever occurs episodically among severe alcoholics and the homeless of large American and European cities.

The crab louse, *Phthirus pubis,* is commonly transmitted among young adults during sexual intercourse. It is not a vector of infectious disease, but it can cause an unpleasant itch.

Ticks

Ticks are arachnids. Arachnids differ from insects in their lack of wings and antennae, and their thorax and abdomen are fused together. Although like insects the immature ticks have three pairs of legs, the adults have four pairs. *Dermacentor andersoni,* the wood tick, is the vector for Rocky Mountain spotted fever caused by the bacterium *Rickettsia rickettsii.* Another tick, *Ixodes scapularis,* transmits with its saliva *Borrelia burgdorferi,* the spirochete that causes Lyme disease. In addition, the saliva of several genera of ticks can produce a profound paralysis, especially in children on whom the tick feeds for several days. Paralyzed humans and animals usually recover rapidly following removal of the tick. ■ Rocky Mountain spotted fever, p. 529 ■ Lyme disease, p. 532

Mites

Mites, like ticks, are arachnids. They are generally tiny, fast moving, and live on the outer surfaces of animals and plants. *Demodex folliculorum* and *D. brevis* are elongated microscopic mites that live in the hair follicles or oil-producing glands usually of the face, typically without producing symptoms. Other species of mites cause human disease.

The disease scabies, caused by a mite, *Sarcoptes scabiei,* is characterized by an itchy rash most prominent between the fingers, under the breasts, and in the genital area. Scabies is easily transmitted by personal contact, and the disease is commonly acquired during sexual intercourse. The female mites burrow into the outer layers of epidermis **(figure 12.19)** feeding and laying eggs over a lifetime of about 1 month. Allergy to the mites is largely responsible for the itchy rash. The diagnosis can only be made by demonstrating the mites, since scabies mimics other skin diseases. Treatment of scabies is easily accomplished with medication applied to the skin. *Sarcoptes scabiei* is not known to transmit infectious agents.

Mites of domestic animals and birds can cause an itchy rash in humans, as can mites sometimes present in hay, grain, cheese, or dried fruits. The dust mites that often live in large numbers in bedrooms can sometimes cause asthma when the mites and their excreta are inhaled.

The mites of rodents can transmit rickettsial diseases to humans. Rickettsial pox, caused by *Rickettsia akari* transmitted by mouse mites, is a mild disease characterized by fever and rash. Epidemics occur periodically in cities of the eastern United States. Serious rickettsial diseases of other parts of the world such as scrub typhus are transmitted by rodent mites.

Helminths

In addition to the arthropods that can lead to disease in humans, the other group of multicellular animals that causes human disease are the **helminths.** In humans, the helminths that cause disease generally belong to one of three classes: the **nematodes,** or roundworms; the **cestodes,** or the tapeworms; and the **trematodes,** or the flukes.

These multicellular parasites have been controlled in the developed nations, but they continue to kill many millions in underdevel-

FIGURE 12.18 ***Pediculus humanus*** A body louse, which is the vector for *Rickettsia prowazekii,* the cause of typhus.

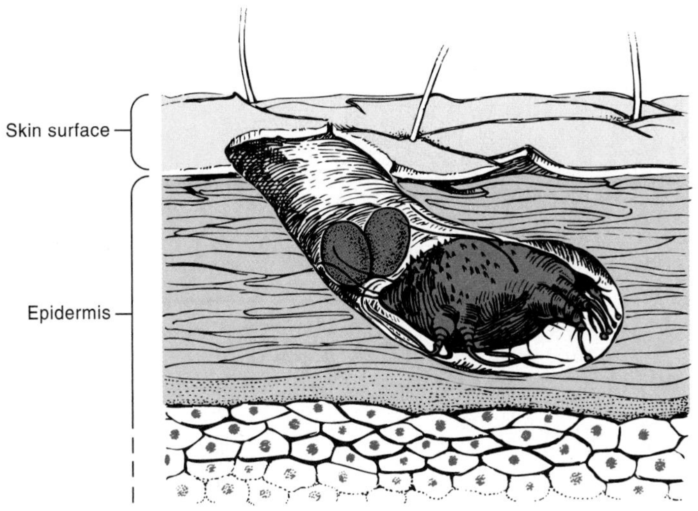

FIGURE 12.19 ***Sarcoptes scabiei*** **(Scabies Mite)** The female burrows into outer skin layers to lay her eggs, causing an intensely itchy rash.

oped parts of the world. Helminths enter the body in a number of ways. They may be eaten in contaminated food, be passed through insect bites, or directly penetrate the skin. They cause disease by invading the host tissues or robbing the host of nutrients. Some helminths have complex life cycles, involving one or more intermediate hosts where early stages of development occur, and a definitive host where the sexually mature forms occur.

Nematodes or Roundworms

The nematodes or roundworms have a cylindrical tapered body with a tubular digestive tract that extends from the mouth to the anus. There are both male and female nematodes. Nematodes include a large number of species. Many nematodes are free-living in soil and water. Others are parasites of human and other animals and plants and produce serious disease.

The nematodes that cause disease can be divided into two groups—the ones that inhabit the gastrointestinal tract of the host, and the ones that are found in the blood and other tissues of the host. Generally, diagnosis of worm infestation depends on microscopic identification of the worms or their ova (eggs), or on blood tests for antibody to the worms. **Table 12.6** summarizes the major diseases caused by these parasites.

Cestodes or Tapeworms

Cestodes or tapeworms have flat, ribbon-shaped bodies that are segmented. The head (scolex) of the tapeworm has suckers for attachment and sometimes has hooks. Directly behind the head is a region that produces the reproductive segments (proglottids). Each segment has both male and female sex organs. The tapeworm does not have a digestive system but rather absorbs nutrients directly. Tapeworms are often associated with beef, lamb, pork, and fish. Transmission of these organisms to humans often occurs when the flesh of these animals is eaten either uncooked or undercooked **(figure 12.20).** Some tapeworms are transmitted to humans from ingesting fleas infected with dog or cat tapeworms. Table 12.6 lists specific tapeworm diseases.

Trematodes or Flukes

Trematodes or flukes are bilaterally symmetrical, flat, and leaf-shaped. They have suckers that hold the organism in place as well as suck fluids from the host. Most species are hermaphroditic (have both sex organs in the same worm). Most trematodes have a complicated life cycle, which may include one or more intermediary hosts. Usually,

TABLE 12.6 Nematodes, Cestodes, and Trematodes

Infectious Agents	Disease	Disease Characteristics
Nematodes (roundworms)		
Pinworms (*Enterobius vermicularis*)	Enterobiasis	Anal itching, restlessness, irritability, nervousness, poor sleep
Whipworm (*Trichuris trichiura*)	Trichuriasis	Abdominal pain, bloody stools, weight loss
Hookworm (*Necator americanus*) and (*Ancylostoma duodenale*)	Hookworm disease	Anemia, weakness, fatigue, physical and mental retardation in children
Threadworm (*Strongyloides stercoralis*)	Strongyloidiasis	Skin rash at site of penetration, cough, abdominal pains, weight loss
Ascaria (*Ascaris lumbricoides*)	Ascariasis	Abdominal pain, live worms vomited or passed in stools
Trichinella (*Trichinella spiralis*)	Trichinosis	Fever, swelling of upper eyelids, muscle soreness
Filaria (*Wuchereria bancrofti*) (*Brugia malayi*)	Filariasis	Fever, swelling of lymph glands, genitals, and extremities
Cestodes (tapeworms)		
Fish tapeworm (*Diphyllobothrium latum*)	Tapeworm disease	Few or no symptoms, sometimes anemia
Beef tapeworm (*Taenia saginata*)	Tapeworm disease	Few or no symptoms, sometimes anemia
Pork tapeworm (*Taenia solium*)	Cysticercosis	Variable symptoms depending on location and number of cysticerci in the body
Trematodes (flukes)		
Cercaria (*Schistosoma mansoni*)	Schistosomiasis	Liver damage, malnutrition, weakness, and accumulation of fluid in the abdominal cavity
Cercaria of birds and other animals	Swimmer's itch	Inflammation of the skin, itching

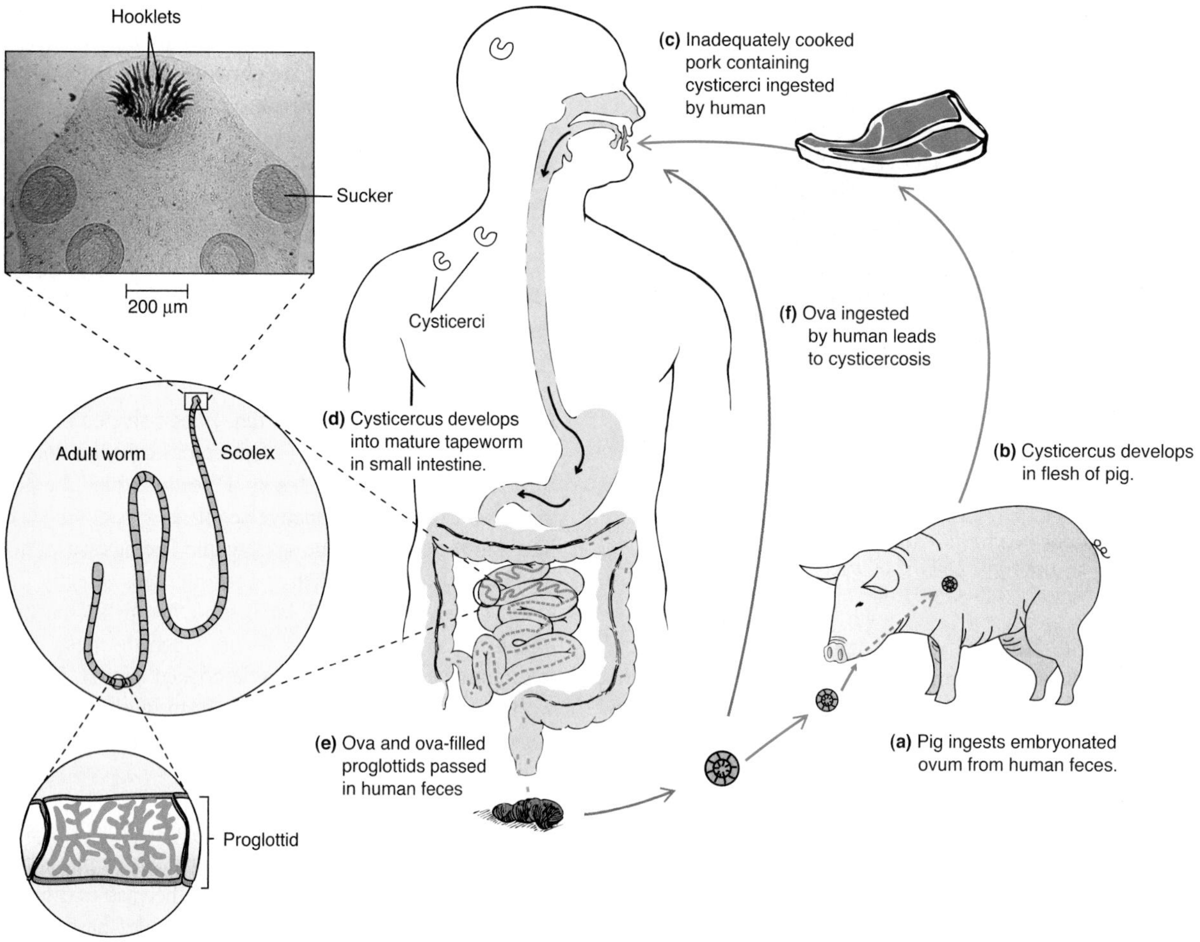

FIGURE 12.20 (a–e) Life Cycle of the Pork Tapeworm, *Taenia solium,* Acquired by Eating Inadequately Cooked Pork If worm ova hatch in the intestine, larval forms called cysticerci can develop throughout the person's tissues. A cysticercus in the brain can cause epilepsy.

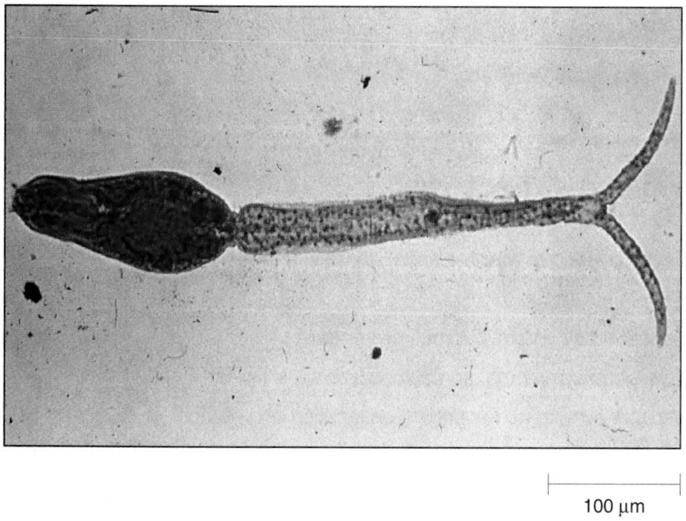

FIGURE 12.21 *Schistosoma mansoni* Cercaria The form that penetrates the skin and initiates the infection. Water bird schistosomes may penetrate the skin of swimmers and then die, causing swimmers itch.

the worms begin with a larval form developing within the egg. These larvae escape into the environment, where they are taken up by one or more intermediate hosts such as a snail. Eventually, the last stage is a tail-bearing larva known as a **cercaria,** which is released from the snail and is ready to attach to the susceptible host **(figure 12.21).** For example, if a human is wading in water and the cercaria of *Schistosoma mansoni* have been discharged into that water, the cercaria can penetrate the skin and work its way through the circulation to the liver and intestine, where it matures and lays eggs.

MICROCHECK 12.5

Arthropods such as mosquitoes, fleas, lice, and ticks act primarily as vectors for the spread of disease. On the other hand, the helminths, which include the roundworms, tapeworms, and flukes, cause serious disease in humans.

- ✓ How are arthropods able to spread disease in humans?
- ✓ What are the major differences among nematodes, cestodes, and trematodes?
- ✓ How would increased travel lead to increased spread of multicellular parasites?

FUTURE CHALLENGES

Fighting Malaria with Effective Vaccines and Inexpensive Drugs

It is estimated that each year a million people die from malaria, of which about 700,000 are children. The disease is found in about 90 countries of the world, and drug-resistant strains are spreading rapidly. More people are dying today from malaria than they did 30 years ago. Recently, more money from both the drug companies and foundations has been put into efforts to find vaccines and new drugs.

The newspapers in recent times have highlighted a push by world health organizations to find a way to control the scourge of malaria. A front page headline in the October 15, 2004, *New York Times* read "Malaria Vaccine Proves Effective." A vaccine tested in Mozambique showed that it could protect children from catching the disease 30% of the time and prevent the disease from becoming life-threatening 58% of the time. Although the rates of prevention of the disease are not high, nonetheless, this is an important step. Children are the most vulnerable to being infected by malaria and many die before age five as a result of the disease. Adults develop immunity to malarial infection and are able to tolerate the ravages of this disease.

Another headline in the Science section of the *New York Times* of January 25, 2005, reads "Millions of Lives on the Line in Malaria Battle." This article announced a pledge by the Bill and Melinda Gates Foundation of $43 million to the efforts of a California biochemist who is working on genetically re-engineering a bacterium to grow a malaria drug that usually grows in plants in Asia. By doing so it is expected that the cost of manufacturing this important drug will be greatly reduced, to allow expanded use in the developing countries.

Finding a cure and/or an effective vaccine for malaria is one of the major challenges for the scientists of the world.

SUMMARY

The Eukaryotic Members of the Microbial World (Figure 12.1)

Cell structure in the ***Eucarya*** is different from that seen in the *Bacteria* or the *Archaea.*

Algae, fungi, and *protozoa* are not accurate classification terms when the rRNA sequences of these organisms are considered. (Figure 12.1)

12.1 Algae

Algae are a diverse group of photosynthetic organisms that contain chlorophyll *a.*

Classification of Algae (Table 12.1, Figure 12.1)

Classification of algae is based on their major photosynthetic pigments.

Organisms are placed on the phylogenetic tree according to rRNA sequences.

Algal Habitats

Algae are found in fresh and salt water as well as in soil.

Unicellular algae make up a significant part of the **phytoplankton.**

Structure of Algae

Algae may be microscopic or macroscopic.

Their cell walls are made of cellulose and other commercially important materials such as agar and carrageenan.

They have membrane-bound organelles including a **nucleus, chloroplasts,** and **mitochondria.**

Algal Reproduction

Algae produce asexually as well as sexually. (Figure 12.4)

Paralytic Shellfish Poisoning

Algae do not directly cause disease, but produce toxins that are ingested by fish and shellfish. (Figure 12.5)

When these fish and shellfish are eaten by humans, dizziness, muscle weakness, and even death may result; cooking does not destroy the toxins.

12.2 Protozoa

Protozoa are microscopic, unicellular organisms that lack chlorophyll, are motile during at least one stage in their development, and reproduce most often by binary fission.

Classification of Protozoa (Figure 12.1)

In classification schemes based on rRNA, protozoa are not a single group of organisms.

Protozoa have traditionally been put into groups based on their mode of locomotion. (Table 12.2)

Sarcomastigophora include the **Mastigophora,** the flagellated protozoa, and **Sarcodina,** which move by means of pseudopodia.

Ciliophora move by means of cilia.

Apicomplexa, also referred to as the sporozoa, include *Plasmodium* sp., the cause of malaria.

Microsporidia, an intracellular protozoa, causes disease in immunocompromised individuals.

Protozoan Habitats

Most protozoa are free-living and are found in marine and fresh water as well as terrestrial environments.

They are important decomposers in many ecosystems and are a key part of the food chain.

Structure of Protozoa

Protozoa lack a cell wall, but most maintain a definite shape using the material lying just beneath the plasma membrane.

Life cycles are often complex and include more than one habitat. (Figure 12.7)

Protozoa feed by either phagocytosis or pinocytosis.

Protozoan Reproduction (Figure 12.8)

Reproduction is often by binary fission; some reproduce by multiple fissions or **schizogony.**

Protozoa and Human Disease (Table 12.2)

Protozoa cause diseases such as malaria, African sleeping sickness, toxoplasmosis, and vaginitis.

12.3 Fungi

Fungi can cause serious disease, primarily in plants.

Fungi produce useful food products.

Classification of Fungi (Table 12.3, Figure 12.1)

Zygomycetes, Ascomycetes, Basidiomycetes, and **Deuteromycetes** or **Fungi Imperfecti** are the four groups of true fungi.

Chytridiomycetes are a close relative.

Yeast, mold, and **mushroom** are common terms that indicate morphological forms of fungi. (Figures 12.9, 12.10, 12.14)

Fungal filaments are called **hyphae** and a group of hyphae is called a **mycelium.** (Figures 12.12, 12.13)

Dimorphic fungi can grow either as a single cell (yeast) or as mycelia.

Fungal Habitats

Fungi inhabit just about every ecological habitat and can spoil a large variety of food materials because they can grow in high concentrations of sugar, salt, and acid.

Fungi can be found in moist environments at temperatures from −6°C to 50°C and pH from 2.2 to 9.6.

Fungi are heterotrophs with enzymes that can degrade most organic materials.

Fungal Disease in Humans (Table 12.4)

Fungi may produce an allergic reaction.

Fungi may produce toxins that make humans ill. These include **ergot,** those in poisonous mushrooms, and **aflatoxin.**

Fungi cause **mycoses** such as **histoplasmosis, coccidioidomycosis,** and **candidiasis.**

Symbiotic Relationships Between Fungi and Other Organisms

Lichens result from an association of a fungus with a photosynthetic organism such as an alga or a cyanobacterium. (Figure 12.15)

Mycorrhizas are the result of an intimate association of a fungus and the roots of a plant.

Economic Importance of Fungi

The yeast *Saccharomyces* is used in the production of beer, wine, and bread.

Penicillium and other fungi synthesize antibiotics.

Fungi spoil many food products.

Fungi cause diseases of plants such as Dutch elm disease and wheat rust.

Fungi have been useful tools in genetic and biochemical studies.

12.4 Slime Molds and Water Molds (Figure 12.1)

Acellular and **cellular slime molds** are important links in the terrestrial food chain. (Figure 12.16)

Oomycetes, also known as **water molds,** cause some serious diseases of plants.

12.5 Multicellular Parasites: Arthropods and Helminths

Arthropods

Arthropods act as vectors for disease. (Table 12.5)

Mosquitoes spread disease by picking up disease-causing organisms when the mosquito bites, and later injecting these organisms into subsequent animals that it bites. (Figure 12.17)

Fleas transmit disease such as plague; lice can transmit trench fever, epidemic typhus, and relapsing fever. (Figure 12.18)

Ticks are implicated in Rocky Mountain spotted fever and Lyme disease.

Mites cause scabies, and dust mites are responsible for allergies and asthma. (Figure 12.19)

Helminths (Table 12.6)

Most **nematodes** or roundworms are free-living, but they may cause serious disease such as pinworm disease, whipworm disease, hookworm disease, and ascariasis.

Cestodes are tapeworms with segmented bodies and hooks to attach to the wall of the intestine.

Most tapeworm infections occur in persons who eat uncooked or undercooked meats; some tapeworms are acquired by ingesting fleas infected with dog or cat tapeworms. (Figure 12.20)

Trematodes, or flukes, often have complicated life cycles that necessarily involve more than one host.

Schistosoma mansoni **cercaria** can penetrate the skin of persons wading in infected waters and cause serious disease. (Figure 12.21)

REVIEW QUESTIONS

Short Answer

1. What are the major differences between the *Eucarya,* the *Bacteria,* and the *Archaea?*
2. What distinguishes algae from all the other eukaryotic microorganisms?
3. Why are algae economically important?
4. Contrast the various modes of locomotion in protozoa.
5. Why are protozoa economically important?
6. What is the difference between a yeast, a mold, and a mushroom?
7. What are fungal diseases called?
8. Why are fungi economically important?
9. Discuss the differences and similarities in the ways algae, protozoa, fungi, helminths, and arthropods cause disease in humans.
10. What is a vector? Give two examples.

Multiple Choice

Choose one or more of these organisms that best answers the question.

1. Members of this group have chitinous cell walls.
   a) Algae b) Protozoa c) Fungi
   d) Helminths e) Arthropods
2. Members of this group are photosynthetic.
   a) Algae b) Protozoa c) Fungi
   d) Helminths e) Arthropods
3. All members of this group are single-celled.
   a) Algae b) Protozoa c) Fungi
   d) Helminths e) Arthropods
4. This group can have both single-celled and multicellular members.
   a) Algae b) Protozoa c) Fungi
   d) Helminths e) Arthropods

5. This group can only cause disease in humans through toxins.
   a) Algae b) Protozoa c) Fungi
   d) Helminths e) Arthropods
6. This group lacks a cell wall.
   a) Algae b) Protozoa c) Fungi
   d) Helminths e) Arthropods
7. These groups are found in plankton.
   a) Algae b) Protozoa c) Fungi
   d) Helminths e) Arthropods
8. Red tides are caused by this group.
   a) Algae b) Protozoa c) Fungi
   d) Helminths e) Arthropods
9. This group helps produce many of the foods that we eat.
   a) Algae b) Protozoa c) Fungi
   d) Helminths e) Arthropods
10. Without these groups the food chains of the world would not exist.
   a) Algae b) Protozoa c) Fungi
   d) Helminths e) Arthropods

Applications

1. A molecular biologist working for a government-run fishery in Vietnam is interested in controlling *Pfisteria* in fish farms. He needs to come up with a treatment that kills *Pfisteria* without harming the fish and other protista and beneficial algae that serve as food for the young fish. What strategy should the biologist consider for developing a selective treatment?
2. Paper recycling companies refuse to collect paper products that are contaminated with food or have been sitting wet for a day. A college sorority member who is running a recycling program on campus wishes to know the reason for this. What reason did the chemist who works for the recycling company probably give her for this policy?

Critical Thinking

1. Explain why it may be more difficult to treat diseases in humans caused by members of the *Eucarya* than diseases caused by the *Bacteria.*
2. Fungi are known for growing and reproducing in a wide range of environmental extremes in temperature, pH, and osmotic pressure. What does this tolerance for extremes indicate about fungal enzymes?

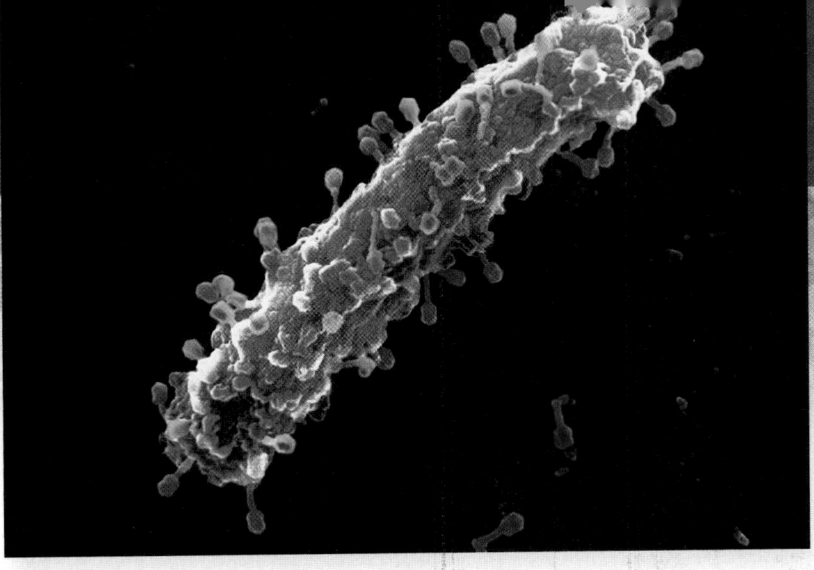

Bacterial viruses attached to a bacterium

CHAPTER THIRTEEN

Viruses of Bacteria

A Glimpse of History

During the late nineteenth century, many bacteria, fungi, and protozoa were identified as infectious organisms. Most of these organisms could be readily seen with a microscope, and they generally could be grown in the laboratory. In the 1890s, D. M. Iwanowsky and Martinus Beijerinck found that a disease of tobacco plants, called **mosaic disease,** was caused by an agent different from anything that was known. About 10 years later, F. W. Twort in England and F. d'Herelle in France showed that infectious agents existed that had the same unusual properties and could destroy bacteria. Both agents were so small that they could not be seen with the light microscope; they passed through filters that retained almost all known bacteria, and they could be grown in media only if it contained living cells. The agents were called **filterable viruses** by Beijerinck. Virus means "poison," a term that once was applied to all infectious agents. With time, the adjective filterable was dropped and only the word virus was retained.

Viruses have many features that are more characteristic of complex chemicals than of cells. For example, tobacco mosaic virus (TMV) can be precipitated from a suspension with ethyl alcohol and still remain infective. A similar treatment destroys the infectivity of bacteria. Further, in 1935, Wendell Stanley of the University of California, Berkeley, crystallized tobacco mosaic virus. Its physical and chemical properties obviously differed from those of cells, which cannot form crystals. Surprisingly, the crystallized tobacco mosaic virus could still cause the disease described by Iwanowsky and Beijerinck 40 years before.

Viruses posed a mystery to scientists as recently as 50 years ago. They were clearly smaller than known bacteria and possessed properties different from those of cells. The nature of these curious agents, some of which infected animals and others, plants, became clearer through the study of viruses that infect bacteria. Because bacterial cells can be grown easily and multiply rapidly, viruses that infect them, can be cultivated much more readily than the viruses that infect other organisms. These viruses have been studied extensively, and the knowledge gained from these studies has contributed enormously to an understanding both of viruses and of the molecular biology of all organisms.

13.1 General Characteristics of Viruses

Focus Points

- Describe the features of viruses that distinguish them from living cells.
- Draw the most common shape of a phage particle and label its parts.

Viruses are non-living entities and therefore are not organisms. These agents can infect all forms of life, including all members of the *Bacteria, Archaea,* and *Eucarya.* They commonly are referred to by the organisms they infect. Those that infect bacteria are **bacteriophage** or **phage** (phage means "to eat"). The word *phage* is both singular and plural when referring to one type of virus. The word *phages* is used when different types of phages are being referenced. This is the same usage as *fish* and *fishes.* Animal viruses infect animals and plant viruses infect plants. These organisms are the hosts for the viruses. Since phages have been isolated from extremophiles of the *Bacteria*

KEY TERMS

Bacteriophage A virus that infects bacteria; often shortened to phage.

Burst size Number of newly formed virus particles released from a single cell following virus replication.

Carrier cells Cells that are capable of releasing virus particles without being killed by the virus.

Latent state The state of a phage when its DNA is integrated into the genome of the host.

Lysogen A bacterium that carries phage DNA (the prophage) integrated into its genome.

Lysogenic conversion The change in properties of a bacterium as a result of carrying a prophage. The phage DNA codes for the new properties.

Maturation The stage in viral replication in which the various components of the virion assemble to form a whole virion.

Productive infection Virus infection in which more virus particles are produced as a result of infection.

Prophage Phage DNA that is integrated into the genome of a host.

Temperate phage A phage that has the ability to integrate its DNA into the chromosome of the host.

Virion A virus in its inert extracellular form.

and *Archaea,* these phages must be capable of multiplying and existing in cells exposed to extreme conditions of high temperature, high salt, and low pH.

Virus Architecture

Each virus particle, also called a **virion,** consists of nucleic acid (DNA or RNA) surrounded by a protective protein coat, termed a **capsid.** Different viruses have different shapes **(figure 13.1).** Some are **isometric,** and are composed of flat surfaces, forming equilateral triangles. The simplest and most common shape of viruses show **icosahedral symmetry.** This shape is a structure with 20 equilateral faces. This shell is the most efficient design for any biological container and requires the least energy to assemble. They appear spherical when viewed with the electron microscope. Others are **helical,** which gives the virion a filamentous or rodlike appearance. Most phages are more **complex** in shape, having an isometric head with a long helical component, the **sheath** or **tail.** It is estimated that more than 10^{23} phage particles of this shape exist in the world.

The shape of a virus is determined by the shape of the protein capsid, either helical or spherical, that encloses the viral nucleic acid genome. The viral capsid together with the nucleic acid that is tightly packed within the protein coat is called the **nucleocapsid (figure 13.2).** The nucleic acid in some viruses is so tightly packed that the internal pressure is 10 times higher than in a champagne bottle. Each capsid is composed of many identical protein subunits, called **capsomers.** All bacterial and animal viruses, but not plant viruses, must be able to attach (adsorb) to specific receptor sites on host cells. In tailless isometric viruses, **attachment proteins** or **spikes** project from the capsid and are involved in attaching the virus to the host cell (see figure 13.2). In isometric viruses with tails (sheaths), tail fibers serve to attach the virus to the host cell (see figure 13.1).

There are two basic types of virions. The outer coat of most phages consists of the protein capsid. This type of virion is called **naked.** Virtually all phages are naked. Many virions that infect humans and other animals, however, have an additional covering over the capsid protein. This consists of a double layer of lipid similar in structure to the cell membrane of the eukaryotic cell. These are termed **enveloped viruses.** Just inside the lipid envelope is often a protein, the **matrix protein,** which is found only in enveloped viruses. The attachment spikes project from the envelope (see figure 13.2).

Most viruses are notable for their small size **(figure 13.3).** They are approximately 100- to 1,000-fold smaller than the cells they infect. The smallest viruses are about 10 nm in diameter, while the largest animal viruses are about 500 nm, the size of the smallest bacterial cells. The smallest viruses contain very little nucleic acid, perhaps as few as 10 genes.

The Viral Genome

The structure of the viral genome is unusual. Viruses contain only a single type of nucleic acid—either RNA or DNA—but never both. The nucleic acids can occur in one of several different forms characteristic of the virus. DNA may be linear or circular, either double-stranded or single-stranded. RNA is usually single-stranded but a few viruses contain double-stranded RNA. Depending on the type of nucleic acid they contain, viruses are frequently referred to as RNA or DNA viruses.

Replication Cycle—Overall Features

Viruses can only multiply within living cells that are actively metabolizing. Viruses lack the cellular components necessary to harvest energy and synthesize protein. They have no mitochondria or ribosomes, or even the enzymes necessary to harvest energy and synthesize proteins. Viruses must use structures and enzymes of cells they infect to support their own reproduction. They are **obligate intracellular parasites.** In all viruses, the nucleic acid separates from its coat before replication begins. ■ mitochondria, p. 78 ■ ribosomes, p. 70

Because viruses contain so little nucleic acid, their few genes can code for only a very limited number of proteins, including enzymes. Every virus, however, must contain the genetic information to encode proteins required to: (1) make the viral protein coat, (2) assure replication of viral nucleic acid, and (3) move the virus into and out of the host cell. Some viruses require enzymes for their replication that are not present in uninfected host cells.

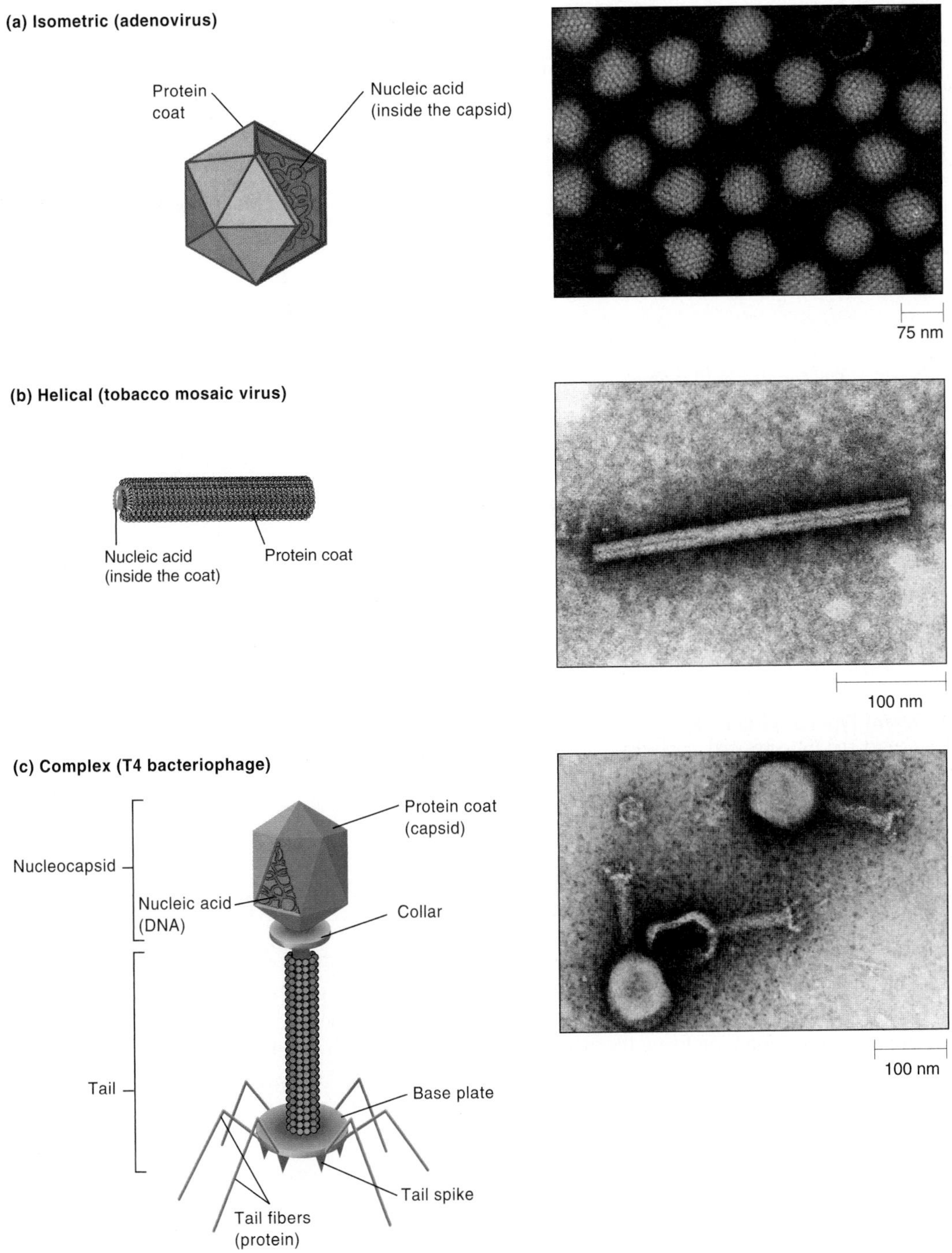

FIGURE 13.1 Common Shapes of Viruses **(a)** Isometric with icosahedral symmetry (adenovirus). **(b)** Helical (tobacco mosaic virus). **(c)** Complex (T4 bacteriophage).

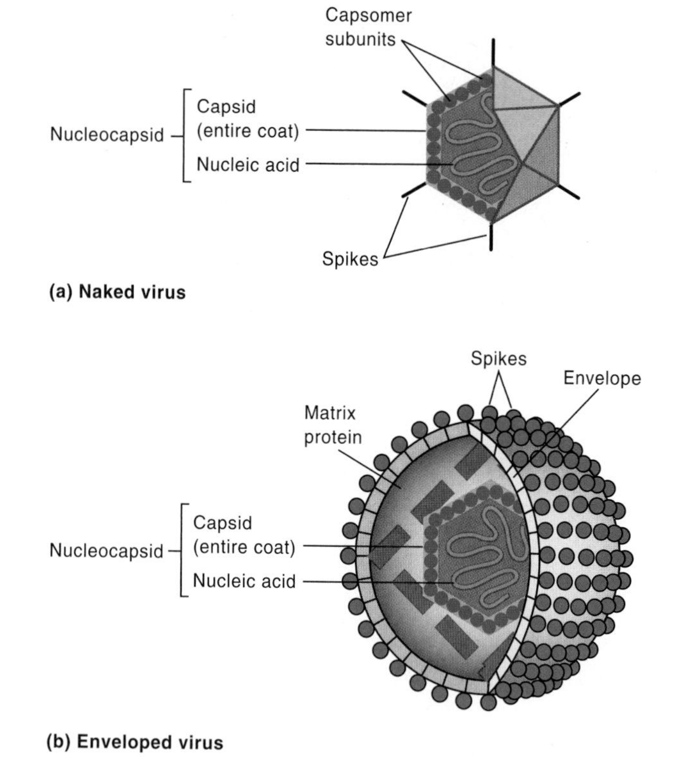

FIGURE 13.2 Two Different Types of Virions **(a)** Naked, not containing an envelope around the capsid and **(b)** enveloped, containing an envelope around the capsid and the matrix protein inside the envelope.

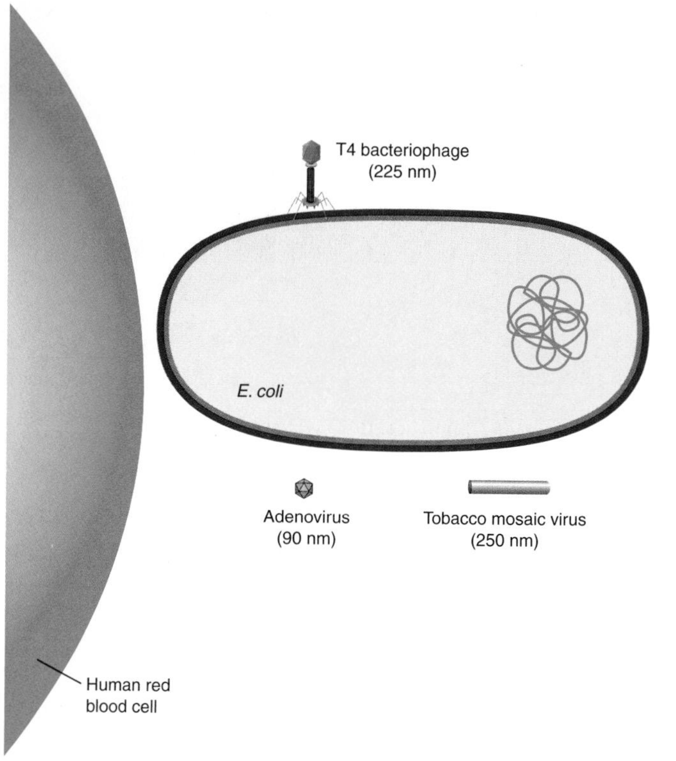

FIGURE 13.3 Virion Size Related sizes of an animal virus (adenovirus), plant virus (tobacco mosaic virus), a bacterial virus, phage T4 and *Escherichia coli,* the host of T4. The bacterial cell is 2,000 nm in length; the red blood cell is 5,000 nm in diameter.

These enzymes are either coded by the nucleic acid of the virion, or the enzymes enter the cell with the virion.

Viruses exist in two distinct phases. Outside of living cells, they are metabolically inert. Essentially, they are only macromolecules. In this state, a virus is referred to as a **virion.** Inside susceptible cells, viruses are in a replication form using the metabolic machinery and pathways of their host cells along with their own genetic information to produce new virions. Viruses and cells are compared in **table 13.1.**

MICROCHECK 13.1

Viruses are non-living agents that consist of nucleic acid surrounded by a protein coat. Viruses only multiply within living cells, because they need certain functions of the host to multiply.

- ✓ List four features of viruses that distinguish them from free-living cells.
- ✓ List three functions that all viruses must perform.
- ✓ An antibiotic is added to a growing culture of *E. coli,* resulting in death of the cells. Bacteriophage are then added. Would the phage replicate in the *E. coli* cells? Explain your answer.

TABLE 13.1 Comparison Between Viruses and Cells

	Viruses	Cells
Size	10–500 nm	Bacteria: 1,000 nm Animal: 200,000 nm Plant: 400,000 nm
Multiplication	Multiply only within cells; outside the cell they are metabolically inert; protein coat and nucleic acid separate prior to multiplication	Most are free-living and multiply in the absence of other cells; entire cell remains intact during multiplication
Nucleic Acid Content	Contain either DNA or RNA, but never both	Always contain both DNA and RNA
Enzyme Content	Contain very few, if any, enzymes	Contain many enzymes
Internal Components	Lack ribosomes and enzymes for harvesting energy	Contain ribosomes and enzymes for harvesting energy

13.2

Virus Interactions with Host Cells

Focus Points

- List the steps in the replication process of a lytic phage and the major feature of each step.
- List the steps in the replication of phage in a latent stage and describe how latency is maintained.

Although viruses as a group infect all kinds of cells, the relationships between even the well studied animal viruses and the host cells they invade are poorly understood in comparison with phage-bacteria systems. This is largely because the eukaryotic host cells of animal viruses are far more complex and grow much more slowly than the prokaryotic host cells of the phage. We will first focus on bacteriophages, which serve as excellent models for all other viruses. What you learn about them will help immensely in understanding similar relationships between viruses and the animal cells they infect, described in chapter 14.

How phages affect the cells they infect depends primarily on the type of phage. Some types multiply inside the cells they invade and escape by lysing the host cell. Since more virus is produced, this interaction is termed a **productive infection** and the phages that lyse the cell are termed **lytic** (*lysis* means dissolution). These viruses take over the metabolism of the cell and direct the cell to produce only phage. Another type of productive infection is carried out by phage that multiply, and then leak out or **extrude** without killing the host cells. These phages take over only some of the metabolic processes of the cell. An example is the filamentous phage, M13. Still other phages, termed **temperate** (*temperatus* means controlled), integrate their DNA into the genome of the bacteria they infect or the DNA replicates as a plasmid. The phage DNA replicates as the bacterial DNA replicates. The infection is termed **latent** because there may be no sign that the cells are infected. The bacterium carrying the phage DNA is a **lysogen** and the cell is in the **lysogenic state.** The phage DNA often codes for proteins that modify the properties of the host, the phenomenon of **lysogenic conversion.** An example of a temperate phage that infects *E. coli* is lambda (λ). These different relationships are shown in **figure 13.4.** ■ plasmid, p. 69

Some of the phages that undergo these three kinds of relationship with their host bacteria are listed in **table 13.2.**

Lytic Phage Replication by Double-Stranded DNA Phages

In all lytic phage infections, the phage nucleic acid enters the bacterium while its protein coat remains on the outside. Since only nucleic acid enters the cell, the nucleic acid must code for the protein in the phage coat. The nucleic acid is replicated as the phage proteins are synthesized, resulting in the formation of many virions. At the end of the replication cycle, phage exit by lysing the bacterium. Phage that go through this productive life cycle are termed **virulent.** An intensively studied virulent phage is the double-stranded DNA phage, T4 (see figure 13.1). Its replication cycle illustrates how a phage can take over the life of a cell and reprogram the cells' activities solely to the synthesis of phage **(figure 13.5).**

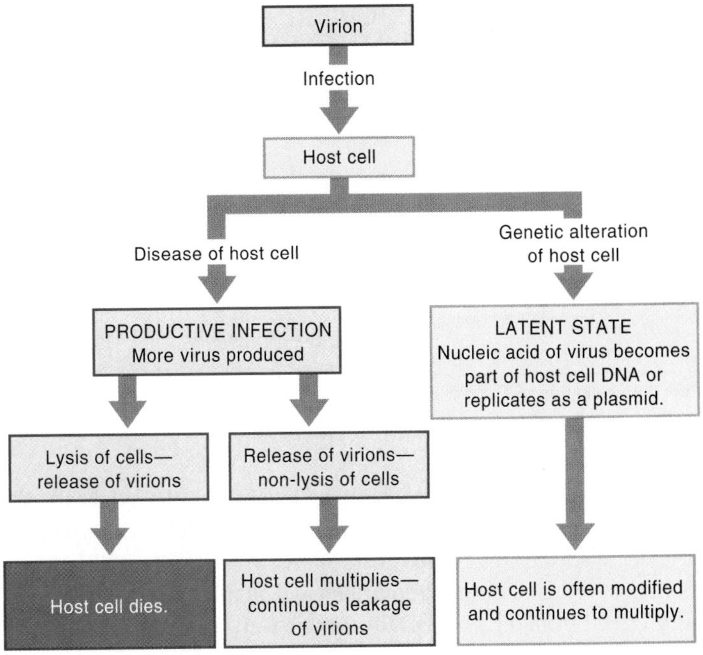

FIGURE 13.4 Major Types of Relationships Between Viruses and the Host Cells They Infect

Step 1: Attachment

When a suspension of T4 phage is mixed with a susceptible strain of *E. coli,* the phages collide by chance with the bacteria. Since viruses do not have flagella, they cannot swim toward their hosts. Protein fibers at the end of the phage tail attach to specific receptors on the bacterial cell wall (Step 1). These receptors generally perform other functions for the cell, such as transport functions. The phage use these structures for their own purposes.

Step 2: Penetration

A few minutes after attachment, an enzyme (lysozyme) located in the tip of the phage tail degrades a small portion of the bacterial cell wall. The tail contracts, and the tip of the tail opens. The double-stranded linear viral DNA in the head passes through the open channel of the phage tail (Step 2). The DNA is literally injected through the cell wall and, by some unknown mechanism, passes through the cytoplasmic membrane and enters the interior of the cell. The protein coat of the phage remains on the outside of the cell. Thus, the protein and nucleic acid separate, a feature of all virus replication.

Step 3: Transcription

Within minutes of the entry of phage DNA into a host cell, a portion is transcribed into mRNA, which is then translated into proteins that are specific for the infecting phage (Step 3). The first proteins produced, termed **early proteins,** are enzymes that are not normally present in the uninfected host cell. They are also known as **phage-encoded proteins,** because they are coded by phage DNA. Some are essential for the synthesis of phage DNA, which contains

TABLE 13.2 Important Bacteriophages

Bacteriophage	Host	Shape	Genome Structure*	Relationship to Host Cell
T4, T1–T7	*Escherichia coli*	Complex	ds DNA	Lytic
M13, fd	*Escherichia coli*	Filamentous	ss DNA	Exit by extrusion
ϕX174	*Escherichia coli*	Isometric	ss DNA	Lytic
Lambda (λ)	*Escherichia coli*	Complex	ds DNA	Latent or lytic
MS2, Qβ	*Escherichia coli*	Isometric	ss RNA	Lytic
Beta (β)	*Corynebacterium diphtheriae*	Isometric	ds DNA	Latent; codes for diphtheria toxin

*ds, double-stranded; ss, single-stranded.

an unusual pyrimidine, and others are involved in the synthesis of phage coat protein. One phage-encoded early protein is a nuclease that degrades the DNA of the host cell. As a result, soon after infection, host cell DNA is not transcribed and all mRNA synthesized is transcribed from the phage DNA. In this way, the phage takes over the metabolism of the bacterial cell for its own purpose, namely the synthesis of more phage. Preexisting bacterial enzymes, however, continue to function. Some supply the energy necessary for phage replication through the breakdown of energy sources in the environment. The host enzymes also synthesize amino acids and nucleotides for the production of phage proteins and nucleic acids, the former being carried out on bacterial ribosomes.

Not all phage-encoded enzymes are synthesized simultaneously. Rather, they are made in a sequential manner during the course of infection. Those required early are synthesized near the beginning of infection; others that are not required until later in infection are made later on. Examples of early phage-encoded enzymes are the nuclease that degrades the host chromosome and the enzymes of phage DNA synthesis. Late phage-encoded enzymes include those concerned with the assembly of capsids and the phage lysozyme that lyses the bacteria to release the newly formed phage.

Step 4: Replication of Phage DNA and Synthesis of Proteins

Phage protein and nucleic acid are synthesized independently of one another. The DNA of the entering phage serves two distinct functions: the template for replication of more phage DNA and the template for the synthesis of mRNA, which is then translated into phage-encoded enzymes and the proteins that form the phage. The DNA and proteins are synthesized by the mechanisms described for bacterial DNA and protein synthesis (Step 4). ■ DNA synthesis, p. 170 ■ protein synthesis, p. 176

Step 5: Assembly

The **assembly** or **maturation** process involves the assembly of phage protein with phage DNA to form intact or mature phage (Step 5). This is a complex, multistep process in the case of T4 phage. The protein structures of the phage, such as the heads, tails (sheaths), tail spikes, and tail fibers, are synthesized independently of one another. Once the phage head is formed, it is packed with DNA; the tail is then attached, followed by the addition of the tail spikes. The synthesis of some of these various components involves a **self-assembly** process, in which the protein components come together spontaneously without any enzyme catalyst to form a specific structure. In other steps, certain phage proteins serve as scaffolds on which various protein components associate. The scaffolds themselves do not become a part of the final structure, much as scaffolding required to build a house does not become part of the house.

Step 6: Release

During the latter stages of the infection period, the phage-encoded enzyme **lysozyme** is synthesized. This enzyme digests the host cell wall from within, resulting in cell lysis and the release of phage (Step 6). If this enzyme were synthesized early in the infection process, it would lyse the host cell before any mature phage could be formed. This is why phage genes are expressed only when the enzymes for which they code are needed.

In the case of the T4 phage, the **burst size,** the number of phage released per cell, is about 200. The time required for the entire cycle from adsorption to release is about 30 minutes. These phage then infect any susceptible cells in the environment, and the process of phage replication is repeated.

Lytic Single-Stranded RNA Phages

Another group of lytic phages that undergo a productive infection are the single-stranded RNA phages. The ones most intensively studied are those that infect *E. coli.* These include MS2 and Qβ, which show many similarities to one another and share several unusual properties (see table 13.2). First, they infect only F^+ strains of *E. coli* because they attach to the sides of the sex pilus. Second, they replicate rapidly and have a burst size of about 10,000. Third, the replication of this phage requires an unusual enzyme, an RNA-dependent RNA polymerase which uses RNA as a template. This enzyme is not present in *E. coli,* so the entering RNA must code for it. ■ sex pilus, p. 68

Phage Replication in a Latent State—Phage Lambda

Some phages can go through a productive lytic infection like T4 or live in harmony with their host bacteria. These latter are known

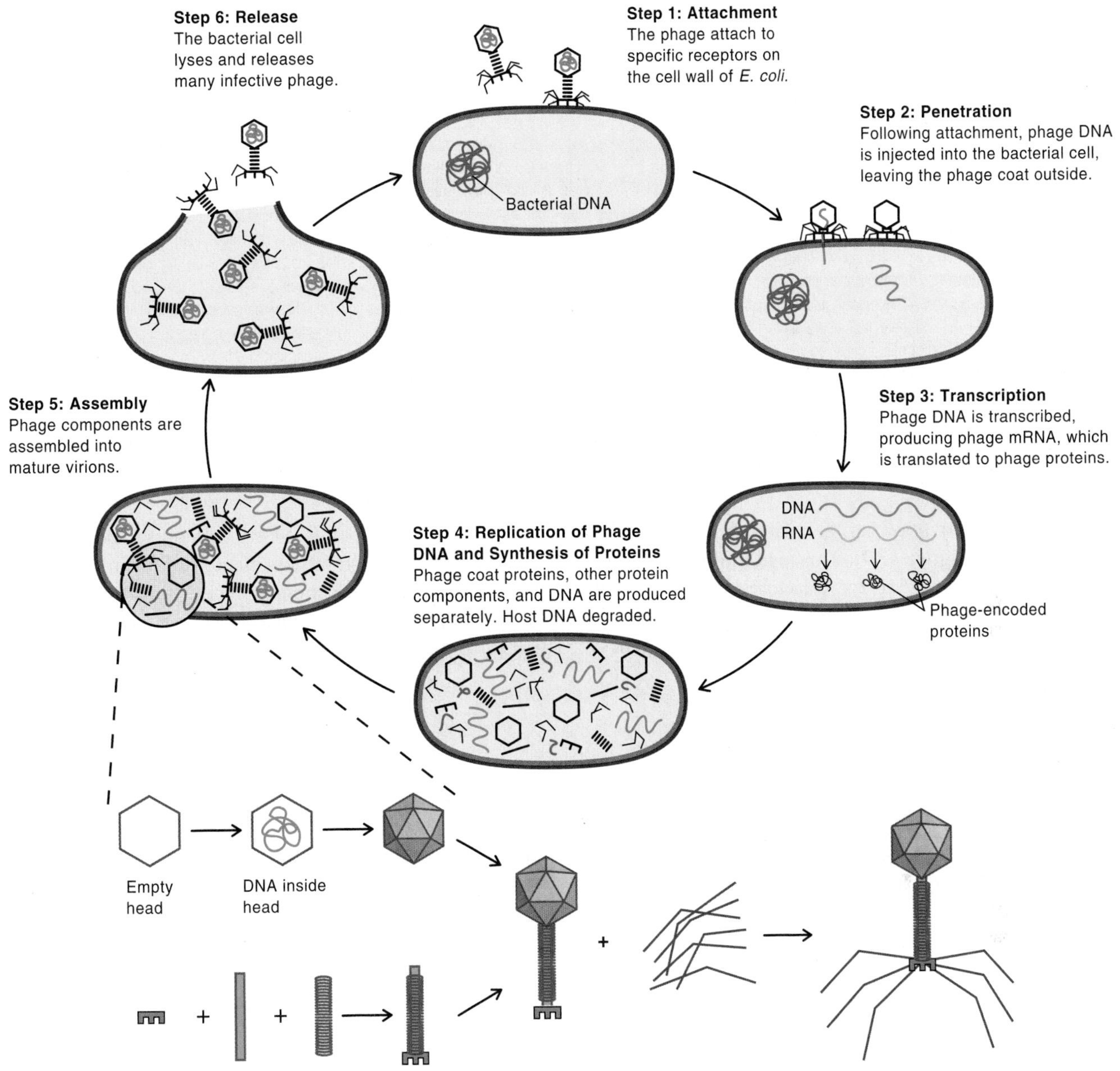
Step 6: Release
The bacterial cell lyses and releases many infective phage.
Step 1: Attachment
The phage attach to specific receptors on the cell wall of E. coli.
Bacterial DNA
Step 2: Penetration
Following attachment, phage DNA is injected into the bacterial cell, leaving the phage coat outside.
Step 5: Assembly
Phage components are assembled into mature virions.
Step 3: Transcription
Phage DNA is transcribed, producing phage mRNA, which is translated to phage proteins.
DNA
RNA
Phage-encoded proteins
Step 4: Replication of Phage DNA and Synthesis of Proteins
Phage coat proteins, other protein components, and DNA are produced separately. Host DNA degraded.
Empty head
DNA inside head

FIGURE 13.5 Steps in the Replication of T4 Phage in *E. coli*

as **temperate phages.** Ninety percent of all phages are temperate. In the harmonious relationship, the entering phage DNA most commonly becomes integrated into the chromosome of the host cell, where it replicates as the host chromosome replicates. When integrated, the phage DNA is called a **prophage** and the bacterial cell carrying a prophage is a **lysogenic cell** or **lysogen.** Some temperate phages multiply as plasmids inside the host cell, another kind of latency. ■ plasmid, p. 69

The most thoroughly studied temperate phage is lambda (λ), which lysogenizes *E. coli.* Its size and shape are similar to T4 phage. Once the phage DNA enters the host cell, one of two events occur. Some of the bacteria will be lysogenized, while others will be lysed **(figure 13.6).** Whether the lambda phage lyses the majority of the cells or lysogenizes them depends largely on chance events that can be tipped in favor of one or the other by modifying the external environment. For example, if the bacteria are growing slowly, because of nutrient deprivation, then the likelihood of the phage DNA becoming integrated increases because phage replicate in a lytic cycle only in actively metabolizing cells.

The Integration of Phage DNA into the Bacterial Chromosome

Phage λ DNA integrates into the *E. coli* genome at a specific site through a process called **site-specific recombination.** Short nucleotide sequences in the DNA of phage λ and the *E. coli* host

PERSPECTIVE 13.1

Viral Soup

For many years viruses have been recognized to cause many very deadly diseases of humans, animals, and plants. Within the past few years, scientists have discovered that they may play another important role in nature—that of being a major component of **bacterioplankton,** the bacteria found in the ocean. In the 1970s and 1980s, bacterial cells were found to be much more abundant than had been believed previously. Earlier estimates of the number of bacteria in aquatic environments were based on the numbers that could be cultured in the laboratory. When direct microscopic counts were made, however, the number of heterotrophic bacteria was estimated to be 10^5 to 10^7 bacteria per ml, much higher than previously estimated. Most carbon fixation in the ocean is carried out by bacteria. The number of cyanobacteria and single-celled eukaryotic algae is also much greater than previously believed. What was most surprising, though, was the number of bacteriophages in aquatic environments. To get an accurate estimate of their numbers, scientists centrifuged large volumes of natural unpolluted waters from various locations. They then counted the number of particles in the pellet. Much to their surprise, up to 2.5×10^8 phages per ml were counted, about 1,000 to 10 million times as high as previous estimates. Why are these new numbers important? First, they may answer the question of why bacteria have not saturated the ocean. The bacteria are most likely held in check by the phages. From the estimates of the numbers of bacteria and phages, it is calculated that one-third of the bacterial population may experience a phage attack each day. Second, the interaction of phages with bacteria in natural water implies that the phages may be actively transferring DNA from one bacterium to another, by the process of transduction.

Thus, the smallest agents in natural waters may have important consequences for the ecology of the aquatic environment. Perhaps viruses have a similar function for eukaryotic organisms. Indeed, it is now known that phages can stop algal blooms.

are identical (homologous), allowing the phage and the bacterial DNA to **synapse** (pair) **(figure 13.7).** This region of homology is located between the genes coding for galactose metabolism and biotin synthesis. Following synapsis, the phage DNA becomes integrated into the bacterial chromosome between these genes. Note that phage DNA is added without replacing any bacterial genes. This differs from the situation following gene transfer by transformation, transduction, or conjugation. In these cases, genes in the recipient cells are replaced by donor DNA. ■ DNA transformation, p. 205 ■ transduction, p. 207 ■ conjugation, p. 210

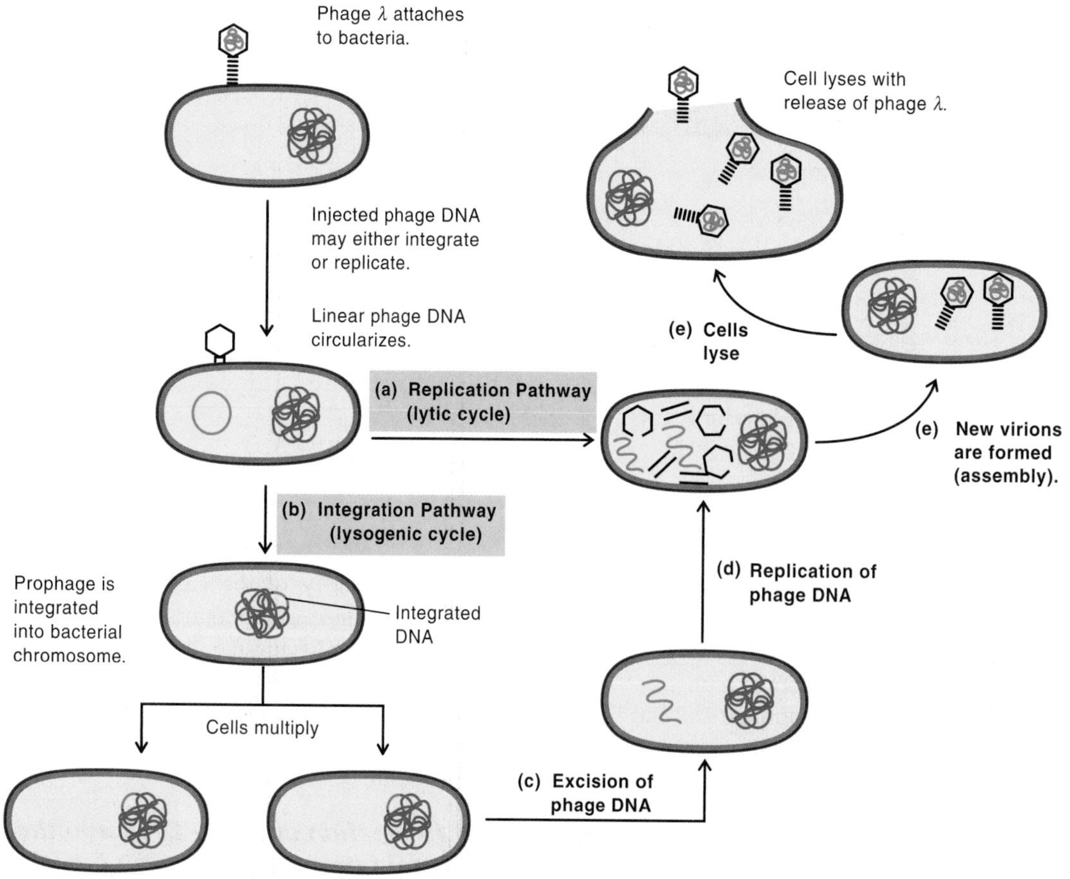

FIGURE 13.6 Lambda Phage (λ) Replication Cycle Depending on the environmental conditions, λ phage may go through the lytic cycle **(a)** or may lysogenize the cell **(b).** As culture conditions change, the phage DNA in a lysogenic cell may be excised **(c)** from the bacterial chromosome and **(d)** enter the lytic cycle and the phage undergo reproduction. Note that unlike the case of phage T4, phage λ does not destroy the bacterial chromosome.

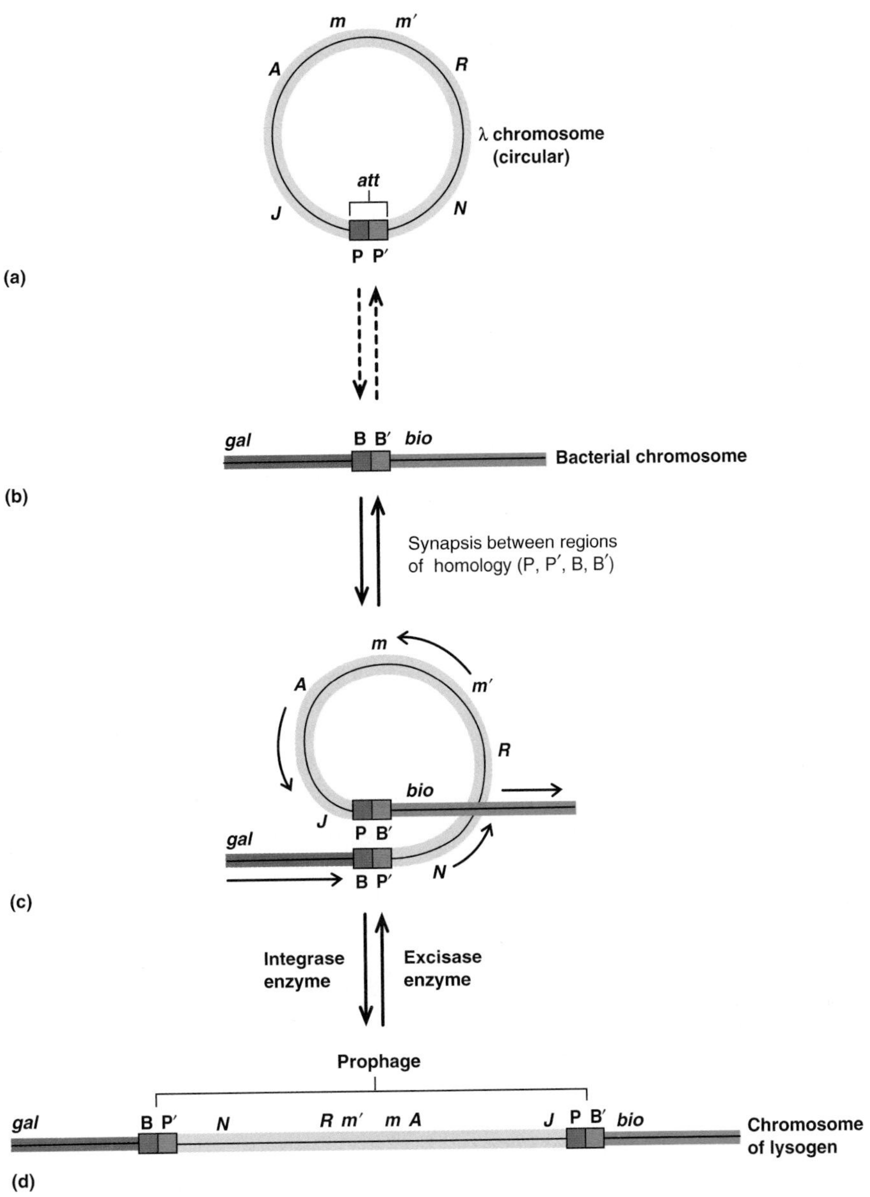

FIGURE 13.7 Reversible Insertion and Excision of Lambda (λ) Phage The λ DNA circularizes **(a),** the phage *att* site, P,P′ synapses with an identical bacterial sequence B,B′ located between *gal* and *bio* **(b)** and is integrated between the *gal* and *bio* operons **(c)** to form the prophage, **(d).** If the process is reversed, the lambda chromosome is excised from the bacterial chromosome and can then replicate and code for the synthesis of phage proteins.

Maintenance of the Prophage in an Integrated State

The phage DNA can remain integrated, replicate along with the bacterial DNA, and be passed on to all daughter cells indefinitely. For this to occur, however, the expression of genes present on the integrated phage DNA must be repressed. These genes code for enzymes that **excise** (remove) the integrated DNA from the host chromosome. If excision occurs, the replication cycle of a productive phage infection ensues. How are these genes repressed to maintain the lysogenic state? One gene in the integrated viral DNA codes for a **repressor** that binds to a viral operator, which controls transcription of the integrated genes required for excision. As long as this repressor is produced, the integrated phage DNA is not excised. If the repressor is no longer synthesized or is inactivated, however, viral genes are transcribed and an enzyme, an **excisase** which removes the viral DNA from the bacterial chromosome, is synthesized. Reproduction with lysis ensues (see figure 13.6d). ■ **repressor, p. 183** ■ **operator, p. 183**

Under ordinary conditions of growth, the phage DNA is excised from the chromosome only about once in 10,000 divisions of the lysogen. If, however, a lysogenic culture is treated with an agent that damages the bacterial DNA (such as ultraviolet light), the repair system, called SOS, comes into play. This system activates a protease that destroys the repressor. As a result, all of the prophage enter the lytic cycle, and a productive infection results. In this way the phage escape from a host that is in deep trouble because its DNA has been damaged. This process, termed **phage induction,** results in complete lysis of the culture. The term *induction* as it is used here should not be confused with induced enzyme synthesis as discussed in chapter 7. ■ **SOS system, p. 200** ■ **ultraviolet light, p. 120** ■ **protease, p. 38**

TABLE 13.3 Some Properties Conferred by Prophage

Microorganism	Medical Importance	Property Coded by Phage
Corynebacterium diphtheriae	Causes diphtheria	Synthesis of diphtheria toxin
Clostridium botulinum	Causes botulism	Synthesis of botulinum toxin
Streptococcus pyogenes	Causes scarlet fever	Synthesis of toxin responsible for scarlet fever
Salmonella	Causes food poisoning	Modification of lipopolysaccharide of cell wall
Vibrio cholerae	Causes cholera	Synthesis of cholera toxin

Immunity of Lysogens

In addition to maintaining the prophage in the integrated state, the repressor protein prevents the second infection of a lysogenic cell by phage of the same type as the phage DNA already carried by the lysogenic cell. Infections are blocked because the repressor binds to the operator in the phage DNA as it enters the cell and inhibits its replication. Consequently, the cell is immune to infection by the same phage but not to infection by other phages, to whose DNA the repressor cannot bind. In this way the phage protects its turf from closely related phages.

Lysogenic Conversion

Lysogenic cells may also differ from their nonlysogenic counterparts in other important ways. The prophage can confer new properties on the cell, the phenomenon of **lysogenic conversion.** For example, strains of *Corynebacterium diphtheriae* that are lysogenic for a certain phage (β phage) synthesize the toxin that causes diphtheria. Similarly, lysogenic strains of *Streptococcus pyogenes* and *Clostridium botulinum* manufacture toxins that are responsible for scarlet fever and botulism, respectively. In all of these cases, if the prophage is eliminated from the bacterium, the cells lose the ability to synthesize toxin. The genes that code for these toxins are phage genes, which are expressed only when the phage DNA is integrated into the bacterial chromosome. Some examples of lysogenic conversion are given in **table 13.3.**

Extrusion Following Phage Replication—Filamentous Phages

In addition to the phages that develop productive (lytic) infections and latency, some phage can develop other relationships with their host cells. A few closely related bacterial viruses that have the appearance of long thin fibers are known as **filamentous phages.** These include the single-stranded DNA phages M13 and fd **(figure 13.8).** They do not lyse the cell; rather, they replicate their DNA and synthesize phage protein but the bacteria continue to multiply. Indeed, these few phages are the only ones that do not lyse their hosts following phage maturation, although the cells grow more slowly.

Replication of Filamentous Phages

Unlike phage T4, filamentous phages adsorb to the tip of the F^+ pilus of *E. coli* and therefore infect only F^+ cells **(figure 13.9).** It is clear that the single-stranded DNA that enters the cell does not completely take over their host's metabolism exclusively for phage production because the bacteria continue to multiply. The phage DNA replicates and also codes for the synthesis of the phage coats. Interestingly, neither mature filamentous phage nor their coats can be detected in the cytoplasm of the host cells. It seems likely that after their synthesis, the phage capsomers are stored in the cytoplasmic membrane of the bacterium. The phage are assembled as they are extruded from the cell. The extrusion occurs continuously, and the phage are not released in a burst. Infected cells, termed **carrier cells,** can be subcultured and stored in the same way as non-infected cells.

Replication of Single-Stranded DNA of Filamentous Phage

The replication of the single-stranded DNA of a filamentous phage has some features that are similar but others that are different from double-stranded DNA replication. The DNA that enters the cell

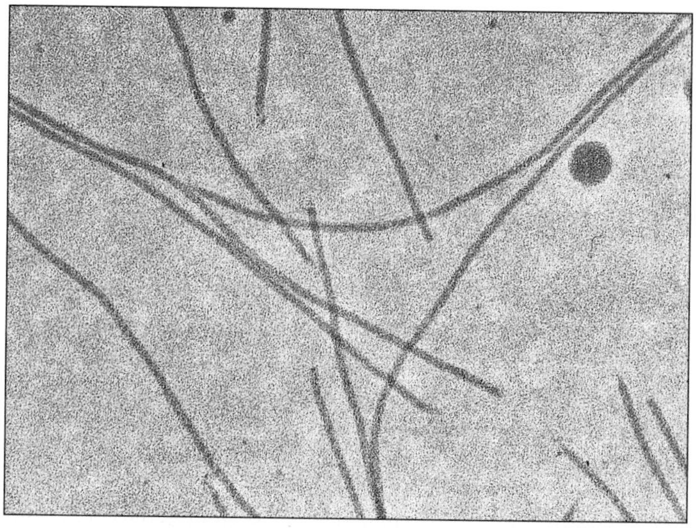

FIGURE 13.8 Electronphotomicrograph of fd Phage This phage only infects cells that have a sex pilus. Each phage is about 900 nm long.

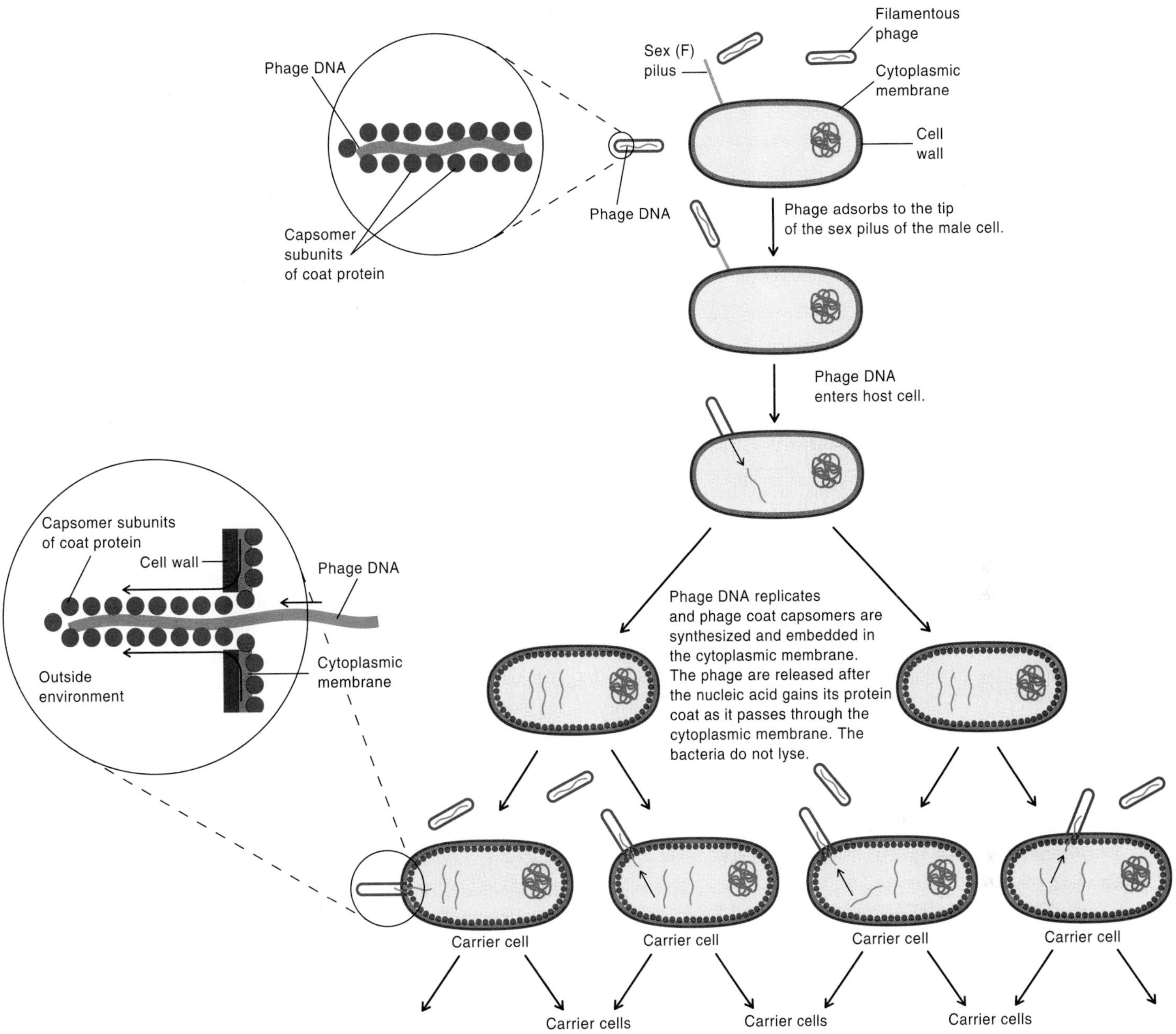

FIGURE 13.9 Replication of a Filamentous Phage The phage coat protein capsomers are embedded in the cytoplasmic membrane of the bacterium. Maturation of the phage occurs as the DNA is extruded through the cytoplasmic membrane. Carrier cells continue to extrude phage as they multiply.

is a positive (+) stranded molecule that is converted to a double-stranded form by enzymes of the host cell **(figure 13.10).** This double-stranded, **replicative form** consists of a positive (+) and a negative (–) strand. The double-stranded replicative form replicates in much the same way as double-stranded DNA of bacteria. This replicative form gives rise to the single-stranded positive (+) strand and a negative (–) strand. The single-stranded DNA that is incorporated into the coat protein as the virus is extruded from the cell is a positive (+) strand, and it is derived from the double-stranded replicative form (see figure 13.10). ■ DNA replication, p. 170 ■ (+) and (–) strand DNA, p. 174

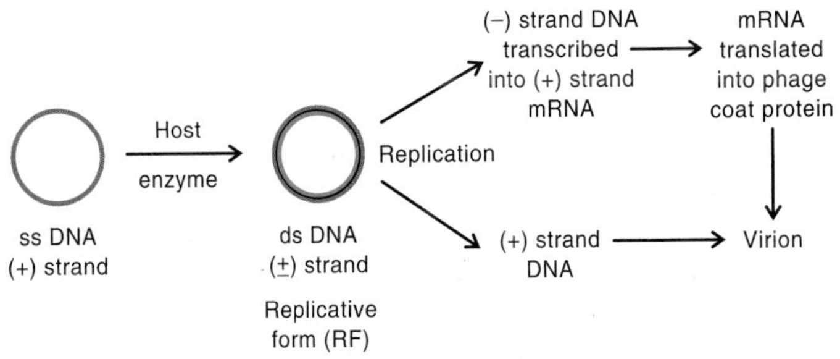

FIGURE 13.10 Macromolecule Synthesis in Filamentous Phage Replication

TABLE 13.4 Features of Interactions of Phages with Host Cells

Phage	Type of Interaction	Type of Nucleic Acid*	Result of Interaction
T4	Productive	ds DNA	Cell lyses
MS2, Qβ	Productive	ss RNA (+) strand	Cell lyses
Lambda (λ)	Latent or Productive	ds DNA	Phage and host often live in harmony
M13, fd	Productive	ss DNA (+) strand	Phage extrudes from cell, which continues to multiply
ϕX174	Productive	ss DNA (+) strand	Cell lyses

*ds, double-stranded; ss, single-stranded.

Lytic Infection by Single-Stranded DNA Phages

Not all phages with single-stranded DNA are extruded. The isometric phage, ϕX174 also contains a positive (+) strand but differs in shape from the filamentous phages and infection is not limited to F^+ cells. This phage goes through a lytic cycle.

Table 13.4 summarizes the salient features of the various interactions of the phages with their host cells.

MICROCHECK 13.2

Some phages lyse their host cells and some are extruded without killing the host. Most live in harmony with them. The latter often code for gene products that confer new properties on the host, which is termed lysogenic conversion.

- ✓ How does T4 phage prevent the infected bacterium from synthesizing bacterial proteins?
- ✓ What are two ways that phage can replicate in harmony with their host?
- ✓ Have phage that are extruded from the bacterial cell surface undergone a productive infection? Are they virulent? Explain your answers.
- ✓ In what way is phage induction an advantage for the phage?

13.3 Transduction

Focus Point

- Describe the differences between generalized and specialized transduction.

Phages play an important role in the transfer of bacterial genes from one bacterium to another. As briefly discussed in chapter 8, DNA can be transferred from one bacterial cell, the donor, to another, the recipient, by phage in the process called **transduction.** There are two types of transduction. In one type, any bacterial gene can be transferred, a process called **generalized transduction.** The phages that carry out this process are termed **generalized transducing phages.** The second type is termed **specialized transduction** since only a few specific genes can be transferred by the phages, which are **specialized transducing phages.** ■ transduction, p. 207

Generalized Transduction

Virulent as well as temperate phages can serve as generalized transducing phages. Recall that some phages in their replication life cycle degrade the bacterial chromosome into many fragments at the beginning of a productive infection. These short DNA fragments can be incorporated inadvertently into the phage head in place of phage DNA during phage maturation (see figure 8.21). Following lysis and release of the phage, the phage binds to another bacterial cell and injects the bacterial DNA. Once inside the new host, the DNA from the donor cell can integrate into the recipient cell DNA by homologous recombination. These recipient cells do not lyse. Since the genetic information transferred can be any gene of the donor cell, this gene transfer mechanism is called generalized transduction. ■ generalized transduction, p. 207 ■ homologous recombination, p. 206

Why do the transducing virulent phage not lyse the cells they invade? Because the bacterial DNA replaces the phage DNA inside the phage's head, the genetic information necessary for the synthesis of phage-encoded proteins is lacking. The phage is termed **defective** because it lacks the DNA necessary to form complete phage and lyse the recipient cell.

Specialized Transduction

Specialized transduction involves the transfer of only a few specific genes and is carried out only by temperate phages. The most actively studied specialized transducing phage is λ, which integrates only at specific sites in the chromosome of *E. coli.* Lambda transduces specific genes by the following means **(figure 13.11).**

Usually, only the phage λ DNA is excised following induction. On rare occasions, however, a piece of bacterial DNA remains attached to the piece of phage DNA that is excised and a piece of phage DNA is left behind in the bacterial chromosome. This loss of phage DNA creates a defective phage. The bacterial genes attached to the phage DNA replicate as the phage DNA replicates. These DNA molecules then become incorporated into mature phage in the maturation process. The defective phage are released from the lysed cells. When the defective phage infect another bacterial cell, both phage and bacterial DNA enter the new host and become integrated into the chromosome. Thus, the resulting lysogens contain bacterial genes

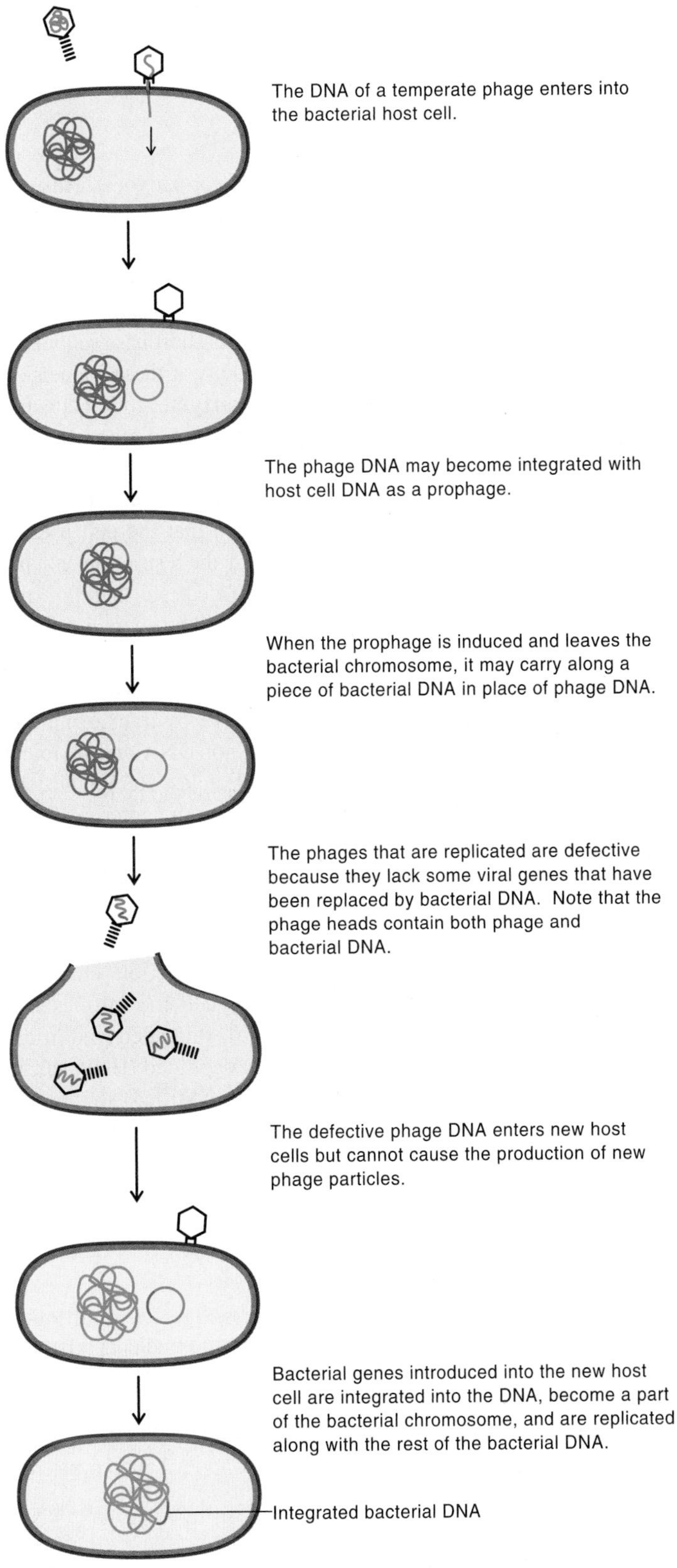

The DNA of a temperate phage enters into the bacterial host cell.
The phage DNA may become integrated with host cell DNA as a prophage.
When the prophage is induced and leaves the bacterial chromosome, it may carry along a piece of bacterial DNA in place of phage DNA.
The phages that are replicated are defective because they lack some viral genes that have been replaced by bacterial DNA. Note that the phage heads contain both phage and bacterial DNA.
The defective phage DNA enters new host cells but cannot cause the production of new phage particles.
Bacterial genes introduced into the new host cell are integrated into the DNA, become a part of the bacterial chromosome, and are replicated along with the rest of the bacterial DNA.
Integrated bacterial DNA

FIGURE 13.11 Specialized Transduction by Temperate Phage Only bacterial genes near the site where the prophage has integrated can be transduced.

from the previously lysogenized cells. Only bacterial genes located near the site of integration of the phage DNA can be transduced.

MICROCHECK 13.3

Bacterial genes from a donor can be transferred to recipient bacteria following the incorporation of bacterial genes in place of phage genes in the virion. After the phage lyse the donor bacteria and infect the recipient cells, the bacterial genes are integrated into the chromosome of the recipient cell, the process of transduction. There are two types of transduction: generalized, in which any gene of the host can be transferred; and specialized, in which only the genes near the site at which the phage DNA integrates into the host chromosome can be transferred. The latter process is carried out only by temperate phages.

- ✓ What is meant by a defective phage?
- ✓ Most temperate phages integrate into the host chromosome, whereas some replicate as plasmids. Which kind of relationship would you think would be more likely to maintain the phage in the host cell? Why?

13.4

Host Range of Phages

Focus Points

- List three mechanisms that reduce infection by phage.
- Describe the activities of the two enzymes in the restriction-modification system.

The number of different bacteria that a particular phage can infect defines its **host range.** Several thousand different phages have been isolated, and the host range of any particular phage is usually limited to a single bacterial species and often to only a few strains of that species. This fact is put to practical use in distinguishing between different bacterial strains, the technique of **phage typing.** Several factors limit the host range of phage. The two most important are (1) the requirement that the phage must attach to specific receptors on the host cell surface to start infection and (2) a restriction-modification system of the host cell must be overcome. The limited host range means that phages seldom transfer DNA between unrelated bacteria. ■ phage typing, p. 258

Receptors on the Bacterial Surface

Receptor sites vary in chemical structure and location. Receptors are usually on the bacterial cell wall, although a few phages attach to pili and a few others attach to sites on flagella **(figure 13.12).** Receptor sites can be altered by two distinct mechanisms, thereby creating a resistant cell. First, the receptor sites can be modified by mutation. In any large population of susceptible cells, some will have a modified (mutant) receptor site that confers resistance to any given phage.

Second, as already discussed, some, but not all, temperate phages that have lysogenized a bacterial cell can alter the cell surface, an

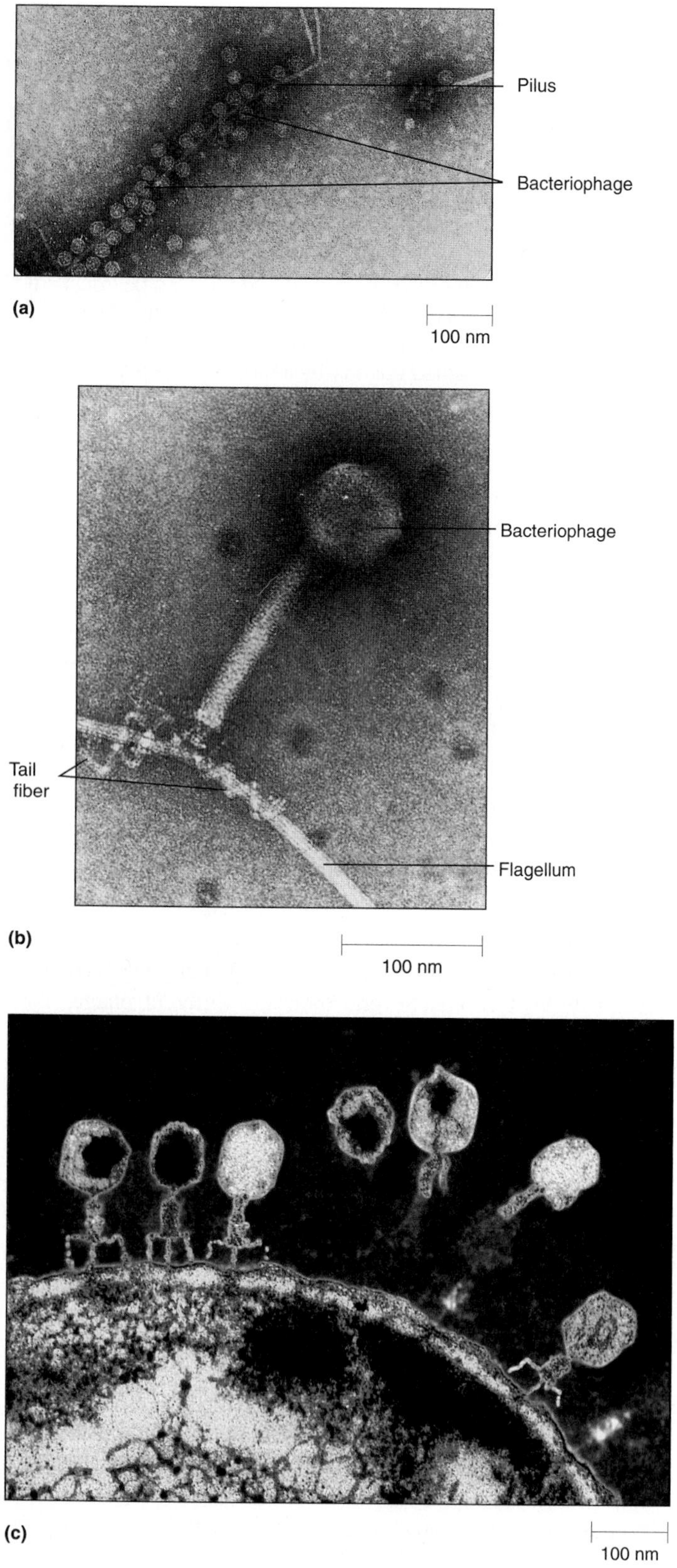

FIGURE 13.12 Adsorption of Bacteriophages on Various Cell Structures **(a)** Bacteriophage on pilus of *E. coli.* **(b)** Bacteriophage tail fiber entwined around flagellum. **(c)** Bacteriophage T4 attached to cell wall of *E. coli.*

example of lysogenic conversion. As a result the original receptor is no longer available. Thus, the prophage protects its host and, in turn, is able to continue replicating inside it.

Restriction-Modification System

Another mechanism of resistance is limited to prokaryotes. This system led to the biotechnology revolution that started when scientists gained the ability to clone genes. Virtually all prokaryotes have two genes located next to each other in the genome that are involved in the **restriction-modification system.** One gene codes for a **restriction enzyme,** an endonuclease that recognizes short base sequences in double-stranded DNA and cleaves the DNA at these sequences. The second gene codes for a **modification enzyme,** which attaches methyl groups to the purine and pyrimidine bases of the nucleotide sequence recognized by the restriction enzyme. These methylated bases are not recognized by the restriction enzyme, and so it does not cleave the DNA. This is the mechanism that the cell uses to protect its own DNA from being degraded by the restriction enzyme present in the cell. Its own DNA is methylated and therefore not degraded, but foreign DNA entering the cell will be degraded unless it is methylated first. ■ restriction enzyme, pp. 220

The restriction-modification system explains why, in general, a recipient bacterium will maintain DNA by transformation, conjugation, or transduction only if the donor DNA and recipient cells are of the same species or even subspecies. Recipient cells restrict any DNA if the methylation pattern of the entering donor DNA differs from its own. Foreign DNA from different species, however, isn't always destroyed when it enters a recipient cell. Why would this be the case in light of the cells having restriction enzymes? When foreign DNA enters a cell, a race ensues between enzymes intent on degrading the DNA (restriction enzymes) and enzymes that are attempting to methylate the purines and pyrimidines of the entering DNA before it is degraded (modification enzymes). In most cases, the DNA is degraded. However, in rare cases, the entering DNA is methylated (modified) so that it is no longer recognized as being foreign. Now the DNA can replicate if it is a replicon or becomes integrated into the genome of the recipient cell in the case of DNA transformation and conjugation. ■ replicon, p. 204 ■ conjugation, p. 210 ■ DNA transformation, p. 205

MICROCHECK 13.4

The host range of bacteriophages is determined by the attachment proteins on the virus recognizing receptors on the bacterial host and by the ability of the entering phage DNA to escape degradation by host restriction-enzymes. Most receptor sites for phage are on the cell wall of the bacterium, although some are on pili and flagella.

- ✓ What kind of enzymatic activity does the modification system have?
- ✓ You add an unknown phage to a mixture of F^+ and F^- cells of *E. coli* and plate out the bacteria. The bacterial colonies that grow are all F^-. How can you explain this phenomenon?
- ✓ A mutation in *E. coli* results in the loss of both restriction and modification enzymes. Would you expect any difference in the frequency of gene transfer by transduction from *Salmonella*? Explain.

FUTURE CHALLENGES

"Take Two Phage and Call Me in the Morning"

More and more bacteria are becoming resistant to an ever greater number of antibiotics, and so the effectiveness of these medications has been greatly reduced. One novel approach to treating infectious diseases is to use phage to kill the disease-causing bacteria. This is not a new idea. Felix d'Herelle, the co-discoverer of phage, believed that they were mainly responsible for natural immunity. He also claimed that phages would be a universal prophylaxis and therapy. So convinced was he that while he was a Professor of Bacteriology at Yale, he also owned a commercial laboratory in Paris that produced preparations of phage that he sold to the pharmaceutical industry. After leaving Yale, he went to the Bacteriophage Research Institute in the USSR state of Georgia. Today, much of the work on the possible use of phage as therapeutic agents is being carried out in this same Institute.

Although in theory the use of phage sounds attractive, in practice many problems are associated with this technology. First, a specific phage will only infect a single species or only a specific strain of a given species. Since it would take too long to isolate the causative infectious bacterium and isolate a phage that could attack it, "cocktails" containing many different phages must be used. Thus, to treat intestinal diseases, a "cocktail" of 17 different phages that attack intestinal pathogens has been developed. To treat burns that may be subject to infection by *Pseudomonas,* a kind of bandage saturated with a cocktail of 5 to 9 different phages has been employed. Whether phages are present that will attack all of the bacteria responsible for the disease, however, is questionable.

Another concern is that great care must be taken in purifying the phage before the preparation is administered. When phages lyse bacteria, a great deal of debris from the lysed cells is mixed in with the phage. This material could be very dangerous if it got into the bloodstream.

A third problem that must be overcome is that phages are recognized as foreign by the body's immune system, and therefore they are quickly eliminated. Some success has been achieved in increasing the time the phages stick around by altering the phage coat.

The fourth hurdle that must be overcome is the need for indepth animal testing and human trials. No clinical trials involving human patients have been carried out but studies from England have reported that mice, calves, and chickens could be protected from disease-causing strains of *E. coli.* Enough statements of success have been made in the use of phage in Russia and countries in the former Soviet Union, that phages are now being seriously considered as therapeutic agents in Western countries. It is the only therapy that increases in amount as it successfully carries out its job.

SUMMARY

13.1 General Characteristics of Viruses (Table 13.1)

Viruses are non-living agents associated with all forms of life. Each virus particle consists of nucleic acid surrounded by a protein coat. They are approximately 100- to 1,000-fold smaller than the cells they infect. (Figures 13.2, 13.3)

Virus Architecture

Different viruses have different shapes. Some are **isometric,** others are **helical** and still others are complex. (Figure 13.1)

The shape is determined by the protein coat (or capsid) that surrounds the nucleic acid. These make up the **nucleocapsid.** Each capsid is composed of **capsomers; attachment proteins** project from the capsid. (Figures 13.1, 13.2)

Some animal viruses have a lipid bilayer surrounding the coat. These viruses are **enveloped.** Viruses without this envelope are **naked.** Virtually all viruses that infect bacteria, **bacteriophages,** are complex and naked. (Figure 13.2)

The Viral Genome

Viruses contain either RNA or DNA, but never both. The nucleic acid may be single-stranded or double-stranded.

Replication Cycle—Overall Features

Viruses only multiply within living cells and use the machinery of the cells to support their own multiplication.

Some viruses take over the metabolism of the host cell completely and kill it; others live in harmony with their hosts.

Viruses exist in two states. Outside the cell they cannot multiply. They are called **virions.** Inside infected cells, they replicate.

13.2 Virus Interactions with Host Cells (Table 13.4, Figure 13.4)

Bacteriophages (phages) have the same relationships to their host as do animal viruses. Phages are much easier to study and serve as excellent model systems.

Some phages multiply inside bacteria and lyse the cells; this is a **productive infection;** the phages are virulent and lytic. Other phages multiply but are extruded from the cell and do not kill it.

Temperate phages transfer their DNA into the host cell, where it multiplies either as a plasmid or more commonly is integrated into the chromosome of the host.

A **latent** infection may show no sign that cells are infected.

Lytic Phage Replication by Double-Stranded DNA Phages (Figure 13.5)

This type of productive infection is one in which the host cell metabolism is taken over by a **virulent** phage and lyses. The infection proceeds through a number of defined steps:

- **Attachment—protein tail fibers** on the tail of the phage adsorb to specific receptors on the cell wall.
- **Penetration**—the DNA passes through the open channel of the **tail** and is injected into the cell. The phage coat remains on the outside.
- **Transcription**—the phage DNA is **transcribed.** Some is transcribed early in infection and other regions are transcribed later. The mRNA is then **translated** into **phage proteins.**

- **Replication** of phage DNA and proteins—the phage DNA and proteins replicate independently of one another. A phage enzyme degrades the bacterial chromosome so that only phage proteins are synthesized.
- **Assembly (maturation)**—this is a highly complex and ordered series of processes, some are catalyzed by enzymes, others not. The net result is the assembly of the phage components into a complete virus particle.
- **Release**—a **phage-encoded** lysozyme lyses the cells resulting in the release of many virus particles per infected cell. This is the **burst size.**

Lytic Single-Stranded RNA Phages

These phages attach to the **sex pilus.**

They replicate rapidly and reach burst sizes of 10,000.

The entering RNA codes for an unusual RNA polymerase that uses RNA as a substrate.

Phage Replication in a Latent State—Phage Lambda (Figure 13.6)

The temperate phage λ can either go through a lytic cycle similar to T4 or integrate its DNA into a specific site in the bacterial chromosome.

Integration of phage DNA into the bacterial chromosome as a prophage occurs by means of site-specific recombination. (Figure 13.7)

The **prophage** is maintained in an integrated state because a repressor prevents expression of genes coding for an enzyme that **excises** the prophage from the chromosome.

Lysogens, the bacteria carrying prophage, are immune to the same phage whose DNA they carry.

Prophage often code for proteins that confer unique properties on the bacteria, a process called **lysogenic conversion.** (Table 13.3)

Extrusion Following Phage Replication—Filamentous Phages (Figures 13.8, 13.9)

The **filamentous phage** attach to the sex pilus of *E. coli,* and the single-stranded DNA enters the cell.

The entering positive (+) single strand of DNA is converted to a double-stranded **replicative form.** This DNA gives rise to the two single-stranded forms, one positive (+), the other **negative** (–).

The negative (–) strand gives rise to its complementary strand, which serves as mRNA for the synthesis of phage proteins.

Filamentous phages do not take over the metabolism of the host cell completely, but multiply productively as the host multiplies.

Phage are released by **extrusion** through the cell wall, a process that does not kill the bacteria.

As the positive strand of DNA is extruded, the DNA becomes surrounded by the capsomers in the cytoplasmic membrane.

Lytic Infection by Single-Stranded DNA Phages

Single-stranded DNA phages exist that lyse cells.

13.3 Transduction

1. There are two types of transduction: **generalized** and **specialized.**

Generalized Transduction (Figure 8.21)

Generalized transduction involves the transfer of any piece of the bacterial chromosome from one cell to another cell of the same species.

Phage genes together with bacterial DNA replicate and the phage DNA codes for the phage coat protein. The coat surrounds the bacterial and phage DNA, and, following lysis, the bacterial DNA is transferred to other bacteria in the environment.

Generalized transduction can be carried out by virulent and temperate phages.

Specialized Transduction (Figure 13.11)

Specialized transduction involves the transfer of specific genes and is carried out only by temperate phages. Lambda is a well-studied **specialized transducing phage.**

Only genes located near the site at which the temperate phage integrates its DNA are transduced. Bacterial genes may remain attached to the phage DNA when the phage DNA excises from the bacterial chromosome.

13.4 Host Range of Phages

Several factors determine the **host range** of phage. These include the requirement that phage attachment proteins must bind to specific receptors on the bacteria, and the phage must circumvent the **restriction-modification** system found in all prokaryotes that degrades foreign DNA.

Receptors on the Bacterial Surface (Figure 13.12)

Most receptors are found primarily on the bacterial cell wall, but some phage attach to pili and flagella.

Restriction-Modification System

All prokaryotes have **restriction enzymes** that recognize short sequences of bases in DNA and cleave, and thereby degrade the DNA at those sites. All prokaryotes have **modification enzymes** that add methyl groups to the bases in the short sequence so that they are not recognized by the endonuclease and are not cleaved. Cells use this mechanism to protect their own DNA from degradation.

When DNA from one strain of *E. coli* enters another strain, a race ensues between the restriction enzyme and the modification enzyme. If the modification enzyme can methylate the sequences before the restriction endonuclease recognizes and cleaves the DNA, then the DNA will be spared from degradation and will replicate. Its pattern of methylation will be identical to the DNA of the cell in which it is replicating, but different from the cell that it came from.

REVIEW QUESTIONS

Short Answer

1. What is the name given to the phage whose DNA can be integrated into the host chromosome? What is the name of the host cell containing the phage DNA?
2. Name the process by which prophages confer new properties on their host cells.
3. Name the two types of transduction. Explain how they differ from each other in the DNA that is transferred.
4. Do all productive infections result in the complete takeover of host metabolism by the phage? Explain your answer.
5. Name three structures of bacteria that contain receptors for phage.
6. List the two mechanisms that allow bacteria to resist phage infection.

7. What is the most common shape of phages?
8. Compare double-stranded DNA phages with single-stranded filamentous DNA phages in terms of cell lysis and number of phages produced.
9. How does UV light induce the synthesis of virions from lysogenic bacteria?
10. In virulent phage infection, why is it important that not all phage-encoded enzymes be synthesized simultaneously? What general classes of enzymes are synthesized first? What class is synthesized last?

Multiple Choice Questions

1. Capsids are composed of
   a) DNA. b) RNA. c) protein.
   d) lipids. e) polysaccharides.
2. Temperate phages often
   1. lyse their host cells.
   2. change properties of their hosts.
   3. integrate their DNA into the host DNA.
   4. kill their host cells on contact.
   5. are rare in nature.
   a) 1, 2 b) 2, 3 c) 3, 4 d) 4, 5 e) 1, 5
3. All phages must have the ability to
   1. have their nucleic acid enter the host cell.
   2. kill the host cell.
   3. multiply in the absence of living bacteria.
   4. lyse the host cell.
   5. have their nucleic acid replicate in the host cell.
   a) 1, 2 b) 2, 3 c) 3, 4 d) 4, 5 e) 1, 5
4. The tail fibers on phages are associated with
   a) attachment.
   b) penetration.
   c) transcription of phage DNA.
   d) assembly of virus.
   e) lysis of host.
5. The phages Qβ and MS2
   1. contain double-stranded RNA.
   2. infect all strains of *E. coli.*
   3. contain single-stranded RNA.
   4. have very large burst sizes.
   5. contain single-stranded DNA.
   a) 1, 2 b) 2, 3 c) 3, 4 d) 4, 5 e) 1, 5
6. T4 is
   1. a phage that contains double-stranded DNA.
   2. a phage that contains single-stranded DNA.
   3. a phage that can lysogenize cells.
   4. a phage that can carry out specialized transduction.
   5. a virulent phage.
   a) 1, 2 b) 2, 3 c) 3, 4 d) 4, 5 e) 1, 5
7. The induction of a temperate phage by ultraviolet light results from
   a) damage to the phage.
   b) formation of thymine dimers.
   c) destruction of excision enzymes.
   d) destruction of a repressor.
   e) killing of the host cell.
8. Filamentous phages
   a) attach to bacterial receptors in the cell wall.
   b) take over metabolism of the host cell.
   c) are extruded from the host cell.
   d) undergo assembly in the cytoplasm of the host cell.
   e) degrade the host cells' DNA.
9. Phages have
   1. only one kind of nucleic acid.
   2. a protective protein coat.
   3. many enzymes.
   4. a single shape.
   5. a wide host range.
   a) 1, 2 b) 2, 3 c) 3, 4 d) 4, 5 e) 1, 5
10. *E. coli* most likely becomes resistant to T4 phage through mutations in
    a) the cell wall.
    b) a restriction enzyme.
    c) a modification enzyme.
    d) the structure of pili.
    e) the cytoplasmic membrane.

Applications

1. A researcher discovered a mutation in *E. coli* that prevented phage T4 but not lambda from lysing the cells. What would you surmise is the nature of this mutation?
2. A public health physician isolated large numbers of phage from rivers used as a source of drinking water in western Africa. The physician is very concerned about humans becoming ill from drinking this water although she knows that phages specifically attack bacteria. Why is she concerned?

Critical Thinking

1. Would transduction or conjugation be the most likely mechanism of gene transfer from a Gram-negative to a Gram-positive organism? Explain the reason for your answer.
2. A filter capable of preventing passage of bacteria is placed at the bottom of a U tube to separate the two sides. Streptomycin-resistant cells of a bacterium are placed on one side of the filter and streptomycin-sensitive cells are placed on the other side. After incubation for 24 hours, the side of the tube that originally contained only streptomycin-sensitive cells now contains some streptomycin-resistant cells. Give three possible reasons for this observation. What further experiments would you do to determine the correct explanation?
3. A suspension of phage when added to a culture of bacteria lyses the cells. When a suspension of the same phage is added to bacteria that have been previously agitated in a blender, no lysis occurs. Explain.
4. Is it surprising that most phages are temperate and not virulent? Explain.
5. Explain how the study of virus host range led to the biotechnology revolution. (Hint: It involves gene cloning technology.)

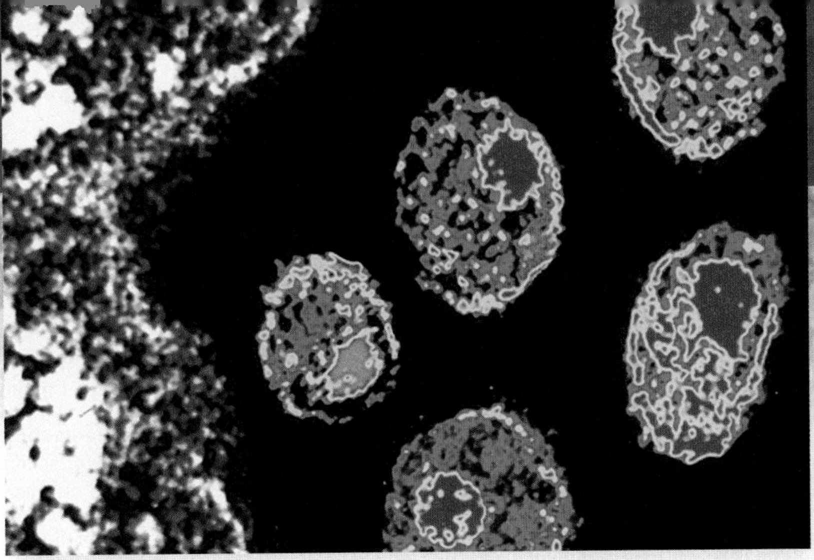

Transmission electron micrograph (TEM) of rotavirus (575,000×)

CHAPTER FOURTEEN

Viruses, Prions, and Viroids: Infectious Agents of Animals and Plants

A Glimpse of History

In December 2003, a cow that had crossed the border from Canada to Washington State was discovered to be suffering from an always fatal neurodegenerative condition called mad cow disease. In the fall of 2004 and January 2005, several more cows were found in Western Canada suffering from the same disease. Finding these few sick cows halted the importation of all beef from Canada into the United States. Such drastic actions were taken because of the tragedies that occurred in the United Kingdom (UK). In the mid-1980s and early 1990s, more than 180,000 cases of mad cow disease, scientific name **bovine spongiform encephalopathy,** were diagnosed in animals in the UK. The disease is so named because the brain of infected animals looks like a sponge with holes. The infected cows were apparently fed meat and bone meal from sheep and cattle that had also been suffering from this disease. The real tragedy unfolded when 11 people died of the disease after eating beef from infected animals. By early 2004, an additional 146 people were diagnosed in the UK as suffering from mad cow disease. Although many people were skeptical at the time of the first diagnosis, there is no question now that the mad cow disease was transmitted from cows to humans.

Mad cow disease is only one of a closely related group of transmissible neurodegenerative diseases that affects both humans and animals. The first example, known for 200 years in Europe, was scrapie, a disease of sheep and goats, so named because affected animals had difficulty standing up and "scraped" along fences for support. In 1936, scientists demonstrated that scrapie could be transmitted by inoculating tissue from diseased animals into healthy sheep and goats—however, it was a year before symptoms appeared. It was assumed that a virus must be the causative agent and the name slow virus disease was given to scrapie in 1954.

In the 1950s, considerable interest developed in a human neurodegenerative disease called kuru that was occurring in epidemic proportions among a native tribe in the highlands of Papua New Guinea. The disease was characterized by symptoms similar to scrapie, and apparently was transmitted through cannibalism. In 1959, Dr. William Hadlow made the connection between kuru and scrapie and suggested that kuru was also a slow virus disease. The next major advance was made when Dr. Carlton Gajdusek demonstrated that kuru was infectious since the symptoms of kuru appeared in chimpanzees 18 to 21 months after he inoculated them with brain tissue from patients with kuru.

From early on, there was no question that these diseases were caused by a transmissible agent, but the nature of this agent was in doubt. Although it was assumed that a virus was the causative agent, no virus could be detected. Further, the agent was resistant to many treatments, such as ultraviolet radiation, nucleases, and treatment with formalin and heat which inactivated most viruses. Also, patients never developed an immune response. All of these properties led some scientists to suggest that perhaps another type of agent was involved. To identify the active agent, brain homogenates were fractionated to identify the portion that was most active in causing disease. The most infectious fractions contained a protease-resistant glycoprotein, which accumulated in affected brains and often formed protein deposits. In 1982, Dr. Stanley Prusiner proposed the term **prion,** from the letters of proteinaceous infectious particle, to distinguish this infectious agent from viruses and viroids. This protein was abbreviated PrP. Initially it was assumed that this protein was encoded by a gene of the slow virus that was still believed to be the causative agent. However, sequencing the PrP led to the astounding discovery that the PrP was very similar in the sequence of amino acids to a protein encoded by a normal chromosomal gene in humans, which is now designated PrP^C (for cellular). Significantly, PrP^C is protease sensitive whereas the prion protein isolated from infected animals, labeled PrP^{SC} (for scrapie), is protease resistant. However, the amino acid sequences of PrP^C and PrP^{SC} are very similar. Therefore, there must be a difference in how

KEY TERMS

Acute infection Infection in which the symptoms appear soon after the pathogen is introduced. Symptoms are short lived.

Antigenic drift Minor changes that occur in the influenza virus antigen as a result of mutations.

Antigenic shift Major changes that occur in influenza virus antigens resulting from reassortment of viral segments following infection of the same cell by different influenza virions.

Budding A mechanism of release of virions through the plasma membrane without cell death.

Chronic infection A persistent infection in which the pathogen can be demonstrated at all times, with or without symptoms.

Endocytosis Process by which animal cells take up particles by enclosing them in a vesicle pinched off from the cell membrane.

Latent infection A persistent infection in which the infectious agent is present but not active. The agent can reactivate and then cause symptoms.

Persistent infection An infection in which the pathogen is continually present with or without disease.

Prion An infectious agent consisting of protein similar in amino acid sequence to a normal protein in the body which causes neurodegenerative disease.

Segmented virus A virion with a genome consisting of multiple different fragments.

Slow infection An infection in which the pathogen increases in number over a very long period of time before symptoms appear.

Zoonoses Natural diseases of animals that can be transmitted to humans as accidental hosts.

these proteins fold to assume their tertiary structure. This in fact is the case. In 1997, Dr. Prusiner was awarded the Nobel Prize for his discovery of prions, and for elucidating the principles that underlie their mode of action.

How can proteins which cannot replicate be infectious? From where did prions arise? Do the more common neurodegenerative diseases that are not infectious also have their basis in modifications in protein folding? The answers to these and other questions about these frightening diseases are beginning to be uncovered and are discussed in this chapter. ■

Much of the basic biology of bacteriophages also applies to animal and plant viruses; however, each viral group has certain unique properties. This chapter presents a general approach to the classification of animal viruses, followed by a discussion of their modes of replication and effects on host cells, including their role in causing certain tumors. A discussion of plant viruses as well as viroids and prions is also included.

14.1

Structure and Classification of Animal Viruses

Focus Points

- Distinguish between naked and enveloped viruses.
- Name three different ways by which viruses can be classified.

The structure of viruses was covered in chapter 13 (see figure 13.2); we give a brief review here. The structures of phage, and animal and plant viruses are similar, namely nucleic acid, either DNA or RNA, surrounded by a protein coat, the **capsid.** The capsid and nucleic acid together are called the **nucleocapsid.** The capsid, composed of a defined number of units called **capsomers,** are held together by non-covalent bonds. If there is no additional covering, the virus is termed **naked.** Many viruses that infect humans and other animals have a lipid membrane or **envelope** that surrounds the protein coat. Such a virus, called an **enveloped** virus, is rarely found among phage or plant viruses. The envelope is usually acquired from the cytoplasmic membrane of the infected cell during viral release from the cell. Thus, the structure of the viral envelope is similar to the membrane of the cell, a lipid bilayer containing various proteins. In certain virus families, a **matrix protein** is found just inside the lipid envelope. The **attachment proteins,** or **spikes,** that bind the virus to the cell project from the envelope or the capsid. Plant viruses, such as tobacco mosaic virus, do not bind to specific sites on the plant cell wall; rather, they enter through wounds and have no protruding attachment proteins.

Another distinguishing feature of some RNA animal and plant viruses is that their genome is divided into more than one RNA molecule in which each molecule carries different genetic information. For example, the influenza virus has eight RNA molecules, each carrying different genetic information. Such viruses are termed **segmented viruses.**

The virion can have a number of shapes **(figure 14.1).** One is **isometric** in which the protein subunits are arranged in groups of equilateral triangles, the most common arrangement being **icosahedral symmetry** in which 20 equilateral triangular faces enclose the nucleic acid. These viruses appear spherical when viewed with the electron microscope. A less common shape in animal viruses is the helical- or rod-shaped structure. Other virions are **pleomorphic**—they have an irregular shape. The most common type of phage, the complex tailed form, does not occur in animal and plant viruses. ■ complex phages, p. 320 ■ icosahedral symmetry, p. 320

Classification of Animal Viruses

The taxonomy of animal viruses changes as more is learned about their properties. The taxonomy likely will continue to evolve, and

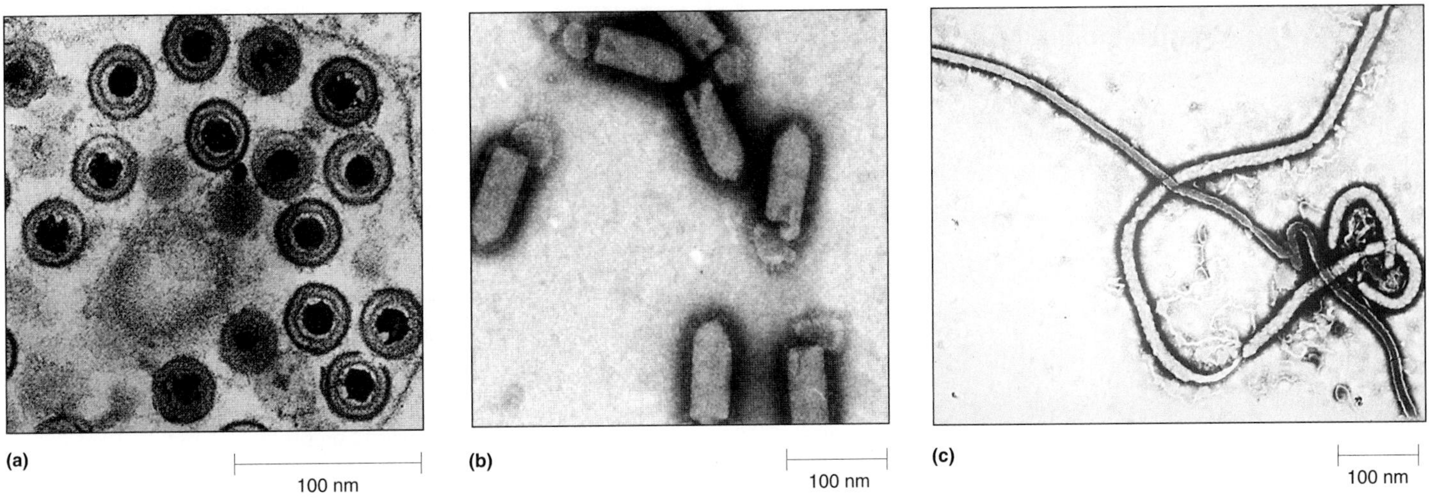

FIGURE 14.1 Shapes of Viruses (a) Electron microscopy of human papillomavirus, an isometric virus whose capsomers can be clearly seen. This virus is a cause of cancer in humans. **(b)** Electron microscopy of rhabdovirus particles, with their characteristic bullet shape. This virus causes rabies. **(c)** Ebola virus, a filamentous virus that occurs in a number of shapes. This virus causes Ebola.

so only general principles are considered here. The most widely employed taxonomic criteria for animal viruses are based on a number of characteristics:

1. Genome structure—DNA or RNA, single-stranded or double-stranded, a single molecule or segmented
2. Virus particle structure—isometric (icosahedral), helical (rod-shaped), or pleomorphic (irregular in shape)
3. Presence or absence of a viral envelope

Based on these major criteria, animal viruses are divided into a number of families, whose names end in *-viridae.* Fourteen families of RNA-containing viruses and seven families of DNA-containing viruses infect vertebrates (**tables 14.1** and **14.2,** respectively). The members of each family are derived from a common ancestor, as shown by nucleic acid hybridization. Evolutionary relationships between families however, cannot be inferred from this taxonomic scheme. The names of the families come from a variety of sources (see tables 14.1 and 14.2). In some cases, the name indicates the appearance of the virion, for example, Coronaviridae coming from *corona,* which means crown. In other cases, the virus is named from the geographic area the virion was first isolated. Bunyaviridae is derived from *Bunyamwera,* a locality in Uganda, Africa. Each family contains numerous genera whose names end in *-virus,* making it a single word, for example, Enterovirus. The species name is the name of the disease the virus causes (for example, polio or poliovirus). The species name is one or two words. In contrast to bacterial nomenclature in which an organism is referred to by its genus and species name, viruses are commonly referred to only by their species name, the name of the disease they cause and the names are not italicized. ■ **nucleic acid hybridization, p. 223**

The classification of the family Picornaviridae, which infects humans, is shown in **table 14.3.** This family contains three genera. The genus Enterovirus contains four species. Each species

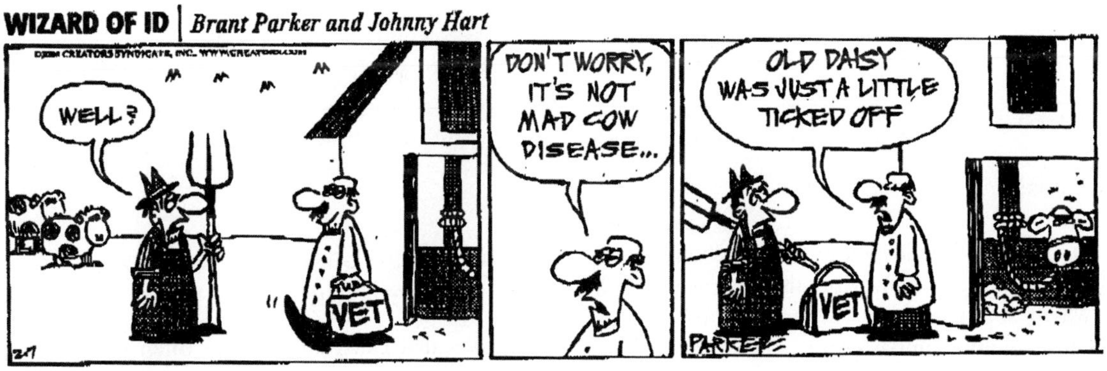

TABLE 14.1 Classification of RNA Viruses Infecting Vertebrates

Family	Drawing of Virion	Virion Structure	Genome Structure*	Representative Pathogenic Members and Some Diseases They Cause
Picornaviridae (*pico,* micro; *rna,* ribonucleic acid)		Naked; isometric	1 molecule, ss RNA	Poliovirus; rhinovirus causes colds Hepatitis A virus
Caliciviridae (*calix,* cup)		Naked; isometric	1 molecule, ss RNA	Norovirus; many members cause gastroenteritis
Togaviridae (*toga,* cloak)		Lipid-containing envelope	1 molecule, ss RNA	Many multiply in arthropods and vertebrates; encephalitis in humans
Flaviviridae (flavus, yellow)		Lipid-containing envelope	1 molecule, ss RNA	Yellow fever virus; dengue virus Hepatitis C virus
Coronaviridae (*corona,* crown)		Lipid-containing envelope	1 molecule, ss RNA	Colds and respiratory tract infections, including severe acute respiratory syndrome (SARS)
Rhabdoviridae (*rhabdos,* rod)	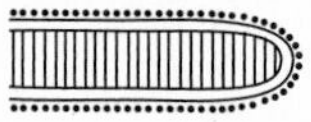	Bullet-shaped; lipid-containing envelope	1 molecule, ss RNA	Rabies virus
Filoviridae, (*filo,* threadlike)	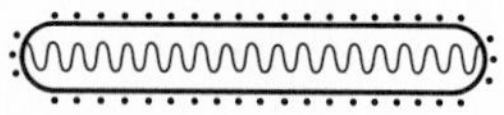	Long filamentous; sometimes circular; lipid-containing envelope	1 molecule, ss RNA	Marburg virus; ebola virus
Paramyxoviridae, (*para,* by the side of; *myxa,* mucus)		Pleomorphic; lipid-containing envelope	1 molecule, ss RNA	Mumps virus; parainfluenza virus measles virus
Orthomyxoviridae (*orthos,* straight; *myxa,* mucus)		Pleomorphic; lipid-containing envelope	7–8 segments of linear ss RNA	Influenza virus
Bunyaviridae (Bunyamwera, a locality in Uganda)		Lipid-containing envelope	3 molecules of ss RNA	Hantaan virus
Arenaviridae (*arena,* sand)		Pleomorphic; lipid-containing envelope	2 molecules of ss RNA with hydrogen-bonded ends	Lassa virus
Reoviridae (respiratory enteric orphan virus)		Naked; isometric	Linear ds RNA divided into 10, 11, or 12 segments	Diarrhea in animals
Birnaviridae (*bi,* two)		Naked; isometric	2 segments of linear ds RNA	No human pathogens; diseases in chickens and fish
Retroviridae (*retro,* backward)		isometric; lipid-containing envelope	2 identical molecules ss RNA	HIV

*ss, single-stranded; ds, double-stranded.

contains numerous "types." Whether these "types" should really be different species is in dispute. Rhinovirus contains a single species, rhinovirus, which in turn contains 100 "types."

In general, viruses with a similar genome structure replicate in a similar way. For example, animal viruses generally follow the same replication strategies as phages with similar genomes.

Groupings Based on Routes of Transmission

Viruses that cause disease are often grouped according to their routes of transmission from one individual to another. These are not taxonomic groupings, and members of more than one family

TABLE 14.2 Classification of DNA Viruses Infecting Vertebrates

Family	Drawing of Virion	Virion Structure	Genome Structure*	Representative Pathogenic Members and Some Diseases They Cause
Hepadnaviridae (*hepa,* liver; *dna,* deoxyribonucleic acid)		Lipid-containing envelope	1 molecule, mainly ds DNA but with a single-stranded gap	Hepatitis B virus
Parvoviridae (*parvus,* small)		Naked; isometric	1 molecule, ss DNA	Outbreaks of gastroenteritis following eating of shellfish
Papovaviridae (papilloma, polyoma, vacuolating agent		Naked; isometric	1 molecule, circular ds DNA	Human papillomaviruses associated with genital and oral carcinomas
Adenoviridae (*adenos,* gland)	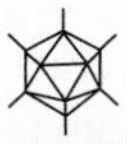	Naked; isometric	1 molecule, ds DNA	Some cause tumors in animals
Herpesviridae (*herpes,* creeping)		Enveloped with surface projections	1 molecule, ds DNA	Herpes simplex virus; cytomegalovirus Chickenpox virus; mononucleosis
Poxviridae (*poc,* pustule)	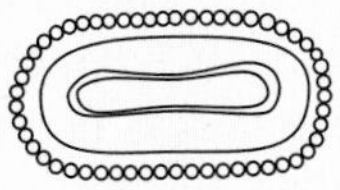	Enveloped; large brick-shaped	ds DNA; covalently closed ends	Smallpox virus; vaccinia virus
Iridoviridae (*irid,* rainbow)	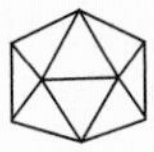	Naked; isometric	1 molecule, ds DNA	No known human pathogens; only animal pathogens

*ss, single-stranded; ds, double-stranded.

may be included in the same group. These groupings, summarized in **table 14.4,** provide examples of such a scheme.

The **enteric viruses** are usually ingested on material contaminated by feces, the **fecal-oral route.** They replicate primarily in the intestinal tract, where they usually remain localized. They often cause **gastroenteritis,** an inflammation of the stomach and intestine. Some, however, such as the poliovirus, replicate first in the intestines but do not cause gastroenteritis. Rather, they cause a systemic disease.

TABLE 14.3 Classification of Human Picornaviruses

Family	Genus	Species
Picornaviridae	Enterovirus	polioviruses 1–3 coxsackieviruses A1–A24 (no A23), B1–B6 echoviruses 1–34 (no 10 or 28) enteroviruses 68–71
	Rhinovirus	rhinoviruses 1–100
	Hepatovirus	hepatitis A virus

Respiratory viruses usually enter the body in inhaled droplets and replicate in the respiratory tract. The respiratory viruses include only those viruses that remain localized in the respiratory tract. Viruses that infect via the respiratory tract but then cause systemic diseases are not considered respiratory viruses. These latter include the viruses that cause mumps and measles.

Viral **zoonoses,** caused by **zoonotic viruses,** are diseases that are transmitted from an animal to a human or to another animal. Humans are accidental hosts and rarely is the disease spread from human to human. Many viruses, such as rabies, are transmitted directly from animals to humans, but humans cannot transmit it to other humans. Others, such as canine distemper, can be transmitted from dogs to African lions. One group of viruses, the arboviruses, are so named because they infect arthropods such as mosquitoes, ticks, and sandflies, where they replicate. Arthropods then bite vertebrates and transmit the virus. Thus, the viruses are arthropod-borne. In many cases, viruses can invade and replicate in widely different species. The same arthropod may bite birds, reptiles, and mammals and transfer viruses among these widely different groups. More than 500 arboviruses are known, and about 80 are known to infect humans. Twenty cause significant diseases such as West Nile fever, yellow fever, Western equine encephalitis, and dengue fever.

Sexually transmitted viruses cause lesions in the genital tract. These include herpesviruses and papillomaviruses. Other viruses that cause systemic infections are often transmitted during sexual activity. They include human immunodeficiency virus (HIV) and hepatitis viruses.

TABLE 14.4 Grouping of Human Viruses Based on Route of Transmission

Virus Group	Mechanism of Transmission	Common Viruses Transmitted
Enteric	Fecal-oral route	Enteroviruses (polio, coxsackie B); rotaviruses (diarrhea)
Respiratory	Respiratory or salivary route	Influenza; measles; rhinoviruses (colds)
Zoonotic	Vector (such as arthropods)	Sandfly fever; dengue
	Animal to human directly	Rabies; cowpox; West Nile fever
Sexually transmitted	Sexual contact	Herpes simplex virus-2 (genital herpes); HIV

MICROCHECK 14.1

The genomic structure and shapes of animal viruses are similar to bacteriophages, except the complex shape is not represented. Many animal viruses have an envelope derived from the host cell membrane surrounding their capsid. Animal viruses are classified based on whether they contain DNA or RNA, whether they are enveloped, and their shape. Viruses that cause disease are often grouped by their routes of transmission.

- ✓ Give two differences in the structure of some animal viruses and bacteriophages.
- ✓ List four ways in which viruses can be transmitted from one organism to another.
- ✓ Why do animal viruses have envelopes and phages rarely do?

14.2 Interactions of Animal Viruses with Their Hosts

Focus Points

- Name the major classes and subclasses of viral infections and describe how they differ from each other.
- Compare the steps in the infection process in an acute infection of an animal with infection of a bacterium by phage T4.

For bacterial viruses, the host organism is a single cell, and so other kinds of cells do not affect the course of the infection. In the case of animals, however, the outcome of viral infection depends on many factors that are independent of the infected cell. Of special importance are the defense mechanisms of the host, such as the presence of protective antibodies that can confer immunity against a virus ordinarily lethal to an individual without such immunity. Devastating epidemics of measles and smallpox, which decimated the indigenous native population following the arrival of Europeans to the Americas, are good examples of the consequences of the lack of immunity to particular viruses.

Sudden epidemics causing widespread deaths are the most dramatic events of virus interactions with humans. The death of the host, however, also means that the virus can no longer multiply. Obviously, this is not in the best interests of the virus. Just as with the vast majority of bacterial viruses, animal viruses may develop a relationship with their normal hosts in which they cause no obvious harm or disease. Thus, the virus infects and persists within the host, in a state of **balanced pathogenicity,** in which neither the virus nor the host is in serious danger. Indeed, most healthy animals, including humans, carry a number of viruses as well as antibodies against these viruses without suffering any ill effects. If, however, a virus is transmitted to an animal that has no immunity against it, disease may result.

Many viruses that are carried by one group of organisms without causing disease may cause serious disease when transferred to another group. For example, Lassa fever virus does not cause disease in rodents, in which it is normally found, but when transferred to humans, it kills a large percentage of the infected population.

The relationship between disease-causing viruses and their hosts can be divided into two major categories based on the disease and the state of the virion in the host. These are **acute** and **persistent.** Acute infections are usually self-limited diseases in which the virus often remains localized **(figure 14.2).** In persistent infections the virus establishes infections that remain for years or even life, often without any disease symptoms.

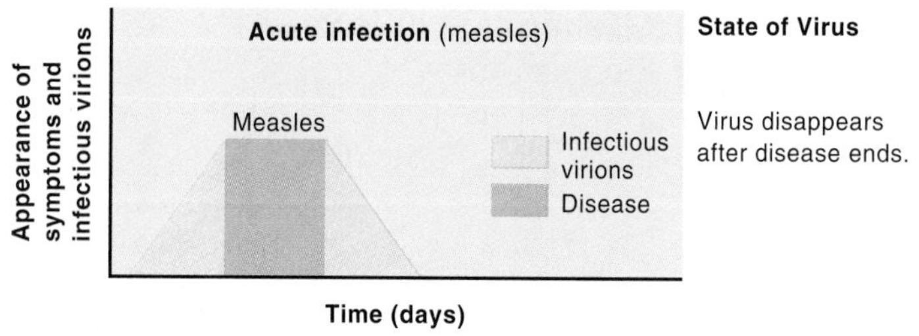

FIGURE 14.2 A Time Course of Appearance of Symptoms of Measles and the Measles Virions

Acute Infections

Acute infections are usually of relatively short duration, and the host organism may develop long-lasting immunity. Viruses that cause acute infections result in productive infections. The infected cells die and may or may not lyse with the release of virions. Viruses that cause lysis of host cells are usually naked, whereas those that do not cause lysis are frequently enveloped. Although infected cells die, this does not mean that the host dies. Disease symptoms result from localized or wide-spread tissue damage following lysis of cells and spreading and infection of new cells. With recovery, the defense mechanisms of the host gradually eliminate the virus over a period of days to months. Examples of acute infections are mumps, measles, influenza, and poliomyelitis. ■ mumps, p. 620 ■ measles, p. 538 ■ influenza, p. 597 ■ polio, p. 695

The reproductive cycle of an animal virus that results in an acute infection with cell lysis can be compared with the productive infection of a bacterium with a virulent phage. Basically the steps are the same except that infection of more complex eukaryotic cells in a multicellular host requires several additional steps. The essential steps include:

- Attachment
- Entry into susceptible cells following attachment
- Targeting of the virion to the site where it will reproduce
- Uncoating of the virion—separation of protein coat from nucleic acid
- Synthesis of protein and replication of nucleic acid
- Maturation of the viral particles
- Cell lysis
- Spreading of the virus within the host
- Shedding of the infectious virions outside the host
- Transmission to the next host, thereby repeating the infection cycle ■ lytic phage replication, p. 323

Step 1: Attachment

The process of attachment (adsorption) is basically the same in all virus-cell interactions, except that the process is more complex in animal viruses than in phages. Animal viruses usually do not contain a single specific attachment appendage, a tail with fibers, as does phage T4, for instance. Rather, surface projections containing attachment proteins or spikes protrude all over the surface of a virion (see figure 13.2). Frequently, there are several different attachment proteins. The receptors to which the viral attachment proteins bind are usually glycoproteins located on the plasma membrane, and often more than one receptor is required for effective attachment. For example, HIV must bind to two key molecules on the cell surface before it can enter the cell. The receptors number in the tens to hundreds of thousands per host cell. As with bacterial phage receptors, the normal function of these glycoproteins is completely unrelated to their role in virus attachment. For example, many receptors are immunoglobulins; other viruses use hormone receptors and permeases. ■ immunoglobulins, p. 392 ■ glycoproteins, p. 31

Different viruses may use the same receptor, and related viruses may use different receptors. Certain viruses can bind to more than one type of receptor and thus be able to invade different kinds of cells. The binding of the attachment proteins to their receptors often changes the shape of viral proteins concerned with entry of the virion and facilitates their entry. Because a virion must bind to specific receptors, frequently a particular virus can infect only a single or a limited number of cell types within a host species, and most viruses can infect only a single species. This may account for the resistance that some animals have to certain diseases. For example, dogs do not contract measles from humans, and humans do not contract distemper from cats. Some viruses however—for example, those that cause zoonoses—can infect unrelated animals such as horses and humans with serious consequences in both.

Step 2: Entry

The mechanism of entry of animal viruses into host cells depends on whether the virion is enveloped or naked. In the case of enveloped viruses, two mechanisms exist. In one mechanism, the envelope of the virion fuses with the plasma membrane of the host after attachment to a host cell receptor **(figure 14.3a).** This fusion is promoted by a specific **fusion protein** on the surface of the virion. In some viruses, such as measles, mumps, influenza, and HIV, the protein, which recognizes a target protein on the cell, changes its shape when it contacts the host cell. Following fusion, the nucleocapsid is released directly into the cytoplasm, where the nucleic acid separates from the protein coat.

In another mechanism, enveloped viruses adsorb to the host cell with their protein spikes, and the virions are taken into the cell in a process termed **endocytosis** (figure 14.3b). In this process, the host cell plasma membrane surrounds the whole virion and forms a vesicle. Then, the envelope of the virion fuses with the plasma membrane of the vesicle. The nucleocapsid is then released into the host's cytoplasm. ■ endocytosis, p. 76

In the case of naked virions, the virion also enters by endocytosis. Since the virus has no envelope, however, it cannot fuse with the plasma membrane. Rather, after being engulfed, the virus dissolves the vesicle, resulting in release of the nucleocapsid into the cytoplasm.

Entry by animal viruses differs from phage penetration in two ways. First, the envelope of the virion and the plasma membrane of the host may fuse. Such fusion is not possible when the outside covering of the host has a rigid cell wall. Second, the entire virion is taken into the cell, whereas in the case of phages, the protein coat remains on the outside of the bacterium.

Step 3: Targeting to the Site of Viral Replication

Following penetration, the virion must be targeted to the site where it will multiply. Most DNA viruses multiply in the nucleus, but how the virion gets to the nucleus is not known.

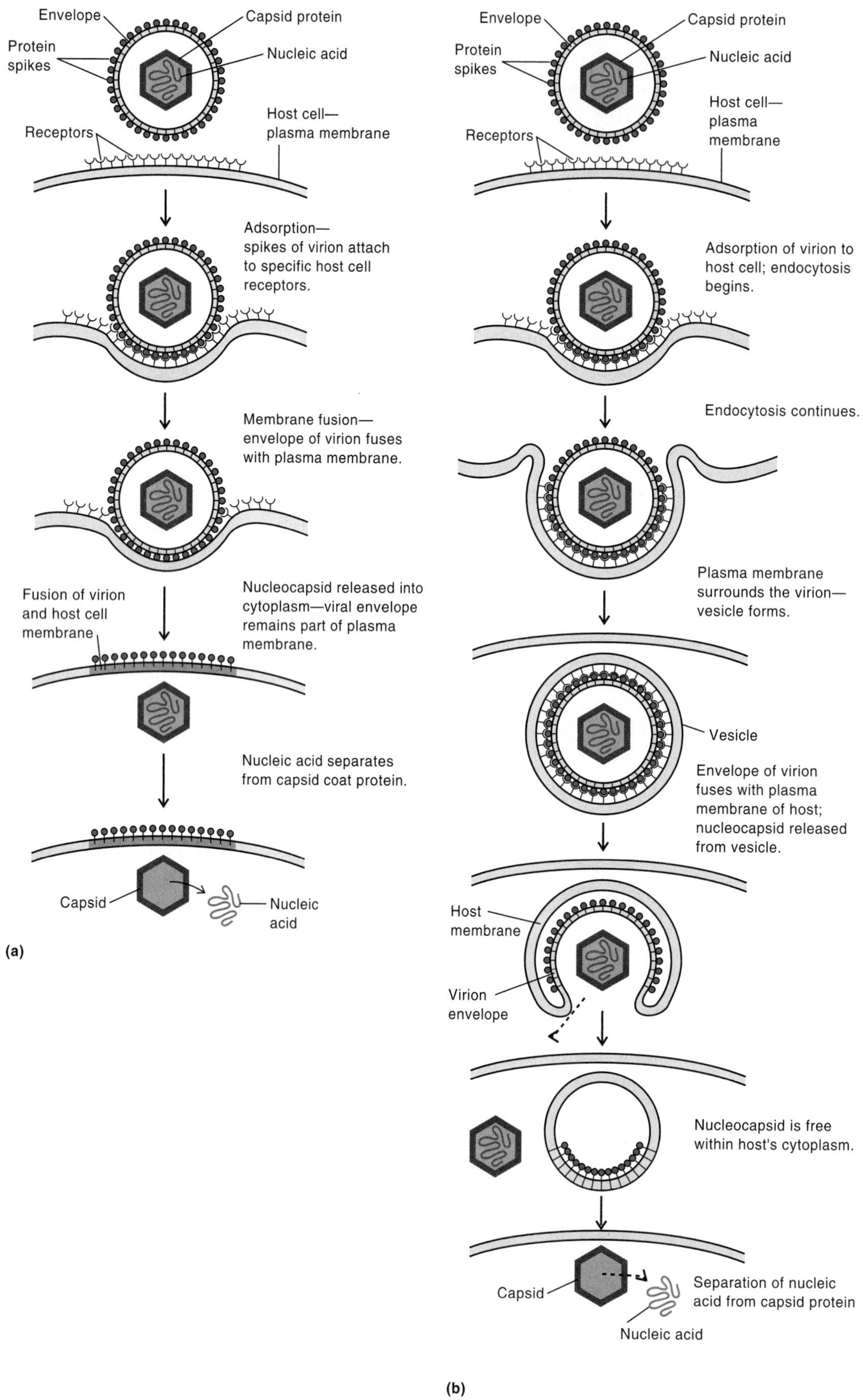

FIGURE 14.3 Entry of Enveloped Animal Viruses into Host Cells (a) Entry following membrane fusion and **(b)** entry by endocytosis.

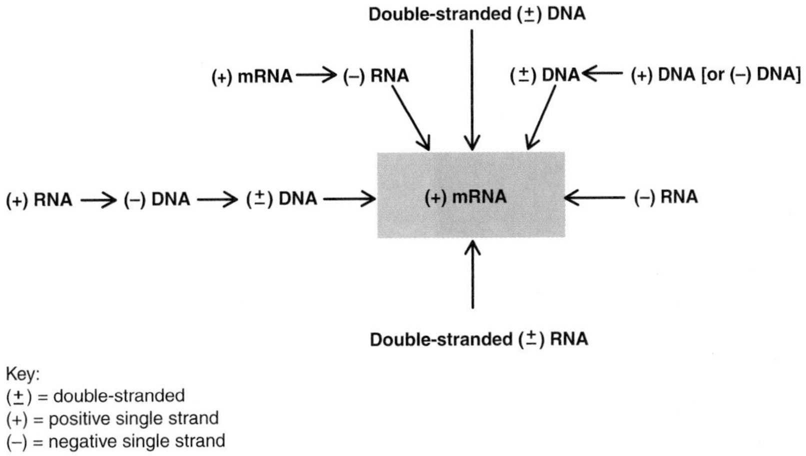

FIGURE 14.4 Strategies of Transcription Employed by Different Viruses Viruses that have the same genome structure follow the same strategy for the synthesis of (+) mRNA, which is then translated into protein. Only (+) mRNA can be translated into protein.
Based on Sherris Medical Microbiology Textbook.

Step 4: Uncoating

In all viruses, the nucleic acid separates from its protein coat prior to the start of replication. This process is termed **uncoating.**

Step 5: Nucleic Acid Replication and Protein Synthesis

The first step in replication is transcription of the nucleic acid of the virion. Diverse strategies are followed by viruses of different families for the synthesis of mRNA. In large part, the transcription strategy depends on whether the virus is RNA or DNA and whether the nucleic acid is single- or double-stranded **(figure 14.4).** For example, in the case of positive single-stranded RNA viruses, the RNA itself functions as a messenger, whereas in the case of negative single-stranded RNA viruses, the RNA must be transcribed into a positive strand. In this case, the RNA-dependent RNA polymerase required for transcription enters the cell as part of the virion since the uninfected cell does not have such an enzyme. Replication of RNA molecules is unique to viruses and generally occurs in the cytoplasm: Replication of viral DNA generally occurs in the nucleus. ■ **nomenclature for nucleic acid strandedness, p. 174**

In all cases, the patterns of transcription of the viral genome follow the same patterns as phages having the same type of genome follow. If a viral enzyme is required for transcription, it may be carried into the cell in the virion or the viral genome may encode the enzyme early in replication. In the case of phages, enzymes do not enter the cell; thus, if host cell enzymes are not available, the enzymes are encoded by the entering viral genome.

In all virus systems, whether phage, animal, or plant, the nucleic acids replicate and proteins are synthesized independently of one another. The replication of viral nucleic acid depends on enzymes present in the host cell prior to infection. Whether enzymes of the host or phage-encoded enzymes are used varies with the virus. In some cases, viral enzymes concerned with virus replication which are not present in the host enter the host cells along with the virion. As a general rule, the larger the viral genome, the fewer host cell enzymes are involved in replication. This is not surprising since enough DNA is present in large viral genomes to encode most enzymes of nucleic acid synthesis. For example, the largest of the DNA animal viruses, the poxviruses, like T4 phage, are totally independent of host cell enzymes for the replication of their nucleic acid. On the other hand, the very small parvoviruses depend so completely on the biosynthetic machinery of the host cell that they require that the host cell actually be synthesizing its own DNA at the time of infection so that viral DNA can also be synthesized. Most animal viruses are between these two extremes. The replication of the genome of many RNA viruses requires enzymes that are not found in the uninfected cell. Obviously, these must be either encoded by the virus or enter the cell with the virion. However, all viruses require that host cells supply the machinery for the generation of energy and the biosynthesis of macromolecules.

In some viruses, a polycistronic message is translated into a **polyprotein** which consists of many proteins strung together. A virus-encoded protease then cleaves the polyprotein to yield individual proteins.

Step 6: Maturation

The final assembly of the nucleic acid with its coat protein, the process of maturation, is preceded by formation of the protein capsid structure that surrounds the viral genome. The maturation process and multistep formation of the viral coat involve the same general principles in all kinds of viruses. In animal viruses, maturation takes place in a variety of organelles such as the nucleus and microtubules, depending on the virus. This process has already been discussed for bacteriophage T4. ■ **assembly, p. 324** ■ **microtubules, p. 77**

The maturation of a tobacco mosaic virus (TMV), a cylindrically shaped plant virus, has been studied extensively and serves as a model for both animal and plant viruses **(figure 14.5).** For TMV many identical protein structural subunits, the capsomers, are first formed and then are added one by one to the growing coat structure that surrounds the viral RNA. The coat elongates in both directions, starting from a specific site on the single-stranded viral

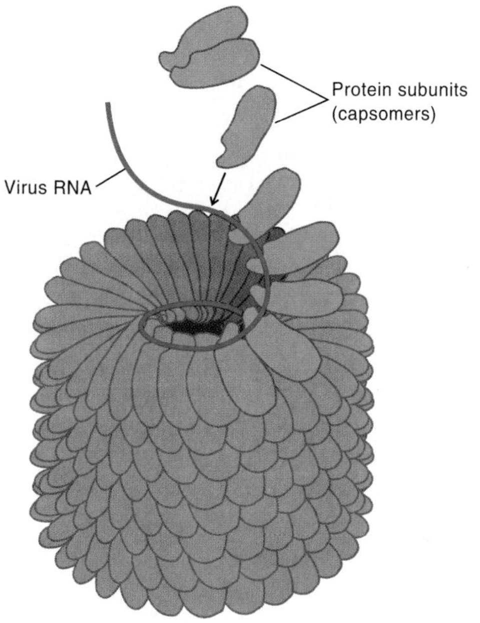

FIGURE 14.5 Tobacco Mosaic Virus Assembly Starting at a specific site on the RNA, the capsomers are added, one by one, to the coat structure to enclose the viral nucleic acid (RNA).

RNA. The RNA interacts with each protein disc as it is added, and when the end of the long RNA molecule is reached, the discs are no longer added. Enzymes are not required for the process, since the coat self assembles. Recall that the maturation of bacteriophage T4 is also, in part, a self-assembly process. It is a far more complicated process in T4 since this virion has many more different parts than the coat of TMV.

Assembly of many animal viruses takes place at specific regions of the membrane which have embedded specific protein components. These regions are termed **lipid rafts.**

Step 7: Release From Cells

Depending on where the virion is assembled, most non-enveloped viruses accumulate within the cytoplasm or nucleus following their assembly. Unlike virulent phages, animal viral nucleic acid does not code for enzymes that lyse the host cells. Infected cells often die because viral DNA and proteins rather than host cell material are synthesized. Thus, functions required for cell survival are not carried out, and cells die. Cell degradation and lysis may also result from the release of degradative enzymes contained in cellular lysosomes. This degradation and release of the virions give rise to **cytopathic effects,** changes in the appearance of cells (see figure 14.13). Dead cells lyse, releasing virions, which may then invade any healthy cells in the vicinity. ■ lysosomes, p. 80

Another mechanism for release is by budding from the plasma membrane **(figure 14.6).** This process is frequently associated with persistent infections, but the process may kill infected cells. An example of the latter is the killing by HIV as it buds from cells of the immune system. This process involves a number of steps. First, the region of the host cell plasma membrane where budding is going to take place acquires the protein spikes coded by the viruses, which eventually are attached to the outside of the virion. These are at the lipid raft regions. Then, the inside of the plasma membrane becomes coated with the matrix protein of the virus. In the next step, the nucleocapsid becomes completely enclosed by the lipid raft region of the plasma membrane into which the spikes and matrix protein are embedded. Most enveloped viruses obtain their envelopes as they exit the cell through the plasma membrane. Some viruses, however, bud through the Golgi apparatus or rough endoplasmic reticulum. Vesicles containing the virus then migrate to the plasma membrane, with which they fuse. The virions are released by **exocytosis.** Thousands of virions can be released over hours or days, often without significant cell damage. For all enveloped viruses, budding is part of the maturation process. The process of budding may not lead to cell death, because the plasma membrane can be repaired following budding. As discussed in chapter 13, filamentous phages also are released from bacterial cells by budding or extrusion, without killing the bacterial cells.
■ filamentous phage, p. 328 ■ Golgi apparatus, p. 80 ■ rough endoplasmic reticulum, p. 79

Step 8: Shedding From Host

To be maintained in nature, infectious virions must exit or be shed from the host. Shedding usually occurs from the same openings or surfaces that viruses use to gain entry. These include mucus or saliva from the respiratory tract during coughing, or sneezing, feces, urine, skin, genital secretions, and blood.

Step 9: Transmission To Other Hosts

Once an infectious virion has been shed from a host, it must be transmitted to another host, whether the same or another species. It enters into the new host and begins the infection cycle again. As previously discussed, human viruses can be classified based on their route of transmission (see table 14.4).

Differences in the various steps in the replication cycle of virulent animal viruses and phages are listed in **table 14.5.**

Persistent Infections

In persistent infections, the viruses are continually present in the body and are released from infected cells by budding. Persistent infections can be divided conveniently into three major categories. These are (a) **latent infections,** (b) **chronic infections,** and (c) **slow infections.** The categories are distinguished from one another largely by whether a virus can be detected in the body during the long period of persistence **(figure 14.7).**

A persistent infection may or may not cause disease, but since the infected person carries the virus, he or she is a potential source of infection to others. A person who sheds the virus is a **carrier** and is able to spread disease. Some persistent infections have features of more than one of these categories. These depend on such circumstances as the time after infection when symptoms appear and the cell type in which the virus is located. For example, infection by HIV has features of latent, chronic, and slow infections.

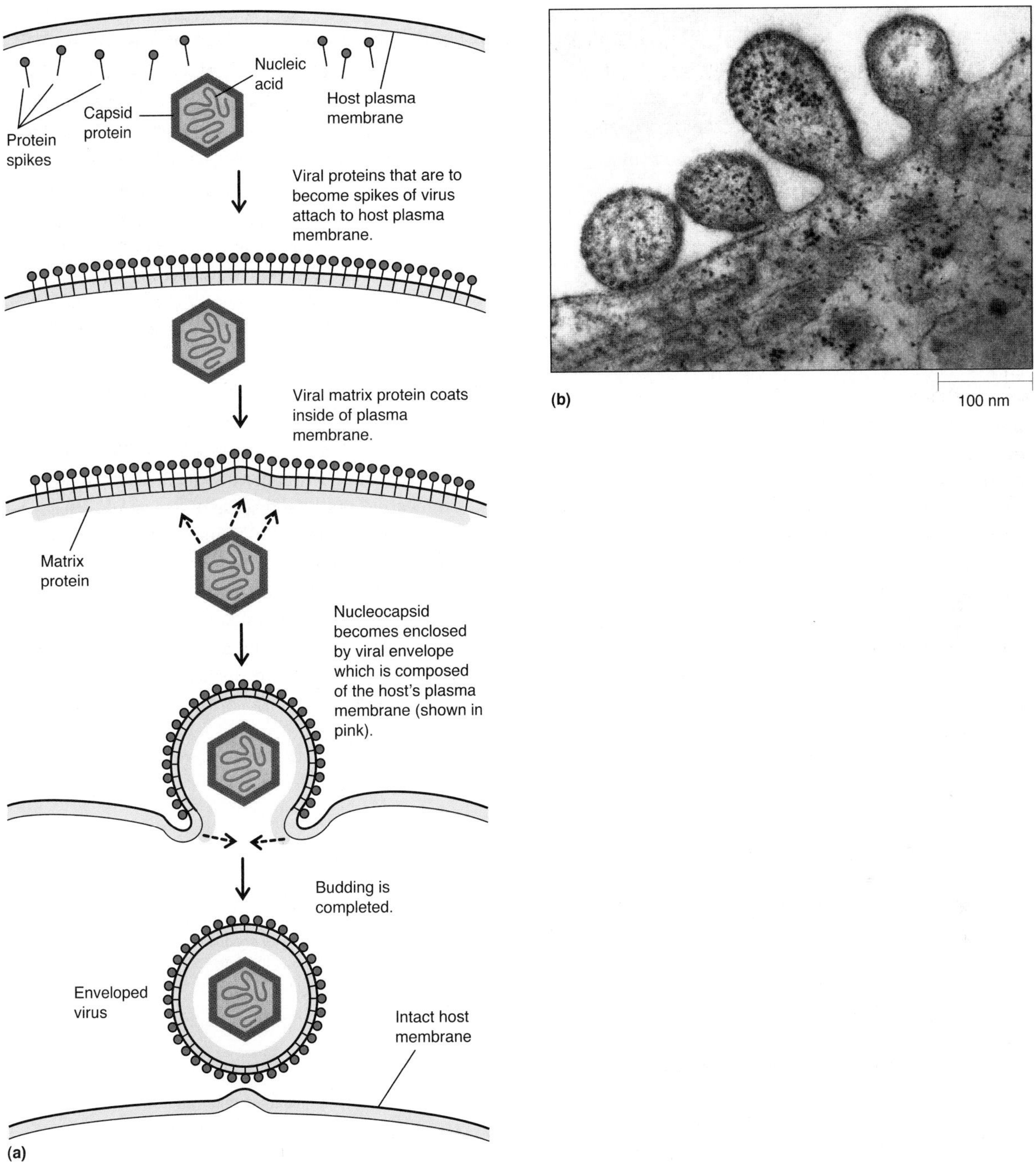

FIGURE 14.6 Mechanism for Releasing Enveloped Virions **(a)** Process of budding. **(b)** Electron micrograph of virus particles budding from the surface of a human cell. The virion on the left has completed the process. The other three are in various degrees of completion. It is clear from the micrograph how the virions gain the plasma membrane of the host cell. Note that the membrane of the host remains intact after budding has been completed.

Latent Infections

Latent infections are persistent infections in which a symptomless period is followed by reactivation of the virus with accompanying symptoms. Infectious virus particles cannot be detected until the disease is reactivated (see figure 14.7a). The symptoms of the initial and reactivated forms of the disease may differ. The viruses causing latent infections can be either DNA or RNA viruses. The best known examples are caused by members of the herpesvirus family (Herpesviridae), which is divided into two herpes simplex types: **HSV-1** and **HSV-2.** The latter, frequently called **genital herpes,** is an important and common sexually transmitted disease.
■ HSV-1, p. 619 ■ HSV-2, p. 619

Initial infection of young children with herpes simplex type 1 (HSV-1) may not lead to any symptoms, but cold sores and fever

TABLE 14.5 Comparison of Replication Cycle of Bacteriophages and Animal Viruses in Virulent Infections

Stage	Bacteriophages	Animal Viruses
Attachment	Fusion of capsid with host membrane does not occur.	Fusion of viral envelope and host membrane common.
Entry	Only nucleic acid enters cell—no enzymes.	Entire virion enters cell, including enzymes of replication.
Targeting of virion	Targeting unnecessary	Targeting to site of viral replication.
Uncoating	Takes place at surface of cell	Takes place inside the cell.
Replication cycle	Depends on whether nucleic acid is DNA or RNA, double- or single-stranded.	Same pattern of replication as phage with the same genome.
Exit	In lytic infection, phage codes for lytic enzyme, which lyses the cell. Budding rare—cells not killed.	Cell dies and lyses with release of virus. Budding common—cells may or may not be killed.

blisters often result. After this initial acute infection, the HSV-1 infects the sensory nerve cells, where it remains in a non-infectious form without causing symptoms of disease **(figure 14.8).** Replication of this virus in the nerve cells is repressed by some unknown mechanism but can be activated by such conditions as menstruation, fever, or sunburn. Following the start of replication, mature infectious virions are produced and are carried to the skin or mucous membranes by the nerve cells, once again resulting in cold sores. After these sores have healed, the virus and host cells once again exist in harmony and, as with other latent infections, no virions are synthesized until the disease recurs. ■ herpes simplex type I, p. 619

Another example of a latent infection is provided by another member of the herpesvirus family, varicella-zoster virus, the cause of **chickenpox (varicella).** Initial infection of normal children results in a rash termed chickenpox. This virus can remain latent for years without producing any disease symptoms. It can then be reactivated and produce the disease called **shingles,** or **herpes zoster.** Thus, chickenpox and shingles are different diseases caused

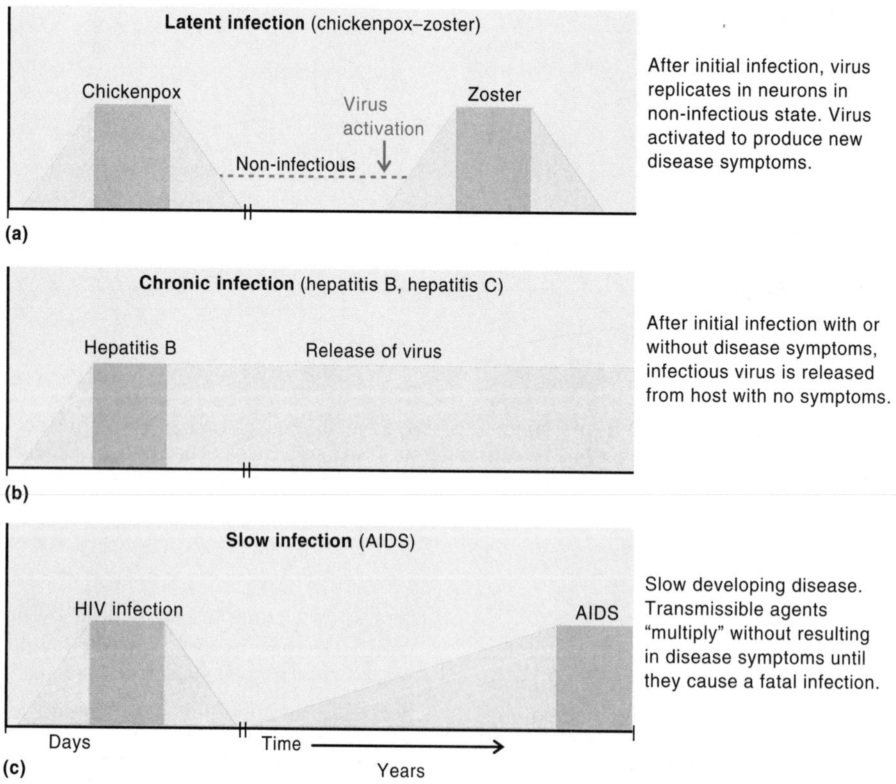

FIGURE 14.7 A Time Course of Appearance of Disease Symptoms and Infectious Virions in Various Kinds of Viral Infections

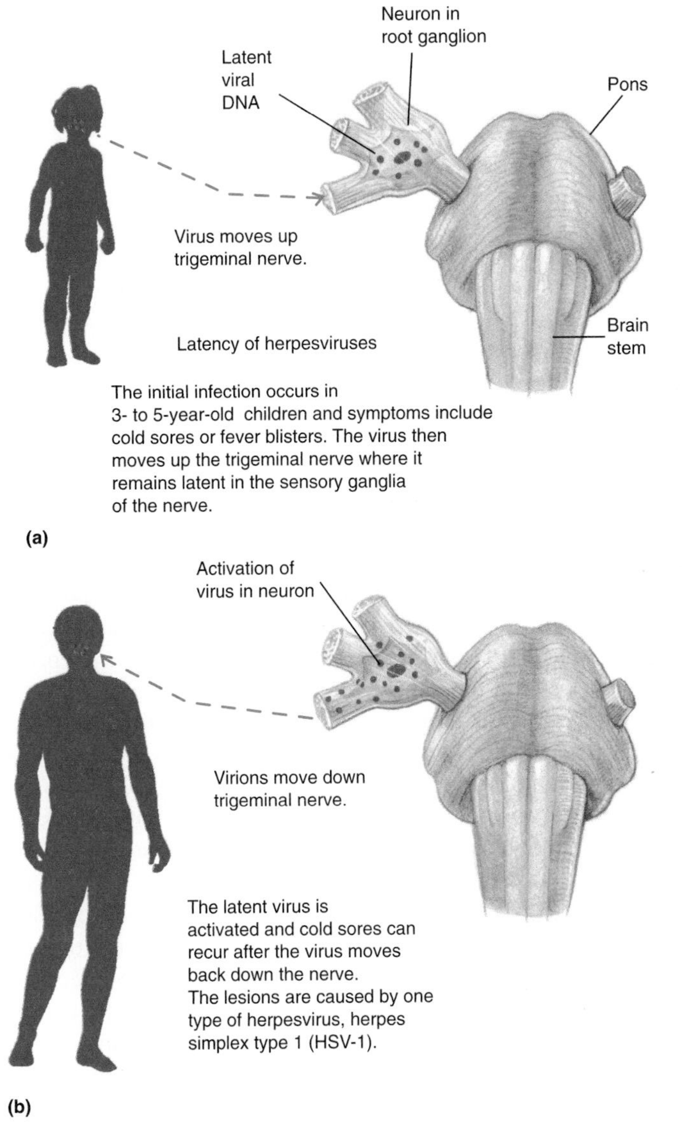
Neuron in
root ganglion
Latent
viral
DNA
Pons
Virus moves up
trigeminal nerve.
Latency of herpesviruses
Brain
stem
The initial infection occurs in 3- to 5-year-old children and symptoms include cold sores or fever blisters. The virus then moves up the trigeminal nerve where it remains latent in the sensory ganglia of the nerve.
(a)
Activation of
virus in neuron
Virions move down
trigeminal nerve.
The latent virus is activated and cold sores can recur after the virus moves back down the nerve.
The lesions are caused by one type of herpesvirus, herpes simplex type 1 (HSV-1).
(b)

FIGURE 14.8 Infection Cycle of Herpes Simplex Virus, HSV-1

by the same virus. Most infections, however, never reactivate. ■ chickenpox, p. 536 ■ shingles, p. 537

Most herpesviruses, including HSV-2, tend to become latent under various conditions. It appears that part or all of the viral DNA becomes integrated into the genome of the host, or copies of the nucleic acid of some herpesviruses may replicate as plasmids in the host cell. Note the similarity to infection by temperate phages. **Table 14.6** gives some examples of latent infections. ■ temperate phages, p. 323 ■ plasmids, pp. 69, 208

Chronic Infections

In chronic infections, the infectious virus can be demonstrated at all times (see figure 14.7b). Disease may be present or absent during an extended period of time or may develop late. The best known chronic human infection is caused by the **hepatitis B virus,** formerly called **serum hepatitis virus.** This disease is transmitted sexually or from the blood of a chronic carrier who shows no symptoms. Some people who contract the virus develop an acute illness marked by nausea, fever, and jaundice. About 300 million people worldwide are carriers of the virus, and a significant number develop cirrhosis or cancer of the liver; more than 1 million people die each year from hepatitis B. ■ hepatitis B, p. 634

In the **carrier state,** infectious virions of hepatitis B are continually produced and can be detected in the bloodstream, saliva, and semen. The viral DNA genome may also occur as a plasmid in liver cells (hepatocytes), where it replicates and produces many infectious virions. Following replication in this plasmid state, the genome can also integrate into the cells of the liver. In this state, only some of the protein components of the virion are synthesized and infectious virions are not produced. Some examples of viruses that cause chronic infections are summarized in **table 14.7.**

Replication of DNA is very unusual in the hepatitis B virus. Unlike all other double-stranded DNA viruses, which replicate their DNA using the viral DNA as a template, the hepatitis B virus synthesizes RNA from the DNA. The RNA is then used as a template for the synthesis of DNA, using a viral-encoded DNA polymerase. This enzyme acts as a **reverse transcriptase,** an unusual enzyme found only in the retroviruses, a group of viruses that will be discussed shortly. Replication can be simply diagrammed as shown here:

$$\text{DNA} \longrightarrow \text{RNA} \xrightarrow[\text{transcriptase}]{\text{Reverse}} \text{DNA}$$

A more detailed discussion of the replication of hepatitis B virus is presented in chapter 25. ■ hepatitis B replication, p. 635

Slow Infections

In slow infections following initial infection, the infectious agent gradually increases in amount over a very long time during which no significant symptoms are apparent. Eventually, a slowly progressive lethal disease ensues (see figure 14.7c). AIDS has features of slow virus infections. ■ AIDS, p. 672

Two groups of unusual agents that cause slow infections have been identified. One genus is the Lentivirus (*lenti* means "slow"), which is in the family Retroviridae (retroviruses; *retro* means backward). Other members of this family cause tumors in animals. The second is the protein infectious particles called **prions.** Both groups cause diseases that have long preclinical phases and result in progressive, invariably fatal diseases. In both groups, the infectious agent can be recovered from infected animals during both the preclinical years when no symptoms are evident and the time that clinical symptoms are present. ■ prions, p. 12

The most common slow virus infection is caused by the human immunodeficiency virus (HIV), which causes AIDS. AIDS results from the invasion and destruction of T lymphocytes and macrophages, important components in the immune system of the body. Without a healthy level of T lymphocytes and macrophages, the body becomes susceptible to a wide variety of infectious diseases. AIDS and HIV infection will be covered in detail in chapter 29. ■ macrophages, p. 372 ■ T lymphocytes, p. 401

TABLE 14.6 Examples of Latent Infections

Virus	Primary Disease	Recurrent Disease	Cells Involved in Latent State
Herpes simplex virus			
HSV-1	Primary oral herpes	Recurrent herpes simplex	Neurons of sensory ganglia
HSV-2	Genital herpes	Recurrent herpes genitalis	Neurons of sensory ganglia
Varicella-zoster virus (herpesvirus family)	Chickenpox	Herpes zoster (shingles)	Satellite cells of sensory ganglia
Cytomegalovirus (CMV; herpesvirus family)	Usually subclinical except in fetus or immunocompromised host	CMV pneumonia, eye infections, mononucleosis-like symptoms	Salivary glands, kidney epithelium, leukocytes
Epstein-Barr virus (herpesvirus family)	Mononucleosis	Burkitt's lymphoma	B cells, which are involved in antibody production

The retroviruses are single-stranded enveloped RNA viruses, many of which infect humans. Many members cause tumors in animals, one causes a leukemia in humans, but the most prominent member is HIV. The HIV genome is unusual in that it consists of two duplicate copies of RNA.

The replication of retroviruses is unusual and has no counterpart in phages. The major feature is that the genetic information in its RNA is converted into DNA, which is then integrated into the genome of the host cell. Its replication is shown in **figure 14.9.** A more complete diagram of all of the steps of the replication cycle is presented in chapter 29. ■ HIV replication cycle, p. 740

Like all retroviruses, the replication of HIV requires that its single-stranded RNA genome be converted into a double-stranded DNA copy. Two Americans, Howard Temin and David Baltimore, independently demonstrated in 1970 that retroviruses contain, in their capsid, an unusual enzyme, **reverse transcriptase,** that enters the host cell as part of the entering nucleocapsid at the time of infection. Reverse transcriptase is not found in uninfected cells. This enzyme copies the single-stranded viral RNA into a complementary strand of DNA. A second strand of DNA complementary to the first DNA strand is then synthesized. The double-stranded DNA is integrated permanently into a chromosome of the host cell as a **provirus.** This provirus is superficially analogous to the phage lambda (λ) when it is present as a prophage in *E. coli.* Recall, however, that lambda integrates at specific sites in the chromosome of *E. coli* whereas HIV DNA integrates randomly into host cell chromosomes. ■ prophage λ, p. 325

The details of how the activity of the provirus is regulated are not nearly so clear as they are in the case of lambda. It is known that some of the infected cells continuously synthesize new virions that bud from the cell. In this situation, the RNA is transcribed by the host cell RNA polymerase to produce one long mRNA molecule that contains all of the viral information, a **polygenic** or **polycistronic** mRNA. This mRNA molecule is translated into a long **polyprotein,** which is then cleaved by a viral-encoded protease to yield the individual proteins. Following cleavage, the individual proteins fold to their proper conformation resulting in the proteins that make up the virion. If the action of this protease is inhibited, then the virus cannot be assembled. Consequently, inhibitors of this viral protease, termed **protease inhibitors,** created in the laboratory are a major weapon against HIV. ■ polycistronic mRNA, p. 174 ■ protease inhibitor, p. 514

Many HIV infected cells can carry the provirus in the latent state, and no virions are produced. Various agents can activate the provirus, however, so that it results in a productive infection in which the virions are released. What these agents are in nature is not known. Small amounts of the virus are present continuously or intermittently in the blood and genital secretions, and carriers can transmit the infection through sexual contact.

DNA polymerase makes very few mistakes in the replication of DNA because of its proofreading ability. Reverse transcriptase, however, has no proofreading activity and makes many mistakes when copying RNA into DNA. As a result, the DNA that codes for a variety of different capsid proteins codes for altered proteins. Many of these proteins are no longer recognized by antibodies that recognized the protein capsid of the original virus. These errors in copying help explain why the virus becomes resistant very quickly to antiviral drugs such as AZT and probably protease inhibitors. ■ proofreading, DNA polymerase, p. 198 ■ AZT, p. 514

TABLE 14.7 Examples of Chronic Infections

Virus	Site of Infection	Location of Infectious Virions in Carrier State	Disease
Hepatitis B	Liver	Plasma, saliva, genital secretions	Hepatitis, cirrhosis, carcinoma
Hepatitis C	Liver	Plasma, saliva, genital secretions	Hepatitis, cirrhosis, carcinoma
Rubella virus	Many organs	Urine, saliva	Congenital rubella syndrome

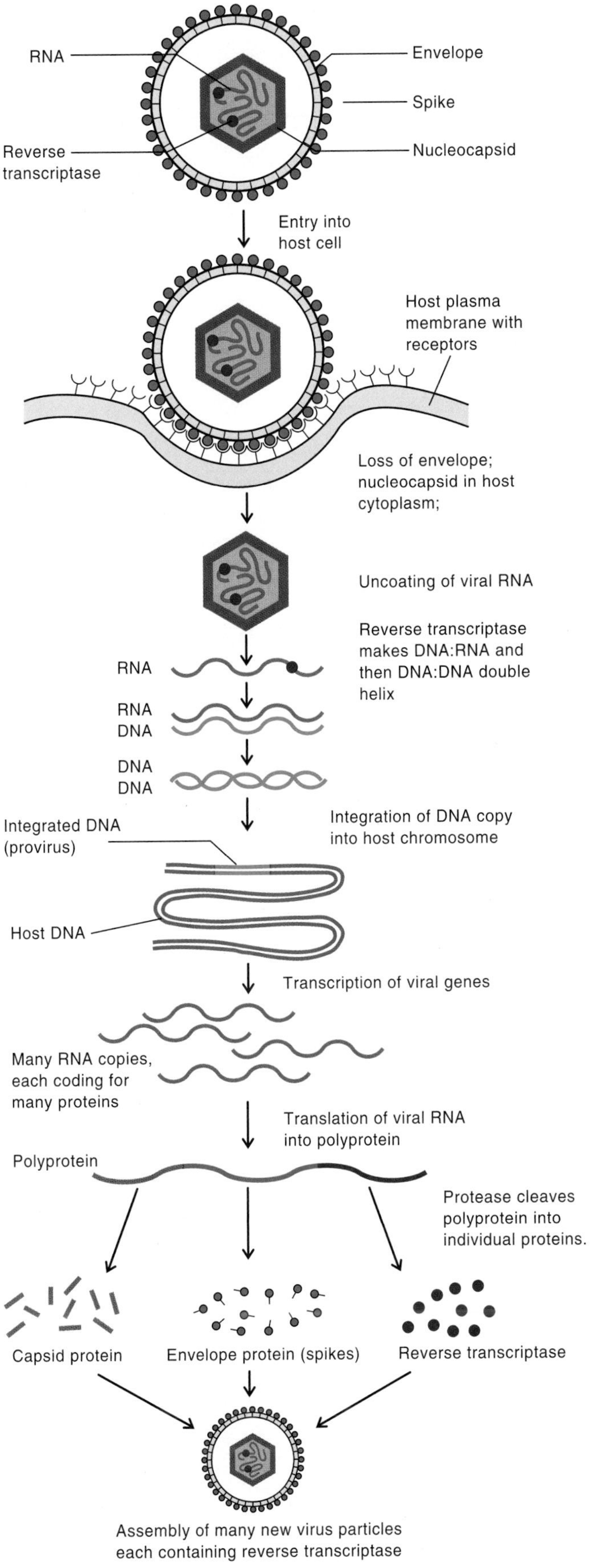

FIGURE 14.9 Replication Cycle of a Retrovirus A retrovirus is the cause of AIDS and many tumors in animals.

MICROCHECK 14.2

Most animal viruses live in harmony with their natural hosts and do not cause serious illness. If the virus infects an unnatural host, a serious disease may result. The various kinds of relationships of animal viruses with their hosts are in general similar to those seen with bacterial viruses and bacteria. Replication of viral nucleic acid depends to varying degrees on the enzymes of nucleic acid replication of the host cells.

A retrovirus, HIV, is responsible for the disease AIDS, which has features of a latent, chronic, and slow infection. The replication of HIV involves an enzyme, reverse transcriptase, which copies the single-stranded RNA of the virion into DNA which then becomes integrated into certain cells of the immune system.

- ✓ Name the two *major* kinds of infections that viruses cause.
- ✓ What is a major difference in the entry of animal viruses and bacterial viruses into their host cells?
- ✓ How do animal viruses cause lysis of the host cell?
- ✓ Explain why HIV becomes resistant to drugs so quickly.

14.3 Viruses and Human Tumors

Focus Points

- Explain how an oncogene can cause cancer.
- Name the two states in which viral DNA can exist inside a cell and cause cancer.

Most human tumors are not caused by viruses, despite intensive efforts to prove otherwise. These numbers are increasing, however, because of the common occurrence of a viral-induced tumor, Kaposi's sarcoma, in AIDS patients.

Considering all viruses, double-stranded DNA viruses are the main cause of virus-induced tumors in humans **(table 14.8).** DNA tumor viruses interact with their host cells in one of two ways. They can go through a productive infection in which they lyse the cells, or they can transform the cells and modify their properties without killing them. The cancers caused by the DNA viruses result from the integration of all or part of the virus genome into the host chromosome. Following integration, the transforming genes or **oncogenes** (from the word *onkos,* which means "mass" or "lump") are expressed, resulting in uncontrolled growth of the host cells. Oncogenes are often altered forms of normal cells' genes coding for proteins involved in regulating cell growth. Thus, these cases of abnormal growth are analogous to lysogenic conversion observed in certain temperate phage infections of bacteria. In both cases, the expression of viral genes integrated into the host's chromosome confers new properties on the host cells. ■ **lysogenic conversion, p. 328**

In the case of some DNA viruses, such as papillomaviruses and herpesviruses, the viral DNA is not integrated but apparently

TABLE 14.8 Viruses Associated with Cancers in Humans*

Virus	Type of Nucleic Acid	Kind of Tumor
Human papillomaviruses (HPV)	DNA	Different kinds of tumors, including squamous cell and genital carcinomas, caused by different HPV types
Hepatitis B	DNA	Hepatocellular carcinoma
Epstein-Barr	DNA	Burkitt's lymphoma; nasopharyngeal carcinoma; B-cell lymphoma
Hepatitis C	DNA	Hepatocellular carcinoma
Human herpes, virus 8	DNA	Kaposi's sarcoma
HTLV-1	RNA (retrovirus)	Adult T-cell leukemia (rare)

*In 2005, the United States government added hep
long before this.

replicates as a plasmid. In the case of the papillomaviruses, on rare occasions, the plasmid may integrate into the host chromosome and this may cause tumors. Certain types of human papillomavirus are linked with most cases of cervical cancer, as well as with vulval, penile, and anal cancers. ■ **papillomavirus, p. 670** ■ **herpesvirus, p. 341** ■ **plasmid, pp. 69, 208**

Kaposi's sarcoma, a cancer of the skin and internal organs common in AIDS patients, is caused by a herpesvirus. How this particular virus causes normal cells to become tumorous is not known. Note that in all cases of virus-induced tumors, the virus does not kill the host cell but instead changes its properties. ■ **Kaposi's sarcoma, p. 747**

The various interactions that viruses display with their hosts are illustrated in **figure 14.10.**

Retroviruses and Human Tumors

Although retroviruses are the main class of viruses causing tumors in animals, it was not until 1980 that a rare human leukemia was also shown to be caused by a retrovirus. It was named human

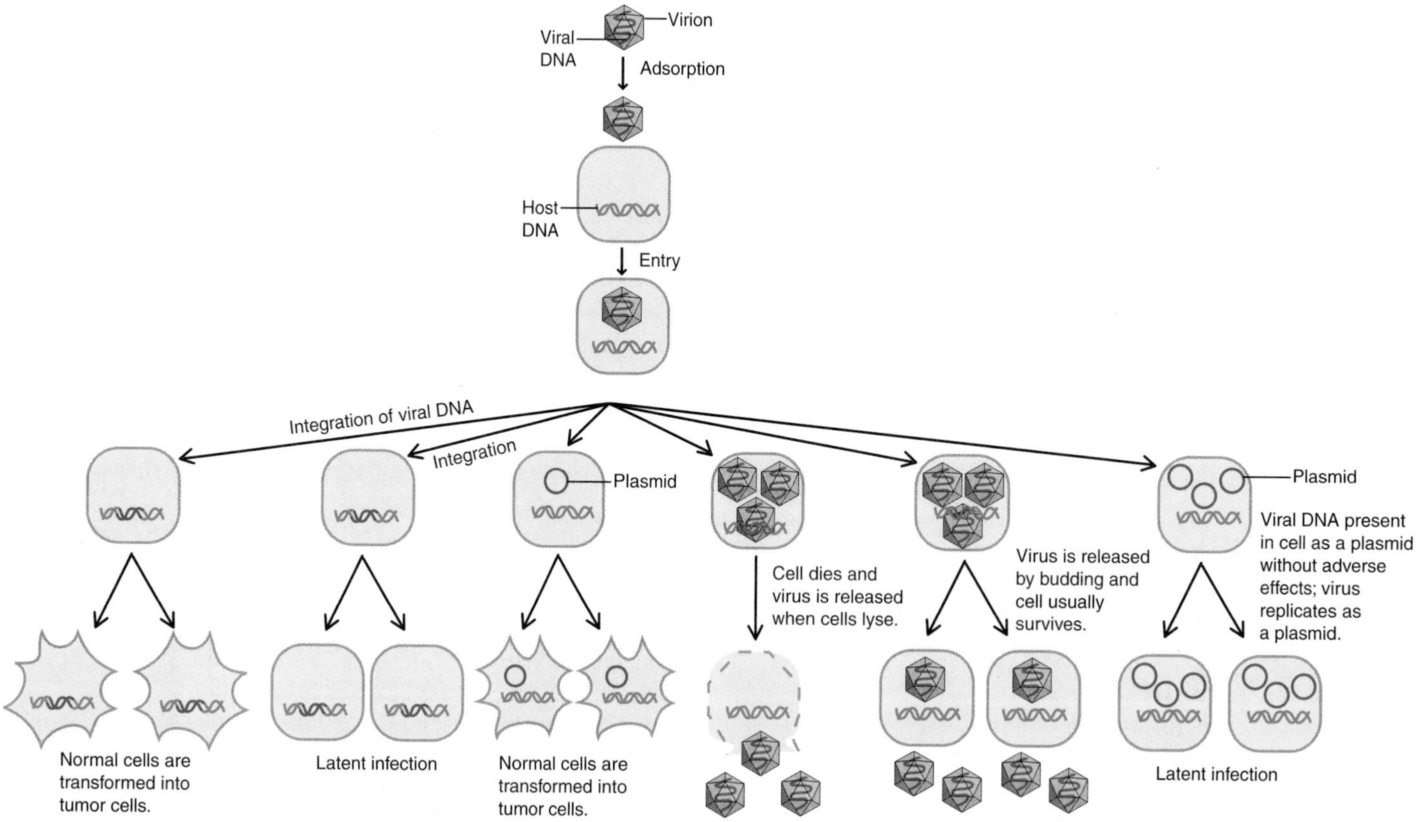

FIGURE 14.10 Various Effects of Animal Viruses on the Cells They Infect

T-cell lymphotrophic virus type 1 (HTLV-1), and this tumor is restricted to certain geographic areas. The virus causes tumors by a somewhat different mechanism than discussed thus far. The virus carries an oncogene that, when integrated into the host cell genome, codes for an activator protein that activates regulatory genes of the cell.

MICROCHECK 14.3

Most human tumors are not caused by viruses but by mutations in certain genes. The most common viral cause of tumors in humans is DNA tumor viruses. One retrovirus is known to cause a rare human tumor.

- ✓ Name three viruses that cause tumors in humans.
- ✓ Name a tumor common in AIDS patients and the virus that causes it.
- ✓ Why is it not surprising that AIDS patients frequently suffer a viral-induced tumor?

14.4 Viral Genetic Alterations

Focus Points

- Describe the process of genetic reassortment?
- What protein of influenza is critical for attachment to host cells?

Most viruses can infect a single species or even only certain cells within an organism. The major limiting factor in host range is the need for the attachment proteins of the virus to bind to specific receptors on the surface of the host. Another less important limitation is that each virion needs different cellular factors and machinery in order to replicate. Some viruses, however, especially those that cause zoonoses, can multiply in widely divergent species. For example, the West Nile virus that has now infected thousands of people across the United States is primarily a disease of birds that have been bitten by infected mosquitoes. The virus can also infect a wide variety of animals.

Genetic alterations in strains as a result of mutation can result in increased virulence for their hosts as well as increased transmissibility between hosts.

Genome Exchange in Segmented Viruses

In addition to mutations, segmented viruses can alter their properties by a process called **genetic reassortment.** This process results from the infection of the same cell by two different viruses, followed by the incorporation of one segment of one infecting virion with the remaining segments coming from the other virion, during viral maturation **(figure 14.11).** This is well illustrated in the case of the influenza virus.

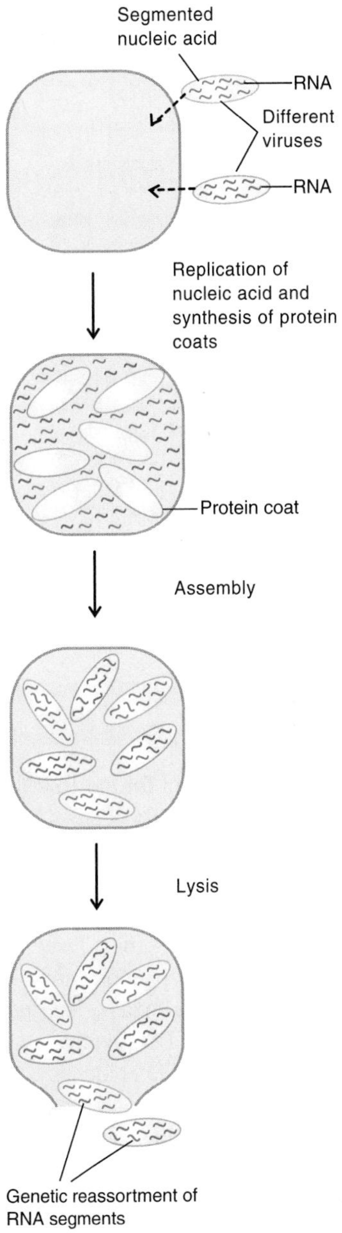

FIGURE 14.11 Genetic Reassortment The virion that undergoes genetic reassortment gives rise to progeny with the same characteristics.

A number of different strains of the influenza virus exist, which can be distinguished by the fact that they are specific for infecting different species of animals and birds. The genome of the influenza virus is divided into eight segments of RNA, each one containing different genetic information. One of the segments codes for **hemagglutinin,** a key protein involved in attachment to host cells. A human with antibodies against hemagglutinin from the human strain is protected against the disease. If, however, the structure of the hemagglutinin gene changes, then the antibodies will not recognize the protein and will not protect against it. Experimental data suggest that avian and human influenza virions can simultaneously infect the same cells in a permissive host such as a pig or duck. The

PERSPECTIVE 14.1

A Whodunit in Molecular Virology

Influenza is a disease that results in symptoms of headache, fever, muscle pain, and coughing. Within a week, these symptoms go away and usually only the elderly or others with a weak immune system die. However, the consequences were much more devastating in two influenza outbreaks in the twentieth century. The "Spanish flu" pandemic of 1918 resulted in more than 20 million deaths around the world, and many of the victims were young adults. In 1997, another deadly influenza virus appeared in Hong Kong of 18 cases that were diagnosed, 6 were fatal. As in the case of the 1918 "Spanish flu" pandemic, many of the victims were young adults. The Hong Kong virus was transmitted from chickens to humans, but rarely from humans to humans. Therefore, the epidemic was stopped in its tracks by killing all of the chickens in Hong Kong. Clearly, the influenza virions that caused each of these epidemics must differ from the influenza virions that result in the usual unpleasant but short-term symptoms of influenza.

What made the virions that caused the "Spanish flu" and Hong Kong outbreaks so deadly? By sequencing the RNA genome of the various strains of the influenza virion, some answers are now beginning to emerge. To study the 1918 virions, tissues were obtained from preserved bodies of the 1918 victims who had died from influenza. These included several soldiers and an Eskimo woman whose body was buried in the Alaskan permafrost. The sequencing of the RNA genome focused on the hemagglutinin gene since this gene is very important in determining the virulence of the virion. What investigators found was that the hemagglutinin gene of the "Spanish flu" virion originated by recombination between a swine influenza virion and a human-lineage virion. The end of the protein that binds to receptors on the host cell was encoded by the swine-lineage influenza, whereas the rest of the molecule was encoded by a gene that came from a human-lineage influenza. Apparently the recombination occurred shortly before the pandemic began in 1918 and may have triggered the pandemic.

The highly virulent virion that caused the Hong Kong epidemic in 1997 is a different, more complicated story. By mixing various combinations of the eight segments of the influenza genome, sequencing the segments and determining the virulence of the various strains, investigators determined that several other genes in addition to the hemagglutinin gene were responsible for the virulence of the Hong Kong strain. These genes included the gene encoding the enzyme neuraminidase, which is required for the spread of the virus within the body, and the gene encoding a protein that blocks the synthesis of interferon, a known viral antagonist.

How these changes in the 1918 "Spanish flu" and the Hong Kong 1997 virions created such deadly strains is not totally understood. However, it seems likely that the new strains were able to circumvent the immune response of the host by expressing new proteins, which the body had not encountered before. Thus the immune cells of the body did not recognize the virions and the body was defenseless. We will likely face new killer strains in the future.

cells then serve as a mixing vessel for the 16 RNA segments of the two virions. On occasion, the RNA segment encoding the avian hemagglutinin is incorporated into the same protein coat along with the seven RNA segments from the human strain. Such a strain is still able to infect humans, but its avian hemagglutinin makes it a new strain now able to evade the host's antibody defense. This is called an **antigenic shift.** This phenomenon likely explains how the virulence of the human influenza virion changes so dramatically every 10 to 30 years (see **Perspective 14.1**). These sudden changes result in deadly worldwide epidemics, called **pandemics,** because the global population does not have protective antibodies. In the twentieth century, four influenza pandemics have occurred, the most devastating being 1918–1920.

In addition to the hemagglutinin experiencing this major genetic change, the hemagglutinin gene, along with other viral genes, can undergo point mutations that result in relatively small changes in the protein. Since RNA replication by RNA dependent RNA polymerase does not involve proofreading of the RNA product, the RNA synthesized suffers numerous mistakes. These changes are termed **antigenic drift.** Both of these processes will be discussed later in terms of the epidemiology of influenza. ■ **antigenic drift and shift, p. 598 ■ antibody, p. 392 ■ antigen, p. 391 ■ point mutation, p. 193**

MICROCHECK 14.4

The properties of animal viruses can be altered if two viruses with different host ranges infect the same cell. Genes of one virus can be incorporated into the protein coat of the other virus in the process of viral assembly, the phenomena of antigenic shift.

- ✓ Differentiate between antigenic shift and antigenic drift in the influenza virus.
- ✓ Is antigenic shift alone likely to lead to influenza pandemics? Explain.

14.5

Methods Used to Study Viruses

Focus Point

- Describe methods for quantifying numbers of animal virions.

A variety of techniques are available to recognize the presence of viruses, identify them, and grow them in large quantities. The focus here is on methods for studying animal viruses, which are far more expensive and time-consuming than the methods used in studying phage.

Cultivation of Host Cells

Since viruses can multiply only inside living cells, such cells are needed to study virus growth. The study of bacterial viruses has advanced much more rapidly than investigations on animal and plant viruses, in large part because bacteria are much easier to grow in large quantities in short time periods. The primary difficulty in studying animal viruses is not so much in purifying the virions as it is in obtaining enough cells to infect. Some viruses can only be cultivated in living animals. Others may be grown in **embryonated chicken eggs,** those that contain developing chicks. Some animal viruses can be grown in cells taken from a human or another animal.

When animal viruses can be grown in isolated animal cells, the host cells are cultivated in the laboratory by a technique called **cell culture** or **tissue culture.** To prepare cells for growth outside the body of the animal (*in vitro*), a tissue is removed from an animal and minced into small pieces **(figure 14.12).** The cells are separated from one another by treating them with a protease enzyme, such as trypsin, that breaks down protein. The suspension

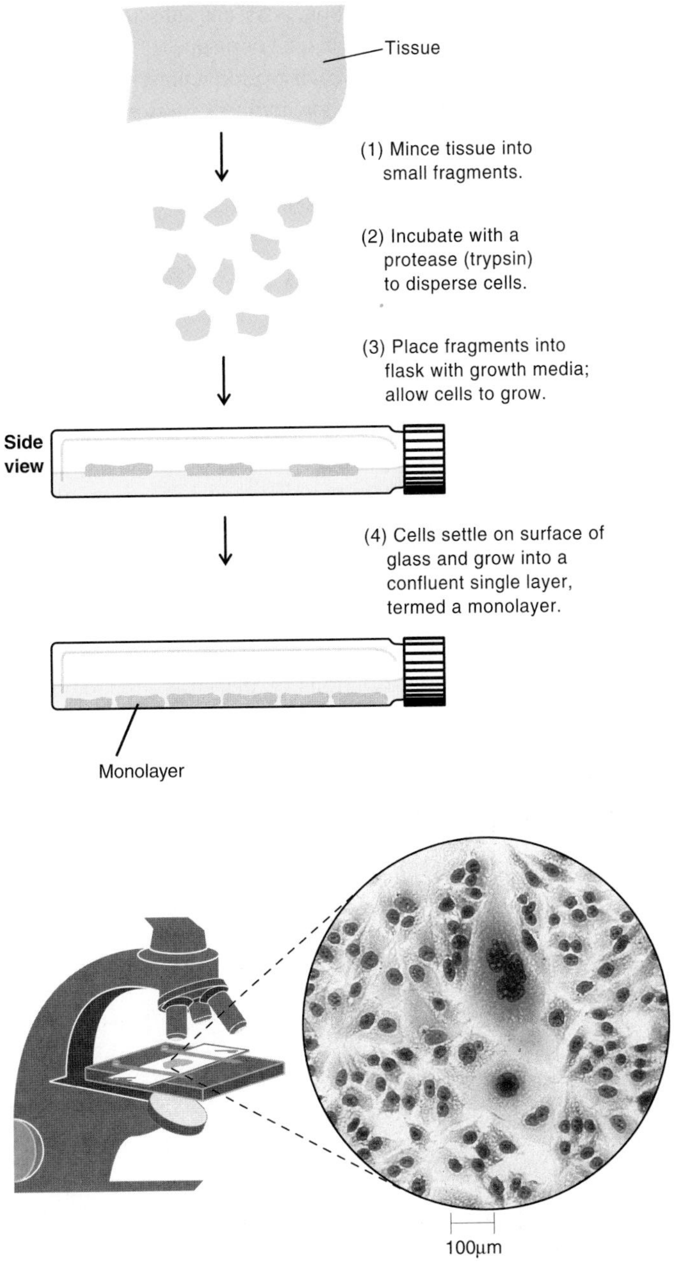

Tissue
(1) Mince tissue into small fragments.
(2) Incubate with a protease (trypsin) to disperse cells.
(3) Place fragments into flask with growth media; allow cells to grow.
Side view
(4) Cells settle on surface of glass and grow into a confluent single layer, termed a monolayer.
Monolayer
100μm

FIGURE 14.12 Preparation of Primary Cell Culture

of cells is then placed in a screw-capped flask in a medium containing a mixture of amino acids, minerals, vitamins, and sugars as a source of energy. The growth of animal cells also requires a number of additional growth factors that have yet to be identified but are present in blood serum. Tissue cultures prepared directly from the tissues of an animal are termed **primary cultures.**

The cells bathed in the proper nutrients attach to the bottom of the flask and divide every several days, eventually covering the surface of the dish with a single layer of cells, a **monolayer.** When cells become crowded, they stop dividing and enter a resting state. One can continue to propagate the cells by treating them with trypsin, removing them from the primary culture, diluting them, and putting the diluted suspension into another flask containing the required nutrients. This results in an **established** cell line.

Cells taken from normal vertebrate tissue die after a certain number of divisions in culture. For example, human skin cells divide 50 to 100 times and then die, even when they are diluted into fresh media. Accordingly, cells must once again be taken from the animal and a new primary culture started.

Cells taken from a tumor, however, can be cultivated *in vitro* indefinitely. Accordingly, they are much easier to use for growing viruses than normal tissue, and several tissue lines have been established from tumors.

Tissue culture is important for growing viruses in the laboratory. The virus is mixed with susceptible cells, and the mixture is incubated until the infected cells are lysed. Following lysis, the unlysed cells and the cell debris are removed by centrifugation. The cells and debris go to the bottom of the centrifuge tube while the light, small virions remain in the liquid, the **supernatant.** This liquid containing the virions is also termed a **lysate.**

Tissue culture cells can also be used in virus detection. When a virus is propagated in tissue culture cells, it often changes the cells' appearance. Often, these changes are characteristic for a particular virus and are referred to as the **cytopathic effect** of the virus (**figure 14.13**). Sometimes the cytopathic effect is localized

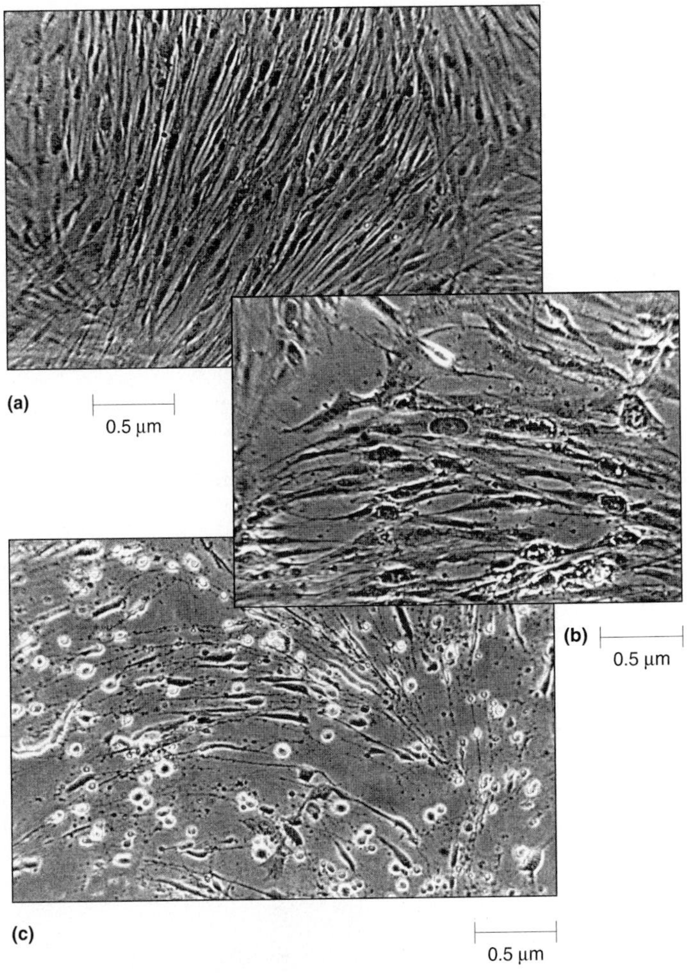

FIGURE 14.13 Cytopathic Effects of Virus Infection on Tissue Culture (a) Fetal tonsil diploid fibroblasts growing as a monolayer, uninfected. **(b)** Same cells infected with adenovirus. **(c)** Same cells infected with herpes simplex virus. Note that the monolayer is totally destroyed.

to particular sites within infected cells. The most common cytopathic effect of this type is termed an **inclusion body.** It is the site at which the virus is being assembled, viral components are being actively synthesized, or cellular damage has occurred. The sites in the cell where inclusion bodies localize vary depending on the virus. Thus, the presence of a virus in an unknown sample and some idea of its identity can often be gained by culturing the specimen on cells in tissue culture.

Quantitation

Tissue culture is also used in virology to study the number of virions in a sample. The most commonly used method for detecting and quantifying the amount of virus present in any sample is the **plaque assay.** A number of other methods can be used for quantitating the number of virions. These include the counting of virions using an electron microscope, **quantal assays,** and in the case of some animal viruses, **hemagglutination.**

Plaque Assay

The plaque assay involves determining the number of viruses in solution by adding a known volume of the solution to actively metabolizing cells in a Petri dish. The infection, lysis, and subsequent infection of surrounding cells leads to a clear zone or plaque surrounded by the uninfected cells **(figure 14.14).** Each plaque represents one virion, initially infecting one cell, and so the number of virions in the original solution can be readily determined. Plaques are only formed by infective viruses and can be used with any viruses that lyse their host cells, including bacteriophage (see figure 14.14b).

It is possible to prepare large numbers of viruses for future studies by adding some liquid to the plate, scraping the surface of the plate with a glass rod, and harvesting the virions.

Counting of Virions with the Electron Microscope

If reasonably pure preparations of virions are obtainable, their concentration may be readily determined by counting the number of virions in a specimen prepared for the electron microscope **(figure 14.15).** This method often may distinguish between infective and non-infective virions (see figure 14.15). From their shape and size, it also provides clues as to the identity of the virus.

Quantal Assays

Quantal assays can often provide an approximate virus concentration. In this assay, several dilutions of the virus preparation are

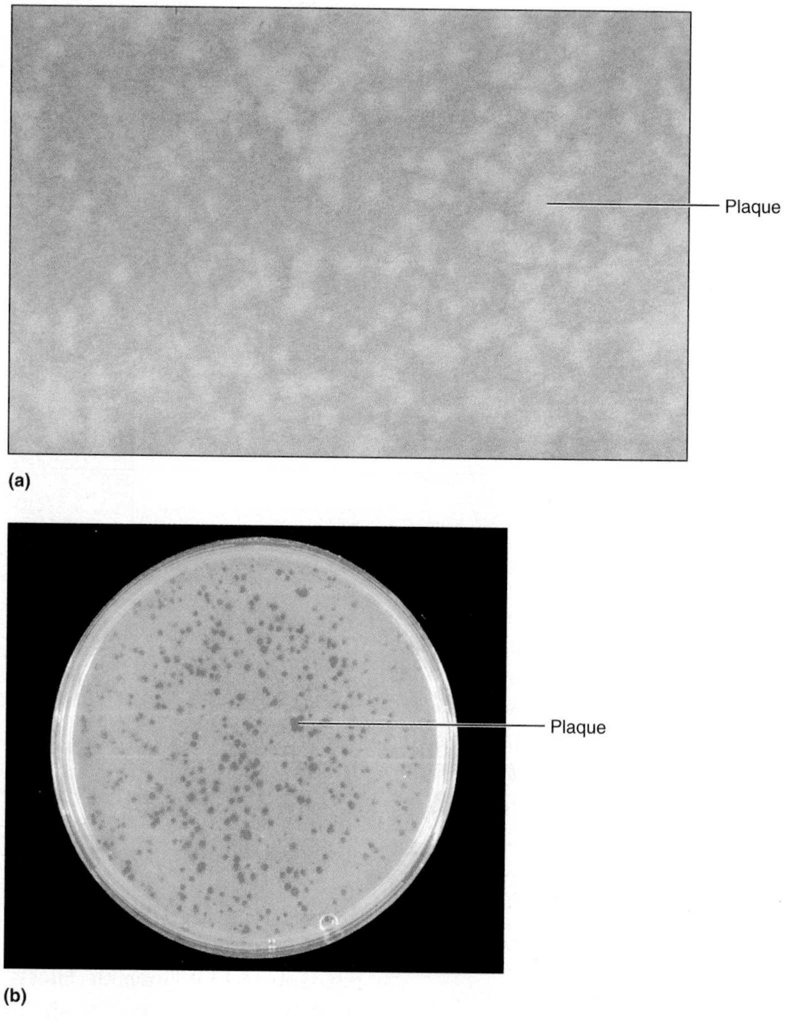

FIGURE 14.14 Viral Plaques **(a)** Plaques formed by the poliovirus infecting a monolayer of cells that have been stained. **(b)** Plaques formed by bacteriophage.

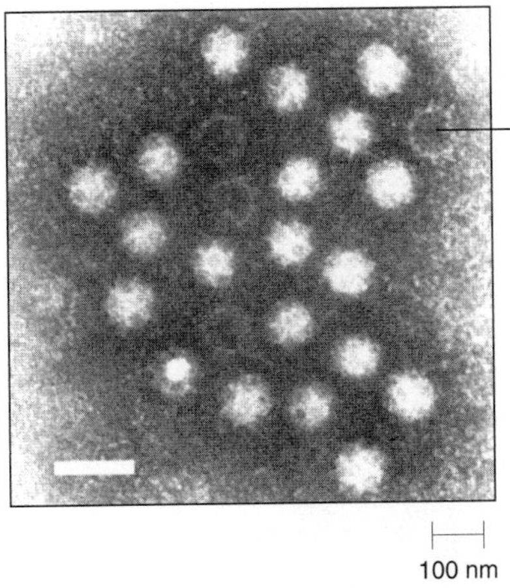

FIGURE 14.15 Electron Micrograph of Calicivirus The number of virions can be counted, and the number of empty capsids also can be readily determined. The latter are not infectious.

administered to a number of animals, cells, or chick embryos, depending on the host specificity of the virus. The **titer** of the virus, or the **endpoint,** is the dilution at which 50% of the inoculated hosts are infected or killed. This titer can be reported as either the $\mathbf{ID_{50}}$, **infective dose,** or the $\mathbf{LD_{50}}$, **lethal dose.**

Hemagglutination

Some animal viruses clump or **agglutinate** red blood cells because they interact with the surfaces of the cells. This phenomenon is called **hemagglutination.** In this process, a virion attaches to two red blood cells simultaneously and causes clumping **(figure 14.16a).** Sufficiently high concentrations of virus cause aggregation of red blood cells, which is readily visible (figure 14.16b). Hemagglutination can be measured by mixing serial dilutions of the viral suspension with a standard amount of red blood cells. The highest dilution showing maximum agglutination is the titer of the virus. One group of animal viruses that can agglutinate red blood cells is the myxoviruses, of which the influenza virus is a member. ■ **hemagglutination, p. 426**

MICROCHECK 14.5

Various hosts are required to grow different viruses. These include whole animals, embryonated chicken eggs, and cells taken from vertebrates. In constrast to normal cells which divide 50 to 100 times, cells taken from tumors divide indefinitely. The animal viruses that lyse their host cells can be assayed by counting plaques.

- ✓ Which of the methods used in quantitating viruses requires an electron microscope?
- ✓ Why is it necessary to continually make new primary cultures of normal cells?
- ✓ Would you expect the number of virions to be the same if you measured them by the plaque assay or by counting using the electron microscope? Explain your answer.

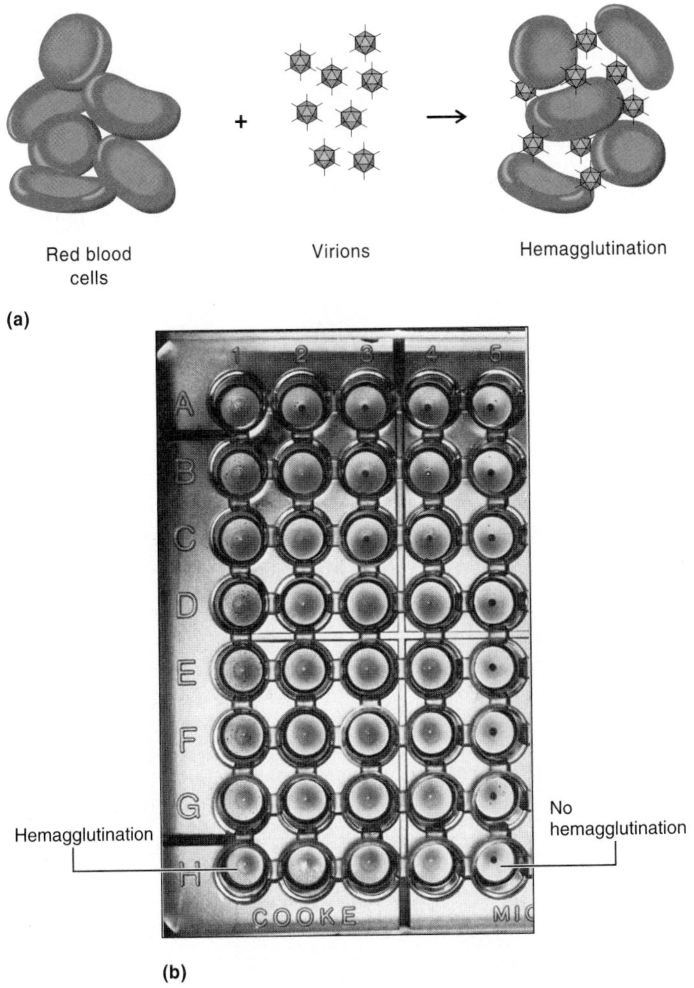

FIGURE 14.16 Hemagglutination (a) Diagram showing virions combining with red blood cells resulting in hemagglutination. **(b)** Assay of viral titer by hemagglutination. Each horizontal series of cups in horizontal lanes (A–H) represents serial twofold dilutions of different preparations of influenza virus mixed with a suspension of red blood cells.

14.6 Plant Viruses

Focus Point

- Compare and contrast the mechanisms by which plant and animal viruses enter host cells.

A great number of plant diseases are caused by viruses. These can be of major economic importance, particularly when they occur in crop plants such as corn, wheat, and rice. Virus infections are especially prevalent among perennial plants (those that live for many seasons), such as tulips and potatoes, and those propagated vegetatively (not by seeds), such as potatoes. Other crops in which viruses cause considerable damage are soybeans and sugar beets. A serious virus infection may reduce yields of these crops in a field by more than 50%.

Infection of plants by viruses may be recognized through various outward signs **(figure 14.17).** Localized abnormalities

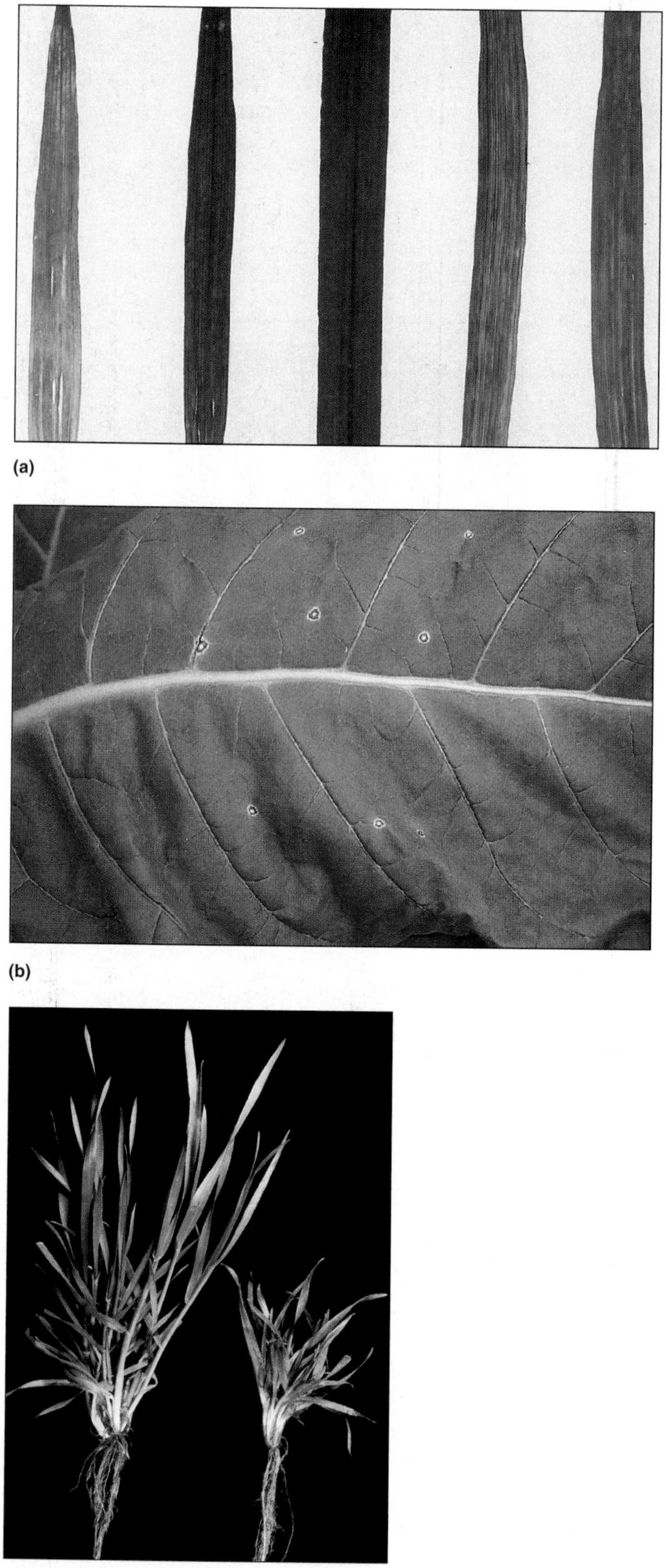

(a)

(b)

(c)

FIGURE 14.17 Symptoms of Viral Diseases of Plants (a) A healthy wheat leaf can be seen in the center. The yellowed leaves on either side are infected with wheat mosaic virus. **(b)** Typical ring lesions on a tobacco plant leaf resulting from infection by tobacco mosaic virus. **(c)** Stunted growth (right) in a wheat plant caused by wheat mosaic virus.

FIGURE 14.18 Tulips The variegated colors of tulips result from viral infection. The virus is transmitted directly from plant to plant.

may result in a loss of green pigment, and entire leaves may turn color. In many cases, rings or irregular lines appear on the leaves and fruits of the infected plant. Individual cells or specialized organs of the plant may die, and tumors may appear. Usually, infected plants become stunted in their growth, although in a few cases growth is stimulated, leading to deformed structures. In the vast majority of cases, plants do not recover from viral infections, for unlike animals, plants are not capable of developing specific immunity to rid themselves of invading viruses. On occasion, however, infected plants produce new growth in which visible signs of infection are absent, even though the infecting virus is still present.

In severely infected plants, virions may accumulate in enormous quantities. As much as 10% of the dry weight of a tobacco mosaic virus (TMV)-infected tobacco plant may consist of virus.

In a few instances, plants have been purposely maintained in a virus-infected state. The best known example of this involves tulips, in which a virus transmitted through the bulbs can cause a desirable color variegation of the flowers **(figure 14.18).** The infecting virus was transmitted through bulbs for a long time before the cause of the variegation was even suspected. The multiplication of viruses in plants is analogous to that of bacterial and animal viruses in most respects.

Spread of Plant Viruses

In contrast to phages and animal viruses, plant viruses do not attach to specific receptors on host plants. Instead, they enter through wound sites in the cell wall, which is very tough and rigid. Once started, infection in the plant can spread from cell to cell through openings, the **plasmodesmata,** that interconnect cells.

Many plant viruses are extraordinarily resistant to inactivation. Tobacco mosaic virus apparently retains its infectivity for up to 50 years, which explains why it is usually difficult to eradicate the virions from a contaminated area. Smokers who garden can transmit TMV to susceptible plants from their cigarette tobacco. The virions are very stable, which is important in maintaining the virus because the usual processes of infection are generally inefficient.

Some viruses are transmitted through soil contaminated by prior growth of infected plants. Some 10% of the known plant viruses transmit disease through contaminated seeds or tubers, or by pollination of flowers on healthy plants with contaminated pollen from diseased plants. Virus infections may also spread through grafting of healthy plant tissue onto diseased plants. Another more exotic transmission mechanism is employed via the parasitic vine, **dodder (figure 14.19).** This vine can establish simultaneous connections with the vascular tissues of two host plants, which serve as conduits for transfer of viruses from one host plant to the other.

Other important infection mechanisms involve vectors of various types. These include insects, worms, fungi, and humans. For example, TMV, which causes a serious disease of tobacco, has no known insect vector. Humans are the major vectors of this disease. Viruses are transmitted to healthy seedlings on the hands of workers who have been in contact with the virus from infected plants or by people who smoke. The most important plant virus vectors are probably insects; thus, insect control is a potent tool for controlling the spread of plant viruses. ■ vector, p. 480

Insect Transmission of Plant Viruses

Plant viruses can be transmitted by insects in several ways. First, in **external** or **temporary transmission,** a virus is associated with the external mouthparts of the vector. In this case, the ability to transmit the virus lasts only a few days. Second, in **circulative transmission,** the virus circulates but does not multiply in the body of the insect; the virus may be transmitted during the lifetime of the insect. Third, the transmission may involve actual multiplication of the virus within the insect. In this case, the virus is infectious for both the insect and a plant cell.

FIGURE 14.19 Dodder Orange-brown twining stems of the parasitic vine dodder wrap around two different hosts so that virions can pass from one host to the other through dodder.

In many instances of insect infection with plant viruses, the viruses are passed from generation to generation of the insect and may be transmitted to plants at any time. The existence of insect-transmitted plant viruses raises several interesting questions about virus evolution. In particular, plant and animal viruses may not be as different as they first appeared.

MICROCHECK 14.6

Plant viruses cause many plant diseases and are of major economic importance. They invade through wound sites in the cell wall, and humans are major vectors for their transmission. Some viruses can multiply in both plants and insects.

- ✓ Why is it especially important for plant viruses to be stable outside the plant?
- ✓ How does a plant virus penetrate the tough outer coat of the plant cell?
- ✓ Why is it surprising that some viruses have the ability to replicate in both plants and animals?
- ✓ Would you expect to find viruses that can infect both animals and bacteria? Explain.

14.7 Other Infectious Agents

Focus Points

- Describe the process by which prions replicate.
- What is the source of infectious prions?

Although viruses are composed of only one type of nucleic acid surrounded by a protective protein coat, other agents that cause serious diseases are even simpler in structure. These are the prions and the viroids.

Prions

In addition to the lentiviruses, which includes HIV, another group of agents that causes slow diseases are **prions,** proteinaceous infectious particles that apparently contain only protein and no nucleic acid (see figure 1.14). They are very similar in amino acid sequence to a protein, the normal prion protein, that is found in all vertebrates. The prion protein is either normal when it is in the vertebrate or abnormal when it causes disease. These agents have been linked to a number of fatal human diseases as well as to diseases of animals. In all of these afflictions, brain function degenerates as neurons die, and brain tissue develops spongelike holes **(figure 14.20).** Thus, the general term **transmissible spongiform encephalopathies** has been given to all of these diseases. The time after infection before symptoms appear is many years. Some of the slow but always fatal infections that have been attributed to prions are listed in **table 14.9.** Before the true nature of prions

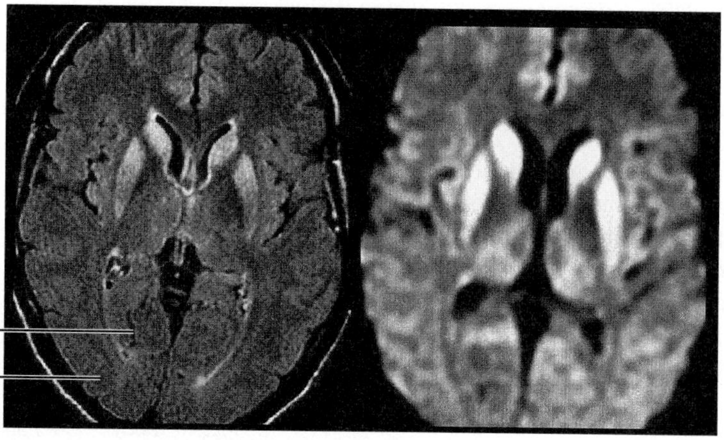

FIGURE 14.20 Appearance of Brain with Spongiform Encephalopathy Left—Normal brain. Right—Brain infected with a prion. Note the spongelike appearance.

was understood, the name **slow virus disease** was given to these diseases. ■ prions, p. 12

Prions differ from viruses in several ways. First, unlike viruses, prions contain no nucleic acid. Second, prions apparently arose following mutations in the gene encoding the normal prion protein in animals and humans. The normal prion protein is abbreviated PrP^{C}. The mutation caused the protein to have different folding properties from the PrP^{C}. It is designated PrP^{SC}, in which the SC stands for scrapie, the first recognized prion disease. The PrP^{SC} is resistant to protease whereas PrP^{C} is sensitive. Both forms are resistant to UV light and nucleases, because, unlike viruses, they do not contain nucleic acid. However, they are inactivated by chemicals that denature proteins.

One of the most intriguing questions regarding prions is how can they replicate if they do not contain any nucleic acid. Recall that only nucleic acids can replicate and code for proteins. An answer to this question is now emerging. The prion protein replicates by converting the normal host protein into prion protein thereby creating more prion protein molecules **(figure 14.21).** Thus, the prion protein is "infectious" because it catalyzes the conversion of normal protein into prion protein by changing the folding properties of the protein. Therefore, only if the cell is synthesizing normal prion protein is the prion protein able to replicate. Further, because the amino acid sequence of the abnormal prion protein and the normal prion protein found in all vertebrates are very similar, the notion that the amino acid sequence of a protein determines its conformation cannot be always true. ■ tertiary structure, p. 29

In most cases, the prion disease is only transmitted to members of the same species, because the amino acid sequence of different prion proteins in different species differs from one another. However, the barrier to prion transmission between species also depends on the strain of prion. It is now clear that the prion that caused mad cow disease in England has killed more than 100 people by causing a disease very similar to Creutzfeldt-Jakob disease. Presumably these people ate beef of infected animals. Thus far, no human deaths have been attributed to eating sheep infected with the scrapie agent or deer and elk infected with the prion causing chronic wasting disease. However, because the incubation period extends over many years,

TABLE 14.9 Slow Infections Caused by Prions

Agent	Host	Site of Infection	Disease
Scrapie agent	Sheep	Central nervous system	Scrapie spongiform encephalopathy
Kuru agent	Humans	Central nervous system	Kuru spongiform encephalopathy
Creutzfeldt-Jakob agent	Humans	Central nervous system	Creutzfeldt-Jakob disease
Gerstmann-Sträussler agent	Humans	Central nervous system	Gerstmann-Sträussler syndrome
Mad cow agent	Cows and humans	Central nervous system	Mad cow spongiform encephalopathy
Chronic wasting disease agent	Deer and elk	Central nervous system	Chronic wasting disease
Transmissible mink agent	Ranched mink	Central nervous system	Transmissible mink encephalopathy

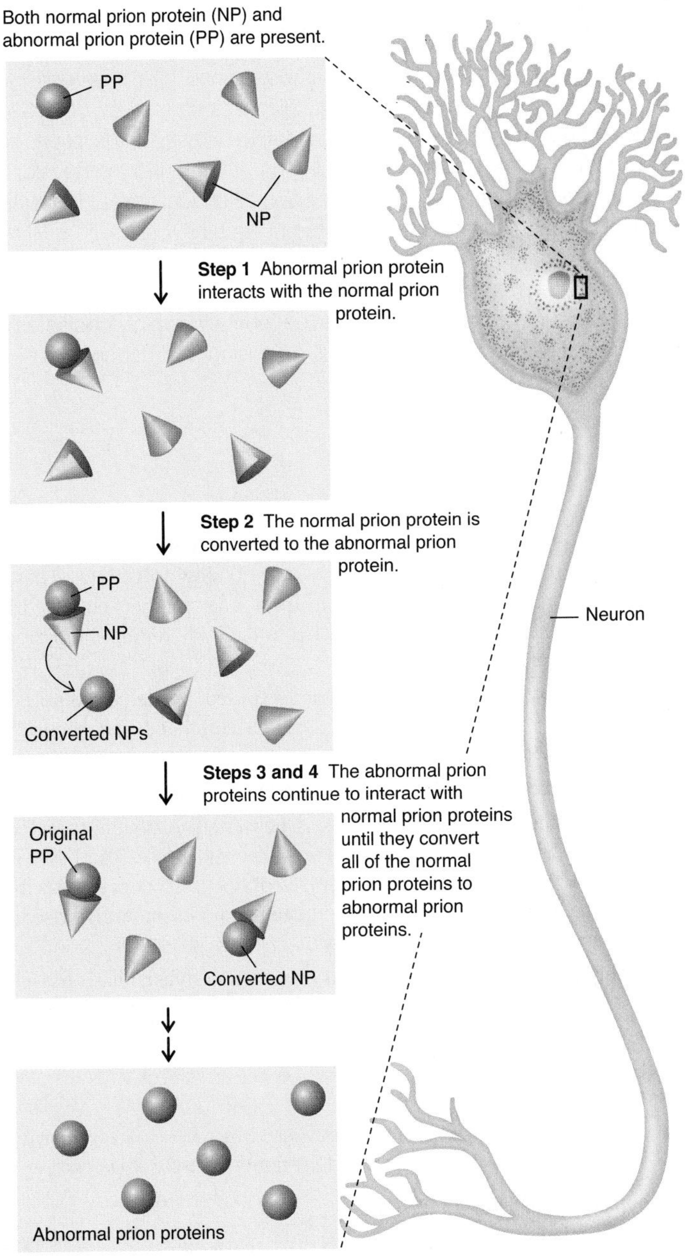
Both normal prion protein (NP) and abnormal prion protein (PP) are present.
PP
NP
Step 1 Abnormal prion protein interacts with the normal prion protein.
Step 2 The normal prion protein is converted to the abnormal prion protein.
PP
NP
Converted NPs
Steps 3 and 4 The abnormal prion proteins continue to interact with normal prion proteins until they convert all of the normal prion proteins to abnormal prion proteins.
Original PP
Converted NP
Abnormal prion proteins
Neuron

FIGURE 14.21 Proposed Mechanism by Which Prions Replicate The normal and abnormal prion proteins differ in their tertiary structures.

the possibility that cross infection can occur in these situations also has not been ruled out entirely. Additional information about the role of prions in human disease is covered in chapter 27. A brief history was covered in the **"A Glimpse of History"** in this chapter.

Viroids

The term **viroid** defines a group of pathogens that are also much smaller and distinctly different from viruses (see figure 1.13). Viroids that have been characterized consist solely of a small, single-stranded RNA molecule that varies in size from 246 to 375 nucleotides. This is about one-tenth the size of the smallest infectious viral RNA known. They have no protein coat and therefore are resistant to proteases.

Their other properties include:

- Viroids replicate autonomously within susceptible cells. No other virions or viroids are required for their replication.
- A single viroid RNA molecule is capable of infecting a cell.
- The viroid RNA is circular and is resistant to digestion by nucleases.

All viroids that have been identified infect only plants, where they cause serious diseases. These diseases include potato spindle tuber, chrysanthemum stunt, citrus exocortis, cucumber pale fruit, hopstunt, and cadang-cadang.

A great deal is known about the structure of viroid RNA, but many questions remain. How do viroids replicate? How do they cause disease? How did they originate? Do they have counterparts in animals, or are they restricted to plants? The answers to these questions will provide insights into new and fascinating features of another unusual member of the microbial world.

MICROCHECK 14.7

Two infectious agents that are structurally simpler than viruses are prions and viroids. Prions contain protein and no nucleic acid; viroids contain only single-stranded RNA and no protein.

- ✓ Distinguish between a prion and a viroid.
- ✓ What are the hosts of prions? Of viroids?
- ✓ Why are viroids resistant to nucleases?
- ✓ Must all prion diseases result from eating infected food? Explain.

FUTURE CHALLENGES

Great Promise, Greater Challenges

Gene therapy, the treatment of disease by introducing new genetic information into the body, is a procedure with tremendous promise, but with disappointing results thus far. In large part, this lack of success results from a number of basic biological and technological problems that have not yet been solved.

Gene therapy is rooted in the advances that have been made in microbial genetics, molecular biology, and virology. The idea that it might be possible to introduce genes into mammalian cells and correct life threatening conditions was first suggested by a number of scientists who worked with microbes and studied gene transfer in bacteria. These included Joshua Lederberg and Edward Tatum, co-discoverers of conjugation in *E. coli.* Lederberg also discovered transduction by a bacterial virus. It was a small step for these investigators to suggest the possibility of gene transfer into mammalian cells by an animal virus.

Viruses are the most popular vectors for introducing genes into cells. They have the ability to be taken up by specific tissues and then induce the cells' machinery to synthesize protein from the introduced genes. The desired genes are merely cloned into the viral genome and these will be introduced into all cells the virus infects.

The major challenge of gene therapy is to design a viral vector that can deliver and express genes in mammalian cells with great efficiency and absolute safety. A long-term goal is to deliver useful genes to the right spot and have them turn on and off at will. Considerable progress is being made to achieve these goals.

The two most common viral vectors currently being used are retroviruses, which include the HIV virus, and adenoviruses, a common cause of colds. The former results in integration of nucleic acid into the host cells, whereas the latter leads only to expression of the viral genes for a short period of time while the virus replicates, referred to as **transient expression.**

The promise of gene therapy has been on a roller coaster. First there was great hope of curing many diseases caused by defective genes, such as cystic fibrosis and hemophilia. However, the issues of safety, resulting from the death of a young patient, and the development of cancer in several others stopped all clinical trials. However, in 2005 clinical trials are set to resume using a new approach, RNA interference, to shut off genes synthesizing harmful products (see chapter 7, Perspective 7.1). Using this technique, scientists hope to treat such conditions as macular degeneration, high cholesterol levels, and HIV. Has a new era in this promising field begun?

SUMMARY

14.1 Structure and Classification of Animal Viruses

Phages and animal and plant viruses are nucleic acid surrounded by a protein coat, the **capsid.** Many animal viruses have an additional covering, an **envelope,** a lipid bilayer similar to the plasma membrane of the host. (Figure 13.2)

Animal and plant viruses containing more than one RNA molecule are **segmented viruses.**

Classification of Animal Viruses

The criteria for classifying animal viruses are **genome structure, particle structure,** and the presence or absence of a **viral envelope.** (Tables 14.1, 14.2)

Groupings Based on Routes of Transmission

Viruses that cause disease can be grouped according to their **routes of transmission**—the **enteric** viruses, **respiratory** viruses, **zoonotic** viruses (transferred from animals to other animals), and **sexually transmitted viruses.** (Table 14.4)

14.2 Interactions of Animal Viruses with Their Hosts

Most viruses infect and persist within their hosts in a state of **balanced pathogenicity** in which the host is not killed.

Viruses cause diseases that can be classified as **acute** or **persistent.**

Acute Infections

Acute infections are self-limited; the virus often remains localized, and diseases are of short duration and lead to lasting immunity. (Figure 14.2)

The replication cycle of virulent animal virus that causes an acute infection is similar to the lytic cycle shown by phage T4. (Table 14.5, Figure 13.5)

The steps in the infection process include **attachment** to specific receptors; **entry of the virion; targeting** to the site of viral replication; **uncoating** of the virion (Figure 14.3); **replication** of virus nucleic acid and synthesis of protein (Figure 14.4); **maturation** of the virion (Figure 14.5); **release** of the virion from cells and infection of other cells (Figure 14.6); **shedding** of the virions from one host and **transmission** to other hosts (Table 14.5).

Persistent Infections

In persistent infections, the virions are continually present in the body and are released from cells by budding. (Figure 14.6)

Persistent infections can be (1) **latent infections** (Table 14.6), (2) **chronic infections** (Table 14.7), and (3) **slow infections.** These categories are distinguished from one another largely by whether a virus can be detected in the body during the period of persistence. (Figure 14.7)

An example of a **latent** infection is caused by herpes simplex, HSV-1, which causes cold sores in childhood and becomes latent in nerve cells. (Figure 14.8)

The most common slow infection is AIDS caused by HIV.

In HIV infection, the viral RNA is converted to double-stranded DNA by the viral enzyme **reverse transcriptase.** The DNA is then integrated into chromosomes of host cells concerned with the immune response, where it can remain latent or give rise to intact virions. (Figure 14.9)

Unlike DNA polymerase, the enzyme reverse transcriptase has no proofreading ability, and so virions undergo numerous uncorrected mutations.

14.3 Viruses and Human Tumors

The relatively few human tumors caused by viruses are primarily caused by double-stranded DNA tumor viruses. (Table 14.8)

Retroviruses and Human Tumors

A rare tumor, a leukemia, is caused by a retrovirus.

14.4 Viral Genetic Alterations

Most viruses can infect only a single species and only certain cells within an organism.

Viruses causing **zoonoses** can multiply in widely divergent species such as birds, mosquitoes, and humans.

Viruses can modify their properties if two viruses with different host ranges infect the same cell.

Genome Exchange in Segmented Viruses (Figure 14.11)

Segmented viruses like influenza can alter their properties through an exchange of genomes following infection of the same cell by two viruses with different host ranges, the process of **genetic reassortment.** This results in changes of many properties of the virion, as a result of **genetic shift.**

This type of exchange likely accounts for the pandemics caused by the influenza virus every 10 to 30 years.

The genome also undergoes small changes as a result of mutations, the process of **genetic drift.**

14.5 Methods Used to Study Viruses

Cultivation of Host Cells

Some viruses can only be cultivated in living animals; others can be grown in **tissue culture.** (Figures 14.12, 14.13)

Quantitation

The **plaque assay** is commonly used to determine the number of infective virions in a sample. (Figure 14.14)

Virions can be counted with an **electron microscope.** (Figure 14.15)

Quantal assays determine the **infective** or **lethal** dose in a viral preparation.

Some viruses can clump red blood cells and their concentration can be measured by determining the dilution of virus able to clump the cells, **hemagglutination.** (Figure 14.16)

14.6 Plant Viruses

Many plant diseases are caused by viruses. (Figure 14.17)

Virions do not bind to receptor sites on plant cells, but enter through wound sites and move to other cells via **plasmodesmata.**

Spread of Plant Viruses

Many plant viruses are very resistant to inactivation.

Viruses are spread in large part by humans, by planting seeds in contaminated soils, through transfer from infected plants by grafting, and through the parasitic plant **dodder,** which can establish connections between an infected and uninfected plant. (Figure 14.19)

Various vectors, like insects and worms, can also spread virions.

Insect Transmission of Plant Viruses

Viruses may be associated with the external mouthparts of an insect or they may multiply within the insect.

14.7 Other Infectious Agents

Prions (Figure 1.11, Table 14.9)

Prions consist of **protein** and no **nucleic acid,** and they cause a number of fatal neurodegenerative diseases called **transmissible spongiform encephalopathies.**

Uninfected cells synthesize a protein almost identical in amino acid sequence to the abnormal prion protein.

Prions replicate by converting the normal cellular prion protein to the abnormal prion protein, which has a different conformation. (Figure 14.21)

Viroids (Figure 1.10)

Viroids are plant pathogens that consist of circular, single-stranded RNA molecules; they are about one-tenth the size of the smallest infectious viral RNA known.

Many unanswered questions remain regarding their origin, how they multiply, and how they cause disease.

REVIEW QUESTIONS

Short Answer

1. What are the criteria on which animal viruses are classified?
2. What are the substrate and product of reverse transcriptase?
3. Name one similarity between prions and HIV in terms of time of onset of symptoms appearing.
4. Distinguish between genetic shift and genetic drift.
5. Compare the mechanisms by which phages, and animal and plant viruses enter their host cells.
6. What is the major difference between a latent and chronic infection in terms of the virus in the host cell?
7. Name two DNA viruses that cause tumors in humans. Name one retrovirus that causes tumors in humans.
8. Distinguish between a prion and a viroid. What hosts does each infect?
9. What family of animal viruses is most closely related to temperate phages in their interaction with host cells?
10. Define genetic reassortment. Explain how it can alter the properties of a virus.

Multiple Choice

Questions 1 to 7 concern the differences and similarities between animal, plant, and bacterial viruses. Answer each question based on the following possibilities by circling the correct letter:

a) Bacteriophages only
b) Animal viruses only
c) Plant viruses only
d) Bacteriophages and animal viruses
e) Animal and plant viruses

1. Bind to specific receptors on the host cell to initiate infection.
   a) b) c) d) e)
2. Only the nucleic acid enters the host cell.
   a) b) c) d) e)
3. Lipid envelopes are common.
   a) b) c) d) e)
4. Reverse transcriptase is involved in the replication cycle.
   a) b) c) d) e)
5. Integration of viral nucleic acid leads to changes in properties of the host.
   a) b) c) d) e)
6. Tumors are caused by these viruses.
   a) b) c) d) e)
7. Restriction enzymes play a role in the host range of these viruses.
   a) b) c) d) e)
8. Prions
   a) contain only nucleic acid without a protein coat.
   b) replicate like HIV.
   c) integrate their nucleic acid into the host genome.
   d) cause diseases of humans.
   e) cause diseases of plants.
9. Viroids
   1. contain only single-stranded RNA and no protein coat.
   2. use reverse transcriptase in their replication.
   3. are similar in structure to bacteriophages.
   4. cause diseases in animals.
   5. cause diseases in plants.
   a) 1, 2 b) 2, 3 c) 3, 4 d) 4, 5 e) 1, 5

10. Acute infections in animals
    1. are a result of productive infection.
    2. generally lead to long-lasting immunity.
    3. result from integration of viral nucleic acid into the host.
    4. are usually followed by chronic infections.
    5. often lead to tumor formation.

    a) 1, 2 b) 2, 3 c) 3, 4 d) 4, 5 e) 1, 5

Applications

1. You are a scientist at a pharmaceutical company in charge of developing drugs against HIV. Discuss four possible targets for drugs that might be effective against this virus.
2. Researchers debate the evolutionary value to the virus of its ability to cause disease. Many argue that viruses accidentally cause disease and only in animals that are not the natural host. They state that this strategy may eventually prove fatal to the virus's future in that host. It is reasoned that the animals will eventually develop immune mechanisms to combat the virus and prevent its spread. Another group of researchers supports the view that disease is a way to enhance the survival of the virus. What rationale would this group use to support its view?

Critical Thinking

1. Would ID_{50} and LD_{50} necessarily be the same for a given virus? Why or why not?
2. The observation that viruses can agglutinate red blood cells suggests to some people that both viruses and red blood cells must have multiple binding sites. Is this a good argument? Why or why not?
3. An agricultural scientist is investigating ways to prevent viral infection of plants. Is preventing the specific attachment of the virus to its host cells a possible way to prevent infection? Why or why not?
4. Why is it virtually impossible to stamp out a disease caused by a zoonotic virus?

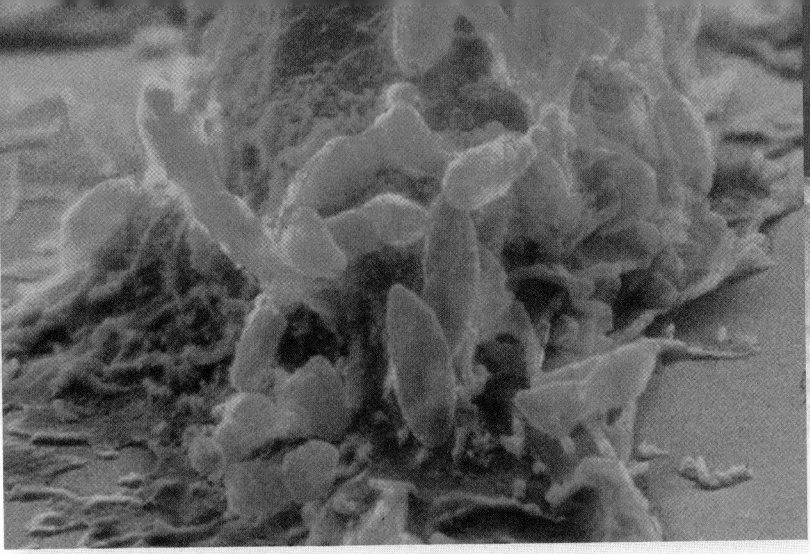

Phagocytic cells engulfing bacteria

CHAPTER FIFTEEN

The Innate Immune Response

A Glimpse of History

Once microorganisms were shown to cause disease, scientists worked to explain how the body defended itself against invasion by microorganisms. Elie Metchnikoff, a Russian-born scientist, theorized that specialized cells within the body destroyed invading organisms. His ideas arose from observations he made while studying the transparent immature larval form of starfish in Sicily in 1882. As he looked at the larvae in the microscope, he could see ameba-like cells within the bodies. He described his observations:

> . . . I was observing the activity of the motile cells of a transparent larva, when a new thought suddenly dawned on me. It occurred to me that similar cells must function to protect the organism against harmful intruders. . . . I thought that if my guess was correct a splinter introduced into the larva of a starfish should soon be surrounded by motile cells much as can be observed in a man with a splinter in his finger. No sooner said than done. In the small garden of our home . . . I took several rose thorns that I immediately introduced under the skin of some beautiful starfish larvae which were as transparent as water. Very nervous, I did not sleep during the night, as I was waiting for the results of my experiment. The next morning, very early, I found with joy that it had been successful.

Metchnikoff reasoned that certain cells present in animals were responsible for ingesting and destroying foreign material. He called these cells **phagocytes,** meaning "cells that eat," and he proposed that they were primarily responsible for the body's ability to destroy invading microorganisms.

When Metchnikoff returned to Russia, he looked for a way to study the ingestion of materials by phagocytes. A water flea that could be infected with a yeast provided a vehicle for such studies. He observed phagocytes ingesting and destroying invading yeast cells within the experimentally infected, transparent water fleas. In 1884, Metchnikoff published a paper that strongly supported his contention that phagocytic cells were primarily responsible for destroying disease-causing organisms. He spent the rest of his life studying this process and other biological phenomena; in 1908, he was awarded the Nobel Prize for these studies of immunity.

From a microorganism's standpoint, the tissues and fluids of the human body are much like a warm culture flask filled with a nutrient-rich solution. Considering this, it may be surprising that the interior of the body—including blood, muscles, bones, and organs—is generally sterile. If this were not the case, microbes would simply degrade our tissues, just as they readily decompose the carcasses of dead animals.

How does the interior of the body remain sterile in this world full of microbes? Like other multicellular organisms, humans have evolved several mechanisms of defense. First, we are covered with skin and mucous membranes that prevent entry of most foreign material, including microbes, into the body. Ready in case the barriers are breached are sensor systems that detect molecules associated with danger. Examples of these "danger signals" include compounds that are unique to bacteria and substances released only when tissues are damaged. The sensors can direct and assist other host defenses, facilitating the destruction of the foreign material. Also lying in wait are host cells that specialize in ingesting and digesting foreign material; if needed, additional reinforcements can be recruited to the site of breach. The protection provided by these systems is termed **innate immunity.**

The components of innate immunity have been called nonspecific defenses, but recent discoveries have shown that most of these components are far from unfocused; instead, they rely on the recognition of certain molecular patterns associated with invading microbes or tissue damage, a feature referred to as **pattern recognition.** Molecular patterns associated with pathogens include various compounds unique to bacterial cell walls (such

KEY TERMS

Apoptosis Programmed cell death that destroys self-cells without eliciting inflammation.

Complement system Series of proteins in blood and tissue fluids that can be activated to facilitate the removal and destruction of invading microbes.

Cytokines Proteins that function as chemical messengers, allowing cells to communicate.

Inflammation Coordinated innate response characterized by swelling, heat, redness, and pain in the infected area, aimed at containing a site of damage, localizing the response, and restoring tissue function.

Innate immunity Host defenses involving anatomical barriers, sensor systems that recognize patterns associated with invading microbes, and phagocytic cells.

Macrophage Type of phagocytic cell always present in tissues to some extent; can be activated to gain more killing power.

Membrane attack complex (MAC) Complement system components that assemble to form pores in membranes of invading cells.

Neutrophil Type of powerful phagocytic cell that quickly moves to an infected area to remove offending microbes.

Opsonization Coating of particles to be ingested by phagocytes with molecules for which the phagocytes have receptors, making it easier for phagocytosis to occur.

Phagocyte Cells that specialize in engulfing and digesting microbes and cell debris.

Phagocytosis The process by which a phagocyte engulfs an invader.

Toll-like receptors (TLRs) Receptors on cell surfaces that recognize specific compounds unique to microbes, enabling cells to sense the presence of invading microbes and then alert other components of the defense systems.

as lipopolysaccharide, lipoteichoic acid, and peptidoglycan) and other molecules. Those associated with damage include various proteins that are normally intracellular and are now outside cells, and substances produced during tissue necrosis and damage. ■ lipopolysaccharide, p. 62 ■ lipoteichoic acid, p. 62 ■ peptidoglycan, p. 61

In addition to innate immunity, vertebrates have evolved a more specialized response, termed the **adaptive immune response;** this develops throughout life and substantially increases the ability of the host to defend itself. Each time the body is exposed to certain types of foreign material, the adaptive defense system first "learns" and then "remembers" the most effective response to that specific material; it then reacts accordingly if the material is encountered again. The foreign material is called an **antigen.** On first exposure to an invading microbe or other antigen, the adaptive response develops relatively slowly, during which time the microbe may cause damage if the innate defenses are unable to contain it. Successive exposures, however, lead to a swift and greater repeat response, generally eliminating the invader before it causes obvious harm.

There are two general mechanisms used by the adaptive immune response to eliminate an invader. If the antigen is within one of the body's own cells, which are referred to as either **host cells** or a **"self" cells,** then the cell may be sacrificed as a means of destroying the invader. If the antigen is extracellular, then the body responds by making **antibodies.** These protein molecules have two functional regions; one binds specifically to the antigen and the other functions as a "red flag," directing other host defenses to remove or destroy the antigen.

The study of the many mechanisms the body uses to defend itself against invading microbes is called **immunology.** It encompasses not only the study of protection against infectious agents, but also cancers and the acceptance or rejection of transplanted cells and organs. Immunologists also study the effects of the immune response that can damage the body, such as **autoimmunity,** which occurs when the immune response is inappropriately directed against the cells of one's own body, and **hypersensitivity,** or allergic reactions.

To simplify the description of a network as complex and intricate as the immune system, it is helpful to consider it as a series of individual parts. This chapter, for example, will focus almost exclusively on innate immunity. Bear in mind, however, that although the various parts are discussed separately, in the body their actions are intimately connected and coordinated. In fact, as you will see in chapter 16, certain components of the innate defenses are instrumental in educating the adaptive defenses, helping them to distinguish antigens that represent danger.

15.1 Overview of the Innate Defenses

Focus Point

- Outline the essential components of the innate defenses.

First-line defenses are the barriers that separate and shield the interior of the body from the surrounding environment; they are the initial obstacles that microorganisms must overcome to invade the tissues. The anatomical barriers, which include the skin and mucous membranes, not only provide physical separation, but they are often bathed in secretions containing substances that have antimicrobial properties.

Sensor systems within the body recognize when the first-line barriers have been breached and then relay that information to other components of the host defenses. Two important groups of sensors that have only recently been discovered are the **toll-like receptors** and **NOD (nucleotide-binding oligomerization domain) proteins,** which are found on or within a variety of different cell types. These receptors recognize families of compounds unique to microbes, enabling the cell to sense invaders and then send chemical signals to alert other components of the host's defense. Another type of sensor is a series of proteins always present in blood and tissue fluids; these proteins are collectively called the **complement system** because they can "complement," or act in conjunction with, the adaptive immune defenses. In response to certain stimuli, the complement proteins become activated, setting off a chain of events that results in removal and destruction of invading microbes.

Phagocytes, cells that specialize in engulfing and digesting microbes and cell debris, act as sentries, alert for signs of invasion of the body. More can be recruited from the blood-stream, serving as reinforcements at the sites in tissues where first-line defenses have been breached.

Cells of the immune system communicate with one another by producing proteins that function as chemical messengers, called **cytokines.** A cytokine produced by one cell diffuses to another and binds to the appropriate cytokine receptor of that cell. When a cytokine binds a receptor, the receptor transmits a signal to the interior of the cell, inducing certain changes in the activities of the cell. Some types of cytokines endow cells with enhanced powers; others prompt cells to migrate to specific locations within the body.

When invading microorganisms or tissue damage is detected, **inflammation** ensues; this is a coordinated response involving many aspects of the innate defenses. During inflammation, the cells that line local blood vessels near the area of invasion or damage undergo changes that allow antibodies, complement proteins, and coagulation proteins in **plasma,** the fluid portion of the blood, to leak into tissues. Other changes allow phagocytic cells in the blood to adhere to the vessels and then squeeze between cells, exiting the bloodstream. Phagocytic cells then migrate to the area of infection or damage where they ingest and destroy foreign material. Some types of phagocytes play a dual role, destroying invaders while also communicating with cells of the adaptive immune system, enlisting their far more powerful effects.

Fever is another of the body's innate defense mechanisms. This increase in internal body temperature acts in several ways to discourage infection.

MICROCHECK 15.1

First-line defenses are the initial obstacles that microbes must overcome to invade the tissues. Within the body are sensor systems such as toll-like receptors, NOD proteins, and the complement system that recognize when the barriers have been breached. Phagocytic cells engulf foreign material; they can communicate with other cells via cytokines. Inflammation is a coordinated response to invasion or tissue damage.

- ✓ How do cytokines function?
- ✓ Describe the dual roles played by some types of phagocytes.
- ✓ What types of molecules that are unique to microbes might toll-like receptors recognize?

15.2 First-Line Defenses

Focus Point

- Describe the first-line defenses, including the physical barriers, antimicrobial substances, and normal flora.

All exposed surfaces of the body, including the skin and the digestive, respiratory, and genitals tracts, are lined with **epithelial cells (figure 15.1).** These cells are tightly packed together and rest on a thin layer of fibrous material, the **basement membrane.** In addition to the physical protection provided by this physical barrier against the outside world, the body's surfaces are bathed with a variety of antimicrobial substances that either kill or inhibit many microbes. Certain microbes, however, are highly adapted to these conditions and actually grow, providing other types of additional protection.

In this section, we will describe the general physical and chemical aspects of the anatomical barriers. We will also discuss the protective contributions of the **normal flora,** those microbes that routinely inhabit the body surfaces. Various other first-line defense mechanisms are discussed more fully in the chapters dealing with each body system. ■ normal flora, p. 453

Physical Barriers

The skin is the most visible barrier, covering the majority of surfaces that are in obvious contact with the environment. **Mucous membranes** line the digestive tract, respiratory tract, and genitourinary tract. These surfaces are often considered to be "inside" the body, but actually they are in direct contact with the external environment **(figure 15.2).** For example, the digestive tract, which begins at the mouth and ends at the anus, is simply a hollow tube that runs through the body, providing the opportunity for intestinal cells to absorb nutrients from food that passes (see figure 25.1); the respiratory tract is a cavity that allows oxygen and carbon dioxide gases to be exchanged (see figure 24.1).

Skin

The skin provides the most difficult barrier for microbes to penetrate; it is composed of two main layers—the dermis and the epidermis

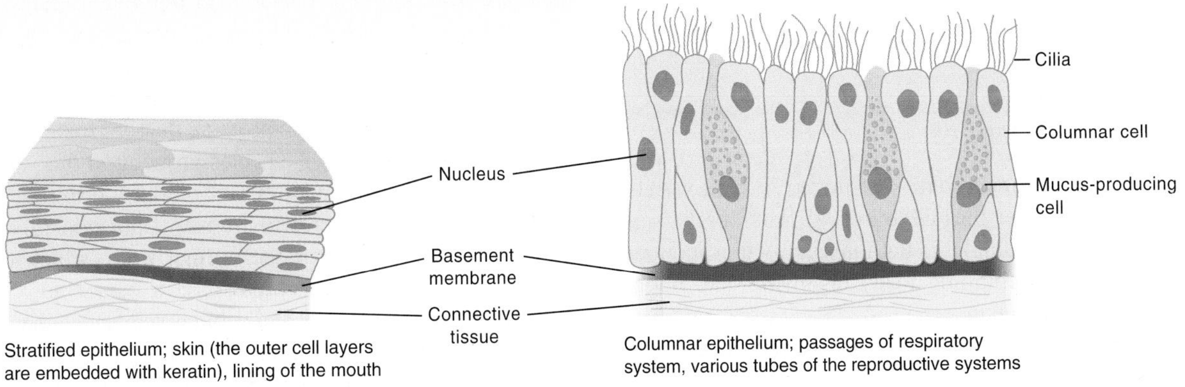

FIGURE 15.1 Epithelial Barriers Cells of these barriers are tightly packed together and rest on a layer of thin fibrous material, the basement membrane. Note that some epithelial cells have cilia which propel material to an area where it can be eliminated.

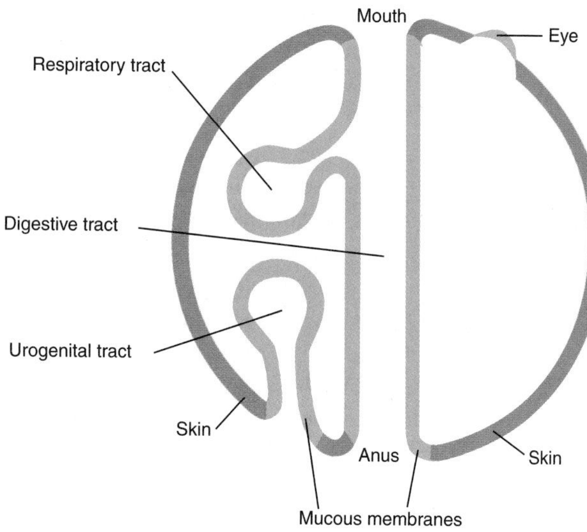

FIGURE 15.2 Physical Barriers These barriers separate the interior of the body from the surrounding environment; they are the initial obstacles microorganisms must overcome to invade tissues. The skin is shown in purple, and mucous membranes in pink.

(see figure 22.1). The **dermis** contains tightly woven fibrous connective tissue, making it extremely tough and durable; the dermis of cows is used to make leather. The **epidermis** is composed of many layers of epithelial cells, which become more progressively flattened towards the exterior. The outermost sheets are made up of dead cells that have been embedded with a water-repelling protein called **keratin,** resulting in the skin being an arid environment. The cells continually slough off, taking with them any microbes that might be adhering. ■ anatomy and physiology of the skin, p. 521

Mucous Membranes

The cells of the mucous membranes, or **mucosa,** are constantly bathed with mucus and other secretions that help wash microbes from the surfaces. Some mucous membranes have mechanisms that propel microorganisms and viruses, directing them toward areas where they can be eliminated more easily. For example, **peristalsis,** the rhythmic contractions of the intestinal tract that propels food and liquid, also helps expel microbes. The respiratory tract is lined with ciliated cells; the hairlike cilia constantly beat in an upward motion, propelling materials including microbes away from the lungs to the throat where they can then be swallowed. The flow of urine regularly flushes organisms from the urinary tract. ■ cilia, p. 77

Antimicrobial Substances

Both the skin and mucous membranes are protected by a variety of **antimicrobial substances** that inhibit or kill microorganisms **(figure 15.3).** Sweat, for example, is high in salt; as it evaporates it leaves a salty residue, inhibiting many organisms that might otherwise proliferate on the skin.

Lysozyme, the enzyme that degrades peptidoglycan, is found in tears, saliva, and in mucus that bathes mucous membranes. It is also found within the body, in phagocytic cells, blood, and the fluid that bathes tissues. Lysozyme is primarily effective against Gram-positive bacteria, whose peptidoglycan is more likely to be exposed and therefore accessible to the enzyme; recall that in Gram-negative bacteria, the peptidoglycan layer is sandwiched between the cytoplasmic and outer membranes (see figures 3.33 and 3.34). ■ lysozyme, p. 65

Peroxidase enzymes are found in saliva and milk; they are also found within body tissues and inside phagocytes. These enzymes break down hydrogen peroxide and, in the process, produce potent oxidizing compounds. For example, the interaction of peroxidase, hydrogen peroxide, and chlorine produces hypochlorite, the active ingredient in bleach. Bacteria that produce the enzyme catalase, however, may avoid the damaging products associated with peroxidase activity; catalase breaks down hydrogen peroxide, potentially destroying the compound before it can interact with peroxidase. Catalase-negative organisms are more sensitive to peroxidase killing. ■ catalase, p. 96

Lactoferrin is an iron-binding protein found in saliva, mucus, and milk; it is also found in some types of phagocytic cells. A similar compound, **transferrin** is found in blood and tissue fluids. Iron, an important part of some enzymes, is one of the major elements required for growth (see table 4.3). By sequestering iron, the lactoferrin and transferrin effectively withhold the essential element from most microbes. Some bacteria, however, make compounds that capture iron in body fluids and secretions, thus circumventing this defense.

Defensins are short antimicrobial peptides found on mucous membranes and within phagocytic cells. They are thought to function by inserting into bacterial membranes, forming pores that disrupt the integrity of the cell.

Normal Flora

The population of microorganisms routinely found growing on the body surfaces of healthy individuals is called the **normal flora** (see figure 19.1). Although these organisms are not technically part of the immune system, the protection they provide is considerable.

One protective effect of the normal flora is competitive exclusion of pathogens. The normal flora prevents invading organisms from adhering to host cells by covering binding sites that might otherwise be used for attachment. The population also consumes available nutrients that could otherwise be used by less desirable organisms. Members of the normal flora also produce compounds that are toxic to other bacteria. In the hair follicles of the skin, for example, *Propionibacterium* species degrade the lipids found in body secretions, releasing fatty acids that inhibit the growth of many pathogens. In the gastrointestinal tract, other strains of *E. coli* synthesize colicins, proteins that are toxic to other strains of bacteria. *Lactobacillus* species growing in the vagina produce lactic acid as a fermentation end product, resulting in an acidic pH that inhibits the growth of many potential disease-causing organisms. Disruption of the normal flora, which occurs when antibiotics are used, can predispose a person to various infections. Examples include antibiotic-associated colitis, caused by the growth of toxin-producing strains of *Clostridium difficile* in the intestine, and vulvovaginitis, caused by excessive growth of *Candida albicans* in the vagina. ■ antibiotic-associated colitis, p. 614 ■ vulvovaginitis, p. 657

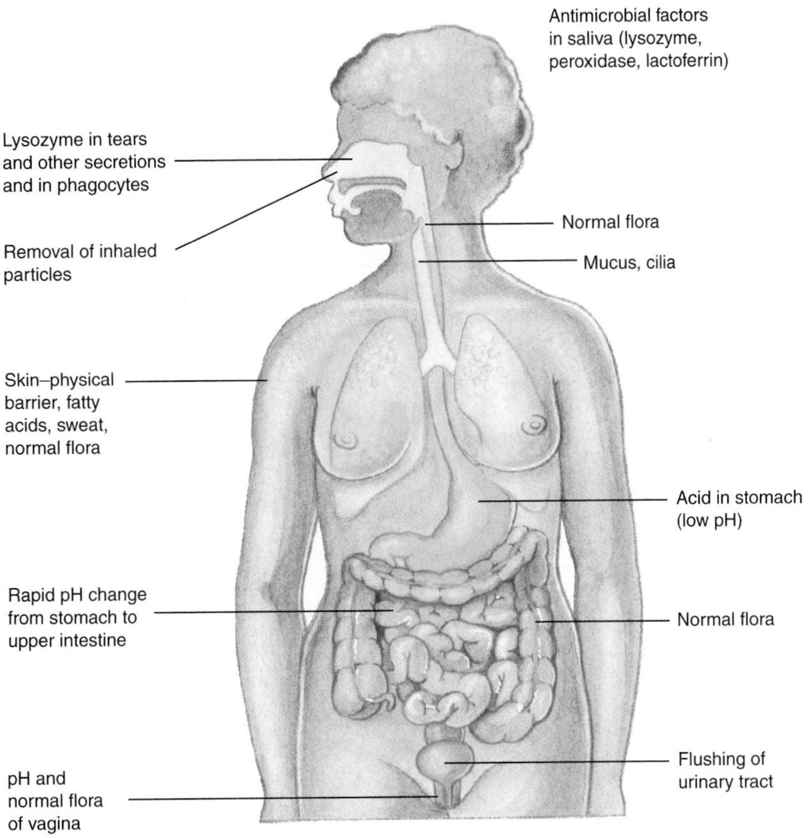

FIGURE 15.3 Antimicrobial Substances and Other First-Line Defenses Physical barriers, such as skin and mucous membranes, antimicrobial secretions, and normal flora work together to prevent entry of microorganisms into the host's tissues.

The normal flora also stimulates the host defenses, effectively providing a moderate amount of "exercise" to the system, thereby enhancing its function. Other aspects of the normal flora will be discussed in chapter 19.

MICROCHECK 15.2

Physical barriers that prevent entry of microorganisms into the body include the skin and mucous membranes. Various antimicrobial substances, including lysozyme, peroxidase enzymes, lactoferrin, and defensins are found on the body surfaces. The normal flora plays a protective role by excluding certain other microbes.

- ✓ What is peristalsis?
- ✓ What is the role of lactoferrin?
- ✓ How would damage to the ciliated cells of the respiratory tract predispose a person to infection?

15.3 The Cells of the Immune System

Focus Point

- Describe the role of granulocytes, mononuclear phagocytes, dendritic cells, and lymphocytes in immunity.

The cells of the immune system can move from one part of the body to another, traveling through the body's circulatory systems like vehicles on an extensive interstate highway system. They are always found in normal blood, but their numbers usually increase during infections, recruited from reserves of immature cells that develop in the bone marrow. Some cells play dual functions, having crucial roles in both innate and adaptive immunity.

The formation and development of blood cells is called **hematopoiesis** (Greek for "blood" and "to make"). All blood cells, including those important in the body's defenses, originate from the same type of cell, the **hematopoietic stem cell,** found in the bone marrow **(figure 15.4).** These stem cells are induced to develop into the various types of blood cells by a group of cytokines called **colony-stimulating factors.** Some of the cells of the immune system are already mature as they circulate in the bloodstream, but others **differentiate,** developing functional properties, after they leave the blood and enter the tissues.

The general categories of blood cells and their derivatives include red blood cells, platelets, and white blood cells. Red blood cells, or **erythrocytes,** carry oxygen in the blood. **Platelets,** which are actually fragments arising from large cells called **megakaryocytes,** are important for blood clotting. White blood cells, or **leukocytes,** are important in all host defenses. Leukocytes can be divided into four broad groups—granulocytes, mononuclear phagocytes, dendritic cells, and lymphocytes **(table 15.1).**

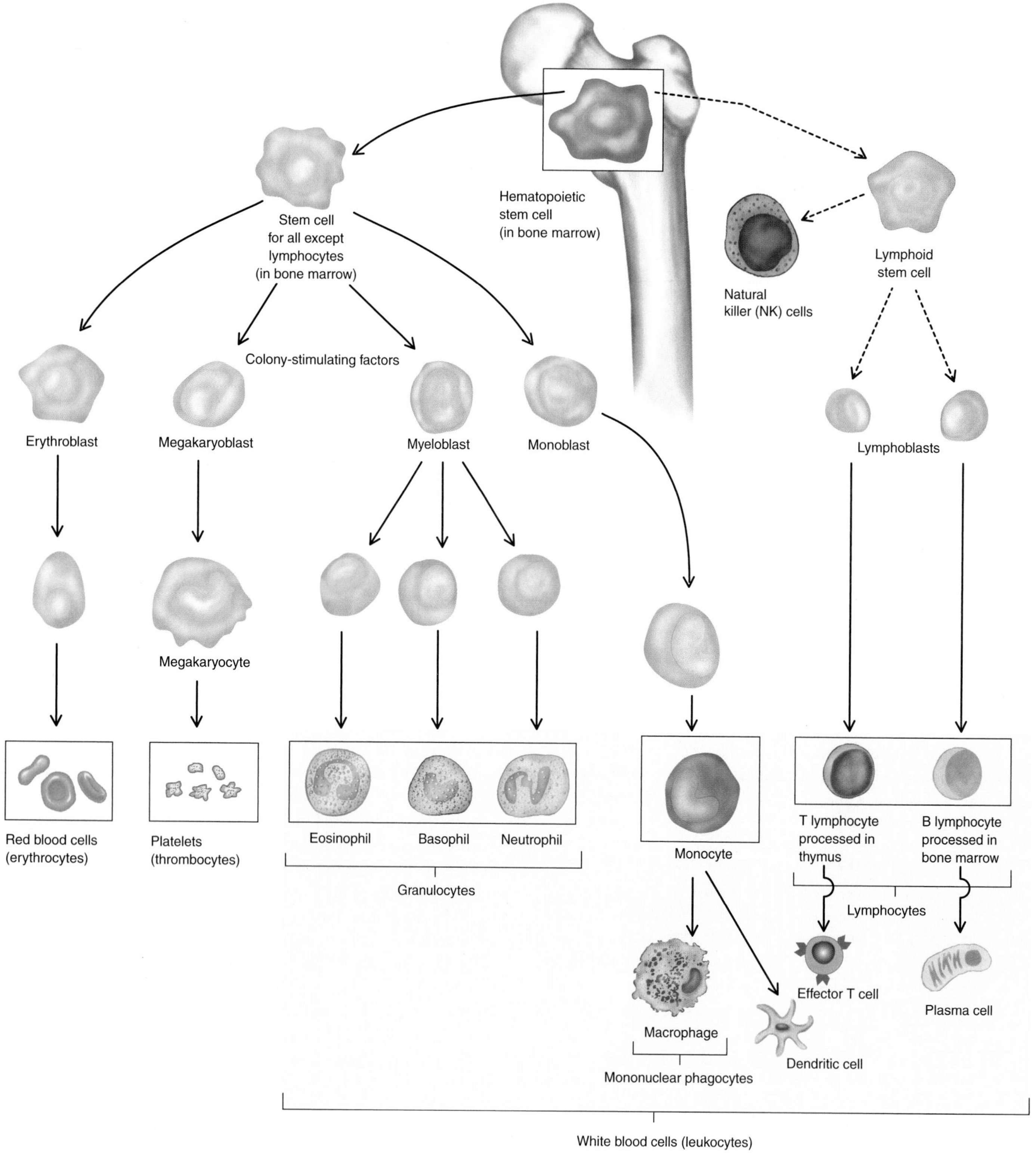

FIGURE 15.4 Blood Cells and Their Derivatives All these descend from hematopoietic stem cells found in the bone marrow. Some of the steps not yet clearly defined are indicated by dotted arrows. Multiple steps occur between the stem cell and the final cells produced. The role of these cells in the immune response will be explained in this chapter and chapter 16.

Granulocytes

Granulocytes all contain prominent cytoplasmic granules, filled with biologically active chemicals that are important in their function. There are three types of granulocytes—neutrophils, basophils, and eosinophils; their names reflect the staining properties of their cytoplasmic granules.

Neutrophils are highly efficient at phagocytizing and destroying foreign material, particularly bacteria, and damaged cells. The contents of their granules, which stain poorly, include many antimicrobial substances and degradative enzymes essential for destruction of materials that the cells engulf. They are the most abundant and important granulocytes of the innate responses and are by far the best understood. Neutrophils are sometimes called **polymorphonuclear neutrophilic leukocytes, polys,** or **PMNs,** names that reflect the appearance of multiple lobes of their single nucleus. They normally account for over 50% of circulating leukocytes, and their numbers increase during most acute bacterial infections. There are generally few in tissues except during inflammation. Because of the importance of neutrophils in innate immunity, they will be described in more detail later in the chapter. ■ specialized attributes of neutrophils, p. 379

Basophils are blood cells involved in allergic reactions and inflammation. Their granules, which are stained dark purplish-blue by the basic dye methylene blue, contain histamine and other chemicals that increase capillary permeability during inflammation. **Mast cells** are similar in appearance and function to basophils but are found in virtually all tissues, rather than in blood. They do not come from the same precursor cells as basophils. Mast cells are important in the inflammatory response and are responsible for many allergic reactions.

Eosinophils are thought to be primarily important in expelling parasitic worms from the body. They seem to be involved in allergic reactions, causing some of the symptoms associated with allergies, but reducing others. Relatively few eosinophils are found in blood, because most leave the bloodstream, ultimately entering local secretions. The granules of eosinophils, which are stained red by the acidic dye eosin, contain antimicrobial substances and also histaminase, an enzyme that breaks down histamine.

TABLE 15.1 Human Leukocytes

Cell Type (% of Blood Leukocytes)		Location in body	Functions
Granulocytes			
Neutrophils (polymorphonuclear neutrophilic leukocytes or PMNs, often called polys; 55%–65%)		Account for most of the circulating leukocytes; few in tissues except during inflammation	Phagocytize and digest engulfed materials
Eosinophils (2%–4%)		Few in tissues except in certain types of inflammation and allergies	Participate in inflammatory reaction and immunity to some parasites
Basophils (0%–1%), Mast cells		Basophils in circulation; mast cells present in most tissues	Release histamine and other inflammation-inducing chemicals from the granules
Mononuclear Phagocytes			
Monocytes (3%–8%)	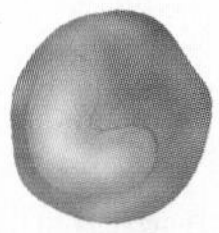	In circulation; they differentiate into either macrophages or dendritic cells when they migrate into tissue	Phagocytize and digest engulfed materials
Macrophages	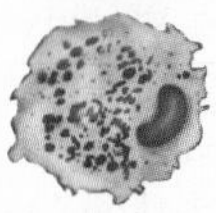	Present in virtually all tissues; given various names based on the tissue in which they are found	Phagocytize and digest engulfed materials
Dendritic cells	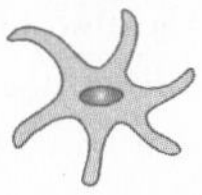	Initially in tissues, but they migrate to secondary lymphoid organs (such as lymph nodes, spleen, thymus, appendix, tonsils)	Gather antigen from the tissues and then bring it to lymphocytes that congregate in the secondary lymphoid organs
Lymphocytes			
Several types (25%–35%)	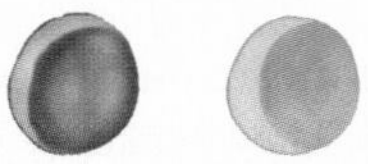	In lymphoid organs (such as lymph nodes, spleen, thymus, appendix, tonsils); also in circulation	Participate in adaptive immune responses

Mononuclear Phagocytes

Mononuclear phagocytes constitute a widespread collection of important phagocytic cells called the **mononuclear phagocyte system (MPS) (figure 15.5).** They include **monocytes,** which circulate in the blood, and the cell types that develop from monocytes as those cells leave the bloodstream and migrate into tissues.

Macrophages, a differentiated form of monocytes, are present in virtually all tissues to at least some extent. They are particularly abundant in liver, spleen, lymph nodes, lungs, and the peritoneal (abdominal) cavity. Unfortunately for the novice, however, they are given various different names based on the tissue in which they are found (see figure 15.5). The role of macrophages in phagocytosis and other aspects of host defense will be discussed in more detail later in the chapter. ■ specialized attributes of macrophages, p. 378

Dendritic cells also develop from monocytes. Their function goes beyond engulfment and destruction of an invader, and so they will be considered separately.

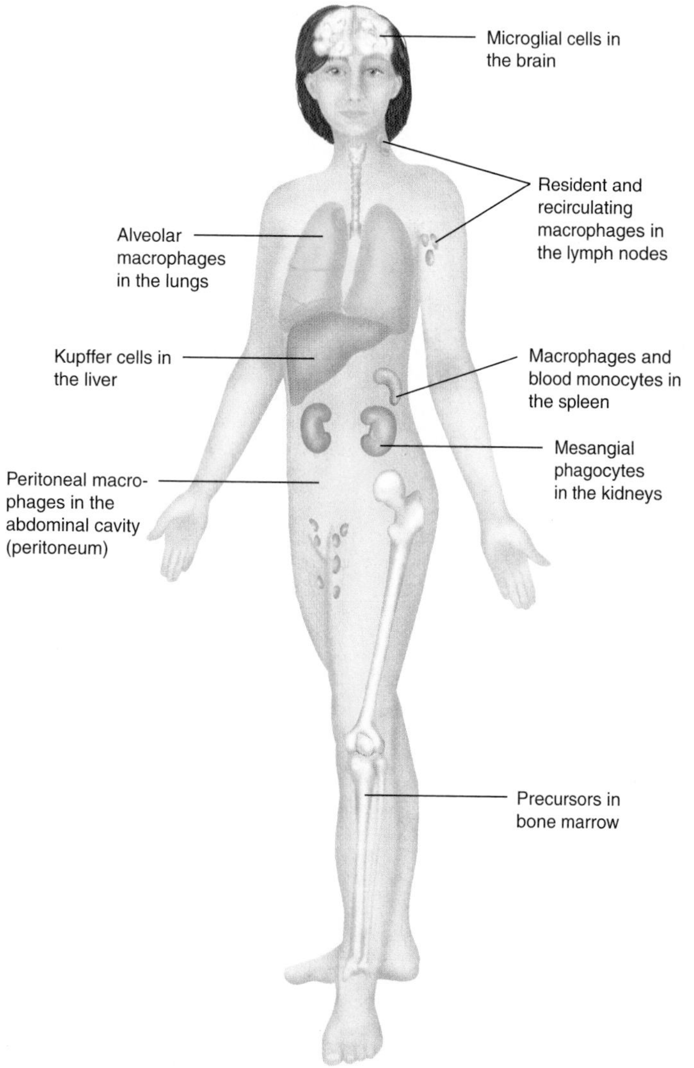

FIGURE 15.5 Mononuclear Phagocyte System This system of monocytes and macrophages was formerly known as the reticuloendothelial system. Many of these cells have special names to denote their location—for example, Kupffer cells (in the liver) and alveolar macrophages (in the lung).

Dendritic Cells

Dendritic cells are branched cells intimately involved in adaptive immunity, functioning as scouts in various tissues throughout the body. They routinely engulf material in the tissues, and then bring it to the cells of the adaptive immune system for "inspection." Dendritic cells develop from monocytes, but some also appear to descend from other cell types. Details regarding the interactions of dendritic cells with the cells of adaptive immunity will be discussed in chapter 16.

Lymphocytes

Lymphocytes are involved in adaptive immunity. In contrast to the generic pattern recognition of antigens by cells of the innate defenses, individual cells of the two major groups of lymphocytes, **B cells** and **T cells,** show remarkable specificity in their recognition of antigen. **Natural killer (NK) cells** are another type of lymphocyte; however, they lack the specificity exhibited by B cells and T cells. Lymphocytes are the center of focus of chapter 16.

MICROCHECK 15.3

Granulocytes include neutrophils, basophils, and eosinophils. Mononuclear phagocytes include monocytes and macrophages. Dendritic cells function as scouts for the adaptive immune system. Lymphocytes are involved in adaptive immunity.

- ✓ Which type of granulocyte is the most abundant?
- ✓ How are macrophages related to monocytes?
- ✓ Why can stem cell transplants be used to replace defective lymphocytes?

15.4 Cell Communication

Focus Point

- Describe the role of surface receptors, cytokines, and adhesion molecules in immunity.

In order for the various cells of the immune system to respond to trauma or invasion in a cooperative fashion, cells must communicate both with their immediate environment and with each other. Cells receive signals from their external environment by producing surface receptors that are able to bind specific chemical messengers; these surface receptors can be considered the "eyes" and "ears" of a cell. The "voices" of a cell are the cytokines, or chemical messengers, that a cell can make. In addition, some cells can make adhesion molecules; these function as "hands," enabling one cell to directly contact another.

Surface Receptors

Surface receptors are membrane proteins to which certain signal molecules bind. They generally span the cell membrane, connecting the outside of the cell with the inside, enabling the inner workings of the cell to sense and respond to signals outside of the cell. Each surface receptor is specific with respect to the compound or compounds it will bind; a molecule that can bind to a given receptor is called a **ligand** for that receptor. When a ligand binds to its surface receptor, the internal portion of the receptor becomes modified in some manner. This modification then elicits some type of response by the cell, such as chemotaxis. Cells can alter the types of surface molecules they make, enabling them to respond only to signals that are relevant when the cell is in a certain location or developmental stage. ■ chemotaxis, p. 68

Cytokines

Cytokines are proteins made by certain cells as a mechanism to communicate with other cells. They bind to certain surface receptors called **cytokine receptors,** which are found on the cells cytokines regulate. Binding of a cytokine to its receptor induces a change in the cell such as growth, differentiation, movement, or cell death. Although cytokines are short-lived, they are very powerful, acting at extremely low concentrations. They can act locally, regionally, or systemically. Often, they act together or in sequence, in a complex fashion. The source and effects of representative cytokines are summarized in **table 15.2.**

Chemokines are cytokines important in chemotaxis of immune cells. Certain types of defense cells have receptors for chemokines, thereby enhancing their ability to migrate to the appropriate region of the body, such as an area of inflammation. Two chemokine receptors, CCR5 and CXCR4, play a critical role in HIV infection; they serve as co-receptors for the virus, influencing which cell types are most likely to become infected. ■ chemotaxis, p. 68 ■ HIV co-receptors, p. 737

Colony-stimulating factors (CSFs) are important in the multiplication and differentiation of leukocytes (see figure 15.4). During the immune response when more leukocytes are needed, a variety of colony-stimulating factors direct immature cells into the appropriate maturation pathways.

Interferons (IFNs) are important in the control of viral infections. In addition to being antiviral, IFN-gamma helps regulate the function of cells involved in the inflammatory response, particularly mononuclear phagocytes, and modulates certain responses of adaptive immunity. The role of interferons in the containment of viral infections will be described in more detail later in the chapter.

Interleukins (ILs), produced by leukocytes, have diverse functions. As a group, they are important in both innate immunity, including the inflammatory response, and adaptive immunity. Their activities often overlap.

Tumor necrosis factors (TNFs) were discovered because of their activities in killing tumor cells, which is how they acquired their name, but they actually have multiple roles. TNF-alpha, which is produced by macrophages and other cell types, plays an instrumental role in initiating the inflammatory response. Tumor necrosis factors can also initiate the process of programmed cell death, or apoptosis. ■ apoptosis, p. 382

TABLE 15.2 Some Important Cytokines

Cytokine	Source	Effects
Chemokines	Various cells	Chemotaxis
Colony-Stimulating Factors (CSFs)	Fibroblasts, endothelium, other cells	Stimulation of growth and differentiation of different kinds of leukocytes
Interferons		
Interferon alpha	Leukocytes	Antiviral; induces fever, contributes to inflammation
Interferon beta	Fibroblasts	Antiviral
Interferon gamma	T lymphocytes	Antiviral; macrophage activation; development and regulation of adaptive immune responses
Interleukins (ILs)		
IL-1	Macrophages, epithelial cells	Proliferation of lymphocytes; macrophage production of cytokines, induce adhesion molecules for PMNs on blood vessel cells; induce fever
IL-2 (T-cell growth factor)	T lymphocytes	Changes in growth of lymphocytes; activation of natural killer cells; promote adaptive cell-mediated immune responses
IL-3	T lymphocytes, mast cells	Changes in growth of precursors of blood cells and also of mast cells
IL-4, IL-5, IL-10, IL-14	T lymphocytes, mast cells, other cells	Promote antibody responses
IL-6	T lymphocytes, macrophages	T- and B-cell growth; production of acute-phase proteins; fever
Tumor Necrosis Factors (TNFs)		
Alpha	Macrophages, T lymphocytes, other cell types, mast cell granules	Initiation of inflammatory response; cytotoxicity for some tumor cells; regulation of certain immune functions; induce fever; chemotactic for granulocytes
Beta	T lymphocytes	Killing of target cells by cytotoxic T cells and natural killer (NK) cells

Groups of cytokines often act together to facilitate a particular response by the host defenses. For example, certain cytokines referred to as **pro-inflammatory cytokines** contribute to inflammation (TNF-alpha, IL-1, IL-6, and others). Others are especially involved in promoting antibody responses (IL-4, IL-5, IL-10, and IL-14). A different group promotes responses that involve certain types of T cells (IL-2, and IFN-gamma, and others).

Adhesion Molecules

Adhesion molecules on the surface of cells allow those cells to adhere to other cells. Some cells use adhesion molecules to "grab" other cells as they pass by. For example, when phagocytic cells in the blood are needed in tissues, the **endothelial cells,** which are the cells that line the blood vessels, synthesize adhesion molecules, snaring passing phagocytic cells. This slows the rapidly moving phagocytic cells, providing them with the opportunity to exit the bloodstream. Other types of adhesion molecules allow cells to make direct contact with one another, thereby enabling cells to target the delivery of cytokines or other compounds to a particular cell.

MICROCHECK 15.4

Surface receptors allow a cell to detect molecules that are present outside of that cell. Cytokines provide cells with a mechanism of communication. Adhesion molecules allow a cell to adhere to other cells.

- ✓ What is a ligand?
- ✓ What is the function of colony-stimulating factors?
- ✓ How could colony-stimulating factors be used as a therapy?

15.5

Sensor Systems

Focus Point

- Describe the outcomes of toll-like receptor engagement, complement system activation, and detection of long dsRNA.

Sensor systems within the blood and tissues lie ready to detect signs of either tissue damage or microbial invasion. They respond to patterns associated with danger, such as bacterial cell wall components, by directly destroying the invading microbe or by recruiting other components of the host defenses.

Toll-Like Receptors and NOD Proteins

Toll-like receptors (TLRs) are pattern recognition receptors that allow cells to "see" molecules that signify the presence of microbes outside of the cell **(figure 15.6); NOD proteins** do the same for the inside of a cell (the cell's cytoplasm). TLRs and NOD proteins have only recently been discovered, and much is still being learned about them, but already they have caused a tremendous resurgence of interest in innate immunity, which many scientists had thought was well understood.

TLRs are part of a family of receptors called Toll receptors, first identified in *Drosophila* species (fruit flies). The name of this family was coined when one of the researchers involved in their discovery exclaimed "toll!" (a German slang word meaning the equivalent of "far out") at the sight of the peculiar developmental defect in fruit fly embryos. The mutation was in a gene that then became known as Toll.

TLRs are found on a variety of cell types including macrophages and cells that line normally sterile body sites. At least 10 TLRs have been described so far, and each recognizes a distinct compound or group of compounds associated with "danger." For example, one recognizes peptidoglycan and another is triggered by lipopolysaccharide. Other bacteria-specific compounds that activate the receptors include flagellin and certain nucleotide sequences that typify bacterial DNA.

When a compound engages a TLR, which appears to occur by either direct or indirect binding, a signal is transmitted to the nucleus of the host cell, inducing that cell to alter the expression of certain genes. For example, lipopolysaccharide triggers a toll-like receptor on monocytes and macrophages, causing the cells to begin producing chemokines that attract additional phagocytes to the area. Engagement of TLRs on endothelial cells that line blood vessels causes those cells to produce pro-inflammatory cytokines.

The discovery of TLRs has led to some intriguing ideas about how they function. Perhaps the triggering of specific combinations of TLRs acts like a bar code, helping the cell identify the invader. If this is true, cells of the innate defenses might be tailoring their responses to fit specific groups of pathogens, such as Gram-positive bacteria.

The NOD proteins are intracellular receptors that recognize bacterial cell wall components within the cytoplasm. Although details regarding the NOD proteins are still being elucidated, a defect in one of the proteins appears to be a predisposing factor in the development of Crohn's disease, an inflammatory bowel disease.

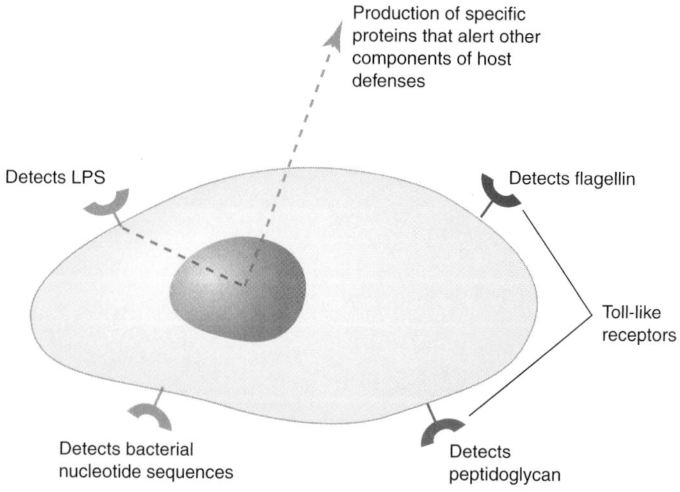

FIGURE 15.6 Toll-Like Receptors These surface receptors are used by the body's cells to detect the presence of pathogen-associated molecular patterns. Engagement of a toll-like receptor transmits a signal to the cell's nucleus, inducing the cell to begin producing certain proteins such as cytokines, alerting other components of host defenses.

The Complement System

The **complement system** is a series of proteins that constantly circulate in the blood and the fluid that bathes the tissues. Early studies showed that these proteins augment the activities of the adaptive immune response; in fact, their name is derived from observations that they "complement" the activities of antibodies. They routinely circulate in an inactive form, but in response to certain stimuli indicating the presence of foreign material, a cascade of reactions occurs. This results in the rapid activation of critical complement system components. These activated forms have specialized functions that cooperate with other host defenses to quickly remove and destroy the offending material.

Three pathways lead to the activation of the complement system **(figure 15.7):**

- **Alternative pathway.** The name of this pathway may seem to imply that it is "second choice," but it actually reflects the fact that it was not discovered first. In fact, the pathway is quickly and easily initiated, providing vital early warning that an invader is present. The alternative pathway relies on the binding of the complement protein C3b to cell surfaces, allowing other complement proteins to subsequently attach and form a complement activating complex. C3b is always present in blood and tissues to at least some extent, so nearly any cell surface automatically triggers the pathway unless regulatory proteins, which are associated with the body's own cells, specifically halt the process. The regulatory proteins function by inactivating bound C3b before the other proteins attach. As we will discuss in chapter 19, some pathogens have developed mechanisms to attract the regulatory proteins to their own surfaces, thwarting complement activation by this pathway.
- **Lectin pathway.** Activation of the lectin pathway requires **mannan-binding lectins (MBLs);** these are pattern-recognition molecules the body uses to detect mannan, a polymer of

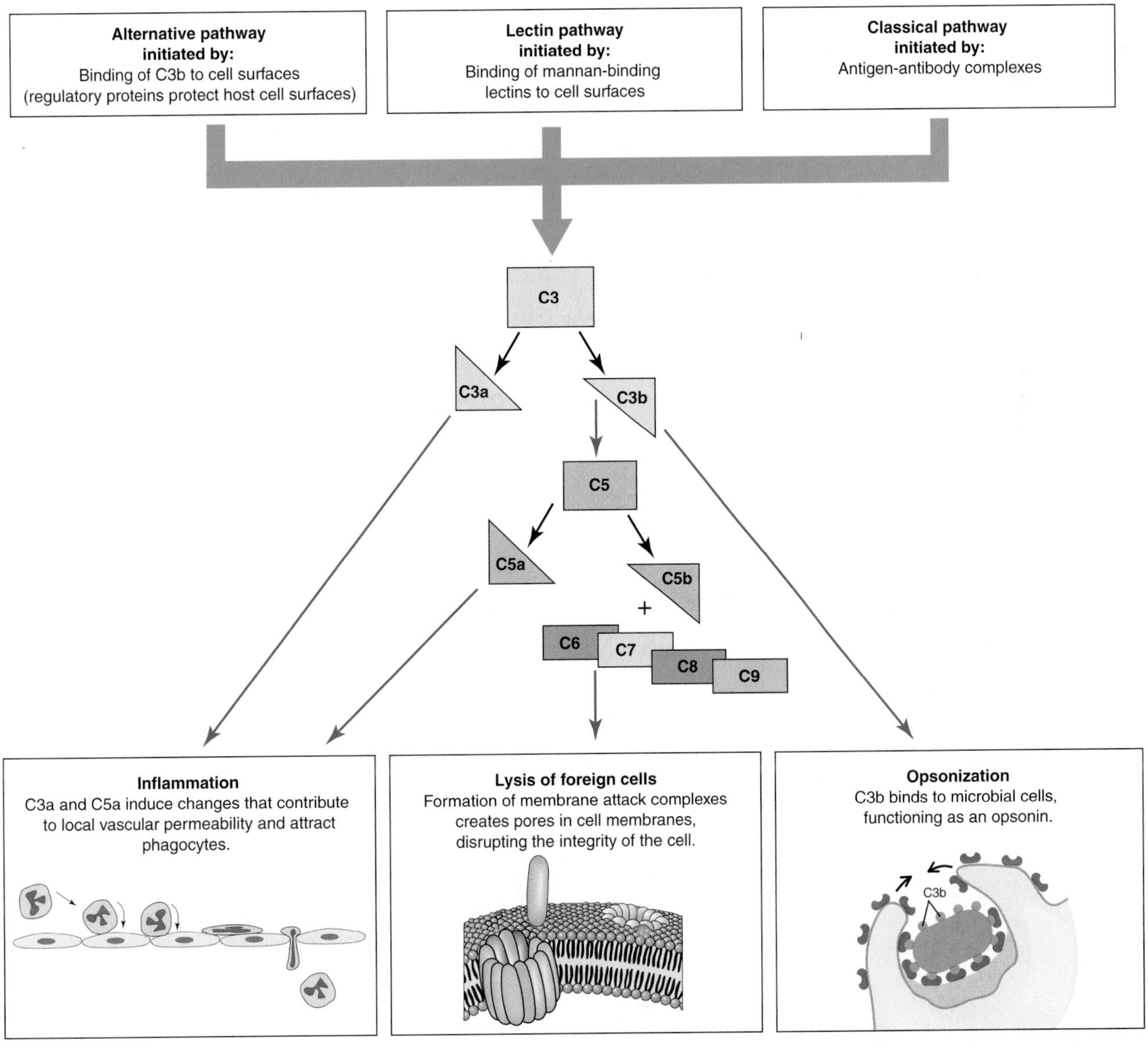

FIGURE 15.7 Complement System Activation of the complement system leads to inflammation, lysis of foreign cells, and opsonization. The three mechanisms that trigger the cascade include the alternative pathway, the lectin pathway, and the classical pathway. Not all of the steps in these pathways are shown.

mannose often found on microbial but rarely on mammalian cells. When MBL attaches to a surface, it can then interact with one of the complement components, activating it. This, in turn, leads to activation of other complement proteins. ■ mannose, p. 32

- **Classical pathway.** Activation by the classical pathway requires antibodies, a component of adaptive immunity. When antibodies bind to antigen, the "red flag" portion of the bound antibodies can then interact with the same complement component involved in activating the lectin pathway. This activates that protein, leading to activation of other complement proteins.

The nature of the complement system allows an exceedingly rapid and powerful response. Its activation occurs by a cascade of reactions; once a specific complement protein becomes activated, it functions as an enzyme, cleaving and therefore activating millions of molecules of the next complement protein in the cascade. In turn, each of those molecules activates multiple molecules of the next protein in the cascade, and so on. Generally, activation involves splitting the protein into two parts, each of which then carries out a specific function. Stringent mechanisms control complement system activation at various points.

The major complement proteins have each been given a number along with the letter C, for complement. The nine major proteins, C1 through C9, were numbered in the order in which they were discovered and not the order in which they react. When one of these is split into two fragments, a lowercase letter is added to the name. For example, the activation of C3 splits it into C3a and C3b. Note that C3 spontaneously splits into C3a and C3b even when the complement system has not been activated, but does so at a very low rate; this spontaneous hydrolysis allows enough C3b to be present to potentially trigger the alternative pathway of complement activation. ■ hydrolysis, p. 26

Activation of the complement system eventually leads to three major protective outcomes:

- **Inflammation.** The complement components **C3a** and **C5a** induce changes in endothelial cells that line the blood vessels, and in mast cells. These effects contribute to the vascular permeability associated with inflammation. **C5a** is also a potent chemoattractant, drawing phagocytes into the area where complement was activated.
- **Lysis of foreign cells.** Complexes of **C5b, C6, C7, C8,** and multiple **C9** molecules, spontaneously assemble in the membranes of cells, forming doughnut-shaped structures each called a **membrane attack complex (MAC) (figure 15.8).** This creates pores in that membrane, disrupting the integrity of the cell. Note that the membrane attack complex has little effect on Gram-positive bacteria because their peptidoglycan layer prevents the complement components from reaching their cytoplasmic membrane. The outer membrane of Gram-negative bacteria, however, renders them susceptible.
- **Opsonization.** The complement protein **C3b** binds to foreign material; phagocytes more easily "grab" particles coated with C3b because phagocytic cells have receptors for the molecule on their surface. The material that C3b has coated is said to be **opsonized** (which means "prepared for eating"); compounds such as C3b that can opsonize material are called **opsonins.** Opsonized material may be viewed as carrying a giant "eat me" sign that can be read by phagocytes. Our own cells are protected from the effects of C3b because our membranes contain regulatory molecules, leading to the inactivation of C3b when it binds. **C3a** and **C5a** cause phagocytes to produce more receptors for C3b on their surfaces. They also directly stimulate metabolic activity of phagocytes.

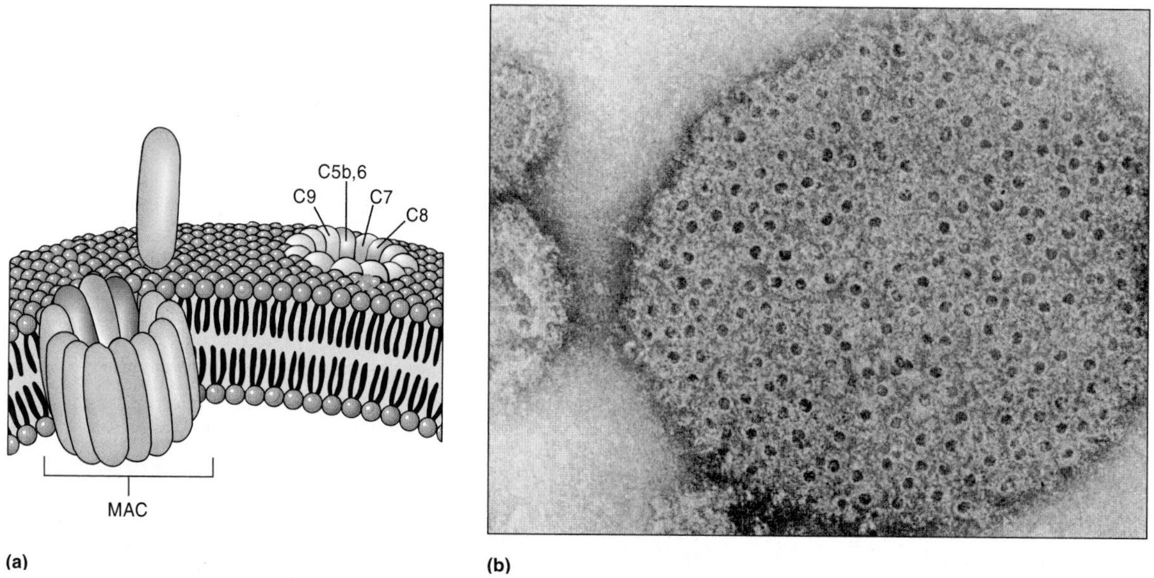

FIGURE 15.8 Membrane Attack Complex (MAC) of the Complement System **(a)** The MAC is formed after C5b, C6, and C7 combine into a complex on the cell surface of bacteria or other foreign cells. This complex, together with C8, causes changes in C9, allowing it to polymerize with the complex and form a MAC. The MAC forms a pore in the membrane, resulting in lysis of the cell. **(b)** An electron micrograph of MACs; each dark dot is a MAC.

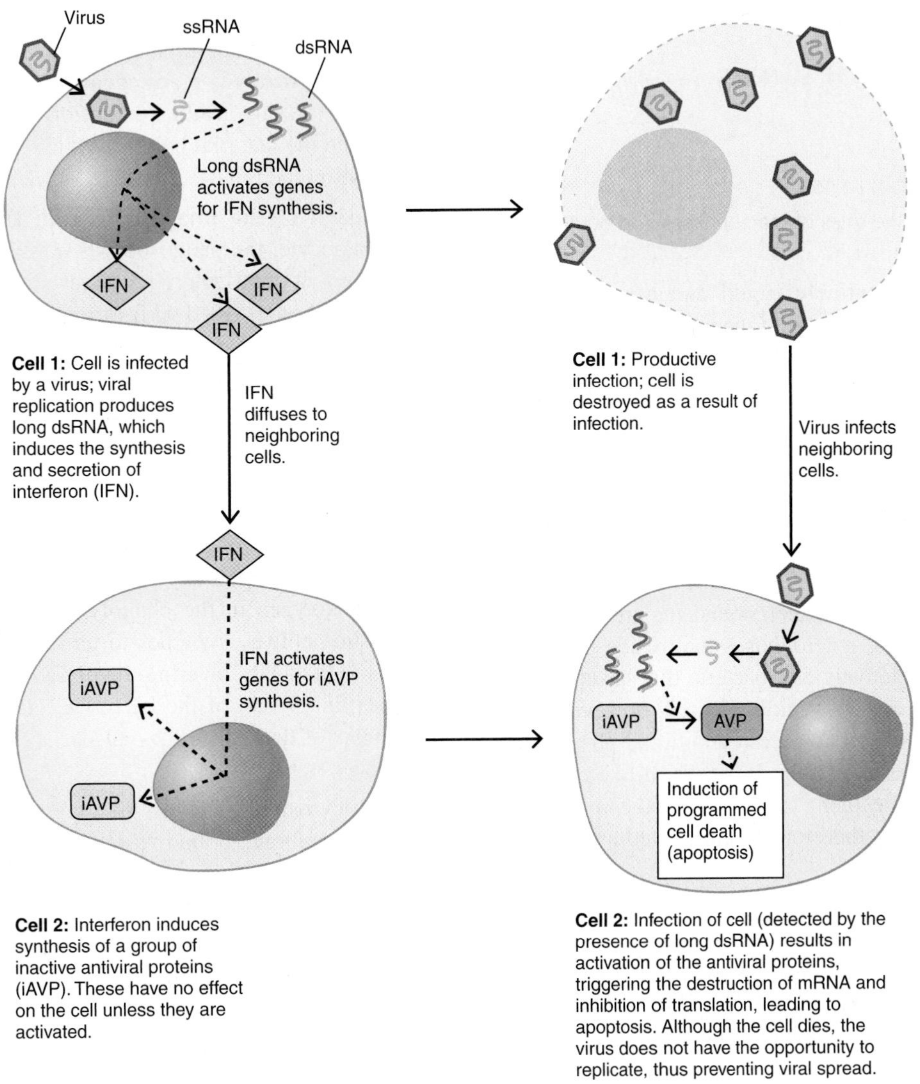

FIGURE 15.9 Antiviral Effects of Interferon

Sensors That Detect Long Double-Stranded RNA (dsRNA)

While recent evidence indicates that cells routinely produce short stretches of dsRNA (see Perspective 7.2), most cells typically do not contain long dsRNA (>30 bp) because only one DNA strand in a gene is used as a template for RNA synthesis. In contrast, cells infected with RNA viruses other than retroviruses routinely have long dsRNA as a result of viral replication. Even cells infected with DNA viruses often have long dsRNA as a consequence of the viruses' efficient use of their relatively small genomes; in some regions of a viral genome, both strands are transcribed into mRNA, generating complementary RNA molecules. Thus, long dsRNA serves as a signal to a cell that it is infected with a virus. Various sensors within cells trigger an antiviral response when they detect the molecule.

Long dsRNA in an animal cell induces synthesis and subsequent secretion of alpha and beta interferons **(figure 15.9).** These molecules then attach to specific receptors on both the infected cell and neighboring cells, causing the cells to express several proteins (protein kinase R, RNAse L, and others) that can be viewed as inactive "suicide enzymes." For convenience, we will refer to these collectively as inactive antiviral proteins (iAVPs). The activated forms of the antiviral proteins (AVPs) degrade mRNA and stop protein synthesis, leading to a programmed cell death ("cell suicide") called **apoptosis.** A key feature of this system is that the iAVPs are activated by dsRNA. Thus, when cells bind interferon, only the infected ones are sacrificed. Their uninfected counterparts remain functional, but are poised to cease vital functions should they too become infected. ■ **apoptosis, p. 382**

MICROCHECK 15.5

Toll-like receptors and NOD proteins enable cells to detect molecules that signify the presence of a microbe. Complement proteins can be activated by three mechanisms, leading to opsonization, lysis of foreign cells, and inflammation. Long dsRNA functions as a signal to a cell that is infected with a virus, triggering an interferon response.

- ✓ What is the role of C3b in opsonization?
- ✓ What is the role of C3b in complement activation?
- ✓ Why would the discovery of toll-like receptors alter the view that innate immunity is non-specific?

15.6

Phagocytosis

Focus Points

- Outline the steps of phagocytosis.
- Compare and contrast the roles of macrophages and neutrophils.

Phagocytes are cells that routinely engulf and digest material, including invading organisms. Yet, with the multitude of different particles in the body, how do the cells determine which ones to engulf? The answer lies in the various pattern recognition receptors that stud the phagocyte surface, binding to certain molecular configurations often found on cell debris and foreign material. Binding of a substance to a phagocyte's receptors induces the cell to engulf that material. A receptor called the **scavenger receptor,** for example, facilitates the engulfment of various materials that have charged molecules on their surface.

In routine situations, such as when organisms are introduced through a minor skin wound, macrophages that reside in the tissues readily destroy the relatively few bacteria that have entered. If the invading microbes are not rapidly cleared, however, macrophages can produce cytokines to recruit additional phagocytes, particularly neutrophils, for extra help. It is the toll-like receptors on macrophages that enable them to sense that the material is microbial in origin, and must therefore be eliminated quickly.

The Process of Phagocytosis

Phagocytosis involves a series of complex steps by which phagocytes engulf and kill invading microorganisms **(figure 15.10).** The steps are particularly relevant medically, because most pathogens have evolved the ability to evade one or more of the steps. Chapter 19 will describe some of the mechanisms microbes use to circumvent this important aspect of innate immunity.

The steps of phagocytosis include:

- **Chemotaxis.** The phagocytic cells are recruited to the site of infection or tissue damage by certain chemical stimuli that act as chemoattractants. These include products of microorganisms, phospholipids released by injured mammalian cells, and the complement component C5a.
- **Recognition and attachment.** Phagocytic cells use various receptors to bind invading microbes either directly or indirectly. Direct binding occurs through receptors that recognize patterns associated with compounds found on microbes. For example, one type of receptor on phagocytic cells binds mannose, a sugar found on the surface of some bacteria and yeasts. Indirect binding occurs when a particle has first been opsonized, dramatically enhancing the phagocytes' ability to attach and subsequently engulf the material. Opsonins include the complement component C3b and certain classes of antibody molecules; phagocytes have receptors for specific parts of these molecules.
- **Engulfment.** The phagocytic cell engulfs the invader, forming a membrane-bound vacuole called a **phagosome.** This process involves rearrangement of the phagocyte's cytoskeleton, forming armlike extensions called pseudopods that surround the material being engulfed. Engulfment itself does not destroy the microbe. ■ cytoskeleton, p. 77 ■ pseudopod, p. 76
- **Fusion of the phagosome with the lysosome.** Within the phagocyte, the phagosome is transported along the cytoskeleton to a point where it can fuse with **lysosomes,** membrane-bound bodies filled with various digestive enzymes, including lysozyme and proteases. The fusion results in the formation of a **phagolysosome.** In neutrophils, the membrane-bound bodies are referred to as **granules.**
- **Destruction and digestion.** Within the phagolysosome, oxygen consumption increases enormously as sugars are metabolized via aerobic respiration, with the production of highly toxic oxygen products such as superoxide, hydrogen peroxide, singlet oxygen, and hydroxyl radicals. As the available oxygen in the phagolysosome is consumed, the metabolic pathway switches to fermentation with the production of lactic acid, lowering the pH. Various enzymes degrade the peptidoglycan of the bacterial cell walls, and other components of the cell. ■ TCA cycle, pp. 137, 146 ■ superoxide, p. 96 ■ hydrogen peroxide, p. 96
- **Exocytosis.** Following the digestion of the microorganisms, the membrane-bound vesicle containing the digested material fuses with the plasma membrane. This expels the material to the external environment. ■ exocytosis, p. 76

Specialized Attributes of Macrophages

Macrophages can be viewed as the scavengers and sentries—routinely phagocytizing dead cells and debris, but always on the lookout, ready to destroy invaders, and able to call in reinforcements when needed. They are always present in tissues to at least some extent, where they either slowly wander or remain stationary. These phagocytic cells play an essential role in every major tissue in the body.

Macrophages live for weeks to months, and maintain their killing power by continually regenerating their lysosomes. As macrophages die they are continually replaced by circulating monocytes that leave the blood and migrate to the tissues; recall that monocytes can differentiate into macrophages. Migration of monocytes is enhanced by certain stimuli associated with invasion and tissue damage.

Macrophages have several important characteristics that allow them to accomplish their diverse tasks. Various toll-like receptors enable them to sense material that signifies danger. When these receptors are triggered, the macrophage produces pro-inflammatory cytokines to alert and stimulate various other cells of the immune system. Macrophages can increase their otherwise limited killing power with the assistance of certain T cells to become **activated macrophages.** This is an example of the cooperation between the innate and adaptive host defenses. Activation of macrophages induces the production of nitric oxide (NO) and oxygen radicals, which more effectively destroy microbes. These products

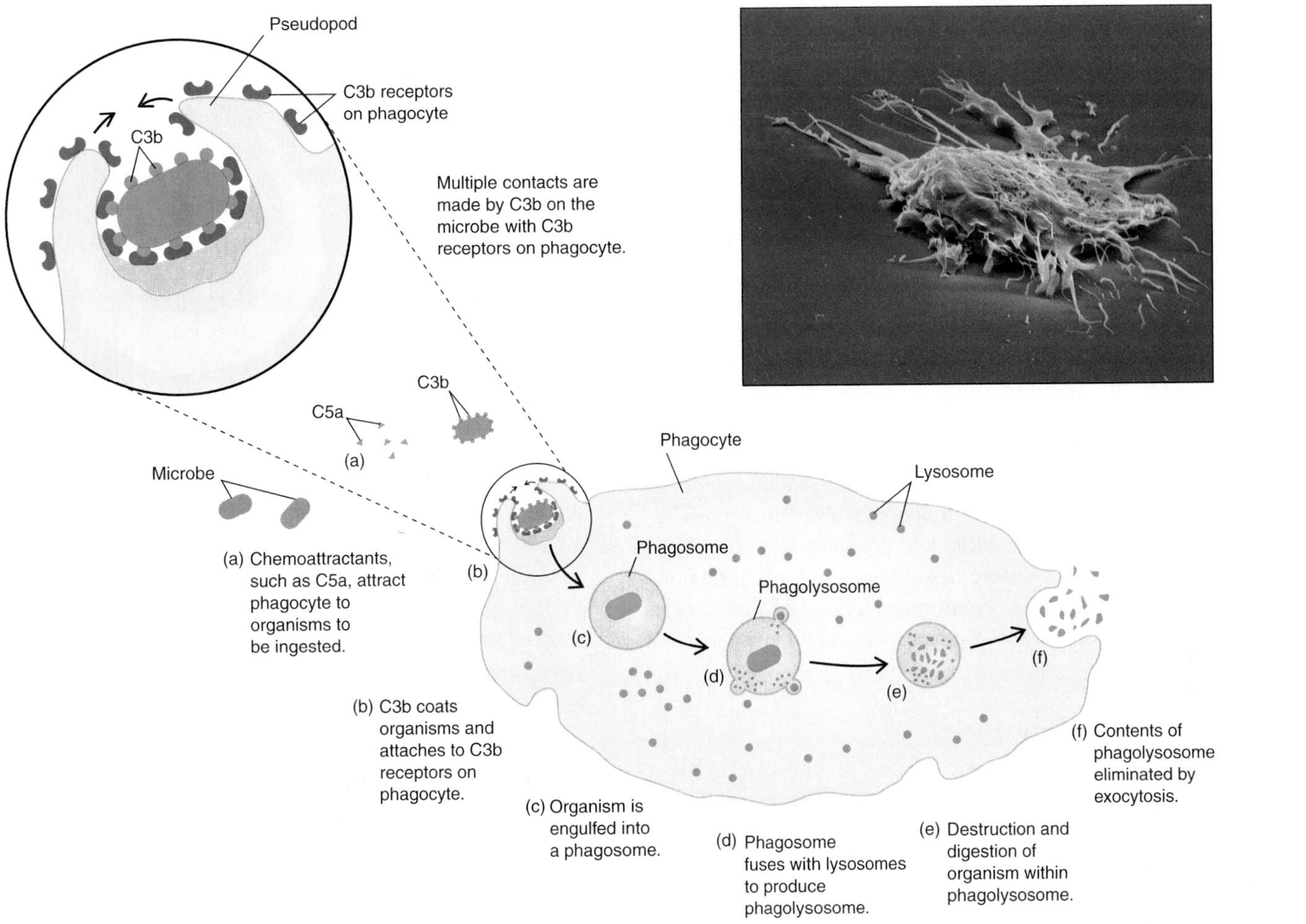

FIGURE 15.10 Phagocytosis and Intracellular Destruction of Phagocytized Material This diagram shows a microbe that has been opsonized by the complement protein C3b; certain classes of antibodies can also function as opsonins.

also damage tissues when they are released, a reason why it would be detrimental for macrophages to continually maintain an activated state. Details of the activation process, including the roles of T cells, will be discussed in chapter 16. ■ macrophage activation, p. 405

If activated macrophages fail to destroy microbes and chronic infection ensues, large numbers of macrophages can fuse together to form **giant cells.** Macrophages, giant cells, and T cells form concentrated groups called **granulomas** that wall off and retain organisms or other material that cannot be destroyed by the cells; again, this is an example of the cooperation between defense systems. This prevents the microbes from escaping to infect other cells (see figure 24.18). Granulomas are part of the disease process in tuberculosis, histoplasmosis, and other illnesses. ■ tuberculosis, p. 593 ■ histoplasmosis, p. 603

Specialized Attributes of Neutrophils

Neutrophils can be viewed as the rapid response team—quick to move into an area of trouble and ready to eliminate the offending invaders. They play a critical role during the early stages of inflammation, being the first cell type recruited from the bloodstream to the site of damage. They inherently have more killing power than macrophages, including those that have been activated. The cost for their effectiveness, however, is a relatively short life span of only 1 to 2 days in the tissues; once they have expended their granules, they die. Many more are in reserve, however, for it is estimated that for every neutrophil in the circulatory system, 100 more are waiting in the bone marrow, ready to be mobilized when needed.

MICROCHECK 15.6

The process of phagocytosis includes chemotaxis, recognition and attachment, engulfment, fusion of the phagosome with the lysosome, destruction and digestion of the ingested material, and exocytosis. Macrophages are long-lived phagocytic cells that are always present in tissues; they can be activated to enhance their killing power. Neutrophils are highly active, short-lived phagocytic cells that must be recruited to the site of damage.

✓ How does a phagolysosome differ from a phagosome?
✓ What is a granuloma?
✓ What could a microorganism do to avoid engulfment?

15.7

Inflammation—A Coordinated Response to Invasion or Damage

Focus Point

- Describe the inflammatory process, focusing on the factors that initiate the response and the outcomes.

When tissues have been damaged, such as when an object penetrates the skin or when microbes are introduced, a coordinated response called the **inflammatory response,** or **inflammation** occurs. Everyone has experienced the signs of inflammation; in fact, the Roman physician Celsus described these four cardinal signs of inflammation in the first century A.D. They are swelling, redness, heat, and pain. A fifth sign, loss of function, is sometimes present.

The vital role of inflammation is to contain a site of damage, localize the response, and restore tissue function. Early inflammatory activation quickly recruits neutrophils, followed by monocytes and other cells, to assist the local macrophages and eosinophils at the site of damage.

Factors That Initiate the Inflammatory Response

Inflammation is initiated in response to invading microbes or tissue damage. In the case of a surface wound, the action that caused the tissue damage is likely to also introduce microbes either residing on the offending instrument or on the skin's surface. Therefore, both factors are often involved in eliciting the response. Events that initiate inflammation include, either singly or in combination:

- Microbial products such as LPS, flagellin, and bacterial DNA trigger the toll-like receptors of macrophages, causing these cells to produce pro-inflammatory cytokines. One of these, tumor necrosis factor alpha, induces the liver to synthesize a group of proteins, termed **acute-phase proteins,** that facilitate phagocytosis and complement activation.
- Microbial cell surfaces can trigger the complement cascade, leading to the production of the C3a and C5a, both of which stimulate changes associated with inflammation. The complement components also induce mast cells to release various pro-inflammatory cytokines (including tumor necrosis factor alpha), histamine, and other substances.
- Tissue damage results in the activation of two enzymatic cascades. One is the coagulation cascade, which results in blood clotting, and the other produces several molecules such as bradykinin that elicit changes involved in inflammation. Current research is seeking to determine if some of the substances released during tissue damage are recognized by toll-like receptors, causing the production of pro-inflammatory cytokines.

The Inflammatory Process

Initiation of the inflammatory process leads to a cascade of events that result in dilation of small blood vessels, leakage of fluids from those vessels, and the migration of leukocytes out of the bloodstream and into the tissues **(figure 15.11).**

The diameter of local blood vessels increases during inflammation due to the action of certain pro-inflammatory chemicals. This results in an increase in blood flow to the area, causing the heat and redness associated with inflammation, accompanied by a decrease in the velocity of blood flow in the capillaries. Because of the dilation, normally tight junctions between endothelial cells are disrupted, allowing fluid to leak from the vessels and into the tissue. This fluid contains various substances such as transferrin, complement system proteins, and antibodies, and thus helps to counteract invading microbes. The increase of fluids in the tissues causes the swelling and pain associated with inflammation. The direct effects of chemicals on sensory nerve endings also cause pain.

Some of the pro-inflammatory cytokines cause endothelial cells in the local area to produce adhesion molecules that loosely adhere to phagocytes. The phagocytes normally flow rapidly through the vessels, but slowly tumble to a halt as they attach to the adhesion molecules. The phagocytic cells themselves then begin producing a different type of adhesion molecule that strengthens the attachment. Then, in response to other cytokines and complement components that function as chemoattractants, phagocytes migrate from the blood vessels into the area. They do this by squeezing between the cells of the dilated permeable vessel, the process of **diapedesis.** Neutrophils (PMNs) are the first type of phagocyte to be lured from the circulation, and soon they predominate in the area. After the influx of neutrophils, monocytes and lymphocytes accumulate. Both monocytes, which mature into macrophages at the site of infection, and neutrophils actively phagocytize foreign material. Clotting factors in the fluid that leaks into the tissues initiate clotting reactions. This helps prevent further bleeding and halts spread of invading microbes by trapping them in the clot. As the inflammatory process continues, large quantities of dead neutrophils accumulate. Along with tissue debris, these dead cells make up **pus.** A large amount of pus constitutes a **boil** or **abscess** (see figure 22.3). ■ boil, p. 525

The extent of inflammation varies, depending on the nature of the injury, but the response is localized, begins immediately upon injury, and increases over a short period of time. This short-term inflammatory response is called **acute inflammation** and is marked by a prevalence of neutrophils. Then, as inflammation subsides, healing occurs. During healing, new capillaries grow into the area and destroyed tissues are replaced; eventually, scar tissue is formed. If acute inflammation cannot limit the infection, **chronic inflammation** occurs. This is a long-term inflammatory process that can last for years. Chronic inflammation is characterized by the prevalence of macrophages, giant cells, and granulomas. ■ giant cells, p. 405 ■ granulomas, p. 405

Outcomes of Inflammation

The inflammatory process can be likened to a sprinkler system that prevents fire from spreading in a building. While the intention of the process—to limit damage and restore function—is positive, the response itself can cause significant harm. One undesirable conse-

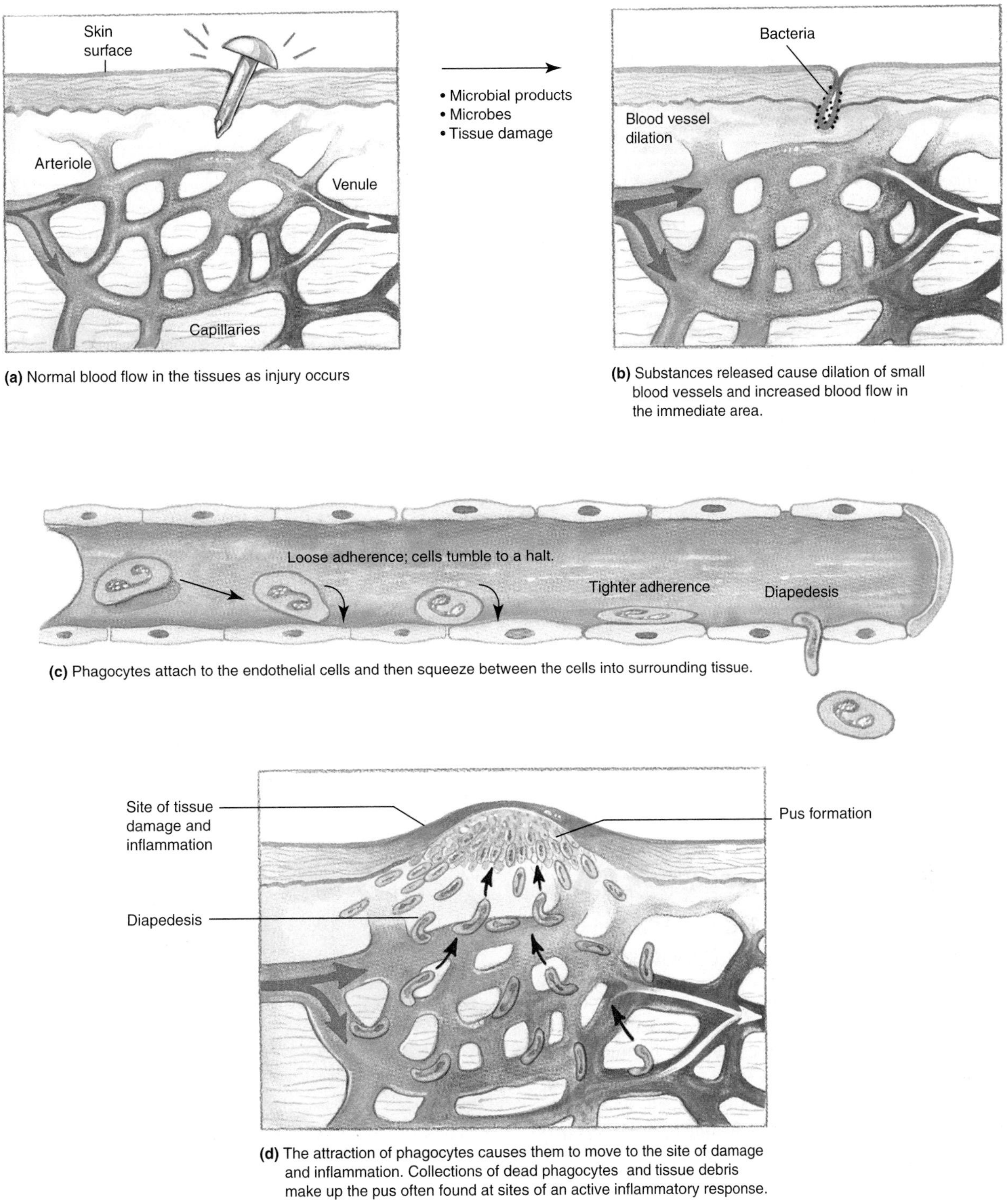

(a) Normal blood flow in the tissues as injury occurs

(b) Substances released cause dilation of small blood vessels and increased blood flow in the immediate area.

(c) Phagocytes attach to the endothelial cells and then squeeze between the cells into surrounding tissue.

(d) The attraction of phagocytes causes them to move to the site of damage and inflammation. Collections of dead phagocytes and tissue debris make up the pus often found at sites of an active inflammatory response.

FIGURE 15.11 The Inflammatory Process This coordinated response to microbial invasion or tissue damage brings phagocytes and other leukocytes to the site. The role of inflammation is to contain a site of damage, localize the response, and restore tissue function.

quence of inflammation, for example, is that some of the enzymes and toxic products contained within phagocytic cells are inevitably released, damaging tissues.

If inflammation is limited, such as in a response to a cut finger, the damage caused by the process is normally minimal. If the process occurs in a delicate system, however, such as the membranes that surrounds the brain and spinal cord, the consequences can be much more severe, even life threatening. Another serious situation occurs in the response to bloodstream infections, particularly those caused by Gram-negative bacteria. The lipopolysaccharide component of their outer membrane, referred to as **endotoxin,** causes a number of responses, including the release of pro-inflammatory cytokines by monocytes, activation of the complement cascade and activation of the clotting cascade.

PERSPECTIVE 15.1

For *Schistosoma,* the Inflammatory Response Delivers

Just as our immune system has evolved to protect us from new and different invasions, it is not surprising that in the opportunistic and adaptable world of microbes, some would find ways to use our defenses to their advantage. The parasitic flatworms that cause schistosomiasis do not shy from the immune response when it comes to procreation; instead they appear to use it to deliver their ova to an environment where they might hatch. Adult females of *Schistosoma* species, which live in the bloodstream of infected hosts, lay their ova in veins near the intestine or bladder; they seem to rely on a robust inflammatory response to expel the ova, completing one portion of a complex life cycle. The ova released in feces or urine can hatch, liberating a larval stage called a *miracidium,* if untreated sewage reaches water. The miracidium then infects a specific freshwater snail host and undergoes asexual multiplication. The infected snail then releases large numbers of another larval form, cercariae, which swim about in search of a human host.

The parasite is acquired when a person wades or swims in contaminated water. The cercariae penetrate the skin by burrowing through it with the aid of digestive enzymes; schistosomes are rare among pathogens because they can actually penetrate intact skin. The larvae then proceed to enter the circulatory system where they can live for over a quarter of a century. *Schisotosoma* species have separate sexes and, remarkably, the male and female worms locate one another in the bloodstream. The male's body has a deep longitudinal groove in which he clasps his female partner to live in copulatory embrace (*shisto-soma* means "split-body," referring to the long slit). The adult worms effectively mask themselves from the immune system by adsorbing various blood proteins; this provides them with a primitive stealth "cloaking device."

Depending on the species, the female worm migrates to the veins of either the intestine or bladder to lay hundreds of ova per day. The body responds vigorously to the highly antigenic eggs, ejecting them in manner that appears similar to what is experienced as a sliver in the skin works its way to the surface. Over half of the ova are not expelled, however, and many of these are instead swept away by the bloodstream to the liver. The inflammatory process and granuloma formation there gradually destroys liver cells, replacing the cells with scar tissue. Malfunction of the liver results in malnutrition and a buildup of pressure in the esophagus. Fluid accumulates in the abdominal cavity and hemorrhage occurs if the engorged esophageal veins rupture.

Despite their complex life cycle, *Schistosoma* species are highly successful. Not only are they adept at avoiding certain immune responses that would otherwise lead to their destruction, they have learned to exploit inflammation for their own dissemination. Over 200 million people worldwide are infected with these parasites, resulting in the death of over 500,000 people each year.

The net result is a rapid loss in blood pressure, leading to shock, extensive tissue damage, and widespread formation of clots that plug the capillaries, cutting off the blood supply; this manifestation of a bloodstream infection (sepsis) is called **septic shock** (see figure 28.3). The cell wall components of Gram-positive bacteria can also elicit septic shock. ■ **meninges, p. 683** ■ **endotoxin, p. 63** ■ **Gram-negative sepsis, p. 713**

Apoptosis—Controlled Cell Death That Circumvents the Inflammatory Process

The inflammatory response represents a potential problem for the host; that is, how to distinguish cell death caused by abnormal events, such as injury, from that caused by normal events such as tissue remodeling that render certain cells unnecessary or potentially harmful. The former merits an inflammatory response whereas the latter does not and, in fact, would be unnecessarily destructive to normal tissue. **Apoptosis** (Greek, *apo* for "falling"; *ptosis* for "off"), or programmed cell death, is a process that destroys self-cells without eliciting inflammation. During apoptosis, the dying cells undergo certain changes. For example, the shape of the cell changes, enzymes cut the DNA, and portions of the cell bud off, effectively shrinking the cell. Some changes appear to signal to macrophages that the remains of the cell are to be engulfed without the commotion associated with inflammation.

The mechanisms and events connected to apoptosis are currently the focus of a great deal of research. It is now recognized that the process is used to eliminate a wide range of the body's own cells, including virally infected cells, as well as those lymphocytes whose function is rendered obsolete by the successful elimination of an antigen.

MICROCHECK 15.7

Inflammation is a cascade of events initiated in response to invading microbes or tissue damage. The outcome is dilation of small blood vessels, leakage of fluids from those vessels, and migration of leukocytes out of the bloodstream and into the tissue. Inflammation can help contain an infection, but the response itself can cause damage. Apoptosis provides a mechanism for the destruction of self-cells without initiating inflammation.

- ✓ Describe three general events that can initiate inflammation.
- ✓ Describe the changes that characterize cells undergoing apoptosis.
- ✓ How could infection of the fallopian tubes lead to sterility and ectopic pregnancy?

15.9 Fever

Focus Point

- Describe the induction and outcomes of fever.

Fever is one of the strongest indications of infectious disease, especially those of bacterial origin, although significant infections can occur without it. There is abundant evidence that fever is an important host defense mechanism in a number of vertebrates, including humans. Within the human body, the temperature is normally kept within a narrow range, around 37°C, by a temperature-regulation center in the hypothalamus of the brain. The hypothalamus controls temperature by regulating blood flow to the skin, and the amount of sweating and respiration. In this way, the heat produced by metabolism is conserved or lost in order to maintain a fairly constant temperature. During an infection, the regulating center continues to function but the body's thermostat is "set" at higher levels. An oral temperature above 37.8°C is regarded as fever.

A higher temperature setting occurs as a result of certain pro-inflammatory cytokines released by macrophages when their toll-like receptors detect microbial products. The cytokines are carried in the bloodstream to the hypothalamus, where they act as messages that microorganisms have invaded the body. These cytokines and other fever-inducing substances are **pyrogens.** Fever-inducing cytokines are called **endogeneous pyrogens,** indicating that the body makes them, whereas microbial products, such as bacterial endotoxins, are called **exogenous pyrogens,** indicating that they are introduced from external sources. The temperature-regulating center responds to pyrogens by raising body temperature. The resulting fever inhibits the growth of many pathogens by at least two mechanisms: (1) elevating the temperature above the optimum growth temperature of the pathogen, and (2) activating and speeding up a number of other body defenses.

The adverse effects of fever on pathogens correlates in part with their ideal growth temperature. Bacteria that grow best at 37°C are less likely to cause disease in people with fever. The growth rate of bacteria often declines sharply as the temperature rises above their optimum growth temperature. A slower growth rate allows more time for other defenses to destroy the invaders.

■ temperature requirements, p. 94

A moderate rise in temperature increases the rate of enzymatic reactions. It is thus not surprising that fever has been shown to enhance the inflammatory response, phagocytic killing by leukocytes, the multiplication of lymphocytes, the release of substances that attract neutrophils, and the production of interferons and antibodies. Release of leukocytes into the blood from the bone marrow is also enhanced. For all these reasons, it is wise to consult a physician before taking drugs to reduce the fever of infectious disease.

MICROCHECK 15.8

Fever results when macrophages release pro-inflammatory cytokines; this occurs when the toll-like receptors on the macrophages are engaged by microbial products.

- ✓ What is an endogenous pyrogen? What is an exogenous pyrogen?
- ✓ How does fever inhibit the growth of pathogens?
- ✓ Syphilis was once treated by intentionally infecting the patient with the parasite that causes malaria, a disease characterized by repeated bouts of fever, shaking, and chills. Why would this treatment cure syphilis?

FUTURE CHALLENGES

Polishing the Magic Bullet

By understanding the body's defense systems, scientists hope to develop a "magic bullet," a drug that can be delivered precisely to the site of disease, effectively treating that disease without harming the patient. Currently, ongoing investigations of the mechanisms of inflammation are providing promising approaches.

Early during the inflammatory response, a family of adhesion molecules called **selectins** is expressed on cells of small blood vessels in the area of injury. Selectins bind to carbohydrate molecules on circulating leukocytes. As the leukocytes roll rapidly through the blood vessels, selectin molecules bind them, stopping them in their tracks. The leukocytes are held captive in the region of inflammation. Other molecules in that area attract the captured white blood cells across the vessel wall and into the injured tissue. Selectin activity is a marker for tissue damage and, therefore, a logical target for delivery of drugs into areas of inflammation resulting from infections. The drugs could be antimicrobials to act against invading microorganisms, or anti-inflammatory agents to lessen the symptoms caused by inflammation.

In some diseases, such as arthritis and other autoimmune diseases, the tissue damage caused by inflammation is the major factor in the disease process. In addition to delivering anti-inflammatory drugs to the area, blocking the actions of selectins by a selectin inhibitor might prevent the development of inflammatory damage.

Scientists working in this area are studying the exact structure of the various selectin molecules and their characteristics. One selectin is stored in cells of the blood vessel and is expressed on the cell surface within minutes of tissue injury. Another is synthesized after injury and expressed on cell surfaces after about 4 hours. The structure of leukocyte surface molecules that will bind to selectins has also been determined. It should be possible to attach antimicrobial or anti-inflammatory drugs to the small portions of binding molecules that actually bind to the selectin. This combination would then be selectively removed from the circulation in the areas of inflammation, the only areas where selectin is produced.

SUMMARY

15.1 Overview of the Innate Defenses

The innate defense system is composed of **first-line defenses,** sensor systems, and **phagocytes.**

15.2 First-Line Defenses (Figures 15.1, 15.2, 15.3)

Physical Barriers

The skin is composed of two main layers—the **dermis** and the **epidermis.**

Mucous membranes are constantly bathed with mucus and other secretions that help wash microbes from the surfaces.

Antimicrobial Substances

Lysozyme, peroxidase enzymes, lactoferrin, and **defensins** inhibit or kill microorganisms.

Normal Flora

Members of the **normal flora** competitively exclude pathogens and stimulate the host defenses.

15.3 The Cells of the Immune System (Figure 15.4, Table 15.1)

Granulocytes

There are three types of **granulocytes—neutrophils, basophils,** and **eosinophils.**

Mononuclear Phagocytes

Monocytes circulate in blood; **macrophages** are found in tissues. (Figure 15.5)

Dendritic Cells

Dendritic cells develop from monocytes; some appear to have other origins.

Lymphocytes

Lymphocytes, which include **B cells, T cells,** and **natural killer (NK) cells,** are involved in adaptive immunity.

15.4 Cell Communication

Surface Receptors

Surface receptors bind ligands that are on the outside of the cell, enabling the cell to detect that the ligand is present.

Cytokines (Table 15.2)

Cytokines include **interleukins (ILs), colony-stimulating factors (CSFs), tumor necrosis factors (TNFs), chemokines,** and **interferons.**

Adhesion Molecules

Adhesion molecules allow cells to adhere to other cells.

15.5 Sensor Systems

Toll-Like Receptors and NOD Proteins (Figure 15.6)

Toll-like receptors and **NOD proteins** enable cells to detect molecules that signify the presence of an invading microbe.

The Complement System (Figure 15.7)

Complement proteins circulate in the blood and the fluid that bathes tissues; in response to certain stimuli that indicate the presence of foreign material, they become activated.

The major protective outcomes of complement activation include **opsonization,** lysis of foreign cells, and initiation of **inflammation.**

Sensors That Detect Long Double-Stranded RNA (dsRNA) (Figure 15.9)

Long dsRNA signifies to a cell that it has been infected with a virus. This induces synthesis of interferons, causing cells in the vicinity to prepare to cease vital cell functions in the event they become infected with a virus.

15.6 Phagocytosis

The Process of Phagocytosis (Figure 15.10)

The steps of phagocytosis include chemotaxis, recognition and attachment, engulfment, destruction and digestion, and exocytosis.

Specialized Attributes of Macrophages

Macrophages are always present in tissues to some extent, but are able to call in reinforcements when needed.

A macrophage can increase its killing power, becoming an **activated macrophage.**

Macrophages, **giant cells,** and T cells form **granulomas** that wall off and retain organisms or other material that cannot be destroyed by macrophages.

Specialized Attributes of Neutrophils

Neutrophils play a critical role during the early stages of inflammation, being the first cell type recruited from the bloodstream to the site of damage.

15.7 Inflammation—A Coordinated Response to Invasion or Damage (Figure 15.11)

Swelling, redness, heat, and pain are the signs of inflammation, the attempt by the body to contain a site of damage, localize the response, and restore tissue function.

Factors That Initiate the Inflammatory Response

Inflammation is initiated when pro-inflammatory cytokines or other inflammatory mediators are released as a result of the engagement of toll-like receptors or activation of the complement system by invading microbes, or when tissue damage occurs.

The Inflammatory Process

The inflammatory process results in dilation of small blood vessels, leakage of fluids from those vessels, and the migration of leukocytes out of the bloodstream and into the tissues.

Acute inflammation is marked by a preponderance of neutrophils; **chronic inflammation** is characterized by the prevalence of macrophages, giant cells, and granulomas.

Outcomes of Inflammation

Inflammation can contain an infection, but the process itself can cause damage; a systemic response can be life threatening.

Apoptosis—Controlled Cell Death That Circumvents the Inflammatory Process

Apoptosis is a mechanism of eliminating self-cells without evoking an inflammatory response.

15.8 Fever

Fever occurs as a result of certain pro-inflammatory cytokines released by macrophages. It inhibits the growth of many pathogens and increases the rate of various body defenses.

REVIEW QUESTIONS

Short Answer

1. Why is iron metabolism important in body defenses?
2. How do phagocytes get into tissues during an inflammatory response?
3. Describe how the skin protects against infection.
4. What are the benefits of saliva in protection against infection? What factors found in saliva aid in protection?
5. Name two categories of cytokines and give their effects.
6. Contrast the classical and alternative pathways of complement activation.
7. How does the activation of a few molecules in early stages of the complement cascade result in the cleavage of millions of molecules of later ones?
8. How do complement proteins cause foreign cell lysis?
9. Describe three mechanisms of triggering inflammation.
10. Describe the purpose of apoptosis.

Multiple Choice

1. Lysozyme does which of the following:
   a) Disrupts cell membranes
   b) Hydrolyzes peptidoglycan
   c) Waterproofs skin
   d) Propels gastrointestinal contents
   e) Propels the cilia of the respiratory tract
2. The hematopoietic stem cells in the bone marrow can become which of the following cell types?
   1. red blood cell 2. T cell 3. B cell
   4. monocyte 5. macrophage
   a) 2, 3 b) 2, 4 c) 2, 3, 4, 5
   d) 1, 4, 5 e) 1, 2, 3, 4, 5
3. All of the following refer to the same type of cell *except*
   a) macrophage. b) neutrophil.
   c) poly. d) PMN.
4. Toll-like receptors are triggered by all of the following compounds *except*
   a) peptidoglycan.
   b) glycolysis enzymes.
   c) lipopolysaccharide.
   d) flagellin.
   e) certain nucleotide sequences.
5. A pathogen that can avoid the complement component C3b would directly protect itself from
   a) opsonization. b) triggering inflammation. c) lysis.
   d) inducing interferon. e) antibodies.
6. Which of the following statements about phagocytosis is *false?*
   a) Phagocytes move toward an area of infection by a process called chemotaxis.
   b) The vacuole in which bacteria are exposed to degradative enzymes is called a phagolysosome.
   c) Phagocytes have receptors that recognize complement proteins bound to bacteria.
   d) Phagocytes have receptors that recognize antibodies bound to bacteria.
   e) Macrophages die after phagocytizing bacteria but neutrophils regenerate their lysosomes and survive.
7. All of the following cell types are found in a granuloma *except*
   a) neutrophils. b) macrophages.
   c) giant cells. d) T cells.
8. All of the following trigger inflammation *except*
   a) engagement of toll-like receptors.
   b) activation of complement.
   c) interferon induction of antiviral protein synthesis.
   d) tissue damage.
9. Which of the following statements about inflammation is *false?*
   a) Vasodilation results in leakage of blood components.
   b) The process can cause damage to host tissue.
   c) Neutrophils predominate at the site during the early stages of acute inflammation.
   d) Apoptosis induces inflammation.
   e) The cardinal signs of inflammation are redness, swelling, heat, and pain.
10. The direct/immediate action of interferon on a cell is to
    a) interfere with the replication of the virus.
    b) prevent the virus from entering the cell.
    c) stimulate synthesis of inactive "suicide enzymes."
    d) stimulate the immune response.
    e) stop the cell from dividing.

Applications

1. Physicians regularly have to treat recurrent urinary tract infections in paralyzed paraplegic patients. What explanation would the physician provide to a patient who asked why the condition keeps coming back in spite of repeated treatment?
2. A cattle farmer sees a sore on the leg of one of his cows. The farmer feels the sore and notices that the area just around the sore is warm to the touch. A veterinarian examines the wound and explains that the warmth may be due to inflammation. The farmer wants an explanation of the difference between the localized warmth and fever. What would be the vet's explanation to the farmer?

Critical Thinking

1. A student argues that phagocytosis is a wasteful process because after engulfed organisms are digested and destroyed, the remaining material is excreted from the cell (see figure 15.10). A more efficient process would be to release the digested material *inside* the cell. This way, the material and enzymes could be reused by the cell. Does the student have a valid argument? Why or why not?
2. According to figure 15.9 *any* cell infected by viruses may die due to the action of interferons. This strategy, however, seems counterproductive. The same result would occur without interferon—any cell infected by a virus might die directly from the virus. Is there any apparent benefit from the interferon action?

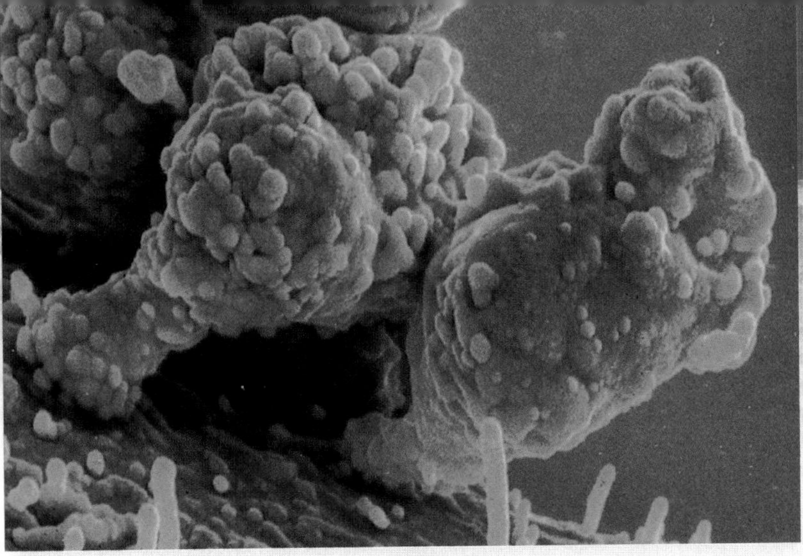

Immune cells

CHAPTER SIXTEEN

The Adaptive Immune Response

A Glimpse of History

Near the end of the nineteenth century, diphtheria was a terrifying disease that killed many infants and small children. The first symptom was a sore throat, often followed by the development of a gray membrane in the throat that made breathing difficult. Death sometimes occurred rapidly, even in the absence of a membrane. Frederick Loeffler, working in Robert Koch's laboratory in Berlin, found club-shaped bacteria growing in the throat of people with the disease but not elsewhere in their bodies. He guessed that the organisms were making a poison that spread through the bloodstream. In Paris, at the Pasteur Institute, Emile Roux and Alexandre Yersin followed up by growing the bacteria in quantity and extracting the poison, or toxin, from strained culture fluids. When injected into guinea pigs, the toxin killed the animals.

Back in Berlin, Emil von Behring injected the diphtheria toxin into guinea pigs that had been previously inoculated with the agent and had recovered from diphtheria. These guinea pigs did not become ill from the toxin, suggesting to von Behring that something in their blood, which he called antitoxin, protected against the toxin. To test this theory, he mixed toxin with serum from a guinea pig that had recovered from diphtheria and injected this mixture into an animal that had not had the disease. The guinea pig remained well. In further experiments, he cured animals with diphtheria by giving them antitoxin.

The results of these experiments in animals were put to the test in people in late 1891, when an epidemic of diphtheria occurred in Berlin. On Christmas night of that year, antitoxin was first given to an infected child, who then recovered from the dreaded diphtheria. The substances in blood with antitoxin properties soon were given the more general name of antibodies, and materials that generated antibody production were called antigens.

Emil von Behring received the first Nobel Prize in Medicine in 1901 for this work on antibody therapy. It took many more decades of investigation before the biochemical nature of antibodies was elucidated. In 1972, Rodney Porter and Gerald Edelman were awarded the Nobel Prize for their part in determining the chemical structure of antibodies.

In contrast to the innate immune response, which is always ready to respond to patterns that signify damage or invasion, the adaptive immune response matures throughout life, developing from the immune system arsenal the most effective response against specific invaders as each is encountered. An important hallmark of the adaptive immune response is that it has memory, a greatly enhanced response to re-exposure. Individuals who survived diseases such as measles, mumps, or diphtheria generally never developed the acute disease again. Vaccination now prevents these diseases by exposing a person's immune system to harmless forms of the causative microbe or its products. While it is true that some diseases can be contracted repeatedly, that phenomenon is generally due to the causative agent's ability to evade the host defenses, a topic we will discuss in chapter 19. The adaptive immune response also has molecular specificity. The response that protects an individual from developing symptoms of measles does not prevent the person from contracting a different disease, for example, chickenpox. The immune system can also discriminate healthy "self," your own normal cells, from "dangerous," such as invading bacteria. If this were not the case, the immune system would routinely turn against the body's own cells, attacking them just as it does an invading microbe. This is not a fail-safe system, however, which is why autoimmune diseases can occur. ■ **acute disease, p. 455** ■ **vaccination, p. 415** ■ **autoimmune disease, p. 444**

The adaptive immune system is extraordinarily complex, involving an intricate network of cells, cytokines, and other compounds. In fact, immunologists are still working out many of its secrets. The recently discovered toll-like receptors, for example, provide insight into how the body learns to distinguish substances

KEY TERMS

Adaptive immunity Host defenses that develop throughout life; involves B cells and T cells.

Antibody Y-shaped protein that binds antigen.

Antigen Molecule that reacts specifically with either an antibody or an antigen receptor on a lymphocyte.

Antigen-presenting cells (APCs) Cells such as B cells, macrophages, and dendritic cells that can present exogenous antigens to naive or memory T cells, activating them.

B cell Type of lymphocyte programmed to make antibodies.

Clonal selection Process in which specific antigen receptor on a lymphocyte binds to a given antigen, allowing the lymphocyte to proliferate.

Cytotoxic T cell Type of lymphocyte programmed to destroy corrupt "self" cells.

Dendritic cell Cell type responsible for activating naive T cells.

Helper T cell Type of lymphocyte programmed to activate B cells and macrophages, and assist other aspects of adaptive immunity.

Lymphocytes White blood cells (leukocytes) that have antigen-specific receptors on their surface; B cells are lymphocytes that mediate humoral immunity, and T cells are lymphocytes that mediate cellular immunity.

Memory lymphocytes Long-lived descendants of activated lymphocytes that can quickly respond when specific antigen is encountered again.

Major histocompatibility complex (MHC) molecules Cell surface molecules that present antigen to T cells. MHC class I molecules present endogenous antigen to cytotoxic T cells; MHC class II molecules present exogenous antigen to helper T cells.

Plasma cell Effector form of a B cell; it functions as an antibody-secreting factory.

T_C cell Effector form of a cytotoxic T cell; it induces apoptosis in infected or cancerous "self" cells.

T_H cell Effector form of a helper T cell; it activates B cells and macrophages, and releases cytokines that stimulate other aspects of the immune system.

that merit an adaptive response from those that do not. Scientists now recognize that the innate immune response, which for many years was viewed as a non-specific and relatively static participant in the host defenses, alerts critical cells of the adaptive response when generic patterns associated with microbes are found. ■ toll-like receptors, p. 374

In this chapter, we will first cover the general strategies the body uses to eliminate invading microbes and acquire the memory that characterizes adaptive immunity. This will then lead to a more detailed description of the various cells and molecules involved. At the end of the chapter, we will focus on the development of the immune system, concentrating on how the cells involved in adaptive immunity gain the specificity required to respond to an incredibly diverse and ever-changing assortment of microbes. Throughout the chapter, we will describe some of the mechanisms used by the adaptive immune system to build **tolerance.** This is the ability to ignore any given molecule, particularly those that characterize healthy "self," such as the proteins that make up your tissues. This process occurs both during the development of the lymphocytes and as a consequence of certain types of exposures to antigen.

16.1 Strategy of the Adaptive Immune Response

Focus Point

- Compare and contrast the general aspects of humoral immunity and cellular immunity.

On first exposure to a given microbe or any other antigen, systemic evidence of the adaptive immune response takes a week or more to develop. During this delay the host depends on the protection provided by innate immunity, which may not be sufficient to prevent disease. This first response to a particular antigen is called the **primary response.** As a result of that initial encounter, the adaptive immune system is able to "remember" the mechanism that proved effective against that specific antigen. As a result, when the same antigen is encountered later in life, there is an enhanced antigen-specific immune response called the **secondary** or **anamnestic response.** The efficiency of the secondary response reflects the memory of the immune system. ■ antigen, p. 366

The adaptive immune response uses two basic strategies for countering foreign material. One response, **humoral immunity,** works to eliminate antigens that are extracellular, for example, bacteria, toxins, or viruses in the bloodstream or in the fluid that surrounds tissues (**figure 16.1**). The other, called **cellular immunity** or **cell-mediated immunity,** deals with antigens residing within a host cell, such as a virus that has infected a cell. Humoral and cellular immunity are both powerful and, if misdirected, can cause a great deal of damage to the body's own tissues. Because of this, the adaptive immune response is tightly regulated; each lymphocyte, the primary participants in the adaptive response, generally requires a "second opinion" from a different type of cell before it can unleash its power. ■ lymphocytes, p. 372

Overview of Humoral Immunity

Humoral immunity is mediated by **B lymphocytes,** or **B cells.** Their name reflects the fact that they develop in an organ called the bursa in birds. In humans, however, B cells develop in the bone marrow. In response to extracellular antigens, B cells may be triggered to proliferate and then differentiate into **plasma cells,** which function as factories that produce Y-shaped proteins called **antibodies.** These molecules bind to antigens, providing protection to the host by mechanisms that will be described shortly. A high degree of specificity is involved in the binding, so a multitude of different antibody molecules are needed to bind to the wide array of antigens that are encountered throughout life. Some of the B

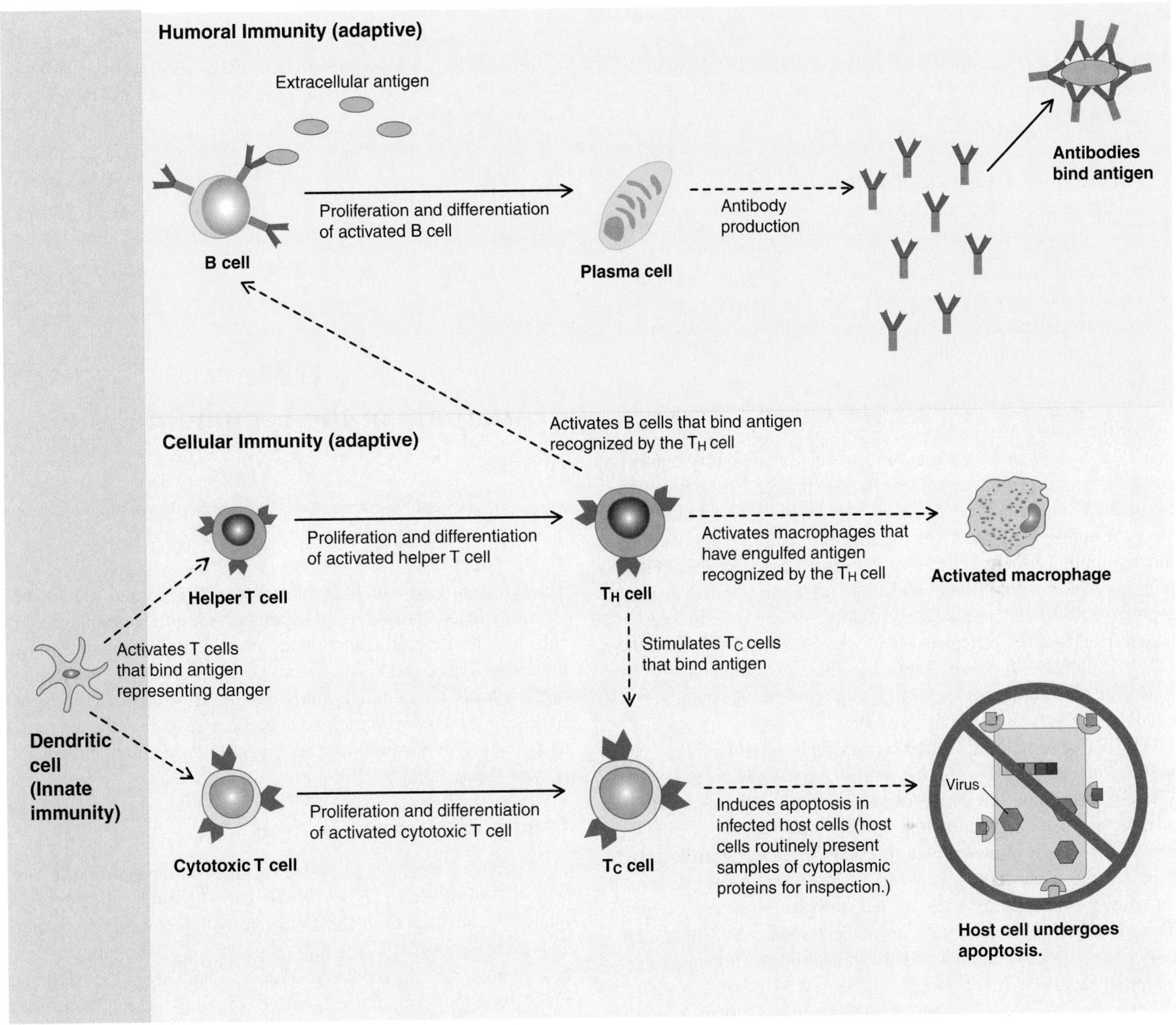

FIGURE 16.1 Overview of Humoral and Cellular Immunity Cellular immunity is also called cell-mediated immunity (CMI).

cells form **memory B cells,** long-lived B cells that respond more quickly if the antigen is encountered again.

Antibody molecules have two functional regions—the two identical arms and the stem of the molecule. It is the arms of the Y that bind to a specific antigen; the amino acid sequence of the end of the arms varies from antibody to antibody, providing the basis for their specificity. The stem of the Y functions as a "red flag," tagging antigen bound by antibody and enlisting other components of the immune system to eliminate the bound molecule.

Antibodies that bind to an antigen protect the host by both direct and indirect mechanisms. Simply by coating an antigen, the antibodies prevent that molecule from attaching to critical sites on host cells. For example, a viral particle that has been coated with antibody cannot bind to its intended receptor on a host cell. Because the virus cannot attach, it is unable to enter the cell. The indirect protective effect is due to the "red flag" region that facilitates elimination of the antigen by the innate defenses. Phagocytes, for example, have receptors for that region of the antibody molecule, enabling them to more easily engulf an antigen coated with bound antibodies; this is the process of opsonization that was described in chapter 15. ■ attachment of viruses, p. 343 ■ opsonization, p. 376

How does a B cell know when to replicate in order to eventually produce antibodies? Each B cell carries on its surface multiple copies of a membrane-bound derivative of the antibody it is programmed to make; each of these molecules is called a **B-cell receptor.** If the B cell encounters an antigen that its B-cell receptors bind, then the cell may gain the capacity to multiply. **Clones,** or copies, of the cell are produced that can eventually differentiate to become plasma cells that make and secrete copious amounts of antibody. Generally, however, before the B cell can multiply, it needs confirmation by another lymphocyte, a T_H cell, that the antigen is indeed dangerous.

Overview of Cellular Immunity

Cellular immunity is mediated by **T lymphocytes,** or **T cells;** their name reflects the fact that they mature in the thymus. T cells include two characterized subsets, **cytotoxic T cells** and **helper T cells.** Both of these have multiple copies of a surface molecule called a **T-cell receptor,** which is functionally analogous to the B-cell receptor, enabling the cell to recognize a specific antigen. Unlike the B-cell receptor, however, the T-cell receptor does not recognize free antigen. Instead, the antigen must be presented by one of the body's own cells.

Like B cells, a T cell must receive confirmation by another cell that the antigen it recognizes signifies danger before it can be triggered to multiply. The cell type responsible for providing the "second opinion" to T cells is the dendritic cell, a component of innate immunity. Once activated, the proliferating T cells differentiate to form effector T cells, which are armed to perform distinct protective roles. For simplicity and clarity, we will refer to effector helper T cells as **T_H cells,** and effector cytotoxic cells as **T_C cells.** Like B cells, both types of T cells are able to form memory cells following activation. These quickly respond if the same antigen is encountered later in life.

In response to intracellular agents such as viruses, T_C cells induce the cells harboring the intruder to undergo apoptosis. While this response obviously harms one's own cells, the sacrifice of infected "self" cells ultimately protects the body. For example, destroying virally infected cells prevents those cells from being used by the virus to produce and release more viral particles. Sacrifice of the cells also releases unassembled viral components. This can strengthen the overall immune response by stimulating production of more antibodies that can then block further cellular infection. ■ apoptosis, p. 382

The critical task for the immune system is to distinguish and destroy only those "self" cells that are infected or otherwise tainted; failure to do this can result in an autoimmune disease. As a means to facilitate detection of intracellular "corruption," all nucleated cells of the body regularly display short fragments of proteins within their cytoplasm in specialized molecules on their cell surface. T_C cells inspect the peptides being presented. If a "self" cell presents an abnormal protein that signifies danger, such as a viral protein, a T_C cell will induce the presenting cell to sacrifice itself.

T_H cells help orchestrate the various responses of humoral and cellular immunity. They provide direction and support to B cells and T cells, and they direct the activation of macrophages.

A third subset of T cells, now dubbed **regulatory T cells** (originally suppressor T cells), appears to help control the immune response. The characteristics and mechanisms of this subset are still being elucidated, but there is great hope that an understanding of these cells will lead to therapies for allergies and autoimmune diseases.

MICROCHECK 16.1

B cells are programmed to eliminate antigens that are extracellular. Cytotoxic T cells are programmed to eliminate antigens that are intracellular. Helper T cells are programmed to orchestrate the adaptive immune response.

- ✓ What are plasma cells?
- ✓ How is the T-cell receptor functionally analogous to the B-cell receptor? How is it different?
- ✓ How would you expect a T_C cell to respond if it encountered a T_H cell that was infected with a virus?

16.2

Anatomy of the Lymphoid System

Focus Point

- Compare and contrast the roles of lymphatic vessels, secondary lymphoid organs, and primary lymphoid organs.

The **lymphoid system** is a collection of tissues and organs that are strategically designed and located to bring the population of B cells and T cells into contact with any and all antigens that enter the body **(figure 16.2).** This is important because lymphocytes are highly specific, recognizing only one or a few different antigens. In order for the body to mount an effective response, the appropriate lymphocyte must actually encounter the given antigen. ■ tissues, p. 72 ■ organs, p. 73

Lymphatic Vessels

Flow within the lymphoid system occurs via the **lymphatic vessels,** or **lymphatics.** These vessels carry a fluid called **lymph,** which is collected from the fluid that bathes the body's tissues. This fluid is formed as a result of the body's circulatory system (see figure 28.1). As oxygenated blood travels from the heart and lungs through the capillaries, much of the fluid portion is extruded into the surrounding tissues, supplying them with the oxygen and nutrients carried by the blood. The majority of the fluid then reenters the capillaries as they return to the heart and lungs, but some enters the lymphatic vessels instead. The lymph, which may contain antigens that have entered the tissues, travels via the lymphatics to the lymph nodes, where materials including protein and cells are removed. The lymph then empties back into the blood circulatory system at a large vein behind the left collarbone. Note that the inflammatory response results in greater accumulation of fluid in the tissues at the site of inflammation; this causes a corresponding increase in the antigen-containing fluids that enter lymphatic vessels.

Secondary Lymphoid Organs

Secondary lymphoid organs are the sites where lymphocytes gather to contact the various antigens that have entered the body. Examples include the lymph nodes, spleen, tonsils, adenoids, and appendix. They are situated at strategic positions in the body so

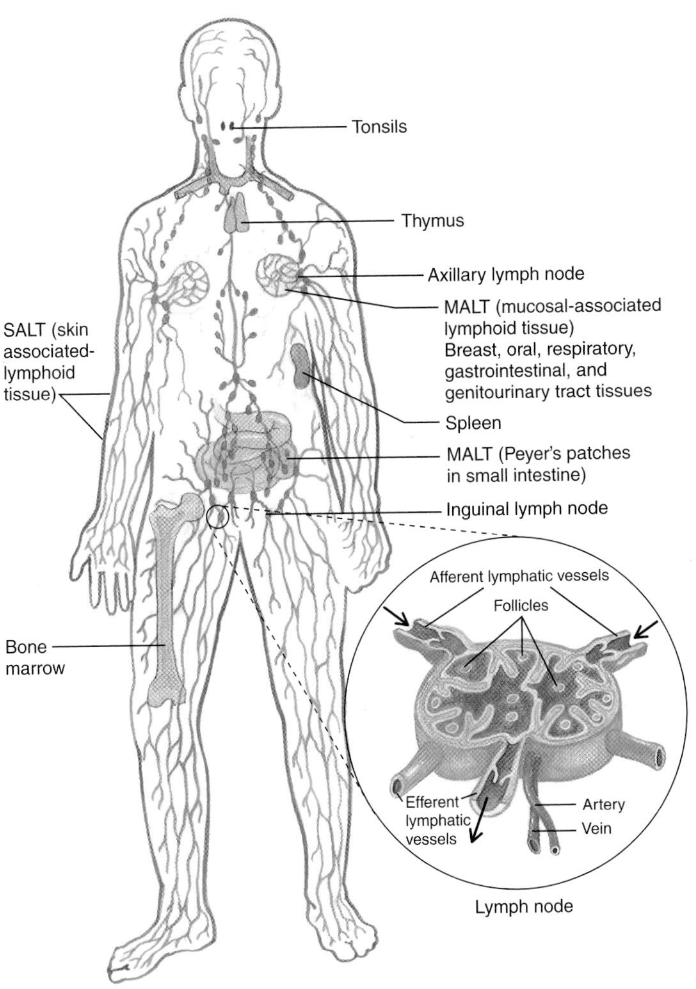

FIGURE 16.2 Anatomy of the Lymphoid System Lymph is distributed through a system of lymphatic vessels, passing through many lymph nodes and lymphoid tissues. For example, lymph enters a lymph node (inset) through the afferent lymphatic vessels, percolates through and around the follicles in the node, and leaves through the efferent lymphatic vessels. The lymphoid follicles are the site of cellular interactions and extensive immunologic activity.

that defensive immune responses can be initiated at almost any location. For example, lymph nodes capture materials from the lymphatics, and the spleen seizes materials from blood.

The secondary lymphoid organs are like busy, highly organized lymphoid coffee shops where many cellular meetings take place and information is exchanged. The anatomy of the organs provides a structured center to facilitate the interactions and transfer of cytokines between various cells of the immune system, including lymphocytes and dendritic cells. No other places in the body have the structure necessary to facilitate the complex interactions required, which is why these organs are the only sites where productive adaptive immune responses can be initiated.

When lymphocytes make contact with a given antigen and receive the required "second opinion," they respond by proliferating to form clones of cells specific for that antigen. The metabolically active and dividing lymphocytes have larger nuclei and more abundant cytoplasm than their resting counterparts.

Some secondary lymphoid organs are less organized in structure than the lymph nodes and spleen, but their purpose remains the same—to capture antigens, bringing them into contact with lymphocytes that have gathered. Among the most important of these organs are the **Peyer's patches,** which sample antigens collected from the small intestine, allowing presentation of the antigen to lymphocytes below the mucosal surface (see figure 19.6). **M cells,** specialized epithelial cells lying over the Peyer's patches, collect material in the intestine and transfer it to the lymphoid tissues beneath. Peyer's patches are part of a network of lymphoid tissues called **mucosal-associated lymphoid tissue (MALT).** These play a critical role in **mucosal immunity,** the element of adaptive immunity that prevents microbes from invading the body via the mucous membranes. Lymphoid tissues under the skin are called **skin-associated lymphoid tissue (SALT).**

Primary Lymphoid Organs

The bone marrow and thymus are the **primary lymphoid organs.** This is where the hematopoietic stem cells destined to become B cells and T cells mature (see figure 15.4). Both B cells and T cells originate in the bone marrow but only B cells mature there; immature T cells migrate to the thymus. Once mature, the lymphocytes gather in the secondary lymphoid organs just described, waiting to encounter antigen. ■ hematopoietic stem cells, p. 369

MICROCHECK 16.2

The lymphatic vessels carry the fluid collected from tissues to the lymph nodes; these and other secondary lymphoid organs are where lymphocytes gather to encounter antigens that have entered the body. The primary lymphoid organs, the bone marrow and thymus, are where hematopoietic stem cells destined to become B cells and T cells mature.

- ✓ How is lymph formed?
- ✓ What are Peyer's patches?

16.3

The Nature of Antigens

Focus Point

- Distinguish between an antigen and an epitope.

The term **antigen** was initially coined in reference to compounds that elicit the production of antibodies; it is derived from the descriptive expression **anti**body **gen**erator. The compounds observed to induce the antibody response are recognized as being foreign to the host by the adaptive immune system. They include an enormous variety of materials, from invading microbes and their various products to plant pollens. Today, the term antigen is used more broadly to describe any molecule that reacts specifically with an antibody or an antigen receptor on a lymphocyte; it does not necessarily imply that the molecule can induce an immune response. When referring specifically to an antigen that elicits an immune response in a given situation, the more restrictive term **immunogen** may be used. The distinction between the

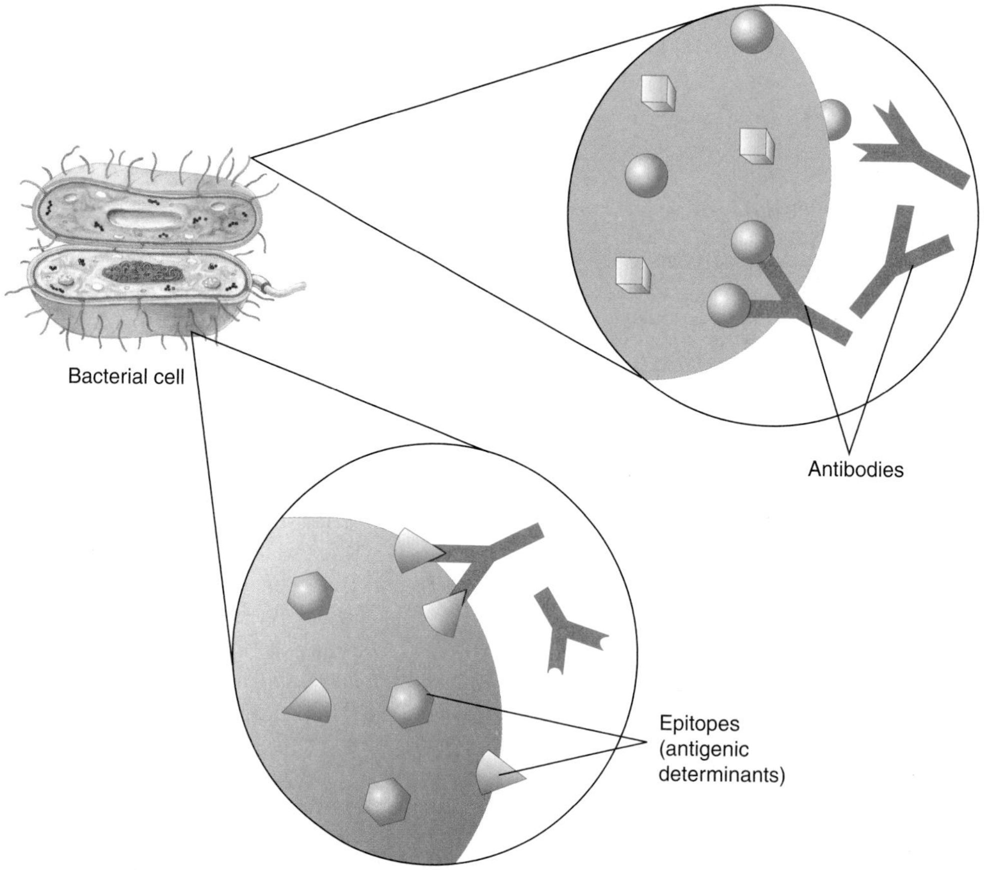

FIGURE 16.3 Antibodies and Antigen Epitopes on a Bacterial Cell

terms antigen and immunogen helps clarify discussions in which a normal protein from host "A" elicits an immune response when transplanted into host "B"; the protein is an antigen because it can react with an antibody or lymphocyte, but it is an immunogen only for host "B," not for host "A."

Various antigens differ in their effectiveness in stimulating an immune response. Proteins and polysaccharides, for example, generally induce a strong response, whereas lipids and nucleic acids often do not. The terms **antigenic** and **immunogenic** are used interchangeably to describe the relative ability of an antigen to elicit an immune response. Substances with a molecular weight of less than 10,000 daltons are generally not immunogenic.

Although antigens are generally large molecules, the adaptive immune response directs its recognition to discrete regions of the molecule known as **antigenic determinants** or **epitopes** **(figure 16.3).** Some epitopes are stretches of 10 or so amino acids, whereas others are three-dimensional shapes such as a protrusion in a globular molecule. A bacterial cell usually has many macromolecules on its surface, each with a number of different epitopes, so that the entire cell has a multitude of various epitopes.

MICROCHECK 16.3

The immune response is directed to epitopes on antigens.

✓ Which macromolecules are most antigenic?

✓ Would a denatured antigen be expected to have the same epitopes as its native (undenatured) counterpart?

16.4

The Nature of Antibodies

Focus Points

- Diagram an antibody, labeling the Fab regions, Fc region, heavy chain, light chain, constant region, variable region, and antigen-binding site.
- Describe six protective outcomes of antibody-antigen binding.
- Compare and contrast the five classes of immunoglobulins.

Antibodies, also called **immunoglobulins,** are Y-shaped proteins that have two functional parts—the arms and the stem **(figure 16.4a).** The two identical arms, called the **Fab regions,** bind antigen. The stem is the **Fc region,** functioning as a "red flag" that enlists other components of the immune system. These names were assigned following early studies that showed that enzymatic digestion of antibodies yielded two types of fragments—fragments that were antigen-binding (Fab) and fragments that could be crystallized (Fc).

Structure and Properties of Antibodies

All antibodies have the same basic Y-shaped structure, called an antibody monomer. It consists of two high molecular weight polypeptide chains, called the **heavy chains,** and two lower molecular weight polypeptide chains, called the **light chains** (see figure 16.4b). Disulfide bonds (S—S) join the two chains, creating a Y-shaped molecule with identical halves. Disulfide bonds also join the two halves of the molecule. At the fork of the Y is a flexible or "hinge" region. In some cases, the arms of the Y move when antigen is attached. Recent evidence indicates that other parts may be pliable as well. For example, some antibodies have been shown to bind to proteins inside crevices on the surface of rhinovirus particles, the cause of the common cold.

There are five major classes of human immunglobulin (Ig) molecules—IgM, IgG, IgA, IgD, and IgE. Each class shares the same basic monomeric structure, but is distinguished by a characteristic amino acid sequence in the constant portion of the heavy chain. Since this is the part of the molecule that interacts with other "players" of the immune system, the various classes differ in their functional properties. The specialized attributes of each class will be described later, after we consider some of the general characteristics of antibodies.

Variable Region

When the amino acid sequence of antibody molecules that bind to different epitopes are compared, tremendous variation is seen in the parts that form the ends of the Fab regions. These parts make up the **variable regions** of the antibody molecule; they contain the antigen-binding sites (see figure 16.4b). The differences provided by the variable regions account for the specificity of antibody molecules.

Each antibody binds via the antigen-binding site to the antigen that induced its production. The interaction depends on close complementarities between the antigen-binding site and the specific antigenic epitope. The fit must be precise, because the bonds that hold the antibody and antigen are non-covalent. Although the forces holding the antigen and antibody together are weak, many such bonds are formed, usually keeping the two together very effectively. Nevertheless, the antigen-antibody interaction is reversible. Upon reversal, both antigen and antibody are unchanged.

Constant Region

The **constant region** encompasses the entire Fc region, as well as part of both the heavy and light chains in the two Fab regions (see figure 16.4b). The amino acid sequence of this region is the same for all antibody molecules of a given class and it imparts the distinct functional properties of the class. The consistent nature of this amino acid sequence allows other components of the immune system to recognize the otherwise diverse antibody molecules.

Protective Outcomes of Antibody-Antigen Binding

The protective outcomes of antibody-antigen binding depend partly on the class of the antibody, and may include these mechanisms **(figure 16.5):**

- **Neutralization.** In order to damage a host cell, toxins and viruses typically must bind specific molecules on the cell surface. A toxin or virus that has been coated with antibodies is prevented from interacting with a cell, and therefore can no longer cause damage.
- **Immobilization and prevention of adherence.** Binding of antibodies to surface structures such as flagella and pili on a bacterium can interfere with such functions as motility and attachment. If these abilities are necessary for the microbe's interaction with the host, binding of antibodies to these structures can protect the host.
- **Agglutination and precipitation.** Binding of antibodies to multiple molecules of antigen causes large antibody-antigen complexes to form, effectively rounding up dispersed antigens to create one large "mouthful" for a phagocytic cell. The complexes form because single antibody molecules can bind adjacent antigens, interconnecting individual antigens to form a network. In the laboratory, the aggregation of antigen and antibody molecules can be seen as either agglutination of particulate antigens or precipitation of soluble antigens.

■ agglutination reactions, p. 426 ■ precipitation reactions, p. 423

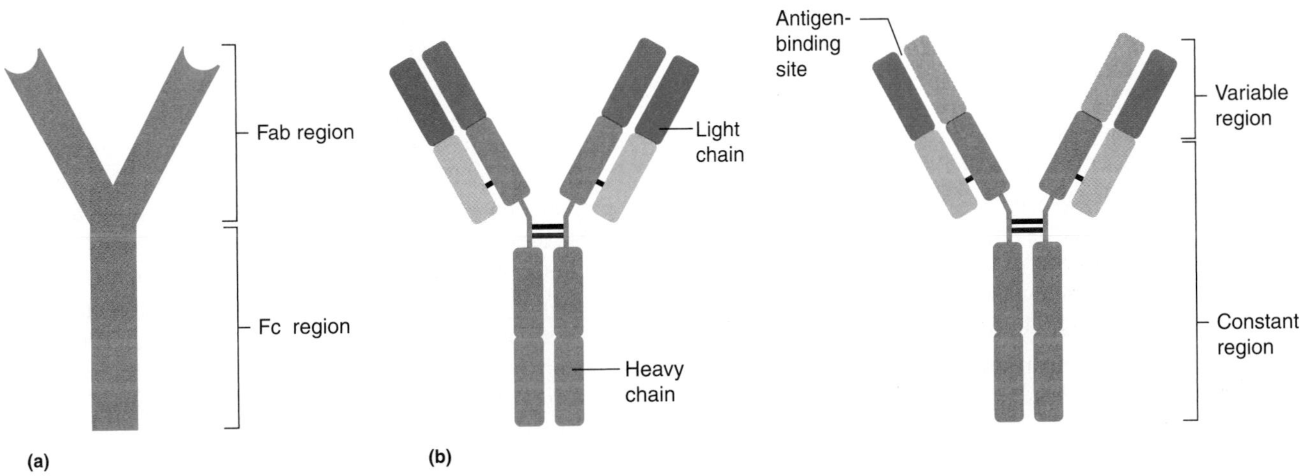

FIGURE 16.4 Basic Structure of an Antibody Molecule **(a)** The Y-shaped molecule; the arms of the Y make up the Fab regions, and the stem is the Fc region. **(b)** The molecule is made up of two identical heavy chains and two identical light chains. Disulfide bonds join the two chains as well as the two halves of the molecule. The constant region is made up of the regions depicted in shades of red. The variable regions differ among antibody molecules, and account for the antigen-binding specificity of antibody molecules.

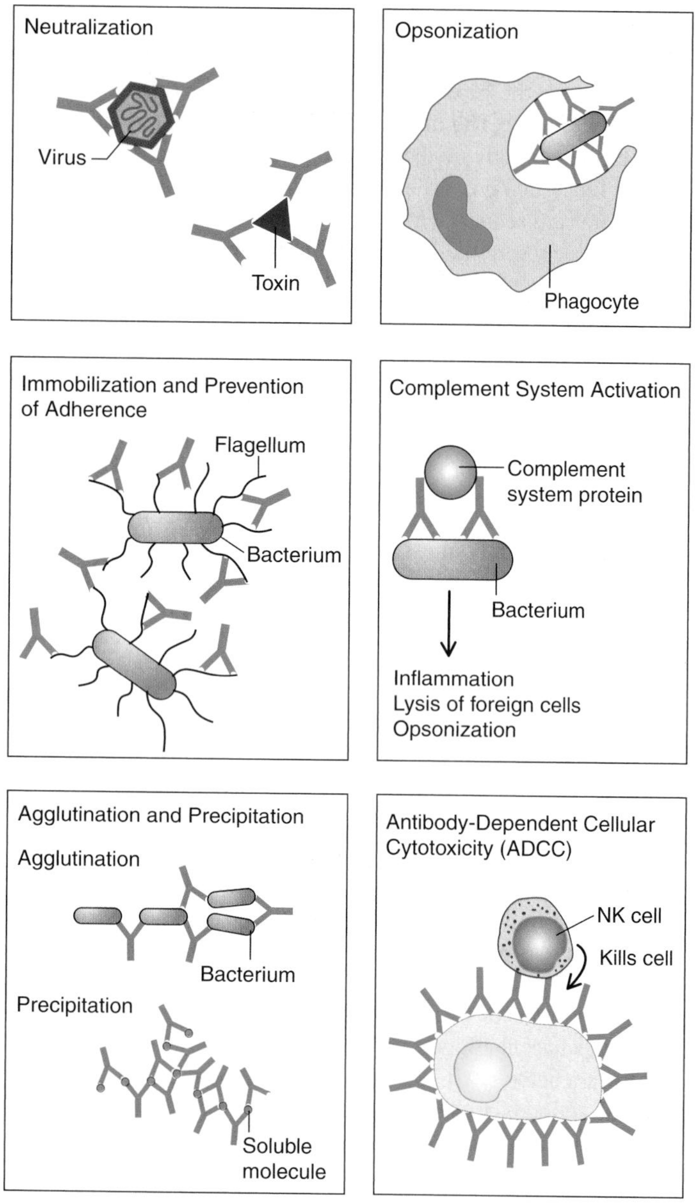

FIGURE 16.5 Protective Outcomes of Antibody-Antigen Binding

- **Opsonization.** Recall from chapter 15 that antigens bound by the complement protein C3b are more easily engulfed by phagocytic cells; the C3b-coated antigens are said to be opsonized. IgG molecules have an analogous effect when they bind to antigen. Macrophages and neutrophils both have receptors for the Fc region of these antibodies on their surface, facilitating the attachment of the phagocytic cell to the antibody-coated antigen as a prelude to engulfment.
- **Complement system activation.** The binding of antibody to antigen can trigger the classical pathway of the complement cascade. When multiple antibodies of certain antibody classes are bound to a cell surface, a specific complement protein attaches to their Fc regions, initiating the cascade. Activation of the complement system results in formation of membrane attack complexes, stimulation of the inflammatory response, and production of the opsonin C3b. ■ complement, p. 375
- **Antibody-dependent cellular cytotoxicity (ADCC).** When multiple IgG molecules bind to a cell, that cell becomes a target for destruction by certain cells. For example, **natural killer (NK) cells** can attach to the Fc regions of those antibodies and once attached, release compounds directly to the target cell, killing that cell. The mechanism by which NK cells destroy target cells will be described later. ■ natural killer cells, pp. 370, 406

Immunoglobulin Classes

All five major classes of immunoglobulin molecules have the same basic structure: two identical light chains connected by disulfide bonds to two identical heavy chains. Each class, however, has a different constant portion of the heavy chain, characterized by distinct amino acid sequences. Some of the immunoglobulins form multimers of the basic monomeric structure. Characteristics of the various classes of human immunoglobulins are summarized in **table 16.1.**

Immunoglobulin M (IgM)

IgM accounts for 5% to 13% of the circulating antibodies and is the first class produced during the primary response to an antigen. It is the only class produced in response to T-independent antigens, a group of antigens that will be discussed later.

IgM found circulating in the blood is a pentamer. Its large size prevents it from crossing from the bloodstream into tissues, so its role is primarily to control bloodstream infections. The five monomeric subunits give IgM a total of 10 antigen-binding sites, making it very effective in agglutination and precipitation. It is the most efficient class in initiating the classical pathway of the complement cascade.

As a fetus is normally sterile until the birth membrane is ruptured, IgM generally begins being made about the time of birth. However, a fetus that is infected *in utero* is capable of making IgM antibodies.

Immunoglobulin G (IgG)

IgG accounts for about 80% to 85% of the total serum immunoglobulin. It circulates in the blood, but readily exits the vessels into tissues with the assistance of receptors on endothelial cells that recognize its Fc region. IgG provides the longest-term protection of any antibody class; its half-life is 21 days, meaning that a given number of IgG molecules will be reduced by approximately 50% after 21 days. In addition, IgG is generally the first and most abundant circulating class produced during the secondary response. The basis for this phenomenon will be discussed later in the chapter. IgG antibodies provide protection by neutralization, agglutination and precipitation, opsonization, complement activation, and antibody-dependent cellular cytotoxicity. ■ serum, p. 421

An important distinguishing characteristic of IgG is that, unlike other immunoglobulin classes, it can cross the placenta from a pregnant woman to the developing fetus. Its Fc region is recognized by receptors in the placenta, permitting transport across to the fetus. Since IgG production is not optimal until the secondary response, women who have not been exposed to certain disease-causing agents that can infect and damage the fetus are warned to take extra precautions during pregnancy. For example, pregnant women are advised not to eat raw meat or become first-time cat owners; this is to avoid a primary infection by *Toxoplasma gondii,* a parasite that can be transmitted in raw meat and the feces of infected cats.

Maternal IgG not only protects the developing fetus against infections, but also the newborn because of the relatively long half-life of this class **(figure 16.6).** The protection provided by these maternal antibodies wanes after about 3 to 6 months, but by this time the infant has begun to produce its own protective antibodies.

IgG is also present in **colostrum,** the first breast milk produced after birth. The intestinal tract of newborns is able to absorb this antibody.

IgA

The monomeric form of IgA accounts for about 10% to 13% of antibodies in the serum. Most IgA, however, is the secreted form, called secretory IgA (sIgA). In fact, IgA is the most abundant immunoglobulin class produced, even though it makes up only a small fraction of the antibodies in blood. The secreted form is important in mucosal immunity and is found on the mucous membranes that line the gastrointestinal, genitourinary, and respiratory tracts and in secretions such as saliva, tears, and breast milk. Secretory IgA in breast milk protects breast-fed infants against intestinal pathogens. ■ mucosal immunity, p. 391

Protection by secretory IgA is primarily due to the direct effect that binding of antibody has on antigens. These include neutralization of toxins and viruses and interference with the attachment of microorganisms to host cells.

Secretory IgA is produced by the plasma cells that reside in the mucosal-associated lymphoid tissues (MALT). Recall that plasma cells are the antibody-secreting form of B cells. The sIgA molecule is a dimer, composed of two monomeric antibody subunits connected by a J-chain (J stands for joining). The dimer binds to the basement membrane side of the epithelial cells of the mucosa and is then transported through those cells to the surface of the mucosal lining. As part of the transport process, a polypeptide called the secretory component is added to the molecule; this component may help protect the antibody from being destroyed by most proteolytic enzymes that might be encountered in the mucosa. ■ MALT, p. 391

IgD

IgD accounts for less than 1% of all serum immunoglobulins. It is involved with the development and maturation of the antibody response, but its functions in serum have not yet been clearly defined.

TABLE 16.1 Characteristics of the Various Classes of Human Immunoglobins

Class and Molecular Weight (daltons)	Structure	Percent of Total Serum Immunoglobulin (Half-life in serum)	Properties and Functions
IgM 970,000	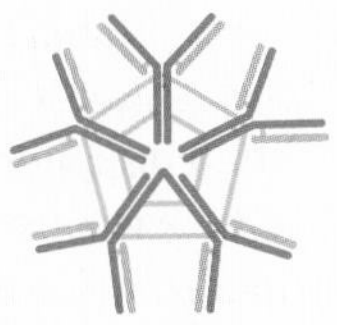 Pentamer	5%–13% (10 days)	First antibody produced during the primary immune response. Only class produced in response to T-independent antigens. Provides direct protection by neutralizing viruses and toxins, immobilizing motile organisms, preventing the adherence of microbes to cell surfaces, and agglutinating/precipitating antigens. Binding of IgM to antigen leads to activation of the complement system (classical pathway).
IgG 146,000	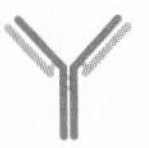 Monomer	80%–85% (21 days)	Most abundant class in the blood and tissue fluids. Provides longest term protection because of its long half-life. Transported across the placenta, providing protection to a developing fetus; long half-life extends the protection through the first several months after birth. Provides direct protection by neutralizing viruses and toxins, immobilizing motile organisms, preventing the adherence of microbes to cell surfaces, and agglutinating/precipitating antigens. Binding of IgG to antigen facilitates phagocytosis, leads to activation of the complement system (classical pathway) and elicits antibody-dependent cellular cytotoxicity.
IgA monomer 160,000; secretory IgA 390,000	 Dimer in secretions	10%–13% (6 days)	Most abundant class produced, but the majority is secreted into mucus, tears, and saliva, providing mucosal immunity. Also found in breast milk, protecting the intestinal tract of breast-fed infants. Protects mucous membranes by neutralizing viruses and toxins, immobilizing motile organisms and preventing attachment of microbes to cell surfaces.
IgD 184,000	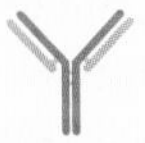 Monomer	< 1% (3 days)	Involved in the development and maturation of the antibody response. Functions in serum have not been clearly described.
IgE 188,000	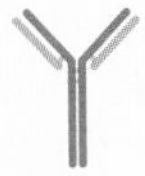 Monomer	< 0.01% (2 days)	Binds via the Fc region to mast cells and basophils; this bound IgE allows those cells to detect parasites and other antigens and respond by releasing their granule contents. Involved in many allergic reactions.

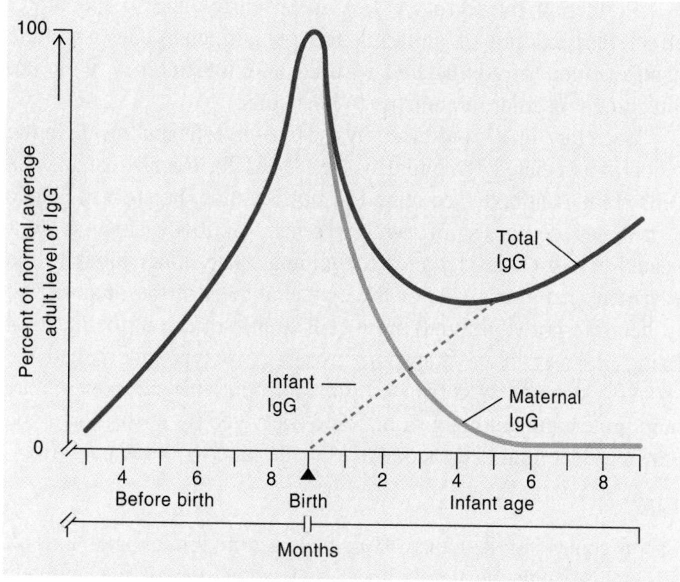

FIGURE 16.6 Immunoglobulin G Levels in the Fetus and Infant During gestation, maternal IgG is transported across the placenta to the fetus. Colostrum also contains IgG. Normally, the fetus does not make appreciable amounts of immunoglobulin; it relies on the maternal antibodies that are transferred passively. After birth, the infant begins to produce immunoglobulins. The maternal antibodies gradually disappear over a period of about 6 months. Usually by 3 to 6 months, most of the antibodies present are those produced by the infant.

IgE

IgE is barely detectable in normal blood, because most is tightly bound via the Fc region to basophils and mast cells, rather than being free in the circulation. The bound IgE molecules allow these cells to detect and respond to antigens. For example, when antigen binds to two adjacent IgE molecules carried by a mast cell, the cell releases a mixture of potent chemicals including histamine, cytokines, and various compounds that contribute to the inflammatory response. Evidence suggests that these responses are important in the elimination of parasites, particularly helminths. ■ **helminths, p. 310**

Unfortunately for allergy sufferers, basophils and mast cells also release their chemicals when IgE binds to normally harmless materials such as dusts and pollens, leading to immediate reactions such as coughing, sneezing, and muscular contractions. In some cases these allergic, or hypersensitivity, reactions can be life-threatening. ■ **hypersensitivity reactions, p. 433**

MICROCHECK 16.4

The results of antibody-antigen binding include neutralization, immobilization and prevention of adherence, agglutination and precipitation, opsonization, complement activation, and antibody-dependent cytotoxicity. Immunoglobulin classes include IgM, IgG, IgA, IgD, and IgE.

- ✓ Why is IgM particularly effective at agglutinating antigens?
- ✓ Which two maternal antibody classes protect a newborn that is breast-fed?
- ✓ In opsonization with IgG, why would it be important that IgG react with the antigen *before* a phagocytic cell recognizes the antibody molecule?

16.5

Clonal Selection and Expansion of Lymphocytes

Focus Point

- Outline the process of clonal selection and expansion.

Early on, immunologists recognized that the immune system is capable of making a seemingly infinite array of antibody specificities, an ability that could potentially be explained by either of two general mechanisms. One hypothesis suggested that antibody-producing cells are able to alter the specificity of the antibodies in response to a particular antigen; in other words, the antigen is able to induce the proper fit. The other hypothesis, proposed in the 1950s, stated that each cell in a large population of antibody-producing cells makes only a single specificity of antibody molecule. Then, when antigen is introduced, only the cells that make the appropriate antibody can bind to the antigen, which promotes their multiplication; this process is called **clonal selection (figure 16.7).** Repeated cycles of cell division generate a population of copies, or **clones,** of the initial cell; this process is called **clonal expansion.**

The model of clonal selection and expansion, now called the **clonal selection theory,** has been shown to be a critical theme in adaptive immunity, pertaining to both B cells and T cells. As lymphocytes mature in the primary lymphoid organs, a population of cells able to recognize a functionally limitless variety of antigens is generated; each individual cell, however, is able to recognize and respond to only one epitope. Thus, if a person's immune system can make antibodies to billions of different epitopes, that person must have billions of different B cells, each interacting with a single epitope. In fact, the body is estimated to have approximately 10^9 (1 billion) B cells, and only one or a few will recognize a given epitope. Since a pathogen has multiple different epitopes, a number of distinct B cells will recognize it. The process of generating the diversity in antigen recognition is random and does not require previous exposure to antigen; the mechanisms will be described later.

The lymphocytes residing in the secondary lymphoid organs are waiting for the "antigen of their dreams," an antigen to which a particular lymphocyte is programmed to respond. When an antigen enters a lymphoid organ, only those rare lymphocytes that specifically recognize it may respond; the specificity of the antigen receptor they carry on their surface (B-cell receptor or T-cell receptor) governs this recognition. Lymphocytes that do not recognize the antigen remain inactive. Recall that in most cases, lymphocytes that recognize antigen require accessory signals, a "second opinion" by another cell type, in order to multiply. This provides a mechanism by which the immune system can avoid mounting a response against "self" molecules.

Some progeny of the lymphocytes that encountered their "dream antigen" leave the secondary lymphoid organs and migrate to the tissues where they continue responding for as long as the antigen is present. Without sustained stimulation by antigen, these cells will undergo apoptosis, curtailing the immune response. ■ **apoptosis, p. 382**

The activities of individual lymphocytes change over the lifetime of the cell, particularly as the cell encounters specific antigen.

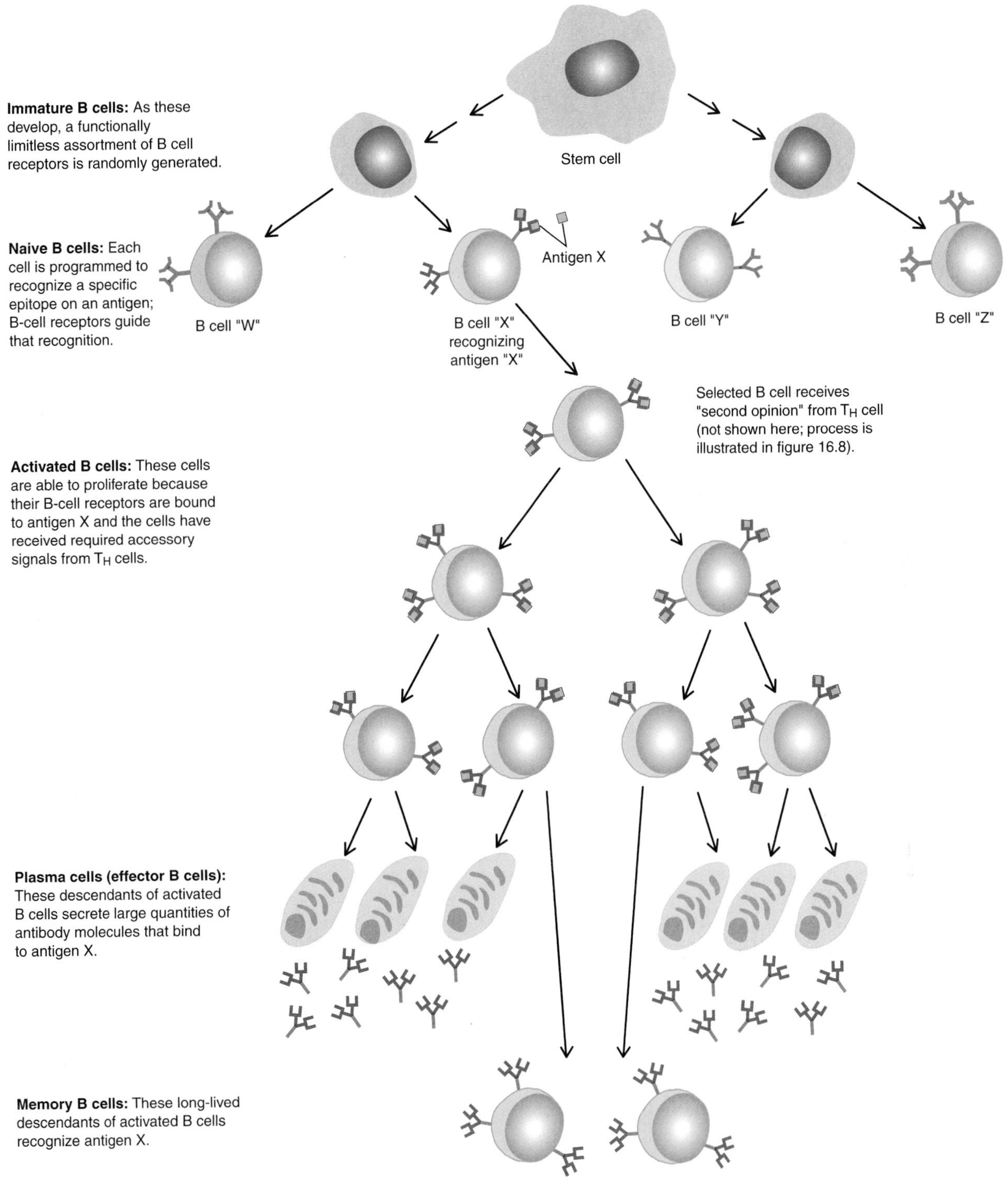
Immature B cells: As these develop, a functionally limitless assortment of B cell receptors is randomly generated.
Stem cell
Naive B cells: Each cell is programmed to recognize a specific epitope on an antigen; B-cell receptors guide that recognition.
Antigen X
B cell "W"
B cell "X" recognizing antigen "X"
B cell "Y"
B cell "Z"
Selected B cell receives "second opinion" from T_H cell (not shown here; process is illustrated in figure 16.8).
Activated B cells: These cells are able to proliferate because their B-cell receptors are bound to antigen X and the cells have received required accessory signals from T_H cells.
Plasma cells (effector B cells): These descendants of activated B cells secrete large quantities of antibody molecules that bind to antigen X.
Memory B cells: These long-lived descendants of activated B cells recognize antigen X.

FIGURE 16.7 Clonal Selection and Expansion During the Antibody Response

As a means of clarifying discussions of lymphocyte characteristics, descriptive terms are sometimes used:

- **Immature lymphocytes** are those that have not fully developed their antigen specific receptor.
- **Naive lymphocytes** have an antigen receptor, but have not yet encountered the antigen to which they are programmed to respond.
- **Activated lymphocytes** are able to proliferate; they have bound antigen by means of their antigen receptor and have received any required accessory signals from another cell, confirming the danger of the antigen.
- **Effector lymphocytes** are descendants of activated lymphocytes that have become armed with the ability to produce specific cytokines or other substances. This endows the cell with specific protective attributes, or **effector functions.** Plasma

cells are effector B cells, T_C cells are effector cytotoxic T cells, and T_H cells are effector helper T cells.

- **Memory lymphocytes** are long-lived descendants of activated lymphocytes; they can quickly change back to the activated form when antigen is encountered again. Memory lymphocytes are responsible for the speed and effectiveness of the secondary response.

MICROCHECK 16.5

In response to antigen, only those lymphocytes that recognize the antigen proliferate. This process gives rise to a population of clones of the original cell. Depending on their developmental stage, lymphocytes may be referred to as immature, naive, activated, effector, or memory cells.

✓ Describe the clonal selection theory.
✓ How does a naive lymphocyte differ from an activated one?
✓ If the heavy chain of an antibody is approximately 450 amino acids long, how much DNA would be required to encode 10^9 separate heavy chain genes?

16.6 B Lymphocytes and the Antibody Response

Focus Points

- Describe the role of T_H cells in B-cell activation.
- Compare and contrast the primary and the secondary responses.
- Compare and contrast the response to T-dependent antigens and T-independent antigens.

When antigen binds to a B-cell receptor, that B cell becomes poised to respond. In most cases, however, the B cell requires confirmation by a T_H cell that a response is truly warranted. Only when this occurs can the B cell become activated to begin dividing, differentiating, and, finally, producing antibodies. Compounds that evoke a response by B cells only with the assistance of T_H cells are called **T-dependent antigens;** these antigens are generally proteins and are the primary focus of this section. We will begin by describing the role of T_H cells in B cell activation. Later in the chapter, we will explain how naïve helper T cells become activated to attain their effector functions. Some carbohydrates and lipids can activate B cells without the aid of T_H cells and are called **T-independent antigens;** they will be covered at the end of this section.

B-Cell Activation

When a T-dependent antigen binds to a B-cell receptor, the B cell internalizes the antigen, enclosing it within a membrane-bound vacuole inside the B cell. Within that vacuole the antigen is degraded into peptide fragments that are delivered to proteins called **MHC class II** molecules that then move to the B-cell surface **(figure 16.8).** This process, called **antigen presentation,** "presents" pieces of the antigen for inspection by T_H cells. Recall that T cells have on their surface multiple copies of an antigen-specific receptor called a T-cell receptor, which is functionally analogous to a B-cell receptor. If the receptor of a T_H cell binds to one of the peptide fragments being presented by the B cell, then that T cell activates the B cell. It does this by delivering cytokines to the B cell, initiating the process of clonal expansion of that particular B cell. If the population of T_H cells fails to recognize any of the fragments being presented by the B cell, then that B cell may become unresponsive to future exposure to the antigen. This induces tolerance to that antigen, endowing the adaptive immune system with a mechanism to avoid erroneous responses against "self" antigens. ■ tolerance, p. 388

Characteristics of the Primary Response

A lag period of approximately 10 days to 2 weeks occurs before a substantial amount of antibody can be detected in the blood following the first (primary) exposure to an antigen **(figure 16.9).** During this delay, the individual could very well experience symptoms of an infection, which could be life-threatening. However, the immune system is actively responding; naive B cells present antigen to T_H cells, resulting in B-cell activation. The activated B cells multiply, generating a population of cells that recognize the antigen. As some of the activated B cells continue dividing, others differentiate to form plasma cells, which secrete thousands of antibody molecules per second **(figure 16.10).** Each plasma cell generally undergo apoptosis after several days, but activated B cells continue proliferating and differentiating, generating increasing numbers of plasma cells as long as antigen is present. The net result is the slow but steady increase in the **titer,** or concentration, of antibody molecules. Over time, some of the proliferating B cells undergo changes, enhancing the immune response. These include:

- **Affinity maturation.** This is a form of natural selection that occurs among proliferating B cells, effectively fine-tuning the quality of the response with respect to antibody specificity **(figure 16.11).** An inordinately large number of mutations naturally occur in certain regions of the antibody genes as the activated B cells replicate their DNA in preparation for division. Some of the mutations result in alterations in the antigen-binding site of the antibody (and therefore the B-cell receptor). B cells that bind antigen most tightly and for the longest duration are most likely to proliferate; others undergo apoptosis.
- **Class switching.** All B cells are initially programmed to differentiate into plasma cells that secrete IgM. Under the direction of cytokines produced by T_H cells, however, some activated B cells switch that genetic program, allowing them to differentiate into plasma cells that secrete another class of antibody. This allows the rare naive B cell that recognized antigen to give rise to an antibody response of the class most effective for a given situation. Circulating B cells most commonly switch to IgG production **(figure 16.12),** whereas B cells that reside in the mucosal-associated lymphoid tissues generally switch to IgA production, providing mucosal immunity.

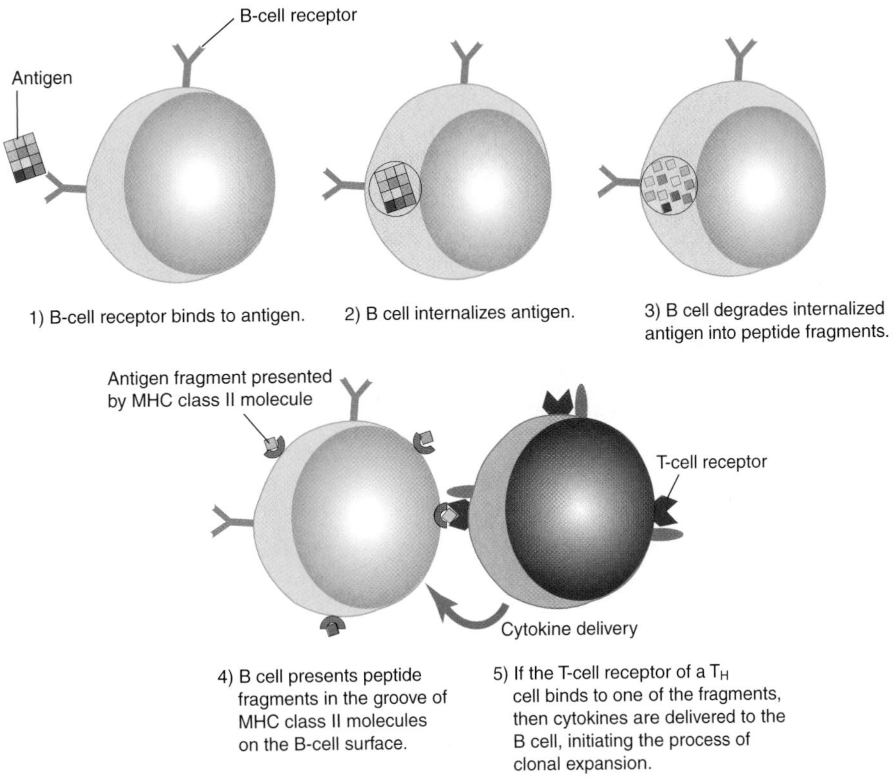
B-cell receptor
Antigen
1) B-cell receptor binds to antigen.
2) B cell internalizes antigen.
3) B cell degrades internalized antigen into peptide fragments.
Antigen fragment presented by MHC class II molecule
T-cell receptor
Cytokine delivery
4) B cell presents peptide fragments in the groove of MHC class II molecules on the B-cell surface.
5) If the T-cell receptor of a TH cell binds to one of the fragments, then cytokines are delivered to the B cell, initiating the process of clonal expansion.

FIGURE 16.8 Antigen Presentation by a B Cell This process enlists the assistance of a T_H cell, which can activate the B cell, allowing it to undergo clonal expansion. The T_H cell also directs affinity maturation, class switching, and the formation of memory cells.

- **Formation of memory cells.** Some of the B cells that have undergone class switching form memory cells. Memory B cells persist in the body for years and are present in numbers sufficient to give a prompt and effective secondary response when the same antigen is encountered again at a later time.

The antibody response begins to wane as the accumulating antibodies clear the antigen. Progressively fewer molecules of antigen remain to stimulate the lymphocytes, and, as a result, the activated lymphocytes undergo apoptosis. Memory B cells, however, are long-lived even in the absence of antigen. In addition, specialized dendritic cells called **follicular dendritic cells** appear to retain antigen in small amounts, using it to continually rejuvenate the memory response. This aspect of immunological memory is not well understood.

Characteristics of the Secondary Response

Memory B cells are responsible for the swift and effective reaction of the secondary response, eliminating identical repeat invaders before they cause noticeable harm. Thus, once a person has recovered from a particular disease, he or she generally has long-lasting immunity to that disease. Vaccination exploits this naturally occurring phenomenon.

Memory B cells that bind antigen can promptly become activated provided they receive necessary signals from T_H cells. When compared to the few naive B cells that initiated the primary response, the memory B cells are markedly faster and more effective. For one thing, there are more cells able to respond to a specific antigen. In addition, the B cells are able to scavenge antigen even when it occurs at low concentration because their receptors have been fine-tuned through affinity maturation to bind antigen more tightly. Likewise, the antibodies coded for by these cells more effectively bind antigen.

Some of the memory B cells that become activated will quickly differentiate to form plasma cells, resulting in the rapid production of antibodies. Because of class switching, most of the circulating

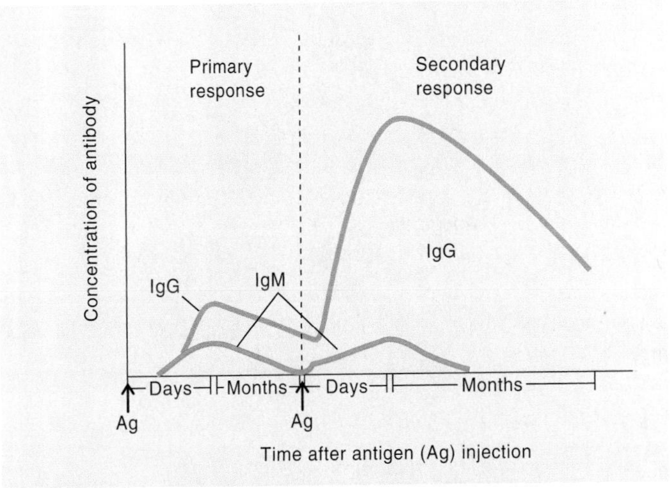
Primary response
Secondary response
Concentration of antibody
IgG
IgM
IgG
Days
Months
Days
Months
Ag
Ag
Time after antigen (Ag) injection

FIGURE 16.9 The Primary and Secondary Responses to Antigen The first exposure to antigen elicits relatively low amounts of first IgM, followed by IgG in the blood. The second exposure, which characterizes the memory of the adaptive immune system, elicits rapid production of relatively large quantities of IgG.

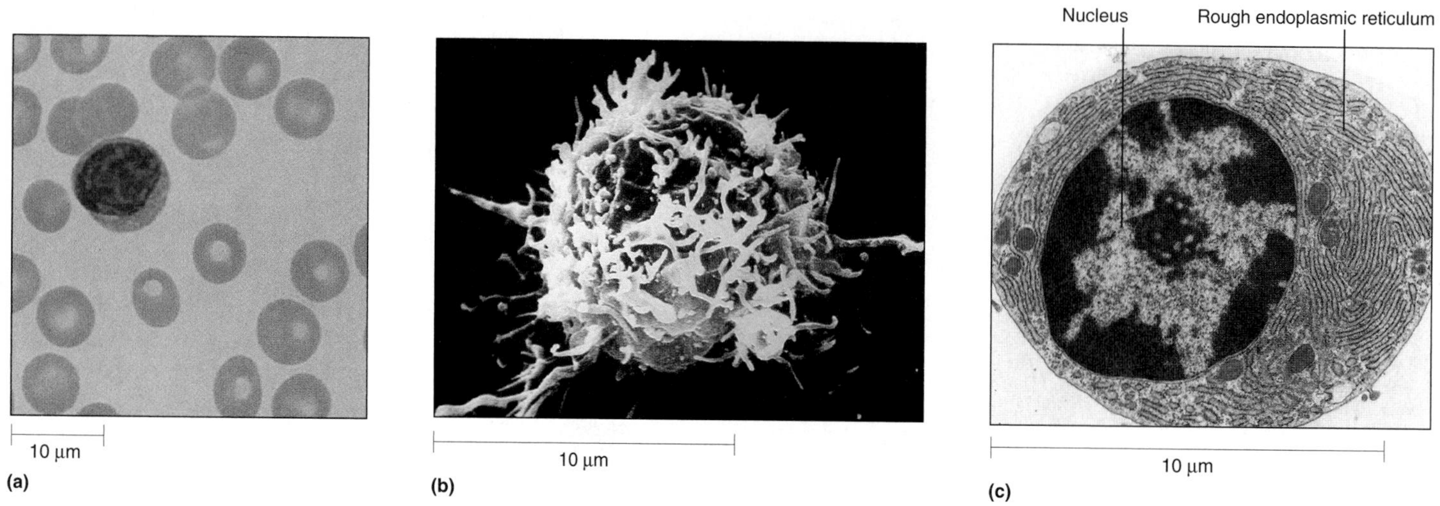

FIGURE 16.10 Lymphocytes and Plasma Cells **(a)** Light micrograph of a T lymphocyte. The morphology is the same as that of a B lymphocyte. **(b)** Scanning electron micrograph of a T lymphocyte. **(c)** Plasma cell, a form of B cell that is highly differentiated to produce large amounts of antibody. Note the extensive rough endoplasmic reticulum, the site of protein synthesis. All of the antibodies produced by a single plasma cell have the same specificity.

antibodies produced are IgG (see figure 16.9). Other activated memory cells begin proliferating, once again undergoing affinity maturation to further enhance the effectiveness of the antibodies they encode. Subsequent exposures to antigen lead to an even stronger response.

The Response to T-Independent Antigens

T-independent antigens can stimulate an antibody response by activating B cells without the aid of T_H cells. Relatively few antigens are T-independent, but they can be very important medically.

Molecules such as polysaccharides that have numerous identical evenly spaced epitopes characterize one type of T-independent antigen. Because of the arrangement of epitopes on the antigen, clusters of B-cell receptors bind the antigen simultaneously, which

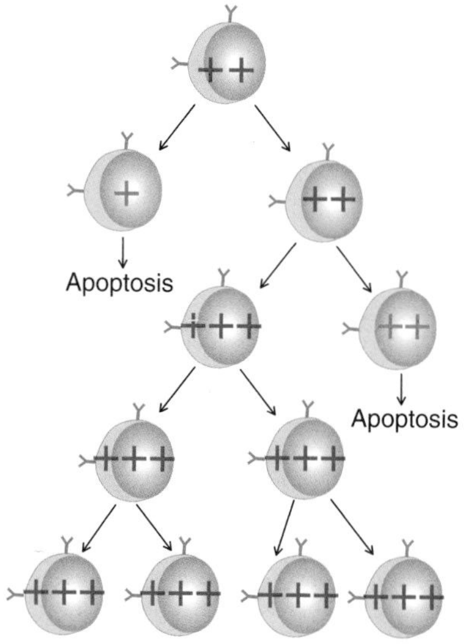

FIGURE 16.11 Affinity Maturation B cells that bind antigen most tightly for the longest duration are the most likely to proliferate. The plus signs indicate the relative quality of binding of the antibody to the antigen; those in green indicate the most "fit" to continue proliferating.

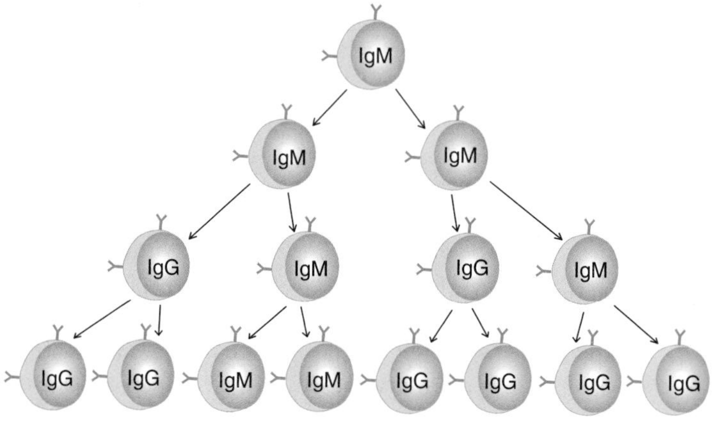

FIGURE 16.12 Class Switching B cells are initially programmed to produce IgM antibodies. With the direction of T_H cells, the activated B cells can switch to express a different class. The plasma cells descended from circulating B cells that have undergone class switching most commonly produce IgG. Plasma cells that descend from B cells residing in the mucosal-associated lymphoid tissues most commonly produce IgA. Note that class switching does not alter the antigen specificity.

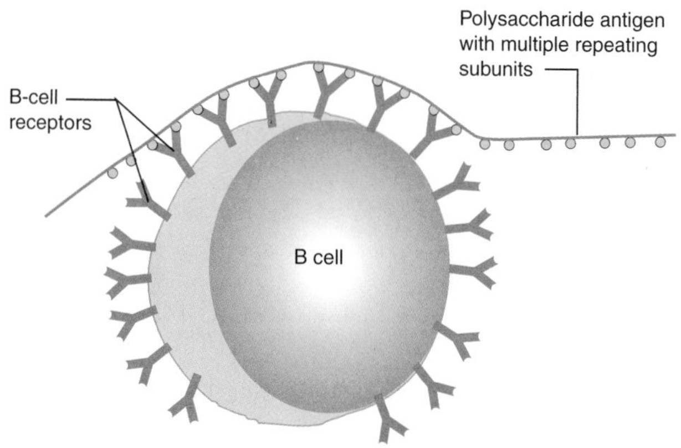

FIGURE 16.13 T-Independent Antigens Antigens such as some polysaccharides have multiple repeating epitopes. Because of the arrangement of epitopes, clusters of B-cell receptors bind to the antigen simultaneously, leading to B-cell activation without the involvement of T_H cells.

leads to B-cell activation without the involvement of helper T cells **(figure 16.13).** These antigens are particularly significant because the immune systems of young children respond poorly to them. This is why children less than 2 years of age are more susceptible to diseases caused by organisms such as *Streptococcus pneumoniae* and *Haemophilus influenzae* that cloak themselves in polysaccharide capsules. Antibodies against the capsules would be protective, but children do not effectively make antibodies against them. Vaccines made from purified capsules are available, but, likewise, they do not elicit a protective response in young children. Fortunately, newer vaccines designed to evoke a T-dependent response have been developed. They will be discussed later, when the role of T_H cells in the antibody response is described in more detail.

Another type of T-independent antigen is lipopolysaccharide (LPS), a component of the outer membrane of Gram-negative bacteria. The constant presence of antibodies against LPS, evoked without the need for T-cell help, is thought to provide an early defense against Gram-negative bacteria that breach the body's barriers.

MICROCHECK 16.6

In most cases, B cells that bind antigen require accessory signals from T_H cells to become activated. Activated B cells proliferate, ultimately producing plasma cells, which secrete antibody, and long-lived memory cells. Affinity maturation and class switching occur in the primary response; these enable a swift and more effective secondary response. T-independent antigens can stimulate an antibody response by activating B cells without the aid of T_H cells.

- ✓ Describe the significance of class switching.
- ✓ How do B cells increase their ability to bind to antigen?
- ✓ Why should B cells residing in the mucosal-associated lymphoid tissues produce IgA?

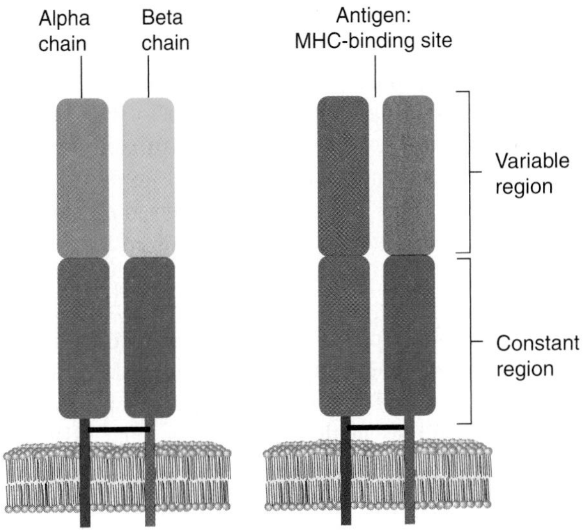

FIGURE 16.14 T-Cell Receptors Each chain has one variable (V) and one constant (C) region. The two chains are connected by a disulfide bond. Unlike antibodies, which have two binding sites for antigen, T-cell receptors have only one.

16.7 T Lymphocytes: Antigen Recognition and Response

Focus Points

- Describe the importance of T-cell receptors and CD markers.
- Describe the role of dendritic cells in T-cell activation.
- Compare and contrast T_H and T_C cells with respect to antigen recognition and the response to antigen.

A discussion of T cells encompasses not only their traits, but also the processes that lead to T-cell activation, and the functions of the resulting effector cells. We will begin by describing the general characteristics of T cells **(table 16.2).** Recognize, however, that the importance of some of these will be more evident as the specific roles of the cells are explained later.

General Characteristics of T Cells

T cells share several important characteristics with B cells. Like B cells, T cells have multiple copies of a receptor on their surface that recognizes a specific antigen. The **T-cell receptor (TCR)** consists of two polypeptide chains (a set of either alpha and beta or gamma and delta), each with a variable and constant region **(figure 16.14).** As in the B-cell receptor, the variable regions make up the antigen-binding sites. The specificity of the T-cell receptor is like that of the B-cell receptor; of the approximately 10^{10} T cells in the body, only one or a few will recognize a given epitope that appears in the body for the first time.

Despite the similarities in certain characteristics, the role of T cells is very different from that of B cells. For one thing, T cells never produce antibody. Instead, the naive cells become armed as effectors that directly interact with other cells, **target cells,** to cause distinct changes in those cells. Another important difference is that

TABLE 16.2 Characteristics of T Cells

T Cell Type/ CD Marker	Effector Form	Effector Function	Potential Target Cell	Antigen Recognition	Source of Antigen
Cytotoxic T cell/CD8	T_c cell	Induces target cell to undergo apoptosis	All nucleated cells	Peptides presented by MHC class I molecules	Endogenous (produced within the target cell)
Helper T cell/CD4	T_H cell	Activates target cell	B cells, macrophages	Peptides presented by MHC class II molecules	Exogenous (produced outside of the target cell)

the T-cell receptor does not interact with free antigen. Instead, the antigen must be "presented" by another host cell. The host cell does this by partly degrading, or **processing,** the antigen and then displaying, or **presenting,** individual peptides of the proteins that make up the antigen. This process is called **antigen presentation.** Dendritic cells present antigen to naive T cells as part of the T-cell activation process. Other cells present antigen to effector T cells, becoming target cells if the antigen is recognized by any of those effector cells.

During antigen presentation, the peptides from the antigen are cradled in the groove of proteins called **major histocompatibility complex molecules,** or **MHC molecules,** which are on the surface of the presenting cell. There are two types of MHC molecules involved in antigen presentation, MHC class I and MHC class II **(figure 16.15).** Each type is shaped somewhat like an elongated bun; it holds the peptide lengthwise, like a bun holds a hot dog. T cells will recognize an antigen only when it is presented by an MHC molecule; the T cell is actually recognizing both the peptide and MHC molecule simultaneously. In other words, the T-cell receptor recognizes the "whole sandwich," the peptide:MHC complex. **Endogenous antigens,** those which have been made within the cell, are presented by MHC class I molecules. **Exogenous antigens,** those that have been taken up by a cell, are presented by MHC class II molecules. All nucleated cells produce MHC class I molecules, but only specialized cell types (dendritic cells, B cells, and macrophages), collectively referred to as **antigen-presenting cells,** produce MHC class II molecules.

Two distinct major functional populations of T cells have been characterized: cytotoxic T cells and helper T cells. Upon activation, naive cytotoxic T cells proliferate and differentiate to become T_C cells, which destroy infected or cancerous "self" cells. In contrast, activated helper T cells multiply and develop into T_H cells, which then activate B cells and macrophages, stimulate other T cells, and orchestrate other immune responses. Cytotoxic T cells (including T_C cells) recognize antigen presented by MHC class I molecules; recall that endogenous antigens are presented by these molecules **(figure 16.16).** In contrast, helper T cells (including T_H cells) recognize antigen displayed by MHC class II molecules; these present exogenous antigens.

The most practical way for scientists to differentiate T cells, which are identical microscopically, is to examine surface proteins called **cluster of differentiation (CD) markers** (or molecules). Most cytotoxic T cells have the CD8 marker and are frequently referred to as CD8 T cells; most helper T cells carry the CD4 marker and are often called CD4 T cells. Note that CD4 is also a receptor for HIV, which explains why the virus infects helper T cells.

There are various subsets of the major cell types we will describe in this section (for example, T_H cells include two subsets—T_H1 and T_H2). Initially, we will focus on only the general characteristics of each cell type; later, we will describe the different roles of the various subsets.

Activation of T Cells

Like B cells, naive T cells require supporting signals in order to become activated. The naive cells slowly circulate among the sec-

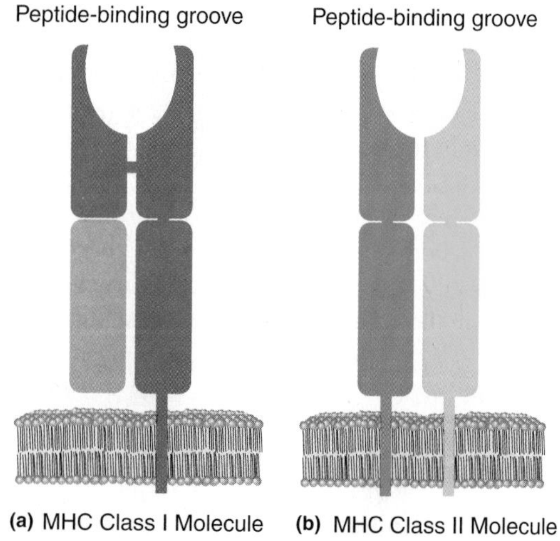
Peptide-binding groove
Peptide-binding groove
(a) MHC Class I Molecule
(b) MHC Class II Molecule

FIGURE 16.15 MHC Molecules (a) MHC class I molecule; cytoplasmic proteins (endogenous antigens) are presented in the groove of these molecules. **(b)** MHC class II molecule; proteins taken in by the cell (exogenous antigens) are presented in the groove of these molecules.

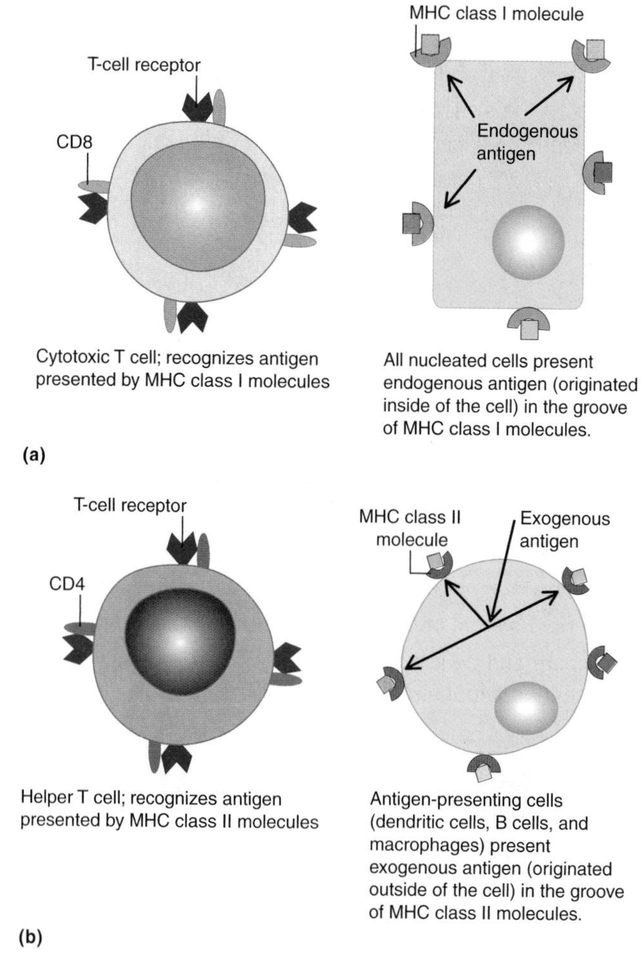
MHC class I molecule
T-cell receptor
CD8
Endogenous antigen
Cytotoxic T cell; recognizes antigen presented by MHC class I molecules
All nucleated cells present endogenous antigen (originated inside of the cell) in the groove of MHC class I molecules.
(a)
T-cell receptor
CD4
MHC class II molecule
Exogenous antigen
Helper T cell; recognizes antigen presented by MHC class II molecules
Antigen-presenting cells (dendritic cells, B cells, and macrophages) present exogenous antigen (originated outside of the cell) in the groove of MHC class II molecules.
(b)

FIGURE 16.16 Antigen Recognition by T Cells (a) Cytotoxic T cell. **(b)** Helper T cell.

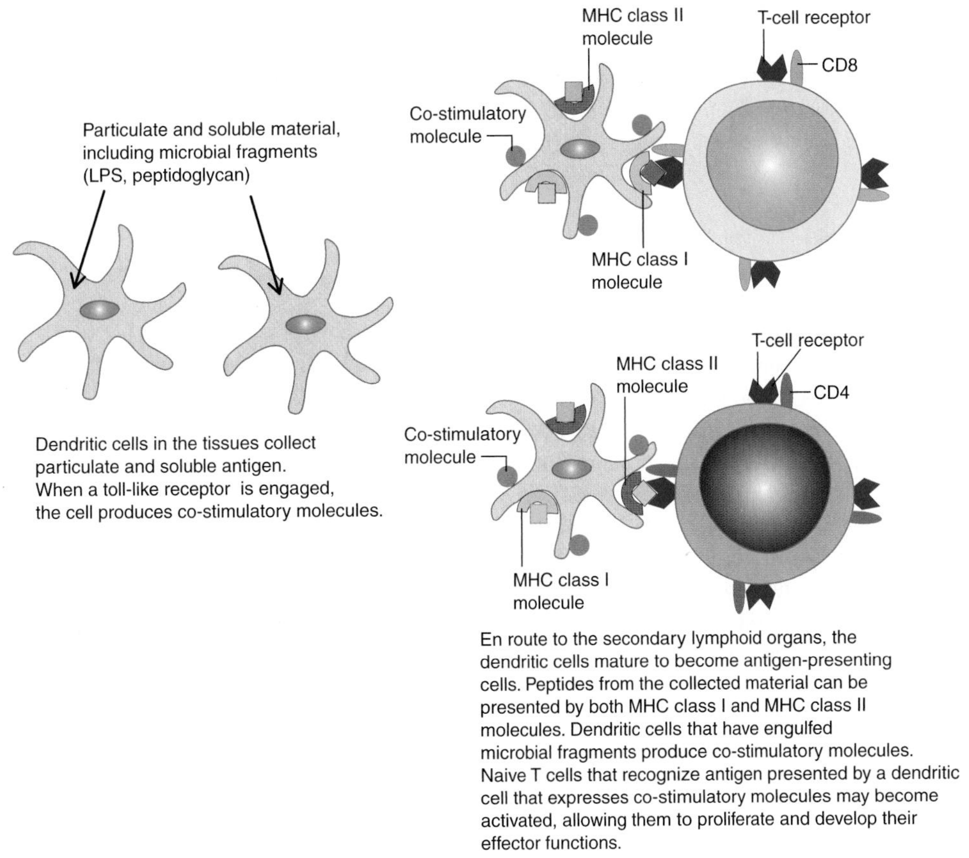

FIGURE 16.17 Activation of T Cells

ondary lymphoid organs to increase their chances of encountering the necessary signals.

Dendritic cells, the scouts of innate immunity, play a crucial role in T-cell activation **(figure 16.17).** Immature dendritic cells reside in peripheral tissues, such as beneath the skin, gathering various materials from those areas. The cells use both phagocytosis and pinocytosis to take up particulate and soluble material that could contain foreign protein. After collecting substances from the periphery, the dendritic cells travel to the secondary lymphoid organs to meet naive T cells; the inflammatory process can trigger the migration.

En route to the secondary lymphoid organs, the dendritic cells mature into a form able to present antigen to naive T cells as a prelude to T-cell activation. A dilemma lies in the fact that the dendritic cell must only activate a given T cell if the material recognized by it represents danger. Antigen presentation alone does not convey the significance of the material being displayed; the fragments could be parts of an invading microbe, which would merit an adaptive immune response, or routine cellular debris, which would not. In fact, a response to cellular debris would harm the host. The sensors of the innate immune response, such as the toll-like receptors, help solve this problem. They enable the dendritic cells to sense the presence of molecules that signify an invading microbe, which, in turn, allows dendritic cells to relay that fact to T cells. When a toll-like receptor on a dendritic cell is engaged, the cell produces surface proteins called **co-stimulatory molecules.** In essence, the co-stimulatory molecules function as "flashing red lights" that interact with the T cell, communicating that the material being presented by the dendritic cell material indicates danger. Dendritic cells displaying co-stimulatory molecules while presenting antigen are able to activate T cells. In contrast, T cells that recognize antigen presented by a dendritic cell not displaying co-stimulatory molecules are generally driven to apoptosis, or may become unresponsive to future encounters with the antigen. Recall that inducing unresponsiveness is one mechanism by which the adaptive immune response eliminates those lymphocytes that recognize "self" proteins.

Dendritic cells present the processed antigen in both types of MHC molecules, class I and class II. This enables them to present antigen to, and therefore activate, cytotoxic T cells as well as helper T cells. T cells that recognize the antigen presented by dendritic cells undergo clonal selection and expansion as described previously, eventually forming effector cells and memory cells that can leave the lymph nodes and migrate in the periphery in search of antigen. Like dendritic cells, macrophages and B cells also present antigen in MHC class II molecules (in other words, they are antigen-presenting cells), and they can produce some co-stimulatory molecules. They do not appear able to contact naive T cells, however; thus they are only able to reactivate memory T cells, which they can encounter in the bloodstream and tissues.

Upon activation, T cells produce both the cytokine that stimulates T cell growth (IL-2) and the receptor for that cytokine, allowing the cells to stimulate their own proliferation. Later, they begin producing additional cytokines and adhesion molecules that allow them to gain their effector functions. The effector T cells can leave the secondary lymphoid organs and circulate in the bloodstream. They can also enter tissues, particularly at sites of infection.

Functions of T_C (CD8) Cells

T_C cells induce apoptosis in "self" cells infected with a virus or other intracellular microbe; they also destroy cancerous "self" cells. How do T_C cells distinguish dysfunctional cells from their normal counterparts? The answer lies in the significance of antigen presentation by MHC class I molecules **(figure 16.18).** All nucleated cells routinely degrade a portion of the proteins they have produced (endogenous proteins) and load peptides from those proteins into the groove of MHC class I molecules to be delivered to the surface of the cell (see figure 16.16a). If a host cell is infected with a virus or a bacterium that resides in the cytoplasm, or if the cell is producing certain abnormal proteins such as those that characterize cancerous cells, then some of the peptides presented by MHC class I molecules will be recognized by circulating T_C cells. This makes the presenting cell a target cell for the lethal effector functions of the T_C cell. In contrast, the peptides presented by MHC class I molecules of normal cells will be parts of standard proteins typically found in the cell. There should be no T_C cells that recognize these because of the constraints of the T-cell activation process. In addition, as we will describe later, most "self"-recognizing T cells are eliminated during T-cell development in the thymus.

When a T_C cell encounters a cell displaying a peptide: MHC class I complex it recognizes, it establishes intimate contact with that cell. The T_C cell then releases several pre-formed **cytotoxins,** molecules lethal to cells, directly to the target cell. The cytotoxins include perforin, a molecule that forms pores in cell membranes, and a group of proteases. Recent evidence indicates that at the concentrations released *in vivo,* perforin simply allows the proteases to enter the target cell. Once inside that cell, the proteases facilitate reactions that induce the target cell to undergo apoptosis. In addition, a specific molecule on the T_C cell can engage a "death receptor" on the target cell, also initiating apoptosis. The remains of the apoptotic cell are then quickly removed by macrophages; the T_C cell survives and can go on to kill other targets. Killing the target cell by inducing apoptosis rather than lysis minimizes the number of intracellular microbes that might spill into the surrounding area and infect other cells. Most microbes remain in cell remnants until they are ingested by macrophages.

In response to antigen recognition, T_C cells also produce various cytokines that allow neighboring cells to become more vigilant against intracellular invaders. One of the cytokines, for example, stimulates antigen processing and presentation in nearby cells, facilitating detection of other infected cells. Another cytokine selectively activates local macrophages whose toll-like receptors have been triggered. Note that a more efficient mechanism of macrophage activation involves T_H cells and will be discussed in more detail shortly.

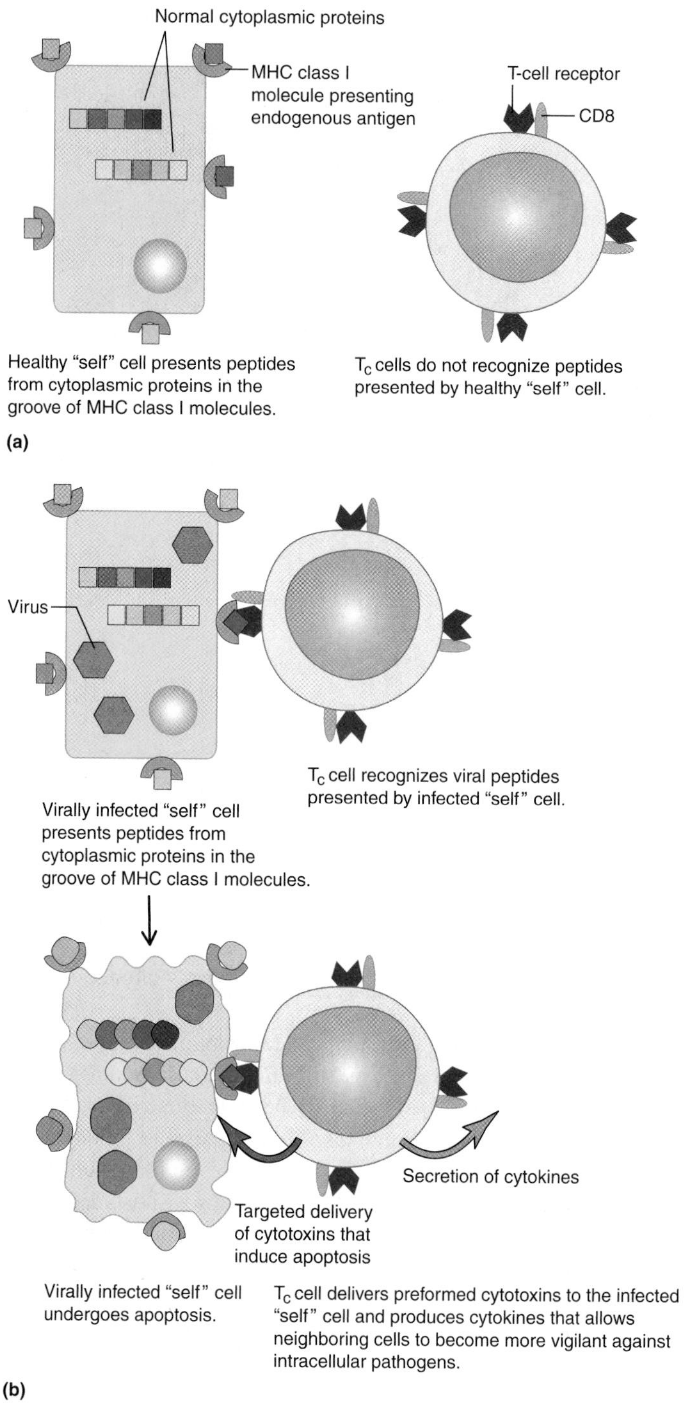
Normal cytoplasmic proteins
MHC class I molecule presenting endogenous antigen
T-cell receptor
CD8
Healthy "self" cell presents peptides from cytoplasmic proteins in the groove of MHC class I molecules.
T_C cells do not recognize peptides presented by healthy "self" cell.
(a)
Virus
T_C cell recognizes viral peptides presented by infected "self" cell.
Virally infected "self" cell presents peptides from cytoplasmic proteins in the groove of MHC class I molecules.
Secretion of cytokines
Targeted delivery of cytotoxins that induce apoptosis
Virally infected "self" cell undergoes apoptosis.
T_C cell delivers preformed cytotoxins to the infected "self" cell and produces cytokines that allows neighboring cells to become more vigilant against intracellular pathogens.
(b)

FIGURE 16.18 Functions of T_C Cells

Functions of T_H (CD4) Cells

T_H cells orchestrate the immune response, directing the activities of B cells, macrophages, and T cells. They recognize antigen presented by MHC class II molecules, which are found only on antigen-presenting cells (APCs). These cells, which include B cells and macrophages, gather, process, and present exogenous antigens (see figure 16.16b). If T_H cell recognizes antigen presented by a B cell or macrophage, it delivers cytokines that activate the presenting cell. Various cytokines are also released, the array of which depends on the subset of T_H cell.

The Role of T_H Cells in B Cell Activation

When a naive B cell binds antigen via its B-cell receptor, the cell brings the antigen in, enclosed within a membrane-bound vesicle called an **endosome.** Proteins within the endosome are degraded to produce short peptides that can then be loaded into the groove of MHC class II molecules (see figure 16.8b). If a T_H cell encounters a B cell bearing the peptide:MHC class II complex it recognizes, it responds by synthesizing cytokines and delivering them to that cell. The cytokines activate the B cell, enabling it to proliferate and undergo class switching. The cytokines also drive the formation of memory B cells. Note that the T-cell receptor could be recognizing any of the various peptides generated from the antigen during antigen processing and presentation. Thus, the epitope to which the T_H cell responds is most likely different from the one that the B-cell receptor recognized. In fact, a B cell that binds to a bacterium is probably recognizing an epitope on the surface of that cell, whereas the helper T cell could very well be responding to a peptide from one of the bacterium's cytoplasmic proteins being presented by the B cell.

Understanding the mechanisms used in antigen processing and presentation is what led to an effective vaccine for children against what was the most common cause of meningitis in children, *Haemophilus influenzae.* Recall that young children are particularly susceptible to meningitis caused by this organism because it produces a polysaccharide capsule, an example of a T-independent antigen to which this age group responds poorly. Polysaccharide antigens can be converted to T-dependent antigens by covalently attaching, or conjugating, them to large protein molecules; this is done to make what is called a **conjugate vaccine.** The polysaccharide component of the vaccine binds to the B-cell receptor and the entire molecule is taken in. The protein component will then be processed and presented to a T_H cell. Although the B cell recognizes the polysaccharide component of the vaccine, the T cell recognizes peptides from the protein component. The T_H cell then activates the B cell, leading to production of antibodies that bind the capsule. ■ conjugate vaccines, p. 417

The requirement for antigen processing and presentation also explains how some people develop allergies to penicillin. This medication is a **hapten,** a molecule that binds a B-cell receptor yet does not elicit the production of antibodies unless it is attached to a protein carrier. In the body, penicillin can react with proteins, forming a penicillin-protein conjugate. This functions in a manner analogous to the *H. influenzae* conjugate vaccine, resulting in antibodies that bind penicillin. The reaction of IgE antibodies with penicillin can result in allergic reactions, precluding the further use of the antimicrobial medication in these reactive individuals. ■ allergy, p. 433, ■ penicillin, pp. 64, 501

The Role of T_H Cells in Macrophage Activation

As discussed in chapter 15, macrophages routinely engulf and degrade invading microbes, rapidly clearing most organisms even before an adaptive response is mounted. Some microbes, however, can evade this method of destruction, enabling them to survive and actually multiply within the phagocytic cell. T_H cells recognize macrophages harboring engulfed microbes resistant to such killing, and then activate those macrophages by delivering cytokines that induce more potent destructive mechanisms.

The steps that lead to macrophage activation are very similar to those described for B-cell activation. When macrophages engulf material, they bring the substance into the cell enclosed within a membrane-bound phagosome **(figure 16.19).** The fate of the proteins within the phagosome is identical to that of proteins within the B cell's endosome, resulting in peptides being loaded into the groove of an MHC class II molecule. If a T_H cell recognizes a peptide presented by a class II molecule on a macrophage, it delivers cytokines directly to that macrophage. This activates the macrophage, leading to several morphological and physiological changes. The macrophage enlarges, the plasma membrane becomes ruffled and irregular, and the cell increases its metabolism so that the lysosomes, each containing antimicrobial substances, increase in number. The activated macrophage also begins producing nitric oxide, a potent antimicrobial chemical, along with various compounds that can be released to destroy extracellular microorganisms. ■ phagosome, p. 378

If the response is still not sufficient to control the infection, activated macrophages are able to fuse together, forming **giant cells.** These, along with other macrophages and T cells, can form granulomas that wall off the offending agent, preventing infectious microbes from escaping to infect other cells. Activated macrophages are an important aspect of the immune response against

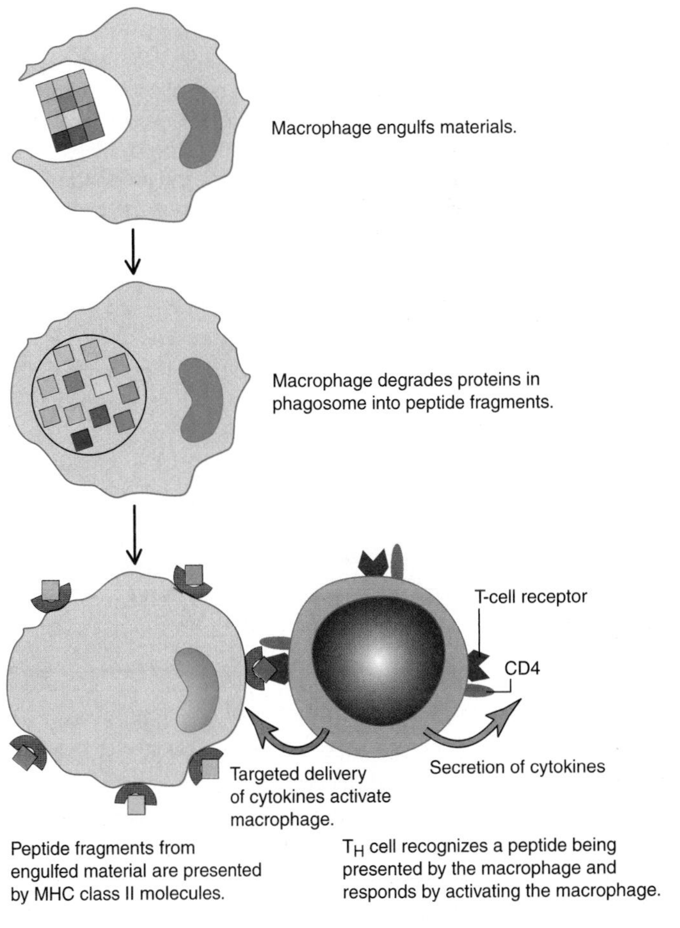
Macrophage engulfs materials.
Macrophage degrades proteins in phagosome into peptide fragments.
T-cell receptor
CD4
Targeted delivery of cytokines activate macrophage.
Secretion of cytokines
Peptide fragments from engulfed material are presented by MHC class II molecules.
T_H cell recognizes a peptide being presented by the macrophage and responds by activating the macrophage.

FIGURE 16.19 The Role of T_H Cells in Macrophage Activation

diseases such as tuberculosis that are caused by organisms capable of surviving within macrophages. ■ giant cell, p. 379 ■ granuloma, p. 379

Subsets of Dendritic Cells and T Cells

Immunologists are currently clarifying the roles of the various subsets of dendritic cells and helper T cells that have been recently discovered. These subsets enable the body to steer the immune response towards either an antibody-mediated response (humoral immunity) or a cell-mediated response (cellular immunity), or to turn down the response. DC1 and DC2 cells, subsets of dendritic cells, appear to be critical in the process. If a DC1 cell presents antigen to a naive helper T cell, the resulting T_H cells will be of the subset T_H1, sometimes called pro-inflammatory T cells. These produce cytokines that direct a cellular response by recruiting and stimulating macrophages, and inducing proliferation and stimulation of activated T cells. In contrast, if a DC2 cell presents antigen to that same naive helper T cell, the resulting T_H cells will be of the subset T_H2. These produce cytokines that direct a humoral response, promoting proliferation, differentiation and most types of class switching by activated B cells, and the eventual transformation of B cells into plasma cells. Interestingly, T_H1 cytokine production suppresses T_H2 cytokine production, and vice versa. The outcome of some conditions, such as Hansen's disease (leprosy), appears to correlate with the type of helper T cell response—T_H1 or T_H2.

MICROCHECK 16.7

T cells are activated when they recognize antigen presented by dendritic cells expressing co-stimulatory molecules. T_C (CD8) cells recognize antigen presented by MHC class I molecules and respond by inducing apoptosis in the target cell and secreting cytokines that stimulate surrounding cells to be more vigilant against intracellular invaders. T_H (CD4) cells recognize antigen presented by MHC class II molecules (found on B cells and macrophages) and respond by activating the target cell and secreting various cytokines that orchestrate the immune response.

✓ Name three types of antigen-presenting cells.

✓ If an effector CD8 cell recognizes antigen presented by an MHC class I molecule, how should it respond?

✓ Why would a person who has AIDS be more susceptible to the bacterium that causes tuberculosis?

16.8

Natural Killer (NK) Cells

Focus Point

- Describe two distinct protective roles of NK cells.

Natural killer (NK) cells descend from lymphoid stem cells, but they lack the antigen-specific receptors that characterize B cells and T cells. Their activities, however, augment the adaptive immune responses. ■ lymphoid stem cells, p. 370

NK cells are important in the process of antibody-dependent cellular cytotoxicity (ADCC), which is a means of killing cells that have been bound by antibody (see figure 16.5). This enables the killing of host cells that have foreign proteins inserted into their membrane, such as those that have been infected by certain types of viruses. NK cells recognize their target by means of Fc receptors for IgG antibodies on their surface; recall that Fc receptors bind the "red flag" portion of antibody molecules. These Fc receptors enable the NK cell to detect and attach to an antibody-coated cell. When multiple receptors on an NK cell bind the Fc regions, the NK cell delivers granules that contain perforin and proteases directly to the target cell. These compounds induce apoptosis in "self" cells.

NK cells also recognize and destroy host cells that do not have MHC class I molecules on their surface. This is important because some viruses have evolved mechanisms to circumvent the action of cytotoxic T cells by interfering with the process of antigen presentation; cells infected with such a virus will be essentially bare of MHC class I molecules and thus cannot be a target of cytotoxic T cells. The NK cells can recognize the absence of MHC class I molecules on those cells and induce them to undergo apoptosis. This can occur because NK cells are actually programmed to destroy "self" cells, but recognition of the MHC class I molecules suppresses that killing action. In the absence of MHC class I molecules, the action can proceed.

MICROCHECK 16.8

Natural killer (NK) cells can mediate antibody-dependent cellular cytotoxicity (ADCC). NK cells also kill cells not bearing MHC class I molecules on their surface.

✓ What mechanism do NK cells use to kill "self" cells?

✓ What can cause a "self" cell to not bear MHC class I molecules on its surface?

✓ What selective advantage would a virus have if it interferes with the process of antigen presentation?

16.9

Lymphocyte Development

Focus Points

- Describe the roles of gene rearrangement, imprecise joining, and combinatorial associations in the generation of diversity of antibody molecules.
- Describe positive and negative selection of self-reactive lymphocytes.

During lymphocyte development, as the cells differentiate from hematopoietic stem cells into either B cells or T cells, they acquire their ability to recognize distinct epitopes. Then, once they have committed to that specificity, they pass through rigorous checkpoints intended to ensure that their antigen-specific receptors are functional yet will not evoke a response against "self" molecules. Most developing lymphocytes fail these tests and, as a consequence, are induced to undergo apoptosis. ■ hematopoietic stem cell, p. 369

PERSPECTIVE 16.1

What Flavor Are Your Major Histocompatibility Complex Molecules?

The major histocompatibility molecules were discovered over half a century ago, long before their critical role in adaptive immunity was recognized. During World War II, bombing raids caused serious burns in many people, stimulating research into the transplantation of skin to replace burned tissue. This research quickly spread to the study of transplantation of a variety of other tissues and organs, including bone marrow, which contains the stem cell precursors of all blood cells in the body. Such transplants were readily rejected, however, due to certain cell surface molecules that differed between tissue donor and recipient. The immune system of the transplant recipient recognized the molecules as foreign and made a vigorous response, resulting in the rejection of the tissue. This led to the development of tissue-typing tests that enabled researchers to more closely match donor and recipient tissues. The typing tests exploit surface structures on leukocytes that serve as markers for tissue compatibility; the structures were called **human leukocyte antigens** or **HLAs.** Later, researchers determined that HLAs were encoded by a cluster of genes, now called the major histocompatibility complex. Unfortunately, the terminology can be confusing because the molecules that transplant biologists refer to as HLAs are called MHC molecules by immunologists.

It is highly unlikely that two random individuals will have identical MHC molecules. This is because the genes encoding them are **polygenic,** meaning they are encoded by more than one **locus,** or position on the chromosome, and each locus is highly **polymorphic,** meaning there are multiple variations **(figure 1).** There are three loci of MHC class I genes, designated HLA-A, HLA-B, and HLA-C; in other words, if MHC molecules were candy, each cell would be covered with pieces of chocolate (HLA-A), taffy (HLA-B), and lollipop (HLA-C). There are more than 100 different **alleles,** or forms, of each of the three genes. Continuing with the candy analogy, the flavor at the chocolate locus could be dark, white, or milk chocolate; the taffy could be peppermint or cinnamon, and so on. The list of known alleles continues to increase, but currently there are at least 229 alleles for HLA-A, 464 for HLA-B, and 111 for HLA-C. In addition, all of the loci are co-dominantly expressed. In other words, you inherited one set of the three genes from your mother and one set from your father; both sets are expressed. Putting this all together, and assuming that you inherited two completely different sets of alleles from your parents, your cells express six different MHC class I molecules—two of the over 229 known HLA-A possibilities, two of the over 464 HLA-B possibilities, and two of the over 111 HLA-C possibilities. As you can imagine, the likelihood that any person you encounter in a day will have those same MHC class I molecules is extremely unlikely, unless you have an identical twin.

Why is there so much diversity in MHC molecules? The answer lies in the complex demands of antigen presentation. MHC class I molecules bind peptides that are only 8 to 10 amino acids in length; MHC class II molecules bind peptides that are only 13 to 25 amino acids in length. Somehow, within that constraint, the MHC molecules must bind as many different peptides as possible in order to ensure that a representative selection from the proteins within a cell can be presented to T cells. The ability to bind a wide variety of peptides is particularly important considering how readily viruses and bacteria can evolve in response to selective pressure. For example, if a single alteration in a viral protein prevented all MHC molecules from presenting peptides from that protein, then a virus with that mutation could routinely overwhelm the body. The ability to bind different peptides is not enough, however, because, ideally, a given peptide should be presented in several slightly different orientations so that distinct aspects of the three-dimensional structures can be inspected by T-cell receptors. No single variety of MHC molecules can accomplish all of these aims, which probably accounts for the diversity in MHC molecules.

The variety of MHC molecules that a person has on his or her cells impacts that individual's adaptive response to certain antigens. This is not surprising since MHC molecules differ in the array of peptides they can bind and manner in which those peptides are held in the molecule. Thus, they impact what the T cells actually "see." In fact, the severity of certain diseases has been shown to correlate with the MHC type of the infected individual. For example, rheumatic fever, which can occur as a consequence of *Streptococcus pyogenes* infection, develops more frequently in individuals with certain MHC types. The most serious manifestations of schistosomiasis have also been shown to correlate with certain MHC types. Epidemics of life-threatening diseases such as plague and smallpox have dramatically altered the relative proportion of MHC types in certain populations, killing those whose MHC types ineffectively present peptides from the causative agent.
■ rheumatic fever, p. 578 ■ schistosomiasis, p. 382

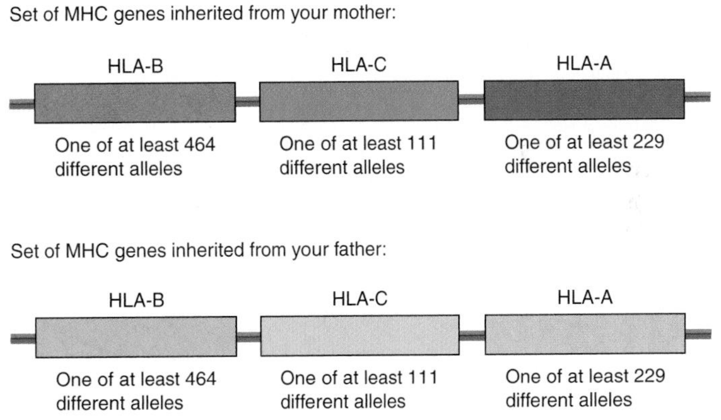

FIGURE 1 MHC Polymorphisms. The order of the MHC class I genes on the chromosome is B, C, and A.

B cells undergo the developmental stages in the bone marrow; T cells go through the maturation process described in this section in the thymus. The events involved in the adaptive immune response, from the maturation of lymphocytes to the development of their effector functions, are summarized in **figure 16.20.**

Generation of Diversity

The mechanisms lymphocytes use to produce a functionally limitless assortment of antibodies and antigen-specific receptors were first revealed in studies using B cells. Because the processes are markedly similar to those employed by T cells, we will use them as a general model to describe the generation of diversity with respect to specificity for antigen.

Each B cell responds to only one epitope, yet it is estimated that the population of B cells within the body can respond to more than 100 million different epitopes. Based on the information presented in chapter 7, it might seem logical to assume that humans have over 100 million different antibody genes, each encoding specificity for a single epitope. This is impossible, however, because the human genome has only 3 billion nucleotides and codes for only about 25,000 genes.

The question of how such tremendous diversity in antibodies could be generated perplexed immunologists until Dr. Susumu Tonegawa solved the mystery. For this work, he was awarded a

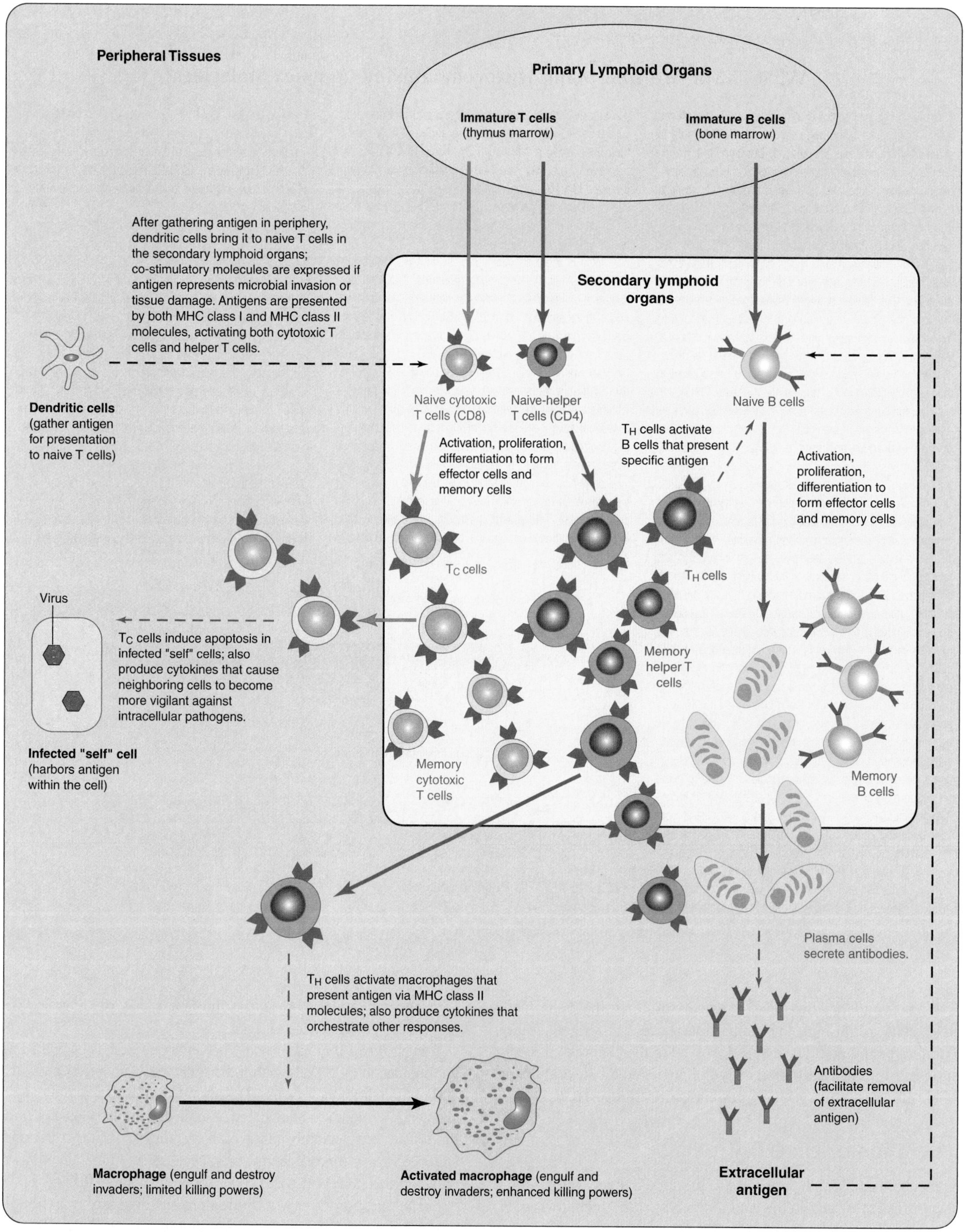
Peripheral Tissues
Primary Lymphoid Organs
Immature T cells (thymus marrow)
Immature B cells (bone marrow)
After gathering antigen in periphery, dendritic cells bring it to naive T cells in the secondary lymphoid organs; co-stimulatory molecules are expressed if antigen represents microbial invasion or tissue damage. Antigens are presented by both MHC class I and MHC class II molecules, activating both cytotoxic T cells and helper T cells.
Secondary lymphoid organs
Dendritic cells (gather antigen for presentation to naive T cells)
Naive cytotoxic T cells (CD8)
Naive-helper T cells (CD4)
Naive B cells
Activation, proliferation, differentiation to form effector cells and memory cells
T_H cells activate B cells that present specific antigen
Activation, proliferation, differentiation to form effector cells and memory cells
T_C cells
T_H cells
Virus
T_C cells induce apoptosis in infected "self" cells; also produce cytokines that cause neighboring cells to become more vigilant against intracellular pathogens.
Memory helper T cells
Infected "self" cell (harbors antigen within the cell)
Memory cytotoxic T cells
Memory B cells
Plasma cells secrete antibodies.
T_H cells activate macrophages that present antigen via MHC class II molecules; also produce cytokines that orchestrate other responses.
Antibodies (facilitate removal of extracellular antigen)
Macrophage (engulf and destroy invaders; limited killing powers)
Activated macrophage (engulf and destroy invaders; enhanced killing powers)
Extracellular antigen

FIGURE 16.20 Summary of the Adaptive Immune Response

Nobel Prize in 1987. Diversity in antibodies involves a combination of gene rearrangement, imprecise joining of gene fragments, and the association of light chains and heavy chains coded for by the rearranged genes.

Gene Rearrangement

A primary mechanism for generating a wide variety of different antibodies using a limited-size region of DNA employs a strategy similar to that of a savvy and well-dressed traveler living out of a small suitcase. By mixing and matching different shirts, pants, and shoes, the traveler can create a wide variety of unique outfits from a limited number of components. Likewise, the maturing B cell selects three gene segments, one each from DNA regions called V (variable), D (diversity), and J (joining), to form an ensemble that encodes a nearly unique variable region of the heavy chain of an antibody **(figure 16.21).**

A human lymphoid stem cell has about 65 different V segments, 27 different D segments, and 6 different J segments in the DNA that encodes the variable region of the heavy chain. As a B cell develops, however, two large regions of DNA are permanently removed, effectively joining discrete V, D, and J regions. The joined segments encode the antibody that the mature B cell is programmed to make. Thus, one B cell could express the combination V5, D3, and J6 to produce its heavy chain, whereas another B cell might use V19, D27, and J6; each combination would result in a unique antibody specificity. Similar rearrangements occur in the genes that encode the light chain of the antibody molecule.

Imprecise Joining

As the various segments are joined during gene rearrangement, nucleotides are readily deleted or added between the sections. This imprecise joining changes the reading frame of the encoded protein so that two B cells that have the same V, D, and J segments for their heavy chain could potentially give rise to antibodies with very different sequences.

Combinatorial Associations

Combinatorial association refers to the specific groupings of light chains and heavy chains that make up the antibody molecule. Both types of chains acquire diversity through gene rearrangement and imprecise joining. Additional diversity is then introduced when these two molecules join; it is the combination of the two chains that creates the antigen-binding site (see figure 16.4b).

Negative Selection of Self-Reactive B Cells

Negative selection is the process of eliminating lymphocytes, including B cells, that recognize "self" molecules. The result is called **clonal deletion.** Failure to eliminate such B cells results in the production of **autoantibodies,** which are antibodies that bind to host components, causing the immune system to attack "self" substances.

After a developing B cell begins producing a functional B-cell receptor, it is then exposed to various other cells and material in the bone marrow. Because the bone marrow is normally free of foreign substances, any B cell that binds material there must be recognizing "self" and therefore ought to be eliminated. This occurs by inducing the cell to undergo apoptosis.

Negative selection also occurs in secondary lymphoid organs. Any naive B cell that recognizes antigen but does not receive agreement from a T_H cell is rendered unresponsive and eventually undergoes apoptosis. This process eliminates cells

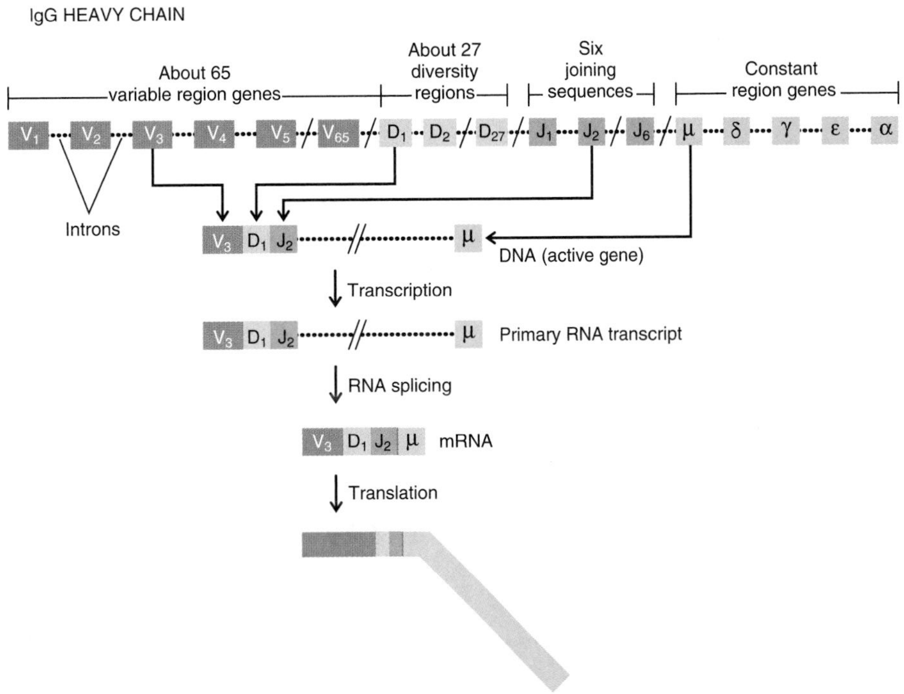

FIGURE 16.21 Antibody Diversity Immunoglobulin gene arrangement in an immature lymphocyte and the mechanism of active gene formation. Only the heavy chain is shown.

that recognize antigens not associated with threat or destruction, a critical aspect of the body's ability to discriminate between "danger" and "harmless."

Positive and Negative Selection of Self-Reactive T Cells

Developing T cells have two phases of trials—positive and negative selection—that seal their fate. **Positive selection** is a process that permits only those T cells that recognize MHC to some extent to develop further. Recall that the T-cell receptor, unlike the B-cell receptor, recognizes a peptide:MHC complex. T cells, therefore, must show at least some recognition of the MHC molecules regardless of the peptide they are carrying. T cells that show insufficient recognition fail positive selection and, as a consequence, are eliminated. Each T cell that passes positive selection is also subjected to negative selection, analogous to that which occurs during B cell development. T cells that recognize "self" peptides presented by MHC molecules are eliminated. Positive and negative selection processes are so stringent that over 95% of developing T cells undergo apoptosis in the thymus.

As occurs with B cells, negative selection also happens in the secondary lymphoid organs. Any naive T cell that recognizes antigen presented by an antigen-presenting cell not expressing co-stimulatory molecules is eliminated.

MICROCHECK 16.9

Mechanisms used to generate the diversity of antigen specificity in lymphocytes include rearrangement of gene segments, imprecise joining of those segments, and combinatorial associations of heavy chains and light chains. Negative selection eliminates B cells and T cells that recognize normal "self" molecules. Positive selection permits only those T cells that show moderate recognition of the MHC molecules to develop further.

- ✓ What three gene segments encode an antibody molecule?
- ✓ What are autoantibodies?
- ✓ How could imprecise joining be considered a type of frameshift mutation?

FUTURE CHALLENGES

Defining "Danger"

For many years immunologists generally accepted the model in which the immune system is able to distinguish "self" from "non-self," tolerating the former and attacking the latter. In many ways, this model makes a great deal of sense. For example, simple observation shows that a strong response is mounted against invading microorganisms, yet the immune system generally does not attack a person's own healthy cells. There are, however, significant flaws in this model, such as the fact that the body does not mount a response against a developing fetus, which is obviously "non-self."

A new hypothesis suggests that the immune system does not mount a response against "non-self" per se, but instead attacks foreign antigens only if they are associated with tissue damage or other signs of "danger." Foreign materials not linked with such signals are tolerated. This **danger model** opens the door to exciting new ideas regarding mechanisms regulating—and methods for treatment of—cancers, allergies, and autoimmune diseases. It is also impacting vaccine development and tissue transplantation strategies.

According to the danger model, a cancerous cell will not be recognized by the immune system as a threat, even if it produces abnormal proteins, unless some sort of "danger" signal is also present. This raises the possibility that scientists may be able to introduce such a danger signal. Coupled with a vaccine against an abnormal protein that characterizes the cancerous cell, this may provide an effective treatment for cancer. An opposite strategy might help in allergy treatment. Allergens are relatively innocuous substances such as mites, fungi, and plant pollens that often have some proteolytic activity. This activity can cause some local damage, triggering an unwarranted immune response. Hiding or minimizing the "danger" signals might help promote tolerance to these compounds. Tolerance is an important aspect in the prevention of transplant rejection as well. The surgical procedures themselves cause tissue damage, eliciting an immune response against the MHC molecules of the donor tissues. Perhaps employing drugs that dampen damaging immune responses while also stimulating tolerance could minimize rejection of transplants. Similar strategies might be useful for treating autoimmune diseases.

SUMMARY

16.1 Strategy of the Adaptive Immune Response (Figure 16.1)

Overview of Humoral Immunity

Humoral immunity is mediated by **B cells;** in response to extracellular antigens, these proliferate and then differentiate into **plasma cells** that function as antibody-producing factories. **Memory B cells** are also formed.

Overview of Cellular Immunity

Cellular immunity is mediated by **T cells;** in response to intracellular antigens, **cytotoxic T cells** proliferate and then differentiate into **T_C cells** that induce apoptosis in "self" cells harboring the intruder. **Memory cytotoxic T cells** are also formed.

Helper T cells proliferate and then differentiate to form **T_H cells** that help orchestrate the various responses of humoral and cellular immunity. **Memory helper T cells** are also formed.

16.2 Anatomy of the Lymphoid System (Figure 16.2)

Lymphatic Vessels

Lymph, which may contain antigens that have entered tissues, flows in the lymphatic vessels to the lymph nodes.

Secondary Lymphoid Organs

Secondary lymphoid organs are the sites at which lymphocytes gather to contact antigens.

Primary Lymphoid Organs

Primary lymphoid organs are the sites where B cells and T cells mature.

16.3 The Nature of Antigens

Antigens are molecules that react specifically with an antibody or lymphocyte; **immunogen** refers specifically to an antigen that elicits an immune response.

The immune response is directed to **antigenic determinants,** or **epitopes,** on the antigen. (Figure 16.3)

16.4 The Nature of Antibodies

Structure and Properties of Antibodies (Figure 16.4)

Antibody monomers have a Y shape with an antigen-binding site at the end of each arm. The tail of the Y is the **Fc region.**

The antibody monomer is composed of two identical **heavy chains** and two identical **light chains.** The **variable region** contains the antigen-binding site; the **constant region** encompasses the entire Fc region as well as part of the Fab regions.

Protective Outcomes of Antibody-Antigen Binding (Figure 16.5)

Antibody-antigen binding results in **neutralization, immobilization** and **prevention of adherence, agglutination** and **precipitation, opsonization, complement activation,** and **antibody-dependent cytotoxicity.**

Immunoglobulin Classes (Table 16.1)

There are five major antibody classes, **IgM, IgG, IgA, IgD,** and **IgE,** and each has distinct functions.

16.5 Clonal Selection and Expansion of Lymphocytes (Figure 16.7)

When antigen enters a secondary lymphoid organ, only the lymphocytes that specifically recognize the antigen will respond; the antigen receptor they carry on their surface governs this recognition.

Lymphocytes may be **immature, naive, activated, effector,** or **memory cells.**

16.6 B Lymphocytes and the Antibody Response

B Cell Activation

B cells present antigen to T_H cells for inspection. If a T_H cell recognizes the antigen, it will deliver cytokines to the B cell, initiating the process of clonal expansion, which ultimately gives rise to plasma cells that produce antibody. (Figure 16.8)

Characteristics of the Primary Response

Under the direction of T_H cells, the expanding B-cell population will undergo affinity maturation and class switching, and form memory cells. (Figures 16.11, 16.12)

Characteristics of the Secondary Response

Memory cells are responsible for the swift and effective **secondary response,** eliminating invaders before they cause noticeable harm. (Figure 16.9)

The Response to T-Independent Antigens

T-independent antigens include polysaccharides that have multiple identical evenly spaced epitopes, and LPS. (Figure 16.13)

16.7 T Lymphocytes: Antigen Recognition and Response

General Characteristics of T Cells (Table 16.2, Figure 16.16)

Cytotoxic T cells (CD8) recognize antigen presented by **major histocompatibility complex (MHC) class I molecules.**

Helper T cells (CD4) recognize antigen presented by **major histocompatibility complex (MHC) class II molecules.**

Activation of T Cells (Figure 16.17)

Dendritic cells sample material in tissues and then travel to secondary lymphoid organs to present antigens to naive T cells. The dendritic cells that detect molecules associated with danger produce **co-stimulatory molecules** and are able to activate both subsets of T cells.

Functions of T_C (CD8) Cells

T_C cells induce apoptosis in cells that present peptides they recognize in MHC class I; they also produce cytokines that allow neighboring cells to become more vigilant against intracellular invaders. (Figure 16.18)

All nucleated cells present peptides from endogenous proteins in the groove of MHC class I molecules.

Functions of T_H (CD4) Cells (Figures 16.8, 16.19)

T_H cells activate cells that present peptides they recognize in MHC class II; various cytokines are released, depending on subset of the responding T_H cell.

Macrophages and B cells present peptides from exogenous proteins in the groove of MHC class II molecules.

Subsets of Dendritic Cells and T cells

DC1 cells drive naive helper T cells to become T_H1 cells, which direct a cellular response.

DC2 cells drive naive helper T cells to become T_H2 cells, which direct a humoral response.

16.8 Natural Killer (NK) Cells

NK cells mediate **antibody-dependent cellular cytotoxicity (ADCC).**

NK cells induce apoptosis in host cells that are not bearing MHC class I molecules on their surface.

16.9 Lymphocyte Development

Generation of Diversity

Mechanisms used to generate the diversity of antigen specificity in lymphocytes include rearrangement of gene segments, imprecise joining of those segments, and combinatorial associations of heavy and light chains. (Figure 16.21)

Negative Selection of Self-Reactive B Cells

Negative selection occurs as B cells develop in the bone marrow; cells to which material binds to their B-cell receptor are induced to undergo apoptosis.

Positive and Negative Selection of Self-Reactive T Cells

Positive selection permits only those T cells that show moderate recognition of the MHC molecules to develop further. Negative selection also occurs.

REVIEW QUESTIONS

Short Answer

1. Which antibody classes can activate complement?
2. Why is IgE so scarce in circulation?
3. Diagram an IgG molecule and label (a) the Fc area and (b) the areas that combine with antigen.
4. How do natural killer cells differ from cytotoxic T cells?
5. How do T-independent antigens differ from T-dependent antigens?
6. How do the roles of T_H1 cells and T_H2 cells differ?
7. Describe clonal selection and expansion in the immune response.
8. Describe the role of dendritic cells in T-cell activation.
9. How does the antigen receptor on T cells differ from the antigen receptor on B cells?
10. What are antigen-presenting cells (APCs)?

Multiple Choice

1. The variable regions of antibodies are located in the
   1. Fc region. 2. Fab region. 3. light chain.
   4. heavy chain. 5. light chain *and* heavy chain.
   a) 1, 3 b) 1, 5 c) 2, 3 d) 2, 4 e) 2, 5
2. Which of the following statements about antibodies is *false?*
   a) If you removed the Fc portion, antibodies would no longer be capable of opsonization.
   b) If you removed the Fc portion, antibodies would no longer be capable of activating the complement system.
   c) If you removed the Fab portion, an antibody would no longer be capable of agglutination.
   d) If IgG were a pentamer, it would be more effective at agglutinating antigens.
   e) If IgE had longer half-life, it would protect newborn infants.
3. Which class of antibody can cross the placenta?
   a) IgA b) IgD c) IgE d) IgG e) IgM
4. A person who has been vaccinated against a disease should have primarily which of these types of antibodies 2 years later?
   a) IgA b) IgD c) IgE d) IgG e) IgM
5. Which of the following statements about B cells/antibody production is *false?*
   a) B cells of a given specificity initially have the potential to make more than one class of antibody.
   b) In response to antigen, all B cells located close to the antigen begin dividing.
   c) Each B cell is programmed to make a single specificity of antibody.
   d) The B-cell receptor enables B cells to "sense" that antigen is present.
   e) The cell type that makes and secretes antibody is called a plasma cell.
6. Which term describes the loss of specific heavy chain genes?
   a) Affinity maturation
   b) Apoptosis
   c) Clonal selection
   d) Class switching
7. Which of the following cell types cannot *replicate* in response to a specific antigen?
   a) B cells b) Cytotoxic T cells c) Helper T cells
   d) Plasma cells
8. Which markers are found on all nucleated cells?
   a) MHC class I molecules
   b) MHC class II molecules
   c) CD4
   d) CD8
9. Which of the following are examples of an antigen-presenting cell (APC)?
   1. Macrophage 2. Neutrophil 3. B cell
   4. T cell 5. Plasma cell
   a) 1, 2 b) 1, 3 c) 2, 4 d) 3, 5 e) 1, 2, 3
10. What is the appropriate response when antigen is presented by MHC class II molecules?
    a) An effector CD8 cell should kill the presenting cell.
    b) An effector CD4 cell should kill the presenting cell.
    c) An effector CD8 cell should activate the presenting cell.
    d) An effector CD4 cell should activate the presenting cell.

Applications

1. Currently there is debate about keeping smallpox virus stored, since the disease has been eradicated. What would be an argument for keeping the virus? What should be done to protect against use of the virus in biological warfare?
2. What kinds of diseases would be expected to occur as a result of lack of T or B lymphocytes?

Critical Thinking

1. The development of primary and secondary immune responses to an antigen differ significantly. The primary response may take a week or more to develop fully and establish memory. The secondary response is rapid and relies on the activation of clones of memory cells. Wouldn't it be better if clones of reactive cells were maintained regardless of prior exposure? In this way, the body could always respond rapidly to *any* antigen exposure. Would there be any disadvantages to this approach? Why?
2. Early investigators proposed two hypotheses to explain the specificity of antibodies. The clonal selection hypothesis states that each lymphocyte can produce only one specificity of antibody. When an antigen appears that binds to that antibody, the lymphocyte is selected to give rise to a clone of plasma cells producing the antibody. The template hypothesis states that any antigen can interact with any lymphocyte and act as a template, causing newly forming antibody to be specific for that antigen. In one experiment to test these hypotheses, an animal was immunized with two different antigens. After several days, lymphocytes were removed from the animal and individual cells placed in separate small containers. Then, the original two antigens were placed in the containers with each cell. What result would support the clonal selection hypothesis? The template hypothesis?

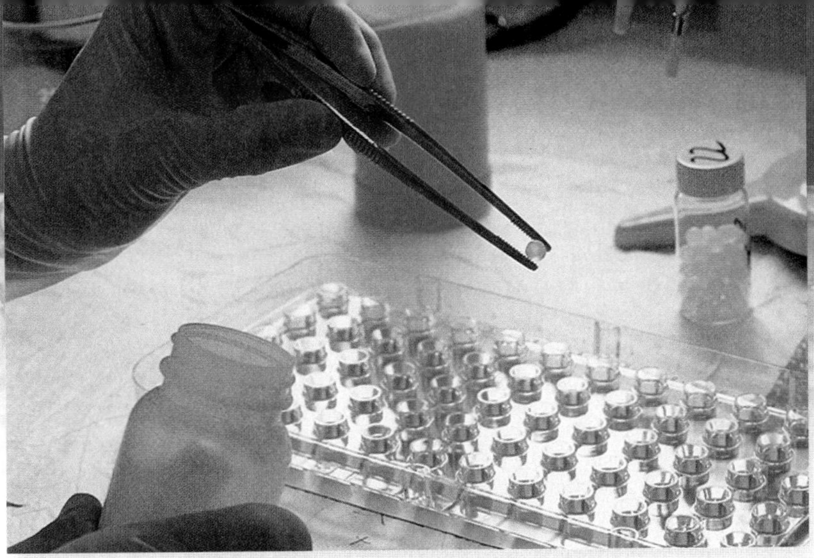

An immunoassay

CHAPTER SEVENTEEN

Applications of Immune Responses

A Glimpse of History

Even before people knew that microorganisms caused disease, it was recognized that individuals who recovered from a disease such as smallpox rarely contracted it a second time. Old Chinese writings dating from the Sung dynasty (A.D. 960–1280) describe a procedure known as variolation, in which small amounts of the powdered crusts of smallpox pustules were inhaled or placed into a scratch made in the skin. Usually the resulting disease was mild, and a permanent immunity to smallpox resulted. Occasionally, however, severe disease developed, often resulting in death.

Although variolation was practiced in China and the Mideast a thousand years ago, it was not widely used in Europe until after 1719. At that time, Lady Mary Wortley Montagu, wife of the British ambassador to Turkey, had their children immunized against smallpox in this way. Variolation subsequently became popular in Europe. Although a person exposed to smallpox through variolation would usually completely recover, he or she would become contagious. Because of the danger of contagion and because the procedure was reasonably expensive, large segments of the population in Europe remained unprotected.

As an apprentice physician, Edward Jenner noted that milkmaids who had suffered cowpox infections rarely got smallpox. Cowpox was a disease of cows that caused few or no symptoms in humans. In 1796 long before bacteria and viruses had been discovered, Jenner conducted a classic experiment in which he deliberately transferred material from a cowpox lesion on the hand of a milkmaid, Sarah Nelmes, to a scratch on the arm of a young boy named James Phipps. Six weeks later, when exposed to pus from a smallpox victim, Phipps did not develop the disease. The boy had been made immune to smallpox when he was inoculated with pus from the cowpox lesion. Using the less dangerous cowpox material in place of the pustules from smallpox cases Jenner and others worked to spread the practice of variolation. Later, Pasteur used the word vaccination (from the Latin vacca for "cow") to describe any type of protective inoculation. By the twentieth century, most of the industrialized world was generally free of smallpox as the result of routine vaccination of large populations.

In 1967, the World Health Organization (WHO) initiated a program of intensive smallpox vaccination. Since there were no animal hosts and no non-immune humans to whom it could be spread, the disease died out. The last case of naturally contracted smallpox occurred in Somalia, Africa, in 1977. Two years later in a ceremony in Nairobi, Kenya, WHO declared the world free of smallpox. Nevertheless, a few laboratories around the world still have the virus. In this age of bioterrorism concerns, some see smallpox as a major threat should the deadly virus ever be released into the largely unprotected populations of the world. Because of this, vaccine stores in the US are being increased.

In chapters 15 and 16, we discussed both innate and adaptive defense systems, becoming acquainted with antibodies and lymphocytes. This chapter will consider how **immunization,** the process of inducing immunity, can be used to protect against disease and how immunization techniques have advanced remarkably in recent years to become safer and more effective. In fact, immunization has probably had the greatest impact on human health of any medical procedure, and even better means of immunization are likely in the near future. We will also explore some useful applications of immunological reactions in diagnostic tests.

KEY TERMS

Active immunity Immunity that results from an immune response in an individual upon exposure to an antigen.

Adjuvant Substance that increases the immune response to antigens.

Agglutination reaction Technique that relies on the clumping observed when antibody molecules bind to and cross-link insoluble antigen molecules as a means to detect antibodies or antigens.

Antiserum A preparation of serum that contains protective antibodies.

Attenuated vaccine Vaccine composed of a weakened form of the pathogen that is generally unable to cause disease.

Enzyme-linked immunosorbent assay (ELISA) Technique that uses enzyme-labeled antibodies to detect antigens or antibodies.

Fluorescent antibody (FA) test Technique that uses fluorescence-labeled antibodies to detect specific antigens in cells affixed to a microscope slide.

Inactivated vaccine Vaccine composed of killed bacteria, inactivated virus, or fractions of the pathogen.

Passive immunity Immunity that results when antibodies are transferred to an individual.

Precipitation reaction Technique that relies on the visible insoluble complexes that form when antibody molecules bind to and cross-link soluble antigens as a means to detect specific antibodies or antigens.

Serology Use of antibodies to detect antigens, or conversely, the use of antigens to detect antibodies.

Western blotting (immunoblotting) Procedure that uses labeled antibodies to detect specific antigens in a mixture of proteins separated according to their molecular weight.

IMMUNIZATION

17.1 Principles of Immunization

Focus Point

- Give examples of naturally acquired active immunity, artificially acquired active immunity, naturally acquired passive immunity, and artificially acquired passive immunity.

Naturally acquired immunity is the acquisition of adaptive immunity through normal events, such as exposure to an infectious agent. Immunization mimics those same events, protecting against disease by inducing what is termed **artificially acquired immunity (figure 17.1).** The protection provided by immunization can be either active or passive.

Active Immunity

Active immunity is the result of an immune response in an individual upon exposure to antigen. Specific B and T cells are activated and then proliferate, providing the individual with the lasting protection associated with immunological memory. Active immunity can develop either naturally from an actual infection or artificially from administration of a vaccine. ■ memory, p. 399

Passive Immunity

Passive immunity occurs naturally during pregnancy; the mother's IgG antibodies cross the placenta and protect the fetus. These antibodies remain active in the newborn infant during the first few months of life, when the neonate's own immune responses are still developing. Consequently, a number of infectious diseases normally do not occur until a baby is three to six months of age, when the maternal antibodies have been degraded. Passive immunity also occurs as a result of breast feeding; the IgA in breast milk protects the digestive tract of the child. Note that passive immunity provides no memory; once the transferred antibodies are degraded, the protection is lost.

Artificially acquired passive immunity involves transferring antibodies produced by other people or animals. This type of immunity can be used to prevent disease before or after likely exposure to an infectious agent, to limit the duration of certain diseases, and to block the action of microbial toxins. A preparation of serum (the fluid portion of blood that remains after blood clots) containing the protective antibodies is referred to as **antiserum.** One that protects against a given toxin is called an **antitoxin.** Passive immunization preparations include **immune globulin,** or gamma globulin, which is the immunoglobulin G (IgG) fraction of pooled blood plasma from many donors. This contains a variety of antibodies that the various donors have made because of infections and vaccination. Immune serum globulin may be given to travelers who visit areas where sanitation is substandard to offer some protection against hepatitis A and other common diseases associated with poor hygiene. It is also useful for immunosuppressed people who have insufficient levels of antibodies. **Hyperimmune globulin,** prepared from the sera of donors with high amounts of antibodies to certain disease agents, is used to prevent or treat specific diseases. Examples include human tetanus immune globulin, rabies immune globulin, and hepatitis B immune globulin. These preparations, given during the incubation period—after exposure, but before disease develops—can often prevent severe diseases from developing.

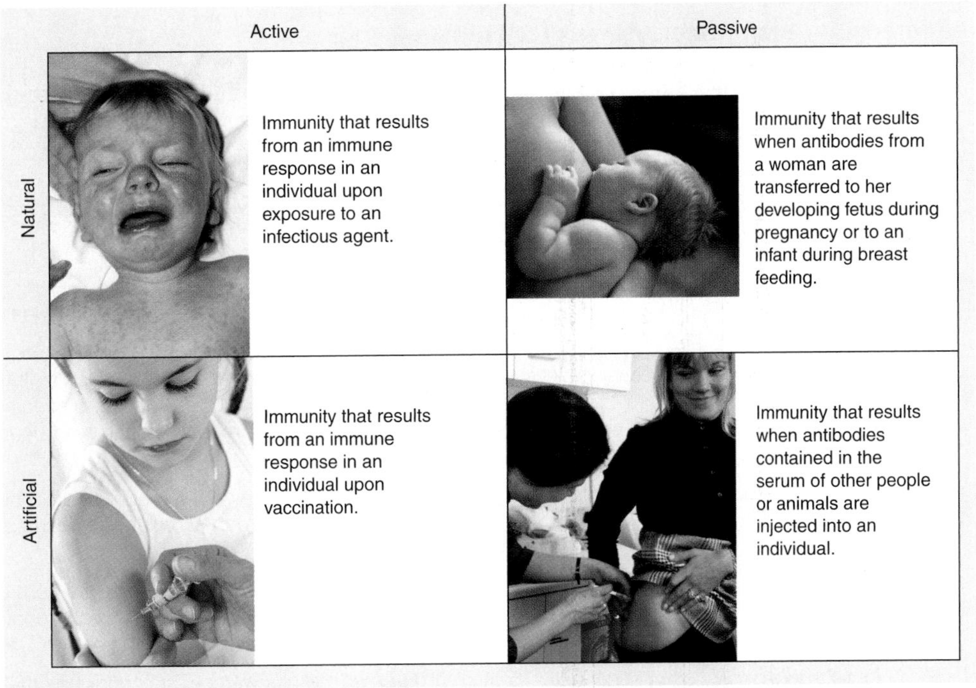

FIGURE 17.1 Acquired Immunity Acquired immunity can be natural or artificial, active or passive.

MICROCHECK 17.1

Immunity is natural or artificial, active or passive. Active immunity occurs naturally in response to infections or other natural exposure to antigens, and artificially in response to vaccine administration. Passive immunity occurs naturally during pregnancy and breast feeding, and artificially through administration of immune serum globulin or hyperimmune globulin.

- ✓ What is an antitoxin?
- ✓ What would be a primary advantage of passive immunity with diseases such as tetanus?

17.2

Vaccines and Immunization Procedures

Focus Points

- Compare and contrast the attributes and risks of attenuated vaccines and inactivated vaccines.
- List six diseases that routine childhood immunizations have reduced in occurrence by at least 95%.

A **vaccine** is a preparation of a pathogen or its products used to induce active immunity. Vaccines not only protect an individual against disease, they can also prevent diseases from spreading in a population. When a critical portion of a population is immune to a disease, either through natural immunity or vaccination, a phenomenon called **herd immunity** develops. This is the inability of an infectious disease to spread because of the lack of a critical concentration of susceptible hosts. Herd immunity is responsible for dramatic declines in childhood diseases, both in the United States and in developing countries. Unfortunately, we periodically see some of these diseases reappear and spread as a direct consequence of parents failing to have their children vaccinated. **Table 17.1** lists a number of human diseases for which vaccines are available. As the table indicates, some are routinely used, whereas others are employed only in special circumstances.

Effective vaccines should be safe, with few side effects, while giving lasting protection against the specific illness. They should induce protective antibodies or immune cells, or both, as appropriate. For example, polio vaccine should induce antibodies that neutralize the virus, thus preventing it from reaching and attaching to nerve cells to cause the paralysis of severe poliomyelitis. On the other hand, an effective vaccine against tuberculosis would induce cellular immunity that can limit growth of the intracellular bacteria. Of course, vaccines ideally should be low in cost, stable with a long shelf life, and easy to administer.

Vaccines fall into two general categories, attenuated and inactivated, based on whether or not the immunizing agent can replicate. Each type has characteristic advantages and disadvantages **(table 17.2).**

Attenuated Vaccines

An **attenuated vaccine** is a weakened form of the pathogen that is generally unable to cause disease. The attenuated strain replicates in the vaccine recipient, causing an infection with undetectable or mild disease that typically results in long-lasting immunity. Because infection with the attenuated strain mimics that of the wild-type strain, the type of immunity it evokes is generally appropriate for

TABLE 17.1 Some Important Immunizing Agents for Humans

Disease	Type of Vaccine	Persons Who Should Receive the Vaccine
Anthrax	Acellular	People in occupations that put them at risk of exposure, such as military personnel
Diphtheria	Toxoid	Children; adults receive a booster every 10 years
Haemophilus influenzae type b infections	Polysaccharide-protein conjugate	Children
Hepatitis A	Inactivated virus	Children who live in selected regions, people traveling to certain parts of the world
Hepatitis B	Protein subunit is produced by genetically engineered *Saccharomyces cereviseae* and purified	Children, adults in high-risk groups such as IV drug abusers, health care workers who might be exposed to infected blood, and contacts of infected people, homosexual men, and people who have multiple sexual partners
Influenza	Two types—inactivated virus, given by injection, and attenuated virus, given as a nasal mist	Children, adults over age 50, medical personnel, and people at increased risk for complications; given yearly, as the antigens of the virus change frequently
Measles	Attenuated virus	Children, people entering college, adults born after 1956 who have not been immunized, travelers to foreign countries, and HIV-infected people without severe immunosuppression
Meningococcal disease	Purified polysaccharide (4 serotypes)	Children and adults with certain conditions that put them at greater risk (for example, those without a spleen or who have certain complement system defects); people traveling to sub-Saharan Africa
Mumps	Attenuated virus	Same as measles
Pertussis (whooping cough)	Acellular vaccine given together with diphtheria and tetanus toxoids (DTaP)	Children
Pneumococcal infection	Two forms—purified polysaccharide (PPV) and polysaccharide protein conjugate (PCV)	Children should receive PCV; adults over 65, people with certain chronic infections, and others in high-risk groups should receive PPV
Rabies	Inactivated virus	People exposed to the virus, people at high risk for exposure, such as veterinarians and other animal handlers
Rubella (German measles)	Attenuated virus	Children, adults (particularly women) who are susceptible, health care workers who are at high risk of exposure
Tetanus	Toxoid	Children; adults receive a booster every 10 years
Tuberculosis	Attenuated BCG strain of tuberculosis bacteria	Used only in special circumstances in the United States; widely used in other countries
Typhoid fever	Two forms—attenuated bacteria (taken orally) and purified polysaccharide	People traveling to certain parts of the world
Varicella-zoster (chickenpox)	Attenuated virus	Children; may also be given to susceptible adults
Yellow fever	Attenuated virus	Travelers to affected areas

controlling the infection. For example, attenuated vaccines given orally induce mucosal immunity (an IgA response), protecting against disease-causing agents that infect via the gastrointestinal tract. Some attenuated vaccines are able to stimulate cytotoxic T cells, inducing cellular immunity.

Production of an attenuated strain often involves successively culturing the microbe under a given set of conditions, resulting in a gradual accumulation of mutations that make it less able to cause disease. Pasteur first produced successful vaccines of attenuated anthrax and chicken cholera by growing the organisms at higher than normal temperatures and in other unusual conditions. Viruses of humans can be attenuated by growing them in cells of a different animal species; mutations occur so that the virus then grows poorly in human cells. Genetic manipulation is now being used to produce strains of pathogens with low virulence. Specific genes are mutated and used to replace wild-type genes. The inserted mutant genes are engineered so they cannot revert to the wild type.

Attenuated vaccines have several advantages compared to their inactivated counterparts. For example, a single dose of an attenuated agent can be sufficient to induce long-lasting immunity. This is because the microbe multiplies in the body, causing the immune system to be exposed to the antigen for a longer period and in greater amounts than with inactivated agents. In addition, the vaccine strain has the added potential of being spread from an individual being immunized to other non-immune people, inadvertently immunizing the contacts of the vaccine recipient.

The disadvantage of attenuated agents is that they have the potential to cause disease in immunosuppressed people, and they can occasionally revert or mutate to become pathogenic again. Care must be taken to avoid giving attenuated vaccines to pregnant women, because some microbes can cross the placenta and damage the developing fetus. Another disadvantage of attenuated vaccines, especially in developing countries where they are desperately needed, is that they usually require refrigeration to keep them active. Attenuated vaccines currently in widespread use include those against measles, mumps, rubella, and yellow fever. The Sabin vaccine against polio is also an attenuated vaccine.

Inactivated Vaccines

An **inactivated vaccine** is unable to replicate, but retains the immunogenicity of the infectious agent or toxin. The advantage of inactivated vaccines is that they cannot cause infections or revert to pathogenic forms. Because they do not replicate, however, the magnitude of the immune response is limited because there is no amplification of the dose *in vivo*. To compensate for the relatively low effective dose, it is usually necessary to give several booster doses of the vaccine to induce protective immunity. Inactivated vaccines fall into two general categories—whole agents and fractions of the agent.

Inactivated whole agent vaccines contain killed microorganisms or inactivated viruses. The vaccines are made by treating the infectious agent with a chemical such as formalin, which does not significantly change the surface epitopes. Such treatments leave the agent immunogenic even though it cannot reproduce. Inactivated whole agent vaccines include those against cholera, influenza, rabies, and the Salk vaccine against polio. ■ formalin, p. 122

Toxoids are inactivated toxins used to protect against diseases due to toxins produced by the invading bacterium. They are prepared by treating the toxins to destroy the toxic part of the molecules while retaining the antigenic epitopes. Diphtheria and tetanus vaccines are toxoids.

Protein subunit vaccines are composed of key protein antigens or antigenic fragments of an infectious agent, rather than whole cells or viruses. Obviously, they can only be developed after research has revealed which of the components of the microbe are most important in eliciting a protective immune response. Their advantage is that parts of the microbe that sometimes cause undesirable side effects are not included. For example, the whooping cough (pertussis) killed vaccine that was previously used for immunizing babies and young children often caused reactions such as pain, tenderness at the site of the injection, fever, and occasionally, convulsions. A subunit vaccine, referred to as the acellular pertussis (aP) vaccine, does not cause these side effects and has now replaced the killed whole cell vaccine. A **recombinant vaccine** is a subunit vaccine produced by a genetically engineered microorganism. An example is the vaccine against the hepatitis B virus; it is produced by yeast cells that have been engineered to produce part of the viral protein coat.

Polysaccharide vaccines are composed of the polysaccharides that make up the capsule of certain organisms. Recall that polysaccharides are T-independent antigens; they generally elicit only an IgM response, provide no memory, and elicit a poor response in young children. **Conjugate vaccines** represent an improvement over purified polysaccharide vaccines because they are effective in young children. Scientists intentionally converted polysaccharides into T-dependent antigens by chemically linking the polysaccharides to proteins. The first conjugate vaccine developed was against *Haemophilus influenzae* type b; it has nearly eliminated meningitis caused by this organism in children. The conjugate vaccine recently developed against certain *Streptococcus pneumoniae* strains promises to do the same for a variety of infections caused by those strains. ■ *Haemophilus influenzae type b*, p. 684 ■ *Streptococcus pneumoniae*, p. 588

Many inactivated vaccines contain an **adjuvant,** a substance that enhances the immune response to antigens. These are necessary additives because purified antigens such as toxoids and subunit vaccines are often poorly immunogenic by themselves because they lack the "danger" signals, the patterns associated with tissue

TABLE 17.2 A Comparison of Characteristics of Attenuated and Inactivated Vaccines

Characteristic	Attenuated Vaccine	Inactivated Vaccine
Antibody response	IgG; IgA if administered orally or nasally	IgG
Cellular immune response	Good	Poor
Duration of protection	Long-term	Short-term
Need for adjuvant	No	Yes
Number of doses	Usually single	Multiple
Risk of mutation to virulence	Very low	Absent
Risk to immunocompromised recipient	Can be significant	Absent
Route of administration	Injection, oral, or nasal	Injection
Stability in warm temperatures	Poor	Good
Types	Attenuated viruses, attenuated bacteria	Inactivated whole agents, toxoids, subunit vaccines, polysaccharide vaccines

damage or invading microbes. These patterns trigger dendritic cells to produce co-stimulatory molecules, allowing them to activate helper T cells, which, in turn, activate B cells. Adjuvants are thought to function by providing the "danger" signals to dendritic cells. Some adjuvants appear to adsorb the antigen, releasing it at a slow but constant rate to the tissues and surrounding blood vessels. Unfortunately, many effective adjuvants evoke an intense inflammatory response, making them unsuitable for use in vaccines for humans. Currently, the only adjuvant approved in the United States for use in vaccines for humans is alum (aluminum hydroxide and aluminum phosphate), although several others are being tested in clinical trials. ■ pattern recognition, p. 365 ■ dendritic cells, pp. 374, 403

An Example of Vaccination Strategy—The Campaign to Eliminate Poliomyelitis

Vaccines against poliomyelitis provide an excellent illustration of the complexity of vaccination strategies. The virus that causes this disease enters the body orally, infects the throat and intestinal tract, and then invades the bloodstream. From there, it may invade nerve cells and cause the disease poliomyelitis (see figure 27.16). There are three types of poliovirus, any of which can cause poliomyelitis. The Salk vaccine, developed in the mid-1950s, consists of inactivated viruses of all three types. It was a huge success in lowering the rate of the disease, but it had the disadvantage of requiring a series of injections over a period of time for maximum protection. In 1961, the Sabin vaccine became available, with the advantage of cheaper oral administration. Even though this attenuated poliovirus vaccine replicates in the intestine, however, it still has to be given in a series of three doses rather than one because of interactions among the three types of virus included in the vaccine. Both attenuated and inactivated polio vaccines induce circulating antibodies and protect against viral invasion of the central nervous system and consequent paralytic poliomyelitis. The Sabin vaccine has a distinct advantage over the Salk vaccine in that it induces mucosal immunity, and thus potentially provides herd immunity. ■ poliomyelitis, p. 695

Polio vaccination was so successful that by 1980 the United States was free of wild-type poliovirus (see figure 27.17). Ironically, poliomyelitis still occurred occasionally, caused by the vaccine strain; approximately one case of poliomyelitis arises for every 2.4 million doses of Sabin vaccine administered. An obvious way to avoid these vaccine-related illnesses is to abandon the Sabin vaccine in favor of the Salk vaccine. As usual, however, the situation is not as simple as it might seem. The Sabin vaccine, unlike the Salk vaccine, prevents transmission of the wild-type virus should it ever be reintroduced to the population. If only the inactivated vaccine is given, the virus can still replicate in the gastrointestinal tract and be transmitted to others, rapidly spreading in a population. Eventually the virus may infect individuals who are susceptible, potentially causing an outbreak of poliomyelitis.

A campaign to eliminate polio worldwide was so successful that by 1991, wild poliovirus had been eliminated from the western hemisphere. By 1997, the worldwide incidence of polio had decreased substantially, minimizing the risk that wild-type polio would be reintroduced into the United States. Because of the continued risk of vaccine-associated paralytic polio, a vaccine strategy that attempted to capture the best of both vaccines was adopted. Children first received doses of the Salk vaccine, protecting them from poliomyelitis. Following these doses the Sabin vaccine was given, providing mucosal protection while also boosting immunity. In mid-1999 the routine use of the Sabin vaccine was discontinued altogether. Although the original goal of global eradication of polio by 2000 was not achieved as was hoped, efforts are currently under way to eliminate it soon. This effort has been interrupted by war in some countries, but it has been possible at times to arrange a cease-fire for National Immunization Days, to permit this vital public health program to continue.

The Importance of Routine Immunizations for Children

Before vaccination was available for common childhood diseases, thousands of children died or were left with permanent disability from these diseases. **Table 17.3** illustrates how dramatically vaccination has decreased the occurrence of certain infectious diseases. Unfortunately, even now, many people become ill or even die every year from diseases that are readily prevented by vaccines.

TABLE 17.3 The Effectiveness of Universal Immunization in the United States

Disease	Cases per Year Before Immunization	Decrease After Immunization
Smallpox	48,164 (1900–1904)	100%
Diphtheria	175,885 (1920–1922)	Nearly 100%
Pertussis (whooping cough)	147,271 (1922–1925)	93.4%
Tetanus	1,314 (1922–1926)	98.1%
Paralytic poliomyelitis	16,316 (1951–1954)	100%
Measles	503,282 (1958–1962)	Nearly 100%
Mumps	152,209 (1968)	99.8%
Rubella (congenital syndrome)	823 (estimated)	99.9%
Haemophilus influenzae type b invasive disease in children	20,000 (estimated)	99.8%

TABLE 17.4 Recommended Childhood and Adolescent Immunization Schedule in the United States (2005)

Vaccine	Birth	1 mo	2 mo	4 mo	6 mo	12 mo	15 mo	18 mo	24 mo	4–6 yrs	11–12 yrs	13–18 yrs
Hepatitis B												
Diphtheria, tetanus (Td), acellular pertussis (DTaP)			DTap	DTap	DTap		DTap			DTap	Td	
Haemophilus Influenzae type b (Hib)												
Poliovirus (IPV—Inactivated polio vaccine)												
Measles-mumps-rubella (MMR)												
Varicella (chickenpox-Var)												
Pneumococcal conjugate												
Influenza							Yearly					

Range of acceptable ages for vaccination indicated by colors:

First dose Second dose Third dose Fourth dose Subsequent doses Catch-up vaccinations

One reason some children are not protected is that parents have refused to have their children vaccinated, fearing the rare chance that immunization procedures might be harmful. Vaccines have, in these cases, become victims of their own success. They have been so effective at preventing diseases that people have been lulled into a false sense of security. Reports of adverse effects of vaccination have led some people to falsely believe that the risk of vaccination is greater than the risk of diseases. Although there is some risk associated with almost any medical procedure, there is no question that the benefits of routine immunizations greatly outweigh the very slight risks. Data show that a child with measles has a 1:2,000 chance of developing serious encephalitic involvement of the nervous system, compared with a 1:1,000,000 chance from measles vaccine. Between 1989 and 1991 measles immunization rates dropped 10% and an outbreak of 55,000 cases occurred, with 120 deaths. Now that immunization rates have increased again, measles outbreaks are rarely seen. The suggestion that the measles, mumps, and rubella (MMR) vaccine is associated with autism in young children, however, is again threatening the acceptance of immunization. Studies so far have not shown evidence of this association, but more work is under way to be sure. Routine immunization against pertussis (whooping cough) caused a marked decrease in its incidence in the United States and saved many lives. Because of some adverse reactions to the killed whole cell vaccine being used at the time, however, many parents refused to allow their babies to get the vaccine. By 1990, this refusal of vaccination resulted in the highest incidence of pertussis cases in 20 years and the deaths of some children, mostly those under one year of age. Currently an acellular subunit pertussis vaccine is used, usually in combination with diphtheria and tetanus toxoids (DTaP). Several large-scale studies have shown the acellular pertussis vaccine to be more effective and have fewer side effects than the whole cell vaccine.

The recommendations of the U.S. Centers for Disease Prevention and Control for childhood and adolescent immunizations are shown in **table 17.4.** Since children need a minimum of 15 separate injections to complete the 2005 recommended childhood immunization schedule from birth to six years, it is desirable that several vaccines be combined into a single preparation. More of these combination vaccines are being licensed for use in the United States each year.

Current Progress in Immunization

Recent advances in understanding the immune system are enabling researchers to make safer and more effective vaccines. Progress is occurring in several fronts—enhancement of the immune response to vaccines, development of new or improved vaccines against certain diseases, and development of new types of vaccines.

An excellent example of how a better understanding of the immune response can lead to the development of more effective vaccines is the introduction of conjugate vaccines, which enlist T-cell help. Another way in which the immune response can be bolstered is to administer certain cytokines along with vaccines, guiding the immune response. The discovery and characterization of toll-like receptors is giving insights into adjuvants that might be incorporated into vaccines to enhance their effectiveness. Discoveries that lead to enhanced immune responses could

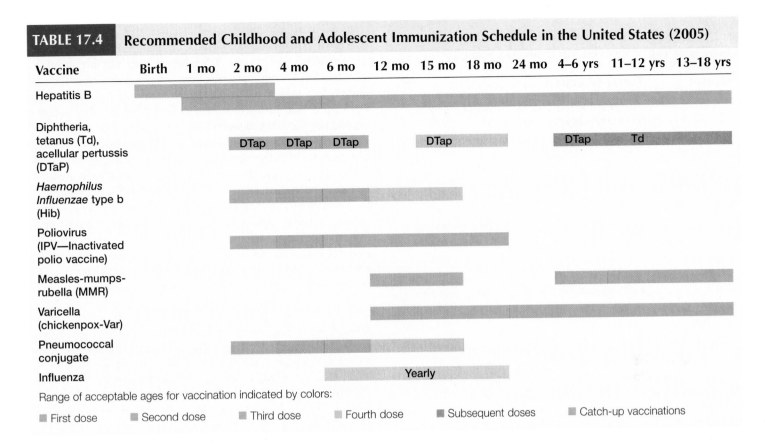

TABLE 17.5 Some Diseases for Which New or Improved Vaccines Are Sought

Disease	Estimated Impact
HIV/AIDS	40 million infected worldwide, with approximately 14,000 new infections daily
Malaria	300–500 million cases/yr and up to 3 million deaths/yr worldwide
Influenza	30–50 million cases/yr worldwide; 10,000–40,000 deaths/yr in the United States
Strep throat	20 million cases/yr in the United States
Genital herpes	45 million infected and 500,000 new infections/yr in the United States
Hepatitis C	170 million infected worldwide
Cancer	1 in 3 in the United States may get cancer, resulting in 560,000 deaths/yr

facilitate the use of some of the new vaccines currently being investigated. ■ toll-like receptors, p. 374

Novel types of vaccines being actively studied include peptide vaccines, edible vaccines, and DNA-based vaccines. Because none of these relies on whole cells, the procedures eliminate the possibility of infection with the immunizing agent; however, some of these vaccines are weakly immunogenic. **Peptide vaccines** are composed of key antigenic peptides from disease-causing organisms. They are stable to heat and do not contain extraneous materials to cause unwanted reactions or side effects. **Edible vaccines** are created by transferring genes encoding key antigens from infectious agents into plants. If appropriate plants can be genetically engineered to function as vaccines, they could potentially be grown throughout the world, eliminating difficulties involving transport and storage. **DNA-based vaccines** are segments of naked DNA from infectious organisms that can be introduced directly into muscle tissue. The host tissue actually expresses the DNA for a short period of time, producing the microbial antigens encoded by the DNA, which induces an immune response.

There are several serious and widespread diseases for which new or more effective vaccines are currently being sought **(table 17.5).** Many of these disease-causing agents have been shown to be particularly adept at avoiding the host defenses, complicating the development of long-lasting effective vaccines. In addition to seeking vaccines that protect against infectious diseases, other uses of vaccines are also being studied. Attempts are being made to develop vaccines to control fertility and hormone activity, and to prevent diabetes and cancer, among other conditions. Vaccines are also being used experimentally in the treatment of cancer.

MICROCHECK 17.2

Attenuated vaccines are weakened forms of the disease-causing agent. Inactivated vaccines are unable to replicate, but they retain the immunogenicity of the infectious agent; they include killed microorganisms, inactivated viruses, and fractions of the agent, including toxoids. Routine childhood immunizations have prevented millions of cases of disease and many deaths during the past decades. Many experimental vaccines are under study or in clinical trials.

- ✓ Compare and contrast attenuated and inactivated vaccines.
- ✓ Since many childhood diseases such as measles and mumps are rare now, why is it important for children to be immunized against them?
- ✓ What would be a primary advantage of using an attenuated agent rather than just an antigen from that agent?

IMMUNOLOGICAL TESTING

The specificity of immunological reactions described in chapter 16 is exploited in **immunoassays,** which are frequently used for diagnosis. For example, antibodies that bind specifically to *Treponema pallidum,* the bacterium that causes syphilis, can be added to a suspension of an unknown bacterium isolated from a patient suspected of having the disease **(figure 17.2).** Binding of the antibodies to the bacterium identifies it as *T. pallidum,* indicating that the patient does indeed have syphilis. Likewise, specific antibodies in a patient's body fluids or tissues can be detected using a known antigen. For instance, if a specimen from a patient suspected of having syphilis is added to proteins specific for *T. pallidum,* and antibodies in that specimen bind to those proteins, then the patient's immune system must have responded to the bacterium at some point, suggesting either previous or current infection.

One of the earliest examples of immunological testing is the PPD skin test (also called the Mantoux test), which is still used for diagnosing tuberculosis. People who have been infected with *Mycobacterium tuberculosis* develop a strong cellular response to the bacterium and its products, which is the basis of the test. If a very small amount of purified protein derivative (PPD) from cultures of *M. tuberculosis* is injected into the skin of someone who has been infected with the organism, redness and a firm swelling usually develop at the site (see figure 24.19). In contrast, people who have not been infected show little, if any, response.

Just as the field of immunology has advanced markedly in the last few decades, so has the technology of immunological testing. New tests are continually being developed, augmenting or gradually replacing many of the older methods. This section will focus primarily on tests commonly used today; information about other

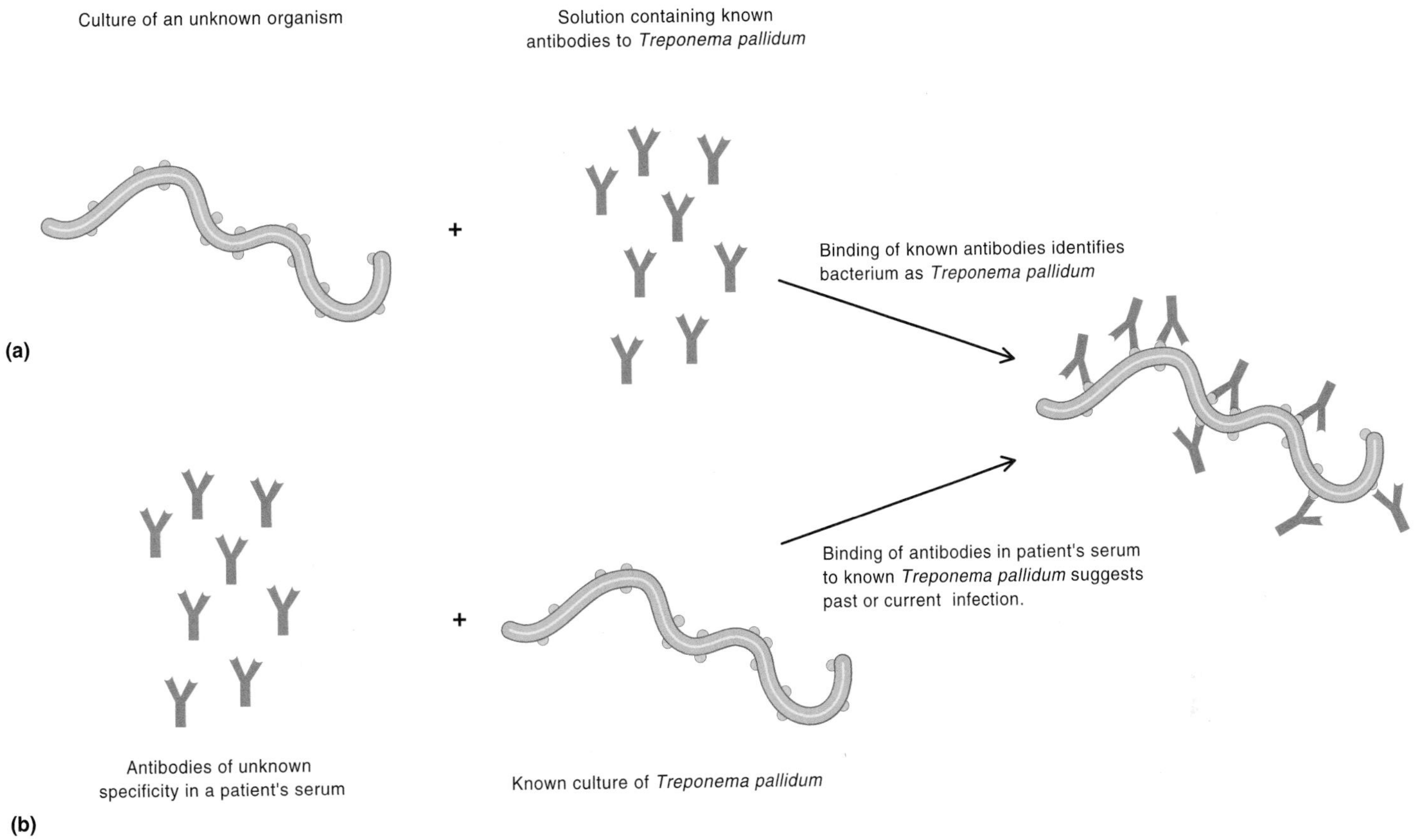

FIGURE 17.2 Principles of Immunoassays These assays can be used to **(a)** identify unknown bacteria (or other antigens); **(b)** detect specific antibodies.

tests such as complement fixation, radioimmunoassay and hemagglutination inhibition—which are declining in use but are historically important and illustrate key immunological principles—can be found in the chapter 17 readings at the Online Learning Center (www.mhhe.com/nester5).

17.3

Principles of Immunological Testing

Focus Points

- Describe the difference between polyclonal and monoclonal antibodies.
- Describe how the antibody titer is determined.

A person who has not been exposed to a given pathogen has no specific antibodies against the agent in their serum, and is referred to as **seronegative.** Once infected, that person will begin producing specific antibodies about a week to 10 days later, becoming **seropositive.** This change from seronegative to seropositive is referred to as **seroconversion.** As the infection progresses, increasing amounts of specific antibodies are produced, causing the amount of those antibodies in the blood to increase. A rise in the amount of specific antibodies, or **titer,** is characteristic of an active infection. In contrast, small but steady amounts of antibodies indicate a previous infection or vaccination.

Obtaining Antibodies

To determine if a patient has antibodies in the blood against a specific infectious agent, then either the patient's serum or plasma is tested. **Serum** is the fluid portion of blood that remains after blood clots; **plasma** is the fluid portion of blood treated with an anticoagulant to prevent clotting. Because serum is so often used as a source of antibodies, the study of *in vitro* antibody-antigen interactions is referred to as **serology.** Cerebrospinal fluid, tissues, and other clinical specimens may also be tested for antibodies.

To obtain antibodies known to bind a certain infectious agent, laboratory animals are used. The animals are immunized with either the whole agent or part of the agent, and the resulting antibodies are then collected by harvesting the animal's serum. The antibody preparation will be **polyclonal,** meaning that multiple naive B cells responded to the immunization, producing a mix of different antibodies that together recognize a variety of epitopes on the antigen. The more complex the antigen, the greater the number of different epitopes recognized by the antibody preparation. For instance, injection of whole bacteria will result in a wider array of antibody specificities than injection of purified toxin. One problem with polyclonal antibodies is that some may bind to closely related organisms, resulting in a false positive reaction. As an example, *Shigella* species have outer membrane proteins in common with *E. coli,* so an animal immunized with whole *Shigella* cells would produce some antibodies that also bind *E. coli* cells. If those antibodies were used in a diagnostic test for *Shigella,* a specimen containing *E. coli* cells but not *Shigella* would yield a false positive result.

PERSPECTIVE 17.1

Monoclonal Antibodies

In 1975, an exciting breakthrough occurred in immunology. Georges Köhler and Cesar Milstein developed techniques that fused normal antibody-producing B lymphocytes with malignant plasma cells (myeloma tumor cells), resulting in clones of cells they termed **hybridomas.** Since these hybridomas are clones, they produce antibodies with a single specificity that, therefore, are known as **monoclonal antibodies (figure 1).**

Plasma cells produce large amounts of antibody, and when they become malignant they grow profusely and indefinitely. Special myeloma cells are used to make hybridomas; they have lost the ability to make their own specificity of antibody but have retained the ability to produce large amounts of immunoglobulin. The normal B cell in the hybridoma supplies the genes for the specific antibody to be produced; the myeloma cell supplies the cellular machinery, the rough endoplasmic reticulum, for producing the antibodies.

Usually, when an animal is injected with an immunizing agent, it responds by making a variety of antibodies directed against different epitopes on the antigen. Therefore, even though there is a single antigen, the result is a mixture of different antibodies (i.e., polyclonal). When these antisera are used in immunological tests, standardizing the results is difficult, since there are differences each time the antiserum is made. Monoclonal antibodies, however, will be of the same immunoglobulin class and have the same variable regions and, thus, the same specificity and other characteristics. With such specificity, tests can be standardized much more easily and with greater reliability.

It was hoped that monoclonal antibodies would also become a useful therapeutic tool. In theory, it should be possible to make monoclonal antibodies that are specific for, say, a cancer cell. Radioactive materials that destroy cancer cells could be attached to the monoclonals, making a sort of "magic bullet." These antibodies would search and find the cancer cells and attach specifically to them, allowing the radioactive material to destroy the cells. In reality, many problems have arisen when the monoclonal antibodies have been used to treat humans. One problem was that mouse cells were used to produce the hybridomas, and humans reacted to the mouse antigens on the hybridoma antibodies, causing them to be rapidly removed from the body. This limited the effectiveness of the monoclonal antibodies to one or a few doses. This and many other unforeseen difficulties are being addressed now, with some encouraging results. For example, genetic engineering is being used to construct antibody genes from human DNA that can be put into hybridomas to produce monoclonal antibodies useful in treating humans.

In the laboratory, monoclonal antibodies are the basis of a number of diagnostic tests. For example, monoclonal antibodies against a hormone can detect pregnancy only 10 days after conception. Specific, monoclonal antibodies are used for rapid diagnosis of hepatitis, influenza, herpes simplex, and chlamydia infections. Köhler and Milstein won the Nobel Prize in 1984 for their work.

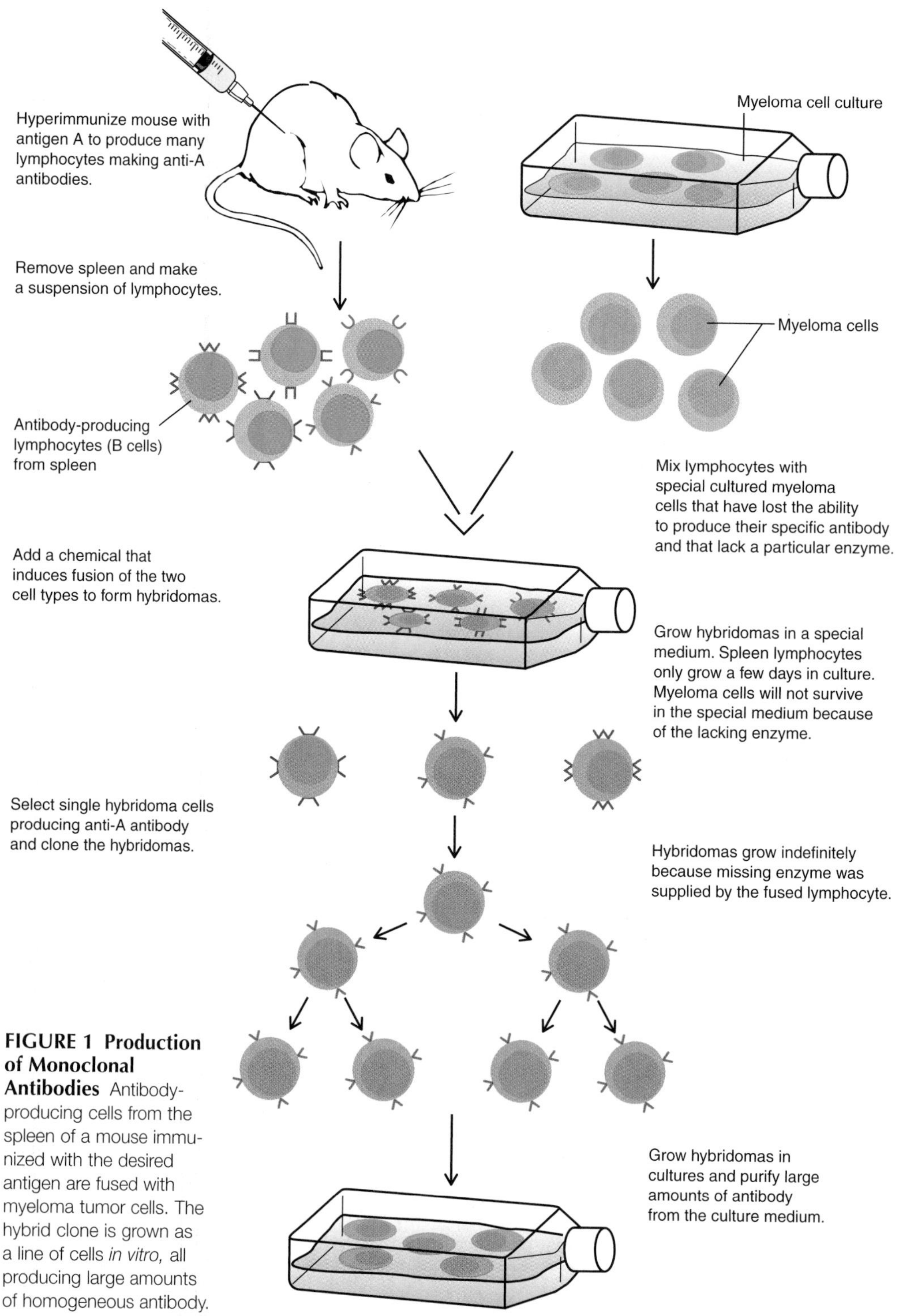

Hyperimmunize mouse with antigen A to produce many lymphocytes making anti-A antibodies.
Myeloma cell culture
Remove spleen and make a suspension of lymphocytes.
Myeloma cells
Antibody-producing lymphocytes (B cells) from spleen
Mix lymphocytes with special cultured myeloma cells that have lost the ability to produce their specific antibody and that lack a particular enzyme.
Add a chemical that induces fusion of the two cell types to form hybridomas.
Grow hybridomas in a special medium. Spleen lymphocytes only grow a few days in culture. Myeloma cells will not survive in the special medium because of the lacking enzyme.
Select single hybridoma cells producing anti-A antibody and clone the hybridomas.
Hybridomas grow indefinitely because missing enzyme was supplied by the fused lymphocyte.
Grow hybridomas in cultures and purify large amounts of antibody from the culture medium.

FIGURE 1 Production of Monoclonal Antibodies Antibody-producing cells from the spleen of a mouse immunized with the desired antigen are fused with myeloma tumor cells. The hybrid clone is grown as a line of cells *in vitro,* all producing large amounts of homogeneous antibody.

Monoclonal antibodies recognize only a single epitope. They are obtained through a laborious process that involves isolating individual B cells from an immunized animal, and then fusing those short-lived B cells with other cells that will divide repeatedly in culture (see **Perspective 17.1**). Because each B cell is programmed to produce antibody molecules that recognize only a single epitope, antibody preparations produced by the descendants (clones) of a single B cell are all identical. Monoclonal antibodies are difficult and expensive to develop and thus are generally available only if they have commercial value due to their widespread use.

Certain serological tests we will be discussing use antibodies that bind to human IgG molecules. These are referred to as **anti-human IgG antibodies.** They are produced by animals that have been immunized with IgG from human serum. In other words, human IgG functions as an antigen when injected into animals, eliciting a humoral immune response. The constant region of human IgG differs from that of other animals, so it is perceived as foreign in the animals. Anti-human IgG antibodies are readily available commercially.

Quantifying Antigen-Antibody Reactions

The concentration of antibody molecules in a specimen such as serum is usually determined by making serial dilutions similar to those done to make plate counts used to enumerate bacterial cells (see figure 4.18). The specimen is prepared by making a series of two-fold or ten-fold dilutions, and then antigen is added to each dilution. The **titer** (concentration) is expressed as the reciprocal of the last dilution that gives a detectable antigen-antibody reaction. Thus, if a positive reaction is observed in the dilution 1:256 but not in 1:512, then the antibody titer is 256.

Serology tests can be set up in test tubes, but this would require many tubes and large quantities of reagents. Therefore, the tests are usually done using plastic **microtiter plates,** which have 96, 384, or 768 wells **(figure 17.3).** Proteins, either antigen or antibody, can be permanently affixed to the tiny plastic wells. The volumes used in each well are a mere fraction of the volumes needed for even a small test tube, so that tests can be done on minute samples. Special equipment allows rapid dilution and mixing of reagents, as well as accurate reading of results.

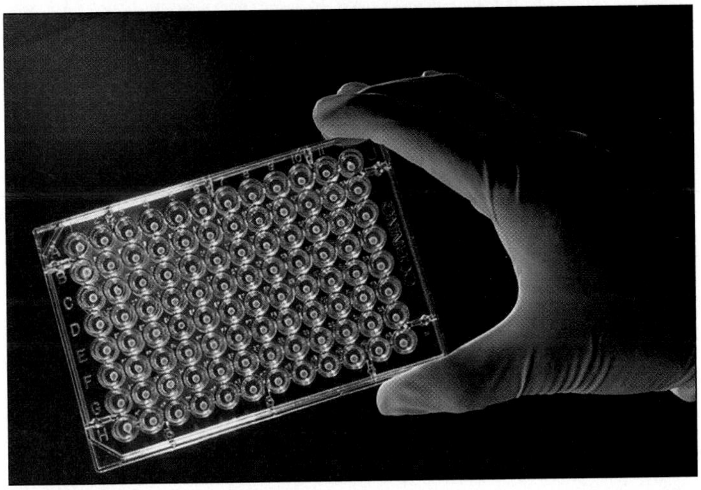

FIGURE 17.3 Microfilter Plate Serological tests can be done in the wells of these small plates, minimizing the volumes of reagents required.

MICROCHECK 17.3

Antibodies used in serological tests may be either polyclonal or monoclonal. Serial dilution of specimens permits quantification of antibodies in a sample.

- ✓ What is the significance of a rise in titer of specific antibodies in serum samples taken early and later during an infectious disease?
- ✓ Would antibodies produced by a patient in response to infection be monoclonal, or polyclonal?

17.4

Observing Antigen-Antibody Aggregations

Focus Point

- Compare and contrast precipitation reactions and agglutination reactions.

Recall from chapter 16 that antigen-antibody complexes form aggregates, creating one large "mouthful" for a phagocytic cell (see figure 16.5). This type of antigen-antibody binding can be readily observed in precipitation and agglutination reactions.

Precipitation Reactions

When antibodies bind to soluble antigens that have multiple epitopes, extensive cross-linking of the two types of molecules may occur, forming latticelike insoluble complexes that then precipitate out of solution. Complete formation of the aggregates can take several hours, and only occurs at certain relative concentrations of antibody and antigen molecules. If there is a great excess of either, the aggregate does not form, and consequently, no precipitate will be seen **(figure 17.4).** The easiest way to achieve this concentration is to place separate antigen and antibody suspensions side by side, and let the two types of soluble molecules diffuse toward each other. A precipitate will form in a distinct region called the **zone of optimal proportions.**

Although the precipitation reactions have historically been done by layering a solution containing antibody over one containing antigen (called the ring precipitation test), they are now most frequently performed by allowing the antigen and antibody to diffuse through agarose or other gels. Common methods include immunodiffusion tests and immunoelectrophoresis. ■ agarose, p. 221

Immunodiffusion tests

Immunodiffusion tests are simply precipitation reactions carried out in a gel such as agarose. The most widely used method is the

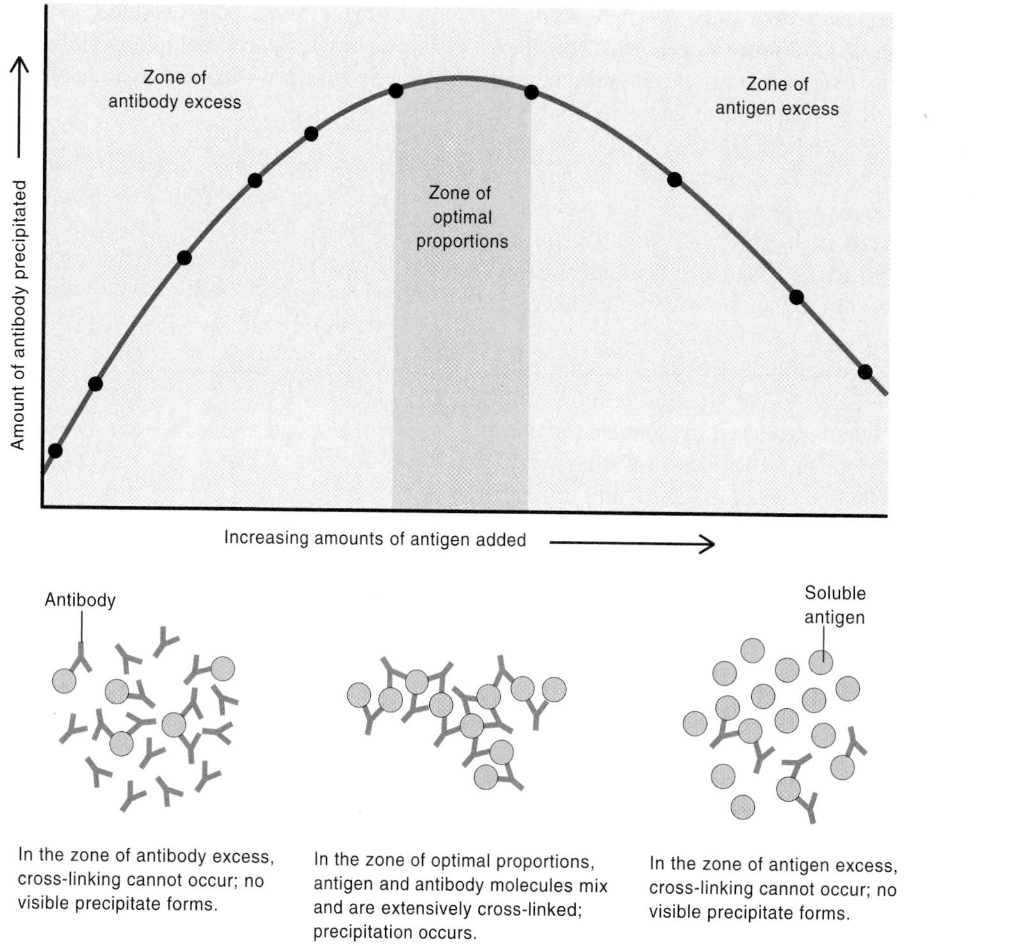

FIGURE 17.4 Antigen-Antibody Precipitation Reactions The maximum amount of precipitate forms in the zone of optimal proportion.

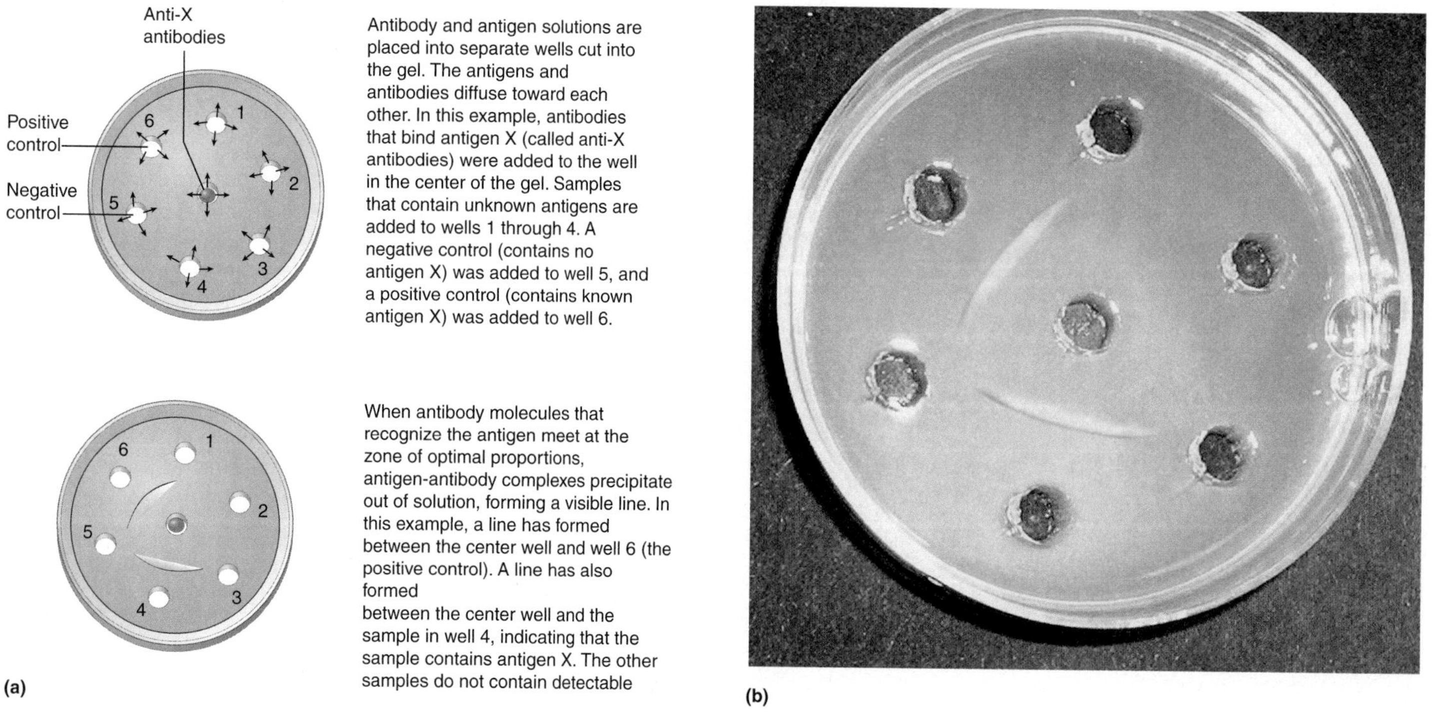

Anti-X
antibodies
Positive
control
Negative
control
1
2
3
4
5
6
Antibody and antigen solutions are placed into separate wells cut into the gel. The antigens and antibodies diffuse toward each other. In this example, antibodies that bind antigen X (called anti-X antibodies) were added to the well in the center of the gel. Samples that contain unknown antigens are added to wells 1 through 4. A negative control (contains no antigen X) was added to well 5, and a positive control (contains known antigen X) was added to well 6.
When antibody molecules that recognize the antigen meet at the zone of optimal proportions, antigen-antibody complexes precipitate out of solution, forming a visible line. In this example, a line has formed between the center well and well 6 (the positive control). A line has also formed
between the center well and the sample in well 4, indicating that the sample contains antigen X. The other samples do not contain detectable
(a)
(b)

FIGURE 17.5 Ouchterlony Procedure **(a)** Method **(b)** Photograph of results.

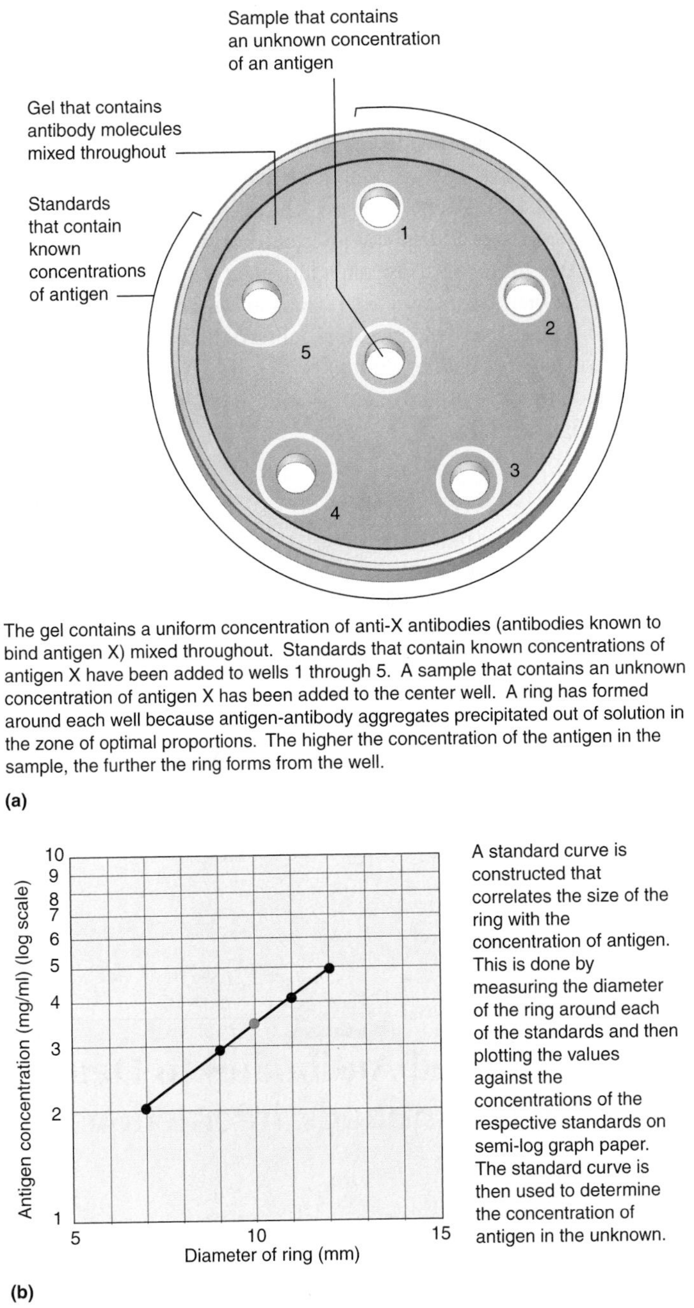
Sample that contains
an unknown concentration
of an antigen
Gel that contains
antibody molecules
mixed throughout
Standards
that contain
known
concentrations
of antigen
1
2
3
4
5
The gel contains a uniform concentration of anti-X antibodies (antibodies known to bind antigen X) mixed throughout. Standards that contain known concentrations of antigen X have been added to wells 1 through 5. A sample that contains an unknown concentration of antigen X has been added to the center well. A ring has formed around each well because antigen-antibody aggregates precipitated out of solution in the zone of optimal proportions. The higher the concentration of the antigen in the sample, the further the ring forms from the well.
(a)
Antigen concentration (mg/ml) (log scale)
Diameter of ring (mm)
A standard curve is constructed that correlates the size of the ring with the concentration of antigen. This is done by measuring the diameter of the ring around each of the standards and then plotting the values against the concentrations of the respective standards on semi-log graph paper. The standard curve is then used to determine the concentration of antigen in the unknown.
(b)

FIGURE 17.6 Radial Immunodiffusion This quantitative test is used to measure the concentration of an antigen in a sample. **(a)** Results, **(b)** standard curve generated from the results.

Ouchterlony procedure, which can be done in a Petri dish **(figure 17.5).** Antigen and antibody solutions are placed into separate wells cut in the gel contained in the dish. These solutions will gradually diffuse outward in the gel, meeting between the wells. If the antibody molecules recognize the antigen, they will form antigen-antibody complexes, resulting in a line of precipitate at the zone of optimal proportions. Since there is often more than one antigen present in the sample and different specificities of antibodies in the serum, more than one line can form, each in its area of optimal proportions.

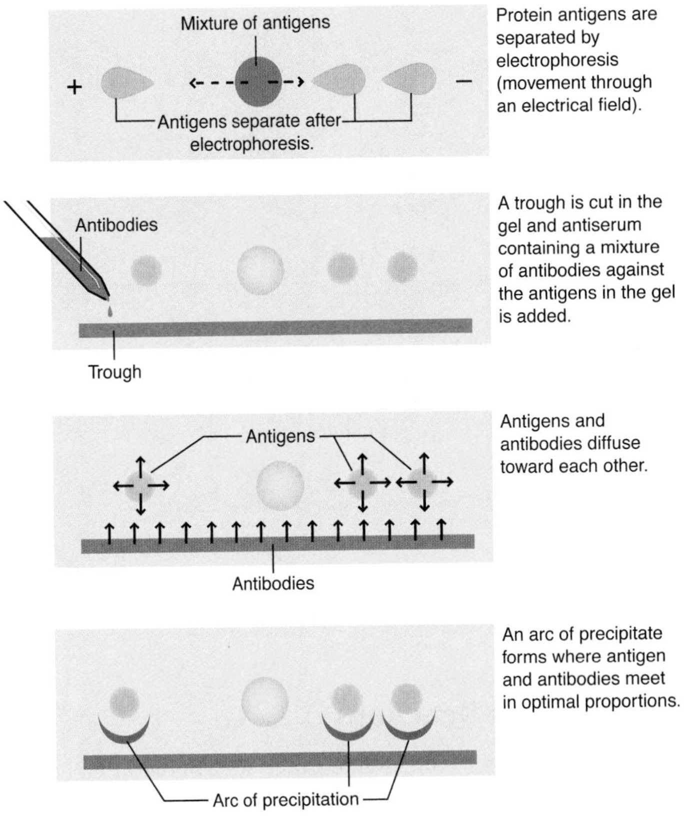

FIGURE 17.7 Immunoelectrophoresis Electrophoresis is used to separate the antigens; then, immunodiffusion is used to identify them.

Unlike the Ouchterlony technique, the **radial immunodiffusion test** is quantitative. To do the test, the antibody is added to the melted, cooled agar before it hardens, generating a uniform concentration of antibody molecules throughout the gel. Then, once the gel has solidified, antigen samples can be added into wells cut in the gel. The antigens will diffuse outward, forming a concentration gradient of antigen around the well. Because antibody molecules have been incorporated into the agar, a ring will form around the well as antibody-antigen aggregates precipitate out of solution in the zone of optimal proportions **(figure 17.6).** The higher the concentration of the antigen in the sample, the further the ring will form from the well. In order to determine the actual antigen concentration, the radial immunodiffusion test includes a separate set of wells into which a series of standards of known concentrations of antigen have been added. The diameter of the ring of precipitation around each of the standards can be used to construct a standard curve, which can then be used to determine the concentration of the unknown.

Immunoelectrophoresis

In **immunoelectrophoresis,** the proteins are first separated using gel electrophoresis **(figure 17.7).** Then, the antibodies are placed in a trough and allowed to diffuse toward the separated proteins. A line of precipitation forms at the location of each protein (antigen) recognized by antibodies. This test is most often used to determine if a patient is producing abnormally high or low levels of certain

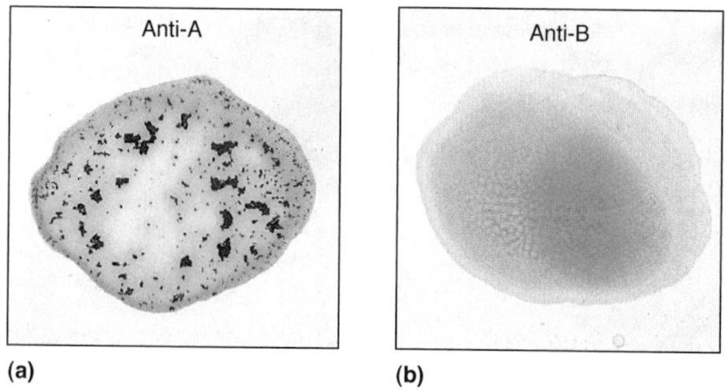

FIGURE 17.8 ABO Blood Typing This method tests for two different antigens (A and B) on red blood cells, using separate antibody suspensions (anti-A and anti-B). The red blood cells in the photographs agglutinated when mixed with anti-A antibodies, but not with anti-B antibodies, indicating that the blood group is Type A.

classes of immunglobulins. High levels of certain classes could indicate myeloma, in which a single plasma cell has given rise to a tumor.

Agglutination Reactions

Agglutination and precipitation reactions are similar in principle; both depend on cross-linking and lattice formation. In agglutination reactions, however, relatively large insoluble particles are involved rather than soluble molecules. Because of this, obvious aggregates are formed, which are much easier to see.

In **direct agglutination tests,** a suspension of specific antibody is mixed with the insoluble antigen, such as red blood cells, bacteria, or fungi. Readily visible clumping is a positive test. The agglutination of red blood cells by antibody binding or other means is referred to as **hemagglutination,** and is used in blood typing **(figure 17.8).**

Passive agglutination tests amplify the outcome of antibody-antigen aggregate formation by attaching either the antibody or the antigen to latex beads or other particles. Agglutination of these insoluble particles is much easier to see than a precipitate of soluble molecules. Latex beads to which specific antibodies have been attached are produced commercially and used to test for various bacteria, fungi, viruses, and parasites, as well as hormones, drugs, and other substances. The beads are mixed with a drop of a body fluid or suspended microbial culture. If the specific antigen is present, easily visible clumps will form. Latex agglutination tests are commonly used to identify beta-hemolytic *Streptococcus* species **(figure 17.9).**

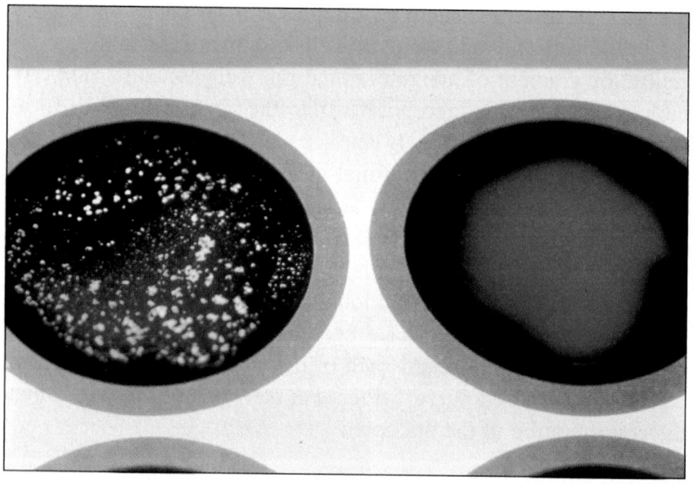

FIGURE 17.9 Latex Agglutination In this example, latex beads coated with antibodies that bind specifically to cell wall antigens of *Streptococcus pyogenes* are mixed with a suspension of a culture suspected of being that species. Visible clumping (shown on the left), confirms that the organism is *S. pyogenes.* Negative test results are shown on the right.

MICROCHECK 17.4

Agglutination and precipitation reactions both depend on cross-linking and lattice formation of antigen-antibody complexes. Large complexes of antibodies and soluble antigens will precipitate out of solution. Complexes of either antibodies and insoluble antigens or soluble antigens and antibody-coated beads will agglutinate.

- ✓ What is the advantage of the radial immunodiffusion test over the Ouchterlony test?
- ✓ How do the antigens used in precipitation reactions differ from those in direct agglutination tests?
- ✓ In precipitation reactions, why can cross-linked lattices not form when there is an excess of antibody?

17.5

Using Labeled Antibodies to Detect Antigen-Antibody Interactions

Focus Points

- Compare and contrast fluorescent antibody tests, ELISAs, and Western blots.
- Describe how the fluorescence-activated cell sorter is used in immunoassays.

Detectable markers such as enzymes, fluorescent dyes, and radioactive tags can be attached to specific antibodies, which are then used to detect the presence of given antigens. Examples of tests that use labeled antibodies include the fluorescent antibody test, enzyme-linked immunosorbent assay (ELISA), and Western blotting. Marking antigens with fluorescently-labeled antibodies also provides a mechanism of sorting antigens.

Fluorescent Antibody (FA) Tests

Fluorescent antibody (FA) tests rely on fluorescence microscopy to locate fluorescently-labeled antibodies bound to antigens fixed to a microscope slide. The antigens are often bacterial cells, and the antibodies may be bound directly or indirectly **(figure 17.10).** Fluorescence microscopy is used to observe the antibody-bound antigens on the slide. ■ fluorescent dyes and tags, p. 52 ■ fluorescence microscopy, p. 46

The **direct FA test** is used to identify an unknown antigen fixed to the slide (see figure 17.10a). Labeled antibodies of known specificity are added, the mix is incubated, and then the slide is washed to remove unbound antibodies. The labeled antibodies bound to the antigen will remain, making the antigen visible under the fluorescence microscope. Since the specificity of the antibodies was known, binding of those molecules to the antigen identifies the antigen. Several different fluorescent dyes, including fluorescein (fluoresces yellow-green) and rhodamine (fluoresces orange-red) can be used to label the antibody. By using various fluorescent dyes, it is possible to locate different antigens in the same preparation.

The **indirect FA test** is used to determine the presence of a given antibody specificity in human serum (see figure 17.10b). A known antigen is fixed to the slide, the test serum is added, and the mixture is incubated. If specific antibodies are present in the serum, they will bind to the antigen. The slide is then washed to remove unbound antibodies. The antigen-antibody complexes cannot be seen however, until they are labeled or tagged in some way, such as with a fluorescent dye. This is done by adding fluorescently-labeled anti-human IgG antibodies, which will bind any antibodies remaining from the human serum. Unbound labeled antibodies are washed away before microscopic examination of the slide. ■ anti-human IgG antibodies, p. 423

Fluorescence polarization immunoassay is a highly sensitive test for antigen-antibody interactions that uses a beam of polarized light to determine the rate of spin of fluorescent antibodies. The assay exploits the fact that large molecules, such as antibody-antigen complexes, spin in a liquid solution more slowly than small molecules, such as free antibodies. As the antigen-antibody complexes form, the molecular aggregates become much larger and the complex spins more slowly. Fluorescently-labeled antigen can be used to detect antibodies in serum or plasma.

Enzyme-Linked Immunosorbent Assay (ELISA)

The **enzyme-linked immunosorbent assay (ELISA)** employs an antibody that has been labeled with a detectable enzyme such as peroxidase from the horseradish plant. When the labeled antibody

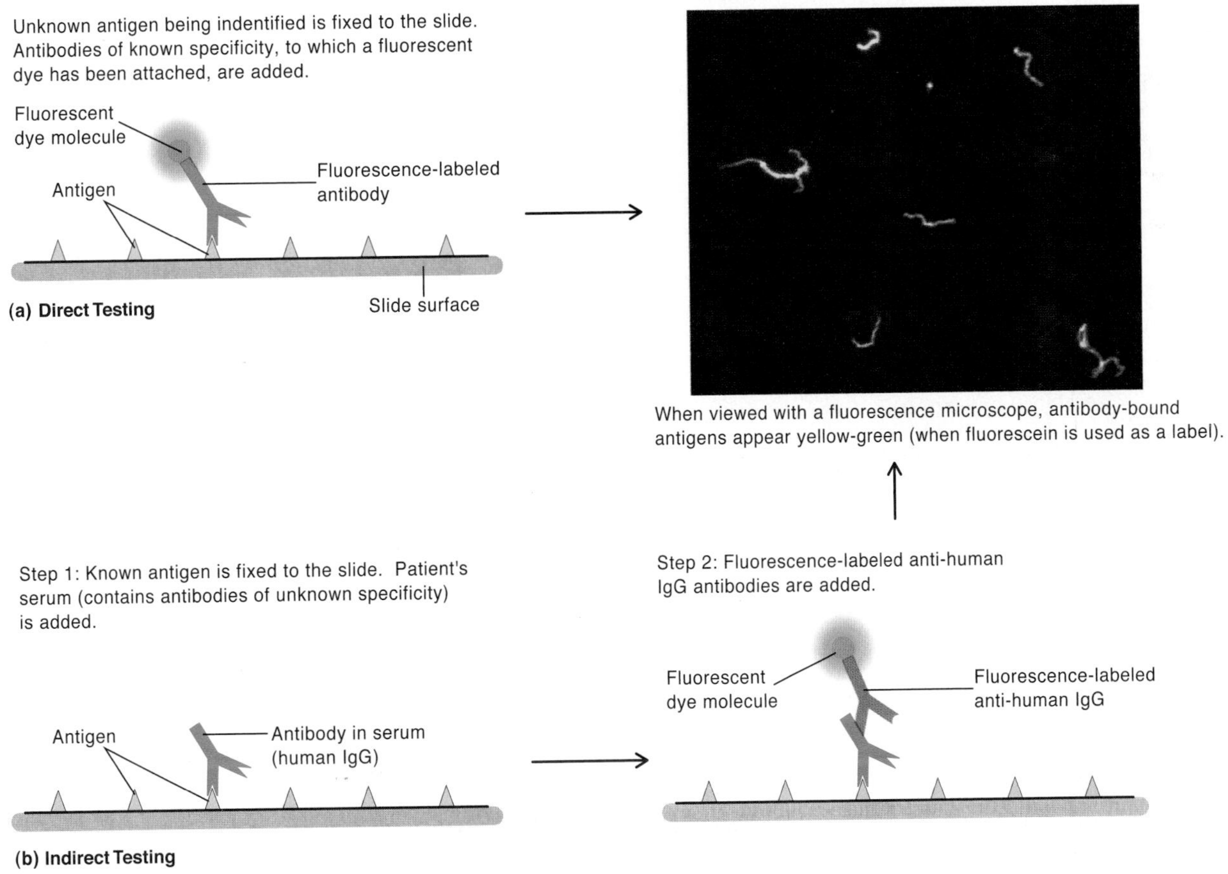

Unknown antigen being indentified is fixed to the slide. Antibodies of known specificity, to which a fluorescent dye has been attached, are added.
Fluorescent dye molecule
Antigen
Fluorescence-labeled antibody
Slide surface
(a) Direct Testing
When viewed with a fluorescence microscope, antibody-bound antigens appear yellow-green (when fluorescein is used as a label).
Step 1: Known antigen is fixed to the slide. Patient's serum (contains antibodies of unknown specificity) is added.
Antigen
Antibody in serum (human IgG)
Step 2: Fluorescence-labeled anti-human IgG antibodies are added.
Fluorescent dye molecule
Fluorescence-labeled anti-human IgG
(b) Indirect Testing

FIGURE 17.10 Fluorescent Antibody (FA) Tests **(a)** Direct testing. **(b)** Indirect testing.

binds directly or indirectly to an antigen fixed to a surface, its location can be determined using a colorimetric assay (**figure 17.11**). This extremely sensitive test is often done in microtiter plates, and is widely used to screen large numbers of specimens for either antigen or antibody. A variety of prepared ELISA plates, as well as commercial modifications, are available from various companies.

Direct ELISA

In the **direct ELISA,** a specimen suspected of containing the antigen of interest is affixed to a surface, such as a well in a microtiter plate. Oftentimes, the antigen is not affixed directly, but is instead "captured" by antibodies that have been attached to the surface (see figure 17.11a). This modification is referred to as the sandwich ELISA. After attachment of the antigen, enzyme-labeled antibodies known to bind the antigen are added and incubated. The unbound antibodies are washed away after incubation. To detect remaining labeled antibodies, a colorless substrate is added that develops a color if acted upon by the enzyme. Examples of commercial modifications of the ELISA test include rapid Group A strep tests done in doctors' clinics, and home pregnancy kits (**figure 17.12**).

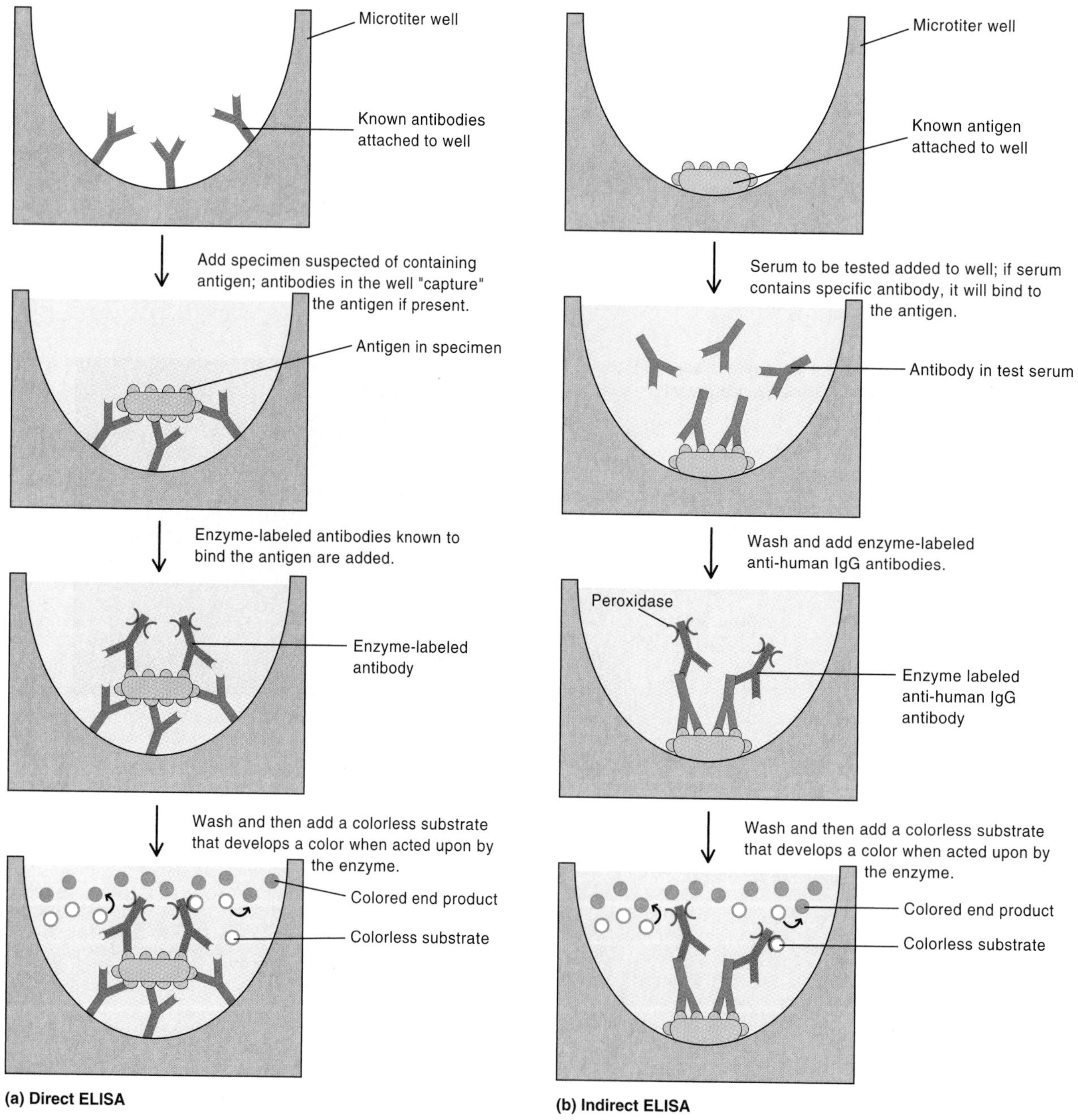
Microtiter well
Known antibodies attached to well
Add specimen suspected of containing antigen; antibodies in the well "capture" the antigen if present.
Antigen in specimen
Enzyme-labeled antibodies known to bind the antigen are added.
Enzyme-labeled antibody
Wash and then add a colorless substrate that develops a color when acted upon by the enzyme.
Colored end product
Colorless substrate
(a) Direct ELISA
Microtiter well
Known antigen attached to well
Serum to be tested added to well; if serum contains specific antibody, it will bind to the antigen.
Antibody in test serum
Wash and add enzyme-labeled anti-human IgG antibodies.
Peroxidase
Enzyme labeled anti-human IgG antibody
Wash and then add a colorless substrate that develops a color when acted upon by the enzyme.
Colored end product
Colorless substrate
(b) Indirect ELISA

FIGURE 17.11 Enzyme-Linked Immunosorbent Assay (ELISA) **(a)** Direct ELISA. **(b)** Indirect ELISA.

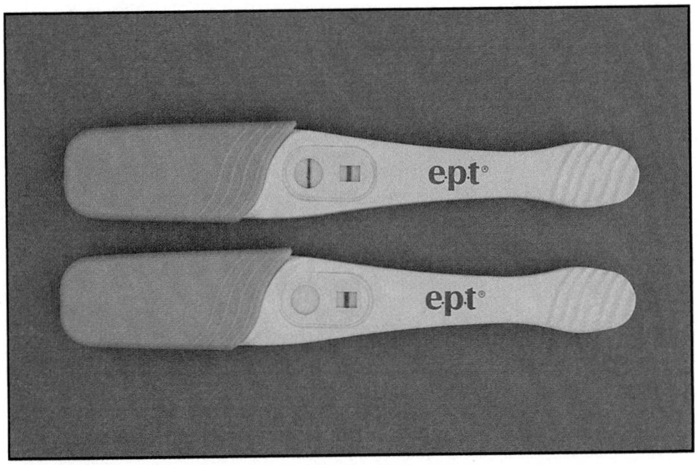

FIGURE 17.12 ELISA Test for Pregnancy The test detects human chorionic gonadotropin (HCG), an antigen present only in pregnant women. A urine sample is applied on the left. Two pink lines indicate reaction of HCG with antibodies, a positive test. A single line indicates absence of HCG in the urine, a negative test.

Indirect ELISA

In the **indirect ELISA,** the known antigen is affixed to a surface, such as a well in a microtiter plate (see figure 17.11b). The serum to be tested is added and incubated. A washing step then removes the unbound antibodies. To allow the antigen-antibody complex to be detected, enzyme-labeled anti-human IgG antibodies are added. These bind any human IgG antibodies remaining from the serum. Unbound labeled antibodies are then washed away. As with the direct ELISA, a colorless substrate of the enzyme is then added. Development of color indicates a positive reaction. The intensity of the color relative to that of a standard is usually quantitative.

The indirect ELISA is routinely used to test donated blood for antibodies against HIV before the blood is used for transfusion. The presence of specific antibodies implies that the virus is present. The ELISA is also used to screen patient serum samples to determine HIV status. A small percentage of the results will be false positive, however. Because of this, a complicated but more reliable test, Western blotting, which will be described next, is used to confirm the positive ELISA results.

Western Blotting

In the **Western blotting** technique, the various proteins that make up an antigen are separated by size before reacting them with antibody. This makes it possible to determine exactly which proteins the antibodies are recognizing, an essential aspect of accurate HIV testing **(figure 17.13).** The basic principles are analogous to those of Southern blotting, but proteins (rather than DNA) are separated and then detected, which is how the Western blotting acquired its name. ■ Southern blotting, p. 228

To separate the proteins, a special type of gel electrophoresis called SDS-PAGE is used. This resolves proteins of different sizes into a series of bands, as smaller proteins move faster than the larger ones. The separated proteins are then transferred to a nylon membrane filter to immobilize them before a solution of antibody molecules is added. The steps after that are very similar to those of an ELISA. To test for antibodies specific for the separated proteins in a patient, a serum sample is added to the blot, and then unbound antibodies are washed off. Enzyme- (particularly luciferase from fireflies) or radioactively-labeled anti-human IgG antibodies are then added, which attach to any antibodies remaining from the serum. Unbound labeled antibodies are then washed off. Finally, the label is detected, generating a bar code–like pattern that indicates which proteins were recognized by the patient's antibodies.

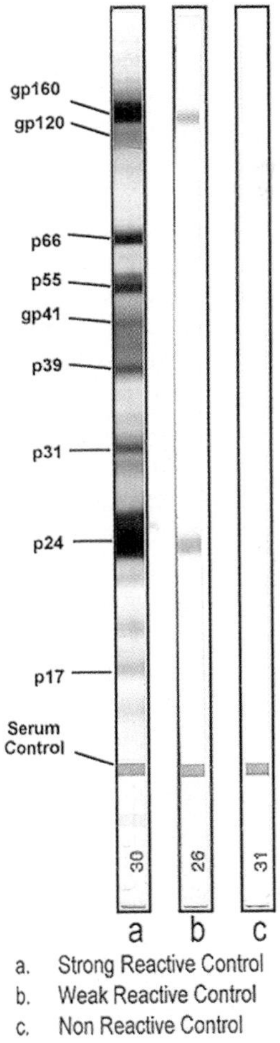

FIGURE 17.13 Western Blotting Results Each strip in this photograph contains HIV proteins that have been separated by gel electrophoresis and then transferred in-place to the strips, along with a serum control. The dark portions of the strips indicate the locations of bound antibodies. The results for the strong reactive control (lane a) indicate that antibodies have bound all HIV proteins on the strip. The results for the weak reactive control (lane b) show binding of antibodies to only certain critical HIV proteins (gp160/120 and p24). The results for the non-reactive control (lane c) show no binding to HIV proteins. When this test is done using antibodies from a patient, strict criteria must be used when interpreting the results.

Fluorescence-Activated Cell Sorter (FACS)

As described in chapter 4, flow cytometry counts cells or other particles by measuring the light scattered as they pass single-file by a laser. A specialized version called the **fluorescence-activated cell sorter (FACS)** can be used to count and separate cells labeled with fluorescent antibodies. For example, subsets of T cells ($CD4^+$ and $CD8^+$) can be counted and even separated by adding monoclonal antibodies against the CD4 and CD8 markers labeled with different fluorescent dyes to the cell mixture before sorting. ■ **flow cytometry, p. 104**

MICROCHECK 17.5

The fluorescence antibody test, ELISA, and Western blot use antibodies labeled with a detectable marker to locate a given antigen. Direct tests use the labeled antibody to identify an antigen. Indirect tests use a labeled antibody to detect a patient's antibody bound to a known antigen. Flow cytometry uses a fluorescence activated cell sorter to separate and count cells labeled with fluorescent antibodies.

- ✓ Compare and contrast the fluorescent antibody test and the ELISA.
- ✓ In HIV testing, why is the Western blot test used to confirm ELISA results?
- ✓ Why is a false positive more significant in HIV testing of patients than in screening donated blood for transfusions?

FUTURE CHALLENGES

Global Immunization

In addition to developing new safe and effective vaccines, a major challenge for the future is delivering available vaccines to populations worldwide. When this was done in the case of smallpox, the disease was eliminated from the world; and poliomyelitis is almost eradicated now. The World Health Organization and the governments that support it deserve much of the credit for these achievements. Much remains to be done, however, and recent gifts totaling well over a billion dollars from Bill Gates, one of the founders of Microsoft, and his wife will go a long way to implementing further progress in this area.

To immunize universally, it is necessary to have vaccines that are easily administered, inexpensive, stable under a variety of environmental conditions, and preferably painless. Instead of expensive needles and syringes and painful injections, vaccines may be delivered in a number of easy ways. For example, naked DNA can be coated onto microscopic gold pellets, which are shot from a gunlike apparatus directly through the skin into the muscle, painlessly. Skin patches deliver antigens slowly through the skin. Vaccines against mucous membrane pathogens can be delivered by a nasal spray, as in some new influenza vaccines, or by mouth. Time-release pills introduce antigen steadily to give a sustained immune response.

In addition to sprays and pills that deliver antigens to mucous membranes in order to induce mucosal immunity, techniques are being developed to get antigens directly to M cells in the gastrointestinal mucosa. These are the cells that can endocytose antigens and deliver them across the membrane to the lymphoid tissue of the Peyer's patches, where immune responses occur. Antigens are incorporated into substances known to bind to M cells, thereby facilitating entry into the M cells and the Peyer's patches. ■ **M cells, p. 391**

Another promising means of immunization, especially for developing nations, is the use of edible vaccines produced in plants. Preliminary studies have shown that genes from various pathogenic organisms can be introduced into plants. For example, potato plants were genetically engineered with a gene for part of an *Escherichia coli* toxin that affects the gastrointestinal tract. The potatoes expressing the harmless fragment of the toxin were then fed to mice, inducing the production of serum and secretory antibodies against the toxin. It is hoped that appropriate genes can be introduced into common plants, such as tomatoes and bananas, resulting in very low cost immunization for whole populations. These investigations, however, are in their early stages.

One of the major remaining challenges is development of an effective vaccine against HIV that can be administered universally. Although many anti-HIV vaccines are under investigation and in clinical trials, there is no indication that a truly effective immunization program for HIV disease is imminent. It is also probable that when HIV disease is brought under control, a new and currently unforeseen challenge will arise during the twenty-first century.

SUMMARY

Immunization

17.1 Principles of Immunization (Figure 17.1)

Active Immunity

Active immunity occurs naturally in response to infections or other natural exposure to antigens, and artificially in response to vaccination.

Passive Immunity

Passive immunity occurs naturally during pregnancy and through breast feeding, and artificially by transfer of preformed antibodies, as in **immune globulin** and **hyperimmune globulin.**

17.2 Vaccines and Immunization Procedures

A **vaccine** is a preparation of a disease-causing agent or its products used to induce active immunity. It protects an individual against disease, and can also provide **herd immunity.** (Table 17.1)

Attenuated Vaccines

An **attenuated vaccine** is a weakened form of the pathogen that can replicate but is generally unable to cause disease.

Inactivated Vaccines

Inactivated vaccines are unable to replicate but they retain the immunogenicity of the infectious agent or toxin. They include inactivated whole agents, **toxoids,** protein subunits, purified polysaccharides, and polysaccharide-protein **conjugates.**

Adjuvants increase the intensity of the immune response to the antigen in a vaccine.

An Example of Vaccination Strategy—The Campaign to Eliminate Poliomyelitis

Both the Sabin and the Salk polio vaccines protect against paralytic poliomyelitis; only the Sabin vaccine induces mucosal immunity.

The Importance of Routine Immunizations for Children (Table 17.3)

Routine childhood immunizations have prevented millions of cases of disease and many deaths during the past decades.

Current Progress in Immunization

Progress in vaccination includes enhancement of the immune response to vaccines, development of new or improved vaccines against certain diseases, and development of new types of vaccines. (Table 17.5)

Immunological Testing

17.3 Principles of Immunological Testing

A **seronegative** individual will **seroconvert,** becoming **seropositive,** a week to 10 days after initial infection with an agent.

Obtaining Antibodies

To determine if a patient has antibodies in the blood against a specific infectious agent, either the patient's **serum** or **plasma** is tested.

Polyclonal antibodies recognize multiple epitopes whereas **monoclonal antibodies** recognize only a single epitope.

Anti-human IgG antibodies are used to detect IgG molecules in a patient specimen.

Quantifying Antigen-Antibody Reactions

The concentration of antibody molecules in a specimen is usually determined by making serial dilutions; the last dilution that gives a detectable antigen-antibody reaction reflects the **titer.**

17.4 Observing Antigen-Antibody Aggregations

Precipitation Reactions (Figure 17.4)

When antibodies bind to soluble antigens that have multiple epitopes, the complexes precipitate out of solution at the **zone of optimal proportion;** examples of tests that involve precipitation reactions include the **Ouchterlony** procedure, the **radial immunodiffusion test,** and **immunoelectrophoresis.** (Figures 17.5, 17.6, 17.7)

Agglutination Reactions (Figures 17.8, 17.9)

Agglutination reactions are similar in principle to precipitation reactions, but insoluble particles are involved, resulting in the formation of obvious aggregates; examples include direct agglutination tests and passive agglutination tests.

17.5 Using Labeled Antibodies to Detect Antigen-Antibody Interactions

Fluorescent Antibody (FA) Tests (Figure 17.10)

Fluorescent antibody (FA) tests rely on fluorescence microscopy to locate fluorescently-labeled antibodies bound to antigens fixed to a microscope slide; examples of FA procedures include the **direct FA test, indirect FA test,** and **fluorescence polarization immunoassay.**

Enzyme-Linked Immunosorbent Assay (ELISA) (Figure 17.11)

The **enzyme-linked immunosorbent assay (ELISA)** employs an antibody that has been labeled with a detectable enzyme; the procedure can be direct or indirect.

Western Blotting (Figure 17.13)

In the **Western blotting** technique, the various proteins that make up an antigen are separated by size before reacting them with antibody.

Fluorescence-Activated Cell Sorter (FACS)

The **fluorescence-activated cell sorter (FACS)** can be used to count and separate antigens labeled with fluorescent antibodies.

REVIEW QUESTIONS

Short Answer

1. Why are acellular subunit vaccines replacing some whole cell vaccines? Discuss an example.
2. What are some ways in which the number of injections needed for childhood immunization could be lessened?
3. Can DNA vaccines cause the disease they are meant to protect against?
4. Which would be expected to be more effective against common childhood diseases, active or passive immunity? Why? Answer in terms of protection and cost-effectiveness.
5. Describe how both active and passive immunization can be used to combat tetanus.
6. In a precipitation reaction, what is meant by optimal proportions?
7. To determine a person's blood type, antibodies against red blood cells bearing the A and/or B antigens are mixed with the person's red cells. Is this an example of a precipitation reaction or an agglutination reaction?
8. What are the advantages of the ELISA test?
9. An ELISA test is used to screen patient specimens for HIV. A positive ELISA test is confirmed by a Western blot test. Why not the other way around, with the ELISA second?
10. What is the purpose of anti-human IgG antibodies in immunological testing?

Multiple Choice

1. All of the following are attenuated vaccines, *except* that against
   a) measles. b) mumps. c) rubella.
   d) Salk polio. e) yellow fever.
2. Examples of active immunization include
   a) giving antibodies against diphtheria.
   b) gamma globulin injections to prevent hepatitis.
   c) Sabin polio immunization.
   d) rabies immune globulin.
   e) tetanus immune globulin.

3. Disease may be caused in immunosuppressed individuals by administration of
   a) inactivated whole agent vaccines.
   b) toxoids.
   c) subunit vaccines.
   d) genetically engineered vaccine against hepatitis B.
   e) attenuated vaccines.
4. Vaccines ideally should be all of the following, *except*
   a) effective in protecting against the disease.
   b) inexpensive.
   c) stable.
   d) living.
   e) easily administered.
5. An important subunit vaccine that is widely used is the
   a) pertussis vaccine. b) Sabin vaccine. c) Salk vaccine.
   d) measles vaccine. e) mumps vaccine.
6. Which of the following about immunological testing is *false?*
   a) Polyclonal antibodies recognize multiple epitopes.
   b) Monoclonal antibodies recognize a single epitope.
   c) Serum and plasma can both be tested for antibodies.
   d) The direct ELISA employs antihuman IgG antibodies.
   e) A rise in specific antibody titer indicates an active infection.
7. Precipitation tests include all of the following, *except*
   a) radial immunodiffusion. b) Ouchterlony.
   c) ELISA. d) immunoelectrophoresis.
8. Which of the following pairs does *not* match?
   a) ELISA—radioactive label
   b) Fluorescence-activated cell sorter—flow cytometry
   c) Radial immunodiffusion—quantitative
   d) Fluorescent antibody test—microscopy
   e) Western blot—gel electrophoresis
9. Which of the following would be most useful for screening thousands of patient specimens for antibodies that indicate a certain disease?
   a) Western blot b) Fluorescent antibody c) ELISA
   d) All of the above e) None of the above
10. In quantifying antibodies in a patient's serum
    a) total protein in the serum is measured.
    b) the antibody is usually measured in grams per ml.
    c) the serum is serially diluted.
    d) both antigen and antibody are diluted.
    e) the titer refers to the amount of antigen added.

Applications

1. A chemist working for the U.S. Department of Agriculture is interested in using simple, fast tests to gather information about the quality of prepared foods sold for human consumption. Explain how immunodiffusion can be used in the food industry to test for food quality.
2. Many dairy operations keep cow's milk for sale and use formula and feed to raise any calves. One farmer noticed that calves raised on the formula and feed needed to be treated for diarrhea more frequently than calves left with their mothers to nurse. He had some tests run on the diets and discovered no differences in the calories or nutritional content. The farmer called a veterinarian and asked him to explain the observations. What was the vet's response?

Critical Thinking

1. In figure 17.4, how would the curve change if the concentration of antibody in the original sample were increased? (Would the shape of the curve change? Would the curve be shifted left, right, up, or down?) Briefly explain your answer.
2. *Staphylococcus aureus* makes a protein called protein A, which binds to the Fc region of antibody molecules from a wide variety of species. How could protein A be exploited in immunoassays?

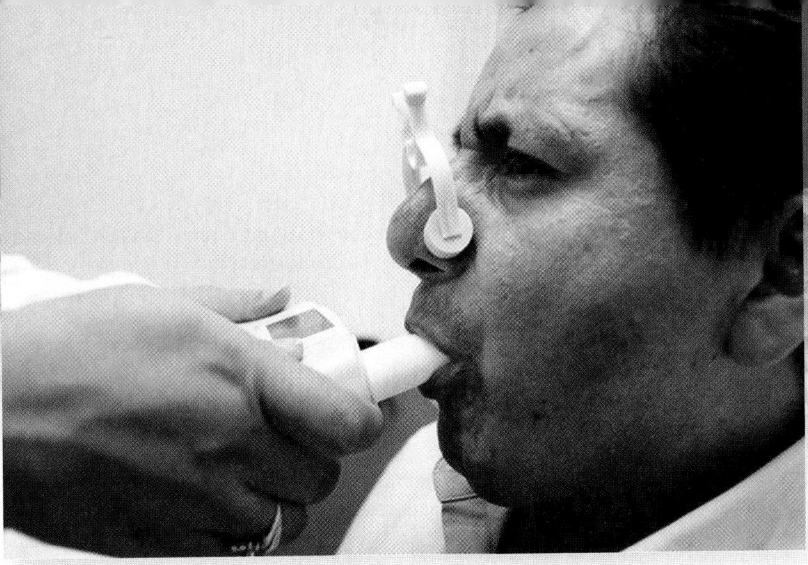

Asthmatic individual using a spirometer

CHAPTER EIGHTEEN

Immunologic Disorders

A Glimpse of History

Pasteur is widely quoted as saying, "Chance favors the prepared mind." This was certainly the case with the physiologist Charles Richet in his discovery of **hypersensitivities,** commonly called allergies, near the end of the nineteenth century. Richet performed some of the early experiments with toxins and antisera. He and his colleague, Paul Portier, while cruising in the South Seas on Prince Albert of Monaco's yacht, hypothesized that the Portuguese man-of-war jellyfish must have a toxin responsible for its ugly stings. They made an extract of the jellyfish tentacles and showed that it was very toxic to rabbits and ducks.

Upon returning to France they began studying the effects of toxins from the tentacles of sea anemones on dogs. Richet and Portier noted that some dogs in their experiments survived the potent toxin, but when these animals were tested with the toxin again, they died a few minutes after receiving a small dose. One very healthy dog survived the first challenge with the toxin. When given a second dose 22 days later, the dog became very ill within a few seconds. It could not breathe, lay on its side, had violent diarrhea, vomited blood, and died within 25 minutes.

Because of the insights they gained from their early work with antisera, Richet and Portier had prepared minds. They recognized that the dogs' reactions were probably immunologically mediated. The reactions, however, represented the opposite effect of prevention of disease, **prophylaxis,** conferred by antisera. Therefore, they named this development of hypersensitivity upon repeat exposure to antigenic substances **anaphylaxis,** the extreme opposite of prophylaxis. For this and other outstanding contributions to medicine, Richet received the Nobel Prize in 1913.

For the most part, the immune system does a superb job protecting the body from invasion by various microorganisms and viruses; however, as Richet showed, the *same mechanisms* that are so effective in protecting us can, under some circumstances, be harmful. The protective responses confer immunity; immune responses that cause tissue injury are referred to as **hypersensitivities.** In addition to hypersensitivities, a second type of immunologic disorder, **autoimmune disease,** results from responses against self-antigens. A third type of immunologic disorder occurs when the immune system responds too little, resulting in **immunodeficiency.**

Exactly the same mechanisms occur in immunological responses, whether the reactions are protective or damaging. The immune response can be likened to fire. Fire is essential for warmth and cooking and in many ways it is beneficial, but exactly the same fire is destructive if it starts in the wrong place or becomes uncontrolled. Similarly, immune responses are essential for protection, but can be destructive if out of control.

Hypersensitivity reactions to usually harmless substances are often called **allergies** or allergic reactions. Antigens that cause allergic reactions are **allergens.** Hypersensitivities are categorized according to which parts of the immune response are involved and how quickly the response occurs. Most allergic or hypersensitivity reactions fall into one of four major types:

- Type I: Immediate IgE-mediated
- Type II: Cytotoxic
- Type III: Immune complex-mediated
- Type IV: Delayed cell-mediated

KEY TERMS

Allergy Hypersensitivity to an allergen, generally mediated by IgE.

Allograft Transplanted tissue from a non-identical individual of the same species.

Anaphylaxis Harmful, as opposed to protective, reactions resulting from prior exposure to a foreign substance. Usually refers to IgE-mediated reactions that potentially could cause shock.

Autoimmune Refers to conditions caused by reactions of the immune system against self-antigens.

Hemolytic disease Conditions resulting from destruction of red blood cells, as in hemolytic disease of the newborn.

Immunodeficiency A condition in which one or more components of the immune system is defective, thereby rendering an individual susceptible to infection.

Immunotherapy Techniques used to modify the immune system action for a favorable effect.

Oral tolerance Decreased reactivity of immune cells resulting from feeding an antigen.

Serum sickness A condition caused by immune complexes arising from antibody formed in response to an antigen (such as snakebite antivenin) injected into the bloodstream.

Urticaria Hives, an IgE-mediated skin reaction characterized by a wheal and flare; an example of type I anaphylaxis.

The main characteristics of the four types of hypersensitivities are shown in **table 18.1.** Allergic reactions occur only in **sensitized** individuals—that is, those who have been immunized or sensitized by prior exposure to that specific antigen.

18.1 Type I Hypersensitivities: Immediate IgE-Mediated

Focus Points

- Describe the immunologic reactions involved in type I hypersensitivities.
- Give four examples of type I hypersensitivities.

Antibodies of the class IgE have a protective role, especially against certain parasitic worms. However, IgE antibodies also cause immediate (type I) hypersensitivity, characterized by a reaction in a sensitized individual within minutes of exposure to antigen. Allergic people develop such a reaction when exposed to substances such as dust, pollens, animal dander, and molds, which do not evoke a response in non-sensitized people. ■ IgE, p. 396

Sensitization occurs when the antigen makes contact with some part of the body (pollen grains contact the mucous membrane of the nose, for example) and induces an antibody response. Tissues under the mucous membranes are rich in B cells committed to IgA and IgE production, and IgE-producing cells are more abundant in allergic than in non-allergic individuals. As IgE is produced in this area, which is rich in mast cells, the IgE molecules attach via their Fc portion to receptors on the mast cells and also on circulating basophils **(figure 18.1).** Once attached, the IgE mol-

TABLE 18.1 Some Characteristics of the Major Types of Hypersensitivities

Characteristic	Type I Hypersensitivity Immediate; IgE-Mediated	Type II Hypersensitivity Cytotoxic	Type III Hypersensitivity Immune Complex-Mediated	Type IV Hypersensitivity Delayed Cell-Mediated
Cell type responsible	B cells	B cells	B cells	T cells
Type of antigen	Soluble	Cell-bound	Soluble	Soluble or cell-bound
Type of antibody	IgE	IgG, IgM	IgG	None
Other cells involved	Basophils, mast cells	Red blood cells, white blood cells, platelets	Various host cells	Various host cells
Mediators	Histamine, serotonin, leukotrienes	Complement, ADCC	Complement, neutrophil proteases	Cytokines
Transfer of hypersensitivity	By serum	By serum	By serum	By T cells
Time of reaction after challenge with antigen	Immediate, up to 30 minutes	Hours to days	Hours to days	Peaks at 48 to 72 hours
Skin reaction	Wheal and flare	None	Arthus	Induration, necrosis
Examples	Anaphylactic shock, hay fever, hives	Transfusion reaction, hemolytic disease of newborns	Serum sickness, farmer's lung, malarial kidney damage	Tuberculin reaction, contact dermatitis, tissue transplant rejection

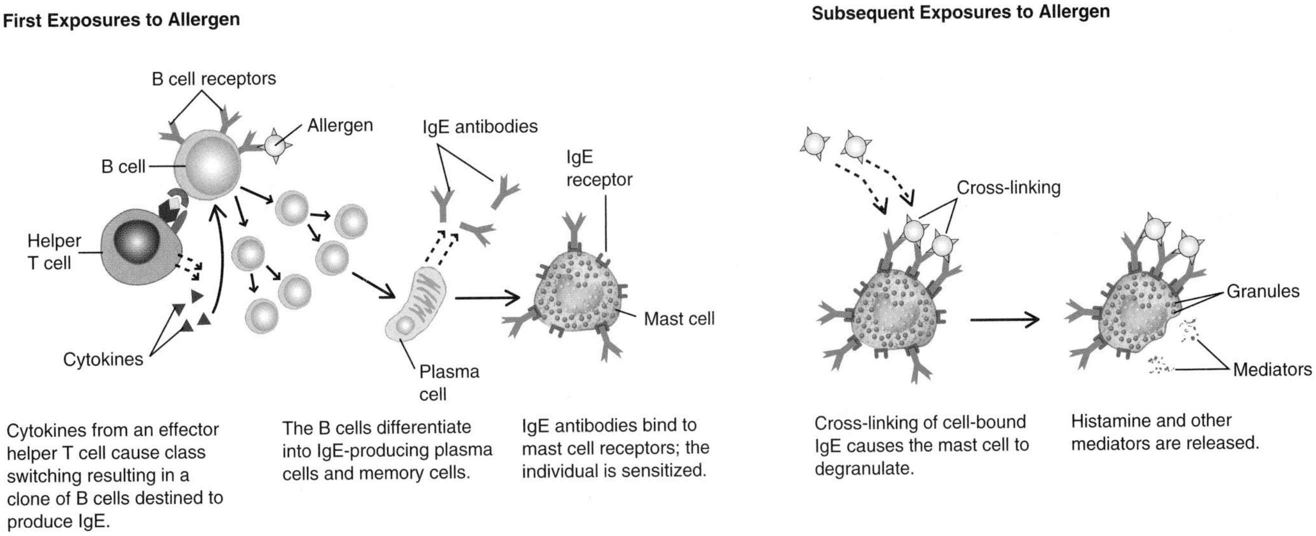
First Exposures to Allergen
B cell receptors
B cell
Allergen
IgE antibodies
IgE
receptor
Helper
T cell
Cytokines
Plasma
cell
Mast cell
Cytokines from an effector helper T cell cause class switching resulting in a clone of B cells destined to produce IgE.
The B cells differentiate into IgE-producing plasma cells and memory cells.
IgE antibodies bind to mast cell receptors; the individual is sensitized.
Subsequent Exposures to Allergen
Cross-linking
Granules
Mediators
Cross-linking of cell-bound IgE causes the mast cell to degranulate.
Histamine and other mediators are released.

FIGURE 18.1 Mechanisms of Type I Hypersensitivity: Immediate IgE-Mediated First exposure to an allergen induces an IgE antibody response leading to sensitization. With subsequent exposures to the allergen, cross-linking of IgE molecules on mast cells results in release of histamine and other substances that can cause dilation and increased leakage of plasma from capillaries, airway constriction, and increased mucus production. These effects can cause itching, swelling, and pain, and conditions such as asthma, hay fever, and anaphylactic shock.

ecules can survive for many weeks with their reaction sites waiting to interact with antigen. The individual is thereby sensitized to that antigen. ■ antibody response, p. 398

People with a type I hypersensitivity will have many IgE antibodies fixed to mast cells throughout their bodies. When such a person is not exposed to antigen, these antibodies are harmless. Upon exposure, however, the antigen readily combines with the cell-fixed IgE antibodies. At least two cell-bound IgE molecules must react with specific antigen, cross-linking the IgE molecules, in order for a reaction to occur (see figure 18.1). Within seconds, the IgE-antigen attachment and cross-linking of IgE in the cell membrane cause the mast cell to degranulate, releasing histamine, leukotrienes, prostaglandins, and cytokines such as IL-4, stored within the granules. These chemical mediators released from the granules are the direct causes of *hives* (urticaria), *hay fever* (allergic rhinitis), asthma, anaphylactic shock, and other allergic manifestations. ■ mast cell, p. 371

The tendency to have type I allergic reactions is inherited. The reactions occur in at least 20% to 30% of the population of the United States. Susceptible people often have higher than normal levels of IgE in the circulation, and increased numbers of eosinophils.

Localized Anaphylaxis

Anaphylaxis is the name given to allergic reactions caused by IgE-mediated release of mast cell granules. Although anaphylaxis may be generalized or local, by far the most usual allergic reactions are examples of localized anaphylaxis. **Hives (urticaria)** is an allergic skin condition characterized by the formation of a wheal and flare; the wheal is an edematous itchy swelling generally resembling a mosquito bite, surrounded by redness, the flare. The wheal and flare reaction is seen also in positive skin tests for allergens **(figure 18.2).** Hives may occur, for example, when a person allergic to lobster eats some of the seafood. Lobster antigen absorbed from the intestinal tract enters the bloodstream and is carried to tissues such as skin, where it reacts with mast cells that have anti-lobster IgE antibody attached to them. Reaction between antibody and antigen on the mast cell surface releases histamine, which in turn causes dilation of tiny blood vessels and the leaking of plasma into skin tissues. Life-threatening respiratory obstruction is possible during a reaction if there is extensive tissue swelling in the throat and larynx. Because histamine is a major mediator in this situation, the reaction is blocked by antihistamines.

Hay fever (allergic rhinitis), marked by itching, teary eyes, sneezing, and runny nose, occurs when allergic persons inhale an antigen such as ragweed pollen to which they are sensitive. The mechanism is similar to that of hives and is also blocked by antihistamines.

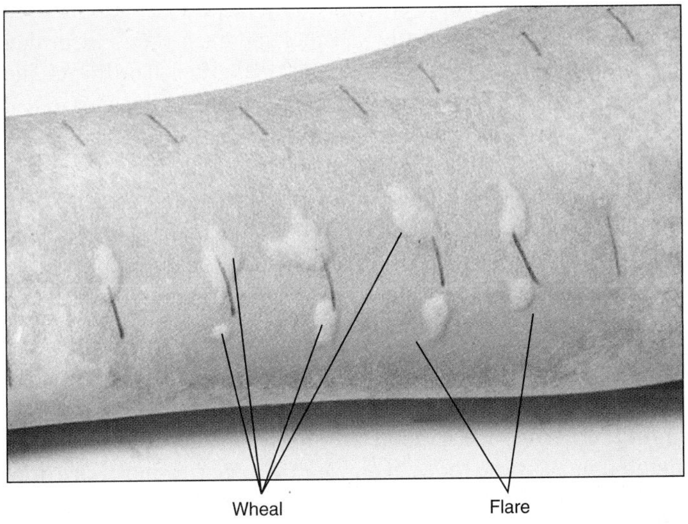
Wheal
Flare

FIGURE 18.2 The Wheal and Flare Skin Reaction of IgE-Mediated Allergies A variety of antigens are injected or placed in small cuts in the skin to test for sensitivity. Immediate wheal and flare reactions occur with antigens to which the person is sensitive.

Asthma is another type of immediate respiratory allergy. Antigen-induced release of chemical mediators from IgE-sensitized mast cell granules and from eosinophils attracted into the area of inflammation causes increased mucus secretion and spasms of the bronchi, markedly interfering with breathing. Mediators other than histamine, mainly lipids such as leukotrienes and prostaglandins and protein cytokines, are responsible for the bronchospasm and increased mucus production. Antihistamines are therefore not effective in treating asthma, but several other drugs are available to block the reaction, such as bronchodilating drugs that relax constricted muscles and relieve the bronchospasm. An example is albuterol, a bronchodilator usually delivered by an inhaler. Steroids are often used to decrease the inflammatory reaction. An anti-IgE therapy is described later.

Generalized Anaphylaxis

Generalized systemic anaphylaxis is a rare but serious form of IgE-mediated allergy. This is the form of anaphylaxis that killed Richet's dog. Antigen enters the bloodstream and becomes widespread. Instead of being localized in areas of the skin or respiratory tract, the reaction affects almost the entire body, causing a drop in blood pressure that can culminate in **shock.** Shock is a state in which the blood pressure is too low to supply the blood flow required to meet the oxygen needs of vital body tissues. In the case of generalized anaphylaxis, large amounts of released mediators cause extensive blood vessel dilation and loss of fluid from the blood, so that blood pressure falls dramatically and there is insufficient blood flow to vital organs such as the brain. Suffocation also occurs, the result of marked constriction of the bronchial tubes. Anaphylactic reactions may be fatal within minutes. Bee stings, peanuts, and penicillin injections probably account for most cases of generalized anaphylaxis. As mentioned in chapter 16, penicillin molecules are changed in the body to a haptenic form that can react with body proteins. In a small percentage of people, this hapten-protein complex causes the formation of IgE antibodies that react with penicillin. Fortunately, only a tiny fraction of people who make the antibodies are prone to anaphylactic shock. Peanuts and their products, such as peanut oil, are found in so many foods that it is often hard to predict where they will be encountered. The problem is widespread enough that peanuts have been barred by some airlines as a snack during flights. Generalized anaphylaxis can usually be controlled by epinephrine (Adrenalin) injected immediately. Anyone who has had a local allergic reaction to bee sting, penicillin, peanuts, or other substance is at risk of anaphylactic shock if exposed to the same substances and should wear a medical-alert bracelet and carry emergency medications.

Immunotherapy

Immunotherapy is a general term for techniques used to modify the immune system for a favorable effect. For example, one way of preventing immediate hypersensitivity reactions is to inject the person with extremely dilute solutions of the antigen, paradoxical in that even tiny amounts of antigen can risk severe generalized anaphylaxis. This form of immunotherapy is called **desensitization** or **hyposensitization.** The concentration of antigen in the injected solution is very gradually increased over a period of months in a series of injections. The individual gradually becomes less and less sensitive to the antigen and may even lose the hypersensitivity entirely. During treatment, there is an increase in the levels of IgG and a decrease in the IgE response to the antigen. The IgG antibodies produced are thought to protect the patient by binding to the offending antigen, thus preventing its attachment to cell-bound IgE (**figure 18.3**). Activation of regulatory T cells may also play a role, through release of cytokines that suppress the IgE-mediated response.

Another approach is to use antibodies to IgE (anti-IgE) to counteract and remove allergy-causing IgE. However, most IgE molecules are attached to receptors on mast cells and basophils. Injected anti-IgE would bind to IgE attached to cell receptors, causing cross-linking of receptors and massive disastrous mediator release. In order to use this form of immunotherapy, a safe and effective anti-IgE molecule had to be *engineered.* A first step was finding the amino acid sequences in the Fc portion of human IgE that bind to the IgE receptor on human cells. Then a monoclonal antibody (Mab) was produced in mouse cells that bound circulating human IgE specifically at that receptor-binding site. This Mab could not react with cell-bound IgE to cause mediator release because the binding site was already blocked by its attachment to cell receptors. Although the Mab blocked the IgE attachment to cells, mouse monoclonal antibodies were not effective in humans for very long because they are foreign molecules and are removed quickly from the body. The next step was to "humanize" the Mab by making a recombinant antibody with the antigen-binding site (anti-IgE) from the mouse Mab and the rest of the molecule from a human antibody. This hybrid recombinant molecule is called

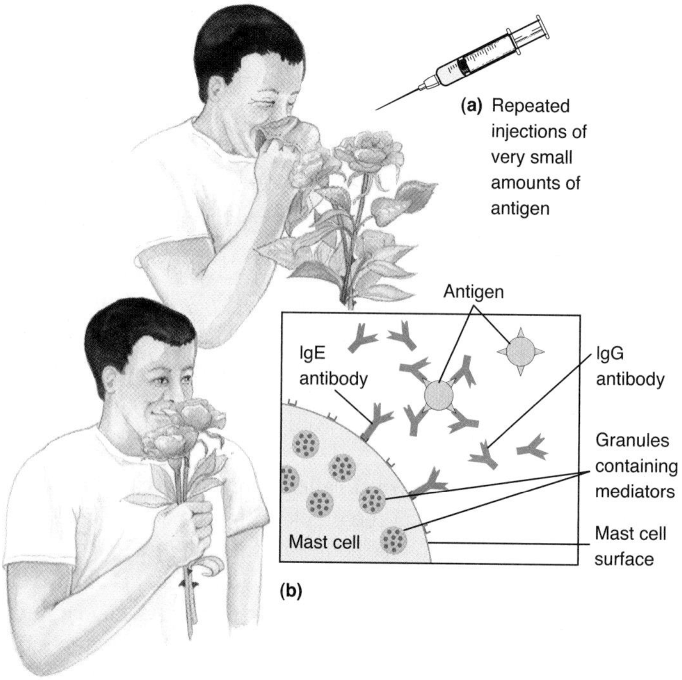

FIGURE 18.3 Immunotherapy for IgE Allergies (a) Repeated injections of very small amounts of antigen are given over several months. **(b)** This regimen leads to the formation of specific IgG antibodies. The IgG reacts with antigen before it can bind to IgE, and therefore it blocks the IgE reaction.

rhuMab (recombinant human Monoclonal antibody). RhuMab, also called omalizumab, injections are well tolerated by asthmatic people and are remarkably effective in treating their asthma, reducing their use of more toxic medications. Long-term use and value in treating other hypersensitivities are still being evaluated.

MICROCHECK 18.1

Hypersensitivity reactions are immunological reactions that cause tissue damage. Type I hypersensitivity reactions mediated by cell-bound IgE antibodies occur immediately after exposure to antigen. The reactions are caused by the release of mediators from mast cell granules. Localized anaphylactic reactions include hives, hay fever, and asthma; generalized reactions lead to anaphylactic shock. Immunotherapy is directed toward inducing IgG rather than IgE. Engineered anti-IgE (omalizumab) is a promising new immunotherapy under evaluation.

- ✓ How do localized and generalized anaphylactic reactions differ?
- ✓ Define allergen and give five common examples of substances that act as allergens.
- ✓ Why would leaking of plasma from blood vessels during an allergic reaction cause a wheal?

18.2

Type II Hypersensitivities: Cytotoxic

Focus Points

- Describe the immunologic reactions involved in type II hypersensitivities and contrast them with type I hypersensitivity reactions.
- Outline the main features of two kinds of type II sensitivity reactions.

In type II hypersensitivity reactions, complement-binding antibody reacting with cell surface antigens may cause injury or death of the cell. This phenomenon is especially striking in the case of red blood cells, because the reaction results in rupture of the cells and a visible release of hemoglobin. The reaction can occur in response to foreign antigenic or haptenic material such as a drug that attaches to erythrocytes or to platelets, but more common examples are transfusion reactions and hemolytic disease of the newborn. In these cases, normal red cells are destroyed as a result of antibodies reacting with erythrocyte epitopes. Cells can be destroyed in type II reactions not only by complement lysis, but also by **antibody-dependent cellular cytotoxicity (ADCC).**

■ epitope, p. 392 ■ complement, p. 375

Transfusion Reactions

Normal erythrocytes have many different antigens on their surfaces, and these antigens differ from one individual to another. When a person receives transfused red blood cells that are antigenically different from his or her own, immune lysis (by antibody and complement) of the red blood cells often results. This lytic reaction is especially likely when the antigens involved are those of the ABO blood group system. People are designated as having blood type A, B, AB, or O, depending on which, if any, ABO polysaccharide is present on the red blood cells. The possible ABO blood types are shown in **table 18.2.**

A locus on human chromosome 9 determines which of the ABO antigens will be present on an individual's red blood cells. Since one gene of the chromosome pair is originally derived from the mother and the other is from the father, the genes of the pair may differ. In the case of the ABO system, there are three possible types of genes for the chromosomal locus: A, B, and O. A and B genes each code for different glycosyltransferases responsible for attaching either A or B polysaccharide antigen to the red cell surface. The O gene does not code for either, indicating a lack of A or B glycosyltransferases. When both an A and a B gene are present, they are codominant, meaning that both antigens are expressed on the red blood cell surface.

One important and unexpected feature of the ABO system is that people who lack A or B erythrocyte polysaccharides have antibodies against the antigen that they lack. Thus, people with blood type O have both anti-A and anti-B antibodies; those of blood type A have anti-B; and those of type B have anti-A. Type AB people have neither anti-A nor anti-B antibodies. These antibodies are called **natural antibodies,** because they are present without any obvious or deliberate stimulus (the anti-A and anti-B antibodies are not present at birth but generally appear before the age of six months). These natural antibodies are mostly of the class IgM and are capable of binding complement and lysing red cells. Since they are IgM, they cannot cross the placenta. They most probably arise because of multiple exposures to small amounts of substances similar to the blood type antigens, substances known to be found in many environmental materials such as bacteria, dust, and foods.

A **transfusion reaction** can occur if a patient receives erythrocytes differing antigenically from his or her own during a blood

TABLE 18.2 Antigens and Antibodies in Human ABO Blood Groups

			Incidence of Type in United States		
Blood Type	**Antigen Present on Erythrocyte Membranes**	**Antibody in Plasma**	**Among Whites**	**Among Asians**	**Among Blacks**
A	A	Anti-B	41%	28%	27%
B	B	Anti-A	10%	27%	20%
AB	A and B	Neither anti-A nor anti-B	4%	5%	7%
O	Neither	Anti-A and anti-B	45%	40%	46%

transfusion. Cross-matching the bloods and other techniques are used to ensure compatibility of donor and recipient. In the case of ABO incompatibility, IgM antibodies cause a type II hypersensitivity reaction. The symptoms of a typical transfusion reaction include fever, low blood pressure, pain, nausea, and vomiting. These symptoms occur because the foreign erythrocytes are agglutinated by the recipient's antibody, complement is activated, and red blood cells are lysed.

Hemolytic Disease of the Newborn

There are a number of other human red cell antigen systems; an important one is the Rhesus, or Rh system (first described in rhesus monkeys). It is the practice to test donor and recipient bloods for Rh and other possible incompatibilities in addition to ABO.

The Rh (Rhesus) blood group system is complex and involves various antigens. If an Rh antigen is present on a person's erythrocytes, he or she is Rh-positive; if it is lacking, the person is Rh-negative. Rh-positive people have the Rh antigen and do not make antibodies to it. An Rh-negative adult, however, may have a transfusion reaction as a result of being immunized against the Rh antigen, through a blood transfusion, organ graft, or pregnancy that might lead to introduction of the antigen and consequent development of anti-Rh antibodies. The Rh-positive cells are destroyed by macrophages in antibody-dependent cellular cytotoxicity, not by complement lysis.

Anti-Rh antibodies formed by a pregnant woman may cross the placenta and damage her baby. The resulting disease is called **hemolytic disease of the newborn** or simply Rh disease **(figure 18.4).** Blood incompatibilities other than Rh may be responsible

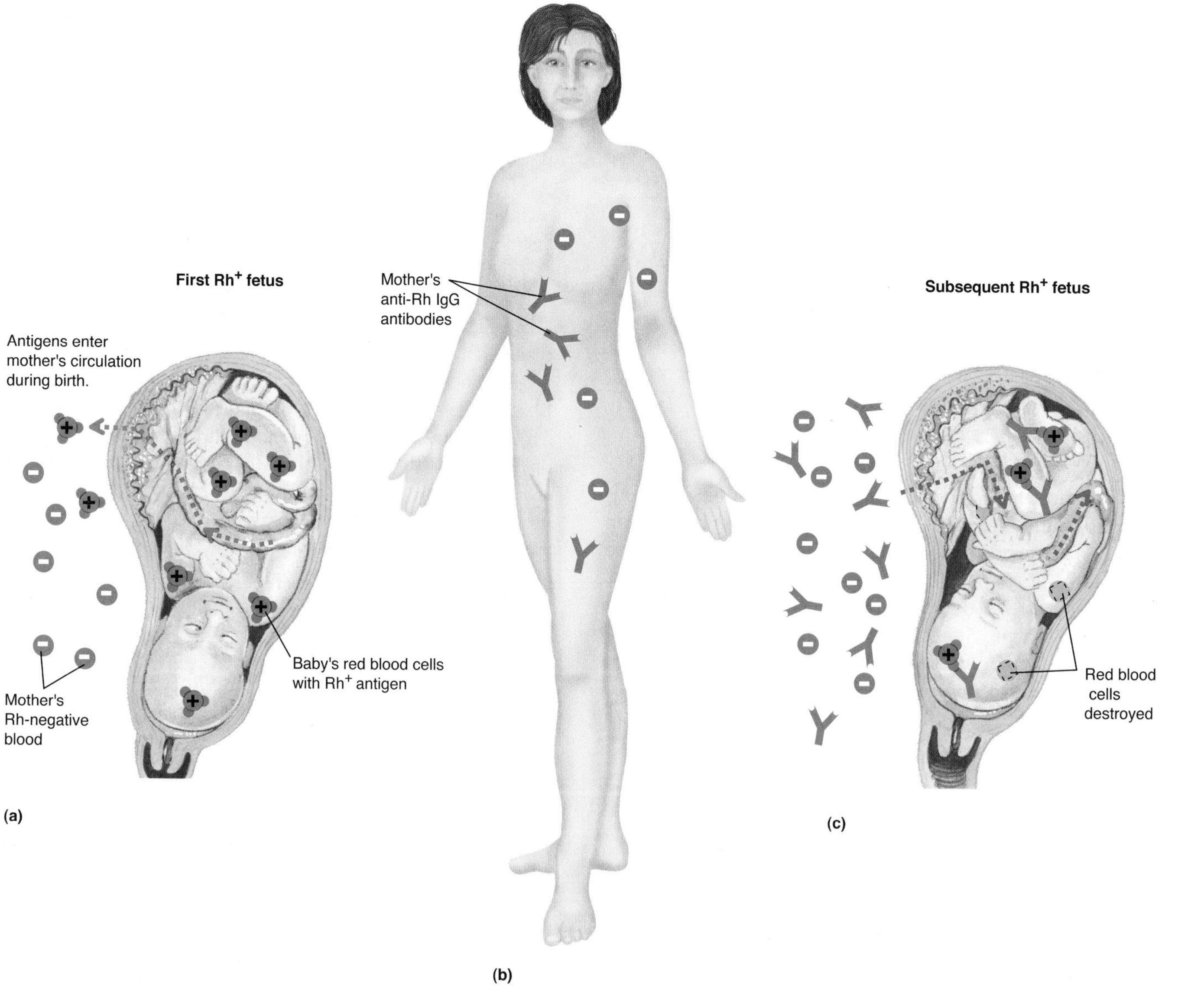

FIGURE 18.4 Hemolytic Disease of the Newborn **(a)** The fetus of an Rh-negative (Rh$^-$) mother may inherit paternal genes for Rh antigens and have Rh-positive (Rh$^+$) blood. During delivery of a first Rh$^+$ baby, enough Rh$^+$ red cells can enter the Rh$^-$ mother to induce an anti-Rh response. **(b)** The mother makes a primary response to Rh antigens and develops memory cells for anti-Rh antibodies. **(c)** During subsequent pregnancies with an Rh$^+$ fetus, the very few fetal red cells that cross the placenta can cause a vigorous secondary response. The IgG anti-Rh antibodies cross the placenta and destroy the baby's red blood cells.

for hemolytic disease of the newborn, but such cases are generally less severe.

While an Rh-negative mother is carrying an Rh-positive fetus, a few fetal red blood cells enter the mother's circulation via the placenta, but usually not enough to cause a primary antibody response. At the time of birth, however, enough of the Rh-positive baby's erythrocytes may enter the mother's circulation to cause an immune response. Induced or spontaneous abortions may also be responsible for immunizing an Rh-negative mother to the Rh antigen. The anti-Rh antibodies formed by the mother cause her no harm, because her red blood cells lack the Rh antigen. With the second and each subsequent Rh-positive fetus, however, even a few Rh-positive cells that might enter the mother's circulation from the fetus are enough to provoke a secondary response. The result is that the mother produces large quantities of anti-Rh antibodies of the class IgG. Like other IgG antibodies, anti-Rh antibodies readily cross the placenta, enter the circulation of the fetus, and cause extensive fetal red cell damage. To save its life, it may be necessary to transfuse the fetus *in utero* repeatedly, using Rh-negative blood. Much more commonly, the disease process only becomes threatening shortly after birth.

The fetus can usually survive the anti-Rh antibody attack while still *in utero* because harmful products of red cell destruction are eliminated from its system by enzymes of the mother. These enzymes are present in only scant amounts in the newborn. As early as 36 hours after birth, jaundice may appear and result in permanent brain damage or even death. Not only does the baby become seriously ill from the toxic products of red cell destruction, but it also develops a severe anemia. In this critical situation, it may be necessary to withdraw a portion of the baby's blood and replace it with Rh-negative blood. Also, irradiation of the baby with light at wavelengths 420 to 480 nm converts the red blood cell breakdown products to a form more readily excretable.

Most cases of hemolytic disease caused by Rh incompatibility are preventable by injecting the Rh-negative mother with anti-Rh antibodies within the first 24 to 48 hours (and preferably within the first few hours) after abortion or delivery. These administered antibodies bind to the baby's Rh-positive red cells that have entered the mother's circulation and prevent the development of a primary response. This treatment does not inhibit the activation of B memory cells or a secondary immune response, and therefore is not helpful if the mother is already sensitized to the Rh antigens. ■ control of antibody responses, p. 398

MICROCHECK 18.2

Type II cytotoxic hypersensitivity reactions are mediated by antibodies, either by complement lysis of cells or by antibody-dependent cellular cytotoxicity. Blood transfusion reactions and hemolytic disease of the newborn are examples.

- ✓ Describe the mechanism of cell damage in a blood transfusion where ABO antigens are mismatched.
- ✓ Why do Rh-negative but not Rh-positive mothers sometimes have babies with hemolytic disease of the newborn?
- ✓ Why is the finding surprising that people lacking the A or B antigen are found to have antibodies to the corresponding antigen (anti-A or anti-B)?

18.3 Type III Hypersensitivities: Immune Complex–Mediated

Focus Points

- Describe the importance of immune complexes in type III hypersensitivity reactions.
- List six medical conditions in which type III hypersensitivities play an important role.

An **immune complex** consists of antigen and antibody bound together, often with some complement components. Immune complexes usually adhere to Fc receptors on cells of the mononuclear phagocyte system and are engulfed and destroyed intracellularly, especially if they are large complexes. Under ordinary circumstances, they are rapidly removed from circulation. In conditions where a moderate excess of antigen over antibody exists, however, small complexes of IgG tightly bound to antigen form. These complexes are not quickly removed and destroyed but persist in circulation or at their sites of formation in tissue. Immune complexes possess considerable biological activity. They initiate the blood clotting mechanism, and they activate components of complement that attract neutrophils into the area and contribute to inflammation **(figure 18.5).** Proteases released from the neutrophils are especially active in inducing tissue damage. Circulating immune complexes are commonly deposited in skin, joints, and the kidneys; deposition of immune complexes in kidneys causes glomerulonephritis. Immune complexes are responsible for the rashes, joint pains, and other symptoms seen in a number of diseases, such as farmer's lung, bacterial endocarditis, early rubella infection, and malaria. Immune complexes can also precipitate a devastating condition, **disseminated intravascular coagulation,** in which clots form in small blood vessels, leading to failure of vital organs. ■ disseminated intravascular coagulation, p. 714 ■ glomerulonephritis, pp. 529, 712

Immune complex disease may arise during a variety of bacterial, viral, and protozoan infections, as well as from inhaled dusts or bacteria and injected medications such as penicillin. The steps in the formation of immune complex pathology are summarized in **table 18.3.**

Immune complex formation is also responsible for the localized injury or death of tissue, known as the **Arthus reaction,** that occurs if antigen is injected into the tissue of a previously immunized animal or person with high levels of circulating specific antibody. The immune complexes form outside the blood vessels, in the tissues, and activate complement, producing complement components that attract neutrophils. The release of neutrophil enzymes contributes to a local inflammatory response that peaks in 6 to 12 hours.

Serum sickness is an immune complex disease caused by passive immunization where an antibody-containing serum from a horse or other animal is injected into humans to prevent or treat a disease such as diphtheria or tetanus. The recipient of the animal serum may make an immune response to antigens in the foreign serum, and after 7 to 10 days enough immune complexes form to cause signs of disease, which include fever, inflammation of

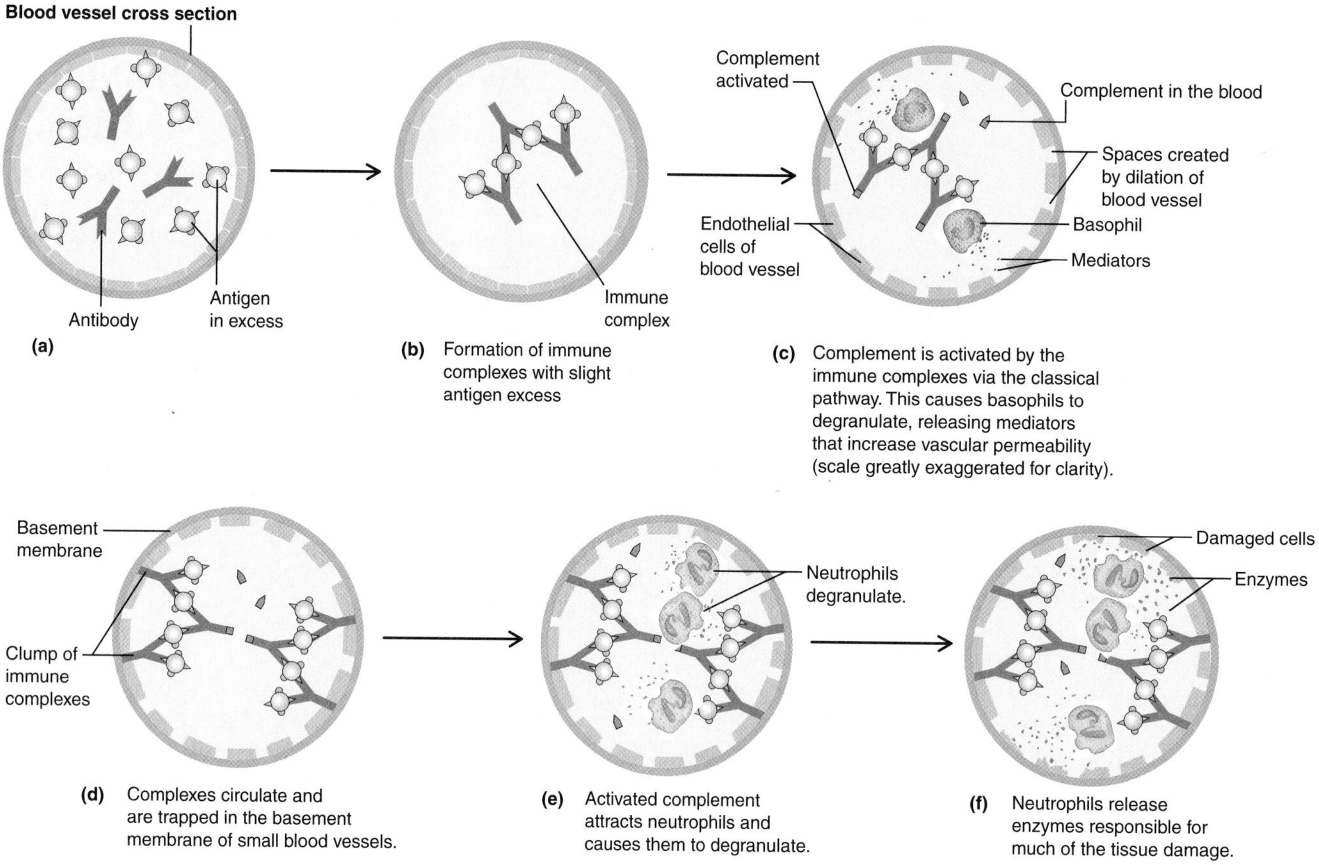

FIGURE 18.5 Type III Hypersensitivity: Immune Complex-Mediated

blood vessels, arthritis, and kidney damage. The disease generally resolves as the antigens of the animal serum are cleared. Of course, horses are no longer used to produce antibodies against diphtheria and tetanus; instead, hyperimmune human sera are used. The serum sickness form of hypersensitivity is rarely seen now, but it can occur following treatment of heart attack patients with the bacterial enzyme streptokinase to dissolve clots, after the use of serum from horses immunized with snake venom to treat snakebites in people, or in a few other rare instances. ■ passive immunity, p. 414

TABLE 18.3 Pathogenesis of Immune Complex Disease

1. IgG antibody combines with excess soluble antigen.
2. The antibody-antigen combination reacts with complement.
3. Complexes are deposited in sites such as skin, kidney, and joints.
4. Fragments of complement cause release of histamine and other mediator substances from mast cells or basophils and also attract neutrophils.
5. Release of the mediators causes increased permeability of blood vessel walls.
6. Immune complexes penetrate or form in blood vessel walls.
7. Neutrophils enter the vessel walls chemotactically.
8. Neutrophils release lysosomal enzymes, especially proteases, that induce tissue injury.

MICROCHECK 18.3

Type III immune complex–mediated hypersensitivities are caused by small complexes of antigen-antibody and complement that persist in tissues or blood and that cause inflammation.

- ✓ Why do immune complexes remain in the circulation or in the tissues in immune complex diseases?
- ✓ How can immune complexes cause tissue damage?
- ✓ Why would the kidneys be particularly prone to immune complex damage?

18.4 Type IV Hypersensitivities: Delayed Cell-Mediated

Focus Points

- Describe the key immunologic reactions involved in type IV hypersensitivities.
- Define the importance of type IV hypersensitivity reactions in infectious diseases.

Harmful effects produced by the mechanisms of cell-mediated immunity are referred to as **delayed hypersensitivity.** The name reflects the slowly developing response to antigen; reactions peak at 2 to 3 days rather than in minutes as in immediate hypersensitivity. As would be expected with cell-mediated responses, T cells are responsible and antibodies are not involved. Delayed hypersensitivity reactions can occur almost anywhere in the body. They are wholly or partly responsible for **contact dermatitis** (such as from poison ivy and poison oak), tissue damage in a variety of infectious diseases, rejection of tissue grafts, and some autoimmune diseases directed against antigens of self.

Tuberculin Skin Test

A familiar example of a delayed hypersensitivity reaction is the positive reaction to a tuberculin skin test that occurs in most people who have been infected with *Mycobacterium tuberculosis.* This test involves the introduction of very small quantities of protein antigens of the tubercle bacillus into the skin. In those with delayed hypersensitivity to *M. tuberculosis,* the site of injection reddens and gradually becomes indurated (thickened) within 6 to 24 hours. The reaction reaches its peak at 2 to 3 days **(figure 18.6).** There is no wheal formation, as would be seen with IgE-mediated reactions. The redness and induration of delayed skin hypersensitivity reactions are the result mainly of the reaction of sensitized T cells with specific antigen, followed by the release of cytokines and the influx of macrophages to the injection site.

Contact Hypersensitivities

Contact hypersensitivity is mediated by T cells. The T cells that have become sensitized to a particular antigen release cytokines when they come into contact again with the same antigen. These cytokines cause inflammatory reactions that attract macrophages to the site. The macrophages then release mediators that add to the inflammatory response, resulting in allergic dermatitis.

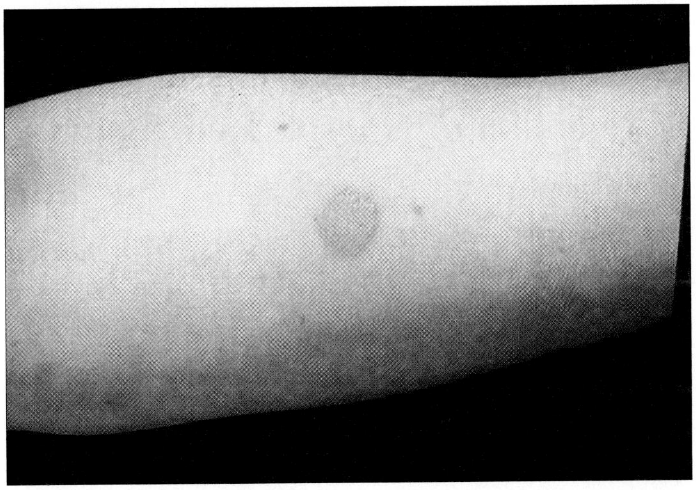

FIGURE 18.6 Positive Delayed (Type IV) Hypersensitivity Skin Test Injection of tuberculin protein into the skin of a person sensitized to the tubercle bacilli causes a firm red plaque to form by 48 to 72 hours. A reaction greater than 10 mm in diameter is considered positive.

Familiar examples of contact hypersensitivity (contact allergy or contact dermatitis) are poison ivy and poison oak **(figure 18.7)** and allergic reactions to the nickel of metal jewelry, the chromium salts in certain leather products, or components of some cosmetics. In the case of poison oak or ivy, a hapten from an oily product of the plant is responsible. With a metal, a soluble salt of the metal acts as a hapten.

Latex products are a frequent cause of contact hypersensitivity reactions, and they also can cause IgE-mediated reactions. Latex, a product of the rubber tree, contains a plant protein that readily induces sensitization. Many products contain latex, such as fabrics, elastics, toys, and contraceptive condoms, but latex gloves probably account for most latex sensitization. Gloves are used extensively by health care and laboratory workers, food preparers, and many others. Typically, a person will notice redness, itching, and a rash on the hands after wearing gloves. To prevent the reaction, latex gloves should be replaced by vinyl or other synthetic gloves. Topical cortisone-like medications are effective treatment.

The causative substance in contact hypersensitivity is commonly detected by patch tests, in which suspect substances are applied to the skin under an adhesive bandage. Positive reactions reach their maximum in about 3 days and consist of redness, itching, and blisters of the skin. **Figure 18.8** shows a severe contact hypersensitivity skin rash.

Delayed Hypersensitivity in Infectious Diseases

The role of cell-mediated immunity in combating intracellular infections through the cell-destroying activity of activated macrophages and T lymphocytes was discussed previously. Although these functions are protective, tissue damage or hypersensitivity also results. These infections may be caused by viruses, mycobacteria and certain other bacteria, protozoa, and fungi. They include leprosy, tuberculosis, leishmaniasis, and herpes simplex, among many others. In particularly slowly progressing infections, delayed hypersensitivity causes extensive cell destruction and progressive impairment of tissue function, such as the damaged sensory nerves in leprosy. The immune response is a two-edged sword, protecting on the one side, but causing damage on the other. ■ **immunity to intracellular infections, p. 388** ■ **leprosy, p. 688**

MICROCHECK 18.4

Type IV delayed hypersensitivity depends on the action of sensitized T cells. The reaction peaks 2 to 3 days after exposure to antigen. Examples are contact dermatitis, damage in a variety of infectious diseases, rejection of tissue grafts, and some autoimmune diseases.

- ✓ Explain the events that occur in the skin during a positive delayed hypersensitivity skin test.
- ✓ Describe a patch test for contact hypersensitivity.
- ✓ In the tuberculin skin test, why would there be no reaction if there is no infection?

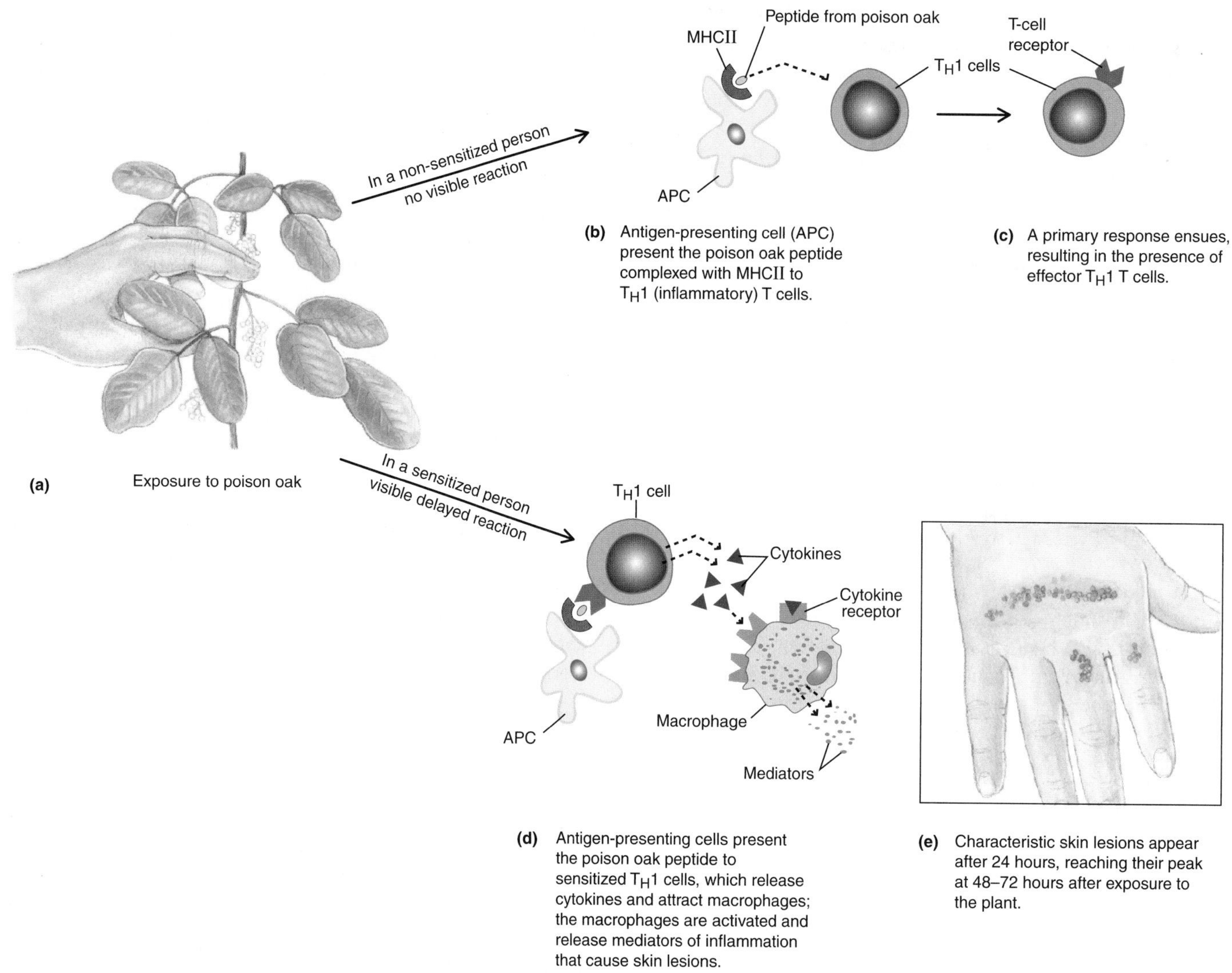

Peptide from poison oak
MHCII
T-cell receptor
T_H1 cells
APC
In a non-sensitized person no visible reaction
(b) Antigen-presenting cell (APC) present the poison oak peptide complexed with MHCII to T_H1 (inflammatory) T cells.
(c) A primary response ensues, resulting in the presence of effector T_H1 T cells.
(a) Exposure to poison oak
In a sensitized person visible delayed reaction
T_H1 cell
Cytokines
Cytokine receptor
Macrophage
APC
Mediators
(d) Antigen-presenting cells present the poison oak peptide to sensitized T_H1 cells, which release cytokines and attract macrophages; the macrophages are activated and release mediators of inflammation that cause skin lesions.
(e) Characteristic skin lesions appear after 24 hours, reaching their peak at 48–72 hours after exposure to the plant.

FIGURE 18.7 Poison Oak Dermatitis Is an Example of Type IV Hypersensitivity: Delayed Cell-Mediated

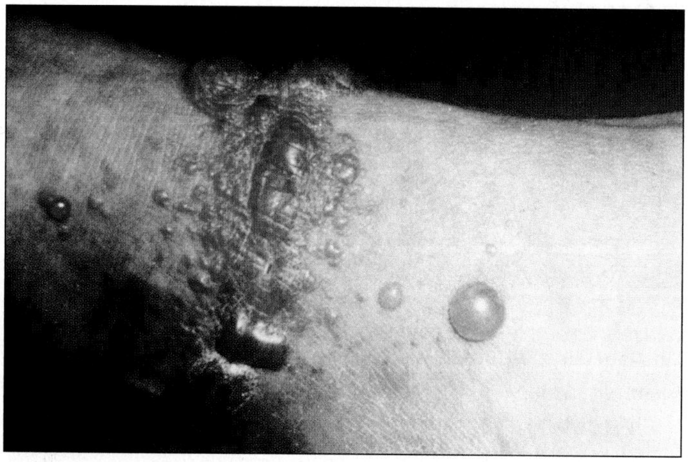

FIGURE 18.8 Severe Contact Hypersensitivity Skin Rash, Showing Redness, Blisters, and Scaling of the Skin

18.5

Rejection of Transplanted Tissues

Focus Points

- Explain why rejection of transplanted tissues occurs.
- Describe the mode of action of medications used to prevent rejection of transplanted tissue.

Transplantation of organs and other tissues between genetically non-identical humans is a well-established clinical procedure. These grafts are called **allografts.** Xenografts, from non-human species, such as pigs, may become more widely available with the development of cloned animals having tissues more closely compatible with humans. The major drawback to graft transplantation is possible immunological rejection of the transplant.

PERSPECTIVE 18.1

The Fetus As an Allograft

Grafts between non-identical members of the same species are **allografts,** and they are normally rejected by immunological mechanisms. The rejection time for grafts that differ in their major histocompatibility antigens is measured in days, about 10 to 14 days in most instances. The rejection process is complex, but it depends principally on host T-cell destruction of grafted cells. For example, when skin allografts are transplanted, the grafted skin appears normal for about a week. Gradually it begins to look bruised and unhealthy, until 10 days to 2 weeks after transplantation. By that time the grafted skin becomes dried and is sloughed off. Microscopic examination of the graft shows that by the end of the first week T cells invade the tissues and within the next few days these lymphocytes have killed the grafted cells. The same events occur in allografts of kidney or other organs, unless effective immunosuppressive therapy is given. There is one kind of allograft that does not follow this sequence and that is not rejected, however—the mammalian fetus.

The fetus is an allograft, with half of its antigens of paternal origin and likely to differ from the other half contributed by the mother. In spite of these major immunological differences, the fetus lives and thrives in the uterus for 9 months and is not rejected. In fact, over a period of years a mother often has several (or even occasionally as many as 20!) children without showing any signs of immunological rejection of the fetus. The mechanisms for survival of the fetal allograft have been the subject of research for many years, but they are not yet fully understood.

It cannot be that paternal antigens from the fetus do not reach the mother's immune system to cause a response. Mothers are known to make antibodies to paternal antigens, such as the Rhesus red blood cell antigens. Also the antibodies used for typing major histocompatibility antigens have long been obtained from women who have borne several children by the same father and have made antibodies to his MHC antigens. Furthermore, various techniques show the presence of small numbers of fetal cells in the maternal circulation during pregnancy. Clearly, paternal antigens can reach the mother's immune system and cause a response. The placenta, however, does prevent most fetal cells from entering the mother and most maternal T cells from reaching the fetus.

The outer layer of the placenta, the trophoblast, forms sort of a buffer zone between the fetus and the mother. The trophoblast does not express MHC class I or II antigens and is not subject to T-cell attack; it also has a mechanism for avoiding destruction by natural killer cells. Thus, the fetus is protected by being in an immunologically privileged site. A few other areas in the body—the brain, the eyes, and the testes—are also immunologically privileged sites. Antigens leaving these sites do not drain through lymphatic vessels and reach lymphoid tissues where antigen-presenting cells are abundant. Also, antigen leaves these privileged sites accompanied by cytokines that are immunosuppressive and direct the immune response toward tolerance, rather than toward active harmful responses. It is well recognized that maternal immune responses are suppressed to some extent during pregnancy, though the reasons for this are not clear.

Thus, one major factor responsible for preventing the rejection of the fetal allograft is the location of the fetus in the uterus, protected by the placental barrier. A second factor is the ability of the pregnancy to cause an immunosuppressive response in the mother.

Body cells vary antigenically from individual to individual, and differences between tissues of the transplant donor and recipient lead to rejection of the graft. Transplantation rejection in this situation is predominantly a type IV cellular immunological reaction showing both specificity and memory. Killing of the graft cells occurs through a complex combination of mechanisms, including direct contact with sensitized T-cytotoxic lymphocytes and natural killer (NK) cells. The ability to overcome immunologic rejection by treatment with immunosuppressive agents allows the grafts to survive. **Perspective 18.1** discusses a very special transplantation situation, the fetus as an allograft. ■ Cytotoxic T cells, p. 390 ■ NK cells, p. 406

There are many different tissue antigens, but those of the major histocompatibility complex (MHC) system are the ones most commonly involved in transplantation graft rejections. Although these MHC antigens are found on many human cells, they are abundant on leukocytes and are called human leukocyte antigens or HLAs. MHC tissue typing is done in an effort to ensure that no major tissue incompatibility exists between a prospective tissue donor and the recipient patient. In addition to carefully matching donor and recipient tissue antigens, it is necessary to use immunosuppressant drugs indefinitely to prevent graft rejection. These drugs are needed because many minor antigens exist and except with identical siblings it is impossible to find a donor compatible in all of these tissue antigens. ■ MHC molecules, p. 402

Radiation and various cytotoxic immunosuppressive drugs interfere with the rejection process, but at the same time they make the patient susceptible to opportunistic infections and also more likely to develop cancer. Cyclosporin A (produced by a fungus) and tacrolimus (produced from a species of *Streptomyces*) are examples of effective immunosuppressants. They interfere with cellular signaling and thereby inhibit clonal expansion of activated T lymphocytes. These drugs specifically suppress T-cell proliferation, and thus they have fewer side effects than other immunosuppressants that affect many cell types.

Combinations of agents are commonly used to prevent allograft rejection. For example, cyclosporin A and a cortisone-like steroid may be given, along with a monoclonal antibody preparation called basiliximab. This preparation blocks IL-2 binding to T-cell receptors thereby preventing activation of the cells.

MICROCHECK 18.5

Successful organ and tissue transplantation depend on matching major histocompatibility antigens and using immunosuppressive agents such as cyclosporin and tacrolimus to minimize the immune response to other antigens of the graft. Rejection of transplants is complex, but type IV cellular immune responses are the major mechanism of rejection for allografts.

- ✓ What are the antigens primarily responsible for allograft rejection?
- ✓ How are allografts rejected?
- ✓ Why is matching of transplant donors and recipients important?
- ✓ What would happen if administration of the antirejection drugs were discontinued?

18.6

Autoimmune Diseases

Focus Points

- Outline the concept of autoimmunity.
- Give four examples of autoimmune diseases and the mechanism of tissue injury in each.

Usually, the body's immune system recognizes its self-antigens and deletes clones of cells that would respond and attack its own tissues. A growing number of diseases are suspected of being caused by an autoimmune process, however, meaning that the immune system responds to tissues of the body as if they were foreign. Some of these diseases are listed in **table 18.4.** Susceptibility to many of them is influenced by the major histocompatibility makeup of the patient, and so, not surprisingly, they often occur in the same family. ■ negative selection, p. 409

Autoimmune diseases may result from reaction to antigens that are similar though not identical to antigens of self. Some bacterial and viral agents evade destruction by the immune system by developing amino acid sequences that are similar to self-antigens. As a result, the immune system may be unable to discriminate between the agent and self. The immune system then destroys the substances of self as well as those of the bacterium or virus. It has been found that the likeness of amino acid sequences need not be exact for this self-destruction; even a 50% likeness may lead to an autoimmune response. Autoimmune responses may also occur after tissue injury in which self-antigens are released from the injured organ, as in the case of a heart attack. The autoantibodies formed react with heart tissue and evidence suggests that they can cause further damage.

The Spectrum of Autoimmune Reactions

Autoimmune reactions occur over a spectrum ranging from organ-specific to widespread responses not limited to any one tissue. Examples of organ-specific autoimmune reactions are several kinds of thyroid disease, in which only the thyroid is affected. Widespread responses include lupus erythematosus and rheumatoid arthritis. Lupus is a disease in which autoantibodies are made against nuclear constituents of all body cells. In rheumatoid arthritis, an immune response is made against the collagen protein of supporting connective tissues. In these widespread diseases, many organs are affected. In both organ-specific and widespread autoimmune diseases, the damage may be caused either by antibodies, immune cells, or both.

Myasthenia gravis, characterized by muscle weakness, is an example of an **autoantibody-mediated disease.** The disease is caused by the production of antibodies to the acetylcholine receptor proteins that are present on muscle membranes where the nerve contacts the muscle. Normally, transmission of the impulses from the nerve to the muscle takes place when acetylcholine is released from the end of the nerve and crosses the gap to the muscle fiber, causing muscle contraction. In myasthenia gravis IgG autoantibodies bind to the acetylcholine receptors, blocking access of acetylcholine to the receptors. These antibodies along with complement cause many of the receptors to be degraded, so that fewer receptors are present on the muscle membranes. Babies born to mothers with myasthenia gravis also experience muscle weakness, since IgG antibodies cross the placenta. Fortunately, the effect is not permanent, as these IgG antibodies decay within a few months and the babies are no longer affected. Treatment of myasthenia gravis includes the administration of drugs that inhibit the enzyme cholinesterase, allowing acetylcholine to accumulate so some contact with receptors can occur. Immunosuppressive medications and thymectomy are helpful in many cases. The role of the thymus in this disease is not understood.

Type 1 diabetes mellitus, also known as insulin-dependent or juvenile onset diabetes, is an autoimmune disease caused by *cellular mechanisms.* Although autoantibodies are present, the major damage is destruction of the insulin-producing β cells of the pancreas by infiltrating cytotoxic T cells. When the β cells are destroyed there is a lack of insulin, resulting in an increase of glucose in the blood. This leads to marked thirst and increased urine production. Although type 1 diabetes can occur at any age, the peak onset of this disease is about 12 years of age. Persons with type 1 diabetes must receive multiple injections of insulin daily to forestall complications such as blindness and kidney failure. In the

TABLE 18.4 Characteristics of Some Autoimmune Diseases

Disease	Organ Specificity	Major Mechanism of Tissue Damage
Graves' disease	Thyroid	Autoantibodies bind thyroid-stimulating hormone receptor, causing overstimulation of thyroid
Myasthenia gravis	Muscle	Autoantibodies bind to acetylcholine receptor on muscle, preventing muscle contraction
Type 1 diabetes mellitus	Pancreas	T-cell destruction of pancreatic β cells
Autoimmune hemolytic anemia	Red blood cells	Antibody, complement, and phagocyte destruction of red cells
Rheumatoid arthritis	Widespread, especially joints	Lymphocyte destruction of joint tissues; immune complexes of IgG and anti-IgG
Systemic lupus erythematosus	Widespread (glomerulonephritis, vasculitis, arthritis)	Autoantibodies to DNA and other nuclear components form immune complexes in small blood vessels

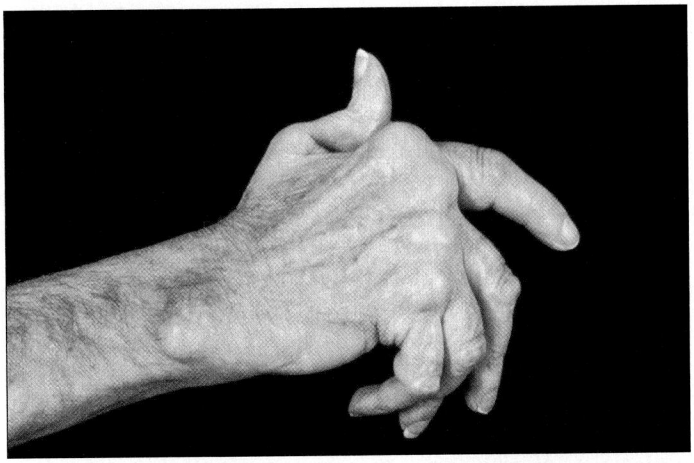

FIGURE 18.9 The Autoimmune Reactions of Rheumatoid Arthritis Cause Chronic Inflammation and Destruction of the Joints

United States there are an estimated one million victims of type 1 diabetes, representing a small fraction of all diabetes cases.

A combination of antibody and cellular mechanisms is active in some autoimmune diseases, such as **rheumatoid arthritis (figure 18.9).** This crippling inflammatory condition is one of the most common autoimmune diseases, occurring in both sexes and in adults and children all over the world. About 1% of males and 3% of females in the United States are affected. Rheumatoid arthritis is most common in women ages 30 to 50. T_H 1 cells, the inflammatory CD4 T cells, infiltrate the joints. When stimulated by specific antigens, the T cells release cytokines that cause inflammation. Autoantibodies are also formed and contribute to widespread tissue damage by forming immune complexes.

In **Graves' disease,** autoantibody is directed at an antigen of the thyroid gland. Normally, this antigen is a receptor for the pituitary hormone TSH (Thyroid Stimulating Hormone). Attachment of the autoantibody does not damage the thyroid gland, but causes it to enlarge and markedly overproduce thyroid hormone. Affected individuals suffer weight loss, heat intolerance, muscle weakness, rapid heartbeat, and other effects of too much thyroid hormone.

Treatment of Autoimmune Diseases

Autoimmune diseases are usually treated with immunosuppressants that kill dividing cells and thus control the response, or drugs that interfere with T-cell signaling, such as cyclosporin. Also, cortisone-like steroids and other anti-inflammatory medications are often used. Replacement therapy is necessary in some of the diseases, such as insulin in type 1 diabetes.

In type 1 diabetes, attempts are made to cure the disease by replacing the tissues destroyed by immune cells. Transplantation of the pancreas or insulin-producing cells of the pancreas has been successful in many cases, but dangerous immunosuppressive agents must be given to prevent rejection. Generally, only those with advanced diabetes who require a kidney transplant, and must take the immunosuppressive drugs anyway, are given pancreas transplants. Research efforts are directed toward developing better methods of transplantation, such as injecting cells harvested from cadaver pancreases into the vein that carries blood to the liver. The cells establish themselves in the liver and produce insulin, often eliminating or decreasing the need for injected insulin. However, the cells usually die off in months or a few years, and the immunosuppressant side effects are often severe. Stem cell research holds greater promise for a cure of type 1 diabetes. ■ stem cells, p. 369

Ideally, it would be better to induce tolerance to the specific antigen causing the immune response. Experimentally, diabetic mice fed with insulin were protected from their diabetes. Rheumatoid arthritis patients often have an active immune response to collagen, a protein present in the joints and surrounding tissues. An experimental treatment involves feeding solutions of animal collagen daily to the patients. The rationale of these experiments depends on a well-known phenomenon called **feeding** or **oral tolerance.** Antigen introduced by the oral route can cause a local intestinal immune response with release of cytokines, down-regulation of antigen receptors, and deletion of immune cells. Trials of oral administration of antigens in people have shown benefit in several autoimmune diseases, but there is much still to be learned about the immunological mechanisms, antigen preparations, doses, and duration of treatment. ■ immunological tolerance, p. 388

MICROCHECK 18.6

Autoimmune disease can result when the immune system reacts to substances of self. Autoimmune diseases cover a spectrum from organ-specific to generalized. They are treated with drugs that suppress immune or inflammatory responses. Attempts are being made to induce specific tolerance to the causative substances.

- ✓ How could viruses or bacteria be implicated in causing autoimmune diseases?
- ✓ Explain what is meant by the spectrum of autoimmune diseases, from organ-specific to generalized.
- ✓ What advantages might stem cells have over pancreatic cell allografts in treating type I diabetes?

18.7

Immunodeficiency Disorders

Focus Points

- Contrast the two main categories of immunodeficiency disorders.
- Explain how immunodeficiency can lead to infection.

The immunologic disorders discussed up to now can be viewed as resulting from the overreaction of the body's immune systems. By contrast, in immunodeficiencies, the body is incapable of making or sustaining an adequate immune response. There are two basic types of immunodeficiency diseases: primary, or congenital; and secondary, or acquired. Primary immunodeficiency can be inborn as the result of a genetic defect or can result from developmental abnormalities. Secondary immunodeficiency can be acquired as the result of infection or other stresses on the immune system such as malnutrition. People with either type of immunodeficiency are subject to repeated infections. The types of these infections will often depend on which part of the immune system is absent or malfunctioning. Some of the more important immunodeficiency diseases are listed in **table 18.5.**

Primary Immunodeficiencies

The genetic or developmental abnormalities that cause primary immunodeficiencies affect B cells, T cells, or both. Some primary immunodeficiencies affect natural killer (NK) cells, phagocytes, or complement components. Primary immunodeficiencies are generally rare. Agammaglobulinemia, a disease in which few or no antibodies are produced, occurs in one in about 50,000 people, and severe combined immunodeficiency (SCID), where neither T nor B lymphocytes are functional, occurs in only about one of 500,000 live births.

Selective IgA deficiency, in which very little or no IgA is produced, is the most common primary immunodeficiency known. It has been reported in different studies to occur as often as one per 333 to 700 people. Although people with this disorder may appear healthy, many have repeated bacterial infections of the respiratory, gastrointestinal, and genitourinary tracts, where secretory IgA is normally protective.

Primary deficiencies may occur in various components of the complement system. For example, the few individuals who lack C3 are prone to develop severe, life-threatening infections with encapsulated and pyogenic bacteria. Patients with deficiencies in the early components of complement such as C1 and C2, may develop immune complex diseases, because these components normally help to clear immune complexes from the circulation. Patients who lack late components of the classical pathway of C activation (C5, C6, C7, C8) have recurrent *Neisseria* infections. Immunity to these bacteria is associated with destruction of the organisms by complement-dependent bactericidal antibodies. People who lack one of the important control proteins of the sequence, C1-inhibitor, experience uncontrolled complement activation. This causes fluid accumulation and potentially fatal tissue swelling, a condition called **hereditary angioneurotic edema.** ■ complement systems, p. 375

In children with DiGeorge syndrome, the thymus fails to develop in the embryo. As a result, T cells do not differentiate and are absent. Affected individuals have other developmental defects as well, such as heart and blood vessel abnormalities, and a characteristic appearance with low-set deformed ears, small mouth, and wide-set eyes. As expected from a lack of T cells, affected people are very susceptible to infections by eukaryotic pathogens, such as *Pneumocystis carinii* and other fungi, as well as viruses and obligate intracellular bacteria. ■ *Pneumocystis carinii*, p. 749

Severe combined immunodeficiency (SCID) results when neither T nor B lymphocytes are produced from bone marrow stem cells. Children with SCID die of infectious diseases at an early age unless they are successfully treated by receiving a bone marrow transplant to reconstitute the bone marrow with healthy cells. There are a variety of gene defects that can cause SCID. One defect is in an enzyme necessary for V, D, and J chain recombination to form B- and T-cell receptors for antigen. Without these receptors, there are no functioning B and T cells. SCID has also been shown to result from mutation in a gene for the interleukin-2 receptor on lymphocytes, such that the cells could not receive the signal to proliferate. Other individuals with SCID lack adenosine deaminase, an enzyme important in the proliferation of B and T cells. A number of these people have responded well to repeated replacement of the adenosine deaminase enzyme. It has been possible to correct this condition temporarily in a few children by collecting their own defective T cells, inserting the adenosine deaminase gene linked to a retrovirus vector, and returning the cells to them. Unfortunately, the genetically altered cells do not live long, and the treatment must be repeated. Still, these results are promising, and there is much excitement about the possibility of treating other severe disorders with gene therapy. Many of the gene defects that cause primary immunological disorders are known and work is under way to correct them. **Table 18.6** lists some of the primary immunodeficiencies for which gene defects have been identified. As the table indicates, deficiencies and defects can occur at any point in the complex steps that lead to an effective immune response. ■ interleukin-2, p. 373 ■ V, D, J gene segments, p. 409 ■ antigen receptors on B and T cells, p. 389 ■ gene therapy, p. 361

TABLE 18.5 Immunodeficiency Diseases

	Disease	Part of the Immune System Involved
Primary Immunodeficiencies		
	DiGeorge syndrome	T cells (deficiency)
	Congenital agammaglobulinemia	B cells (deficiency)
	Infantile X-linked agammaglobulinemia	Early B cells (deficiency)
	Selective IgA deficiency	B cells making IgA (deficiency)
	Severe combined immunodeficiency (SCID)	Bone marrow stem cells (defect)
	Chediak-Higashi disease	Phagocytes (defect)
	Chronic granulomatous disease	Phagocytes (defect)
Secondary Immunodeficiencies		
	Acquired immunodeficiency syndrome (AIDS)	T cells (destroyed by virus)
	Monoclonal gammopathy	B cells (multiply out of control)

TABLE 18.6 Some Primary Immunodeficiency Diseases for Which Genetic Defects Are Known

Severe combined immunodeficiency (SCID)	X-linked hyper-IgM syndrome
X-linked SCID	Wiscott-Aldrich syndrome
MHC class II deficiency	Ataxia telangiectasia
CD3 deficiency	Chronic granulomatous disease
CD8 deficiency	Leukocyte adhesion deficiency
X-linked agammaglobulinemia	Many complement deficiencies

Chronic granulomatous disease involves the phagocytes, which fail to produce hydrogen peroxide and certain other active products of oxygen metabolism, due to a defect in an oxidase system normally activated by phagocytosis. Hence, the phagocytes are unable to kill some organisms, especially the catalase-positive *Staphylococcus aureus.* In Chediak-Higashi disease, the phagocyte lysosomes are deficient in certain enzymes and thus cannot destroy phagocytized bacteria. People with this condition suffer from recurring pyogenic bacterial infections. In another primary immunodeficiency involving phagocytes, leukocyte adhesion deficiency, white blood cells fail to localize at sites of infection. Most victims of this disease have very high white blood counts and infections that are difficult to detect in time for effective treatment. ■ pyogenic bacterial infections, p. 552

Secondary Immunodeficiencies

Secondary, or acquired, immunodeficiency diseases result from environmental rather than genetic factors. Malignancies, advanced age, certain infections (especially viral infections), immunosuppressive drugs, or malnutrition may all lead to secondary immunodeficiencies. Often, an infection will cause a depletion of certain cells of the immune system. The measles virus, for example, replicates in lymphoid cells, killing many of them and leaving the body temporarily open to other infections. Syphilis, leprosy, and malaria affect the T-cell population and also macrophage function, causing defects in cell-mediated immunity. Malnutrition also causes decreased immune responses, especially the cell-mediated response.

Malignancies involving the lymphoid system often decrease effective antibody-mediated immunity. For example, multiple myeloma is a malignancy arising from a single plasma cell that proliferates out of control and in most cases produces large quantities of immunoglobulin. This overproduction of a single kind of molecule results in the body using its resources to produce immunoglobulin of a single specificity at the expense of those needed to fight infection. The result is an overall immunodeficiency. Other lymphoid disorders include macroglobulinemia (overproduction of IgM) and some forms of leukemia.

One of the most serious and widespread secondary immunodeficiencies is AIDS (acquired immunodeficiency syndrome), caused by human immunodeficiency virus (HIV). This RNA virus of the retrovirus group infects and destroys helper T cells, leaving the affected person highly susceptible to infections, especially with opportunistic agents. AIDS and opportunistic infections are covered in chapter 29. ■ retrovirus, p. 349

MICROCHECK 18.7

Immunodeficiencies may be primary, either genetic or developmental defects in any components of the immune response, or they may be secondary, acquired as a result of infection or environmental influences.

- ✓ What is the defect in severe combined immunodeficiency? What could cause it?
- ✓ Multiple myeloma is a plasma cell tumor in which a clone of malignant plasma cells produces large amounts of immunoglobulin. With all this excess immunoglobulin, how can a person with multiple myeloma be immunodeficient?
- ✓ Why is infection with opportunistic agents a particular problem in individuals with AIDS?

FUTURE CHALLENGES

New Approaches to Correcting Immunologic Disorders

In recent years many of the genes responsible for immunodeficiency diseases have been identified. It has been possible to correct some of these gene defects in cells in the laboratory and, rarely, in patients. In the near future, research will be directed toward developing the existing technology for gene transfer to make it more effective in correcting these gene defects in human patients. It is important also to continue the search for other defective genes; it is likely that with increasing knowledge of the human genome more will be found soon. A continuing challenge is finding ways to overcome graft rejection to make bone marrow and other transplants more acceptable. The challenge of treating cancer and of preventing rejection of essential transplants may be met, at least in part, by the development of gene transfer technology and by better understanding of the mechanisms of cellular immunological mechanisms.

One interesting line of research stems from the observation that parasitic worm infestations appear to protect people from allergies and autoimmune diseases. Experiments with mice support this idea and also show that feeding mice parasitic worms effectively treats experimental autoimmune disease. The effect appears to be due at least in part to down-regulation of the immune response. Research into understanding the regulation of immune responses will help in controlling autoimmune and immunodeficiency disease, and it will permit development of improved vaccines.

A promising and challenging area is the development of human stem cell research. Stem cells have an almost unlimited capacity to divide, and some of them can differentiate into most of the tissues in the body. They could be used to generate cells for transplantation and to replace defective or injured tissues such as nerve tissue. They might also be used to test the effects of drugs on human cells, without the danger of testing on human beings. A major stumbling block is the fact that the stem cells come from fetal material, either from early stage embryos obtained from fertility treatments or from non-living fetuses from terminated pregnancies. The legal and ethical guidelines for the use of these cells are matters of considerable debate.

SUMMARY

18.1 Type I Hypersensitivities: Immediate IgE-Mediated (Table 18.1)

IgE attached to mast cells or basophils reacts with specific antigen, resulting in the release of powerful mediators of the allergic reaction. (Figure 18.1)

Localized Anaphylaxis

Localized anaphylactic (type I) reactions include **hives (urticaria), hay fever (allergic rhinitis),** and **asthma.** (Figure 18.2)

Generalized Anaphylaxis

Generalized or systemic anaphylaxis is a rare but serious reaction that can lead to **shock** and death.

Immunotherapy

Desensitization or immunotherapy is often effective in decreasing the type I hypersensitivity state. (Figure 18.3)

A new treatment, using an engineered anti-IgE, promises to be effective in treating asthma.

18.2 Type II Hypersensitivities: Cytotoxic (Table 18.1)

Type II hypersensitivity reactions, or cytotoxic reactions, are caused by antibodies that can destroy normal cells by complement lysis or by **antibody-dependent cellular cytotoxicity (ADCC).**

Transfusion Reactions (Table 18.2)

The ABO blood group antigens have been the major cause of **transfusion reactions.**

Hemolytic Disease of the Newborn (Figure 18.4)

The Rhesus blood group antigens are usually responsible for this potentially fatal disease.

Injected anti-Rh antibody helps prevent Rh sensitization of Rh negative mothers.

18.3 Type III Hypersensitivities: Immune Complex-Mediated (Table 18.1)

Type III hypersensitivity reactions are mediated by small antigen-antibody complexes that activate complement and other inflammatory systems, attract neutrophils, and contribute to inflammation.

The small **immune complexes** are often deposited in small blood vessels in organs, where they cause inflammatory disease—for example, glomerulonephritis in the kidney or arthritis in the joints. (Figure 18.5, Table 18.3)

18.4 Type IV Hypersensitivities: Delayed Cell-Mediated (Table 18.1)

Delayed hypersensitivity reactions depend on the actions of sensitized T lymphocytes.

Tuberculin Skin Test (Figure 18.6)

A positive reaction to protein antigens of the tubercle bacillus introduced under the skin peaks 2 to 3 days after exposure to antigen.

Contact Hypersensitivities

Contact allergy, or **contact dermatitis,** occurs frequently in response to substances such as poison ivy, nickel in jewelry, and chromium salts in leather products. (Figures 18.7, 18.8)

Delayed Hypersensitivity in Infectious Diseases

Delayed hypersensitivity is important in responses to many chronic, long-lasting infectious diseases.

18.5 Rejection of Transplanted Tissues

Transplantation rejection of **allografts** is caused largely by type IV cellular reactions.

18.6 Autoimmune Diseases

Responses against substances of self can lead to **autoimmune diseases.** (Table 18.4)

The Spectrum of Autoimmune Reactions

Autoimmune diseases may be organ-specific or widespread.

Some autoimmune diseases are caused by antibodies produced to body components, and others by cell-mediated reactions or a combination of antibodies and immune cells.

Treatment of Autoimmune Diseases

Autoimmune diseases are usually treated with drugs that suppress the immune and/or inflammatory responses.

18.7 Immunodeficiency Disorders

Immunodeficiencies may be primary genetic or developmental defects in any components of the immune response, or they may be secondary and acquired. (Table 18.5)

Primary Immunodeficiencies (Table 18.6)

B-cell immunodeficiencies result in diseases involving a lack of antibody production, such as agammaglobulinemias and selective IgA deficiency.

T-cell deficiencies result in diseases such as DiGeorge syndrome.

Lack of both T- and B-cell functions results in combined immunodeficiencies, which are generally severe.

Defective phagocytes are found in chronic granulomatous disease and Chediak-Higashi disease.

Secondary Immunodeficiencies

Acquired immunodeficiencies can result from malnutrition, immunosuppressive agents, infections (such as AIDS), and malignancies such as multiple myeloma.

REVIEW QUESTIONS

Short Answer

1. Why are antihistamines useful for treating many IgE-mediated allergic reactions but not effective in treating asthma?
2. Penicillin is a very small molecule, yet it can cause any of the types of hypersensitivity reactions, especially type I. How can this occur?
3. What are some major differences between an IgE-mediated skin reaction, such as hives, and a delayed hypersensitivity reaction, such as a positive tuberculin skin test?
4. What causes insulin-dependent diabetes mellitus?
5. Give the evidence showing that myasthenia gravis results from antibody activities.
6. Give an example of an organ-specific autoimmune disease and one that is widespread, involving a variety of tissues and organs.
7. Describe an Arthus reaction.
8. Why might malnutrition lead to immunodeficiencies?
9. What is the most common primary immunodeficiency disorder?
10. How can genetic abnormalities leading to immunodeficiency disorders be corrected? Give an example.

Multiple Choice

1. An IgE-mediated allergic reaction
   a) reaches a peak within minutes after exposure to antigen.
   b) occurs only to polysaccharide antigens.
   c) requires complement activation.
   d) requires considerable macrophage participation.
   e) is characterized by induration.
2. Which of the following statements is true of the ABO blood group system in humans?
   a) A antigen is present on type O red cells.
   b) B antigen is the most common antigen in the population of the United States.
   c) Natural anti-A and anti-B antibodies are of the class IgG.
   d) People with blood group O do not have natural antibodies against A and B antigens.
   e) In blood transfusions, incompatibilities cause complement lysis of red blood cells.
3. All of the following are true of immune complexes, *except*
   a) the most common complexes consist of antigen-IgE-complement.
   b) an immune complex consists of antigen attached to antibody.
   c) usually complement components are included in antigen-antibody complexes.
   d) immune complexes activate strong inflammatory reactions.
   e) immune complexes deposit in kidneys, joints, and skin.
4. Delayed hypersensitivity reactions in the skin
   a) are characterized by a wheal and flare reaction.
   b) peak at 4 to 6 hours after exposure to antigen.
   c) require complement activation.
   d) show induration because of the influx of sensitized T cells and macrophages.
   e) depend on activities of the Fc portion of antibodies.
5. Organ transplants, such as of kidneys
   a) are experimental at present.
   b) can be successful only if there are exact matches between donor and recipient.
   c) survive best if radiation is used for immunosuppression.
   d) survive best if B cells are suppressed.
   e) are rejected by a complex process in which cellular mechanisms predominate.
6. All of the following are true of autoimmune disease, *except*
   a) many of them show association with particular major histocompatibility types.
   b) some of them often occur in members of the same family.
   c) during heart attacks heart antigens are released, but no response occurs to them.
   d) disease may result from reaction to viral antigens that are similar to antigens of self.
   e) some are organ-specific and some are widespread in the body.
7. Autoantibody-induced autoimmune diseases
   a) can sometimes be passively transferred from mother to fetus.
   b) include diabetes mellitus.
   c) are always organ-specific.
   d) are never organ-specific.
   e) cannot be treated.
8. All of the following are approaches being used to treat autoimmune diseases, *except*
   a) cytotoxic drugs to prevent lymphoid cell proliferation.
   b) cyclosporin.
   c) antibiotics.
   d) steroid with anti-inflammatory action.
   e) replacement therapy, as with insulin in diabetes.
9. Patients with primary immunodeficiencies in the complement system
   a) who lack late-acting components (C5, C6, C7, C8) show increased susceptibility to *Neisseria* infections.
   b) who lack C3 are prone to develop tuberculosis.
   c) generally have no symptoms.
   d) only show defects in the major components, C1 through C9.
   e) usually handle infections normally.
10. One of the most serious of the secondary immunodeficiencies is
   a) acquired immunodeficiency syndrome, caused by the human immunodeficiency virus.
   b) severe combined immunodeficiency.
   c) DiGeorge syndrome.
   d) chronic granulomatous disease.
   e) Chediak-Higashi disease.

Applications

1. Patients with advanced leprosy do not give positive type IV reactions to any of a variety of antigens that normal people are exposed to and usually respond to with a positive delayed hypersensitivity skin reaction. Why might this be? What is another disease where lack of the

ability to give a positive delayed hypersensitivity reaction could be a useful diagnostic criterion?

2. The BCG vaccine against tuberculosis is not very effective, and great efforts are being made to produce a better vaccine. Nevertheless, BCG vaccine does give some protection and it is routinely used in many countries of the world, but not the United States. Since tuberculosis is far from eradicated in the United States, why would the BCG vaccine not be used?

Critical Thinking

1. Hypersensitivity reactions, by definition, lead to tissue damage. Can they also be beneficial? Explain.
2. Why does blood need to be cross-matched before transfusion? Why not just type the blood and use compatible ABO types?
3. What hypothesis could explain why primary immunodeficiencies are generally rare?

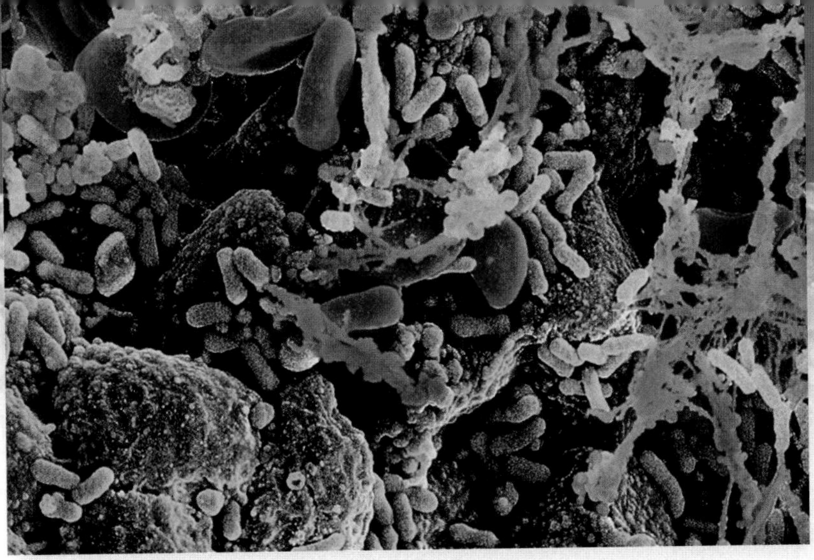

Bacterial cells adhering to a body surface

CHAPTER NINETEEN

Host-Microbe Interactions

A Glimpse of History

The ancients thought epidemics and diseases were divine punishment of the people for their sins. By the time of Moses, however, the Egyptians and Hebrews had come to believe that leprosy could be transmitted by contact with lepers. In Europe, around 430 B.C. Thucydides had concluded that some plagues were contagious. By the Middle Ages, many believed this, and fled cities to escape the diseases. Fracastorius, in 1546, first proposed a theory that communicable diseases were caused by living agents, passed from one person or animal to another. He had no way to test this theory, however.

With the discovery of microorganisms in the late seventeenth century by Leeuwenhoek, people began to suspect that microorganisms might cause disease, but the techniques of the times could not prove this. It was not until 1876 that Robert Koch offered convincing proof of the "germ theory" of disease. He showed that *Bacillus anthracis* is the cause of anthrax, an often fatal disease of humans, sheep, and other animals. With his microscope, he observed *B. anthracis* cells in the blood and spleen of dead sheep. He then inoculated mice with the infected sheep blood and was able to recover *B. anthracis* from the blood of the mice. In addition, he grew the bacteria in pure culture and showed that they caused anthrax when injected into healthy mice. From these experiments and later work with *Mycobacterium tuberculosis,* Koch formalized a group of criteria for establishing the cause of an infectious disease, known as Koch's Postulates.

Every day we have intimate contact with an enormous number and variety of microorganisms. Every breath introduces some to our upper respiratory system, others are ingested with each bite of food or sip of a drink, and still more adhere to our skin whenever we touch an object or surface. The vast majority of these microbes generate no ill effects whatsoever. Some may colonize the body surfaces, taking up residence with the variety of other organisms that live there without causing harm, while others are sloughed off with dead epithelial cells. Most of those swallowed are eventually eliminated in feces.

Relatively few microbes are able to inflict any noticeable damage, invading tissues or producing toxic substances. Those organisms that can, and do, are called **pathogens.** They have distinct patterns of interaction with the host that enable them to gain the upper hand in the relationship and elude at least some of the body's defenses. The mechanisms pathogens use to counter our innate and adaptive defenses, and subsequently cause damage, are the focus of a great deal of research. These studies are unraveling an impressive array of ploys that certain microorganisms and viruses have acquired for subverting and circumventing our sophisticated defense systems. Advances in genomics, immunology, and other areas over the last two decades have given new insight into the pathogenic strategies, fueling hope that therapies targeted to specific relationships between disease-causing microbes and the human host can be developed.

This chapter will explore some of the ways in which microbes colonize the human host, living either as members of the normal flora in harmony with the host or subverting the host defenses and causing disease. We will also discuss how pathogens are able to at least temporarily evade or overcome the host responses and damage the host.

KEY TERMS

Acute infection An infection characterized by symptoms that have a rapid onset but last only a short time.

Chronic infection An infection that develops slowly and lasts for months or years.

Colonization Establishment and growth of a microorganism on a body surface.

Disease Condition that results in noticeable impairment of body function.

Endotoxin The lipopolysaccharide (LPS) component of the outer membrane of Gram-negative bacteria; lipid A is responsible for the toxic properties of LPS.

Exotoxin A toxic protein produced by a microorganism.

Immunocompromised A host with weaknesses or defects in the innate or adaptive defenses.

Latent infection Infection in which the infectious agent is present but not active.

Normal flora The population of microorganisms routinely found growing on the body surfaces of healthy individuals.

Opportunistic pathogen A microorganism or virus that causes disease only when introduced into an unusual location or into an immunocompromised host.

Primary pathogen A microorganism or virus that is able to cause disease in an otherwise healthy individual.

Virulence determinants Attributes of a microorganism or virus that promote pathogenicity.

MICROBES, HEALTH, AND DISEASE

Many people think of microorganisms as "germs" that should routinely be avoided, failing to recognize that the microbial cells on the body actually outnumber human cells. Nearly all of these microbes co-exist peacefully with the human body, often providing beneficial aspects. The organisms that routinely reside on the body's surfaces are called the **normal flora.** It is a delicate balancing act, however; the normal flora, as well as microbes that make incidental contact with humans, are quite able to exploit body fluids and tissues as a source of nutrients should the opportunity arise.

Pathogens have developed the ability to make products such as damaging toxins or molecules to subvert defense systems, causing a disruption in the delicate balance. Weaknesses or defects in the innate or adaptive defenses can leave people vulnerable to invasion even by members of their own normal flora; the individual is said to be **immunologically compromised,** or **immunocompromised.** Factors that can lead to an individual becoming immunocompromised include malnutrition, cancer, AIDS or other diseases, surgery, wounds, genetic defects, alcohol or drug abuse, and immunosuppressive therapy that accompanies procedures such as organ transplants.

19.1 The Anatomical Barriers As Ecosystems

Focus Point

- Compare and contrast mutualism, commensalism, and parasitism.

The skin and mucous membranes provide anatomical barriers against invading microorganisms, but they also supply the foundation for a complex **ecosystem,** an interacting biological community. The microbial community that resides on humans is important from a medical standpoint because it offers protection from some disease-causing organisms. At the same time, members of the normal flora are a common cause of infection in people who are immunocompromised.

The intimate interactions between the microorganisms and the human body are an example of **symbiosis,** meaning living together; symbionts are different organisms that live close together on more or less a permanent basis.

Symbiotic Relationships Between Microorganisms and Hosts

Microorganisms that inhabit the human body can have a variety of symbiotic relationships with each other and the human host. These relationships may take on different characteristics depending on the closeness of the association and the relative advantages to each partner. Symbiotic associations can be one of several forms, and these may change, depending on the state of the host and the attributes of the microbes:

- **Mutualism** is an association in which both partners benefit. In the large intestine, for example, some bacteria synthesize vitamin K and certain B vitamins. These nutrients are then available for the animal host to absorb, providing an important source of essential vitamins, particularly for hosts lacking a well-balanced diet. The bacteria residing in the intestine benefit as well, as they are supplied with warmth and a variety of different energy sources.
- **Commensalism** is an association in which one partner benefits but the other remains unharmed. Many bacteria found living on the skin are thought to be neither harmful nor advantageous to the human host, but the bacteria gain by obtaining food and other necessities from the host.
- **Parasitism** is an association in which one organism, the **parasite,** derives benefit at the expense of the other organism, the **host.** All pathogens are parasites, but medical microbiologists often reserve the word parasite for eukaryotic organisms such as protozoa and helminths that cause disease.

MICROCHECK 19.1

Depending on the relative benefit to each partner in a relationship, such as a human host and a microorganism, the relationship can be described as mutualism, commensalism, or parasitism.

✓ How is mutualism different from commensalism?

19.2

The Normal Flora

Focus Points

- List two ways that our normal flora plays a protective role in our overall health.
- Describe how the composition of normal flora can change over time.

The **normal flora** is the population of microorganisms routinely found growing on the body of healthy individuals **(figure 19.1).** Microbes that typically inhabit body sites for extended periods are **resident flora,** whereas those that are only temporary are **transient flora.** Many different species make up the normal flora, and they occur in large numbers. In fact, there are more bacteria in just one person's mouth than there are people in the world!

The Protective Role of the Normal Flora

The most significant contributions of the normal flora to the overall health of the human host include protection against potentially harmful microorganisms, and stimulation of the immune system. When members of the normal flora are killed or their growth suppressed, as can happen during treatment of the host with antibiotics, harmful organisms may colonize and cause disease. For example, oral administration of antibiotics can suppress normal intestinal flora, allowing the overgrowth of toxin-producing strains of *Clostridium difficile,* causing the disease antibiotic-associated colitis. ■ antibiotic-associated colitis, p. 614

As we discussed in chapter 15, the presence and multiplication of normal flora competitively excludes pathogens by several different mechanisms. These include covering binding sites that might otherwise be used for attachment, consuming available nutrients, and producing compounds that are toxic to other bacteria. ■ normal flora, p. 368

The normal flora also plays an important role in priming the adaptive immune system. The response mounted against members of the normal flora, which routinely breach the body's anatomical barriers in small numbers, may cross-react with pathogens that could be encountered later. The importance of the normal flora in the development of immune responses is shown in mice reared in a microbe-free environment. These animals lack a normal flora and have greatly underdeveloped mucosal-associated lymphoid tissues (MALT). ■ MALT, p. 391

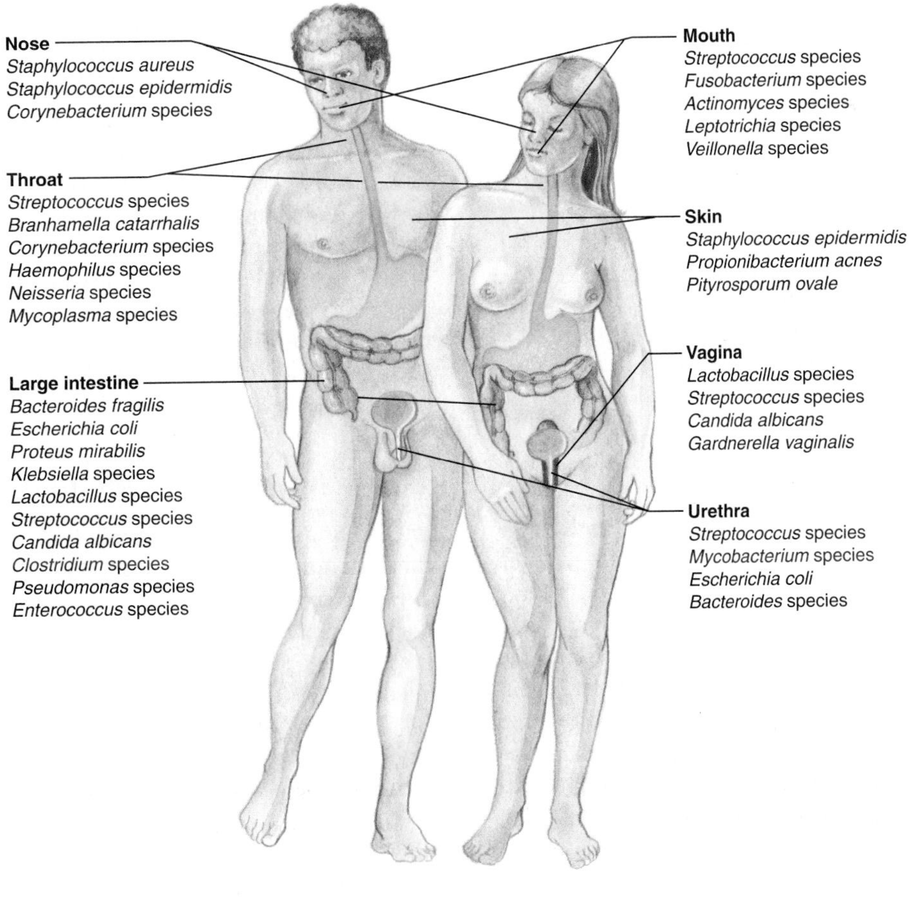

FIGURE 19.1 Normal Flora Many different organisms are part of the normal flora of the male and female human body.

The Dynamic Nature of the Normal Flora

A healthy human fetus is sterile until the protective membrane that surrounds it ruptures as a prelude to birth. During the passage through the birth canal, the baby is exposed to a variety of microbes that take up residence on its skin and in its digestive tract. Various microorganisms in food, on other humans, and in the environment soon also become established as residents on the newborn.

Once established, the composition of the normal flora is dynamic. At any one time the makeup of this complex ecosystem represents a balance of many forces that may dramatically or discreetly alter the bacterial population's quantity and composition. Changes occur in response to physiological variations within the host, such as hormonal changes, and as a direct result of the activities of the human host, such as the type of food consumed. Further, each member of the ecosystem is influenced by the presence and condition of others. Most antibiotics will kill or inhibit not only pathogens, but also some of the normal flora, allowing unwanted organisms to proliferate. For example, the *Lactobacillus* species that predominate in the vagina of mature females normally suppress growth of the yeast *Candida albicans.* During intensive, unrelated, treatment with certain antibiotics, however, the normal bacterial flora may be inhibited, allowing the fungi to overgrow and cause disease.

MICROCHECK 19.2

The normal flora provides protection against potentially harmful organisms and stimulates the immune system.

- ✓ What factor favors the growth of *Clostridium difficile* in the intestine?
- ✓ Why would the immune response to members of the normal flora cross-react with pathogens?

19.3

Principles of Infectious Disease

Focus Points

- Define the terms primary pathogen, opportunist, and virulence.
- Compare and contrast acute, chronic, and latent infections.

Colonization of a host by a microorganism implies that the microbe has become established and is multiplying on a body surface. If the microbe has a parasitic relationship with the host, then the term **infection** may be used. That is, a member of the normal flora is said to have colonized the host, but an organism capable of causing illness is described as having either colonized or infected the host. Infection does not always lead to noticeable adverse effects. It can be **subclinical** or **inapparent,** meaning that symptoms either do not appear or are mild enough to go unnoticed.

An infection that results in **disease,** a noticeable impairment of body function, is called an **infectious disease.** Diseases are characterized by symptoms and signs; **symptoms** are the effects of the disease experienced by the patient, such as pain and nausea, whereas **signs** are the effects of the disease that can be observed by examining the patient, such as rash, pus formation, and swelling.

One disease may leave a person predisposed to developing another. For example, various respiratory illnesses make a person more likely to develop pneumonia. The initial infection is a **primary infection;** an additional infection that occurs as a result of the primary infection is a **secondary infection.**

Pathogenicity

Some microorganisms and viruses are able to cause disease in otherwise healthy individuals; a microbe that is able to do this is referred to as a **primary pathogen** or, more simply, a **pathogen.** Diseases such as plague, malaria, measles, influenza, diphtheria, tetanus, and tuberculosis are caused by primary pathogens. A microbe that is able to cause disease only when the body's innate or adaptive defenses are compromised, or when introduced into an unusual location, is called an **opportunistic pathogen,** or **opportunist.** Opportunists may be members of the normal flora or common in the environment. For instance, *Pseudomonas* species are ubiquitous and routinely come into contact with healthy individuals without harmful effect, yet they can cause fatal infections in individuals who have the genetic disease cystic fibrosis and also in burn patients (see figure 23.6). Ironically, as our health care systems improve, extending the life span of many patients through surgery and immunosuppressive drugs, diseases caused by opportunists are becoming more common. Also, many organisms not previously recognized as able to cause disease have now been shown to do so in some severely immunocompromised patients.

The term **virulence** refers to the degree of pathogenicity of an organism. An organism described as highly virulent has more disease-promoting attributes than do other less virulent strains of the same species; the virulent organism is more likely to cause disease, particularly severe disease, than might otherwise be expected. *Streptococcus pyogenes* causes strep throat, for example, but certain strains are particularly virulent, causing diseases such as necrotizing fasciitis ("flesh-eating disease"). ■ necrotizing fasciitis, p. 554

Characteristics of Infectious Disease

Infectious diseases that spread from one host to another are called **communicable** or **contagious diseases.** Some contagious diseases, such as colds and measles, are easily transmitted. The ease of spread of a contagious disease partly reflects the **infectious dose,** or the number of microbes necessary to establish an infection. For example, the intestinal disease shigellosis is quite contagious in humans because only 10 to 100 cells of a *Shigella* species need be ingested to establish infection; in contrast, salmonellosis, which is not as contagious, requires ingestion of as many as 10^6 cells of *Salmonella* Enteritidis. The difference in these infectious doses reflects, in part, the ability of *Shigella* species to survive the acidic conditions encountered during passage through the stomach. Generally, the infectious dose is expressed as the

ID_{50}, an experimentally derived figure that indicates the number of microbes administered that resulted in disease in 50% of a population. ■ *Shigella,* p. 625 ■ *Salmonella* Enteritidis, p. 629

Course of Infectious Disease

The course of an infectious disease includes several stages **(figure 19.2).** The interval between introduction of an organism to a susceptible host and the onset of illness is the **incubation period.** The incubation period may vary considerably, from only a few days for the common cold, to several weeks for hepatitis A, to many months for rabies, and even years for Hansen's disease (leprosy). The length of the incubation period depends on the number of organisms encountered, the condition of the host, and many other factors.

A phase of **illness** follows the incubation period. During this period a person will experience the signs and symptoms of the disease. After the illness subsides, there is a period of **convalescence,** the stage of recuperation and recovery from the disease. Even though there is no indication of infection during the incubation and convalescent periods, many infectious agents can still be spread. Some individuals, called **carriers,** may harbor infectious agents for months or years and continue to spread pathogens, even though they themselves show no signs or symptoms of the disease. The impact of carriers on spread of disease will be discussed in chapter 20. ■ carriers, p. 478

Following recovery from infection, or after immunization, the host normally will have developed specific antibodies and memory lymphocytes that prevent reinfection with the same organism or virus. In most cases, the host is no longer susceptible to infection with that particular infectious agent.

Duration of Symptoms

Infections and the associated diseases are often described according to the timing and duration of the symptoms (see figure 19.2):

- **Acute** infections are characterized by symptoms that have a rapid onset but last only a short time; an example is strep throat.
- **Chronic** infections develop slowly and last for months or years; an example is tuberculosis.
- **Latent** infections are never completely eliminated; the microbe continues to exist in host tissues, often within host cells, for years without causing any symptoms. If there is a decrease in immune response, the latent infection may become reactivated and symptomatic. Note that the symptomatic phase of the disease may be either acute or chronic. For example, the infection caused by the varicella-zoster virus results in the characteristic rash and illness of chickenpox, an acute illness. The illness is halted by an effective immune response, leaving the host immune against reinfection. The virus, however, is not completely eliminated. It takes refuge in sensory nerves, held in check by the immune system. Later in life, if there is a decrease in immunity, infectious viral particles are produced, causing the skin disease called shingles (herpes zoster). In tuberculosis, the mycobacteria are often initially confined within a small area by host defense mechanisms, causing no symptoms; much later, if the host becomes immunocompromised, the bacteria may begin multiplying and destroying tissue, resulting in a chronic illness. Other diseases in which the causative agent becomes latent include cold sores, genital herpes, and typhus. ■ varicella virus, p. 536 ■ tuberculosis, p. 593

Distribution of the Pathogen

Infections are often described according to the distribution of the causative agent in the body. In a **localized** infection, the microbe is limited to a small area; an example is a boil caused by *Staphylococcus aureus.* In a **systemic** or **generalized** infection, the infectious agent is spread, or **disseminated,** throughout the body; an example is measles.

The suffix -emia means "in the blood." Thus, **bacteremia** indicates that bacteria are circulating in the bloodstream. Note that this term does not necessarily imply a disease state. A person can become transiently bacteremic after vigorous tooth brushing. **Toxemia** indicates that toxins are circulating in the bloodstream. The organism that causes tetanus, for instance, produces a localized infection yet its toxins circulate in the bloodstream. The term **viremia** indicates that viral particles are circulating in the bloodstream. **Septicemia** is an acute, life-threatening illness caused by infectious agents or their products circulating in the bloodstream.

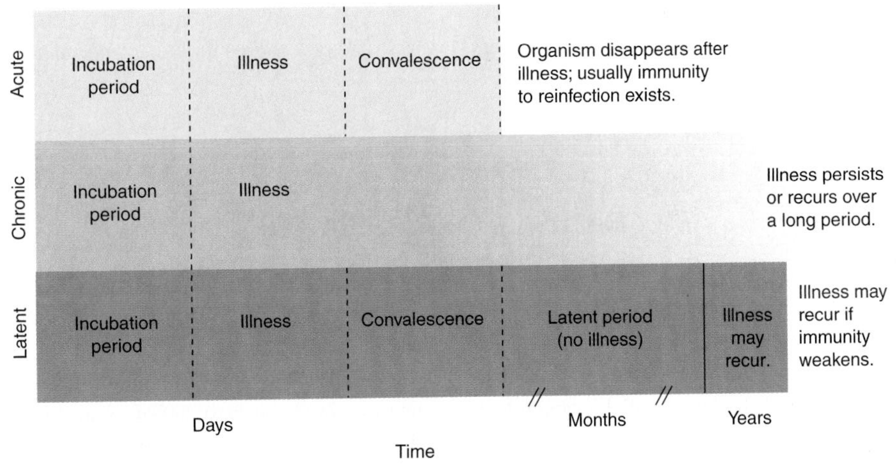

FIGURE 19.2 The Course of Infectious Diseases Diseases may be acute, chronic, or latent.

MICROCHECK 19.3

A primary pathogen can cause disease in an otherwise healthy individual; an opportunist causes disease in an immunocompromised host. The course of infectious disease includes an incubation period, illness, and a period of convalescence. Infections can be acute or chronic, latent, localized, or systemic.

- ✓ Why are opportunists causing disease more frequently?
- ✓ Give an example of a latent disease.
- ✓ What factors might contribute to a long incubation period?

19.4 Establishing the Cause of Infectious Disease

Focus Point

- List Koch's postulates, and compare them to the Molecular postulates.

Koch's postulates, the criteria that Robert Koch used to establish that *Bacillus anthracis* causes anthrax (see **A Glimpse of History**), provide a foundation for establishing that a given microbe causes a specific disease. These are now supplemented and often supplanted by **Molecular postulates,** which use precise genetic techniques to determine the pathogenicity of microorganisms and viruses.

Koch's Postulates

Robert Koch proposed that in order to conclude that a microbe causes a particular disease, these postulates must be fulfilled:

1. The microorganism must be present in every case of the disease.
2. The organism must be grown in pure culture from diseased hosts.
3. The same disease must be produced when a pure culture of the organism is introduced into susceptible hosts.
4. The organism must be recovered from the experimentally infected hosts.

Koch used these postulates to prove that *Bacillus anthracis* causes anthrax in sheep. He grew *B. anthracis* from all cases of anthrax examined; he introduced pure cultures of the organisms grown in the laboratory into healthy susceptible mice, again causing the disease anthrax; and finally, he recovered the organism from the experimentally infected mice.

It is important to note that there are many situations in which Koch's postulates cannot be carried out. In some cases the organism cannot be cultured in the laboratory. In other cases, it would not be ethical to test the postulates on humans because of safety concerns, and suitable experimental animal hosts are not available.

Molecular Postulates

The **Molecular postulates** are similar in principle to Koch's postulates, but they rely on molecular techniques to study a microbe's virulence factors. They are particularly relevant when studying bacteria such as *Streptococcus pyogenes,* which can cause a number of different diseases, depending on the virulence factors of a given strain.

The Molecular postulates state:

1. The virulence factor gene or its product should be found in pathogenic strains but not in non-pathogenic strains of the suspected pathogen.
2. Introduction of a cloned virulence gene should change a non-pathogenic to a pathogenic strain, whereas disrupting the function of the virulence gene should reduce the virulence of the organism.
3. The genes for virulence must be expressed during the disease process.
4. Antibodies or immune cells specific for the virulence gene products should be protective.

As with the traditional Koch's postulates, it is not always possible to apply all of these criteria, but they provide many new approaches to determining the causative agents of infectious diseases.

MICROCHECK 19.4

Koch's postulates can be used to prove the cause of an infectious disease. The Molecular postulates are used to identify the virulence factors responsible for disease.

- ✓ How were Koch's postulates used to prove the cause of anthrax?
- ✓ In two of Koch's postulates (#2 and #3), a pure culture of the organism is required. What would be the consequence of using a culture that was not pure?

MECHANISMS OF PATHOGENESIS

From a microbe's perspective, the interior of the human body is a lucrative source of nutrients, provided that some of the obstacles of the innate and adaptive defenses can be overcome. The ability to subvert these defenses and cause damage is what separates pathogenic microbes from the multitudes of other microorganisms that inhabit this planet. The methods that disease-causing microbes use to evade the host defenses and then cause damage are called **mechanisms of pathogenicity.** The arsenal of mechanisms that an individual strain possesses is collectively referred to as its **virulence determinants.** The DNA encoding these virulence factors can sometimes be transferred to other bacteria. ■ genetic transfer of virulence factors, p. 213

The innate and adaptive defenses do not need to be overcome indefinitely, simply long enough for the pathogen to multiply and then successfully exit the host. In fact, a pathogen that is too adept at overcoming the host defenses and causing damage is actually at a disadvantage because its opportunity to be transmitted may be limited and it loses an exclusive source of nutrients if the host dies. Pathogens and their hosts generally evolve over time to a state of **balanced pathogenicity.** The pathogen becomes less virulent while simultaneously the host becomes less susceptible. This was demonstrated when the myxoma virus was intentionally introduced into Australia in the early 1950s to kill the burgeoning rabbit population. Shortly after introduction of the virus, the rabbit population plummeted. Eventually, however, the numbers of rabbits again began increasing. Viruses recovered from surviving rabbits were shown to be less virulent than the original strain, while at the same time the rabbits themselves were more resistant to the original virus strain.

The mechanism by which a microorganism causes disease generally follows one of several patterns:

- **Production of exotoxins that are then ingested.** The microorganism does not grow on or in the host, so this is not an infection but rather a **foodborne intoxication,** a form of food poisoning. The only virulence determinant these microbes require is toxin production. Relatively few organisms cause foodborne intoxication, but these include *Clostridium botulinum,* which causes botulism, and toxin-producing strains of *Staphylococcus aureus,* which cause staphylococcal food poisoning. ■ exotoxin, p. 464 ■ botulism, p. 690 ■ *Staphylococcus aureus* foodborne intoxication, p. 806
- **Colonization of surface of the host, followed by exotoxin production.** The microorganism multiplies to high numbers on a host surface, such as the respiratory or intestinal tract. There, the microbes produce a toxin that interferes with cell function, sometimes structurally damaging the cell. Examples of bacteria that use this strategy include *Vibrio cholerae,* which causes cholera, *E. coli* O157:H7, which causes bloody diarrhea, and *Corynebacterium diphtheriae,* which causes diphtheria. ■ cholera, p. 623 ■ *E. coli* O157:H7 diarrhea, p. 627 ■ diphtheria, p. 579
- **Invasion of host tissues.** The microbe penetrates the first-line defenses, breaching the body's barriers, and then multiplies within the tissues. Organisms that use this strategy generally have mechanisms to avoid destruction by macrophages; additionally, some have mechanisms to avoid detection by antibodies. There are numerous examples of bacteria that use this strategy, including *Mycobacterium tuberculosis, Yersinia pestis, Salmonella* species, and *Streptococcus pyogenes.* ■ *Mycobacterium tuberculosis,* p. 593 ■ *Yersinia pestis,* p. 717 ■ *Salmonella,* p. 628 ■ *Streptococcus pyogenes,* p. 577
- **Invasion of host tissues, followed by exotoxin production.** These organisms are similar to those in the previous category, but in addition to their other attributes, they also make toxins. Examples include *Shigella dysenteriae* and certain strains of *Streptococcus pyogenes.* ■ *Shigella,* p. 625

Awareness of the pathogenic strategies of microorganisms and viruses is important because they illustrate why only certain microbes are able to cause disease in a healthy host. They also help explain the epidemiology and symptoms associated with the various diseases described later in the textbook.

In the next sections we will describe mechanisms that pathogens use to adhere to and colonize host tissue, avoid innate defenses, avoid adaptive defenses, and, finally, cause the damage associated with disease. We will focus on mechanisms used by bacterial pathogens because these are by far the most thoroughly characterized; later in the chapter we will discuss mechanisms of pathogenicity of viruses and eukaryotic organisms. As we describe various virulence determinants, recognize that their attributes are not mutually exclusive; a single structure on a cell can serve more than one purpose.

19.5 Establishment of Infection

Focus Points

- Compare and contrast adherence and colonization.
- Explain the role of type III secretion systems in infection.

In order to cause disease, most pathogens must first adhere to a body surface; once they have attached, they then multiply to high enough numbers to either produce an appreciable amount of toxin or invade. In some cases, after they have colonized a surface they deliver molecules to epithelial cells, inducing a specific change in those cells.

Adherence

Because the first-line defenses are very effective in removing organisms, a pathogen must adhere to host cells as a necessary first step in the establishment of infection. Microorganisms that attach to cells, however, do not necessarily cause disease. Many members of the normal flora adhere to epithelial cells with no ill effect whatsoever. Other factors such as toxin production and invasive ability of the microbe generally must come into play before disease results. ■ first-line defenses, p. 367

To bind to host cells, bacteria use **adhesins.** These are often located at the tips of pili, the filamentous protein structures found on the surface of the cell (**figure 19.3;** see figure 3.41). Pili used for attachment are often called **fimbriae.** Adhesins can also be a component of other surface structures such as capsules or various cell wall proteins (see figure 3.36). The streptococci that cause tooth decay produce a capsule, allowing them to attach to the tooth surface; other bacteria then adhere to this sticky surface, forming a biofilm. ■ pili, p. 68 ■ glycocalyx, p. 66 ■ biofilm, p. 89

The surface receptors on animal cells to which the bacterial adhesins attach are typically glycoproteins (protein molecules that have various sugars attached) or glycolipids; the adhesin binds to the sugar component of the receptor. Note that the surface receptor serves a distinct role for the cell that produces it; the microbe merely exploits the molecule for its own use. *Neisseria*

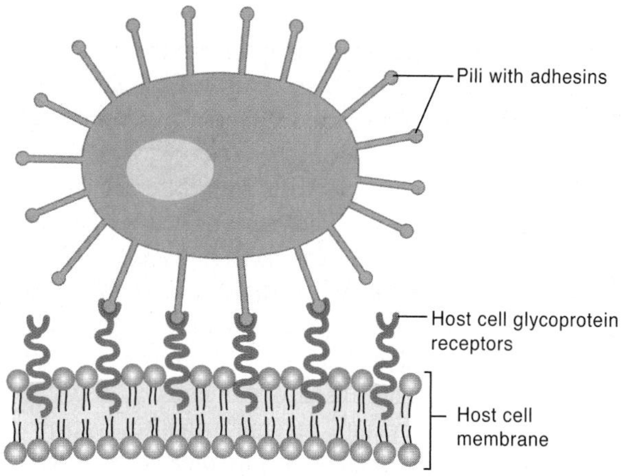

FIGURE 19.3 Pili Attachment to Host Cell Protein adhesins of microorganisms attach to glycoprotein or glycolipid receptors on host cells.

gonorrhoeae adheres to mucosal epithelial cells by means of a molecule called CD46; the normal function of this molecule is to bind certain complement system components, facilitating their degradation before they trigger responses that can damage the host cell. ■ complement system, p. 375

The binding of an adhesin to a surface receptor is highly specific, dictating the type of cells to which the bacterium can attach. The adhesin of common strains of *E. coli* allows them to adhere to cells that line the large intestine. Certain pathogenic strains, however, have other additional adhesins, broadening the range of tissues to which they can attach. Strains of *E. coli* that cause urinary tract infections generally produce a type of pili called P pili; these pili mediate specific attachment to cells that line the bladder. *E. coli* strains that cause watery diarrhea produce a type of pili that allows the bacteria to attach specifically to cells of the small intestine. These strains, enterotoxigenic *E. coli* (ETEC), are often species-specific. Some ETEC strains infect humans, whereas other strains infect only certain domestic animals. ■ enterotoxigenic *E. coli*, p. 627

Colonization

A microorganism must multiply in order to colonize the host, a prerequisite for infectious disease. To colonize a site populated by normal flora, the new arrival must compete successfully with established organisms for space and nutrients, and overcome their toxic products such as fatty acids. They also must counter the body's defenses aimed at protecting the surfaces.

IgA antibodies that recognize adhesin molecules and bind to them may prevent attachment of pathogens to the mucosal surfaces, thwarting their attempts at colonization. Microbes, however, have developed counterstrategies. These include: rapid turnover of pili, which effectively sheds antibody that has bound; antigenic variation, which can alter the type of pili produced; and **IgA proteases,** which cleave the antibody molecule. ■ antigenic variation, p. 187

One of the limiting nutrients for bacteria is often iron; recall that the body uses lactoferrin and transferrin to sequester iron. Some pathogens produce their own iron-binding molecules, **siderophores,** which compete with the host proteins; others are able to use the iron that has bound to the host proteins. ■ lactoferrin and transferrin, p. 368

Delivery of Effector Molecules to Host Cells

Once they have colonized a surface, some bacteria are able to deliver certain molecules directly to host cells, inducing changes in those cells. This characteristic appears to be particularly common among gastrointestinal pathogens. In some cases, the compounds delivered induce changes that damage the recipient cell, such as loss of microvilli; in others, they direct the uptake of the bacterial cell, a process that will be discussed in the next section. ■ microvilli, p. 611

Gram-negative bacteria use type III secretion systems to deliver proteins to eukaryotic cells. These structures resemble short flagella and function as microscopic hypodermic needles **(figure 19.4).** The secretion systems and transferred proteins are often encoded by pathogenicity islands. ■ pathogenicity island, p. 213

MICROCHECK 19.5

Pathogens use adhesins, often on pili, to bind to a body surface. To colonize a surface, the pathogen must often compete with normal flora, prevent binding of IgA, and obtain iron. Some bacteria deliver certain molecules to epithelial cells, inducing a specific change in those cells.

- ✓ What are siderophores?
- ✓ What is a type III secretion system?
- ✓ Why is it a good strategy for a microbe to adhere to a receptor that plays a critical function for a host cell?

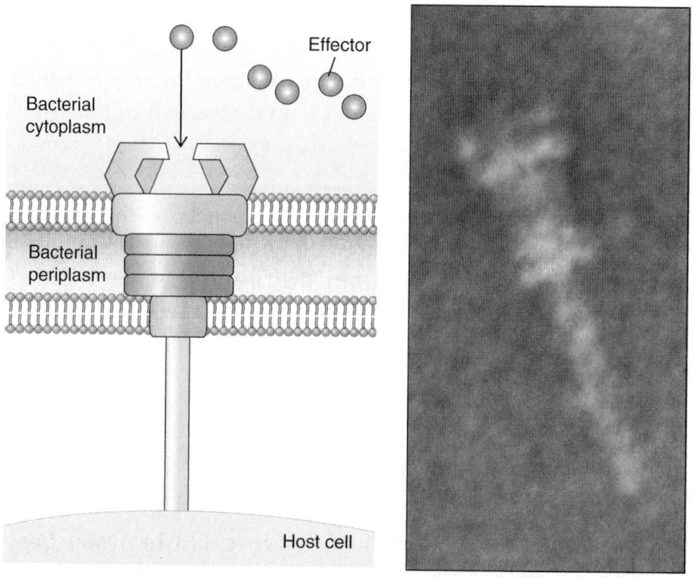

FIGURE 19.4 Type III Secretion Systems Gram-negative bacteria use type III secretion systems to deliver certain molecules directly to host cells, inducing changes in those cells.

19.6

Invasion—Breaching the Anatomical Barriers

Focus Point

- Describe the mechanisms pathogens use to penetrate the skin and mucous membranes.

Some bacterial pathogens cause disease while remaining on the mucosal surfaces, but many others breach the anatomical barriers. By traversing the epithelial cell barrier and accessing the nutrient-rich tissue, these invading microbes can enjoy an exclusive source of nutrients, multiplying without competition.

Penetration of Skin

Skin is the most difficult anatomical barrier for a microbe to penetrate. Bacterial pathogens that invade via this route rely on trauma of some sort that destroys the integrity of the skin. *Staphylococcus aureus,* a common cause of wound infections, accesses tissues via the lesion. *Yersinia pestis,* the causative agent of plague, exploits fleas, relying on them to inject the microbe through the skin via a flea bite. ■ plague, p. 717

Penetration of Mucous Membranes

Invasion of mucous membranes is the most common route of entry for most pathogens, but the invasive processes are complex and inherently difficult to study. *In vitro* techniques that employ bacteria added to eukaryotic cells growing in tissue culture give important insights, but they do not necessarily demonstrate what actually happens in the complex environment of a mucous membrane. Studies involving mice or other animals can often be used to confirm the results of tissue culture, but some pathogens behave quite differently in non-human hosts. It appears, however, that there are at least two general mechanisms used for invasion—directed uptake by cells and exploitation of antigen-sampling processes.

Directed Uptake by Cells

Some pathogens induce non-phagocytic cells to use the process of endocytosis to take up the bacterial cells. The pathogen first attaches to a cell, then triggers that cell to engulf the bacterium. In many cases, specialized proteins that cause changes in the host cell's cytoskeleton are delivered by the type III secretion systems to induce the uptake. The directed disruption of the cytoskeleton causes obvious morphological disturbances in the cell membrane called **ruffling (figure 19.5).** The bacteria appear to sink into the ruffles, leading to their eventual engulfment. *In vitro* studies show that *Salmonella* species can induce their own uptake by intestinal epithelial cells. *Shigella* species do the same, but they enter the mucosal epithelial cells at their base; they must first pass through an M cell to access the basement membrane side of epithelial cells. The mechanism they use to do this will be described in the next section. ■ endocytosis, p. 76 ■ basement membrane, p. 367 ■ M cell, p. 391

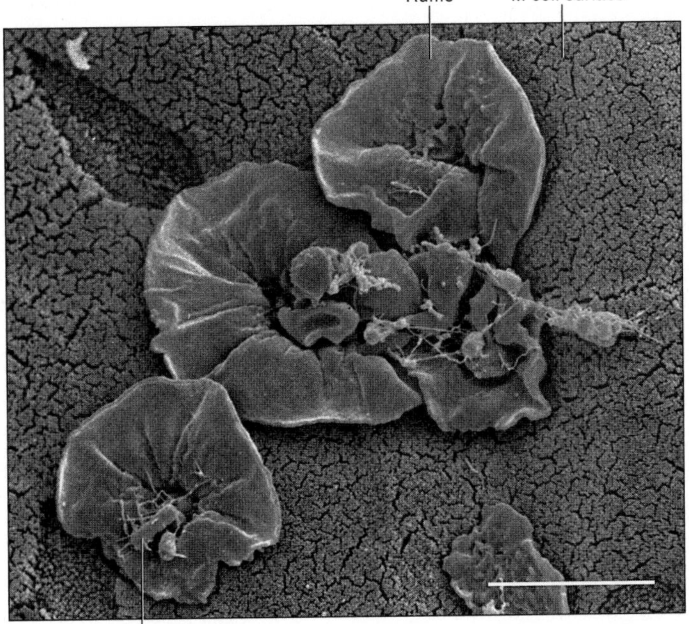

FIGURE 19.5 Ruffling *Salmonella* Typhimurium inducing ruffles on an M cell (a specialized epithelial cell) leading to uptake of the bacterial cells (scale bar = 10 μm).

Exploitation of Antigen-Sampling Processes

Recall that components of the immune system are located at strategic sites so that antigens that enter the body or pass through the intestine can be sampled. Some bacteria exploit the sampling process in order to access deeper tissues.

Several intestinal pathogens gain access to tissue by way of the M cells that overlie the Peyer's patches in the intestine. Recall that M cells are specialized cells that function as a conduit between the intestinal lumen and the lymphoid tissues of the Peyer's patches. They routinely sample intestinal contents and deliver them to macrophages in the lymphoid tissues beneath; this process of transferring material from one side of the cell to the other is called **transcytosis.** Most microbes transcytosed by M cells are destroyed by the macrophages that receive them, but pathogens have evolved mechanisms to avoid this demise. *Shigella* species use M cells to traverse the epithelial barrier; once on the other side, the macrophages ingest them, but the bacteria are able to survive the phagocytic process, eventually escaping by inducing apoptosis in the phagocytic cells **(figure 19.6).** *Shigella* cells then adhere to specific receptors at the base of the epithelial cells and then induce these non-phagocytic cells to engulf them. ■ survival within the phagocyte, p. 462 ■ Peyer's patch, p. 391

Some pathogens invade by means of alveolar macrophages, which engulf material that enters the lungs. *Mycobacterium tuberculosis* produces surface proteins that facilitate their uptake by the alveolar macrophages that reside in the lung. While this might seem disadvantageous, it actually allows the organism to avoid a process that could otherwise lead to macrophage activation. *Mycobacterium* cells can survive within macrophages that have not been activated.

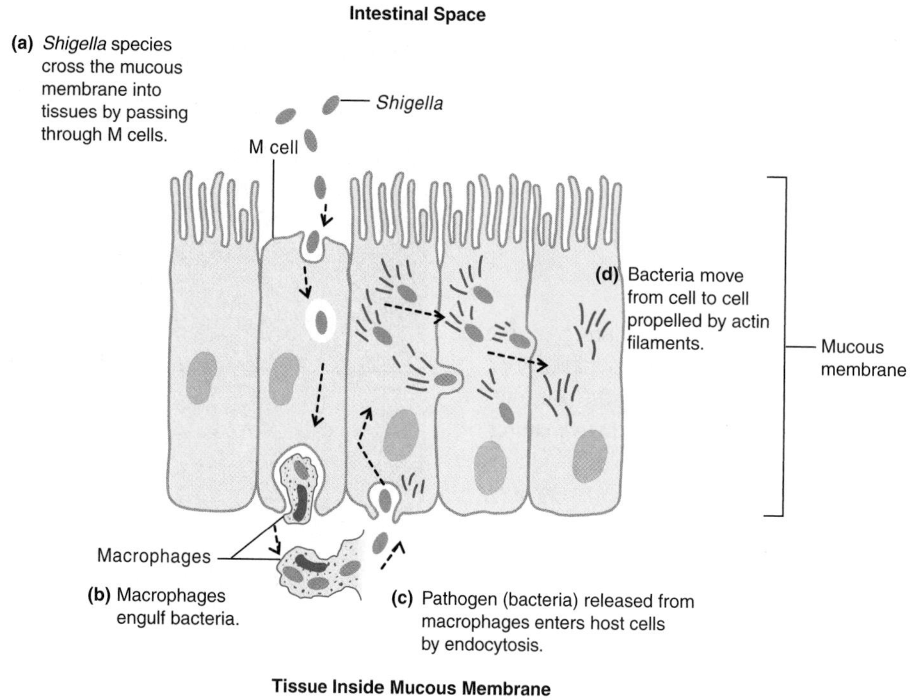
Intestinal Space
(a) Shigella species cross the mucous membrane into tissues by passing through M cells.
Shigella
M cell
(d) Bacteria move from cell to cell propelled by actin filaments.
Mucous membrane
Macrophages
(b) Macrophages engulf bacteria.
(c) Pathogen (bacteria) released from macrophages enters host cells by endocytosis.
Tissue Inside Mucous Membrane

FIGURE 19.6 Antigen-Sampling Processes Provide a Mechanism for Invasion *Shigella* species use M cells to traverse the epithelial barrier. Once on the other side, macrophages ingest them, but the bacteria are able to escape and then infect other cells.

MICROCHECK 19.6

Skin is the most difficult barrier for a microbe to penetrate. Some pathogens induce mucosal epithelial cells to engulf the bacterium. Some pathogens exploit antigen-sampling processes, including transcytosis by M cells and phagocytosis.

- ✓ How do *Shigella* species enter intestinal epithelial cells?
- ✓ Why does *Mycobacterium tuberculosis* facilitate its own uptake by macrophages?
- ✓ Why would some pathogens behave differently in a non-human host?

19.7

Avoiding the Host Defenses

Focus Point

- Describe mechanisms that bacteria use to avoid complement system proteins, antibodies, and destruction by phagocytes.

Inside the body, invading microorganisms soon encounter the innate and adaptive defenses. Pathogens as a group have evolved a variety of mechanisms to circumvent the otherwise lethal effects of these defenses.

Hiding Within a Host Cell

Some bacteria evade certain components of the host defenses by remaining inside host cells, out of the reach of the phagocytes, complement, and antibodies. An example is *Shigella* species; recall that these organisms induce their own uptake by intestinal epithelial cells. Once inside a host cell, the bacteria can orchestrate their transfer to adjacent cells. They do this by causing the rapid polymerization of host cell actin at one end of the bacterial cell, effectively forming an "actin tail." This action propels the bacterium within the cell. It can also propel a cell with such force that it drives the bacterium out of one cell and into another. *Listeria monocytogenes* also polymerizes host cell actin to facilitate its own movement (**figure 19.7**). ■ actin, p. 77

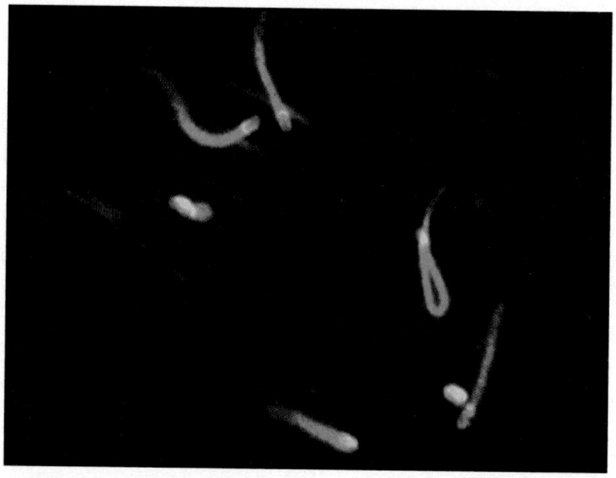

FIGURE 19.7 Actin Tail of Intracellular *Listeria monocytogenes* Rapid polymerization of host cell actin (green) at one end of the bacterial cell (orange) propels the bacterium within the cell.

Avoiding Killing by Complement System Proteins

As we discussed in chapter 15, activation of the complement system leads to three primary outcomes—lysis of foreign cells by the membrane attack complex (MAC), opsonization, and inflammation (see figure 15.7). Because the latter two outcomes are associated with phagocytosis, mechanisms that bacteria use to subvert them will be discussed in the next section. Here, we will focus on mechanisms used to avoid the lethal effects of the MAC. Recall that Gram-negative bacteria are susceptible to the MAC because their outer membrane serves as a target; the MAC has little effect on Gram-positive organisms. ■ complement system, p. 375

Gram-negative bacteria that circumvent killing by the complement proteins are said to be **serum resistant.** Strains of *Neisseria gonorrhoeae* that cause disseminated gonococcal infection, a systemic disease characterized by symptoms including fever, rash, and arthritis, are serum resistant. These strains are able to capture the mechanism that host cells use to prevent their own surfaces from activating the complement system, thereby preventing MAC formation. Recall that the alternative pathway of complement system activation can be initiated when the complement component C3b binds to a cell surface (see figure 15.7). Host cells are protected because they bind complement regulatory proteins that quickly inactivate any C3b that binds to the cell, preventing the alternative pathway from being triggered. Invasive *N. gonorrhoeae* strains effectively hijack the protective mechanism normally used by host cells, thwarting the events that would otherwise lead to formation of MAC **(figure 19.8).** ■ disseminated gonococcal infection, p. 662

Avoiding Destruction by Phagocytes

Phagocytosis involves multiple steps—including chemotaxis, recognition and attachment, engulfment, and fusion of the phagosome with the lysosome—that lead to the destruction and digestion of an invading microbe (see figure 15.10). Pathogenic bacteria have evolved a variety of ingenious mechanisms to avoid the destructive effects of phagocytosis **(figure 19.9).**

Preventing Encounters with Phagocytes

Some pathogens prevent phagocytosis by avoiding macrophages and neutrophils altogether. One way they do this is by destroying the complement component that attracts phagocytes; the other way is to kill phagocytic cells as they arrive. The mechanisms involved include:

- **C5a peptidase.** This enzyme degrades the complement component C5a, a chemoattractant that recruits phagocytic cells to an area where complement has been activated. *Streptococcus pyogenes,* which causes strep throat, is an example of a bacterium that makes C5a peptidase. ■ C5a, p. 376 ■ *Streptococcus pyogenes,* p. 577
- **Membrane-damaging toxins.** These kill phagocytes and other cells, often by forming pores in their membranes. *S. pyogenes* makes a membrane-damaging toxin called streptolysin O. ■ membrane-damaging toxins, p. 464

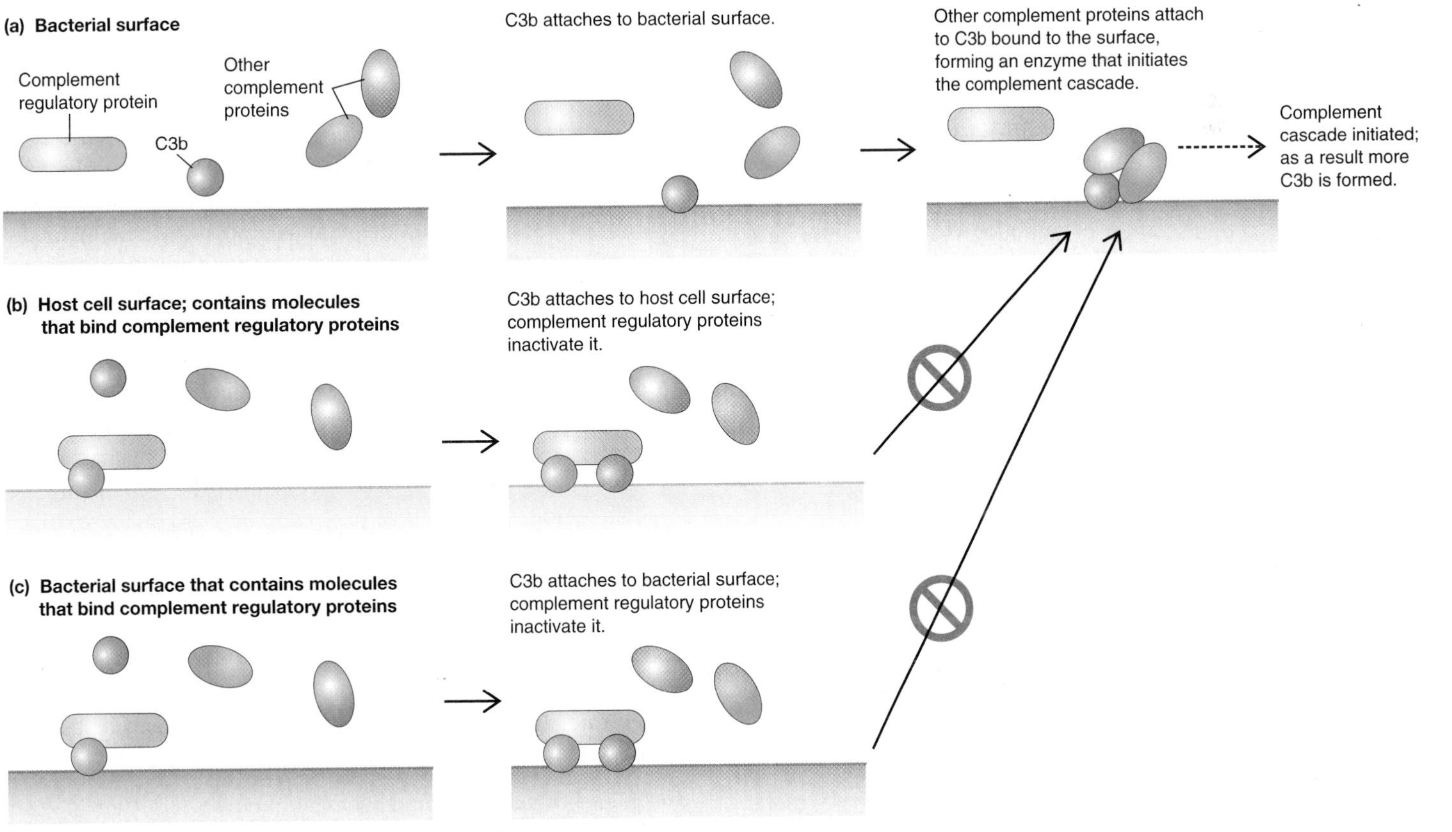

FIGURE 19.8 Avoiding the Alternative Pathway of Complement Activation Some bacterial pathogens foil the activation of the complement system by carrying surface components that attach to host cell regulatory proteins. The regulatory proteins inactivate C3b that has bound to a surface.

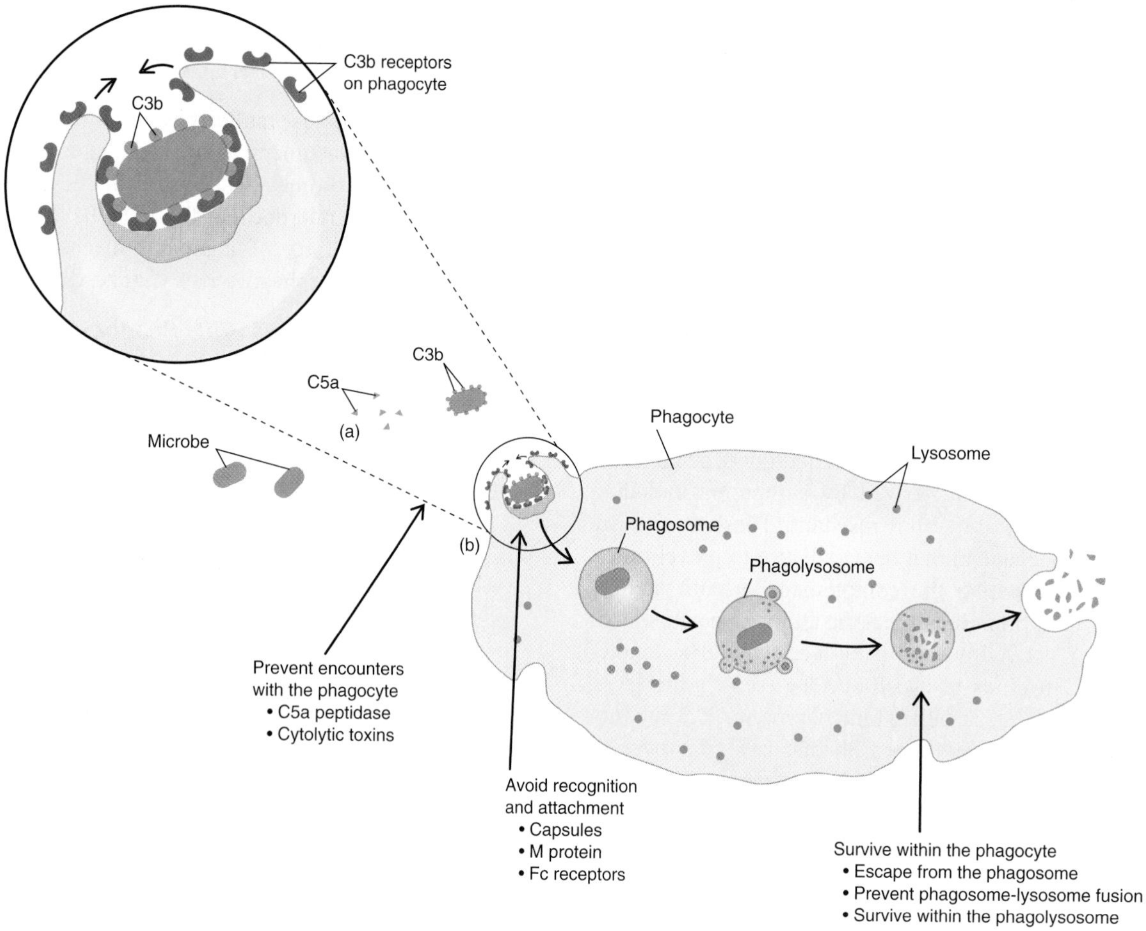

FIGURE 19.9 Avoiding Destruction by Phagocytes

Avoiding Recognition and Attachment

Recall that recognition and attachment of phagocytes to foreign material is most efficient if either the complement system component C3b or certain classes of antibody molecules have first opsonized the material. Mechanisms that bacteria use to avoid recognition and attachment include:

- **Capsules.** Capsules have long been recognized for their ability to prevent phagocytosis. Often, they interfere with the alternative pathway of complement activation. They do this by binding to host cell complement regulatory proteins that inactivate C3b that has bound to a surface; this mechanism is identical to that described earlier for serum-resistant bacteria (see figure 19.8). Rapid inactivation of C3b also prevents the molecule from being an effective opsonin. *Streptococcus pneumoniae* is an example of an organism that produces a capsule that prevents phagocytosis.
- **M protein.** This component of the cell wall of *Streptococcus pyogenes* functions in a manner similar to that of the *Streptococcus pneumoniae* capsule; it binds to a complement regulatory protein that inactivates C3b, interfering with complement activation and the subsequent formation of more C3b. Rapid inactivation of C3b also prevents it from being an effective opsonin.
- **Fc receptors.** These proteins are found on the surface of *Staphylococcus aureus* (protein A) and *Streptococcus pyogenes* (protein G). The Fc receptors foil opsonization by antibodies; they outfox the immune system by binding the Fc region of antibody molecules, reversing the intended orientation of the molecule on the cell **(figure 19.10).** Recall that antibodies have two parts—the Fab region, which binds specifically to antigens, and the Fc region, which functions as a "red flag," directing the fate of the antigen. Bacterial cells that have Fc receptors are able to coat themselves with antibody molecules in a manner that obscures the cell from phagocytes. The phagocytic cell has no mechanism for recognizing the Fab region, which will be projecting outward on these cells.

Surviving Within the Phagocyte

Some bacteria make no attempt to avoid engulfment, instead using phagocytosis as an opportunity. It allows them to hide from antibodies, control some aspects of the immune response, and obtain a "free ride" to other locations in the body. Mechanisms used to survive within phagocytes include:

- **Escape from the phagosome.** Some bacteria are able to escape from the phagosome before it fuses with the lysosome; these organisms are then able to multiply within the cyto-

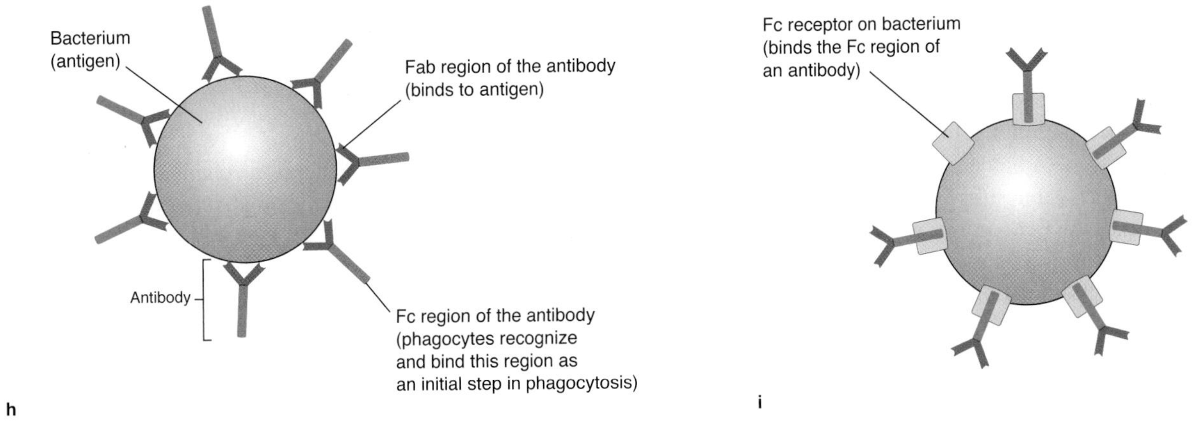

FIGURE 19.10 Fc Receptors Foil Opsonization by Antibodies **(a)** The defense system's intended orientation of antibody molecules on the surface of a bacterium; note that the Fc region of the antibody projects from the bacterial cell, making it available for a phagocyte to recognize and bind. **(b)** The effect of Fc receptors on a bacterial cell's surface; the receptors reverse the defense system's intended orientation of the antibody molecules on the cell, preventing the Fc region from interacting with the phagocyte cell.

plasm of the phagocyte, protected from other host defenses. *Listeria monocytogenes* produces a molecule that is activated to form pores in membranes once inside the phagosome, allowing the bacteria to escape to the cytoplasm. *Shigella* species are also able to lyse the phagosome before it fuses with the lysosome.

- **Preventing phagosome-lysosome fusion.** Bacteria that prevent phagosome-lysosome fusion avoid the otherwise inevitable exposure to the degradative enzymes and other toxic components of the lysosome. *Salmonella* species are able to sense they have been ingested by a macrophage, and respond by producing a protein that blocks the fusion process.
- **Surviving within the phagolysosome.** Relatively few organisms are able to survive the destructive environment within the phagolysosome. *Coxsiella burnetii,* however, an obligate intracellular parasite that causes Q fever, is able to withstand the conditions. It appears that once the organism has been ingested by a macrophage, it can delay fusion of the phagosome with the lysosome, allowing the microbe additional time to equip itself for growth within the phagolysosome.

Avoiding Antibodies

Pathogens that survive the initial assault of the innate defenses soon encounter an additional obstacle, the adaptive defenses. For most bacteria, the most formidable of these are antibodies. Mechanisms for avoiding antibodies include:

- **IgA protease.** This enzyme cleaves IgA, the class of antibody found in mucus and other secretions. *Neisseria gonorrhoeae* and a variety of other pathogens produce IgA protease. This enzyme may also have other roles.
- **Antigenic variation.** Some pathogens routinely alter the structure of their surface antigens. This allows them to stay ahead of antibody production by altering the very molecules antibodies would otherwise recognize. *Neisseria gonorrhoeae* is able to vary the antigenic structure of its pili; antibodies produced by the host in response to one variation of the pili cannot bind effectively to another. ■ antigenic variation, p. 187
- **Mimicking host molecules.** An essential aspect of the immune system is the development of tolerance for molecules that the body perceives as healthy "self." Pathogens can exploit this by covering themselves with molecules that resemble normal "self" molecules. Certain strains of *Streptococcus pyogenes* have a capsule composed of hyaluronic acid, a polysaccharide found in tissues.

MICROCHECK 19.7

Serum-resistant bacteria avoid the killing effects of complement system proteins. Mechanisms bacteria use to avoid destruction by phagocytes include preventing encounters with phagocytes, avoiding recognition and attachment, and surviving within the phagocyte. Mechanisms for avoiding antibodies include IgA protease, antigenic variation and mimicking host molecules.

✓ Describe the effects of the Fc receptor on the surface of a bacterial cell.

✓ Describe three mechanisms that bacteria can use to survive within a phagocytic cell.

✓ Encapsulated organisms can be phagocytized once antibodies against the capsule have been formed. Why would this be so?

19.8 Damage to the Host

Focus Points

- Describe the difference between exotoxins and endotoxins.
- Compare and contrast neurotoxins, enterotoxins, and cytotoxins, giving two examples of each.
- Explain how inflammation and antibody production can be damaging.

In order to cause disease, a pathogen must evoke some type of damage to the host. In many cases, the damage facilitates dispersal of the organism, enabling it to infect other hosts. *Vibrio cholerae,* which causes cholera, induces watery diarrhea; up to 20 liters of microbe-containing fluid can be excreted in one day. In areas of the world with inadequate sewage treatment, this can lead to contaminated water supplies and widespread outbreaks. *Bordetella pertussis,* which causes whooping cough, facilitates its airborne dispersal by causing severe bursts of coughing. Damage due to infection can be the result of direct effects of the pathogen, such as toxins produced, or indirect effects, such as the immune response.

Exotoxins

A number of Gram-positive and Gram-negative bacterial pathogens produce **exotoxins,** proteins that have very specific damaging effects **(table 19.1).** These proteins are among the most potent toxins known and are often a major cause of damage to an infected host.

Exotoxins are either secreted by the bacterium or leak into the surrounding fluid following lysis of the bacterial cell. In most cases, the pathogen must colonize a body surface or tissue to produce enough toxin to cause damage. With foodborne intoxication, however, the bacterial cells multiply in a food product where they produce toxin that is then consumed. In the case of botulism, caused by ingestion of botulinum toxin produced by *Clostridium botulinum,* ingestion of minute amounts of toxin is sufficient to cause paralysis. Like most other exotoxins, botulinum toxin can be destroyed by heating. ■ botulism, p. 690

Exotoxins can act locally, or they may be carried in the bloodstream throughout the body, causing systemic effects. *Corynebacterium diphtheriae,* the organism that causes diphtheria, grows and releases its exotoxin in the throat. There, the toxin destroys local cells, leading to the formation of a pseudomembrane composed of dead host cells, pus, and blood. This membrane can dislodge and obstruct the airway. The toxin can also be absorbed and carried to the heart and other organs, causing additional damage. ■ diphtheria, p. 579

Because exotoxins are proteins, the immune system can generally produce protective antibodies. Unfortunately, many exotoxins are so powerful that fatal damage can occur before an adequate immune response is mounted. This is why vaccination, using a toxoid, is important in preventing otherwise common diseases such as tetanus and diphtheria (see table 17.1). Passive immunity to a given toxin can be provided by administering an antitoxin; for example, a person who develops symptoms of botulism is administered botulinum antitoxin. Although vaccines against botulinum toxin exist, they are not routinely used because the risks of developing the disease are negligible if prudent food preparation procedures are followed. ■ toxoid, p. 417 ■ antitoxin, p. 414

Many exotoxins can be grouped into functional categories according to the tissues they adversely impact (see table 19.1). **Neurotoxins** damage the nervous system, causing symptoms such as paralysis. **Enterotoxins** cause symptoms associated with intestinal disturbance, such as diarrhea and vomiting. **Cytotoxins** damage a variety of different cell types, either by interfering with essential cellular mechanisms or by lysing the cell. Some exotoxins do not fall into any of these groups, instead causing symptoms associated with excessive stimulation of the immune response.

Most exotoxins fall into three general categories that reflect their structure and general mechanism of action—A-B toxins, membrane-damaging toxins and superantigens.

A-B Toxins

A-B toxins consist of two parts—one constitutes the toxic, or active, part (the A subunit) and another (the B subunit) binds to specific receptors on cells **(figure 19.11).** In other words, the A subunit, usually an enzyme, is responsible for the effects the toxin has on a cell, whereas the B subunit dictates the type of cell to which the toxin is delivered.

The structure of A-B toxins offers novel approaches for the development of vaccines and therapies. For example, a fusion protein that contains diphtheria toxin is now being used to treat cutaneous T-cell lymphoma. By fusing the toxin to the cytokine IL-12, the toxin is delivered to T cells, including cancerous ones. The B subunit of cholera toxin is being used to develop an orally administered vaccine against cholera. Antibodies that bind the B subunit should prevent cholera toxin from binding to intestinal cells, thus protecting the vaccine recipient. Researchers are now experimenting with attaching other compounds to B subunits, allowing those compounds to be delivered specifically to the cell type targeted by the B subunit.

Membrane-Damaging Toxins

Membrane-damaging toxins disrupt plasma membranes, causing the cell to lyse. Because they damage a variety of different cell types, they are cytotoxins. Many also lyse red blood cells, causing hemolysis that can be observed when the organisms are grown on blood agar; thus, many of these toxins are also referred to as **hemolysins.** They are also called **cytolysins.** ■ hemolysis, p. 101 ■ blood agar, p. 100

Some membrane-damaging toxins insert themselves into membranes, forming pores that allow fluids to enter. One pore-forming toxin is streptolysin O, the compound responsible for the characteristic β-hemolysis of *Streptococcus pyogenes* grown anaerobically on blood agar (see figure 4.11). Recall that this membrane-damaging toxin enables *S. pyogenes* to avoid phagocytosis.

Phospholipases are a group of membrane-damaging toxins that enzymatically remove the polar head group of the phospholipids in the plasma membrane, destabilizing its integrity. The α-toxin of *Clostridium perfringens,* which causes gas gangrene, is a phospholipase. ■ phospholipid, p 36 ■ gas gangrene, p. 559

Superantigens

Superantigens override the specificity of the T-cell response, causing toxic effects due to the massive release of cytokines by an inordinate number of T_H cells (effector helper T cells). They include toxic shock syndrome toxin (TSST) as well as several other toxins produced by *Staphylococcus aureus* and *Streptococcus pyogenes.* ■ helper T cells, p. 390

Superantigens effectively short-circuit the normal control mechanisms inherent in antigen processing and presentation. They do this

TABLE 19.1 Exotoxins Produced by Various Primary Pathogens

Toxins	Name of Disease; Name of Toxin	Characteristics of the Disease	Mechanism	Page Reference
A-B TOXINS—Composed of two subunits, A and B. The A subunit is the toxic, or active, part; the B subunit binds to the target cell.				
Neurotoxins				
Clostridium botulinum	Botulism; botulinum toxin	Flaccid paralysis	Blocks transmission of nerve signals to the muscles by preventing the release of acetylcholine.	p. 690
Clostridium tetani	Tetanus; tetanospasmin	Spastic paralysis	Blocks the action of inhibitory neurons by preventing the release of neurotransmitters.	p. 557
Enterotoxins				
Enterotoxigenic *E. coli*	Traveler's diarrhea; heat-labile enterotoxin (cholera-like toxin)	Severe watery diarrhea	Modifies a regulatory protein in intestinal cells, causing those cells to continuously secrete electrolytes and water.	p. 627
Vibrio cholerae	Cholera; cholera toxin	Severe watery diarrhea	Modifies a regulatory protein in intestinal cells, causing those cells to continuously secrete electrolytes and water.	p. 624
Cytotoxins				
Bacillus anthracis	Anthrax; edema factor, lethal factor	Inhaled form—septic shock; cutaneous form—skin lesions	Edema factor modifies a regulatory protein in cells, causing accumulation of fluids. Lethal factor inactivates proteins involved in cell signaling functions.	p. 591
Bordetella pertussis	Pertussis (whooping cough); pertussis toxin	Sudden bouts of violent coughing	Modifies a regulatory protein in respiratory cells, causing accumulation of respiratory secretions and mucus. Other factors also contribute to the symptoms.	p. 591
Corynebacterium diphtheriae	Diphtheria; diphtheria toxin	Pseudomembrane in the throat; heart, kidney damage	Inhibits protein synthesis by inactivating an elongation factor of eukaryotic cells. Kills local cells (in the throat) but can also be carried in the bloodstream to various organs.	p. 580
E. coli O157:H7	Bloody diarrhea, hemolytic uremic syndrome; shiga toxin	Diarrhea that may be bloody; kidney damage	Inactivates the 60S subunit of eukaryotic ribosomes, halting protein synthesis.	p. 627
Shigella dysenteriae	Dysentery, hemolytic uremic syndrome; shiga toxin	Diarrhea that contains blood, pus, and mucus; kidney damage	Inactivates the 60S subunit of eukaryotic ribosomes, halting protein synthesis	p. 626
MEMBRANE-DAMAGING TOXINS (cytotoxins)—Disrupts plasma membranes.				
Clostridium perfringens	Gas gangrene; α-toxin	Extensive tissue damage	Removes the polar head group on the phospholipids in the membrane, destablizing membrane integrity.	p. 559
Staphylococcus aureus	Wound and other infections; leukocidin	Accumulation of pus	Inserts into membranes, forming pores that allow fluids to enter.	p. 525
Streptococcus pyogenes	Pharyngitis and other infections; streptolysin O	Accumulation of pus	Inserts into membranes, forming pores that allow fluids to enter.	p. 577
SUPERANTIGENS—Overrides the specificity of the T-cell response.				
Staphylococcus aureus (certain strains)	Foodborne intoxication; staphylococcal enterotoxins	Nausea and vomiting	How the ingested toxins lead to the characteristic symptoms of foodborne intoxication is not understood.	p. 806
Staphylococcus aureus (certain strains)	Staphylococcal toxic shock; toxic shock syndrome toxin (TSST)	Fever, vomiting, diarrhea, muscle aches, rash, low blood pressure	Systemic toxic effects due to the resulting massive release of cytokines.	p. 658
Streptococcus pyogenes (certain strains)	Streptococcal toxic shock; streptococcal pyrogenic exotoxins (SPE)	Fever, vomiting, diarrhea, muscle aches, rash, low blood pressure	Systemic toxic effects due to the resulting massive release of cytokines.	p. 578
OTHER TOXIC PROTEINS				
Staphylococcus aureus	Scalded-skin syndrome; exfoliatin	Separation of the outer layer of skin	Thought to break ester bonds that hold the layers of skin together.	p. 526
Various organisms	Various diseases; proteases, lipases, and other hydrolases	Tissue damage	Degrades proteins, lipids, and other compounds that make up tissues.	

by binding simultaneously to the outer portion of the major histocompatibility (MHC) class II molecule on antigen-presenting cells and the T-cell receptor **(figure 19.12).** Whereas most antigens stimulate about one in 10,000 T cells, superantigens can stimulate as many as one in five T cells. The resulting release of cytokines by an inordinate number of T cells leads to symptoms including fever, nausea, vomiting, and diarrhea. Shock may occur, with failure of many organ systems, circulatory collapse, and even death. In addition, the immune response is suppressed because many T cells undergo apoptosis following the excessive stimulation. Superantigens are also suspected of contributing to autoimmune diseases; by overriding the control mechanisms that normally characterize adaptive immunity, they may induce the proliferation of those few T cells that respond to healthy "self." ■ **MHC class II molecules, p. 402** ■ **apoptosis, p. 382**

The family of related exotoxins produced by *Staphylococcus aureus* strains that cause foodborne intoxication are superantigens. Although they cause nausea and vomiting and are therefore referred to as enterotoxins, the manner in which they function and the symptoms they cause are distinct from those of the enterotoxins of *Vibrio cholerae* and certain *E. coli* strains. The spectrum of symptoms associated with the ingestion of a staphylococcal enterotoxin is also different from that of other superantigens. The precise mechanism by which they induce vomiting is poorly understood, but they seem to affect inflammatory functions of subepithelial macrophages and cause a change in local vascular permeability. Unlike most other exotoxins, the enterotoxins produced by *Staphylococcus aureus* are heat-stable. Even thorough

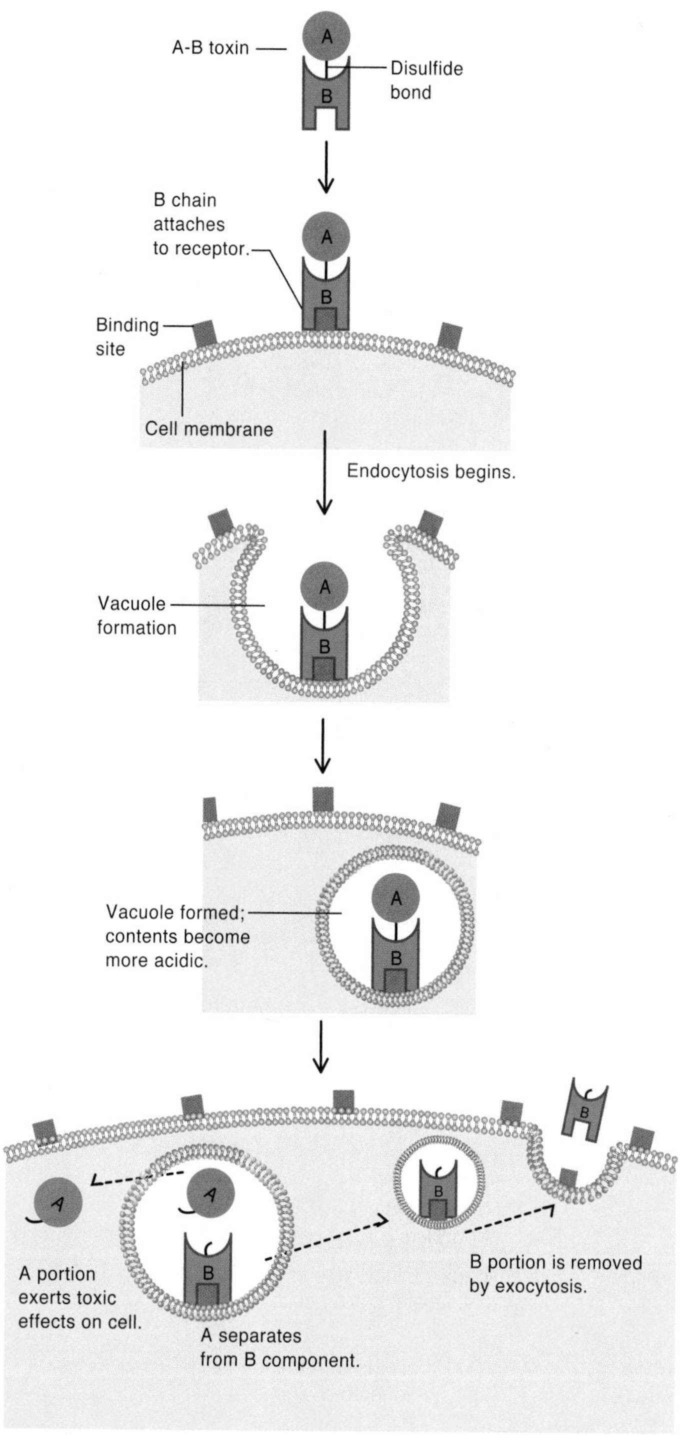

FIGURE 19.11 The Action of A-B Toxins The A portion is toxic and the B portion binds to specific receptors on cells. After binding, the A-B molecule is taken up by endocytosis. After endocytosis, the contents of the vacuole become more acidic, causing the A and B portions to separate. The B portion remains in the vacuole and is removed by exocytosis, while the A portion enters the cytoplasm of the cell and exerts its toxic effect.

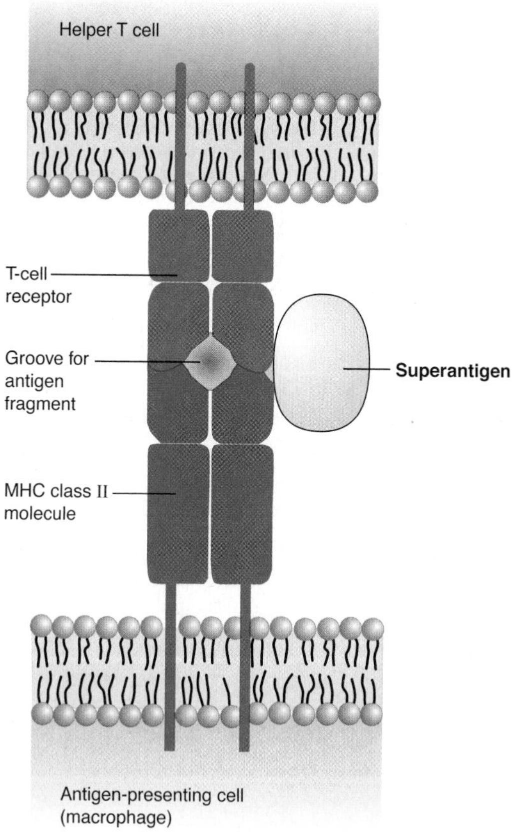

FIGURE 19.12 Superantigens These exotoxins override the specificity of the T-cell response, causing systemic toxic effects due to the massive release of cytokines by an inordinate number of effector T cells. The superantigens effectively short-circuit the normal control mechanisms inherent in antigen processing and presentation by binding simultaneously to the outer portion of the MHC class II molecule and the T-cell receptor.

cooking of foods that have been contaminated with these toxins will not prevent illness. ■ *Staphylococcus aureus* food poisoning, p. 806

Other Toxic Proteins

Various proteins that are not A-B toxins, superantigens, or membrane-damaging toxins can have detrimental effects. An important example is the exfoliating toxin produced by certain strains of *Staphylococcus aureus*. This toxin, exfoliatin, destroys material that binds together the layers of skin, causing the outer layer to separate (see figure 22.4). The organism may be growing in a small, localized lesion but the toxin can spread systemically.

Various hydrolytic enzymes including proteases, lipases, and collagenases can break down tissue components. Along with destroying tissues, some of these enzymes facilitate the spread of the organism.

Endotoxin and Other Bacterial Cell Wall Components

The host defenses are primed to respond to various bacterial cell wall components, including lipopolysaccharide and peptidoglycan, in order to contain an infection. A systemic response to these compounds, however, can overwhelm the system and cause toxic effects.

Endotoxin

Endotoxin is lipopolysaccharide (LPS), the molecule that makes up the outer leaflet of the outer membrane of Gram-negative bacteria (see figure 3.34). Thus, endotoxin is a fundamental part of Gram-negative organisms. The nomenclature is somewhat unfortunate, because it implies that endotoxin is "inside the cell" and exotoxins are "outside the cell"; in fact, endotoxin is an integral part of the outer membrane, whereas exotoxins are proteins produced by a bacterium that may or may not be secreted. Unlike most exotoxins, endotoxin cannot be converted to an effective toxoid for immunization. **Table 19.2** summarizes some of the other differences between exotoxins and endotoxin. ■ lipopolysaccharide molecule, p. 63

Recall from chapter 3 that the lipopolysaccharide molecule is composed of two medically important parts—lipid A and the O-specific polysaccharide side chain. The lipid A component is responsible for the toxic properties of LPS. The symptoms associated with endotoxin are due to a vigorous innate immune response. When lipid A is present in a localized region, the magnitude of the response helps clear an infection. It is a different situation entirely, however, when the infection is systemic, such as septicemia. Imagine a state in which inflammation occurs throughout the body—extensive leakage of fluids from permeable blood vessels and widespread activation of the coagulation cascade. The overwhelming response in such bloodstream infections has profound effects, causing fever, a dramatic drop in blood pressure and disseminated intravascular coagulation. This array of symptoms associated with systemic bacterial infection is called **septic shock;** when it is caused by endotoxin, it may also be called **endotoxic shock.**

Lipid A is embedded in the outer membrane and does not evoke a response unless it is released. This occurs primarily when the bacterium lyses, which can happen as a result of phagocytosis, formation of membrane attack complexes by complement components, and treatment with certain types of antibiotics.

Once released from a cell, the LPS molecules can activate the innate and adaptive defenses by a variety of mechanisms. Monocytes, macrophages, and other cells have toll-like receptors that detect liberated LPS, inducing the cells to produce pro-inflammatory cytokines. LPS also functions as a T-independent antigen; at high concentrations it activates a variety of different B cells, regardless of the specificity of their B-cell receptor. ■ toll-like receptors, p. 374 ■ T-independent antigens, p. 400

Endotoxin is heat-stable; it is not destroyed by autoclaving. Consequently, solutions intended for intravenous administration must not only be sterile, but free of endotoxin as well. Disastrous results including death have resulted from administering intravenous fluids contaminated with minute amounts of endotoxin. To verify that fluids are not contaminated with endotoxin, a very sensitive test known as the *Limulus* amoebocyte lysate (LAL) assay is used. This test employs proteins extracted from blood of the horseshoe crab *Limulus polyphemus* that form a gel-like clot in the presence of endotoxin; as little as 10 to 20 picograms (1 picogram = 10^{-12} grams) of endotoxin per milliliter can be

TABLE 19.2 Comparison of Exotoxins and Endotoxin

Property	Exotoxins	Endotoxin
Bacterial source	Gram-positive and Gram-negative species	Gram-negative species only
Location in the bacterium	Synthesized in the cytoplasm; may or may not be secreted	Component of the outer membrane
Chemical nature	Protein	Lipopolysaccharide (the lipid A component)
Ability to form a toxoid	Generally	No
Heat stability	Generally inactivated by heat	Heat-stable
Mechanism	A distinct toxic mechanism for each	Innate immune response; a systemic response leads to fever, a dramatic drop in blood pressure, and disseminated intravascular coagulation.
Toxicity	Generally very potent; some are among the most potent toxins known.	Not very toxic; small amounts in a localized area lead to an appropriate response that helps clear an infection.

detected using the LAL. Horseshoe crabs are one of this planet's more unique and ancient life forms. The critical role they play in this test has led to an increased awareness of the importance of their habitat, and a non-lethal system of capture, blood sampling, and release has been developed.

Other Bacterial Cell Wall Components

Peptidoglycan and other bacterial cell wall components can elicit symptoms similar to those that characterize the response to endotoxin. The systemic response leads to septic shock.

Damaging Effects of the Immune Response

Although the intent of the immune response is to eliminate the invading microbe, the tissues of the host can inadvertently be damaged as well. Note that the reactions to endotoxin and other cell wall components can be viewed as damaging effects of the immune response, but are typically considered a toxic effect of the bacterium because the reactions may be immediate and overwhelming. The damaging responses discussed next generally manifest themselves more slowly.

Damage Associated with Inflammation

The inflammatory response itself can destroy tissue because phagocytic cells recruited to the area inevitably release some of the enzymes and toxic products they contain. The life-threatening aspects of bacterial meningitis, for example, are due to the inflammatory response itself. Complications of certain sexually transmitted diseases are also due to the damage associated with inflammation. If *Neisseria gonorrhoeae* or *Chlamydia trachomatis* infections ascend from the cervix to involve the fallopian tubes, the inflammatory response can lead to scarring that obstructs the tubes, either predisposing a woman to an ectopic pregnancy or preventing fertilization altogether.

Damage Associated with Antibodies

Antibodies generated during an immune response can also lead to damaging effects by these mechanisms:

- **Antigen-antibody complexes.** These complexes can form during the immune response and settle in the kidneys and joints. There they may activate the complement system, causing destructive inflammation. Acute glomerulonephritis, a complication that can follow strep throat and impetigo caused by *Streptococcus pyogenes,* is due to antigen-antibody complexes that settle in the kidney, eliciting a response that damages kidney structures called glomeruli. ■ **acute glomerulonephritis, p. 529**
- **Cross-reactive antibodies.** Certain antibodies produced in response to an infection bind to the body's own tissues, promoting an autoimmune response. Some evidence indicates that acute rheumatic fever, a complication that can follow strep throat, may be due to the binding of antibodies produced in response to *Streptococcus pyogenes* to a normal tissue protein. This occurs most frequently in people with certain MHC types (see Perspective 16.1). ■ **acute rheumatic fever, p. 578**

MICROCHECK 19.8

Damage can be due to exotoxins, including A-B toxins, superantigens, membrane-damaging toxins, and other toxic proteins. Endotoxin and other cell wall components can elicit a host response so strong that septic shock may result. The inflammatory response can cause tissue damage that leads to scarring. Antigen-antibody complexes can trigger damaging inflammation in the kidneys and joints; cross-reactive antibodies can lead to an autoimmune response.

✓ What is an A-B toxin?

✓ How is an enterotoxin different from endotoxin?

✓ Home-canned foods should be boiled before consumption to prevent botulism. Considering that this treatment does not destroy endospores, why would it prevent the disease?

19.9

Mechanisms of Viral Pathogenesis

Focus Point

- Describe three general mechanisms of viral pathogenicity.

The mechanisms of viral pathogenesis are somewhat different from those of bacteria. First, viruses "live" only within the context of a cell. All viruses are parasites, according to our earlier definitions. However, some viruses have very long-term relationships with their hosts—perhaps even across generations. Thus, viral pathogenesis is more a matter of degree than it is with bacteria. The virus must recognize its host, enter the cell, find a way to utilize or subvert the physiological processes of the cell for replication, keep the host from recognizing and destroying the infected cell during viral replication, and then move to new cells or hosts. In carrying out these functions, many viruses damage host cells and induce inflammatory responses, causing the signs and symptoms of disease.

Binding to Host Cells and Invasion

As discussed in chapter 14, all viruses have proteins on their surface that interact with specific receptors on the surface of certain host cells, enabling the virus to attach to the target cell. Once attached, many types of viruses are taken up because they stimulate the host cell to "collect receptors" from the surface and internalize them in the process of receptor-mediated endocytosis. Others carry proteins that lead to fusion of the viral envelope with the cell membrane, releasing the viral capsid into the cell (see figure 14.3a). ■ **receptor-mediated endocytosis, p. 76**

The receptor used by a particular virus influences the host range and tissue specificity of that virus; only cells that bear the specific receptor can be infected. HIV uses CD4 as a receptor; recall that this is found on helper T cells. Picorna viruses and reoviruses bind to receptors on M cells in the Peyer's patches of the intestinal tract. ■ **CD4, p. 402**

The viruses released from the infected cell may infect neighboring cells or they may disseminate in the bloodstream or lymphatic system to other tissues. Polioviruses for example, initially infect cells in the throat and intestinal tract. Upon release from these cells, the virus may spread via the bloodstream to infect motor nerve cells of the brain and spinal cord. ■ polio, p. 695

Avoiding Immune Responses

As intracellular obligate parasites, viruses must subvert or avoid mechanisms the body has developed to maintain a healthy internal environment. These include the production of interferon, induction of apoptosis, recognition of altered MHC class I expression, production and action of neutralizing antibodies, and production of cytotoxic T cells capable of killing infected cells.

Avoiding the Antiviral Effects of Interferons

Early in the interaction between the body and a virus, interferons play a large role in limiting viral spread (see figure 15.9). Interferons induce cells to produce enzymes that, when activated, prevent viral replication. To avoid this, some viruses encode proteins that shut down expression of host genes. Some circumvent interferon's effects by interferring with activation of the enzymes. ■ interferon, p. 377

Regulation of Host Cell Death by Viruses

A hallmark of viral infection recognized in the early days of virology was damage and death of infected cells. Many of the viruses studied took control of cellular machinery and converted a large fraction of the total mass of the cell into viral components, leading to the loss of cell structure and integrity. As the study of viruses has expanded, we have learned that interactions between viruses and their host cells can be much more complex. Some viruses kill the host cell after production of a large number of viral copies to allow them to spread to other cells. Others control certain aspects of immune surveillance to avoid premature death of their host cell.

Some types of viruses induce apoptosis, or programmed cell death, in their host cell to limit the inflammatory response and the resulting stimulation of the immune response. Many viral products, particularly double-stranded RNA intermediates, initiate apoptosis.

Certain viruses inhibit apoptosis, giving the virus more time to replicate and produce new copies of itself. They do this by controlling a protein called p53 that regulates apoptosis activation in the cell. The inhibition of the p53 protein in the host cell is often associated with tumor development. Papillomaviruses, a group of viruses that cause various types of warts, interfere with the normal function of p53. ■ apoptosis, p. 382 ■ papillomavirus, p. 670

Some viruses block antigen presentation by MHC class I molecules, the mechanism the immune system uses to recognize "corrupt cells." Normally, pieces of endogenous proteins are placed into the groove of MHC class I molecules and brought to the cell surface for "inspection" by the T_C cells (effector cytotoxic T cells) of the adaptive immune response. Some viruses such as herpesviruses block the processing and movement of MHC class I to the surface, making the immune system less aware of their presence in the body. The immune system has developed mechanisms to thwart this widespread "hijacking" of the normal mechanisms for identifying infected cells. Natural killer (NK) cells recognize cells that have "too few" MHC class I molecules and destroy them. Some viruses have also adapted methods to counteract this NK mechanism. Cytomegalovirus (CMV), a herpesvirus that causes severe problems in immunocompromised people, makes "counterfeit" MHC class I proteins and displays them on the surface of its host cells to trick the body into believing "all is well in this cell" **(figure 19.13).** These counterfeit molecules do not identify the infection to the immune system and buy time for the virus to replicate. ■ antigen presentation by MHC class I, p. 404 ■ herpesviruses, p. 341 ■ natural killer cells, p. 406 ■ cytomegaloviruses, p. 752

Antibodies and Viruses

Antibodies generally control the spread of virus from cell to cell by neutralizing extracellular viral particles (see figure 16.5). To subvert the role of antibodies, some viruses have developed methods to directly transfer virus from one cell to its immediate neighbors. Other viruses remain intracellular by forcing all the cellular neighbors to join a "commune," fusing to form what is called a **syncytium.** Viruses like HIV avoid the neutralizing activity of antibodies by inducing syncytia formation.

Some viruses actually use antibodies to enhance their ability to infect cells. These viruses use the "free ride" given by Fc-mediated uptake of viral-antibody complexes into macrophages to enhance infection and damage the host. This is referred to as antibody-mediated enhancement of infection.

Another way viruses deal with the development of antibodies is to outpace the body's capacity to produce them by altering viral surface antigens. RNA viruses contain, on average, one mutation per new viral particle. Their polymerases copy RNA without any proofreading, so the mutation frequency is about 1 base in 100,000. There are more than 100,000 bases in the average RNA virus, so about 1 error per new virus. The accumulation of mutations by these viruses generates pools of genetically altered viruses. These mutants come into dominance as the "parent" viruses are rapidly neutralized by antibody. Thus, the body keeps selecting for new viral "strains" over the course of infection. Many of these viruses are eventually cleared as a result of an immune response against essential proteins that cannot tolerate extensive mutations. Other viruses, like HIV, exploit this method to infect the host for a very long time.

Viruses and Damage to the Host

Viruses can damage host cells in many ways. Some viruses just take over the host cell, use up the internal components, and then burst it to release new copies of themselves. The combination of tissue damage and presence of viral antigens evokes the innate and adaptive immune responses. Damage is caused by a combination of events including the inflammatory response and the destruction of host cells by both the virus and T_C cells.

Other viruses cause host cell death by activation of apoptosis, either by design or accident. Apoptotic death generally minimizes local inflammatory responses and retards development of an immune response. In critical tissues such as nerves, however, even slight damage can be symptomatic. If enough cells are lost even in non-critical tissues, functional changes occur in the host, signaling danger and eliciting a response from the host defenses.

In other instances, like the common cold, the body responds vigorously to the infection and causes many cycles of damage and response—far out of proportion with the damage done directly by

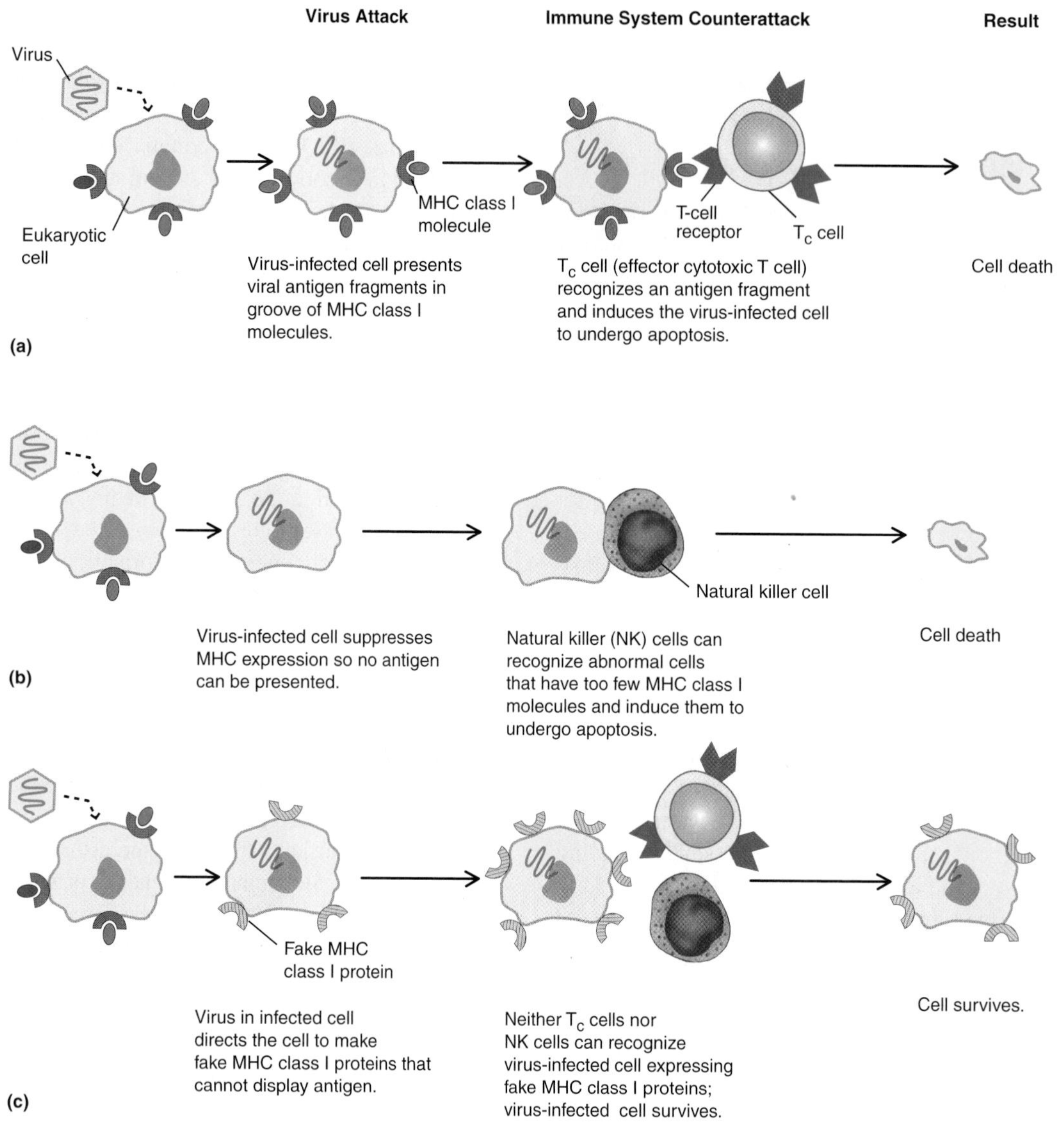
Virus Attack
Immune System Counterattack
Result
Virus
Eukaryotic cell
MHC class I molecule
T-cell receptor
T_C cell
Virus-infected cell presents viral antigen fragments in groove of MHC class I molecules.
T_C cell (effector cytotoxic T cell) recognizes an antigen fragment and induces the virus-infected cell to undergo apoptosis.
Cell death
(a)
Natural killer cell
Virus-infected cell suppresses MHC expression so no antigen can be presented.
Natural killer (NK) cells can recognize abnormal cells that have too few MHC class I molecules and induce them to undergo apoptosis.
Cell death
(b)
Fake MHC class I protein
Virus in infected cell directs the cell to make fake MHC class I proteins that cannot display antigen.
Neither T_C cells nor NK cells can recognize virus-infected cell expressing fake MHC class I proteins; virus-infected cell survives.
Cell survives.
(c)

FIGURE 19.13 Cytomegalovirus-Immune Cell Interactions **(a)** Normal reaction to virus-infected cell by a T_C cell. **(b)** Some viruses can evade destruction of their host cell by suppressing MHC expression, but NK cells of host can induce apoptosis in cells lacking MHC molecules. **(c)** Virus causes cell to produce fake MHC that neither T_C cells nor NK cells can recognize, and so the virus-infected cell survives.

the virus. Thus, we suffer a long time from the common cold even after the virus has moved on.

MICROCHECK 19.9

Proteins on the surface of virus particles function as adherence factors. Viruses, as a group, have evolved mechanisms to avoid the antiviral effects of interferon and to control apoptosis of the host cell. Damage is often due to the host response.

- ✓ From a virus's perspective, why would it be beneficial to prevent apoptosis?
- ✓ From a virus's perspective, why would it be beneficial to induce apoptosis?
- ✓ Why would various unrelated viral infections often include a similar set of symptoms (fever, headache, fatigue, and runny nose)?

19.10 Mechanisms of Eukaryotic Pathogenesis

Focus Point

- Describe some of the virulence determinants of fungi and eukaryotic parasites.

Pathogenesis of eukaryotic cells including fungi and protozoa involve the same basic scheme as that of bacterial pathogens—colonization, evasion of host defenses, and damage to the host. The mechanisms, however, are generally not well understood.

Fungi

Most fungi, such as yeasts and molds, are **saprophytes,** meaning that they acquire nutrients from dead and dying material; those that can cause disease are generally opportunists, although notable exceptions exist.

A group of fungi referred to as **dermatophytes** can cause superficial infections of hair, skin, and nails but do not invade deeper tissues. These fungi have keratinase enzymes that break down the keratin in superficial tissues, resulting in diseases such as ringworm and athlete's foot.

Fungi in the normal flora, especially the yeast *Candida albicans,* can cause disease in immunocompromised hosts. Generally this leads to infection of the mucous membranes, causing thrush, an infection of the throat and mouth, or vaginitis. Factors that may lead to excessive growth of *C. albicans* include disruption of normal flora due to hormonal influences or antibiotic treatment, AIDS, uncontrolled diabetes, and severe burns.

The most serious fungal infections are caused by a group of fungi that are **dimorphic;** they occur as molds in the environment, but assume other forms, usually yeasts, when they invade tissues. Infection occurs when the small airborne spores of the molds are inhaled, lodging deep within the lungs. These infections are generally controlled by the immune system and do not cause serious disease unless there is an overwhelming infection or if the person is immunocompromised.

Some fungi produce toxins, collectively referred to as mycotoxins, which can cause disease. For example, *Aspergillus flavus,* a fungus that grows on certain grains and nuts, including peanuts, produces aflatoxin. If this toxin is ingested it can damage the liver, perhaps leading to cancer. The spores and other fungal elements can cause hypersensitivities in some people.

Eukaryotic Parasites

Most eukaryotic parasites either live within the intestinal tract or enter the body via the bite of an arthropod. *Schistosoma* species, however, can enter the skin directly (see Perspective 15.1).

Like bacteria and viruses, eukaryotic parasites attach to host cells via specific receptors. *Plasmodium vivax,* one of the two most common causes of malaria, attaches to the Duffy blood group antigen on red blood cells. Most people of West African ancestry lack this antigen and are therefore resistant to infection by this species. *Giardia lamblia* uses a disc that functions as a suction cup to attach to the intestine; it appears that it also has an adhesin associated with the disc that facilitates the initial attachment.

Eukaryotic parasites use a variety of mechanisms to avoid antibodies. Some hide within cells, thus avoiding exposure to antibodies as well as certain other defenses. Malarial parasites produce enzymes that allow them to penetrate red blood cells. These host cells do not present antigen to T_C cells, enabling the parasite to escape the cellular immune defenses as well. *Leishmania* species are able to survive and multiply within macrophages when phagocytized. Parasites such as the African trypanosomes, the cause of sleeping sickness, escape from the effects of antibody by routinely varying their surface antigens, repeatedly activating different genes. *Schistosoma* species coat themselves with host proteins, effectively disguising themselves. Some parasites appear to suppress immune responses in general.

The extent and type of damage caused by parasites varies tremendously. In some cases, the parasites compete for nutrients in the intestinal tract, contributing to malnutrition of the host. Helminths may accumulate in high enough numbers or grow long enough to cause blockage of the intestines or other organs. Some parasites can produce enzymes that digest host tissue, causing direct damage. In other cases, damage is due to the immune response; high fevers that characterize malaria, and the granulomatous response to schistosoma eggs are examples.

MICROCHECK 19.10

Pathogenic mechanisms of fungi and eukaryotic parasites are not as well understood as those of bacteria; however, they involve the same basic scheme—colonization, evasion of host defenses, and damage to the host.

- ✓ What is the importance of keratinase?
- ✓ How do the African trypanosomes avoid the effects of antibodies?
- ✓ Why would relatively few people of West African ancestry have the Duffy blood group antigen?

FUTURE CHALLENGES

Genetics of Pathogenicity

Study of the pathogenesis of infectious diseases has come a long way since the first bacterial toxins were discovered little more than a century ago. Many questions, however, remain unanswered. Advances in genetic techniques have opened many areas of investigation. The availability of genetic sequence data has shown similarities in the virulence factors of diverse organisms. The discovery of pathogenicity islands bearing genes for a number of virulence factors in a cluster that is readily transferred opens the door to new approaches to understanding virulence.

One challenge is to understand how these virulence genes are regulated. It is known that bacteria express only the virulence genes appropriate for each host cell environment. Control is complex, and its study offers a fertile field of research.

Other challenges arise in trying to better understand interactions between microorganisms and host cells and tissues. Tools such as "knock-out mice" will be useful. These are mice in which specific genes have been inactivated or "knocked-out." It may be possible to use the host's immune system to modify the infectious process.

Of course, microorganisms are constantly changing and evolving. New pathogens will continue to emerge as a result of transfers of genetic information, such as pathogenicity islands. Use of the Molecular postulates will permit identification of new pathogens. New techniques will produce better diagnostic methods and new approaches to control and treatment of infectious diseases.

SUMMARY

Microbes, Health, and Disease

19.1 The Anatomical Barriers As Ecosystems

Symbiotic Relationships Between Microorganisms and Hosts

In **mutualism,** both partners benefit, in **commensalism** one partner benefits while the other is unaffected, and in **parasitism,** the **parasite** benefits at the expense of the host.

19.2 The Normal Flora (Figure 19.1)

The Protective Role of Normal Flora

The **normal flora** excludes pathogens by covering binding sites that might otherwise be used for attachment, consuming available nutrients, and producing compounds toxic to other bacteria.

The normal flora primes the adaptive immune system.

The Dynamic Nature of the Normal Flora

The composition of the normal flora continually changes in response to host factors including hormonal changes, type of food consumed, and antibiotics.

19.3 Principles of Infectious Disease

Pathogenicity

A **primary pathogen** causes disease in otherwise healthy individuals; an **opportunist** causes disease only when the body's innate or adaptive defenses are compromised.

Virulence refers to the degree of pathogenicity of an organism.

Characteristics of Infectious Disease

Communicable or **contagious diseases** spread from one host to another; ease of spread partly reflects the **infectious dose.**

Stages of infectious disease include the **incubation period, illness,** and **convalescence;** during the illness a person experiences **signs** and **symptoms** of the disease. (Figure 19.2)

Infections can be described as **acute, chronic,** or **latent,** depending on the timing and duration of symptoms.

Infections can be **localized** or **systemic.**

19.4 Establishing the Cause of Infectious Disease

Koch's Postulates

Koch's postulates are used to establish the cause of infectious disease.

Molecular Postulates

Molecular postulates are used to identify virulence factors that contribute to disease.

Mechanisms of Pathogenesis

19.5 Establishment of Infection

Adherence

Bacteria use **adhesins** to bind to host cells. (Figure 19.3)

Colonization

Rapid turnover of pili, antigenic variation, and **IgA proteases** enable bacteria to avoid the effects of IgA.

Siderophores enable microbes to scavenge iron.

Delivery of Effector Molecules to Host Cells

Type III secretion systems of Gram-negative bacteria allow them to deliver compounds directly to host cells. (Figure 19.4)

19.6 Invasion—Breaching the Anatomical Barriers

Penetration of Skin

Bacteria take advantage of trauma that destroys the integrity of the skin or rely on arthropods to inject them.

Penetration of Mucous Membranes

Some pathogens induce mucosal epithelial cells to engulf bacterial cells; others exploit antigen-sampling processes. (Figures 19.5, 19.6)

19.7 Avoiding the Host Defenses

Hiding Within a Host Cell

Some bacteria can evade the innate defenses, as well as some aspects of the adaptive defenses, by remaining inside host cells.

Avoiding Killing by Complement System Proteins

Some **serum-resistant** bacteria are able to postpone the formation of the membrane attack complex by interfering with activation of the complement system via the alternative pathway. (Figure 19.8)

Avoiding Destruction by Phagocytes (Figure 19.9)

Mechanisms to prevent encounters with phagocytes include **C5a peptidase** and **membrane-damaging toxins.**

Mechanisms to avoid recognition and attachment by phagocytes include **capsules, M protein,** and **Fc receptors.** (Figure 19.10)

Mechanisms to survive within the phagocyte include escape from the phagosome, preventing phagosome-lysosome fusion, and surviving within the phagolysosome.

Avoiding Antibodies

Mechanisms to avoid antibodies include **IgA protease, antigenic variation,** and mimicking "self."

19.8 Damage to the Host

Exotoxins (Table 19.1)

Exotoxins are proteins that have very specific damaging effects; they may act locally or cause dramatic systemic effects. Many can be grouped into categories such as **neurotoxins, enterotoxins,** or **cytotoxins.**

The toxic activity of **A-B toxins** is mediated by the A subunit; binding to specific cells is mediated by the B subunit. (Figure 19.11)

Superantigens override the specificity of the T-cell response, causing systemic effects due to the massive release of cytokines. (Figure 19.12)

Membrane-damaging toxins disrupt cell membranes either by forming pores or by removing the polar head group on phospholipids in the membrane.

Various other proteins can have detrimental effects; hydrolytic enzymes can break down tissue components.

Endotoxin and Other Bacterial Cell Wall Components

The symptoms associated with endotoxin are due to a vigorous host response. **Lipid A** of lipopolysaccharide is responsible for its toxic properties.

Peptidoglycan and certain other components induce various cells to produce pro-inflammatory cytokines.

Damaging Effects of the Immune Response

The release of enzymes and toxic products from phagocytic cells can damage tissues.

Antigen-antibody complexes can cause kidney and joint damage; cross-reactive antibodies can promote an autoimmune response.

19.9 Mechanisms of Viral Pathogenesis

Binding to Host Cells and Invasion

Viruses attach to specific receptors on the target cell.

Avoiding Immune Responses

Some viruses can avoid the effects of interferon; some can regulate apoptosis of the host cell. (Figure 19.13)

To subvert the role of antibodies, some viruses transfer directly from cell to cell; the surface antigens of some viruses change quickly, outpacing the production of antibodies.

Viruses and Damage to the Host

Mechanisms of damage include direct damage by the virus, virally induced apoptosis, and the immune response to the infection.

19.10 Mechanisms of Eukaryotic Pathogenesis

Fungi

Saprophytes are generally opportunists; dermatophytes cause superficial infections of skin, hair, and nails. The most serious fungal infections are caused by dimorphic fungi.

Eukaryotic Parasites

Eukaryotic parasites attach to host cells via specific receptors. They use a variety of mechanisms to avoid antibodies; the extent and type of damage they cause varies tremendously.

REVIEW QUESTIONS

Short Answer

1. Describe three types of symbiotic relationships.
2. Describe two situations that can lead to changes in the composition of the normal flora.
3. What is the difference between acute, chronic, and latent infection?
4. Why are Koch's postulates not sufficient to establish the cause of all infectious diseases?
5. Describe the four general mechanisms by which microorganisms cause disease.
6. Describe two mechanisms that bacteria use to invade mucous membranes.
7. Explain how capsules enable an organism to be serum resistant and avoid phagocytosis.
8. Give an example of a neurotoxin, an enterotoxin, and a cytotoxin.
9. Describe two mechanisms a virus might use to prevent the induction of apoptosis in an infected cell.
10. How do *Schistosoma* species avoid antibodies?

Multiple Choice

1. Opportunistic pathogens are *least* likely to affect which of the following groups:
   a) AIDS patients b) Cancer patients c) College students
   d) Drug addicts e) Transplant recipients
2. Capsules are thought to interfere with which of the following:
   a) Opsonization by complement proteins
   b) Opsonization by antibodies
   c) Recognition by T cells
   d) Recognition by B cells
   e) Phagosome-lysosome fusion
3. The C5a peptidase enzyme of *Streptococcus pyogenes* breaks down C5a, resulting in
   a) lysis of the *Streptococcus* cells.
   b) lack of opsonization of *Streptococcus* cells.
   c) killing of phagocytes.
   d) decreased accumulation of phagocytes.
   e) inhibition of membrane attack complexes.
4. All of the following are known mechanisms of avoiding the effects of antibodies *except*
   a) antigenic variation.
   b) mimicking "self."
   c) synthesis of an Fc receptor.
   d) synthesis of IgG protease.
   e) remaining intracellular.
5. Which of the following statements about diphtheria toxin is *false?* It
   a) is an example of an endotoxin.
   b) is produced by a species of *Corynebacterium.*
   c) inhibits protein synthesis.
   d) can cause local damage to the throat.
   e) can cause systemic damage (that is, to organs such as the heart).
6. Which of the following statements about botulism is *true?*
   a) It is caused by *Bacillus botulinum,* an obligate aerobe.
   b) The toxin is resistant to heat, easily withstanding temperatures of 100°C.
   c) The organism that causes botulism can cause disease without avoiding the immune response.
   d) Vaccinations are routinely given to prevent botulism.
   e) Symptoms of botulism include uncontrolled contraction of muscles.
7. Superantigens
   a) are exceptionally large antigen molecules.
   b) cause a very large antibody response.
   c) elicit a response from a large number of T cells.
   d) attach non-specifically to B-cell receptors.
   e) assist in a protective immune response.

8. Which of the following statements about endotoxin is *true?* It
   a) is an example of an A-B toxin.
   b) is a component Gram-positive bacteria.
   c) is highly antigenic.
   d) is heat-stable.
   e) causes T cells to release cytokines.
9. The tissue damage caused by *Neisseria gonorrhoeae* is primarily due to
   a) cross-reactive antibodies.
   b) exotoxins.
   c) hydrolytic enzymes.
   d) the inflammatory response.
   e) all of the these.
10. Which of the following statements about viruses is *false?* They may
    a) colonize the skin.
    b) enter host cells by endocytosis.
    c) enter host cells by fusion of the viral envelope with the cell membrane.
    d) induce apoptosis in infected host cells.
    e) suppress expression of MHC class I molecules on host cells.

Applications

1. A group of smokers suffering from the outcome of severe *Staphylococcus aureus* infections are suing the cigarette companies. They claim that the disease was aggravated by cigarette smoking. The group is citing studies indicating that phagocytes are inhibited in their action by compounds in cigarette smoke. A statement prepared by their lawyers states that the *S. aureus* would not have caused such a severe disease if the phagocytes and immune system overall were functioning properly. During the proceedings, a microbiologist was called in as a professional witness for the court. What were her conclusions about the validity of the claim?
2. A microbiologist put forth a grant proposal to study the molecules bacteria use to communicate. His principal rationale was that the damaging effects of many pathogenic microorganisms could be prevented by inactivating the molecules these bacteria use to communicate. Is this a reasonable proposal? Why or why not?

Critical Thinking

1. A student argued that no distinction should be made between commensalism and parasitism. Even in commensalism, the microorganisms are gaining some benefit (such as nutrients) from the host and this represents a loss to the host. In this sense the host is being damaged. Does the student have a valid argument? Why or why not?
2. A microbiologist argued that there is no such thing as "normal" flora in the human body, since the population is dynamic and is constantly changing depending on diet and external environment. What would be an argument against this microbiologist's view?

Community water supply in a developing country

CHAPTER TWENTY

Epidemiology

A Glimpse of History

Puerperal fever, an illness we now recognize is the result of a bacterial infection of the uterus following childbirth, has occurred at least since the time of Hippocrates (460–377 B.C.). In the eighteenth century, when it became popular for women to deliver their babies in hospitals, the incidence of the disease rose to epidemic proportions. In Prussia between 1816 and 1875, more than 363,600 women died of puerperal fever. In the middle of the nineteenth century in the hospitals of Vienna, the major medical center of the world at that time, about one of every eight women died of puerperal fever following childbirth.

In 1841, Ignaz Semmelweis, a Hungarian, traveled to Vienna to study medicine. After finishing medical school, he became the first assistant to Professor Johann Klein at the Lying-In Hospital. There were two sections of the hospital. The first section was under the management of Professor Klein and the medical students. Midwives and midwifery students served the second section. Being an astute observer, Semmelweis soon noticed that the incidence of puerperal fever in the first section often rose as high as 18%, four times that in the second section. When he investigated the conditions in the two sections, they appeared to be the same except in terms of their management. Semmelweis was dismissed from his post when he implicated Professor Klein and the students in the spread of the disease, but he was reinstated a few months later when others intervened on his behalf.

Semmelweis recognized that disease symptoms that led to the death of a friend who had incurred a scalpel wound while doing an autopsy were similar to puerperal fever. He reasoned that the "poison" that killed his friend probably also contaminated the hands of the medical students who did autopsies. These students were transferring the "poison" from the cadavers to the women in childbirth. Midwives did not perform autopsies. Since this was before Pasteur and Koch established the germ theory of disease, Semmelweis had no way of knowing that the "poison" being transferred was probably *Streptococcus pyogenes,* a common cause of many infections, including puerperal fever. Those being autopsied had likely died of streptococcal disease as well. To test his hypothesis, Semmelweis instituted the practice of having physicians and students wash their hands with a solution of chloride of lime, a strong disinfectant, before attending their patients. The result was a drop in the incidence of puerperal fever to one-third its previous level. Instead of accepting these findings, Semmelweis's colleagues refused to admit responsibility for the deaths of so many patients. His work was so fiercely attacked that he was forced to leave Vienna and return to his native Hungary. There he was again able to use disinfection techniques to achieve a remarkable reduction in the number of deaths from puerperal fever.

Semmelweis became increasingly outspoken and bitter, finally becoming so deranged that he was confined to a mental institution. Ironically, he died one month later of a generalized infection similar to the kind that had killed his friend and the many women who had contracted puerperal fever following childbirth. The infection originated from a finger wound received before his confinement. Some said he deliberately infected himself from a cadaver while performing an autopsy.

Epidemiology combines diverse disciplines including ecology, microbiology, sociology, statistics, and psychology to study the cause and distribution of health states, both positive and negative, in populations. **Epidemiologists** are the "health detectives" who do most of this work. They collect and compile data to describe disease outbreaks, much as a criminal detective describes the scene of a crime. Many habits in the daily routine of life, from handwashing to waste disposal, reflect a current understanding of epidemiology.

KEY TERMS

Attack rate The proportional number of cases developing in a population exposed to the infectious agent.

Communicable disease An infectious disease that can be transmitted from one host to another.

Endemic A disease or other occurrence that is constantly present in a population.

Epidemic A disease or other occurrence that has a much higher incidence than expected.

Herd immunity A phenomenon that occurs when a critical concentration of immune hosts prevents the spread of an infectious agent.

Incidence The number of new cases of a disease in a population at risk during a specified time period.

Index case The first identified case of a disease in an outbreak or epidemic.

Morbidity Illness. Most often expressed as the rate of illness in a given population at risk.

Mortality Death. Most often expressed as a rate of death in a given population at risk.

Outbreak A cluster of cases occurring during a brief time interval and affecting a specific population; an outbreak may herald the onset of an epidemic.

Pandemic A worldwide epidemic.

Prevalence The total number of cases of a disease in a given population at risk at a point in time.

Reservoir of infection The natural habitat of a pathogen.

20.1 Principles of Epidemiology

Focus Points

- Describe why epidemiologists are most concerned with the rate of disease rather than absolute number of cases.
- Describe how a pathogen gets from its reservoir to the next host. Focus on the types of reservoirs, portals of exit, mechanisms of transmission, and portals of entry.
- Describe three factors that influence the epidemiology of disease.

Diseases that can be transmitted from one host to another, such as measles, colds, and influenza, are communicable diseases. In order for a communicable disease to spread, a specific chain of events must occur. First, the pathogen must have a suitable environment in which to live. That natural habitat, the **reservoir of infection** may be on or in an animal, including humans, or in an environment such as soil or water **(figure 20.1a).** A pathogen must then leave its reservoir in order to be transmitted to the susceptible host. If the reservoir is an animal, the body orifice or surface from which a microbe is shed is called the **portal of exit.** Disease-causing organisms must then be transmitted to the next host, usually through direct contact or via contaminated food, water, or air (figure 20.1b). They enter the next host through a body surface or orifice called the **portal of entry** (figure 20.1c).

Diseases that do not spread from one host to another are called **non-communicable diseases.** Microorganisms that cause these diseases most often arise from an individual's normal flora or from an environmental reservoir. Prevention of non-communicable illness is often disease-specific.

Rate of Disease in a Population

Epidemiologists are most concerned with the **rate** of a disease (the proportion of a given population infected), rather than the absolute number of cases. For example, 100 people in a large city developing disease X in a given period may not be abnormal, whereas 100 people in a small rural community developing the same disease would indicate a much higher rate and thus be of greater concern to the epidemiologist. A related concept is the **attack rate,** which is the number of cases developing in a group of people who were exposed to the infectious agent. For example, if 100 people at a party ate chicken that was contaminated with *Salmonella,* and 10 people came down with symptoms of salmonellosis, then the attack rate was 10%. The attack rate reflects many factors, including the infectious dose of the organism and the immunity of the population.

Other rates are also often used to express the effect of a disease on a population. **Morbidity rate** is calculated as the number of cases of an illness in a given time period divided by the population at risk. Contagious diseases such as influenza often have a high morbidity rate because each infected individual may transmit the infection to several others. **Mortality rate** reflects the percentage of a population that dies from the disease. Diseases such as plague and Ebola hemorrhagic fever are feared because of their very high mortality rate. The **incidence** of a disease reflects the number of new cases in a specific time period in a given population at risk, whereas the **prevalence** reflects the number of total existing cases both old and new in a given population at risk. Usually these rates are expressed as the number of cases per 100,000 people. The prevalence is useful to assess the overall impact of the disease on society because it takes the duration of the disease into account, whereas the incidence provides a means of measuring the risk of an individual contracting the disease.

Diseases that are constantly present in a given population are called **endemic.** Both the common cold and influenza are endemic in the United States. An unusually large number of cases in a population constitutes an **epidemic.** Epidemics may be caused by diseases not normally present in a population, such as cholera being reintroduced to the Western Hemisphere, or by endemic diseases such as influenza and pneumonia **(figure 20.2).** A related term is **outbreak,** which generally implies a cluster of cases occurring during a brief time interval and affecting a specific population; an outbreak may herald the onset of an epidemic. When an epidemic spreads worldwide, such as we have seen with AIDS, it is called a **pandemic.**

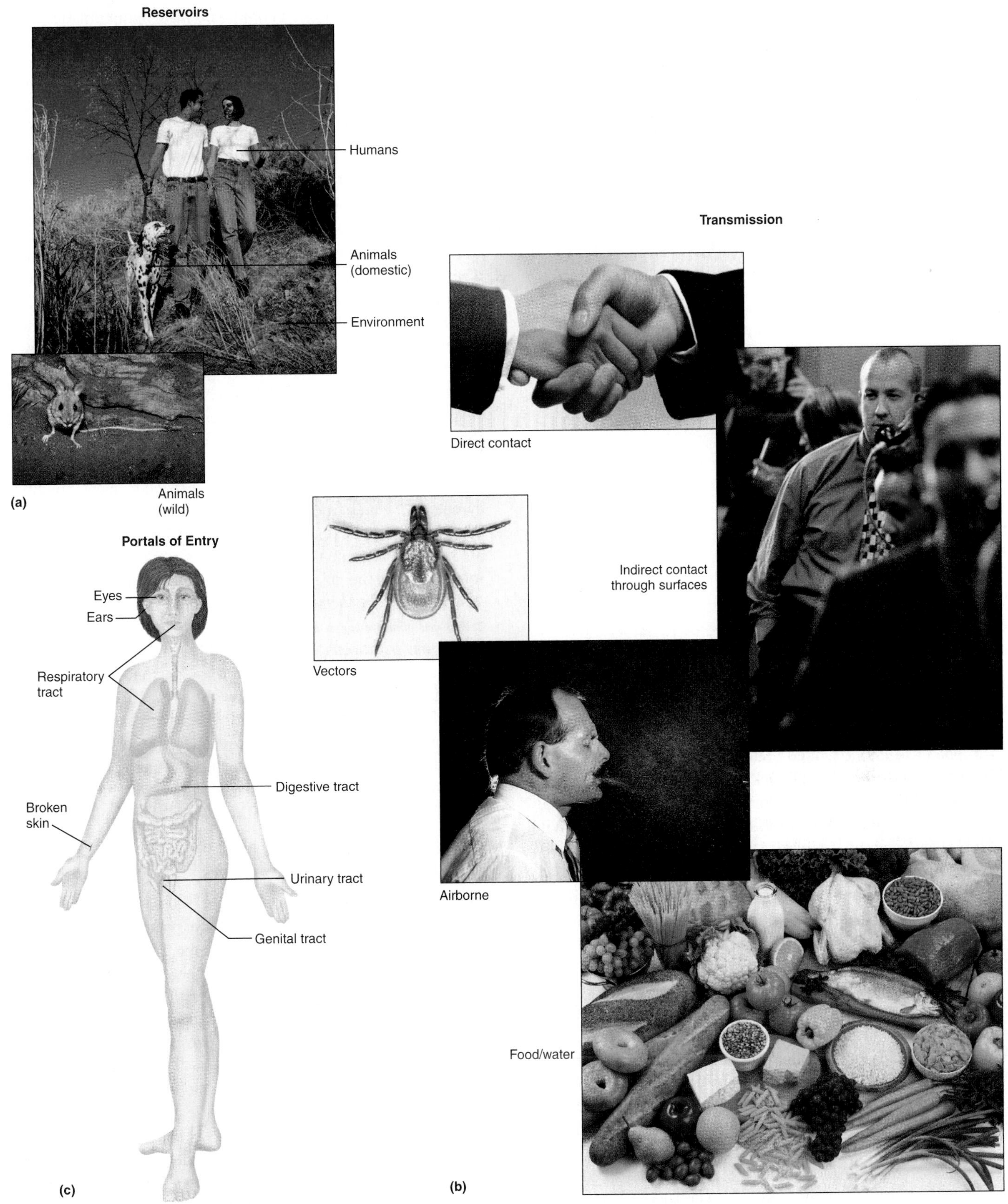

FIGURE 20.1 Spread of Pathogens **(a)** Reservoirs of infection, **(b)** transmission, and **(c)** portals of entry are necessary for the spread of communicable diseases.

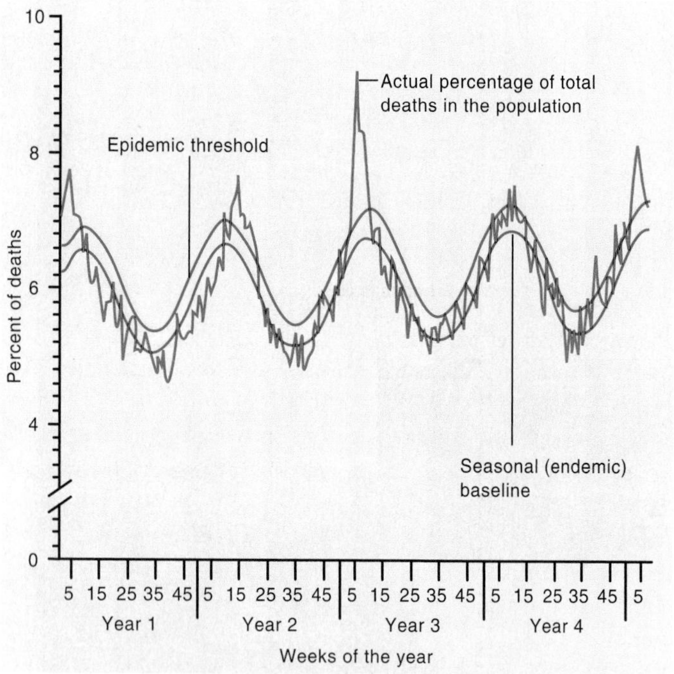

FIGURE 20.2 Endemic Disease that Can Be Epidemic Example of yearly fluctuation of pneumonia and influenza mortality (expressed as a percentage of all deaths).

Reservoirs of Infection

The reservoir of infection is important because it affects the extent and distribution of a disease. Recognizing the reservoir can help protect a population from disease, because measures can then be instituted to prevent the people from coming into contact with that source. The fact that the United States does not have epidemics of plague, the disease that killed over one-quarter of the European population in the fourteenth century, is in part because we recognize the importance of controlling its rodent reservoir. Wild rats, mice, and prairie dogs are the natural reservoir of *Yersinia pestis,* the bacterium that causes plague. By avoiding a buildup of garbage in cities and homes, we prevent rodent infestation of our living quarters. ■ *Yersinia pestis,* p. 717

Human Reservoirs

Infected humans are the most significant reservoir of the majority of communicable diseases. In some cases, humans are the only reservoir. In other instances, the pathogenic organism can exist not only in humans but in other animals and, occasionally, the environment as well. If infected humans are the only reservoir, then theoretically the disease is easier to control. This is because it is more feasible to institute prevention and control programs in humans than it is in wild animals. The eradication of smallpox is an excellent example. The combined effects of widespread vaccination programs, which resulted in fewer susceptible people, and the successful isolation of those who did become infected, eliminated the smallpox virus from nature. The virus no longer had a reservoir in which to multiply.

Symptomatic Infections People who have symptomatic illnesses are an obvious source of infectious agents, and ideally they understand the importance of taking precautions to avoid transmitting their illness to others. Staying home and resting while ill both helps the body recover and protects others from exposure to the disease-causing agent. Even conscientious people, however, can unintentionally be a source of infection to others. For example, people who are in the incubation period of mumps still shed virus. ■ mumps, p. 620 ■ incubation period, p. 455

Asymptomatic Carriers A person can harbor a pathogen with no ill effects whatsoever, acting as a **carrier** of the disease agent. These people may shed the organism intermittently or constantly for months, years, or even a lifetime.

Some carriers have an **asymptomatic infection;** their immune system is actively responding to the invading microorganism, but they have no obvious clinical symptoms. Because these people often have no reason to consider themselves a reservoir, they move freely about, spreading the pathogen. People with asymptomatic infections are a significant complicating factor in the control of sexually transmitted diseases such as gonorrhea. Up to 50% of women infected with *Neisseria gonorrhoeae* have no obvious symptoms, which means they often unknowingly transmit the disease to their sexual partners. In contrast, most infected men are symptomatic and therefore seek medical treatment. Gonorrhea infections can be treated with antibacterial drugs, but tracking down sexual contacts of infected people is difficult and costly. ■ *Neisseria gonorrhoeae,* p. 661

Some pathogens can colonize the skin or mucosal surfaces, establishing themselves as part of a person's microbial flora. For instance, many people carry *Staphylococcus aureus* as a part of their nasal or skin flora. *S. aureus* carriers may never have any illness or disease as a result of the organism, but they remain a potential source of infection to themselves and others. Unfortunately, ridding a colonized carrier of the infectious organism is often difficult, even with the use of antimicrobial drugs. ■ *Staphylococcus aureus,* p. 525

Non-Human Animal Reservoirs

Non-human animal reservoirs are the source of some pathogens. Poultry are a reservoir of gastrointestinal pathogens such as species of *Campylobacter* and *Salmonella.* In the United States, raccoons, skunks, and bats are the reservoir of the rabies virus. Recall that rodents are the reservoir of *Yersinia pestis,* the causative agent of plague. Occasional transmission of plague to humans is still reported in the southwestern states where *Y. pestis* is endemic in prairie dogs and other rodents, but rodent control has helped prevent epidemics of the disease. Rodents, particularly the deer mouse, are also the reservoir for hantavirus. ■ *Campylobacter,* p. 630 ■ *Salmonella,* p. 628

Diseases such as plague and rabies that can be transmitted to humans but primarily exist in other animals are called **zoonotic** diseases or **zoonoses.** Zoonotic diseases are often more severe in humans than in the normal animal host because the infection in humans is accidental; there has been no evolution toward the balanced pathogenicity that normally exists between a host and parasite. ■ balanced pathogenicity, p. 457

Environmental Reservoirs

Some pathogens have environmental reservoirs. *Clostridium botulinum,* which causes botulism, and *Clostridium tetani,* which causes tetanus, are both widespread in soils. Unfortunately, pathogens that have environmental reservoirs are probably impossible to eliminate. ■ *Clostridium botulinum,* p. 690 ■ *Clostridium tetani,* p. 557

Portals of Exit

Microorganisms must leave one host in order to be transmitted to another. Those that inhabit the intestinal tract are routinely shed in the feces. Pathogens such as *Vibrio cholerae* that cause massive volumes of watery diarrhea may have an evolutionary advantage because the large volumes discharged can enhance their dispersal. Respiratory organisms are expelled in droplets of saliva when people talk, laugh, sing, sneeze, or cough (see figure 20.1b). Pathogens such as *Mycobacterium tuberculosis* and various respiratory viruses exit the body via this route. Meanwhile, organisms that inhabit the skin are constantly shed on skin cells. Even as you read this text you are shedding skin cells, some of which may have *Staphylococcus aureus* on their surface. Genital pathogens such as *Neisseria gonorrhoeae* can be carried in semen and vaginal secretions. Hantavirus is found in the saliva, urine, and droppings of the deer mouse. ■ *Vibrio cholerae,* p. 624 ■ *Neisseria gonorrhoeae,* p. 661 ■ *Mycobacterium tuberculosis,* p. 593 ■ *Staphylococcus aureus,* p. 525

Transmission

A successful pathogen must somehow be passed from its reservoir to the next susceptible host. Transmission of a pathogen from one person to another through contact, ingestion of food or water, or via a living agent such as an insect is called **horizontal transmission.** This contrasts with **vertical transmission,** which is the transfer of a pathogen from a pregnant woman to the fetus, or from a mother to her infant during childbirth or breast feeding.

Contact

Transmission of a pathogen from one person to another often involves some form of contact. This contact can be either direct or indirect.

Direct Contact **Direct contact** occurs when one person physically touches another. It can be an act as simple as a handshake, or a more intimate contact such as sexual intercourse. In some cases, direct contact is the primary way in which an organism is transmitted. This is particularly true if the transfer of even very low numbers of an organism can initiate an infection. For example, the infectious dose of *Shigella* species, which are intestinal pathogens, is approximately 10 to 100 cells, a number easily passed when shaking hands. Once on the hands, the organisms can inadvertently be ingested. This is just one example of how **fecal-oral transmission,** the consumption of organisms that originate from the intestine, can occur. Handwashing, a fairly simple routine that physically removes organisms, is important in preventing this type of spread of disease. Even washing in plain water reduces the numbers of potential pathogens on the hands, which in turn decreases the possibility of transferring or ingesting sufficient numbers of cells to establish an infection. In fact, routine handwashing is considered to be the single most important measure for preventing the spread of infectious disease. ■ *Shigella sp.,* p. 625

Pathogens that cannot survive for extended periods in the environment must generally, because of their fragile nature, be transmitted through direct contact. *Treponema pallidum,* which causes syphilis, and *Neisseria gonorrhoeae,* which causes gonorrhea, both die quickly when exposed to a relatively cold dry environment and thus require intimate sexual contact for their transmission. ■ *Treponema pallidum,* p. 664 ■ *Neisseria gonorrhoeae,* p. 661

Indirect Contact Indirect transmission involves transfer of pathogens via inanimate objects, or **fomites,** such as clothing, tabletops, doorknobs, and drinking glasses. As an example, carriers of *Staphylococcus aureus* may inoculate their fingers with the organism when touching a skin lesion or colonized nostril. Organisms on the fingers can then easily be transferred to a fomite. Another person can then readily acquire the microbes when handling that object. Again, handwashing is an important control measure.

Droplet Transmission Large microbe-laden respiratory droplets generally fall to the ground no farther than a meter (approximately 3 feet) from release. People in close proximity can inhale those droplets, however, resulting in the spread of respiratory disease via **droplet transmission.** Although physical contact is not necessary, droplet transmission is considered contact transmission because of the close range involved. Droplet transmission is particularly important as a source of contamination in densely populated buildings such as schools and military barracks. Desks or beds in such locations ideally should be spaced more than 4 feet and preferably 8 to 10 feet apart to minimize the transfer of infectious agents. Another way to minimize the spread of respiratory diseases is to educate people about the importance of covering their mouths with a tissue when they cough or sneeze.

Food and Water

Pathogens, particularly those that infect the digestive tract, can be transmitted through contaminated food or water. Foods can become contaminated in a number of different ways. Animal products such as meat and eggs may harbor pathogens that originated from the animal itself. This is the case with poultry contaminated with species of *Salmonella* or *Campylobacter* and hamburger contaminated with *E. coli* O157:H7. Pathogens can also be inadvertently added during food preparations. *Staphylococcus aureus* carriers who do not wash their hands thoroughly prior to preparing food can easily contaminate the food. **Cross-contamination** results when pathogens from one food are transferred to another. A cutting board used first to carve raw chicken and then to cut cooked potatoes can serve as a fomite, transferring *Salmonella* species from the chicken onto the potatoes. Because many foods are a rich nutrient source, microorganisms can multiply to high numbers if the contaminated food is improperly stored. Sound food-handling methods, including sanitary preparation as well as thorough cooking and proper storage, can prevent foodborne diseases. ■ food storage, p. 126

Waterborne disease outbreaks can involve large numbers of people because municipal water systems distribute water to large areas. The 1993 waterborne outbreak of *Cryptosporidium parvum,* an intestinal parasite, in Milwaukee, Wisconsin, was estimated to have involved approximately 400,000 people. Prevention of waterborne diseases requires chlorination and filtration of drinking water and proper disposal and treatment of sewage. ■ *Cryptosporidium parvum*, p. 639 ■ drinking water treatment, p. 786 ■ sewage treatment, p. 780

Air

Respiratory diseases can also be transmitted through the air, When particles larger than 10 μm are inhaled, they are usually trapped in the mucus lining of the nose and throat and eventually swallowed. Smaller particles, however, can enter the lungs, where any pathogens they carry can potentially cause disease.

As mentioned earlier, when people talk, laugh, or sneeze they continually discharge microorganisms in liquid droplets. While large droplets quickly fall to the ground, the smaller droplets dry, leaving one or two organisms attached to a thin coat of the dried material, creating **droplet nuclei.** The droplet nuclei can remain suspended indefinitely in the presence of even slight air currents. Other airborne particles, including dead skin cells, household dust, and soil disturbed by the wind, may also carry respiratory pathogens. An air conditioning system can distribute air contaminated by people or with organisms growing within the system.

The number of viable organisms in air can be estimated by using a machine that pumps a measured volume of air, including any suspended dust and particles, against the surface of a nutrient-rich medium in a Petri dish. This technique has shown that the number of bacteria in the air sampled rises in proportion to the number of people in a room **(figure 20.3).**

Understandably, airborne transmission of pathogens is very difficult to control. To prevent the buildup of airborne pathogens, modern public buildings have ventilation systems that constantly change the air. Hospital microbiology laboratories can be kept under a slight vacuum so that air flows in from the corridors, preventing microorganisms and viruses from being swept out of the lab to other parts of the building. Air in some laboratories, specialized hospital rooms, and jetliners is circulated through high-efficiency particulate air (HEPA) filters to remove airborne organisms that may be present. ■ HEPA filters, p. 119

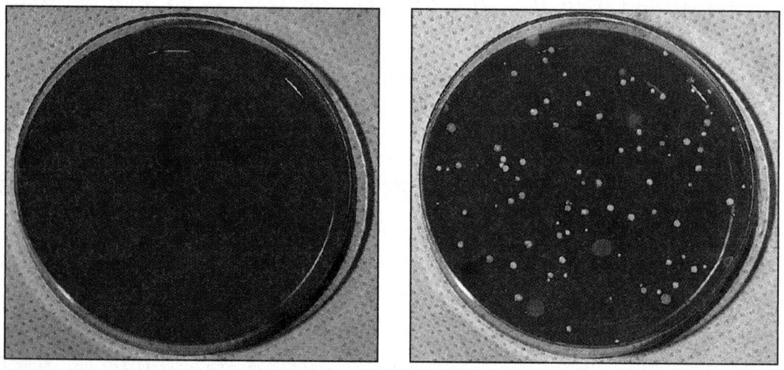

(a) (b)

FIGURE 20.3 Air Sample Cultures (a) Air from a clean, empty hospital room. **(b)** Air from a small room containing 12 people. In both situations, 5 cubic feet of air was sampled.

Vectors

A **vector** such as a mosquito or flea can transmit certain diseases. The term vector applies to any living organism that can carry a disease-causing microbe, but most commonly these are arthropods such as mosquitoes, fleas, lice, and ticks. A vector may carry a pathogen externally or internally.

Flies that land on feces can pick up intestinal pathogens such as *Escherichia coli* O157:H7 and *Shigella* species on their legs. If the fly then moves to a food, it transfers the microorganisms to a source that could be consumed. In this case, the fly serves as a **mechanical vector,** carrying the microbe on its body from one place to another.

Diseases such as malaria, plague, and Lyme disease are transmitted via arthropods that harbor the pathogen internally. The vector either injects the infectious agent while taking a blood meal or defecates, depositing the pathogen onto a person's skin where it can then be inadvertently inoculated when the individual scratches the bite. For example, infected fleas inject *Yersinia pestis* while attempting to take a blood meal. In the case of malaria, caused by species of the eukaryotic pathogen *Plasmodium,* the mosquito is not only the transmitter of the parasite but also serves as an essential part of its reproductive life cycle. A vector that is required as a part of a parasite's life cycle is called a **biological vector.** An important significance of a biological vector is that the pathogen can multiply to high numbers within the vector.

Prevention of vector-borne disease relies on control of arthropods. Malaria, once endemic in the continental United States, was successfully eliminated from the nation through a combination of mosquito elimination and prompt treatment of infected patients. Unfortunately, worldwide eradication efforts that initially showed great promise ultimately failed, in part due to the decreased vigilance that accompanied the dramatic but short lived decline of the disease.

Portals of Entry

To cause disease, not only must a pathogen be transmitted from its reservoir to a new host, it must also colonize a surface of or enter that new host. Colonization is generally a prerequisite for causing disease. Cells of a *Shigella* species may be transferred via a handshake, for example, but they will only cause disease if the person then transfers them to his or her mouth or to food and inadvertently ingests them, allowing the pathogen the opportunity to establish itself in the intestinal tract. Respiratory pathogens released into the air during a cough generally cause disease only when someone inhales them. Many organisms that cause disease if they enter one body site are harmless if they enter another. For instance, *Enterococcus faecalis* may cause a bladder infection if it enters the normally sterile urinary tract, but it is harmless in the intestine where it frequently resides as a member of the normal flora.

The importance of the route of entry in disease development is illustrated in the case of plague transmission. When a flea that normally resides on the rodent reservoir becomes infected and then bites a person, *Yersinia pestis* is injected and the form of plague called **bubonic plague** develops. The bacteria multiply rapidly inside lymph nodes, resulting in a disease that is not contagious but has a mortality rate of 50% to 75% if not treated promptly. In a small percentage of people with bubonic plague, however, the organism spreads to the lungs, resulting in a different manifestation of the disease, **pneumonic plague.** Pneumonic plague presents a much more severe situation, because it is readily transmitted from person to person through respiratory droplets and is nearly always fatal. ■ *Yersinia pestis,* p. 717

Factors That Influence the Epidemiology of Disease

An infectious agent transmitted to a new host can potentially cause disease in that host. The outcome of such transmission events, however, is affected by many different factors including the dose, the incubation period, and characteristics of the host.

The Dose

The probability of infection and disease is generally lower when an individual is exposed to small numbers of a pathogen. This is because there must be a certain minimum number of cells of the pathogen in the body to produce enough damage to cause disease symptoms. If 30 *Salmonella* Typhi cells are ingested in contaminated drinking water yet 1,000,000 are required to produce typhoid fever symptoms, then it will take some time for the bacterial population to increase to that number. Because host defenses are being mobilized at the same time and are racing to eliminate the bacteria, small doses often result in a higher percentage of asymptomatic infections. The immune system sometimes eliminates the organism before symptoms appear. On the other hand, there are few if any infections for which immunity is absolute. An unusually large exposure to a pathogen, such as can occur in a laboratory accident, may produce serious disease in a person who has immunity to ordinary doses of the pathogen. Therefore, even immunized persons should take precautions to minimize exposure to infectious agents. This principle is especially important for medical workers who attend patients with infectious diseases. ■ *Salmonella* Typhi, p. 629

The Incubation Period

The extent of the spread of an infectious agent is influenced by the incubation period. Diseases with typically long incubation periods can spread extensively before the first cases appear. An excellent example of this was the spread of typhoid fever from a ski resort in Switzerland in 1963. As many as 10,000 people had been exposed to drinking water containing small numbers of *Salmonella* Typhi, the causative agent of the disease. The long incubation period of the disease, 10 to 14 days, allowed widespread dissemination of the organisms by the skiers, since they flew home to various parts of the world before they became ill. As a result, there were more than 430 cases of typhoid fever in at least six countries. ■ incubation period, p. 455

Population Characteristics

Certain population groups are more likely to be affected by a given disease-causing agent. Population characteristics that influence the occurrence of disease include:

- **Immunity to the pathogen.** Previous exposure or immunization of a population to a disease agent or an antigenically related agent influences the number of people who become ill. A disease is unlikely to spread very widely in a population in which 90% of the individuals are immune to the disease agent. When an infectious agent cannot spread in a population because it lacks a critical concentration of non-immune hosts, a phenomenon called **herd immunity** results. The non-immune individuals are essentially protected by the lack of a reservoir of infection. Unfortunately, some infectious agents are able to undergo antigenic variation so that they can continue to propagate even in a previously exposed population. ■ antigenic variation, pp. 187, 463
- **General health.** Malnutrition, overcrowding, and fatigue increase the susceptibility of people to infectious diseases and enhance the diseases' spread. Infectious diseases have generally been more of a problem in poor areas of the world where individuals are crowded together without proper food or sanitation. Factors that promote good general health result in increased resistance to diseases such as tuberculosis. When infection does occur in a healthy individual, it is more likely to be asymptomatic or to result in mild disease.
- **Age.** The very young and the elderly are generally more susceptible to infectious agents. The immune system of young children is not fully developed, and consequently, they are predisposed to certain diseases. For example, young children are particularly susceptible to meningitis caused by *Haemophilus influenzae.* The elderly are more prone to disease because the immune system wanes over time. Influenza outbreaks in nursing homes can have fatal consequences. ■ meningitis, p. 684 ■ influenza, p. 597
- **Gender.** In some cases, gender influences disease distribution. Women are more likely to develop urinary tract infections because their urethra, the tube that connects the bladder to the external environment, is relatively short. Microbes can ascend the urethra into the bladder. Pregnant women are more susceptible to listeriosis, caused by *Listeria monocytogenes.* ■ *Listeria monocytogenes,* p. 687
- **Religious and cultural practices.** The distribution of disease is also influenced by religious and cultural practices. Infants who are breast-fed are less likely to have infectious diarrhea because of the protective effects of antibodies in the mother's milk. Groups who eat traditional dishes made from raw freshwater fish are more likely to acquire tapeworm, a parasite normally killed by cooking.
- **Genetic background.** Natural immunity can vary with genetic background, but it is usually difficult to determine the relative importance of genetic, cultural, and environmental factors. In a few instances, however, the genetic basis for resistance to infectious disease is known. For example, many people of black African ancestry are not susceptible to malaria caused by *Plasmodium vivax* because they lack a specific red blood cell receptor used by the organism. Some populations of Northern European ancestry are less susceptible to HIV infection because they lack a certain receptor on their white blood cells.

MICROCHECK 20.1

The reservoir of a disease agent can be infected people, other animals, or the environment. In order to spread, infectious organisms must exit a host. Handwashing and vector control can prevent many diseases; airborne transmission of pathogens is difficult to control. The portal of entry can affect the outcome of disease. The outcome of transmission is affected by the dose, the incubation period, and characteristics of the host population.

- ✓ Explain why smallpox was successfully eradicated but rabies probably never will be.
- ✓ Contrast the transmission of bubonic plague with that of pneumonic plague.
- ✓ Considering that circulating blood is not normally released from the body, describe how blood-borne microbes might exit.

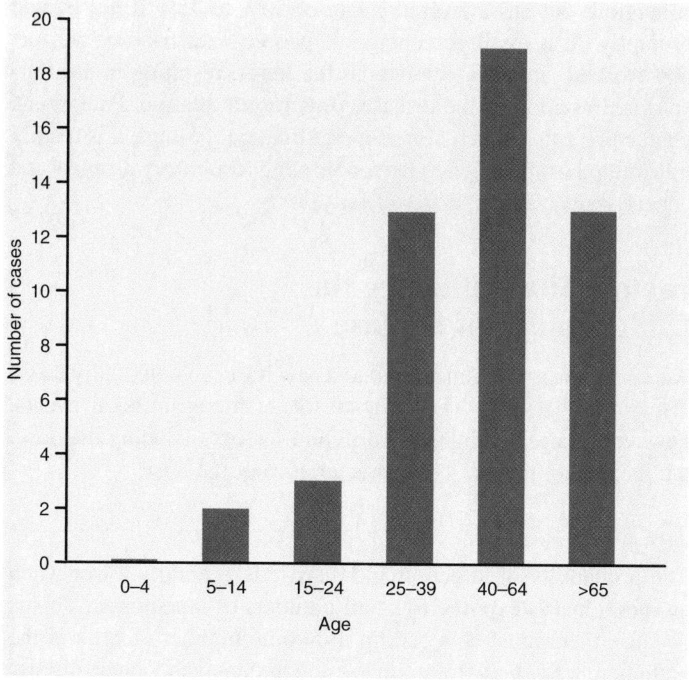

FIGURE 20.4 Typical Incidence of Tetanus by Age Group

20.2 Epidemiological Studies

Focus Point

- Compare and contrast descriptive studies, analytical studies, and experimental studies.

Epidemiologists investigate a disease outbreak to determine the causative agent as well as its reservoir and route of transmission so as to recommend ways to minimize the spread. The British physician John Snow illustrated the power of a well-designed epidemiological study over a century ago. Years before the relationship between microbes and disease was accepted, he documented that the cholera epidemics plaguing England from 1849 to 1854 were due to contaminated water supplies. He did this by carefully comparing the conditions of households that were affected by cholera to those that were not, eventually determining that the primary difference was their water supply. At one point, he ordered the removal of the handle of a public water pump in the neighborhood of an outbreak; this simple act helped halt an epidemic that in 10 days had killed more than 500 people. ■ cholera, p. 623

Descriptive Studies

After a disease outbreak, epidemiologists conduct a **descriptive study** to define characteristics such as the person, the place, and the time. That information is then used to compile a list of possible risk factors involved in the spread of disease.

The Person

Determining the profile of those who become ill is critical to defining the population at risk. Variables such as age, sex, race/ethnicity, occupation, personal habits, previous illnesses, socioeconomic class, and marital status may all yield clues about risk factors for developing the disease. For example, the fact that adults are more likely than children to develop tetanus may indicate that they are not receiving adequate immunizations, which are recommended once every 10 years **(figure 20.4).**

The Place

The geographic location of disease acquisition identifies the general site of contact between the person and the infectious agent. This helps pinpoint the exact source. The location may also give clues about potential reservoirs, vectors, or geographical boundaries that may affect disease transmission. For example, malaria can only be transmitted in regions that have the appropriate mosquito vector.

The Time

The timing of the outbreak may also yield helpful clues. A rapid rise in the numbers of people who became ill suggests that they were all exposed to a single common source of the infectious agent, such as contaminated chicken at a picnic. This is called a **common-source epidemic.** In contrast, if the numbers of ill people rise gradually, then the disease is likely contagious, with one person transmitting it to several others, who each then transmit it to several more, and so on. This is called a **propagated epidemic (figure 20.5).** The first case in such an outbreak is called the **index case.** In a propagated epidemic, if a direct chain of contacts can be established, the time between the onset of symptoms in one case and the next reflects the incubation period of the disease.

The season in which the epidemic occurs may also be significant. Respiratory diseases including influenza, respiratory syncytial virus infections, and the common cold are more easily transmitted in crowded indoor conditions during the winter **(figure 20.6).** Conversely, vector-and foodborne disease are more often transmitted in warm weather when people are more likely to be exposed to mosquitoes and ticks, or eating picnic food that has not been stored properly **(figure 20.7).**

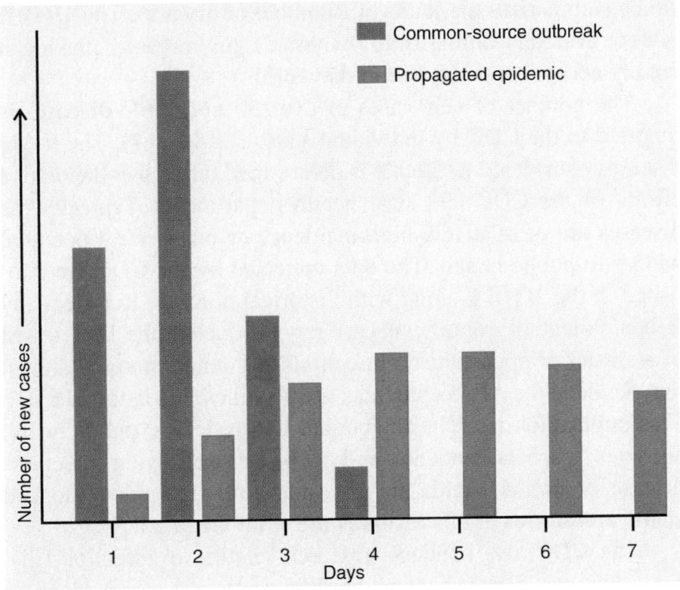

FIGURE 20.5 Comparison of Propagated Versus Common-Source Epidemics The graph depicts the number of new cases that develop over a period of days.

Analytical Studies

Analytical studies are designed to determine which of the potential risk factors identified by the descriptive studies are actually relevant in the spread of the disease.

Cross-Sectional Studies

A **cross-sectional study** surveys a range of people to determine the prevalence of any of a number of characteristics including

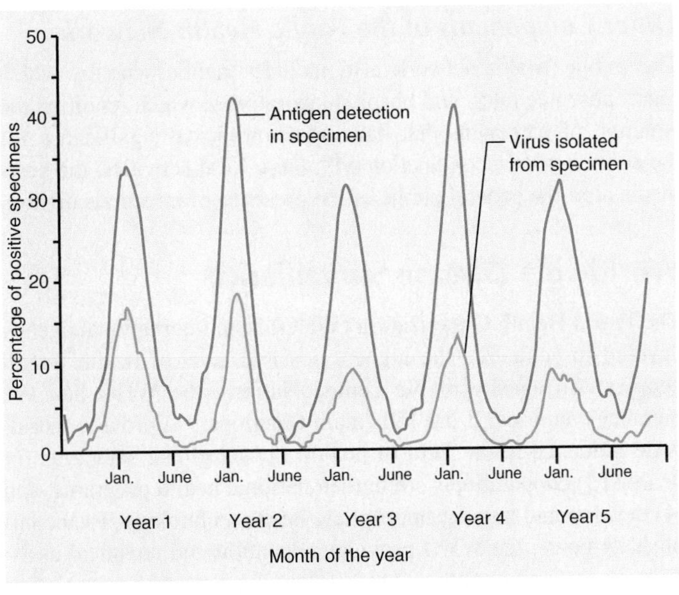

FIGURE 20.6 Typical Seasonal Occurrence of Respiratory Infections Caused by Respiratory Syncytial Virus

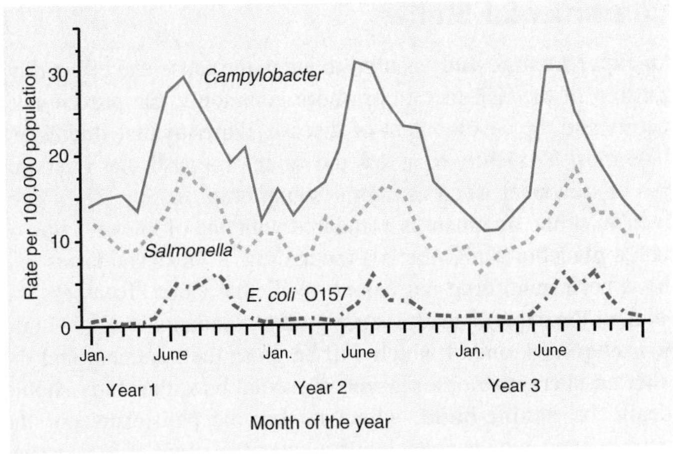

FIGURE 20.7 Seasonal Occurrence of Gastrointestinal Diseases

disease, risk factors associated with disease, or previous exposure to a disease-causing agent. This survey provides a rapid assessment of the features of a population at a given point in time and may suggest associations between risk factors and disease. These associations can then be explored using other types of analytical studies. The cross-sectional survey does not attempt to follow a certain group, nor does it establish cause of disease.

Retrospective Studies

A **retrospective study** is done following a disease outbreak. It compares the actions and events surrounding clinical cases (individuals who developed the disease) against appropriate controls (those who remained healthy). Thus, a case-control study starts by looking at the effect, which is the disease, and attempts to identify the causative chain of events. The activity or event that was common among the cases but not the controls is likely to have been a factor in the development of the disease. It is important to select controls that match the cases with respect to variables not thought to be associated with disease. Matching these variables, which might include factors such as age, sex, and socioeconomic status, ensures that all controls had equal probability of coming in contact with the disease agent. Otherwise, the bias can skew the results.

Prospective Studies

A **prospective study** looks ahead to see if the risk factors identified by the retrospective study predict a tendency to develop the disease. **Cohort groups,** which are study groups that have a known exposure to the risk factor, are selected and then followed over time. The incidence of disease in those who were exposed to the risk factor and those who were not are then compared. By following cohort groups, the study attempts to determine if the hypothesized cause does indeed correlate with the expected effect. This type of study is less prone to bias than a retrospective study because the groups are selected before disease occurs. It is generally more time-consuming and expensive, however, particularly when examining a disease that has a long incubation period. Also, an error in the initial identification of the risk factor renders the entire study useless.

Experimental Studies

An **experimental study** is used to judge the cause and effect relationship of the risk factors or, more commonly, the preventative factors and the development of disease. Experimental studies are done most frequently to assess the value of a particular intervention or treatment, such as antimicrobial drug therapy. The effectiveness of the treatment is compared with one of known value or with a **placebo.** A placebo is a mock drug; it looks and tastes like the experimental drug but has no medicinal value. To assess the value of the experimental drug, a group of patients is divided into two subgroups, one of which will be given the treatment and the other an alternative or a placebo. To avoid bias, the study should ideally be **double-blind,** where neither the physicians nor the patients know who is receiving the actual treatment. Ethical issues sometimes necessitate the use of experimental animals rather than patients in experimental studies.

MICROCHECK 20.2

Descriptive epidemiological studies attempt to identify the potential risk factors that lead to disease. Analytical studies try to determine which factors are actually relevant to disease development. Experimental studies are generally used to evaluate the effectiveness of a treatment or an intervention in preventing disease.

- ✓ On what three factors does a descriptive study focus?
- ✓ What is the value of a double-blind experimental study?
- ✓ Why is it important to include a placebo in a scientific study to assess the effectiveness of a drug?

20.3

Infectious Disease Surveillance

Focus Point

- Compare and contrast the roles of the Centers for Disease Control and Prevention, state public health departments, and the World Health Organization.

Infectious disease surveillance both nationally and worldwide is one of the most important aspects of disease prevention.

National Disease Surveillance Network

Infectious disease control nationwide depends heavily on a network of agencies across the country that monitors disease development. It is partly because of this network that infectious diseases do not claim more lives in the United States.

Centers for Disease Control and Prevention

The Centers for Disease Control and Prevention (CDC) is part of the U.S. Department of Health and Human Services and is located in Atlanta, Georgia. It provides support for infectious disease laboratories in the United States and abroad and collects data on diseases of public health importance. Each week, the CDC publishes a booklet, the *Morbidity and Mortality Weekly Report (MMWR),* which summarizes the status of a number of diseases. The *MMWR* is now available online (http://www.cdc.gov/mmwr/), making it readily accessible to anyone in the world.

The number of new cases of over 50 **notifiable diseases** is reported to the CDC by individual states **(table 20.1).** The list of diseases considered notifiable is determined through collaborative efforts of the CDC and state health departments. Typically the diseases are of relatively high incidence or otherwise a potential danger to public health. The data collected by the CDC are published in the *MMWR* along with historical numbers to reflect any trends. Potentially significant case reports, such as the 1981 report of a cluster of opportunistic infections in young homosexual men that heralded the AIDS epidemic, are also included in the *MMWR.* This publication is an invaluable aid to physicians, public health agencies, teachers, students, and anyone else studying infectious disease or public health. In fact, many of the epidemiological charts and stories in this textbook are from the *MMWR.*

The CDC also conducts research relating to infectious diseases and can dispatch teams worldwide to assist with identifying and controlling epidemics. In addition, the CDC provides refresher courses that update the knowledge of laboratory and infection control personnel.

Public Health Departments

Each state has a public health laboratory responsible for infection surveillance and control as well as other health-related activities. Individual states have the authority to mandate which diseases must be reported by physicians to the state laboratory. The prompt response of health authorities in Washington State that led to the cessation of an outbreak of *Escherichia coli* O157:H7 in 1993 caused by contaminated hamburger patties was partly because Washington then was one of the few states with surveillance and reporting measures for the organism. The epidemic had actually started in other states but had gone unrecognized.

Other Components of the Public Health Network

The public health network also includes public schools, which report absentee rates, and hospital laboratories, which report on the isolation of pathogens that have epidemiological significance for the community. In conjunction with these local activities, the news media alert the general public of the presence of infectious disease.

Worldwide Disease Surveillance

The World Health Organization (WHO) is an international agency devoted to achieving the highest possible level of health for all peoples. An agency of the United Nations, the WHO has 192 member countries. It has four main functions: (1) provide worldwide guidance in the field of health; (2) set global standards for health; (3) cooperatively strengthen national health programs; and (4) develop and transfer appropriate health technology. To accomplish its goals, the WHO provides education and technical assistance to member countries. One of their most recent successes has been the establishment of truces between various factions in war-torn countries in order to allow vaccination efforts to proceed.

The WHO disseminates information through a series of periodicals and books. For example, the *Weekly Epidemiological*

TABLE 20.1 Notifiable Infectious Diseases

Individual states and territories require physicians to report cases of these notifiable diseases. In turn, the number of cases is reported to the CDC, where they are collated and published in the *MMWR.*

- AIDS
- Anthrax
- Arboviral neuroinvasive and non-neuroinvasive diseases
- Botulism
- Brucellosis
- Chancroid
- *Chlamydia trachomatis,* genital infections
- Cholera
- Coccidioidomycosis
- Cryptosporidiosis
- Cyclosporiasis
- Diphtheria
- Ehrlichiosis
- Enterohemorrhagic *Escherichia coli*
- Giardiasis
- Gonorrhea
- *Haemophilus influenzae,* invasive disease
- Hansen's disease (leprosy)
- Hantavirus pulmonary syndrome
- Hemolytic uremic syndrome, post-diarrheal
- Hepatitis, viral, acute and chronic
- HIV infection
- Influenza-associated pediatric mortality
- Legionellosis (Legionnaires' disease)
- Listeriosis
- Lyme disease
- Malaria
- Measles
- Meningococcal disease
- Mumps
- Pertussis
- Plague
- Poliomyelitis, paralytic
- Psittacosis
- Q fever
- Rabies, animal and human
- Rocky Mountain spotted fever
- Rubella
- Rubella, congenital syndrome
- Salmonellosis
- Severe acute respiratory syndrome-associated coronavirus (SARS-CoV) disease
- Shigellosis
- Smallpox
- Streptococcal disease, invasive, group A
- Streptococcal toxic shock syndrome
- *Streptococcus pneumoniae,* drug-resistant, invasive disease
- *Streptococcus pneumoniae,* invasive in children < 5 years
- Syphilis
- Syphilis, congential
- Tetanus
- Toxic shock syndrome
- Trichinosis
- Tuberculosis
- Tularemia
- Typhoid fever
- Vancomycin-intermediate *Staphylococcus aureus* (VISA)
- Vancomycin-resistant *Staphylococcus aureus* (VRSA)
- Varicella
- Yellow fever

Record reports timely information about epidemics of public health importance, particularly those of global concern.

MICROCHECK 20.3

Across the country, a network of agencies including the Centers for Disease Control and Prevention and state and local public health departments monitors disease development. It is partly because of the success of this network that infectious diseases do not claim more lives in the United States. The WHO is devoted to achieving the highest possible level of health for all peoples.

✓ What is the *MMWR?*

✓ Explain why we have relatively accurate data on the number of cases of measles that occur in the United States but not on the number of cases of the common cold.

20.4 Trends in Disease

Focus Points

- Name one disease that has been eradicated.
- Describe six factors that contribute to the emergence and reemergence of disease.

The rapid scientific advances made over the past several decades led some people to speculate at one point that the war against infectious diseases, particularly those caused by bacteria, had been won. Microorganisms have occupied this planet far longer than have humans, however, evolving to occupy every habitat having the potential for life, including the human body. Perhaps it should be no surprise, then, that new and previously unrecognized pathogens are emerging, and that some of those we had previously controlled are now making a comeback.

Reduction and Eradication of Disease

Humans have been enormously successful in developing the means to eliminate or reduce the occurrence of certain diseases through such efforts as improved sanitation, reservoir and vector control, vaccination, and antibiotic treatment **(figure 20.8).** One disease, smallpox, has been globally eradicated, eliminating the natural occurrence of a disease that had a 25% mortality rate, and left many of those who survived permanently disfigured **(figure 20.9).** The World Health Organization hopes to eradicate polio, measles, and dracunculiasis soon. Political and social upheaval, complacency, and lack of financial support can result in a resurgence of diseases unless the pathogens are completely eliminated. ■ polio, p. 695 ■ measles, p. 538

In the United States, many diseases that were once common and claimed many lives are now relatively rare, Successful vaccination programs have led to dramatic decreases in the number of

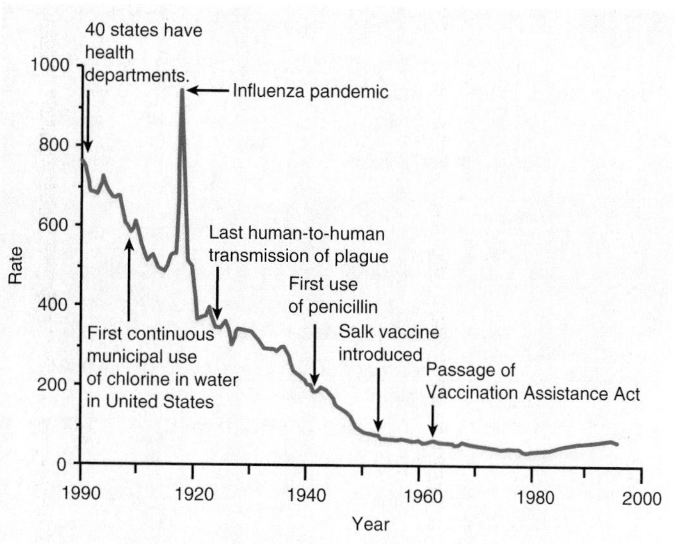

FIGURE 20.8 Crude Death Rate for Infectious Diseases, United States, Per 100,000 Population per Year

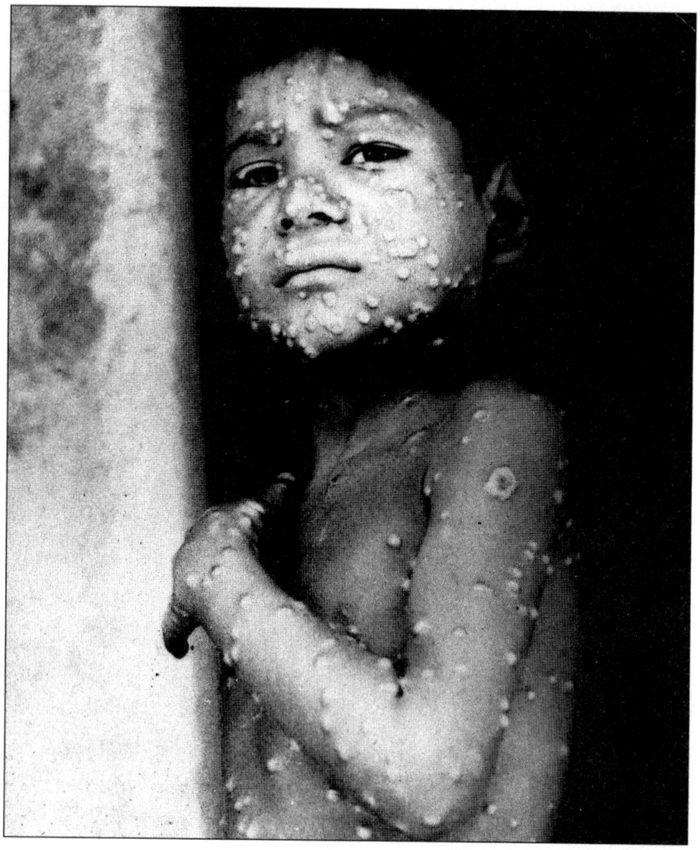

FIGURE 20.9 A Case of Smallpox, a Disease That Has Now Been Eradicated

deaths caused by *Haemophilus influenzae, Corynebacterium diphtheriae, Clostridium tetani,* and *Bordetella pertussis.* Meanwhile, recognizing and controlling the source of diseases such as malaria, plague, and cholera have been effective in limiting their spread.

Emerging Diseases

Just as humans have been successful in reducing and eliminating certain diseases, microorganisms are equally adept at taking advantage of new opportunities in which to thrive and multiply. As human lifestyles change due to advancing technologies, increasing populations, and shifting social behaviors, new diseases emerge while those that have been controlled in the past sometimes make a comeback.

Diseases that have increased in incidence in the past two decades are referred to as **emerging diseases.** These include new or newly recognized diseases such as SARS as well as familiar ones such as malaria that are reemerging after years of decline (see figure 1.4). Some of the factors that contribute to the emergence and reemergence of diseases include:

- **Microbial evolution.** The emergence of some diseases is due to the natural evolution of microorganisms. For example, a new serotype of *Vibrio cholerae,* designated O139, appears to be nearly identical to the strain that most commonly causes cholera epidemics, *V. cholerae* O1, except that it has gained the ability to produce a capsule. The consequence of the new serotype is that even people who have immunity against the earlier strain are susceptible to the new one. Resistance to the effects of antimicrobial drugs is contributing to the reemergence of many diseases, including malaria. ■ *V. cholerae,* p. 624 ■ malaria, p. 725
- **Complacency and the breakdown of public health infrastructure.** As infectious diseases are controlled and therefore of lessening concern, complacency can develop, paving the way for the resurgence of a disease. The preliminary success of the plan to eliminate tuberculosis in the United States by the year 2000 resulted in less public attention being paid to the disease. News reports, education, and research money were all diverted to more common diseases. Simultaneously, the AIDS crisis developed and funding for some social welfare programs was curtailed, resulting in an increase in the number of people at risk of developing active tuberculosis due to poor health and living conditions. Consequently, tuberculosis reemerged as an increasing threat. Fortunately, increased public health measures, including direct observation of drug therapy compliance, brought the disease back under at least temporary control (see figure 24.16). ■ tuberculosis, p. 593
- **Changes in human behavior.** Changes in society's behavior can inadvertently create opportunities for microorganisms to spread and flourish. For example, day care centers, where diapered infants mingle, oblivious to sanitation and hygiene, are a relatively new component of American society. For obvious reasons, the centers can be hotbeds of contagious diseases. Many young children have not yet acquired immunity to common communicable diseases. As a consequence, illnesses such as colds and diarrhea are readily transmitted among this susceptible population. This is particularly true with intestinal pathogens such as *Giardia* and *Shigella* that have a low infectious dose, because infants often explore through taste and touch and are thus likely to ingest fecal organisms. ■ *Giardia,* p. 638 ■ *Shigella,* p. 625

- **Advances in technology.** Technology can make life easier but can inadvertently create new habitats for microorganisms. The advent of contact lenses to correct vision gave microorganisms the opportunity to grow in a new location, the lenses and storage solutions of users who did not employ proper disinfection techniques. In turn, this resulted in new types of eye infections.
- **Population expansion.** The increase in world population, and the subsequently denser living conditions, create situations in which diseases can be more readily transmitted. In areas where the population has expanded outward, people are coming in contact with previously unknown reservoirs of disease such as that of the Ebola virus. The reservoir of Ebola still has not been determined.
- **Development.** Dams, which provide important sources of power necessary for economic development, have inadvertently extended the range of certain diseases. Transmission of the disease schistosomiasis relies on the presence of an aquatic snail that serves as a host for the *Schistosoma* parasite. Construction of dams such as the Aswan dam on the Nile River has increased the habitat for the snail, thus extending the distribution of the disease. ■ schistosomiasis, p. 382
- **Mass distribution and importation of food.** Foodborne illness has always existed, but the ease with which we can now transport items worldwide can create new problems. Widespread distribution of foods contaminated with pathogens can result in a similarly broad outbreak of disease. Contaminated raspberries grown in Guatemala were linked to a 1996 multistate outbreak of diarrheal disease in the United States, affecting more than 900 people, caused by the intestinal parasite *Cyclospora*. ■ *Cyclospora*, p. 640
- **War and civil unrest.** Wars and civil unrest can disrupt the infrastructure on which disease prevention relies. Refugee camps that crowd people into substandard living quarters lacking toilet facilities and safe drinking water are hotbeds of infectious diseases such as cholera and dysentery. Unfortunately, war also disrupts disease eradication efforts. ■ cholera, p. 623 ■ dysentery, p. 623
- **Climate changes.** Changes in temperature and rainfall may affect the incidence of certain diseases. Warm temperatures favor the reproduction and survival of some arthropods, which in turn can serve as vectors for diseases such as malaria. The heavy rainfall and flooding that resulted in a surge of cholera cases in Africa may have been due to the effects of El Niño. ■ malaria, p. 725 ■ cholera, p. 623

MICROCHECK 20.4

Humans have been successful in reducing and eliminating certain diseases, but microorganisms are adept at taking advantage of new opportunities in which to thrive and multiply.

- ✓ Explain why diarrheal diseases spread so easily in day care centers.
- ✓ Describe two factors that can contribute to the reemergence of an infectious disease.
- ✓ What political and societal factors might lead to a decrease in childhood immunizations?

20.5 Nosocomial Infections

Focus Points

- List four species that commonly cause nosocomial infections.
- Describe four reservoirs of infectious agents in hospitals and three mechanisms by which the agents can be transferred to patients.
- Describe the role of Infection Control Committees in preventing nosocomial infections.

A hospital can be seen as a high-density population made up of unusually susceptible people where the most antimicrobial-resistant and virulent pathogens can potentially circulate. Considering this, it is not surprising that hospital-acquired infections, or **nosocomial infections,** have been a problem since hospitals began (nosocomial is derived from the Greek word for hospital). Modern medical practices, however, including the extensive use of antimicrobial drugs and invasive therapeutic procedures, have changed the nature of the problem. In the United States alone, it is estimated that 5% to 6% of patients admitted to the hospital develop a nosocomial infection, adding over $4.5 billion to the price of health care. Many of these infections originate from the patient's own normal flora, but approximately one third are potentially preventable. **Figure 20.10** shows the relative frequency of different types of nosocomial infections.

Nosocomial infections may range from very mild to fatal. Sometimes, because of a long incubation period, the infection may not be discovered until after the patient has been discharged. Many factors determine which microorganisms or viruses are responsible

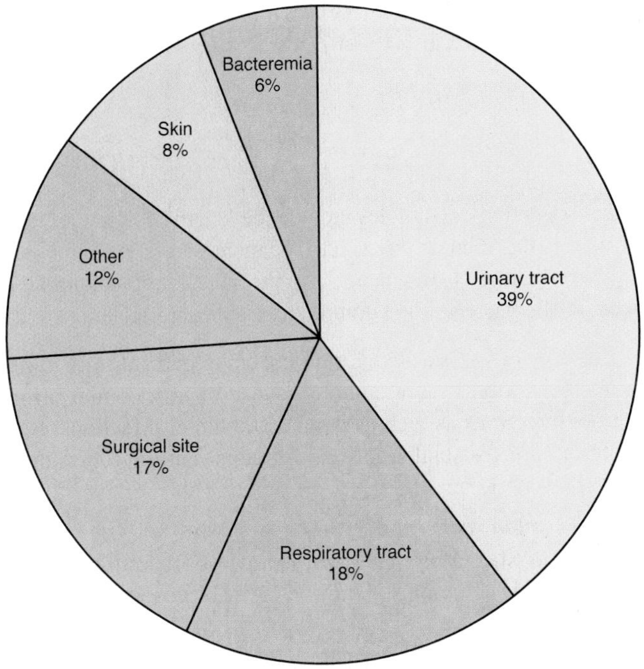

FIGURE 20.10 Relative Frequency of Different Types of Nosocomial Infections

PERSPECTIVE 20.1

Standard Precautions—Protecting Patients and Health Care Personnel

One of the biggest challenges for a hospital has always been the prevention of spread of disease within that confined setting. A century ago, patients with infectious diseases were segregated in separate hospitals; those with similar diseases were sometimes housed in clusters on the same floor. In 1910, a cubicle system of isolation was introduced in which patients were placed in multiple-bed wards. Aseptic nursing procedures were aimed at preventing the transmission of infectious agents to other patients and personnel. These scrupulous measures were so successful that general hospitals were able to incorporate infectious disease patients, ultimately resulting in the closure of many infectious disease hospitals beginning in the 1950s. To assist general hospitals with isolation procedures, in 1970 the CDC began publishing a manual that recommended a category system of seven isolation procedures for patients based on their diagnosis. These procedures included Strict Isolation, Respiratory Precautions, Protective Isolation, Enteric Precautions, Wound and Skin Precautions, Discharge Precautions, and Blood Precautions. Over the years, some of these categories were changed or deleted.

In the early 1980s it became increasingly apparent that health care workers were acquiring hepatitis B and, later, HIV from contact with the blood or other body fluids of patients, including those who were not suspected of having blood-borne disease. Existing guidelines were primarily aimed at preventing patient-to-patient transmission of disease, rather than patient-to-personnel. In response, the CDC recommended an additional set of guidelines, the **Universal (Blood and Body Fluid) Precautions,** to be followed when working with any patient, regardless of the diagnosis. These defined the situations in which gloves, gowns, masks, and eye protection were required to prevent contact with blood. Many hospitals then broadened this concept, requiring the use of gloves to isolate all moist and potentially infectious body substances. This approach, **Body Substance Isolation,** made the traditional diagnosis-dependent isolation procedures largely unnecessary.

The advent of Universal Precautions and Body Substance Isolation, in addition to the previous diagnosis-dependent isolation procedures, resulted in a such a mix of recommendations that it generated a great deal of confusion. No existing single set of guidelines was sufficient, and it was not clear which one should be used when. In response, the CDC and the Hospital Infection Control Program Advisory Committee established a new set of guidelines in 1996 that incorporates the strength of each of the alternatives. These new guidelines have two tiers of isolation procedures. The fundamental measures are the **Standard Precautions,** designed for the care of all patients in all hospitals. The **Transmission-Based Precautions** are supplementary measures to be used in addition to the Standard Precautions if a patient is, or might be, infected with highly transmissible or epidemiologically important pathogen. These are separated into three sets—Airborne Precautions, Droplet Precautions, and Contact Precautions—which are used singly or in combination as appropriate.

The Standard Precautions can be summarized as:

Handwashing. Wash hands with soap and water after touching blood, body fluids, secretions, excretions, and contaminated items, whether or not gloves are worn.

Gloves. Clean disposable gloves are worn whenever there is possible contact with blood, body fluids, secretions, excretions, mucous membranes, skin wounds, and contaminated items. Change gloves between procedures on the same patient after contact with material that may contain high concentrations of microbes. Remove gloves immediately after use and wash hands thoroughly, Gloves should always be removed in a reverse manner so as not to touch the contaminated surface.

Mask, eye protection, face shield, gown. When doing a procedure that is likely to generate splashes or sprays of blood, body fluids, secretions, and excretions, wear a mask and eye protection or a face shield to protect the mucous membranes of the eyes, nose, and mouth. Wear a clean gown. Remove the soiled gown as soon as possible and wash hands.

Patient-care equipment. Handle used patient-care equipment soiled with blood, body fluids, secretions, and excretions in a manner that prevents skin and mucous membrane exposure, and contamination and transfer to other patients and environments. Reusable equipment must be cleaned and processed appropriately. Single-use items must be disposed of properly.

Environmental control. Use adequate procedures for the routine care, cleaning, and disinfection of environmental surfaces, bed rails, and other frequently touched surfaces.

Linen. Soiled, reusable items are placed in protective bags to prevent leaking and contamination.

Occupational health and blood-borne pathogens. All needles and sharp objects are discarded in a rigid, puncture-proof container without touching them or replacing needle caps.

Patient placement. Private rooms are used for any patient who contaminates the environment or might soil other people and their surroundings.

From: http://www.cdc.gov/ncidod/hip/ISOLAT/Isolat.htm The Public Health Services, U.S. Department of Health and Human Services, Centers for Disease Control and Prevention. Garner, J. Hospital Infection Control Practices and Advisory Committee. Guidelines for Isolation Precautions in Hospitals. *Infection Control and Hospital Epidemiology* 1996; 17: 53–80, and *American Journal of Infection Control* 1996; 24: 24–52.

for these infections. Examples include the length of time the person is exposed, the manner in which a patient is exposed, the virulence and number of organisms, and the state of the patient's host defenses. The bacteria most commonly implicated include:

- ***Enterococcus* species.** Enterococci, a part of the normal intestinal flora, are a common cause of nosocomial urinary tract infections as well as wound and blood infections. Some strains are resistant to all conventional antimicrobial drugs. ■ enterococci, p. 272
- ***Escherichia coli* and other members of the *Enterobacteriaceae*.** *Escherichia coli* is a part of the normal intestinal flora. It is the most common cause of nosocomial urinary tract infections. ■ *E. coli*, p. 652 ■ *Enterobacteriaceae*, p. 279
- ***Pseudomonas* species.** These bacteria grow readily in many moist, nutrient-poor environments such as the water in the humidifier of a mechanical ventilator. *Pseudomonas* species are resistant to many disinfectants and antimicrobial drugs. They are a common cause of hospital-acquired pneumonia and infections of the urinary tract and burn wounds. ■ *Pseudomonas*, p. 555
- ***Staphylococcus aureus*.** Many people including health care personnel are carriers of this organism. Because it survives for prolonged periods in the environment, it is readily transmissible on fomites. It is a common cause of nosocomial pneumonia and surgical site infections. Hospital strains are often resistant to a variety of antimicrobial drugs. ■ *Staphylococcus aureus*, p. 525
- ***Staphylococcus* species other than *S. aureus*.** These normal skin flora can colonize the tips of intravenous catheters (small plastic tubes inserted into the veins). The resulting biofilms continuously seed organisms into the bloodstream and increase the likelihood of a systemic infection. ■ biofilm, p. 89

Reservoirs of Infectious Agents in Hospitals

The organisms that cause nosocomial infections may originate from other patients, the hospital environment, medical personnel, or from the patient's own normal flora. Because of the widespread use of antimicrobial drugs in hospitals, many organisms that cause nosocomial infections are resistant to these medications.

Other Patients

Because of the very nature of hospitals, infectious agents are always present. Patients are often hospitalized because they have a severe infectious disease. The pathogens that these patients harbor can be discharged into the environment via skin cells, respiratory droplets, and other body secretions and excretions. Scrupulous cleaning and the use of disinfectants minimize the spread of these pathogens.

Hospital Environment

Some Gram-negative rods, particularly the common opportunistic pathogen *Pseudomonas aeruginosa,* can thrive in certain hospital environments such as sinks, respirators, and toilets. Not only is *P. aeruginosa* resistant to the effects of many disinfectants and antimicrobial drugs, it requires few nutrients, enabling it to multiply in environments containing little other than water. Many nosocomial infections have been traced to soaps, disinfectants, and other aqueous solutions that have become contaminated with the organism.

Health Care Workers

Outbreaks of nosocomial infections are sometimes traced to infected health care personnel. Clearly, those who report to work with even a mild case of influenza can expose patients to an infectious agent that has serious or fatal consequences to those with impaired health. A more troublesome source of infection is a health care worker who is a carrier of a pathogen such as *Staphylococcus aureus* or *Streptococcus pyogenes.* These personnel often do not recognize they pose a risk to patients until they have been implicated in an outbreak. Carriers who are members of a surgical team pose a particular threat to patients, because inoculation of a pathogen directly into a surgical site can result in a systemic infection.

Patient's Own Normal Flora

Many hospital-acquired infections originate from the patient's own flora. Nearly any invasive procedure can transmit microorganisms that are part of the normal flora to otherwise sterile body sites. When intravenous fluids are administered, for example, *Staphylococcus epidermidis,* a common member of the normal skin flora, can potentially gain access to the bloodstream. While the immune system can usually readily eliminate these normally benign organisms, the underlying illness of many hospitalized patients compromises their immunity and they can develop a bloodstream infection. Patients who undergo intestinal surgery are prone to surgical site infection by their normal bowel flora. Similarly, patients who are on certain medications or have impaired cough reflexes can inadvertently inhale their normal oral flora, resulting in hospital-acquired pneumonia.

Severely immunocompromised patients, such as people who have undergone cancer chemotherapy or are on immunosuppressive drugs, are prone to activation of latent infections their immune system was previously able to control. For example, latent infections of *Toxoplasma gondii,* a protozoan parasite commonly acquired during childhood, can become activated and cause a life-threatening disease. ■ latent infection, p. 455

Transmission of Infectious Agents in Hospitals

Diagnostic and therapeutic procedures during hospitalization can potentially transmit infectious agents to patients. This is particularly true in intensive care units (ICUs), where patients generally have indwelling catheters used to deliver intravenous fluids or monitor the patient's condition **(figure 20.11).**

Medical Devices

Nosocomial infections most often result from medical devices that breach the first-line barriers of the normal host defense. Catheterization of the urinary tract can readily introduce microorganisms into the normally sterile bladder. Because urine is an excellent growth medium, the urinary tract often becomes infected. Urinary tract infections are the most common type of nosocomial infection (see figure 20.10).

Just as urinary catheters can introduce bacteria into the bladder, intravenous (IV) catheters can introduce microorganisms into the bloodstream. This can happen when normal skin flora colonize the tip of an indwelling catheter or when environmental organisms contaminate IV fluids or the lines that deliver them. Even normally benign skin flora can cause life-threatening bacteria when they gain access to the bloodstream.

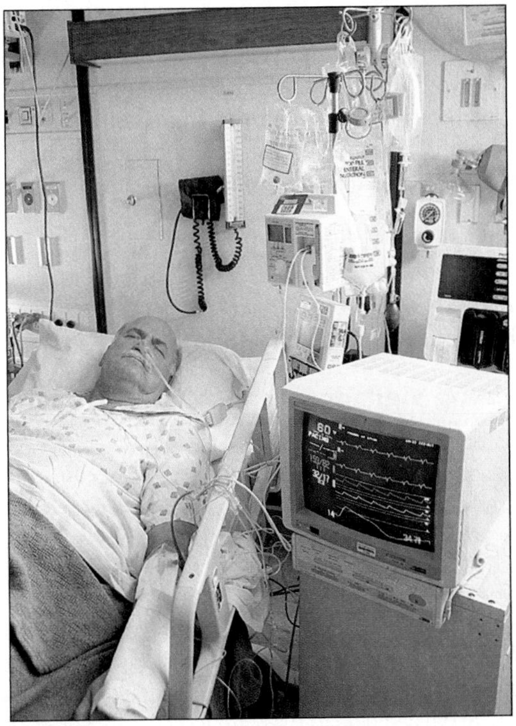

FIGURE 20.11 Patient in an Intensive Care Unit

Mechanical respirators that assist a patient's breathing by pumping air directly into the trachea can potentially deliver microorganisms to the lungs. This is particularly a problem if a nutritionally versatile organism such as *Pseudomonas* can gain access to water droplets in the machine, allowing it to multiply.

Inadequately sterilized instruments that are used in invasive procedures such as surgery or biopsy can also transmit infectious agents. Endoscopes and other heat-sensitive instruments are often treated with chemical sterilants to render them microbe-free. Improper use of these chemicals, however, can result in the survival of some organisms. ■ sterilants, p. 121

Health Care Personnel

Health care personnel must be extremely vigilant to avoid transmitting infectious disease agents, particularly from patient to patient. What Ignaz Semmelweis found to be true in the 1800s is equally true today—handwashing between contact with individual patients helps prevent the spread of disease (see **A Glimpse of History**). Unfortunately, this relatively simple procedure is too often overlooked.

Health care personnel should routinely wash or disinfect their hands after touching one patient before going on to the next. A more thorough hand scrubbing, requiring 10 minutes and using a strong disinfectant, should be performed by nurses, physicians, and other personnel before participating in an operation, or when working in a nursery, or an intensive care or isolation unit. Gloves are also worn whenever there is contact with blood, mucous membranes, broken skin, or body fluids.

Airborne

Most hospitals are designed to minimize the airborne spread of microorganisms. Airflow to operating rooms is usually regulated so that it is supplied under slight pressure, thereby preventing contaminated air in the corridors from flowing into the room. Floors are washed with a damp mop or floor washer rather than swept in order to avoid resuspending microbes into the air. To exclude airborne microorganisms and viruses from rooms in which exquisitely susceptible patients reside, such as those who have recently undergone a bone marrow transplant, high-efficiency particulate air filters (HEPA) are employed. These filter out most airborne particles, including microorganisms. ■ HEPA filters, p. 119

Preventing Nosocomial Infections

The most important steps in preventing nosocomial infections are to first recognize their occurrence and then establish policies to prevent their development. To accomplish this, nearly every hospital has an Infection Control Committee, composed of representatives of the various professionals in the hospital, such as nurses, physicians, dietitians, housekeeping staff, and microbiology laboratory personnel. On this committee, and sometimes chairing it, is often a **hospital epidemiologist,** a professional specially trained in hospital infection control. Hospitals may employ an **infection control practitioner (ICP),** whose role is to perform active surveillance of the types and numbers of infections that arise in the hospital. The Infection Control Committee, in conjunction with the ICP, drafts and implements preventative policies following the guidelines suggested by the Standard Precautions and the Transmission-Based Precautions (see **Perspective 20.1**).

The CDC also takes an active role in preventing nosocomial infections, and in the early 1990s established the Hospital Infection Control Program Advisory Committee (HICPAC). The role of this national committee is to provide advice to hospitals and recommend guidelines for surveillance, prevention, and control of nosocomial infections.

MICROCHECK 20.5

Nosocomial infections may originate from other patients, the hospital environment, medical personnel, or the patient's own normal flora. Diagnostic and therapeutic procedures can potentially transmit infectious agents. The most important steps in preventing nosocomial infections are to first recognize their occurrence and then establish policies to prevent their development.

- ✓ Explain why an IV catheter poses a risk to a patient.
- ✓ Describe two ways in which infectious agents can be transmitted to a patient.
- ✓ The rate of nosocomial infections is often relatively high in emergency room settings. Explain why this might be so.

FUTURE CHALLENGES

Maintaining Vigilance Against Bioterrorism

Today, an unfortunate challenge in epidemiology is to maintain vigilance against biological warfare. Even as we work to control, and seek to eradicate, some diseases, we must be aware that microbes pose a threat as potent biological weapons. Experts in the field of bioterrorism list four diseases—anthrax, botulism, plague, and smallpox—as the greatest threats.

While it is hoped that a biological weapons attack will never occur again, it is crucial to be prepared for the possibility. Prompt recognition of such an event, followed by rapid and appropriate isolation and treatment procedures, can help to minimize the consequences. The CDC, in cooperation with the Association for Professionals in Infection Control and Epidemiology (APIC), has prepared a bioterrorism readiness plan to be used as a template by health care facilities. Many of the recommendations are based on the Standard Precautions already employed by hospitals to prevent the spread of infectious agents (see Perspective 20.1). Some of the most relevant characteristics of the diseases that are the most likely candidates for biological weapons include:

- ***Anthrax.*** This was the agent used in the bioterrorism events of 2001. The most severe outcome results from the inhalation of the airborne endospores of *Bacillus anthracis,* which can rapidly result in a fatal systemic illness. Anthrax can be prevented by vaccination, but that option is not widely available. Prophylaxis with antimicrobial medications is possible for those who might have been exposed, but this requires prompt recognition of exposure. Fortunately, person-to-person transmission of anthrax is not likely.

- ***Botulism.*** Botulism is caused naturally by the ingestion of botulinum toxin, produced by *Clostridium botulinum.* Aerosolized toxin could also be used as a weapon, however, because any mucous membrane can absorb the toxin. Botulism can be prevented by vaccination, but that option is not widely available. An antitoxin is also available. Botulism is not contagious.
- ***Plague.*** Pneumonic plague, caused by inhalation of *Yersinia pestis,* is the most likely form of plague to result from a biological weapon. Although no effective vaccine is available, post-exposure prophylaxis with antimicrobial medications is possible. Special isolation precautions must be used for patients who have pneumonic plague because the disease is easily transmitted by respiratory droplets.
- ***Smallpox.*** Although a vaccine is available, routine immunization was stopped over 30 years ago because the natural disease has been eradicated. As is the case with nearly all infections caused by viruses, effective drug therapy is not available. Special isolation precautions must be used for smallpox patients because the virus may be acquired through droplet, airborne, or contact transmission.

SUMMARY

20.1 Principles of Epidemiology

Epidemiologists study the frequency and distribution of disease in order to identify its cause, source, and route of transmission.

Rate of Disease in a Population

Epidemiologists focus on the rate of disease.

Diseases that are constantly present in a population are **endemic;** an unusually large number of cases in a population constitutes an **epidemic.** (Figure 20.2)

Reservoirs of Infection

Preventing susceptible people from coming in contact with a **reservoir of infection** can prevent infectious disease.

People who have asymptomatic infections or are colonized with a pathogen are **carriers** of the infectious agent.

Zoonotic diseases are those such as plague and rabies that can be transmitted to humans but exist primarily in other animals.

Pathogens that have environmental reservoirs are probably impossible to eliminate.

Portals of Exit

Pathogens may be shed in feces, in respiratory droplets, on skin cells, in genital secretions, and in urine.

Transmission

Handwashing is a key control measure in preventing diseases that are spread through direct or indirect contact, as well as those that spread via contaminated food.

Direct contact occurs when one person physically touches another.

Indirect contact involves transfer of pathogens via **fomites.**

Droplet transmission of respiratory pathogens is considered contact because of the close proximity involved.

Foodborne pathogens can originate from the animal reservoir or from contamination during food preparation.

Waterborne pathogens often originate from sewage contamination.

Airborne transmission of pathogens is the most difficult to control.

Prevention of vector-borne disease relies on mosquito, tick, and insect control.

Portals of Entry

The portal of entry of a pathogen can affect the outcome of disease.

Factors That Influence the Epidemiology of Disease

The probability of infection and disease is generally lower if an individual is exposed to small numbers of pathogens.

Diseases with a long incubation period can spread extensively before the first cases appear.

A disease is unlikely to spread very widely in a population in which 90% of the people are immune to the disease agent.

Malnutrition, overcrowding, and fatigue increase the susceptibility of people to infectious diseases.

The very young and the elderly are generally more susceptible to infectious agents.

Natural immunity can vary with genetic background, but it is difficult to determine the relative importance of genetic, cultural, and environmental factors.

20.2 Epidemiological Studies

Descriptive Studies

Descriptive studies attempt to identify potential risk factors that correlate with the development of disease.

Determining the time that the illness occurred helps distinguish a **common-source epidemic** from **a propagated epidemic.** (Figure 20.5)

Analytical Studies

Analytical studies try to determine which risk factors are actually relevant to disease development.

A **retrospective study** compares the activities of **cases** with **controls** to determine the cause of the epidemic.

A **prospective study** compares **cohort groups,** to determine if the identified risk factors predict a tendency to develop disease.

Experimental Studies

Experimental studies are generally used to evaluate the effectiveness of a treatment or intervention in preventing disease.

20.3 Infectious Disease Surveillance

National Disease Surveillance Network

The Centers for Disease Control and Prevention collects data on diseases of public health importance and summarizes their status in the ***Morbidity and Mortality Weekly Report** (MMWR);* other activities of the CDC include research, assistance in controlling epidemics, and support for infectious disease laboratories.

State public health departments are involved in infection surveillance and control.

Worldwide Disease Surveillance

The World Health Organization (WHO) is devoted to achieving the highest possible level of health for all peoples.

20.4 Trends in Disease

Reduction and Eradication of Disease

Smallpox has been eradicated. The WHO hopes to soon eliminate polio, measles, and dracunculiasis.

Emerging Diseases

Emerging diseases include those that are new or newly recognized and familiar ones that are reemerging after years of decline.

Factors that contribute to the emergence and reemergence of diseases include microbial evolution, the breakdown of public health infrastructure, changes in human behavior, advances in technology, population expansion, economic development, mass distribution and importation of food, war, and climate changes.

20.5 Nosocomial Infections

Reservoirs of Infectious Agents in Hospitals

The organisms that cause nosocomial infections may originate from other patients, the hospital environment, medical personnel, or the patient's own flora.

Transmission of Infectious Agents in Hospitals

Nosocomial infections can result from medical devices that breach the first-line barriers of the normal host defense.

Health care personnel should routinely wash or disinfect their hands after touching one patient before going on to the next in order to prevent transmission of disease-causing organisms.

Preventing Nosocomial Infections

The most important steps in preventing nosocomial infections are to first recognize their occurrence and then establish policies to prevent both their development and spread.

REVIEW QUESTIONS

Short Answer

1. Explain the difference between incidence and prevalence.
2. What is the epidemiological significance of people who have an asymptomatic infection?
3. Explain why zoonotic diseases are severe in humans.
4. Name the most important control measure for preventing person-to-person transmission of a disease.
5. Explain why *Shigella* and *Giardia* species are readily transmitted in day care centers.
6. Explain how smallpox was eradicated.
7. Describe three factors that contribute to the emergence of disease.
8. Draw a representative graph (time versus number of people ill) depicting both a propagated and common-source epidemic.
9. What are three important factors that a descriptive epidemiological study attempts to determine?
10. Describe the difference between a retrospective (case-control) study and a prospective (cohort) study.

Multiple Choice

1. Which of the following is an example of a fomite?
   a) Table b) Flea
   c) *Staphylococcus aureus* carrier
   d) Water e) Air
2. Which of the following would be the easiest to eradicate?
   a) A pathogen that is common in wild animals but sometimes infects humans
   b) A disease that occurs exclusively in humans, always resulting in obvious symptoms
   c) A mild disease of humans that often results in no obvious symptoms
   d) A pathogen found in marine sediments
   e) A pathogen that readily infects both wild animals and humans
3. Which of the following methods of disease transmission is the most difficult to control?
   a) Airborne b) Foodborne c) Waterborne
   d) Vector-borne e) Direct person to person
4. Which of the following statements is *false?*
   a) A botulism epidemic that results from improperly canned green beans is an example of a common-source outbreak.
   b) Bubonic plague has a higher mortality rate than pneumonic plague.
   c) Congenital syphilis is an example of a disease acquired through vertical transmission.
   d) Plague is endemic in the prairie dog population in parts of the United States.
   e) The first case in an outbreak is called the index case.
5. Which of the following statements is *false?*
   a) A disease with a long incubation period might spread extensively before an epidemic is recognized.
   b) A person exposed to a low dose of a pathogen might not develop disease.
   c) The young and the aged are more likely to develop certain disease.
   d) Malnourished populations are more likely to develop certain diseases.
   e) Herd immunity occurs when a population does not engage in a given behavior, such as eating raw fish, that would otherwise increase their risk of disease.
6. The purpose of an analytical study is to
   a) identify the person, place, and time of an outbreak.
   b) identify risk factors that result in high frequencies of disease.
   c) assess the effectiveness of preventative measures.
   d) determine the effectiveness of a placebo.
   e) None of the above

7. Which of the following causes of emerging diseases is thought to be a new pathogen?
   a) *Giardia* b) *Vibrio cholerae* O139
   c) *Mycobacterium tuberculosis* d) *Shigella dysenteriae*
   e) *Schistosoma*
8. All of the following are thought to contribute to the emergence of disease, *except*
   a) advances in technology.
   b) breakdown of public health infrastructure.
   c) construction of dams.
   d) mass distribution and importation of food.
   e) widespread vaccination programs.
9. Which of the following common causes of nosocomial infections is an environmental organism that grows readily in nutrient-poor solutions?
   a) *Enterococcus* b) *Escherichia coli*
   c) *Pseudomonas aeruginosa* d) *Staphylococcus aureus*
10. What is the most common type of nosocomial infection?
   a) Bloodstream infection b) Gastrointestinal infection
   c) Pneumonia d) Surgical wound infection
   e) Urinary tract infection

Applications

1. The television news station reported a story about a potentially fatal epidemic disease occurring in a small Laotian village. An epidemiologist from the CDC was interviewed to discuss the disease and was very distressed that it was not being contained. Why did the epidemiologist feel the disease was a concern for people in North America?
2. An international research team was gathered to discuss how funding should be spent to eliminate human infectious disease. There is only enough for this project to eliminate one disease. How would the scientists go about choosing the next disease to be eliminated from the planet?

Critical Thinking

1. *Yersinia pestis* and hantavirus are both found in wild rodents in the southwestern United States. What is the risk of trying to stop a hantavirus epidemic by destroying rodents in that region?
2. A student disagreed with the presentation of the examples in figure 20.5. She claimed that the number of cases from a common-source outbreak could remain high over a much longer period of time in some cases and not decrease to zero. Is the student's claim reasonable? Why or why not?

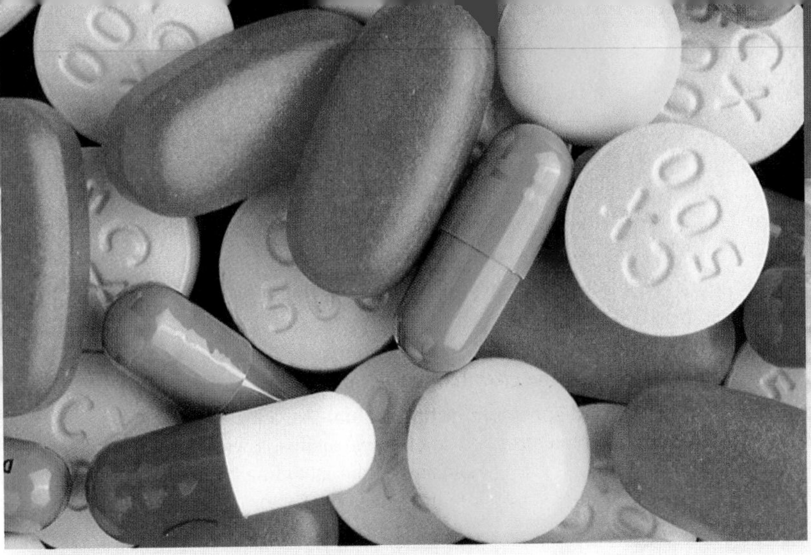

A few of the many important antimicrobial medications

CHAPTER TWENTY-ONE

Antimicrobial Medications

A Glimpse of History

Paul Ehrlich (1854–1915), a German physician and bacteriologist, was born into a wealthy family. As the only son after many daughters, family and servants indulged his interests, even though his large collection of frogs and snakes occasionally entered the laundry room. As an adult, he was rarely without a good cigar and habitually scribbled notes on his shirt cuffs. After receiving a degree in medicine in 1878, he became intrigued with the way various types of body cells differ in their ability to take up dyes and other substances. When he observed that certain dyes stain bacterial cells but not animal cells, indicating that the two cell types are somehow fundamentally different, it occurred to him that it might be possible to find a chemical that selectively harms bacteria without affecting human cells.

Ehrlich began a systematic search attempting to find a "magic bullet," a term he used to describe a drug that would kill a microbial pathogen without harming the human host. He began by looking for a chemical that would cure the sexually transmitted disease syphilis, which is caused by the bacterium *Treponema pallidum.* Much of the mental illness during this time resulted from tertiary syphilis, a late stage of the disease. Ehrlich knew that an arsenic compound had shown some success in treating a protozoan disease of animals, and so he and his colleagues began tediously synthesizing hundreds of different arsenic compounds in search for a cure for syphilis. In 1910, the 606th compound tested, arsphenamine, proved to be highly effective in treating the disease in laboratory animals. Although the drug itself was potentially lethal for patients, it did cure infections that were previously considered hopeless. The drug was given the name Salvarsan, a term derived from the words salvation and arsenic. The use of Salvarsan to cure syphilis proved that chemicals could selectively kill pathogens without permanently harming the human host.

Think back to the last time you were prescribed an antimicrobial medication. Could you have recovered from the infection without the drug? The prognosis for people with common diseases such as bacterial pneumonia and severe staphylococcal infection was grim before the discovery and widespread availability of penicillin in the 1940s. Physicians were able to identify the cause of the disease, but were generally unable to recommend treatments other than bed rest. Today, however, antimicrobials are routinely prescribed, and the simple cure they provide for so many infectious diseases is often taken for granted. Unfortunately, the misuse of these life-saving medications, coupled with bacteria's amazing ability to adapt, has led to an increase in the number of drug-resistant organisms. Some people even speculate that we are in danger of seeing an end to the era of antimicrobial medications. In response, scientists are scrambling to develop new drugs.

21.1 History and Development of Antimicrobial Drugs

Focus Point

- Describe the discovery of antimicrobial drugs and antibiotics, and how new generations of antimicrobial drugs are developed.

To appreciate the unique antibiotic era in which we now live, it is helpful to understand the history and development of these life-saving remedies.

Discovery of Antimicrobial Drugs

The development of Salvarsan by Paul Ehrlich was the first documented example of a chemical used successfully as an antimicrobial medication. The next breakthrough in the developing

KEY TERMS

Acquired resistance Resistance that develops through mutation or acquisition of new genes.

Antibiotic A compound naturally produced by mold or bacteria that inhibits the growth of or kills other microorganisms.

Antimicrobial drug A chemical that inhibits the growth of or kills microorganisms; the term encompasses antibiotics and chemically synthesized drugs.

Antiviral drug A drug that interferes with the replication of viruses.

Bactericidal drug An antimicrobial drug that kills bacteria.

Bacteriostatic drug An antimicrobial drug that inhibits the growth of bacteria.

Broad-spectrum antimicrobial An antimicrobial drug that is effective against a wide range of microorganisms, often including both Gram-positive and Gram-negative bacteria.

Chemotherapeutic agent A chemical used to treat disease.

Innate (intrinsic) resistance Resistance due to inherent characteristics of the organism.

Narrow-spectrum antimicrobial An antimicrobial drug that is effective against a limited range of microorganisms.

R plasmid A plasmid that encodes resistance to one or more antimicrobial drugs.

science of antimicrobial chemotherapy came almost 25 years later. In 1932, the German chemist Gerhard Domagk, using the same dogged persistence demonstrated by Ehrlich, discovered that a red dye called Prontosil was dramatically effective in treating streptococcal infections in animals. Surprisingly, Prontosil had no effect on streptococci growing in test tubes. It was later discovered that enzymes in the blood of the animal split the Prontosil molecule, producing a smaller molecule called **sulfanilamide;** this breakdown product acted against the infecting streptococci. Thus, the discovery of sulfanilamide, the first **sulfa drug,** was based on luck as well as scientific effort. If Prontosil had only been screened against bacteria in test tubes and not given to infected animals, its effectiveness might never have been discovered.

Salvarsan and Prontosil were the first documented examples of chemicals used successfully as antimicrobial medications. Any chemical that is used to treat a disease is called a **chemotherapeutic agent.** One used to treat microbial infections can also be called an **antimicrobial drug** or, more simply, an **antimicrobial.**

Discovery of Antibiotics

Alexander Fleming, a British scientist, was working with cultures of *Staphylococcus* when he noticed that colonies growing near a contaminating mold looked as if they were dissolving. Recognizing that the mold might be secreting a substance that killed the bacteria, he proceeded to study it more carefully. He identified the mold as a species of *Penicillium* and found it was indeed producing a bacteria-killing substance; he called this **penicillin.** Even though Fleming was unable to purify penicillin, he showed it was remarkably effective in killing many different kinds of bacteria and could be injected into rabbits and mice without adverse effects. Fleming recognized the potential medical significance of his discovery, but he became discouraged with his inability to purify the compound and eventually abandoned his study of it.

Ten years after Fleming's discovery, two other scientists in Britain, Ernst Chain and Howard Florey, were successful in their attempts to purify penicillin. In 1941, the drug was tested for the first time on a police officer with a life-threatening *Staphylococcus aureus* infection. He improved so dramatically that within 24 hours his illness seemed under control. Unfortunately, the supply of purified penicillin ran out, and the man eventually died of the infection. Later, with greater supplies of the drug, the experiment was repeated and two deathly ill patients were successfully cured.

World War II spurred a cooperation of British and American scientists to determine the chemical structure of penicillin and to develop the means for its large-scale production so that it could be used to treat infected soldiers and workers. Several different penicillins were found in the mold cultures, and were designated alphabetically. **Penicillin G** (or benzyl penicillin) was found to be the most suitable for treating infections. This was the first of what we now call **antibiotics,** antimicrobial drugs naturally produced by microorganisms.

Soon after the discovery of penicillin, Selman Waksman isolated a bacterium from soil, *Streptomyces griseus,* that produced an antibiotic he called **streptomycin.** The realization that bacteria as well as molds could produce medically useful antimicrobial drugs prompted researchers to begin laboriously screening hundreds of thousands of different strains of microorganisms for antibiotic production. Even today, pharmaceutical companies examine soil samples from around the world for organisms that produce novel antibiotics.

Development of New Generations of Drugs

In the 1960s scientists discovered that they could alter the chemical structure of drugs such as penicillin G, giving them new properties. For example, penicillin G, which is mostly active against Gram-positive bacteria, can be altered to produce ampicillin, a drug that kills additional Gram-negative species as well. Other changes to penicillin created the drug methicillin, which is less susceptible to enzymes used by some bacteria to inactivate penicillin. Thus, methicillin can be used to treat infections caused by certain penicillin-resistant organisms. Today a variety of penicillin-like medications exist, making up what is referred to as the family of penicillins **(figure 21.1).** Other unrelated antimicrobial drugs have also been altered to give them new characteristics.

MICROCHECK 21.1

Antimicrobials are chemotherapeutic agents that are effective in treating microbial infections. Antibiotics are antimicrobial chemicals naturally produced by particular microorganisms.

- ✓ How is the microbe that makes penicillin different from the one that makes streptomycin?
- ✓ Define and contrast the terms *chemotherapeutic agent, antimicrobial,* and *antibiotic.*
- ✓ How might *Streptomyces griseus* cells protect themselves from the effects of streptomycin?

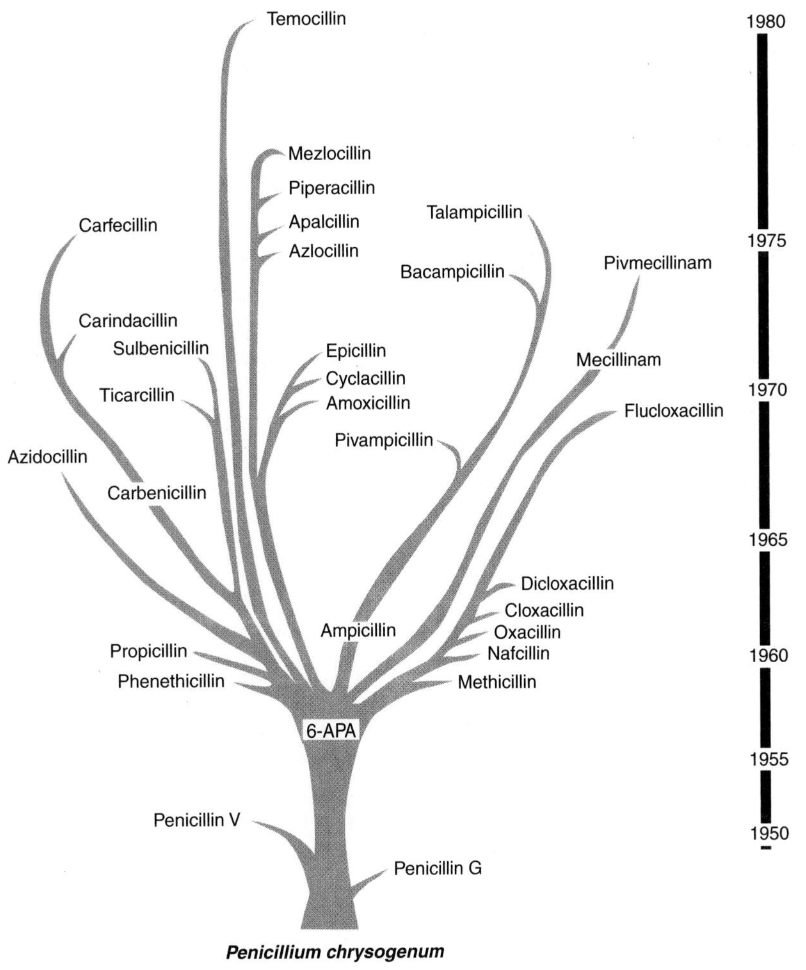

FIGURE 21.1 Family Tree of Penicillins All of the derivatives contain 6-aminopenicillanic acid (6-APA), the core portion of penicillin G.

21.2

Features of Antimicrobial Drugs

Focus Point

- Describe the important features of antimicrobial drugs that physicians must consider when prescribing an appropriate medication, including selective toxicity; antimicrobial action; spectrum of activity; tissue distribution, metabolism, and excretion; effects of combinations of antimicrobial drugs; adverse effects; resistance to antimicrobials; and cost.

Most modern antibiotics come from microorganisms that normally reside in the soil; these include species of *Streptomyces* and *Bacillus* (bacteria), and *Penicillium* and *Cephalosporium* (fungi). To commercially produce an antibiotic, a carefully selected strain of the appropriate species is inoculated into a broth medium and incubated in a huge vat. As soon as the maximum antibiotic concentration is reached, the drug is extracted from the medium and extensively purified. In many cases, the antibiotic is chemically altered after purification to impart new characteristics such as increased stability. These chemically modified compounds are called **semisynthetic.** In some cases, the entire drug can be synthesized in the laboratory. By convention, these partially or totally synthetic chemicals are still called antibiotics because microorganisms naturally produce them. Numerous different antimicrobial drugs are now available, each with characteristics that make it more or less suitable for a given clinical situation. Hundreds of tons and many millions of dollars' worth of antibiotics are now produced each year.

Selective Toxicity

Medically useful antimicrobial drugs exhibit **selective toxicity,** causing greater harm to microorganisms than to the human host. They do this by interfering with essential biological structures or biochemical processes that are common in microorganisms but not human cells.

While the ideal antimicrobial drug is non-toxic to humans, most can be harmful at high concentrations. In other words, selective toxicity is a relative term. The toxicity of a given drug is expressed as the **therapeutic index,** which is the lowest dose toxic to the patient divided by the dose typically used for therapy. Antimicrobials that have a high therapeutic index are less toxic to the patient, often because the drug acts against a vital biochemical process of bacteria that does not exist in human cells. For example, penicillin G, which interferes with bacterial cell wall synthesis, has a very high therapeutic index. When an antimicrobial that has a low therapeutic index is administered, the concentration in the patient's blood must be carefully monitored to ensure it does not reach a toxic level. Drugs that are too toxic for systemic use can sometimes be used for topical applications, such as first-aid antibiotic skin ointments.

Antimicrobial Action

Antimicrobial drugs may either kill microorganisms or inhibit their growth. Those that inhibit bacterial growth are called **bacteriostatic.** These drugs depend on the normal host defenses to kill or eliminate the pathogen after its growth has been inhibited. For example, sulfa drugs, which are frequently prescribed for urinary tract infections, inhibit the growth of bacteria in the bladder until they are eliminated during the normal process of urination. Drugs that kill bacteria are **bactericidal.** These drugs are particularly useful in situations in which the normal host defenses cannot be relied on to remove or destroy pathogens. A given drug can be bactericidal in one situation yet bacteriostatic in another, depending on the concentration of the drug and the growth stage of the microorganism.

Spectrum of Activity

Antimicrobial drugs vary with respect to the range of microorganisms they kill or inhibit. Some kill or inhibit a narrow range of microorganisms, such as only Gram-positive bacteria, whereas others affect a wide range, generally including both Gram-positive and Gram-negative organisms. Antimicrobials that affect a wide range of bacteria are called **broad-spectrum** antimicrobials. These are very important in the treatment of acute life-threatening diseases when immediate antimicrobial therapy is essential and there is no time to culture and identify the disease-causing agent. The disadvantage of broad-spectrum antimicrobials is that, by affecting a wide range of organisms, they disrupt the normal flora that play an important role in excluding pathogens. This in turn can leave the patient predisposed to other infections. Antimicrobials that affect a limited range of bacteria are **narrow-spectrum** antimicrobials. Their use requires identification of the pathogen, but they cause less disruption to the normal flora. ■ normal flora, pp. 368, 453

Tissue Distribution, Metabolism, and Excretion of the Drug

Antimicrobials differ not only in their action and activity, but also in how they are distributed, metabolized, and excreted by the body. For example, only some drugs are able to cross from the blood into the cerebrospinal fluid, an important factor for a physician to consider when prescribing a drug to treat meningitis. Drugs that are unstable at low pH are destroyed by stomach acid when taken orally, and so these drugs must instead be administered through intravenous or intramuscular injection. ■ meningitis, p. 684

Another important characteristic of an antimicrobial is its rate of elimination, which is expressed as the **half-life.** The half-life of a drug is the time it takes for the body to eliminate one-half of the original dosage in the serum. The half-life of a drug dictates the frequency of doses required to maintain an effective level in the body. Penicillin V, which has a very short half-life, needs to be taken four times a day, whereas azithromycin, with a half-life of over 24 hours, is taken only once a day or less. Patients who have kidney or liver dysfunction often excrete or metabolize drugs more slowly, and so their drug dosages must be adjusted accordingly.

Effects of Combinations of Antimicrobial Drugs

Combinations of antimicrobials are sometimes used to treat infections, but care must be taken when selecting the combinations because some drugs will counteract the effects of others. When the action of one drug enhances the activity of another, the combination is called **synergistic.** In contrast, combinations in which the activity of one interferes with the other are called **antagonistic.** Combinations that are neither synergistic nor antagonistic are called **additive.**

Adverse Effects

As with any medication, several concerns and dangers are associated with antimicrobial drugs. It is important to remember, however, that antimicrobials are extremely valuable drugs that have saved countless lives when properly prescribed and used.

Allergic Reactions

Some people develop hypersensitivities or allergies to certain antimicrobials. An allergic reaction to penicillin or other related drugs usually results in a fever or rash but can abruptly cause life-threatening anaphylactic shock. For this reason, people who have allergic reactions to a given antimicrobial must alert their physicians and pharmacists so that an alternative drug can be prescribed. A bracelet or necklace that records that information should also be worn in case of emergency. ■ anaphylactic shock, p. 436

Toxic Effects

Several antimicrobials are toxic at high concentrations or occasionally cause adverse reactions. Aminoglycosides can damage kidneys, impair the sense of balance, and even cause irreversible deafness. Patients taking these drugs must be closely monitored because of the very low therapeutic index. Some antimicrobials have such severe potential side effects that they are reserved for only life-threatening conditions. For example, in rare cases, chloramphenicol causes the potentially lethal condition **aplastic anemia,** in which the body is unable to make white and red blood cells. For this reason, chloramphenicol is usually used only when no other alternatives are available.

Suppression of the Normal Flora

The normal flora plays an important role in host defense by excluding pathogens. When the composition of the normal flora is altered, which happens when a person takes an antimicrobial, pathogens normally unable to compete may multiply to high numbers. Patients who take broad-spectrum antibiotics orally sometimes develop the life-threatening disease called **antibiotic-associated colitis,** caused by the growth of toxin-producing strains of *Clostridium difficile.* This organism is not usually able to establish itself in the intestine due to competition from other bacteria. When members of the normal intestinal flora are inhibited or killed, however, *C. difficile* can sometimes flourish and cause disease. ■ normal flora, pp. 368, 453 ■ *Clostridium difficile,* p. 614

Resistance to Antimicrobials

Just as humans are assembling a vast array of antimicrobial drugs, microorganisms have their own genetic toolbox of mechanisms to avoid their effects. In some cases, certain types of bacteria are inherently resistant to the effects of a particular drug; this is called **innate** or **intrinsic resistance.** Members of the genus *Mycoplasma* lack a cell wall, so, not surprisingly, they are resistant to any drug such as penicillin that exerts its action by interfering with cell wall synthesis. Many Gram-negative organisms are intrinsically resistant to certain drugs because the lipid bilayer of their outer membrane excludes entry of the drug. In other instances, previously sensitive organisms develop resistance through spontaneous mutation or the acquisition of new genetic information; this is called **acquired resistance.** The mechanisms and acquisition of resistance will be discussed later. ■ **characteristics of bacteria that lack a cell wall, p. 65** ■ **Gram-negative cell wall, p. 62**

Cost

While the price of a drug is not a concern from a purely scientific standpoint, it can significantly affect the overall expense of health care. In general, newly introduced drugs are far more expensive than their traditional counterparts. One relatively new addition to the family of penicillins is 20 times more costly than the original version. This higher price partially reflects the inherent expense of the research and development of new drugs. Unfortunately, the rapidly increasing resistance of microorganisms to traditional antimicrobials is affecting the cost of health care.

MICROCHECK 21.2

When choosing an antimicrobial to prescribe, a physician must consider a variety of factors including the therapeutic index, antimicrobial action, spectrum of activity, effects of combinations of antimicrobials, tissue distribution, half-life, adverse effects, resistance of the microbe, and cost of the drug.

- ✓ Which would you rather take: an antimicrobial that has a low therapeutic index or one that has a high therapeutic index? Why?
- ✓ In what clinical situation is it most appropriate to use a broad-spectrum antimicrobial?
- ✓ Why would antimicrobials that have toxic side effects be used at all?

21.3

Mechanisms of Action of Antibacterial Drugs

Focus Points

- Compare and contrast the antimicrobial drugs that inhibit cell wall synthesis.
- Compare and contrast the antimicrobial drugs that inhibit protein synthesis.
- Compare and contrast the antimicrobial drugs that inhibit nucleic acid synthesis.
- Compare and contrast the antimicrobial drugs that inhibit metabolic pathways.
- Describe the antimicrobial drugs that interfere with cell membrane integrity.
- Describe the antibacterial medications used to treat infections caused by *Mycobacterium tuberculosis.*

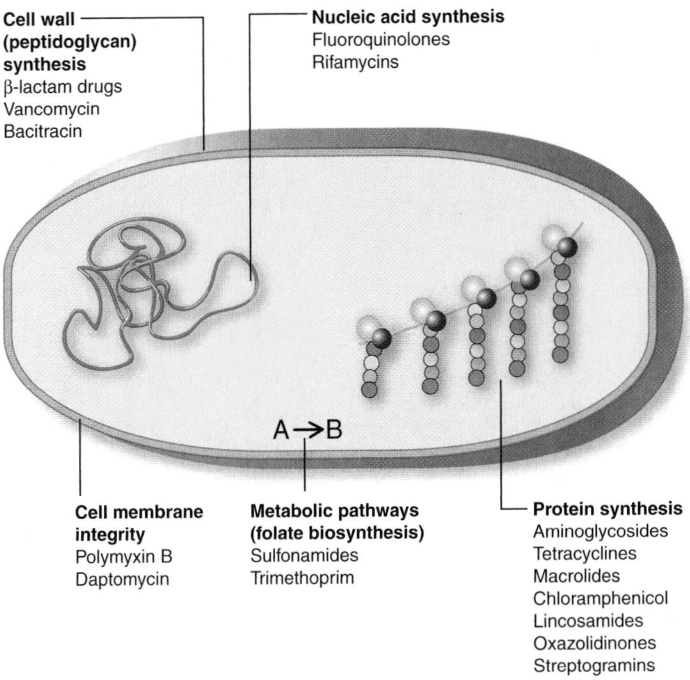

FIGURE 21.2 Targets of Antibacterial Medications

A number of bacterial processes utilize enzymes or structures that are either different, absent, or not commonly found in eukaryotic cells. Several microbial processes, including the synthesis of bacterial cell walls, proteins, and nucleic acids, metabolic pathways, and the integrity of the cytoplasmic membrane, are the targets of most antimicrobial drugs **(figure 21.2).**

This section will discuss the bacterial processes commonly targeted by antimicrobial medications. To illustrate how these targets are affected, the mechanism of action of some of the most widely used antimicrobials will be described **(table 21.1).** A group of antibiotics called β-lactam drugs will be covered in the greatest detail, because they serve as excellent examples of some of the important features of antimicrobials.

Antibacterial Medications That Inhibit Cell Wall Synthesis

Bacterial cell walls are unique in that they contain peptidoglycan (see figures 3.33 and 3.34). Because of this, antimicrobial medications that interfere solely with synthesis of this cell wall component do not affect eukaryotic cells, generally resulting in a very high therapeutic index (**figure 21.3,** p. 501).

TABLE 21.1 Characteristics of Antibacterial Drugs

Target/Drug	Comments/Characteristics
Cell Wall Synthesis	
β-lactam drugs	Bactericidal against a variety of bacteria; inhibits penicillin-binding proteins. Resistance is due to synthesis of β-lactamases, decreased affinity of penicillin-binding proteins, or decreased uptake.
Penicillins	A family of antimicrobial medications; different groups vary in their spectrum of activity and their susceptibility to β-lactamases.
Natural penicillins: penicillin G, penicillin V	Active against Gram-positive bacteria and some Gram-negative cocci. Penicillin G is destroyed by stomach acid, and so it usually must be administered by injection. Penicillin V can be taken orally.
Penicillinase-resistant: methicillin, dicloxicillin	Similar to natural penicillins, but resistant to inactivation by the penicillinase of staphylococci.
Broad-spectrum: ampicillin, amoxicillin	Similar to the natural penicillins, but more active against Gram-negative organisms.
Extended-spectrum: ticarcillin, piperacillin	Increased activity against Gram-negative rods, including *Pseudomonas* species.
Cephalosporins Cephalexin, cephradine, cefaclor, cefprozil, cefixime, cefibuten, cefepime	A family of antimicrobial medications. The later generations are generally more effective against Gram-negative bacteria and less susceptible to destruction by β-lactamases.
Carbapenems Imipenem, meropenem	Resistant to inactivation by β-lactamases. Imipenem must be given in combination with a drug that inhibits certain kidney enzymes in order to avoid its inactivation.
Monobactams Aztreonam	Resistant to β-lactamases; can be given to patients who are allergic to penicillin. Primarily active against members of the family *Enterobacteriaceae.*
Vancomycin	Bactericidal against Gram-positive bacteria; binds to the peptide side chain of *N*-acetylmuramic acid. Used to treat serious systemic infections and antibiotic-associated colitis. In enterococci, resistance is due to a plasmid-encoded altered target.
Bacitracin	Bactericidal against Gram-positive bacteria; interferes with the transport of peptidoglycan precursors. Common ingredient in non-prescription antibiotic ointments.
Protein Synthesis	
Aminoglycosides Streptomycin, gentamicin, tobramycin, amikacin, neomycin	Bactericidal against aerobic and facultative bacteria; binds to the 30S ribosomal subunit, blocking the initiation of translation and causing the misreading of mRNA. Toxicity limits the use. Resistance is due to a plasmid-encoded inactivating enzyme, alteration of the target molecule, or decreased uptake by a cell. Neomycin is commonly used in non-prescription topical antibiotic ointments.
Tetracyclines Tetracycline, doxycycline	Bacteriostatic against some Gram-positive and Gram-negative bacteria; binds to the 30S ribosomal subunit, blocking the attachment of tRNA. Resistance is generally due to decreased accumulation, either through decreased uptake or increased efflux.
Macrolides Erythromycin, clarithromycin, azithromycin	Bacteriostatic against many Gram-positive bacteria as well as the most common causes of atypical pneumonia; binds to the 50S ribosomal subunit, preventing the continuation of protein synthesis. Used for treating patients who are allergic to β-lactam drugs. Resistance is due to an inactivating enzyme, alteration of the target molecule, or decreased uptake by a cell.
Chloramphenicol	Bacteriostatic and broad-spectrum; binds to the 50S ribosomal subunit, preventing peptide bonds from being formed. Generally used only as a last resort for life-threatening infections. Resistance is often due to a plasmid-encoded inactivating enzyme.
Lincosamides Lincomycin, clindamycin	Bacteriostatic against a variety of Gram-positive and Gram-negative bacteria, including the anaerobe *Bacteroides fragilis.* Binds to the 50S ribosomal subunit, preventing the continuation of protein synthesis. Associated with an even greater risk of developing antibiotic-associated colitis.
Oxazolidinones Linezolid	Bacteriostatic against a variety of Gram-positive bacteria. Binds to the 50S ribosomal subunit, interfering with the initiation of protein synthesis.
Streptogramins Quinupristin, dalfopristin	A synergistic combination of two drugs that bind to two different sites on the 50S ribosomal subunit, inhibiting distinct steps of protein synthesis. Individually each drug is bacteriostatic, but together they are bacteriocidal. Effective against a variety of Gram-positive bacteria.

TABLE 21.1 Characteristics of Antibacterial Drugs *(continued)*

Target/Drug	Comments/Characteristics
Nucleic Acid Synthesis	
Fluoroquinolones	Bactericidal against a wide variety of Gram-positive and Gram-negative bacteria; inhibits topoisomerases. Resistance is most often due to structural alterations in the topoisomerase target.
Ciprofloxacin, ofloxacin	
Rifamycins	Bactericidal against Gram-positive and some Gram-negative bacteria. Binds RNA polymerase, blocking the initiation of RNA synthesis. Primarily used to treat infections caused by *Mycobacterium tuberculosis* and as prophylaxis for patients who have been exposed to *Neisseria meningitidis.*
Rifampin	
Folate Biosynthesis	
Sulfonamides	Bacteriostatic against a variety of Gram-positive and Gram-negative bacteria. Structurally similar to para-aminobenzoic acid (PABA) and therefore inhibits the enzyme for which PABA is a substrate. Resistance is most commonly due to a plasmid-encoded alternative enzyme.
Trimethoprim	Often used in combination with a sulfa drug for a synergistic effect; inhibits the enzyme that catalyzes a step following the one inhibited by the sulfonamides. Resistance is commonly due to a plasmid-encoded alternative enzyme; the genes that encode resistance to sulfa drugs are often carried on the same plasmid.
Cell Membrane Integrity	
Polymyxin B	Bactericidal against Gram-negative cells by damaging cell membranes. Its toxicity limits its use primarily to topical applications, but it is a common ingredient in non-prescription antibiotic ointments.
Daptomycin	Bactericidal against Gram-positive bacteria by damaging the cytoplasmic membrane.
Mycobacterium tuberculosis	
Ethambutol	Inhibits the synthesis of a component of the mycobacterial cell wall.
Isoniazid	Inhibits synthesis of mycolic acid, a major component of the mycobacterial cell wall.
Pyrazinamide	Mechanism unknown.

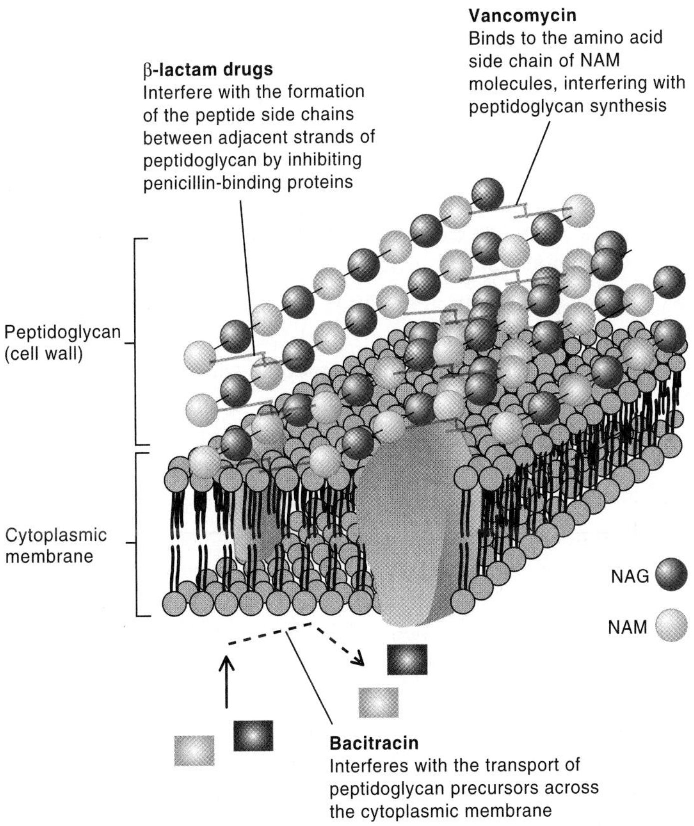
Vancomycin
Binds to the amino acid side chain of NAM molecules, interfering with peptidoglycan synthesis
β-lactam drugs
Interfere with the formation of the peptide side chains between adjacent strands of peptidoglycan by inhibiting penicillin-binding proteins
Peptidoglycan (cell wall)
Cytoplasmic membrane
NAG
NAM
Bacitracin
Interferes with the transport of peptidoglycan precursors across the cytoplasmic membrane

FIGURE 21.3 Antibacterial Medications that Interfere with Cell Wall Synthesis

Penicillins, Cephalosporins and Other β-Lactam Drugs

Penicillins and cephalosporins are members of a group of antimicrobial medications collectively referred to as **β-lactam drugs.** This group, which also includes the monobactams and carbapenems, all have a shared chemical structure called a **β-lactam ring (figure 21.4).**

The β-lactam drugs competitively inhibit a group of enzymes that catalyze formation of peptide bridges between adjacent glycan strands, an essential step in the final stages of peptidoglycan synthesis (see figure 3.32). This disruption in cell wall biosynthesis leads to weakening of the wall and ultimately results in cell lysis **(figure 21.5).** Because cell walls are only synthesized in actively multiplying cells, the β-lactam drugs are only effective against growing bacteria. ■ competitive enzyme inhibition, p. 142

The enzymes that β-lactam drugs inhibit are commonly called **penicillin-binding proteins (PBPs),** reflecting the fact that they bind penicillin and were initially discovered during experiments to study the effects of the medication. Unfortunately, the name seems to imply that the natural biological function of the enzymes is to bind penicillin, when, in fact, their function is peptidoglycan biosynthesis. The name also fails to highlight the fact that PBPs may bind any number of β-lactam drugs, not just the penicillins.

The different β-lactam drugs vary in their spectrum of activity. Some are more active against Gram-positive bacteria,

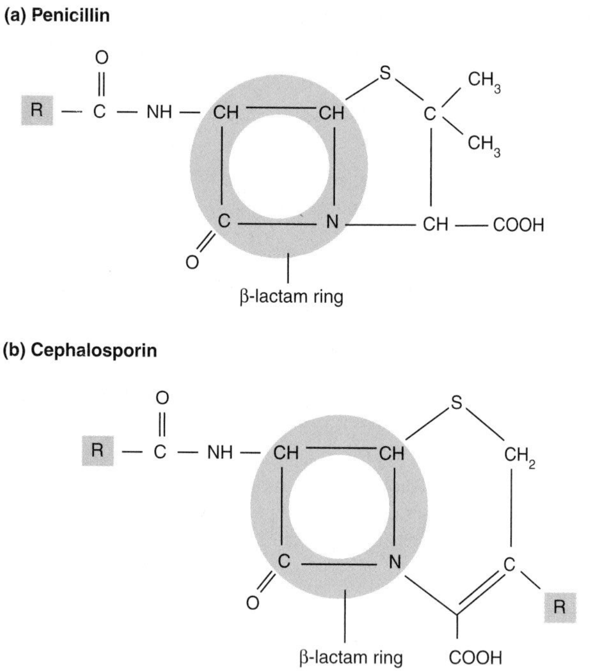

FIGURE 21.4 The β-Lactam Ring of Penicillins and Cephalosporins The core chemical structure of **(a)** a penicillin; **(b)** a cephalosporin. The β-lactam rings are marked by an orange circle. The R groups vary among different penicillins and cephalosporins.

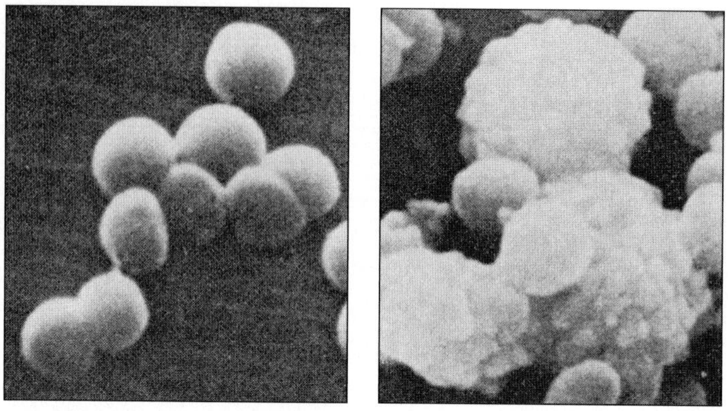

FIGURE 21.5 Effect of a β-Lactam Drug on a Cell The drug disrupts cell wall synthesis, leading to weakening of the cell wall, ultimately causing the cells to lyse.

whereas others are more active against Gram-negative organisms. One reason for this difference arises from the architecture of the cell wall. The peptidoglycan layer of Gram-positive organisms directly contacts the outside environment, making the enzymes that synthesize it readily accessible to drugs. In contrast, the outer membrane of Gram-negative bacteria excludes many antimicrobials, making many of these organisms innately resistant to many medications, including certain β-lactam drugs. Another difference is the affinity of an organism's penicillin-binding proteins for a particular β-lactam drug. The PBPs of Gram-positive bacteria differ somewhat from those of Gram-negative bacteria, and the PBPs of obligate anaerobes differ from those of aerobes. Differences in affinity can even exist among related organisms such as Gram-positive cocci.

Some bacteria can resist the effects of certain β-lactam drugs by synthesizing an enzyme, a **β-lactamase,** that breaks the critical β-lactam ring, destroying the activity of the antibiotic. Just as there are many β-lactam drugs, there are various β-lactamases; these differ in the range of drugs they destroy. A β-lactamase that was originally detected in some strains of staphylococci only inactivates members of the penicillin family. To reflect this fact, it is often called a **penicillinase.** In contrast, some of the β-lactamases produced by Gram-negative organisms inactivate a wide variety of β-lactam drugs. The **extended-spectrum β-lactamases** inactivate both the penicillins and the cephalosporins. As a whole, Gram-negative bacteria can produce a much more extensive array of β-lactamases than can Gram-positive organisms.

The Penicillins Each member of the family of penicillins shares a common basic structure. Only the side chain has been modified in the laboratory to create penicillin derivatives, each with unique characteristics **(figure 21.6).** Currently the family of penicillins can be loosely grouped into several categories, each of which consists of several different drugs:

- **Natural penicillins.** These are the original penicillins produced naturally by the mold *Penicillium chrysogenum.* Natural penicillins are narrow-spectrum antibiotics, effective against Gram-positive bacteria and some Gram-negative cocci. Strains of bacteria that produce penicillinase are resistant to the natural penicillins. Penicillin V is more stable in acid and, therefore, better absorbed than penicillin G when taken orally.
- **Pencillinase-resistant penicillins.** These drugs were developed in the laboratory as a response to the problem of penicillinase-producing staphylococci. Their side chains prevent penicillinase from inactivating them. Unfortunately, some strains of penicillinase-producing *Staphylococcus aureus* have responded by synthesizing altered PBPs to which β-lactam drugs, including the penicillins, no longer bind. Penicillinase-resistant penicillins include methicillin and dicloxicillin.
- **Broad-spectrum penicillins.** The modified side chains of these drugs give them a broad spectrum of activity. They retain their activity against penicillin-sensitive Gram-positive bacteria, yet they are also active against Gram-negative organisms. Unfortunately, they can be inactivated by many β-lactamases. Broad-spectrum penicillins include ampicillin and amoxicillin.
- **Extended-spectrum penicillins.** These have greater activity against *Pseudomonas* species, Gram-negative bacteria that are unaffected by many conventional antimicrobial drugs. The extended-spectrum penicillins, however, have less activity against Gram-positive organisms. Like the other broad-spectrum penicillins, they are destroyed by many β-lactamase-producing organisms. Extended-spectrum penicillins include ticarcillin and piperacillin.
- **Penicillins + β-lactamase inhibitor.** Rather than a new drug, this is a novel combination of therapeutic agents. β-lactamase inhibitors are chemicals that interfere with the

activity of some types of β-lactamases. When a β-lactamase inhibitor is administered with one of the penicillins, the medication is protected against enzymatic destruction. An example is Augmentin®, a combination of amoxicillin and clavulanic acid.

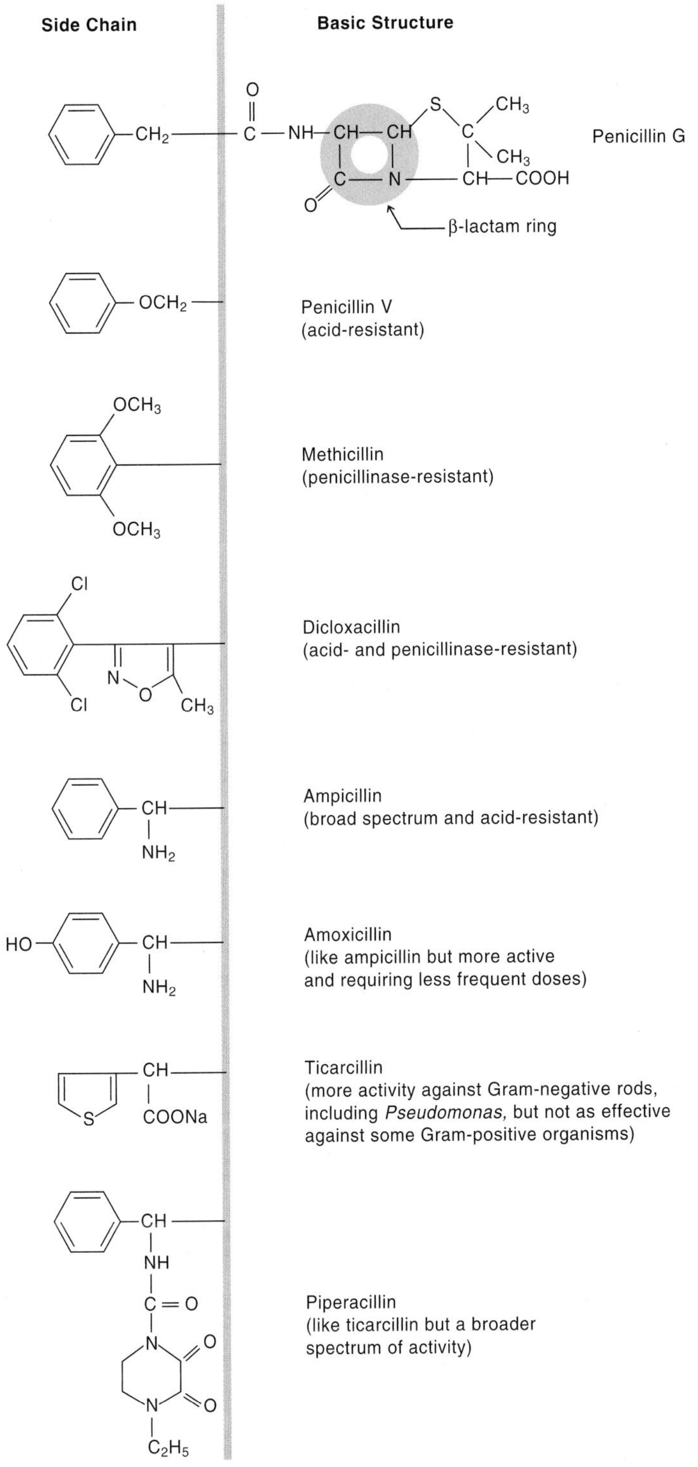

FIGURE 21.6 Chemical Structures and Properties of Representative Members of the Penicillin Family The entire structure of penicillin G and the side chains of other penicillins are shown.

The Cephalosporins The **cephalosporins** are derived from an antibiotic produced by the fungus *Acremonium cephalosporium* (formerly called *Cephalosporium acremonium*). Generally included in this family of drugs are a closely related group of antibiotics made by members of a genus of filamentous bacteria related to *Streptomyces.*

The chemical structure of the cephalosporins makes them resistant to inactivation by certain β-lactamases, but some have a low affinity for penicillin-binding proteins of Gram-positive bacteria, thus limiting their effectiveness against these organisms. Like the penicillins, the cephalosporins have been chemically modified to produce a family of various related antibiotics. They are grouped as the first-, second-, third-, and fourth-generation cephalosporins. These include cephalexin and cephradine (first generation), cefaclor and cefprozil (second generation), cefixime and cefibuten (third generation), and cefepime (fourth generation). The later generations are generally more effective against Gram-negative bacteria and are less susceptible to destruction by β-lactamases.

Other β-Lactam Antibiotics Two other groups of β-lactam drugs, carbapenems and monobactams, are very resistant to β-lactamases. The carbapenems are effective against a wide range of Gram-negative and Gram-positive bacteria. Two types are available, imipenem and meropenem. Imipenem is rapidly destroyed by a kidney enzyme and is therefore administered in combination with a drug that inhibits that enzyme. The only monobactam used therapeutically, aztreonam, is primarily effective against members of the family *Enterobacteriaceae,* which are Gram-negative rods. Structurally, it is slightly different from other β-lactam drugs; this characteristic is important because aztreonam can be given to patients who have developed an allergy to penicillin.
■ *Enterobacteriaceae,* p. 279

Vancomycin

Vancomycin binds to the terminal amino acids of the peptide side chain of NAM molecules that are being assembled to form glycan chains. By doing so, it blocks synthesis of peptidoglycan, resulting in weakening of the cell wall and, ultimately, cell lysis. Vancomycin does not cross the outer membrane of Gram-negative bacteria; consequently, these organisms are innately resistant. It is, however, a very important medication for treating infections caused by Gram-positive bacteria that are resistant to β-lactam drugs. In addition, it is sometimes the preferred drug for treating severe cases of antibiotic-associated colitis. Because vancomycin is poorly absorbed from the intestinal tract, it must be administered intravenously except when used to treat intestinal infections. Acquired resistance to vancomycin is most often due to an alteration in the peptide side chain of the NAM molecule that prevents vancomycin from binding.

Bacitracin

Bacitracin inhibits cell wall biosynthesis by interfering with the transport of peptidoglycan precursors across the cytoplasmic membrane. Its toxicity limits its use to topical applications; however, it is a common ingredient in non-prescription first-aid ointments.

Antibacterial Medications That Inhibit Protein Synthesis

Several types of antibacterial drugs inhibit prokaryotic protein synthesis **(figure 21.7).** While all cells synthesize proteins, the structure of the prokaryotic 70S ribosome, which is composed of a 30S and a 50S subunit, is different enough from the eukaryotic 80S ribosome to make it a suitable target for selective toxicity. The mitochondria of eukaryotic cells also have 70S ribosomes, however, which may partially account for the toxicity of some of these drugs. ■ ribosome structure, p. 70 ■ protein synthesis, p. 176

The Aminoglycosides

The **aminoglycosides** are bactericidal drugs that irreversibly bind to the 30S ribosomal subunit, causing it to distort and malfunction. This blocks the initiation of translation and causes misreading of mRNA by ribosomes that have already passed the initiation step. Aminoglycosides are actively transported into bacterial cells by a process that requires respiratory metabolism. Consequently, they are generally not effective against anaerobes, enterococci, and streptococci. To extend their spectrum of activity, the aminoglycosides are sometimes used in a synergistic combination with a β-lactam drug. The β-lactam drug interferes with cell wall synthesis, which, in turn, allows the aminoglycoside to more easily enter cells that would otherwise be resistant. Examples of aminoglycosides include streptomycin, gentamicin, tobramycin, and amikacin. Unfortunately, these all can cause severe side effects including hearing loss and kidney damage; consequently, they are generally used only when other alternatives are not available. Recently, a form of tobramycin that can be administered through inhalation rather than injection was developed, making treatment of lung infections in cystic fibrosis patients caused by *Pseudomonas aeruginosa* safer and more effective. Another aminoglycoside, neomycin, is too toxic for systemic use; however, it is a common ingredient in nonprescription topical ointments. ■ active transport, p. 59

The Tetracyclines

The **tetracyclines** reversibly bind to the 30S ribosomal subunit, blocking the attachment of tRNA to the ribosome and preventing the continuation of protein synthesis. These bacteriostatic drugs are actively transported into prokaryotic but not animal cells, which effectively concentrates them inside bacteria. This, in part, accounts for their selective toxicity. The tetracyclines are effective against certain Gram-positive and Gram-negative bacteria. The newer tetracyclines such as doxycycline have a longer half-life, allowing less frequent doses. Resistance to the tetracyclines is primarily due to a decrease in their accumulation by the bacterial cell, either by decreased uptake or increased excretion. Tetracyclines can cause discoloration in teeth when used by young children.

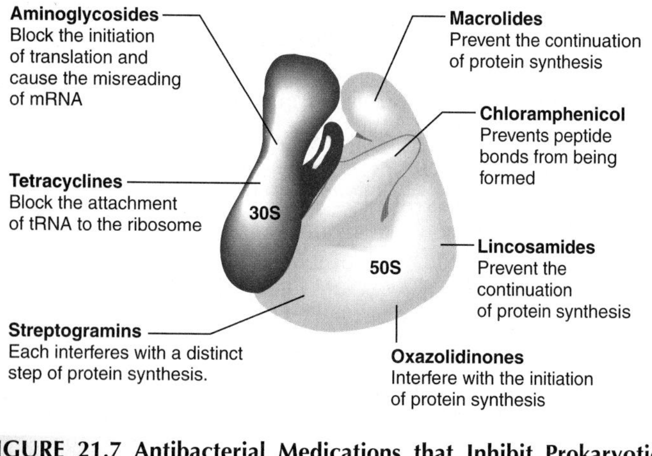
Aminoglycosides
Block the initiation of translation and cause the misreading of mRNA
Tetracyclines
Block the attachment of tRNA to the ribosome
30S
50S
Streptogramins
Each interferes with a distinct step of protein synthesis.
Macrolides
Prevent the continuation of protein synthesis
Chloramphenicol
Prevents peptide bonds from being formed
Lincosamides
Prevent the continuation of protein synthesis
Oxazolidinones
Interfere with the initiation of protein synthesis

FIGURE 21.7 Antibacterial Medications that Inhibit Prokaryotic Protein Synthesis These medications bind to the 70S ribosome.

The Macrolides

The **macrolides** reversibly bind to the 50S ribosomal subunit and prevent the continuation of protein synthesis. Macrolides as a group are bacteriostatic against a variety of bacteria, including many Gram-positive organisms as well as the most common causes of atypical pneumonia ("walking pneumonia"). They often serve as the drug of choice for patients who are allergic to penicillin. Macrolides are not effective against members of the family *Enterobacteriaceae,* however, because the outer membrane of these organisms excludes the drug. Examples of macrolides include erythromycin, clarithromycin, and azithromycin. Both clarithromycin and azithromycin have a longer half-life than erythromycin, so that they can be taken less frequently. Resistance to all the macrolides can occur through modification of the ribosomal RNA target. Other mechanisms of resistance include the production of an enzyme that chemically modifies the drug and alterations that result in decreased uptake of the drug. ■ walking pneumonia, p. 590

Chloramphenicol

Chloramphenicol binds to the 50S ribosomal subunit, preventing peptide bonds from being formed and, consequently, blocking protein synthesis. Although it is bacteriostatic against a wide range of bacteria, it is generally only used as a last resort for life-threatening infections in order to avoid a rare but lethal side effect. This complication, aplastic anemia, is not related to dose and is characterized by the inability of the body to form white and red blood cells.

The Lincosamides

The **lincosamides** bind to the 50S ribosomal subunit and prevent the continuation of protein synthesis, inhibiting a variety of Gram-negative and Gram-positive organisms. They are particularly useful for treating infections resulting from intestinal perforation because they inhibit *Bacterioides fragilis,* a member of the normal intestinal flora that is frequently resistant to other antimicrobials. Unfortunately, the risk for people taking lincosamides developing antibiotic-associated colitis is greater than for some other antimicrobials because *Clostridium difficile* is generally resistant to these drugs. The most commonly used lincosamide is clindamycin.

The Oxazolidinones

The **oxazolidinones** are a promising new class of antimicrobial drugs. They bind to the 50S ribosomal subunit and interfere with the initiation of protein synthesis. They are bacteriostatic against a variety of Gram-positive bacteria and are useful in treating infections caused by bacteria that are resistant to β-lactam drugs and vancomycin. Linezolid is the first drug of this class to be approved for use.

The Streptogramins

Two **streptogramins,** quinupristin and dalfopristin, are administered together in a recently approved medication called Synercid®. These act as a synergistic combination, binding to two different sites on the 50S ribosomal subunit and inhibiting distinct steps of protein synthesis. Individually, each drug is bacteriostatic but together they are bactericidal. Synercid® is effective against a variety of Gram-positive bacteria, including some of those that are resistant to β-lactam drugs and vancomycin.

Antibacterial Medications That Inhibit Nucleic Acid Synthesis

Enzymes required for nucleic acid synthesis are the targets of some groups of antimicrobial drugs. These include the fluoroquinolones and the rifamycins.

The Fluoroquinolones

The synthetic drugs called the **fluoroquinolones** inhibit one or more of a group of enzymes called **topoisomerases,** which maintain the supercoiling of closed circular DNA within the bacterial cell. One type of topoisomerase, called **DNA gyrase** or **topoisomerase II,** breaks and rejoins strands to relieve the strain caused by the localized unwinding of DNA during replication and transcription. Consequently, inhibition of this enzyme prevents these essential cell processes. The fluoroquinolones are bactericidal against a wide variety of bacteria, including both Gram-positive and Gram-negative organisms. Examples of fluoroquinolones include ciprofloxacin and ofloxacin. Acquired resistance is most commonly due to an alteration in the DNA gyrase target. ■ supercoiled DNA, p. 69

The Rifamycins

The **rifamycins** block prokaryotic RNA polymerase from initiating transcription. Rifampin, which is the most widely used rifamycin, exhibits bactericidal activity against many Gram-positive and some Gram-negative bacteria as well as members of the genus *Mycobacterium.* It is primarily used to treat tuberculosis and Hansen's disease (leprosy) and to prevent meningitis in people who have been exposed to *Neisseria meningitidis.* In some patients, a reddish-orange pigment appears in urine and tears. Resistance to rifampin develops rapidly and is due to a mutation in the gene that encodes RNA polymerase.

Antibacterial Medications That Inhibit Metabolic Pathways

Relatively few antibacterial medications interfere with metabolic pathways. Among the most useful are the folate inhibitors—sulfonamides and trimethoprim. These each inhibit different steps in the pathway that leads initially to the synthesis of folic acid and ultimately to the synthesis of a coenzyme required for nucleotide biosynthesis **(figure 21.8).** Animal cells lack the enzymes in the folic acid synthesis portion of the pathway, which is why folic acid is a dietary requirement. ■ coenzyme, p. 140

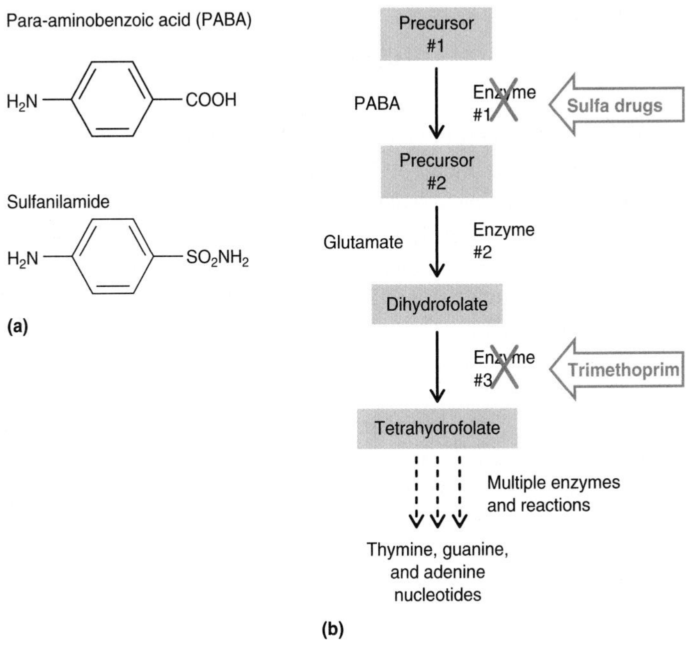

FIGURE 21.8 Inhibitors of the Folate Pathway (a) The chemical structure of PABA and a sulfa drug (sulfanilamide). **(b)** The sulfonamides and trimethoprim interfere with different steps of the pathway that leads initially to the synthesis of folic acid and ultimately to the synthesis of a coenzyme required for nucleotide biosynthesis.

The Sulfonamides

Sulfonamides and related compounds, collectively referred to as **sulfa drugs,** inhibit the growth of many Gram-positive and Gram-negative bacteria. They are structurally similar to para-aminobenzoic acid (PABA), a substrate in the pathway for folic acid biosynthesis. Because of this similarity, the enzyme that normally binds PABA preferentially binds sulfa drugs, resulting in its competitive inhibition (see figure 6.13). Human cells lack this enzyme, providing the basis for the selective toxicity of the sulfonamides. Resistance of bacteria to the sulfonamides is most often due to the acquisition of a plasmid-encoded enzyme that has a lower affinity for the drug. ■ competitive inhibition, p. 142

Trimethoprim

Trimethoprim inhibits the bacterial enzyme that catalyzes a metabolic step following the one inhibited by sulfonamides. Fortunately, the drug has little effect on the analogous enzyme in human cells. The combination of trimethoprim and a sulfonamide has a synergistic effect, and they are often used together to treat urinary tract infections. The most common mechanism of resistance is a plasmid-encoded alternative enzyme that has a lower affinity for the drug. Unfortunately, the genes encoding resistance to trimethoprim and sulfonamide are often carried on the same plasmid.

Antibacterial Medications That Interfere with Cell Membrane Integrity

A few antimicrobial drugs damage bacterial membranes. **Polymyxin B,** a common ingredient in first-aid skin ointments, binds to the membrane of Gram-negative cells and alters the permeability, leading to leakage of cellular contents and eventual death of the cells. Unfortunately, these drugs also bind to eukaryotic cells, though to a lesser extent, which generally limits their use to topical applications. **Daptomycin** binds to the bacterial cytoplasmic membrane, resulting in death of the cell by a mechanism not yet fully understood. Its recent approval increases the arsenal of antimicrobial medications available for treating infections caused by Gram-positive bacteria resistant to other drugs. It is not effective against Gram-negative bacteria, however, because it cannot penetrate the outer membrane.

Antibacterial Medications That Interfere with Processes Essential to *Mycobacterium tuberculosis*

Only a limited range of antimicrobials can be used to treat infections caused by *Mycobacterium tuberculosis* and related species. This is due to several factors, including the chronic nature of the disease caused by these organisms, their slow growth, and their waxy cell wall, which is impervious to many drugs. A group of five medications, called the **first-line** drugs, are preferred because they are the most effective as well as the least toxic. These are generally given in combination of two or more to patients who have active tuberculosis. This combination therapy prevents the development of resistant mutants; if some cells in the infecting population spontaneously develop resistance to one drug, the other drug will eliminate them. The **second-line** medications can be used if the first-line drugs are not an option; however, they are either less effective or more toxic. ■ *Mycobacterium tuberculosis,* p. 593

Of the first-line medications, some specifically target the unique cell wall that characterizes the mycobacteria. **Isoniazid** inhibits the synthesis of mycolic acids, a primary component of the cell wall. **Ethambutol** inhibits enzymes that are required for synthesis of other mycobacterial cell wall components. The mechanism of **pyrazinamide** is unknown. Other first-line drugs include rifampin and streptomycin, which have already been discussed.

MICROCHECK 21.3

Bacterial processes that utilize enzymes or structures that are different, absent, or not commonly found in eukaryotic cells are the targets of most medically useful antimicrobial drugs. The targets of antimicrobial drugs include biosynthetic pathways for peptidoglycan, protein, nucleic acid, and folic acid and the integrity of membranes. Drugs used to treat tuberculosis often interfere with processes unique to *Mycobacterium tuberculosis.*

- ✓ Explain the normal biological role of penicillin-binding proteins.
- ✓ What is the target of the macrolides?
- ✓ Why would co-administration of a bacteriostatic drug interfere with the effects of penicillin?

21.4

Determining the Susceptibility of a Bacterial Strain to an Antimicrobial Drug

Focus Points

- Describe how the minimum inhibitory concentration (MIC) and the minimum bactericidal concentration (MBC) of an antimicrobial drug are determined.
- Compare and contrast the Kirby-Bauer disc diffusion test with commercial modifications of antimicrobial susceptibility testing.

In many cases, susceptibility of a pathogenic organism to a specific antimicrobial drug is unpredictable. Unfortunately, it has often been the practice to try one drug after another until a favorable response is observed or, if the infection is very serious, to give several together. Both approaches are undesirable. With each unnecessary drug given, needless risks of toxic or allergic effects arise and the normal flora may be altered, permitting the overgrowth of pathogens resistant to the drug. A better approach is to determine the susceptibility of the specific pathogen to various antimicrobial drugs and then choose the drug that acts against the offending organism but against as few other bacteria as possible.

Determining the Minimum Inhibitory and Bactericidal Concentrations

The **minimum inhibitory concentration (MIC)** is a quantitative test to determine the lowest concentration of a specific antimicrobial drug needed to prevent the growth of a given organism *in vitro.* It is determined by examining the test bacterial strain's ability to grow in broth cultures containing different concentrations of the antimicrobial. Serial dilutions generating decreasing concentrations of the drug are first prepared in tubes containing a suitable growth medium **(figure 21.9).** Then, a known concentration of the organism is added to each tube. The tubes are incubated for at least 16 hours and then are examined for visible growth or turbidity. The lowest concentration of the drug that prevents growth of the microorganism is the minimum inhibitory concentration. The fact that an organism is inhibited by a given concentration of drug, however, does not necessarily mean that an infection can be successfully treated with the drug. For example, an organism with a MIC of 20 μg/ml of a drug is sensitive to that concentration *in vitro.* Nevertheless, the organism would be considered resistant for the purposes of treatment if the level that can be achieved in blood were only 5 μg/ml. Microorganisms requiring inhibitory concentrations on the borderline between susceptible (treatable) and resistant (untreatable) are called intermediate.

The **minimum bactericidal concentration (MBC)** is the lowest concentration of a specific antimicrobial drug that kills 99.9% of cells of a given strain of bacteria. The MBC is determined by assaying for live organisms in those tubes from the MIC test that showed no growth. A small sample from each of those tubes is transferred to fresh, antibiotic-free medium. If growth occurs, then

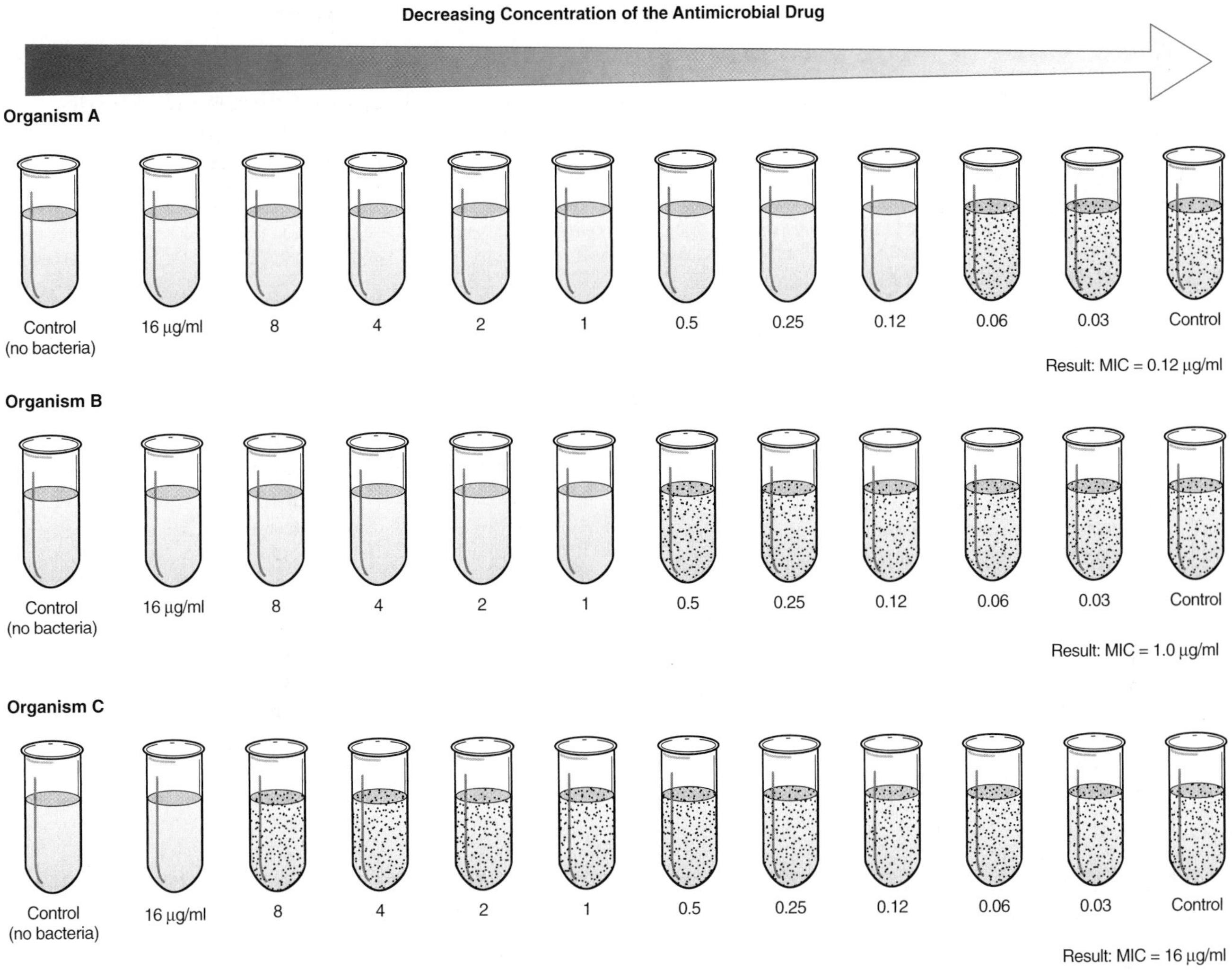

FIGURE 21.9 Determining the Minimum Inhibitory Concentration (MIC) of an Antimicrobial Drug The lowest concentration of drug that prevents growth of the culture is the MIC.

living organisms remained in the original tube. Conversely, if no growth occurs, then no living organisms remained, indicating that the antibiotic was bactericidal at that concentration.

Determining the MIC and MBC using these conventional methods gives precise information regarding an organism's susceptibility. The techniques, however, are labor-intensive and consequently expensive. In addition, individual sets of tubes must be inoculated to determine susceptibility to each different antimicrobial tested.

Conventional Disc Diffusion Method

The **Kirby-Bauer disc diffusion test** is routinely used to qualitatively determine the susceptibility of a given bacterial strain to a battery of antimicrobial drugs. A standard concentration of the strain is first uniformly spread on the surface of an agar plate. Then 12 or so discs, each impregnated with a specified amount of a selected antimicrobial drug, are placed on the surface of the medium **(figure 21.10).** During incubation, the various drugs diffuse outward from the discs at a rate inversely proportional to their

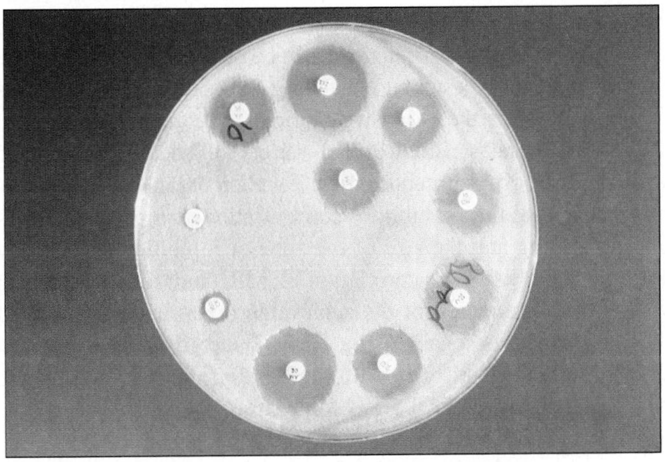

FIGURE 21.10 Kirby-Bauer Method for Determining Drug Susceptibility The size of the zone of inhibition surrounding the disc reflects, in part, the sensitivity of the bacterial strain to the drug. Because zone size is influenced by characteristics of the drug such as molecular weight, however, a chart must be consulted that correlates zone size to susceptibility.

PERSPECTIVE 21.1

Measuring the Concentration of an Antimicrobial Drug in Blood or Other Body Fluids

There are many situations in which it is necessary to determine the concentration of an antimicrobial drug in a patient's blood or other body fluid. For example, patients who are being administered an aminoglycoside must often be carefully monitored to ensure that the concentration of drug in their blood does not reach an unsafe level, particularly if they have kidney or liver dysfunction that interferes with normal elimination. Likewise, new drugs must be tested to determine achievable levels in the blood, urine, or other body fluids.

A technique called the **diffusion bioassay** is used to measure the concentration of an antimicrobial in a fluid specimen. The test relies on the same principle as the Kirby-Bauer test, except in this case it is the concentration of drug, not the sensitivity of organism, being assayed. A culture of a stock organism that is highly susceptible to the drug is added to melted cooled agar, and the mixture is poured into an agar plate and allowed to solidify. This results in a solid medium that is uniformly inoculated throughout with the sensitive organism. Cylindrical holes are then punched out of the agar, creating wells. **Standards,** or fluids containing known concentrations of the drug, are then added to some of the wells, while others are filled with the body fluid being tested. Following overnight incubation, zones of inhibition form around the agar wells, the sizes of which correspond to the concentrations of the drug **(figure 1).** The higher the concentration of antimicrobial, the larger is the zone of inhibition. The zone sizes around the standards are measured, and from this a **standard curve** is constructed by plotting the zone sizes against the corresponding drug concentration. A line relating zone size to concentration is obtained, from which the concentration of the antimicrobial drug in the body fluid can be read.

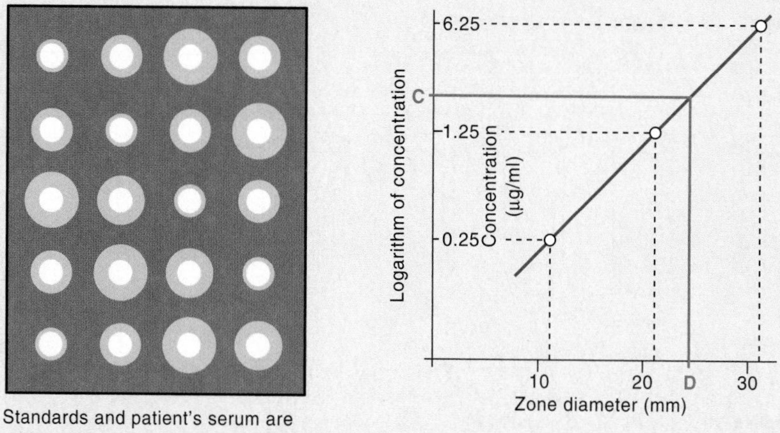

(a) Standards and patient's serum are added to agar that has been seeded with susceptible strain of bacteria.

(b) A standard curve that correlates the size of the zone with the concentration of antibiotic is constructed. The concentration of the antimicrobial drug in the body fluid can be read from the line relating zone size to concentration.

FIGURE 1 Biological Assay to Determine the Concentration of an Antimicrobial Drug in a Patient's Body Fluid

size, forming a concentration gradient of drug around each disc. A clear **zone of inhibition** around an antimicrobial disc reflects, in part, the degree of susceptibility of the organism to the drug. The zone size is also influenced by characteristics of the drug including its molecular weight and stability, as well as the amount in the disc.

Special charts have been prepared correlating the size of the zone of inhibition to susceptibility of bacteria to the drug. Based on the size of the zone, organisms can be described as susceptible, intermediate, or resistant to the drug. These seemingly simple categories reflect the extensive work of researchers who tested the antimicrobial sensitivity of a variety of bacteria that had a wide range of drug susceptibilities. For each organism, they determined the minimum inhibitory concentration of a particular antimicrobial drug and the size of the zone of inhibition around that antimicrobial disc. The correlation of MIC and zone size, along with the determination of the achievable blood levels of each of the various drugs, enabled the Kirby-Bauer disc diffusion test to become a standard method to guide physicians in prescribing appropriate antimicrobial drugs for treating patients.

Commercial Modifications of Antimicrobial Susceptibility Testing

Commercial modifications of the conventional methods offer certain advantages. They are less labor-intensive, and the results can be read in as little as 4 hours. One system utilizes a small card with miniature wells containing specific antimicrobial concentrations. The highly automated system inoculates and incubates the cards, determines the growth rate by reading the turbidity, and uses mathematical formulas to interpret the results and derive the MICs in 6 to 15 hours **(figure 21.11).**

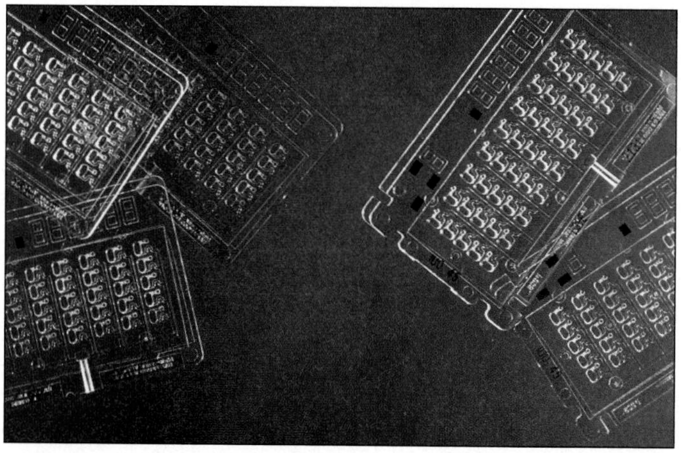

FIGURE 21.11 Automated Tests Used to Determine Antimicrobial Susceptibility The miniature wells in the card contain specific concentrations of an antimicrobial drug. An automated system inoculates and incubates the cards, determines the growth rate by reading turbidity, and uses mathematical formulas to interpret the results and derive the MICs.

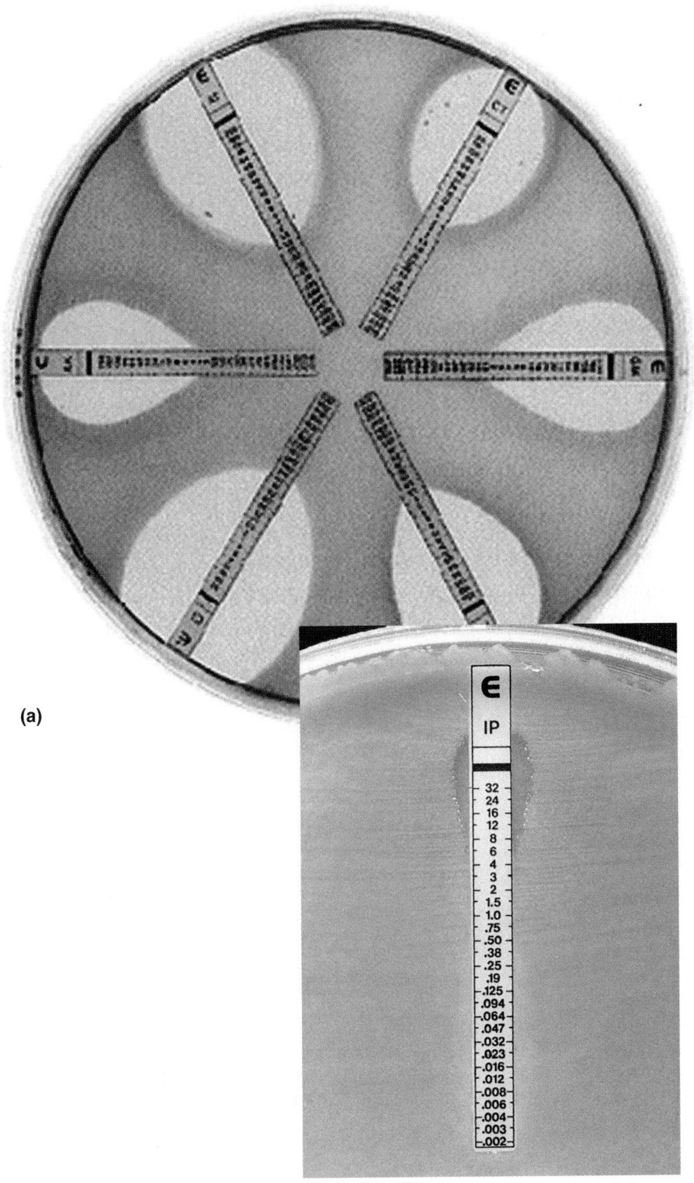

(a)

(b)

FIGURE 21.12 The E Test The strip is impregnated with a gradient of concentrations of a given antimicrobial drug. The MIC is determined by reading the number on the strip at the point at which growth intersects the strip.

The E test, a modification of the disc diffusion test, utilizes a strip impregnated with a gradient of concentrations of an antimicrobial drug. Multiple strips, each containing a different drug, are placed on the surface of an agar medium that has been uniformly inoculated with the test organism. During incubation the test organism will grow, and a zone of inhibition will form around the strip, but because of the gradient of drug concentrations, the zone of inhibition will be shaped somewhat like a teardrop that intersects the strip at some point **(figure 21.12).** The MIC is determined by reading a number off the numerical scale printed on the strip at the point where the bacterial growth intersects it.

MICROCHECK 21.4

The minimum inhibitory concentration and minimum bactericidal concentration are quantitative measures of a bacterial strain's susceptibility to an antimicrobial drug. Disc diffusion tests can determine whether an organism is sufficiently susceptible to a specific drug for it to successfully be used in treatment. Commercial tests for determining antimicrobial sensitivity are less labor-intensive and often more rapid.

- ✓ Explain the difference between the MIC and the MBC.
- ✓ List two factors other than an organism's sensitivity to a drug that can influence the size of the zone of inhibition around an antimicrobial disc.
- ✓ Why would it be important for the Kirby-Bauer disc diffusion test to use a standard concentration of the bacterial strain being tested?

21.5

Resistance to Antimicrobial Drugs

Focus Points

- Describe four general mechanisms of antimicrobial resistance.
- Describe how antimicrobial resistance can be acquired.
- List four examples of emerging antimicrobial resistance.
- Describe how the emergence and spread of antimicrobial resistance can be slowed.

After the introduction of sulfa drugs and penicillin, there was great hope that such drugs would soon eliminate most bacterial diseases. It is now recognized, however, that drug resistance limits the usefulness of all known antimicrobials. As these drugs are increasingly used and misused, the resistant bacterial strains have a selective advantage over their sensitive counterparts **(figure 21.13).** For example, when penicillin G was first introduced, less than 3% of *Staphylococcus aureus* strains were resistant to its effects. Heavy use of the drug, measured in hundreds of tons per year, progressively eliminated sensitive strains, so that 90% or more are now resistant. This development is understandably of great concern to health professionals because of the impact on the cost, complications, and outcomes of treatment. Understanding the mechanisms and the spread of antimicrobial resistance is an important step in curtailing the problem, and it may also allow pharmaceutical companies to develop new drugs that foil common resistance mechanisms.

Mechanisms of Acquired Resistance

Bacteria can resist the effects of antimicrobials through a variety of mechanisms. In some cases this resistance is innate, but in many others it is acquired. **Figure 21.14** depicts the most common mechanisms of acquired antimicrobial resistance.

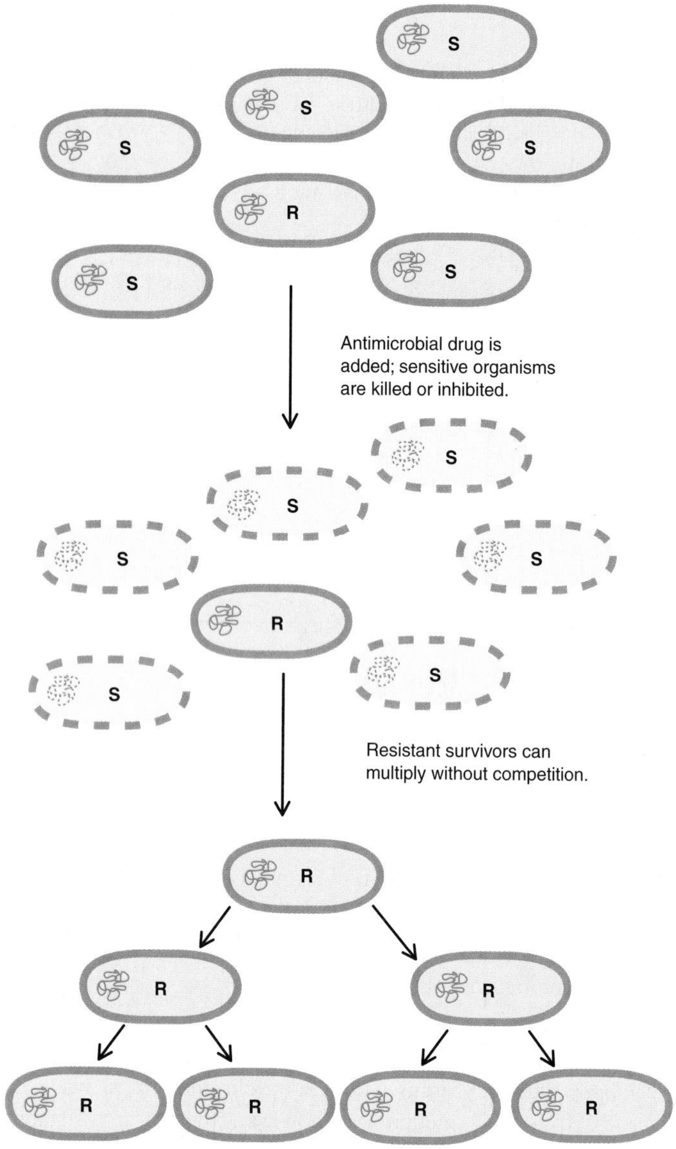
S
S
S
S
R
S
S
Antimicrobial drug is added; sensitive organisms are killed or inhibited.
S
S
S
S
R
S
S
Resistant survivors can multiply without competition.
R
R
R
R
R
R
R

FIGURE 21.13 The Selective Advantage of Drug Resistance When antimicrobial drugs are used, bacterial strains that are resistant (R) to their effects have a selective advantage over their sensitive (S) counterparts.

Drug-Inactivating Enzymes

Some organisms produce enzymes that chemically modify a specific drug in such a way as to render it ineffective. Recall that bacteria that synthesize the enzyme penicillinase are resistant to the bactericidal effects of penicillin. As another example, the enzyme chloramphenicol acetyltransferase chemically alters the antibiotic chloramphenicol.

Alteration in the Target Molecule

An antimicrobial drug generally acts by recognizing and binding to a specific target molecule in a bacterium, interfering with its function. Minor structural changes in the target can prevent the drug from binding. Alterations in the penicillin-binding proteins prevent β-lactam drugs from binding to them. Similarly, a change in the ribosomal RNA, the target for the macrolides, prevents those drugs from interfering with ribosome function.

Decreased Uptake of the Drug

The porin proteins in the outer membrane of Gram-negative bacteria selectively permit small hydrophobic molecules to enter a cell. Alterations in these proteins can therefore alter permeability and prevent certain drugs from entering the cell. By excluding entry of a drug, an organism avoids its effects. ■ porins, p. 62

Increased Elimination of the Drug

The systems that bacteria use to transport detrimental compounds out of a cell are called **efflux pumps.** Alterations that result in the increased expression of these pumps can increase the overall capacity of an organism to eliminate a drug, thus enabling the organism to resist higher concentrations of that drug. In addition, structural changes might influence the array of drugs that can be actively pumped out. Resistance that develops by this mechanism is particularly worrisome because it potentially enables an organism to become resistant to several drugs simultaneously. ■ efflux pumps, p. 59

Acquisition of Resistance

Antimicrobial resistance can be due to either spontaneous mutation, which alters existing genes, or acquisition of new genes (see figure 8.1). Acquisition of resistance through spontaneous

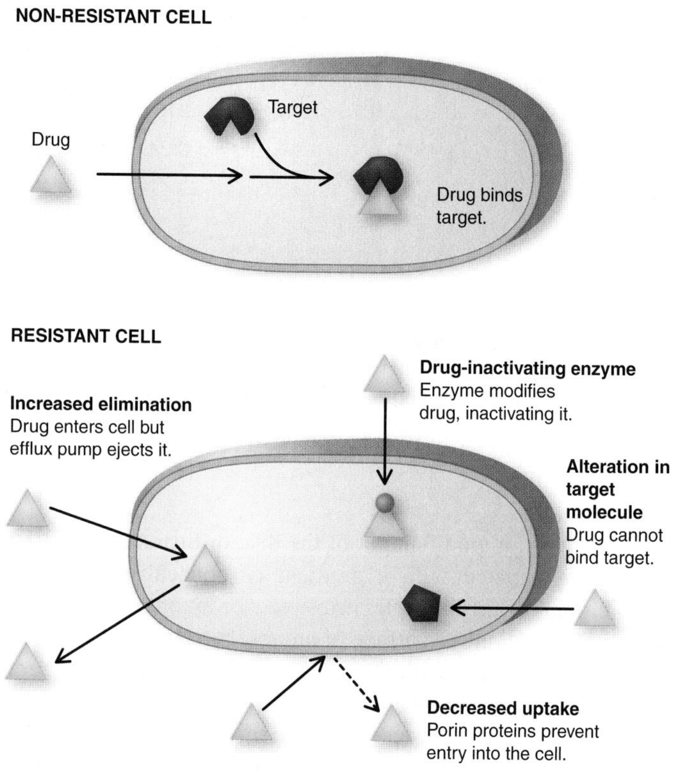
NON-RESISTANT CELL
Drug
Target
Drug binds target.
RESISTANT CELL
Increased elimination
Drug enters cell but efflux pump ejects it.
Drug-inactivating enzyme
Enzyme modifies drug, inactivating it.
Alteration in target molecule
Drug cannot bind target.
Decreased uptake
Porin proteins prevent entry into the cell.

FIGURE 21.14 Common Mechanisms of Acquired Antimicrobial Drug Resistance

mutation is called **vertical evolution,** because it affects only the progeny of the altered cell. In contrast, acquisition of resistance through gene transfer is called **horizontal evolution;** even entirely unrelated organisms can gain new traits this way.

Spontaneous Mutation

As cells replicate, spontaneous mutations occur at a relatively low rate. Even at a low rate, however, such mutations can ultimately have a profound effect on the resistance of a bacterial population to an antimicrobial drug. For instance, resistance to the aminoglycoside streptomycin results from a single base-pair change in the gene encoding the ribosomal protein to which streptomycin binds; that point mutation alters the target sufficiently to render the drug ineffective. When a streptomycin sensitive bacterium is grown in streptomycin-free medium to a population of 10^9 cells, it is probable that at least one cell in the population has that particular mutation in its genome. Through spontaneous mutation, that particular cell has acquired resistance to streptomycin. If streptomycin is then added to the medium, only that cell and its progeny will be able to replicate, generating a population of streptomycin-resistant clones.

When an antimicrobial drug has several different potential targets or has multiple binding sites on a single target, it is more difficult for an organism to develop resistance through spontaneous mutation. This is because several different mutations are required to prevent binding of the drug. Unlike streptomycin, the newer aminoglycosides bind to several sites on the ribosome, making resistance due to spontaneous mutation less likely.

Drugs such as streptomycin to which single point mutations can confer resistance are sometimes used in combination with one or more other drugs to prevent survival of resistant mutants. If any organism spontaneously develops resistance to one drug, another drug will still kill it. The chance of an organism simultaneously developing mutational resistance to multiple drugs is extremely low.

Gene Transfer

Given the mobility of DNA, genes encoding resistance to an antimicrobial drug can spread to different strains, species, and even genera. The most common mechanism of transfer of resistance is through the conjugative transfer of **R plasmids.** R plasmids frequently carry several different resistance genes, each one mediating resistance to a specific antimicrobial drug. Thus, when an organism acquires an R plasmid, it acquires resistance to several different medications simultaneously. ■ R plasmid, p. 209

In some cases, the resistance gene that was transferred from one organism to another originated through spontaneous mutation of a common bacterial gene, such as one encoding the target of the drug. In other cases, the gene may have originated from the soil microbe that naturally produces that antibiotic. For example, a gene coding for an enzyme that chemically modifies an aminoglycoside likely originated from the *Streptomyces* species that produces that aminoglycoside.

Examples of Emerging Antimicrobial Resistance

Some of the problems associated with the increasing resistance of bacteria to antimicrobial drugs are highlighted by the following examples.

Enterococci

One of the most dramatic examples of antimicrobial resistance is the enterococci, a group of bacteria that are part of the normal intestinal flora and a common cause of nosocomial infections. Enterococci are intrinsically less susceptible to many common antimicrobials. For example, their penicillin-binding proteins have low affinity for certain β-lactam antibiotics. In addition, many enterococci have plasmid-borne resistance genes. Some strains, called **vancomycin-resistant enterococci (VRE),** are even resistant to vancomycin. This drug is usually reserved as a last resort for treating life-threatening infections caused by Gram-positive organisms that are resistant to all β-lactam drugs. Because vancomycin resistance in these strains is encoded on a plasmid, the resistance is transferable to other organisms. ■ nosocomial infections, p. 487

Staphylococcus aureus

Staphylococcus aureus, another common cause of nosocomial infections, is becoming increasingly resistant to antimicrobials. Over the past 50 years, most strains have acquired resistance to penicillin due to their acquisition of a gene encoding the enzyme penicillinase. Up until recently, infections caused by these strains could be treated with methicillin or other penicillinase-resistant penicillins. New strains have emerged, however, that not only produce penicillinase, but also have penicillin-binding proteins with low affinity for all β-lactam drugs. These strains, called **methicillin-resistant *Staphylococcus aureus*** or **MRSA,** are resistant to methicillin as well as all other β-lactam drugs. Infections caused by these strains are generally treated with vancomycin. A few hospitals, however, have reported isolates that are no longer susceptible to normal levels of vancomycin. So far, strict hospital guidelines designed to immediately halt the spread of these **vancomycin-intermediate *S. aureus*** **(VISA)** and **vancomycin-resistant *S. aureus*** **(VRSA)** strains have been successful.
■ *Staphylococcus aureus,* p. 525

Streptococcus pneumoniae

Until recently, *Streptococcus pneumoniae,* the leading cause of pneumonia in adults, has remained exquisitely sensitive to penicillin. Some isolates, however, are now resistant to the drug. This acquired resistance is due not to the production of a β-lactamase, but rather to modifications in the chromosomal genes coding for four different penicillin-binding proteins, decreasing their affinities for the drug. The nucleotide changes do not appear to have arisen through a series of point mutations as one might expect; instead, they are due to the acquisition of chromosomal DNA from other species of *Streptococcus.* As you may recall from earlier reading, *S. pneumoniae* undergoes DNA-mediated transformation.
■ *Streptococcus pneumoniae,* p. 588 ■ DNA-mediated transformation, p. 205

Mycobacterium tuberculosis

Treatment of *Mycobacterium tuberculosis* active infections has always been a long and complicated process, requiring a combination of two or more different drugs taken for a period of 6 months or more. Unfortunately, the first-line drugs (the preferred therapeutic agents) are often those to which spontaneous mutations readily occur. Because large numbers of organisms are found in an active infection, the probability that one has developed spontaneous resistance to a single drug is likely, which is why multiple drug therapy is required. The length of treatment is due to the tediously slow growth of *M. tuberculosis.* ■ *Mycobacterium tuberculosis,* p. 593

Many tuberculosis patients do not comply with the complex treatment regime, skipping doses or stopping treatment too soon, and as a consequence, strains of *M. tuberculosis* are developing resistance to the first-line drugs. This results in even lengthier, more costly treatments that are also less effective. Strains that are resistant to two of the favored drugs for tuberculosis treatment, isoniazid and rifampin, are called **multiple-drug-resistant *M. tuberculosis*** or **MDR-TB.** To prevent the emergence of these strains, some cities are utilizing **directly observed therapy** in which health care workers routinely visit patients in the community and watch them take their drugs to ensure they comply with their prescribed antimicrobial treatment.

Slowing the Emergence and Spread of Antimicrobial Resistance

To reverse the alarming trend of increasing antimicrobial resistance, everyone must cooperate. On an individual level, physicians as well as the general public must take more responsibility for the appropriate use of these life-saving drugs. On a global scale, countries around the world need to make important policy decisions about what is, and what is not, an appropriate use of these medications.

The Responsibilities of Physicians and Other Health Care Workers

Physicians and other health care workers need to increase their efforts to identify the specific causative agent of a given infection and only if appropriate, prescribe suitable antimicrobials. They must also educate their patients about the proper use of prescribed drugs in order to increase patient compliance. While these efforts may be more expensive in the short term, they will ultimately save both lives and money.

The Responsibilities of Patients

Patients need to carefully follow the instructions that accompany their prescriptions, even if those instructions seem inconvenient. It is essential to maintain the concentration of the antimicrobial in the blood at the required level for a specific time period. When a patient skips a scheduled dose of a drug, the blood level of the drug may not remain high enough to inhibit the growth of the least sensitive members of the population. If these less sensitive organisms then have a chance to grow, they will give rise to a population that is not as sensitive as the original. Likewise, failure to complete the prescribed course of treatment may not kill the least sensitive organisms, allowing their subsequent multiplication. Misusing antimicrobials by skipping doses or failing to complete the prescribed duration of treatment promotes the gradual emergence of resistant organisms. In essence, the patient is selecting for the step-wise development of resistant mutants.

The Importance of an Educated Public

A greater effort must also be made to educate the public about the appropriateness and limitations of antibiotics in order to ensure they are utilized wisely. First and foremost, people need to understand that antibiotics are not effective against viruses. Taking antibiotics will not cure the common cold or any other viral illness. A few antiviral drugs are available, but they are effective against only a limited group of viruses such as HIV and herpesviruses. Unfortunately, surveys indicate that far too many people erroneously believe that antibiotics are effective against viruses and often seek prescriptions to "cure" viral infections. This misuse only selects for antibiotic-resistant bacteria in the normal flora. Even though these organisms are not pathogenic themselves, they can serve as a reservoir for R plasmids, eventually transferring their resistance genes to an infecting pathogen.

Global Impacts of the Use of Antimicrobial Drugs

Worldwide, there is growing concern about the overuse of antimicrobial drugs. Countries may vary in their laws and social norms, but antimicrobial resistance recognizes no political boundaries. An organism that develops resistance in one country can quickly be transported globally. In many parts of the world, particularly in developing countries, antimicrobial drugs are available on a nonprescription basis. Because of the consequences of inappropriate use, there is a growing opinion that over-the-counter availability of these drugs should be curtailed or eliminated. Another worldwide concern is the use of antimicrobial drugs in animal feeds. Low levels of these drugs in feeds result in larger, more economically productive animals, and therefore, less expensive meat, a seemingly attractive option. This use, like any other, however, selects for drug-resistant organisms, which has caused some scientists to question its ultimate wisdom. In fact, infections caused by drug-resistant *Salmonella* strains have been linked to animals whose feed was supplemented with those drugs. In response to these concerns, there is growing pressure worldwide to ban the use of antimicrobial drugs in animal feeds.

MICROCHECK 21.5

Mutations and transfer of genetic information have enabled microorganisms to develop resistance to each new antimicrobial drug developed. Drug resistance affects the cost, complications, and outcomes of medical treatment. Slowing the emergence and spread of resistant microbes involves the cooperation of health care personnel, educators, and the general public.

- ✓ Explain how using a combination of two antimicrobial drugs helps prevent the development of spontaneously resistant mutants.
- ✓ Explain the significance of a member of the normal flora that harbors an R plasmid.
- ✓ A student argued that "spontaneous mutation" meant that a drug could cause mutations. Is the student correct? Why or why not?

21.6

Mechanisms of Action of Antiviral Drugs

Focus Points

- Describe the antiviral drugs that interfere with viral uncoating.
- Describe the antiviral drugs that interfere with nucleic acid synthesis.
- Describe the antiviral drugs that interfere with the assembly and release of viral particles.

Viruses rely almost exclusively on the host cell's metabolic machinery for their replication, making them extremely difficult targets for selective toxicity. Viruses have no cell wall, ribosomes, or any other structure targeted by commonly used antibiotics. Thus, they are completely unaffected by antibiotics. Some viruses encode their own polymerases, however, and these are potential targets of antiviral drugs **(figure 21.15).** Relatively few other targets have been discovered.

Many researchers and pharmaceutical companies are currently trying to develop more effective antiviral drugs. The relatively few drugs available are generally effective against only a specific type of virus; none can eliminate latent viral infections. **Table 21.2** summarizes the characteristics of the most common antiviral drugs. ■ latent viral infections, p. 347

Viral Uncoating

After a virus enters a host cell, the protein coat must dissociate from the nucleic acid in order for replication to occur. Drugs that interfere with the uncoating step thus prevent viral replication. The only effective drugs that target this step, however, are those that block influenza A viruses. ■ influenza A virus, p. 598

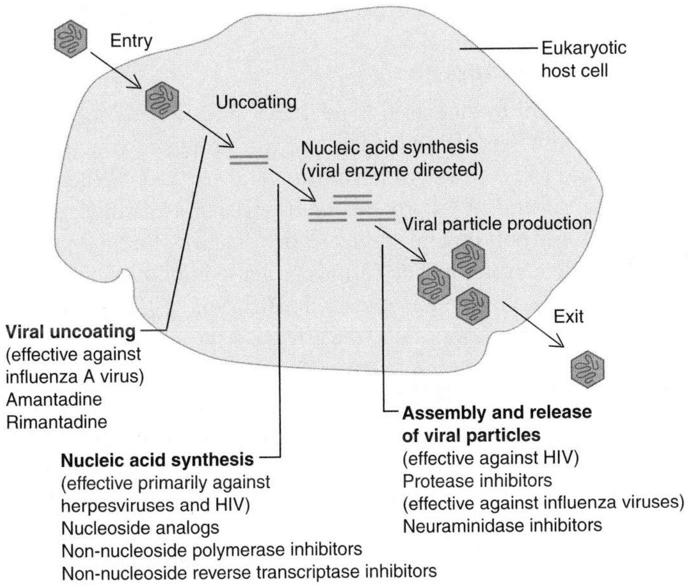

FIGURE 21.15 Targets of Antiviral Drugs

Amantadine and Rimantadine

Two drugs, amantadine and rimantadine, which are similar in both their chemical structure and mechanism of action, block the uncoating of influenza A virus after it enters a cell. Consequently, they prevent or reduce the severity and duration of the disease. The drugs are only used until active immunization can be achieved, since immunization is important for long-term protection. Unfortunately, resistance develops frequently and may eventually limit the usefulness of the drugs.

Nucleic Acid Synthesis

Many of the most effective antiviral drugs exploit the error-prone virally encoded enzymes used to replicate viral nucleic acid. With few exceptions, however, the use of these drugs is generally limited to treating infections caused by the herpesviruses and HIV.

Nucleoside Analogs

A growing number of antiviral drugs are **nucleoside analogs,** compounds similar in structure to a nucleoside. These analogs can be phosphorylated *in vivo* by a virally encoded or normal cellular enzyme to form a **nucleotide analog,** a chemical structurally similar to the nucleotides of DNA and RNA. In some cases, incorporation of the nucleotide analog results in termination of the growing nucleotide chain. In other cases, incorporation of the analog results in a defective strand with altered base-pairing properties. ■ nucleotide, p. 33 ■ DNA sequencing, pp. 230, 236

The basis for the selective toxicity of most nucleoside analogs is the fact that virally encoded enzymes are much more prone to incorporating the corresponding nucleotide analogs than are host polymerases. Thus, more damage is done to the rapidly replicating viral genome than to host cells. The analogs, however, are only effective against replicating viruses. Because viruses such as herpesvirus and HIV can remain latent in cells, the drugs do not cure these infections; they simply limit the duration of the active infection. Latent virus can still undergo reactivation, causing a reoccurrence of symptoms.

Most nucleoside analogs are reserved for severe infections because of their significant side effects. An important exception to this principle is **acyclovir,** a drug used to treat herpesvirus infections. This drug causes little harm to uninfected cells because the conversion of acyclovir to a nucleotide analog does not utilize a normal cellular enzyme but instead requires a virally encoded enzyme. The enzyme is only present in cells infected by herpesviruses such as herpes simplex virus (HSV) and varicella-zoster virus (VZV). Thus, acyclovir does not get converted to a nucleotide analog in uninfected cells. Other nucleoside analogs include ganciclovir, which is used to treat life-threatening or sight-threatening cytomegalovirus (CMV) infections in immunocompromised patients, and ribavirin, which is used to treat respiratory syncytial virus infections (RSV) in newborns. ■ herpes simplex virus, pp. 619, 670 ■ varicella-zoster, p. 536

TABLE 21.2 Characteristics of Antiviral Drugs

Target/Drug Examples	Comments/Characteristics
Viral Uncoating	
Amantadine and rimantadine	Used to treat influenza A infections.
Nucleic Acid Synthesis	
Nucleoside analogs Acyclovir, ganciclovir, ribavirin, zidovudine (AZT), didanosine (ddl), lamivudine (3TC)	Primarily used to treat infections caused by herpesviruses and HIV; they do not cure latent infections. The drugs are converted within eukaryotic cells to a nucleotide analog; virally encoded enzymes are prone to incorporate these, resulting in premature termination of synthesis or improper base-pairing of the viral nucleic acid. Acyclovir is used to treat herpes simplex virus (HSV) and varicella-zoster virus (VZV) infections. Ganciclovir is used to treat cytomegalovirus infections in immunocompromised patients. Ribavirin is used to treat respiratory syncytial virus (RSV) infections in newborns. Combinations of nucleoside analogs such as zidovudine (AZT), didanosine (ddl), and lamivudine (3TC) are used to treat HIV infections.
Non-nucleoside polymerase inhibitors Foscarnet	Primarily used to treat infections caused by herpesviruses. They inhibit the activity of viral polymerases by binding to a site other than the nucleotide-binding site. Foscarnet is used to treat ganciclovir-resistant cytomegalovirus (CMV) and acyclovir-resistant herpes simplex virus (HSV).
Non-nucleoside reverse transcriptase inhibitors Nevirapine, delavirdine, efavirenz	Used to treat HIV infections. They inhibit the activity of reverse transcriptase by binding to a site other than the nucleotide-binding site and are often used in combination with nucleoside analogs.
Assembly and Release of Viral Particles	
Protease inhibitors Indinavir, ritonavir, saquinavir, nelfinavir	Used to treat HIV infections. They inhibit protease, an essential enzyme of HIV, by binding to its active site.
Neuraminidase inhibitors Zanamivir, oseltamivir	Used to treat influenza virus infections.

A number of different nucleoside analogs are used to treat HIV infection by interfering with the activity of reverse transcriptase. Unfortunately, the virus rapidly develops mutational resistance against these drugs, which is why they are often used in combination with other anti-HIV drugs. Nucleoside analogs that interfere with reverse transcription include zidovudine (AZT), didanosine (ddI), and lamivudine (3TC). Two of these are often used in combination for HIV therapy.

Non-Nucleoside Polymerase Inhibitors

Non-nucleoside polymerase inhibitors are compounds that inhibit the activity of viral polymerases by binding to a site other than the nucleotide-binding site. One example, foscarnet, is used to treat infections caused by ganciclovir-resistant CMV and acyclovir-resistant HSV.

Non-Nucleoside Reverse Transcriptase Inhibitors

Non-nucleoside reverse transcriptase inhibitors inhibit the activity of reverse transcriptase by binding to a site other than the nucleotide-binding site. They are often used in combination with nucleoside analogs to treat HIV infections. The medications include nevirapine, delavirdine, and efavirenz.

Assembly and Release of Viral Particles

Virally encoded enzymes required for the production and release of viral particles are the targets of medications used to treat certain viral infections.

Protease Inhibitors

Protease inhibitors are used to treat HIV infections. These medications inhibit the HIV-encoded enzyme protease, which plays an essential role in the production of viral particles. When HIV replicates, several of its proteins are translated as a single amino acid chain, or polyprotein; protease then cleaves the polyprotein into individual proteins. The various protease inhibitors, including indinavir, ritonavir, saquinavir, and nelfinavir, differ in several aspects including dosage and side effects. ■ HIV protease, p. 737

Neuraminidase Inhibitors

Neuraminidase inhibitors inhibit **neuraminidase,** an enzyme encoded by influenza viruses that is essential for the release of infectious viral particles from infected cells. Two neuraminidase inhibitors are currently available—zanamivir, which is administered by inhalation, and oseltamivir, which is administered orally. Both limit the duration of influenza infections when taken within two days of the onset of symptoms.

MICROCHECK 21.6

Viral replication generally uses host cell machinery; thus, there are few targets for selectively toxic antiviral drugs. Most antiviral drugs are virus-specific and target nucleic acid synthesis.

- ✓ Explain why acyclovir has fewer side effects than do other nucleoside analogs.
- ✓ Why are nucleoside analogs active only against replicating viruses?

21.7 Mechanisms of Action of Antifungal Drugs

Focus Points

- Describe the antifungal drugs that interfere with plasma membrane synthesis and function.
- Describe the mechanism of echinocandins.
- Describe the mechanism of griseofulvin.
- Describe the mechanism of flucytosine.

Eukaryotic pathogens such as fungi more closely resemble human cells than do bacteria. It is not surprising, therefore, that relatively few drugs are available for systemic use against fungal pathogens. The targets of antifungal drugs are illustrated in **figure 21.16. Table 21.3** summarizes the characteristics of the most common antifungal drugs.

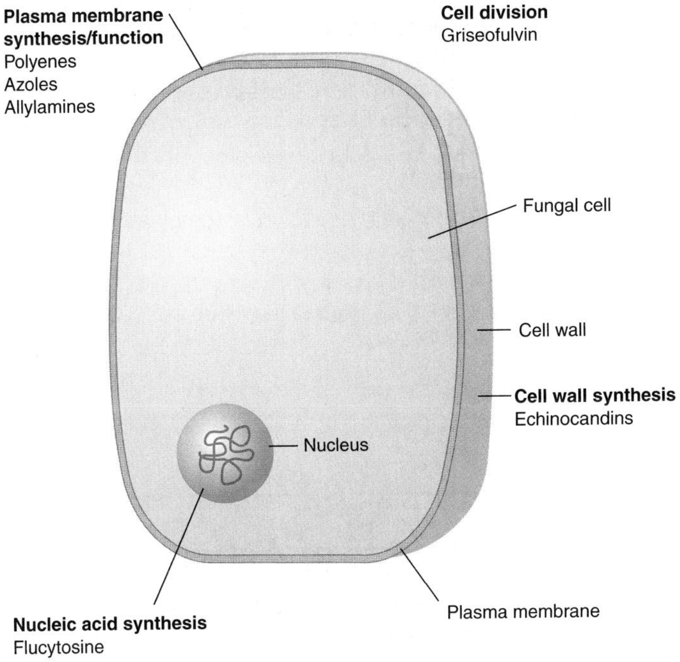

FIGURE 21.16 Targets of Antifungal Drugs

Plasma Membrane Synthesis and Function

The target of most antifungal drugs is the chemical compound **ergosterol,** which is found in the plasma membrane of fungal but not human cells.

Polyenes

The polyenes, a group of antibiotics produced by *Streptomyces,* bind to ergosterol. This disrupts the fungal membrane, causing leakage of the cytoplasmic contents and leading to cell death. Unfortunately, the polyenes are quite toxic to humans, which limits their systemic use to life-threatening infections. Amphotericin B causes severe side effects, but it is the most effective drug for treating many systemic infections. Newer lipid-based emulsions are less toxic but are more expensive. Nystatin is too toxic to be given systemically, but it is used topically.

Azoles

The **azoles** are a large family of chemically synthesized drugs, some of which have antifungal activity. They include two classes, the imidazoles and the newer triazoles; the latter are generally less toxic. Both classes inhibit the synthesis of ergosterol, resulting in defective fungal membranes that leak cytoplasmic contents. Fluconazole and itraconazole, which are triazoles, are increasingly being used to treat systemic fungal infections. Ketoconazole, an imidazole, is also used systemically, but it is associated with more severe side effects. Other imidazoles, including miconazole and clotrimazole, are commonly used in nonprescription creams, ointments, and suppositories to treat vaginal yeast infections. They are also used topically to treat dermatophyte infections. ■ dermatophyte, p. 545

Allylamines

The **allylamines** inhibit an enzyme in the pathway of ergosterol synthesis. Naftifine and terbinafine can be administered topically to treat dermatophyte infections. Terbinafine can also be taken orally.

Cell Wall Synthesis

Fungal cell walls contain some components not produced by animal cells. Synthesis of these is an effective target for antifungal medications.

Echinocandins

Echinocandins are a family of antifungal agents that interfere with synthesis of the β-1, 3 glucan component of fungal cell walls. Caspofungin, the first member to be approved, is used to treat *Candida* infections as well as invasive aspergillosis that resists other treatments.

Cell Division

The target of one antifungal drug, griseofulvin, is cell division.

Griseofulvin

The exact mechanism of **griseofulvin** is unknown, but it appears to interfere with the action of tubulin, a necessary factor in

TABLE 21.3 Characteristics of Antifungal Drugs

Drug Target/Drug	Comments
Plasma Membrane	
Polyenes Amphotericin B, nystatin	Bind to ergosterol, disrupting the plasma membrane and causing leakage of the cytoplasm. Amphotericin B is very toxic but the most effective drug for treating life-threatening infections; newer lipid-based emulsions are less toxic but very expensive. Nystatin is too toxic for systemic use, but it can be used topically.
Azoles *Imidazoles:* ketoconazole, miconazole, clotrimazole *Triazoles:* fluconazole, itraconazole	Interfere with ergosterol synthesis, leading to defective cell membranes; active against a wide variety of fungi. Used to treat a variety of systemic and localized fungal infections. Triazoles are less toxic than imidazoles.
Allylamines Naftifine, terbinafine	Inhibit an enzyme in the pathway of ergosterol synthesis. Administered topically to treat dermatophyte infections. Terbinafine can be taken orally.
Cell Wall Synthesis	
Echinocandins Capsofungin	Interfere with β-1,3 glucan synthesis. Used to treat *Candida* infections as well as invasive aspergillosis that resists other treatments.
Cell Division	
Griseofulvin	Used to treat skin and nail infections. Taken orally for months; concentrates in the dead keratinized layers of the skin; taken up by fungi invading those cells and inhibits their division. Active only against fungi that invade keratinized cells.
Nucleic Acid Synthesis	
Flucytosine	Used to treat systemic yeast infections; enzymes within yeast cells convert the drug to 5-fluorouracil, which inhibits an enzyme required for nucleic acid synthesis; not effective against most molds; resistant mutants are common.

nuclear division. Because tubulin is a part of all eukaryotic cells, the selective toxicity of this drug may be due to its greater uptake by fungal cells. When the drug is taken orally for months, it is absorbed and eventually concentrated in the dead keratinized layers of the skin. The fungi that then invade keratin containing structures such as skin and nails take up the drug, which prevents their multiplication. It is only active against fungi that invade keratinized cells and is used to treat skin and nail infections. ■ **tubulin, p. 77** ■ **keratin, p. 522**

Nucleic Acid Synthesis

Nucleic acid synthesis is a common feature of all eukaryotic cells, which generally makes it a poor target for antifungal drugs. The drug flucytosine, however, is taken up by yeast cells and then converted by yeast enzymes to an active, inhibitory form.

Flucytosine

Flucytosine is a synthetic derivative of cytosine, one of the pyrimidines found in nucleic acids. Enzymes within infecting yeast cells convert flucytosine to 5-fluorouracil, which inhibits an enzyme required for nucleic acid synthesis. Unfortunately, resistant mutants are common, and therefore, flucytosine, is used mostly in combination with amphotericin B or as an alternative drug for patients with systemic yeast infections who are unable to tolerate amphotericin B. Flucytosine is not effective against molds.

MICROCHECK 21.7

Because fungi are eukaryotic cells, there are relatively few targets for selectively toxic antifungal drugs. Most antifungal drugs interfere with the function or synthesis of ergosterol, which is found in the membrane of fungal but not human cells. Other targets of antifungal drugs include cell wall synthesis, cell division, and nucleic acid synthesis.

- ✓ Why is amphotericin B, a polyene, used only for treating life-threatening infections?
- ✓ Why is flucytosine generally used only in combination with other drugs?
- ✓ If griseofulvin were not concentrated in keratin containing structures, would it still be toxic to fungi that invade these structures? Why or why not?

21.8 Mechanisms of Action of Antiprotozoan and Antihelminthic Drugs

Focus Point

- Describe five antiprotozoan drugs and four antihelminthic drugs.

Most antiparasitic drugs probably interfere with biosynthetic pathways of protozoan parasites or the neuromuscular function of worms. Unfortunately, compared with antibacterial, antifungal, and antiviral drugs, little research and development goes into these drugs, because most parasitic diseases are concentrated in the poorer areas of the world where people simply cannot afford to spend money on expensive medications.

Some of the most important antiparasitic drugs and their characteristics are summarized in **table 21.4.**

TABLE 21.4 Characteristics of Some Antiprotozoan and Antihelminthic Drugs

Causative Agent/Drug	Comments
Intestinal protozoa	
Iodoquinol	Mechanism unknown. Poorly absorbed but taken orally to eliminate amebic cysts in the intestine.
Nitroimidazoles Metronidazole	Activated by the metabolism of anaerobic organisms. Interferes with electron transfer and alters DNA. Does not reliably eliminate the cyst stage. Metronidazole is also used to treat infections caused by anaerobic bacteria.
Quinacrine	Mechanism of action is unknown, but it may be due to interference with nucleic acid synthesis.
Plasmodium (Malaria) and Toxoplasma	
Folate antagonists Pyrimethamine, sulfonamide	Interferes with folate metabolism. Used to treat toxoplasmosis and malaria.
Malarone®	A synergistic combination of atovaquone and proguanil hydrochloride used to treat malaria. Atovaquone interferes with mitochondrial electron transport while proguanil disrupts folate synthesis. The combination is active against both the blood stage and early liver stage of *Plasmodium* species.
Quinolones Chloroquine, mefloquine, primaquine, tafenoquine	The mechanism of action is not completely clear. Chloroquine is concentrated in infected red blood cells and is the drug of choice for preventing or treating the red blood cell stage of the malarial parasite. Its effects may be due to inhibition of an enzyme that protects the parasite from the toxic by-products of hemoglobin degradation. Primaquine and tafenoquine destroy the liver stage of the parasite and are used to treat relapsing forms of malaria. Mefloquine is used to treat infection caused by chloroquine-resistant strains of the malarial parasite.
Trypanosomes and Leishmania	
Eflornithine	Used to treat infections caused by some types of *Trypanosoma.* It inhibits the enzyme ornithine decarboxylase.
Heavy metals Melarsoprol, sodium stibogluconate, meglumine antimonate	These inactivate sulfhydryl groups of parasitic enzymes, but they are very toxic to host cells as well. Melarsoprol is used to treat trypanosomiasis, but the treatment itself is often lethal. Sodium stibogluconate and meglumine antimonate are used to treat leishmaniasis.
Nitrofurtimox	Widely used to treat acute Chagas' disease; it forms reactive oxygen radicals that are toxic to the parasite as well as the host.
Intestinal and Tissue Helminths	
Avermectins Ivermectin	Ivermectin causes neuromuscular paralysis in parasites. It is used to treat infections caused by *Strongyloides* and tissue nematodes.
Benzimidazoles Mebendazole, thiabendazole, albendazole	Mebendazole binds to tubulin of helminths, blocking microtubule assembly and inhibiting glucose uptake. It is poorly absorbed in the intestine, making it effective for treating intestinal, but not tissue, helminths. Thiabendazole may have a similar mechanism, but it is well absorbed and has many toxic side effects. Albendazole is used to treat tissue infections caused by *Echinococcus* and *Taenia solium.*
Phenols Niclosamide	Absorbed by cestodes in the intestinal tract, but not by the human host.
Piperazines Piperazine, diethylcarbamazine	Piperazine causes a flaccid paralysis in worms and can be used to treat infections caused by *Ascaris.* Diethylcarbamazine immobilizes filarial worms and alters their surface, which enhances killing by the immune system. The resulting inflammatory response, however, causes tissue damage.
Pyrazinoisoquinolines Praziquantel	A single dose of praziquantel is effective in eliminating a wide variety of trematodes and cestodes. It is taken up but not metabolized by the worm, ultimately causing tetanic contractions of the worm.
Tetrahydropyrimidines Pyrantel pamoate, oxantel	Pyrantel pamoate interferes with neuromuscular activity of worms, causing a type of paralysis. It is not readily absorbed from the gastrointestinal tract and is active against intestinal worms including pinworm, hookworm, and *Ascaris.* Oxantel can be used to treat *Trichuris* infections.

FUTURE CHALLENGES

War with the Superbugs

With respect to antimicrobial drugs, the future challenge is already upon us. The challenge is to maintain the effectiveness of antimicrobials by (1) preventing the continued spread of resistance, and (2) developing new drugs that have even more desirable properties. New ways must be developed to fight infections caused by the ever greater numbers of bacterial strains that are resistant to the effects of conventional antimicrobial drugs. Several strategies are being used to develop potential weapons against these "superbugs."

One way to combat resistance is to continue developing modifications of existing antimicrobial drugs. Researchers constantly work to modify drugs chemically, trying to keep at least one step ahead of bacterial resistance. Another method to foil drug resistance is to interfere with the resistance mechanism itself, as is done currently in using β-lactamase inhibitors in combination with β-lactam drugs to protect the antimicrobial drug from enzymatic destruction. Likewise, it may be possible to thwart resistance using other mechanisms—for example, developing chemicals that can be used to inactivate or interfere with bacterial efflux systems.

Other researchers are focusing on developing new drugs that are entirely unrelated to conventional antimicrobials. One example is a class of compounds called **defensins,** which are short peptides, approximately 29 to 35 amino acids in length, produced naturally by a variety of eukaryotic cells to fight infections. Various defensins and related compounds are being intensively studied as promising antimicrobials.

Accumulating knowledge of the genetic sequences of pathogens and identification of genes associated with pathogenicity may allow development of antimicrobials that interfere directly with those processes. The "master switch" that controls expression of virulence determinants is one such potential target. Nucleotide sequence information and determination of the three-dimensional conformation of proteins may uncover new targets for antimicrobial drug therapy.

SUMMARY

21.1 History and Development of Antimicrobial Drugs

Discovery of Antimicrobial Drugs

Salvarsan, developed by Paul Ehrlich, was the first documented example of an antimicrobial medication.

Discovery of Antibiotics

Alexander Fleming discovered that a species of the fungus *Penicillium* produces **penicillin,** which kills some bacteria.

Development of New Generations of Drugs

Antimicrobial drugs can be chemically modified to give them new properties.

21.2 Features of Antimicrobial Drugs

Most modern antibiotics come from *Streptomyces* and *Bacillus* (bacteria) and *Penicillium* and *Cephalosporium* (fungi)

Selective Toxicity

Medically useful antimicrobials are **selectively toxic;** the relative toxicity of a drug is expressed as the **therapeutic index.**

Antimicrobial Action

Bacteriostatic drugs inhibit the growth of bacteria; drugs that kill bacteria are **bactericidal.**

Spectrum of Activity

Broad-spectrum antimicrobials affect a wide range of bacteria; those that affect a narrow range are called **narrow-spectrum.**

Tissue Distribution, Metabolism, and Excretion of the Drug

Some antimicrobials cross the blood-brain barrier into the cerebrospinal fluid; these can be used to treat meningitis.

Drugs that are unstable in acid must be administered through injection.

Drugs that have a long **half-life** need to be administered less frequently.

Effects of Combinations of Antimicrobial Drugs

Combinations of antimicrobial drugs may be **synergistic, antagonistic,** or **additive.**

Adverse Effects

Some people develop allergies to certain antimicrobials.

Some antimicrobials can have potentially damaging side effects such as kidney damage.

When the composition of the normal flora is altered, which happens when a person takes antimicrobials, pathogens normally unable to compete may grow to high numbers.

Resistance to Antimicrobials

The resistance of certain types of bacteria to a particular drug is **intrinsic** or **innate.**

Previously sensitive microorganisms can develop resistance through spontaneous mutation or the acquisition of new genetic information.

Cost

Newly introduced drugs are generally far more expensive than their traditional counterparts.

21.3 Mechanisms of Actions of Antibacterial Drugs (Table 21.1, Figure 21.2)

Antibacterial Medications That Inhibit Cell Wall Synthesis (Figure 21.3)

The β-lactam drugs, which include the **penicillins, cephalosporins, carbapenems,** and **monobactams,** irreversibly inhibit **penicillin-binding proteins (PBPs),** ultimately leading to cell lysis. (figure 21.4)

Vancomycin binds to the terminal amino acids of the peptide side chain of NAM, blocking peptidoglycan synthesis.

Bacitracin interferes with the transport of peptidoglycan precursors across the cytoplasmic membrane; it is a common ingredient in non-prescription ointments.

Antibacterial Medications That Inhibit Protein Synthesis (Figure 21.7)

Antibiotics that inhibit protein synthesis by binding to the 70S ribosome include the **aminoglycosides,** the **tetracyclines,** the **macrolides, chloramphenicol,** the **lincosamides,** the **oxazolidinones,** and the **streptogramins.**

Antibacterial Medications That Inhibit Nucleic Acid Synthesis

The **fluoroquinolones** interfere with DNA replication and transcription by inhibiting one or more topoisomerases.

The **rifamycins** block prokaryotic RNA polymerase from initiating transcription.

Antibacterial Medications That Inhibit Metabolic Pathways (Figure 21.8)

Sulfa drugs competitively inhibit an enzyme in the metabolic pathway leading to folic acid synthesis because they are structurally similar to a substrate in the pathway.

Trimethoprim inhibits the enzyme that catalyzes a metabolic step following the one inhibited by sulfonamides.

Antibacterial Medications That Interfere with Cell Membrane Integrity

Polymyxin B damages bacterial membranes.

Daptomycin damages the cytoplasmic membrane.

Antibacterial Medications That Interfere with Processes Essential to Mycobacterium tuberculosis

First-line medications that specifically target *Mycobacterium* species include **isoniazid, ethambutol,** and **pyrazinamide.**

21.4 Determining the Susceptibility of a Bacterial Strain to an Antimicrobial Drug

Determining the Minimum Inhibitory and Bactericidal Concentrations (Figure 21.9)

The **minimum inhibitory concentration (MIC)** is the lowest concentration of a specific antimicrobial drug needed to prevent the growth of a given organism *in vitro.*

The **minimum bactericidal concentration (MBC)** is the lowest concentration of a specific antimicrobial drug that kills 99.9% of cells of a given strain of bacterial *in vitro.*

Conventional Disc Diffusion Method (Figure 21.10)

The **Kirby-Bauer disc diffusion test** qualitatively determines the susceptibility of a bacterial strain to a battery of antimicrobial drugs.

Commercial Modifications of Antimicrobial Susceptibility Testing (Figure 21.11)

Automated methods can determine antimicrobial susceptibility in as little as 4 hours.

21.5 Resistance to Antimicrobial Drugs (Figure 21.13)

Mechanisms of Acquired Resistance (Figure 21.14)

Enzymes that chemically modify a drug render it ineffective.

Structural changes in the target can prevent the drug from binding.

Altered porin proteins prevent drugs from entering cells.

Efflux pumps actively pump drugs out of cells.

Acquisition of Resistance

Vertical evolution is the acquisition of resistance through spontaneous mutation; **horizontal evolution** is the acquisition of resistance through gene transfer.

The most common mechanism of transfer of antibiotic resistance genes is through the conjugative transfer of **R plasmids.**

Examples of Emerging Antimicrobial Resistance

Vancomycin-resistant enterococci (VRE), methicillin-resistant *Staphylococcus aureus* (MRSA), vancomycin-intermediate *S. aureus* (VISA), vancomycin-resistant *S. aureus* (VRSA), penicillin-resistant *Streptococcus pneumoniae,* and multiple-drug-resistant *Mycobacterium tuberculosis* (MDR-TB) are all examples of emerging antimicrobial resistance.

Slowing the Emergence and Spread of Antimicrobial Resistance

Physicians should prescribe antimicrobial medications only when appropriate.

The public must be educated about the appropriateness and limitations of antimicrobial therapy. Patients need to carefully follow prescribed instructions when taking antimicrobials.

21.6 Mechanisms of Action of Antiviral Drugs (Figure 21.15, Table 21.2)

Viral Uncoating

Amantadine and **rimantadine** block the uncoating of influenza A virus after it enters a cell.

Nucleic Acid Synthesis

Most antiviral drugs take advantage of the error-prone virally encoded enzymes used to replicate viral nucleic acid.

Nucleoside analogs are phosphorylated *in vivo* to form **nucleotide analogs;** when these are incorporated into viral DNA they interfere with replication.

Assembly and Release of Viral Particles

Protease inhibitors bind to and inhibit protease, the enzyme required for the production of infectious HIV particles.

Neuraminidase inhibitors interfere with the release of influenza virus particles from a cell.

21.7 Mechanisms of Action of Antifungal Drugs (Figure 21.16, Table 21.3)

Plasma Membrane Synthesis and Function

The **polyenes** disrupt fungal cell membranes by binding to ergosterol.

The **azoles** inhibit the synthesis of ergosterol.

The **allylamines** inhibit an enzyme in the pathway of ergosterol synthesis.

Cell Wall Synthesis

Echinocandins interfere with the synthesis of β-1, 3 glucan.

Cell Division

Griseofulvin is concentrated in keratinized skin cells, where it inhibits fungal cell division.

Nucleic Acid Synthesis

Flucytosine is taken up by yeast cells and converted by yeast enzymes to an active form.

21.8 Mechanisms of Action of Antiprotozoan and Antihelminthic Drugs (Table 21.4)

Most antiparasitic drugs are thought to interfere with biosynthetic pathways of protozoan parasites or the neuromuscular function of worms.

REVIEW QUESTIONS

Short Answer

1. Describe the difference between what is implied by the terms antibiotic and antimicrobial.
2. Define therapeutic index and explain its importance.
3. Explain the role of penicillin-binding proteins in drug susceptibility.
4. Name three of the first-line drugs used to treat tuberculosis.
5. Name three antimicrobial medications that target ribosomes.
6. Compare and contrast the method for determining the minimum inhibitory concentration of an antimicrobial drug with the Kirby-Bauer disc diffusion test.
7. Name three targets that can be altered sufficiently via spontaneous mutation to result in resistance to an antimicrobial drug.
8. What is MRSA? Why is it significant?
9. Why is it difficult to develop antiviral drugs?
10. Explain the difference between the mechanism of action of an azole and that of a polyene.

Multiple Choice

1. Which of the following targets would you expect to be the most selective with respect to toxicity?
   a) Cytoplasmic membrane function
   b) DNA synthesis
   c) Glycolysis
   d) Peptidoglycan synthesis
   e) 70S ribosome
2. Penicillin has been modified to make derivatives that differ in all of the following, *except*
   a) spectrum of activity.
   b) resistance to β-lactamases.
   c) potential for allergic reactions.
   d) A and C.
3. Which of the following is the target of β-lactam antibiotics?
   a) Peptidoglycan synthesis
   b) DNA synthesis
   c) RNA synthesis
   d) Protein synthesis
   e) Folic acid synthesis
4. Which of the following statements is *false?*
   a) A bacteriostatic drug stops the growth of a microorganism.
   b) The lower the therapeutic index, the less toxic the drug.
   c) Broad-spectrum antibiotics are associated with the development of antibiotic-associated colitis.
   d) Azithromycin has a longer half-life than does penicillin V.
   e) Chloramphenicol can cause a life-threatening type of anemia.
5. All of the following interfere with the function of the ribosome, *except*
   a) fluoroquinolones. b) lincosamides. c) macrolides.
   d) streptogramins. e) tetracyclines.
6. The target of the sulfonamides is
   a) cytoplasmic membrane proteins.
   b) folic acid synthesis.
   c) gyrase.
   d) peptidoglycan biosynthesis.
   e) RNA polymerase.
7. Routine antimicrobial therapy to treat tuberculosis involves taking
   a) one drug for 10 days.
   b) two or more drugs for 10 days.
   c) one drug for at least 6 months.
   d) two or more drugs for at least 6 months.
   e) five drugs for 2 years.
8. Strains of *Staphylococcus aureus* referred to as MRSA are sensitive to
   a) methicillin.
   b) penicillin.
   c) cephalosporin.
   d) vancomycin.
   e) none of the above.
9. Acyclovir is
   a) a nucleoside analog.
   b) a non-nucleoside polymerase inhibitor.
   c) a protease inhibitor.
   d) none of the above.
10. The antifungal drug griseofulvin is used to treat
    a) vaginal infections.
    b) systemic infections.
    c) nail infections.
    d) hair infections.

Applications

1. A physician was treating one young female and one elderly patient for urinary tract infections caused by the same type of bacterium. Although the patients had similar body dimensions and weight, the physician gave a smaller does of drug to the older patient. What was the physician's rationale for this decision?
2. An advocacy group in Washington, D.C., is petitioning the United States Department of Agriculture (USDA) to stop the use of low-dosage antimicrobial agents used to enhance the growth of cattle and chickens. Why is the group against this practice? Why does the USDA permit it?

Critical Thinking

1. Figure 21.12 shows the E-test procedure for determining an MIC value. How would the zone of inhibition appear if the drug concentrations in the strip were decreased slightly?
2. Why is acyclovir converted to a nucleotide analog only in cells infected with herpes simplex virus?

APPENDIX I

Microbial Mathematics

Because prokaryotes are very tiny and can multiply to very large numbers of cells in short time periods, convenient and simple ways are used to designate their numbers without resorting to many zeros before or after the number. In the study of microbiology, it is important to gain an understanding of the metric system, which is used in scientific measurements.

The basic unit of measure is the meter, which is equal to about 39 inches. All other units are fractions of a meter:

1 decimeter is one tenth = 0.1 meter
1 centimeter is one hundredth = 0.01 meter
1 millimeter is one thousandth = 0.001 meter

Because prokaryotes are much smaller than a millimeter, even smaller units of measure are used. A millionth of a meter is a micrometer = 0.000001 meter, and is abbreviated µm. This is the most frequently used size measurement in microbiology, since bacteria are in this size range. For comparison, a human hair is about 75 µm wide.

Since it is inconvenient to write so many zeros in front of the 1, an easier way of denoting the same number is through the use of superscript, or exponential, numbers (exponents). One hundred dollars can be written 10^2 dollars. The 10 is called the base number and the 2 is the exponent. Conversely, one hundredth of a dollar is 10^{-2} dollars; thus the exponent is negative. The base most commonly used in biology is 10 (which is designated as $\log_{10}$). The above information can be summarized as follows:

1 millimeter = 1 mm = 0.001 meter = 10^{-3} meter
1 micrometer = 1 µm = 0.000001 meter = 10^{-6} meter
1 nanometer = 1 nm = 0.000000001 meter = 10^{-9} meter

The same prefix designations can be used for weights. The basic unit of weight is the gram, abbreviated g. Approximately 450 grams are in a pound.

1 milligram = 1 mg = 0.001 gram = 10^{-3} g
1 microgram = 1 µg = 0.000001 gram = 10^{-6} g
1 nanogram = 1 ng = 0.000000001 gram = 10^{-9} g
1 picogram = 1 pg = 0.000000000001 gram = 10^{-12} g

Note that the number of zeros before the 1 is one less than the exponent.

The value of the number is obtained by multiplying the base by itself the number of times indicated by the exponent.

Thus, $10^1 = 10 \times 1 = 10$
$10^2 = 10 \times 10 = 100$
$10^3 = 10 \times 10 \times 10 = 1{,}000$

When the exponent is negative, the base and exponent are divided into 1.

For example, $10^{-2} = 1/10 \times 1/10 = 1/100 = 0.01$

When multiplying numbers having exponents to the same base, the exponents are added.

For example, $10^3 \times 10^2 = 10^5$ (not 10^6)

When dividing numbers having exponents to the same base, the exponents are subtracted.

For example, $10^5 \div 10^2 = 10^3$

In both cases, only if the bases are the same can the exponents be added or subtracted.

APPENDIX II

Microbial Terminology

Singular and Plurals

Singular	Plural	Singular	Plural
alg*a*	alg*ae*	fung*us*	fung*i*
ameb*a*	ameb*ae*	hydroly*sis*	hydrolys*es*
bacill*us*	bacill*i*	hyph*a*	hyph*ae*
bacteri*um*	bacteri*a*	inocul*um*	inocul*a*
cili*um*	cili*a*	medi*um*	medi*a*
clostridi*um*	clostridi*a*	mucos*a*	mucos*ae*
cocc*us*	cocc*i*	myceli*um*	myceli*a*
conidi*um*	conidi*a*	mycos*is*	mycos*es*
dat*um*	dat*a*	phyl*um*	phyl*a*
diagnos*is*	diagnos*es*	pil*us*	pil*i*
fimbri*a*	fimbri*ae*	nucle*us*	nucle*i*
flagell*um*	flagell*a*	sept*um*	sept*a*
foc*us*	foc*i*	synthes*is*	synthes*es*

Meanings of Prefixes and Suffixes

Prefix or Suffix	Meaning	Example
a-, an-	not, without	avirulent (lacking virulence), anaerobic (without air)
aer-	air	aerobic
anti-	against	antiseptic
-ase	enzyme	penicillinase
chlor-	green	chlorophyll
-chrom-	color	metachromatic (staining differently with the same dye)
-cide	causing death	germicide
co-, com-, con-	together	coenzyme
-cyan-	blue	pyocyanin (a blue bacterial pigment)
de-	down, from	dehydrate (remove water)
-dem-	people, district	epidemic
endo-	within	endospore (spore within a cell)
-enter-	intestine	enteritis (inflammation of the intestine)
epi-	upon	epidermis
erythro-	red	erythocyte (red blood cell)
eu-	well, normal	eukaryotic (true nucleus)
exo-	outside	exoenzyme (enzyme that acts outside the cell that produced it)
extra-	outside of	extracellular
flav-	yellow	flavoprotein (a protein containing a yellow enzyme)
-gen	produce, originate	antigen (a substance that induces a production of antibodies)

Prefix or Suffix	Meaning	Example
glyc-	sweet	glycemia (the presence of sugar in the blood)
hetero-	other	heterotroph (organism that obtains carbon from organic compounds)
homo-	common, same	homologous (similar in structure or origin)
hydr-	water	dehydrate
hyper-	excessive, above	hypersensitive
hypo-	under	hypotonic (having low osmotic pressure)
iso-	same, equal	isotonic (having the same osmotic pressure)
-itis	inflammation	appendicitis, meningitis
leuko-	white	leukocyte (white blood cell)
ly-, -lys, -lyt-	loosen; dissolve	bacteriolysis (dissolution of bacteria)
meso-	middle	mesophilic (preferring moderate temperatures)
meta-	changed	metachromatic (staining differently with the same dye)
micro-	small; one-millionth part	microscopic
milli-	one-thousandth part	millimeter (10^{-3} meter)
mito-	thread	mitochondrion (small, rod-shaped or granular organelle)
mono-	single	monotrichous (having a single flagellum)
multi-	many	multinuclear (having many nuclei)
myc-	fungus	mycotic (caused by fungus)
myx-	mucus	myxomycete (slime mold)
-oid	resembling	lymphoid (resembling lymphocytes)
-ose	a sugar	lactose (milk sugar)
-osis	disease of	coccidioidomycosis (disease caused by *Coccidioides*)
pan-	all	pandemic (widespread epidemic)
para-	beside	parasite (an organism that feeds in and at expense of the host)
patho-	disease	pathogenic (producing disease)
peri-	around	peritrichous (having flagella on all sides)
-phag-	eat	phagocyte (a cell that ingests other cell substances)
-phil	like, having affinity for	eosinophilic (staining with the dye eosin)
-phot-	light	photosynthesis
-phyll	leaf	chlorophyll (green leaf pigment)
pleo-	more	pleomorphic (occurring in more than one form)
poly-	many	polymorphonuclear (having a many-shaped nucleus)
post	after	postnatal (after birth)
pyo-	pus	pyogenic (producing pus)
-sta-	stop	bacteriostatic (inhibiting bacterial multiplication)
sym-, syn-	together	symbiosis (life together)
thermo-	heat	thermophilic (liking heat)
trans-	through, across	transfusion
-trich-	hair	monotrichous (having a single flagellum)
-troph	nourishment	autotroph (organism that obtains carbon from CO_2)
tox-	poison	toxin
zym-	ferment	enzyme

APPENDIX III

Pronunciation Key for Bacterial, Fungal, Protozoan, and Viral Names

A

Acetobacter (a-see′-toe-back-ter)
Achromobacter (a-krome′-oh-back-ter)
Acinetobacter calcoaceticus (a-sin-et′-oh-back-ter kal-koh-ah-see′-ti-kus)
Actinomyces israelii (ak-tin-oh-my′-seez iz-ray′-lee-ee)
Actinomycetes (ak-tin-oh-my′-seats)
Adenovirus (ad′-eh-no-vi-rus)
Agrobacterium tumefaciens (ag-rho-bak-teer′-ee-um too-meh-faysh′-ee-enz)
Alcaligenes (al-ka-li′-jen-ease)
Amoeba (ah-mee′-bah)
Arbovirus (are′-bow-vi-rus)
Aspergillus niger (ass-per-jill′-us nye′-jer)
Aspergillus oryzae (ass-per-jill′-us or-eye′-zee)
Azolla (aye-zol′-lah)
Azotobacter (ay-zoh′-toe-back-ter)

B

Bacillus anthracis (bah-sill′-us an-thra′-siss)
Bacillus cereus (bah-sill′-us seer′-ee-us)
Bacillus coagulans (bah-sill′-us coh-ag′-you-lans)
Bacillus fastidiosus (bah-sill′-us fas-tid-ee-oh′-sus)
Bacillus stearothermophilus (bah-sill′-us steer-oh-ther-maw′-fill-us)
Bacillus subtilis (bah-sill′-us sut′-ill-us)
Bacillus thuringiensis (bah-sill′-us thur′-in-jee-en-sis)
Bacteroides (back′-ter-oid′-eez)
Baculovirus (back′-you-low-vi-rus)
Beggiatoa (beg-gee-ah-toe′-ah)
Beijerinckia (by-yer-ink′-ee-ah)
Bordetella pertussis (bor-deh-tell′-ah per-tuss′-iss)
Borrelia burgdorferi (bor-real′-ee-ah berg-dor′-fir-ee)
Bradyrhizobium (bray-dee-rye-zoe′-bee-um)
Branhamella (bran-ham-el′-lah)
Brucella abortus (bru-sell′-ah ah-bore′-tus)

C

Campylobacter jejuni (kam′-peh-low-back-ter je-june′-ee)
Candida albicans (kan′-did-ah al′-bi-kanz)
Caulobacter (caw′-loh-back-ter)
Ceratocystis ulmi (see′-rah-toe-sis-tis ul′-mee)
Chlamydia trachomatis (klah-mid′-ee-ah trah-ko-ma′-tiss)
Claviceps purpurea (kla′-vi-seps purr-purr′-ee-ah)
Clostridium acetobutylicum (kloss-trid′-ee-um a-seat-tow-bu-till′-i-kum)
Clostridium botulinum (kloss-trid′-ee-um bot-you-line′-um)
Clostridium difficile (kloss-trid′-ee-um dif′-fi-seal)
Clostridium perfringens (kloss-trid′-ee-um per-frin′-gens)
Clostridium tetani (kloss-trid′-ee-um tet′-an-ee)
Coccidioides immitis (cock-sid-ee-oid′-eez im′-mi-tiss)
Coronavirus (kor-oh′-nah-vi-rus)
Corynebacterium diphtheriae (koh-ryne′-nee-bak-teer-ee-um dif-theer′-ee-ee)
Coxsackievirus (cock-sack-ee′-vi-rus)
Cryptococcus neoformans (krip-toe-cock′-us knee-oh-for′-manz)
Cytophaga (sigh-taw′-fa-ga)

D

Desulfovibrio (dee-sul-foh-vib′-ree-oh)

E

Eikenella corrodens (eye-keh-nell′-ah kor-roh′-denz)
Entamoeba histolytica (en-ta-mee′-bah his-toh-lit′-ik-ah)
Enterobacter (en′-ter-oh-back-ter)
Enterococcus faecalis (en′-ter-oh-kock′-us fee-ka′-liss)
Enterovirus (en′-ter-oh-vi-rus)
Epidermophyton (eh-pee-der′-moh-fy-ton)
Escherichia coli (esh-er-ee′-she-ah koh′-lee)

F

Filobasidiella neoformans (fee-loh-bah-si-dee-ell′-ah knee-oh-for′-manz)
Flavivirus (flay′-vih-vi-rus)
Flavobacterium (flay-vo-back-teer′-ee-um)
Francisella tularensis (fran-siss-sell′-ah tu-lah-ren′-siss)
Frankia (frank′-ee-ah)
Fusobacterium (fu′-zoh-back-teer-ee-um)

G

Gallionella (gal-ee-oh-nell′-ah)
Gardnerella vaginalis (gard-nee-rel′-lah va-jin-al′-is)
Giardia intestinalis (jee-are′-dee-ah in-test′-tin-al-is)
Giardia lamblia (jee-are′-dee-ah lamb′-lee-ah)
Gluconobacter (glue-kon-oh-back′-ter)
Gonyaulax (gon-ee-ow′-lax)
Gymnodinium breve (jim-no-din′-i-um brev-eh)

H

Haemophilus influenzae (hee-moff'-ill-us in-flew-en'-zee)
Helicobacter pylori (he'-lih-koh-back-ter pie-lore'-ee)
Hepadnavirus (hep-ad'-nah-vi-rus)
Hepatitis virus (hep-ah-ti'-tis vi-rus)
Herpes simplex (her'-peas sim'-plex)
Herpes zoster (her'-peas zoh'-ster)
Histoplasma capsulatum (his-toh-plaz'-mah cap-su-lah'-tum)
Hyphomicrobium (high-foh-my-krow'-bee-um)

I

Influenza virus (in-flew-en'-za vi-rus)

K

Klebsiella pneumoniae (kleb-see-ell'-ah new-moan'-ee-ee)

L

Lactobacillus brevis (lack-toe-ba-sil'-lus bre'-vis)
Lactobacillus bulgaricus (lack-toe-ba-sil'-lus bull-gair'-i-kus)
Lactobacillus casei (lack-toe-ba-sil'-us kay'-see-ee)
Lactobacillus plantarum (lack-toe-ba-sil'-us plan-tar'-um)
Lactobacillus thermophilus (lack-toe-ba-sil'-us ther-mo'-fil-us)
Lactococcus lactis (lack-toe-kock'-us lak'-tiss)
Legionella pneumophila (lee-jon-ell'-ah new-moh'-fill-ah)
Leptospira interrogans (lep-toe-spire'-ah in-ter-roh'-ganz)
Leuconostoc citrovorum (lew-kow-nos'-tok sit-ro-vor'-um)
Listeria monocytogenes (lis-tear'-ee-ah mon'-oh-sigh-to-jen'-eze)

M

Malassezia (mal-as-seez'-e-ah)
Methanobacterium (me-than'-oh-bak-teer-ee-um)
Methanococcus (me-than-oh-ko'-kus)
Microsporum (my-kroh-spore'-um)
Mobiluncus (moh-bi-lun'-kus)
Moraxella catarrhalis (more-ax-ell'-ah kah-tah-rah'-liss)
Moraxella lacunata (more-ax-ell'-ah lak-u-nah'-tah)
Mucor (mu'-kor)
Mycobacterium leprae (my-koh-bak-teer'-ee-um lep-ree)
Mycobacterium tuberculosis (my-koh-bak-teer'-ee-um too-ber-kew-loh'-siss)
Mycoplasma pneumoniae (my-koh-plaz'-mah new-moan'-ee-ee)

N

Neisseria gonorrhoeae (nye-seer'-ee-ah gahn-oh-ree'-ee)
Neisseria meningitidis (nye-seer'-ee-ah men-in-jit'-id-iss)
Neurospora sitophila (new-rah'-spor-ah sit-oh-phil'-ah)

O

Orthomyxovirus (or-thoe-mix'-oh-vi-rus)
Oscillatoria (os-sil-la-tor'-ee-ah)

P

Papillomavirus (pap-il-oh'-ma-vi-rus)
Parainfluenza virus (par-ah-in-flew-en'-zah vi-rus)
Paramecium (pair'-ah-mee-see-um)
Paramyxovirus (par-ah-mix'-oh-vi-rus)
Parvovirus (par'-vo-vi-rus)
Pasteurella multocida (pass-ture-ell'-ah mul-toe-sid'-ah)
Pediococcus soyae (ped-ih-oh-ko'-kus soy'-ee)
Penicillium camemberti (pen-eh-sill'-ee-um cam-em-bare'-tee)
Penicillium roqueforti (pen-eh-sill'-ee-um rok-e-for'-tee)
Peptostreptococcus (pep'-to-strep-to-ko-kus)
Phytophythora infestans (fy'-toe-fy-thor-ah in-fes'-tanz)
Picornavirus (pi-kor'-na-vi-rus)
Plasmodium falciparum (plaz-moh'-dee-um fall-sip'-air-um)
Plasmodium malariae (plaz-moh'-dee-um ma-lair'-ee-ee)
Plasmodium ovale (plaz-moh'-dee-um oh-vah'-lee)
Plasmodium vivax (plaz-moh'-dee-um vye'-vax)
Pneumocystis carinii (new-mo-sis'-tis car'-i'-nee-ee)
Poliovirus (poe'-lee-oh-vi-rus)
Polyoma virus (po-lee-oh'-mah vi-rus)
Propionibacterium acnes (proh-pee-ah-nee-bak-teer'-ee-um ak'-neez)
Propionibacterium shermanii (proh-pee-ah-nee-bak-teer'-ee-um sher-man'-ee-ee)
Proteus mirabilis (proh'-tee-us mee-rab'-il-us)
Pseudomonas aeruginosa (sue-dough-moan'-ass aye-rue-gin-o'-sa)

R

Rabies virus (ray'-bees vi-rus)
Retrovirus (re'-trow-vi-rus)
Rhabdovirus (rab'-doh-vi-rus)
Rhinovirus (rye'-no-vi-rus)
Rhizobium (rye-zoh'-bee-um)
Rhizopus nigricans (rise'-oh-pus nye'-gri-kanz)
Rhizopus stolon (rise'-oh-pus stoh'-lon)
Rhodococcus (roh-doh-koh'-kus)
Rickettsia rickettsii (rik-kett'-see-ah rik-kett'-see-ee)
Rotavirus (row'-tah-vi-rus)
Rubella virus (rue-bell'-ah vi-rus)
Rubeola virus (rue-bee-oh'-la vi-rus)

S

Saccharomyces carlsbergensis (sack-ah-row-my'-sees karls-berg-en'-siss)
Saccharomyces cerevisiae (sack-ah-row-my'-sees sara-vis'-ee-ee)
Saccharomyces rouxii (sack-ah-row-my'-sees roos'-ee-ee)
Salmonella enteritidis (sall-moh-nell'-ah en-ter-it'-id-iss)
Salmonella typhi (sall-moh-nell'-ah tye'-fee)
Salmonella typhimurium (sall-moh-nell'-ah tye-fe-mur'-ee-um)
Serratia marcescens (ser-ray'-sha mar-sess-sens)
Shigella dysenteriae (shig-ell'-ah diss-en-tair'-ee-ee)
Spirillum minus (spy-rill'-um my'-nus)
Sporothrix schenckii (spore'-oh-thrix shenk-ee-ee)
Staphylococcus aureus (staff-ill-oh-kok'-us aw'-ree-us)
Staphylococcus epidermidis (staff-ill-oh-kok'-us epi-der'-mid-iss)
Streptobacillus moniliformis (strep-tow-bah-sill'-us mon-ill-i-form'-is)
Streptococcus agalactiae (strep-toe-kock'-us a-ga-lac'-tee-ee)
Streptococcus cremoris (strep-toe-kock'-us kre-more'-iss)
Streptococcus mutans (strep-toe-kock'-us mew'-tanz)

Streptococcus pneumoniae (strep-toe-kock′-us new-moan′-ee-ee)
Streptococcus pyogenes (strep-toe-kock′-us pie-ah-gen-ease)
Streptococcus salivarius (strep-toe-kock′-us sal-ih-vair′-ee-us)
Streptococcus sanguis (strep-toe-kock′-us san′-gwis)
Streptococcus thermophilis (strep-toe-kock′-us ther-moh′-fill-us)
Streptomyces griseus (strep-toe-my′-seez gree′-see-us)

T

Thiobacillus (thigh-oh-bah-sill′-us)
Torulopsis (tore-you-lop′-siss)
Treponema pallidum (tre-poh-nee′-mah pal′-ih-dum)
Trichomonas vaginalis (trick-oh-moan′-as vag-in-al′-iss)
Trichophyton (trick-oh-phye′-ton)
Trypanosoma brucei (tri-pan′-oh-soh-mah bru′-see-ee)

V

Varicella-zoster virus (var-ih-sell′-ah zoh′-ster vi-rus)
Veillonella (veye-yon-ell′-ah)
Vibrio anguillarum (vib′-ree-oh an-gwil-air′-um)
Vibrio cholerae (vib′-ree-oh kahl′-er-ee)

Y

Yersinia enterocolitica (yer-sin′-ee-ah en-ter-oh-koh-lih′-tih-kah)
Yersinia pestis (yer-sin′-ee-ah pess′-tiss)

Metabolic Pathways

FIGURE IV-1 The Entner-Doudoroff Pathway

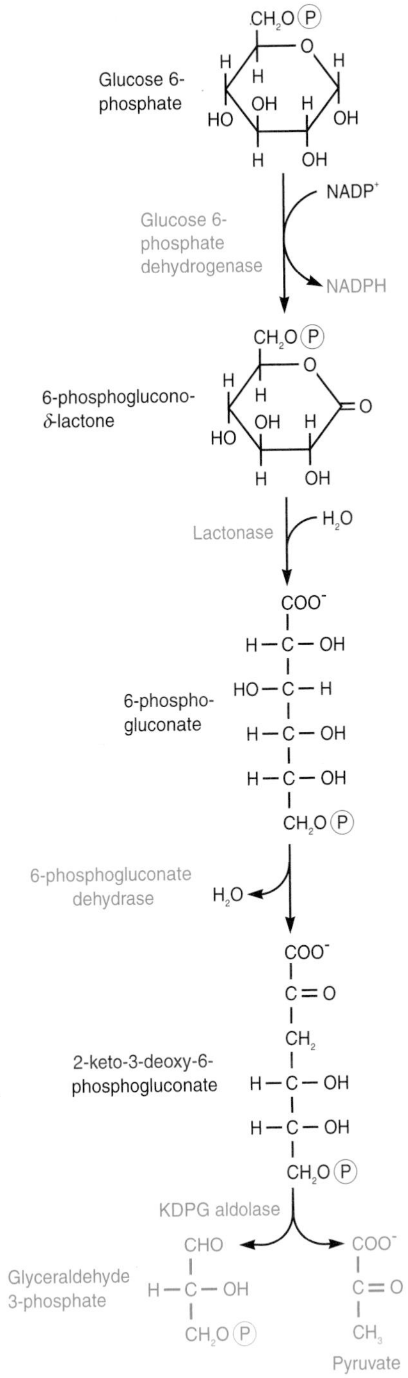

FIGURE IV-2 The Embden-Meyerhof-Parnas Pathway
Commonly called glycolysis or the glycolytic pathway.

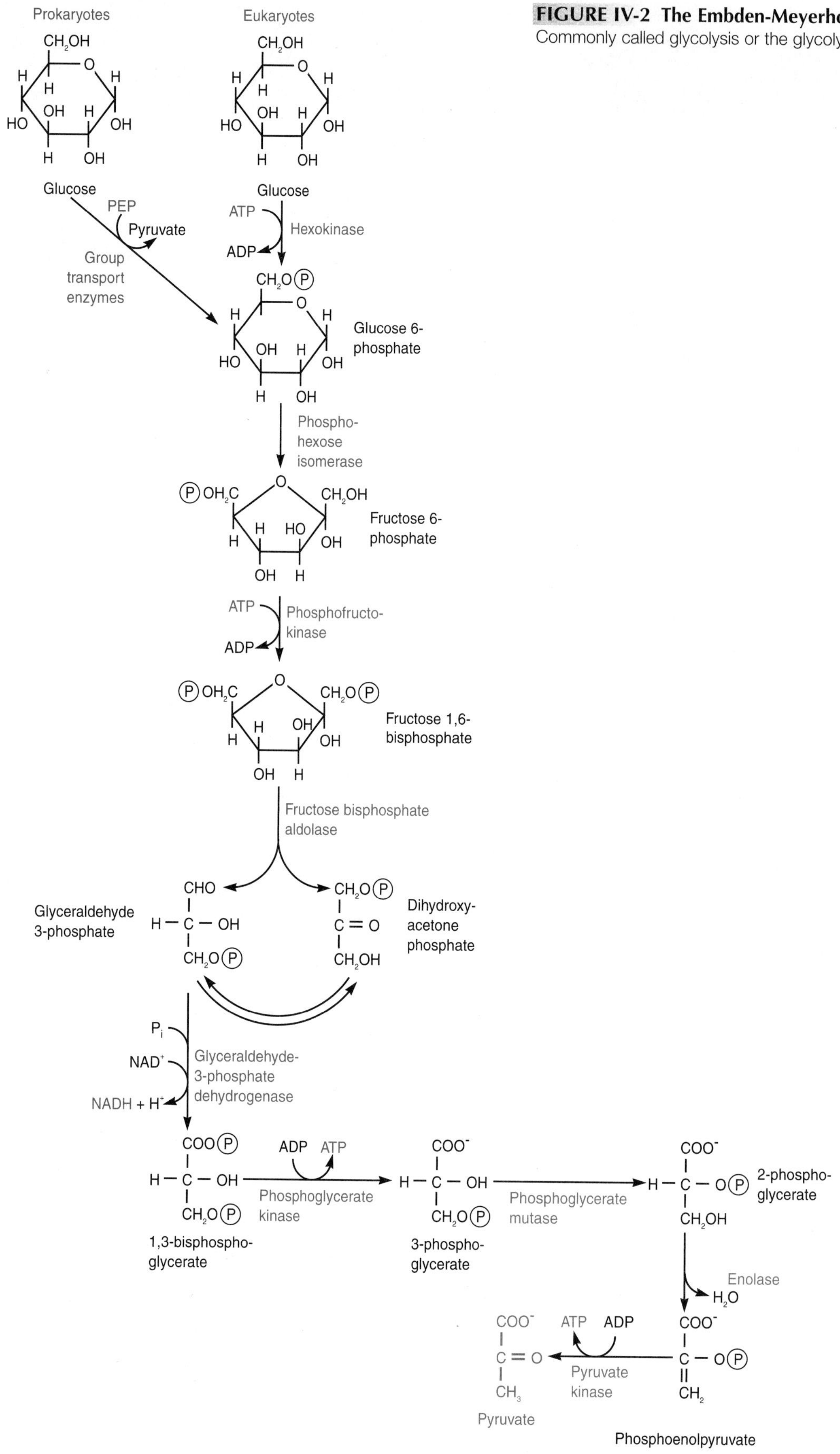

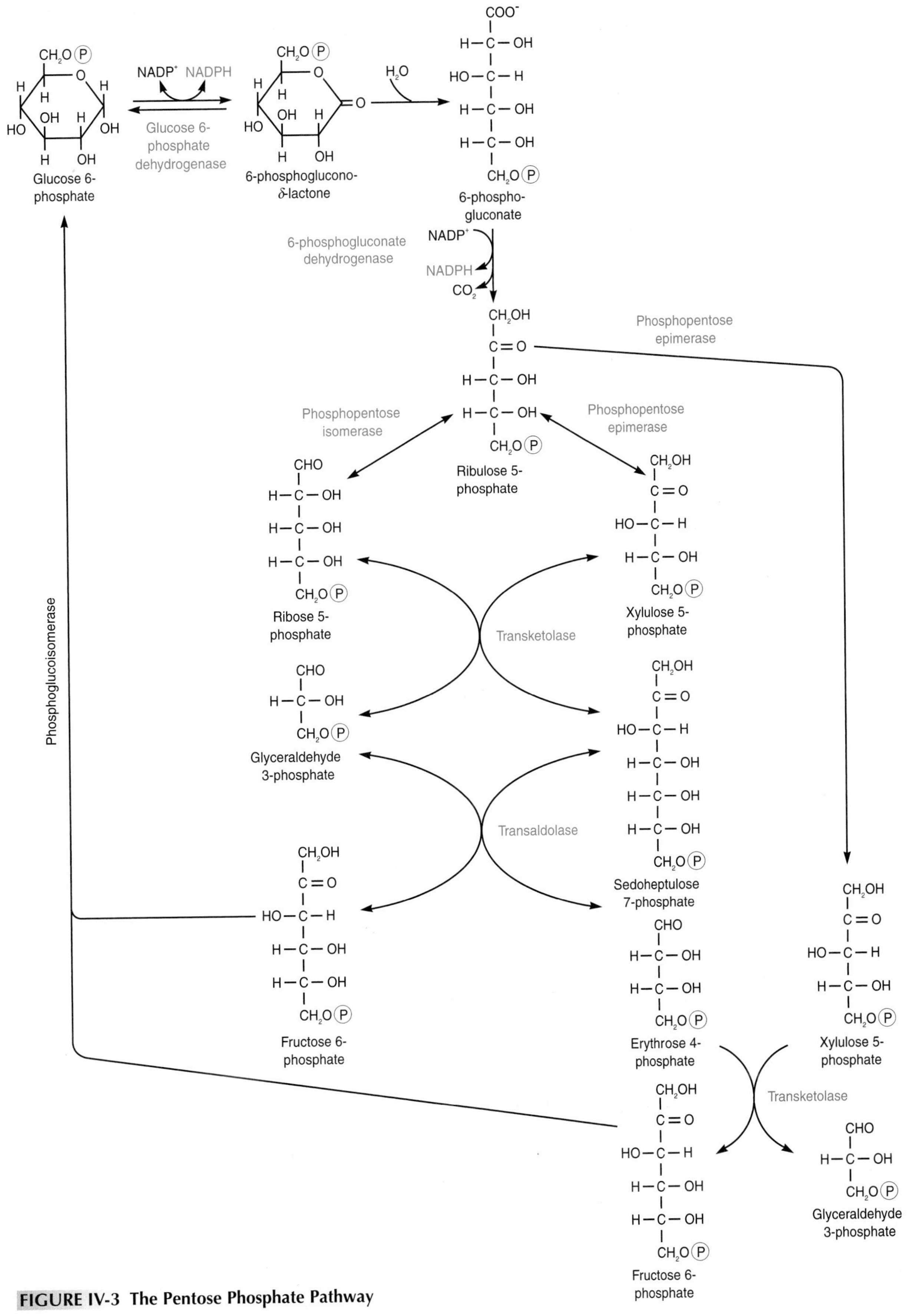

FIGURE IV-3 The Pentose Phosphate Pathway

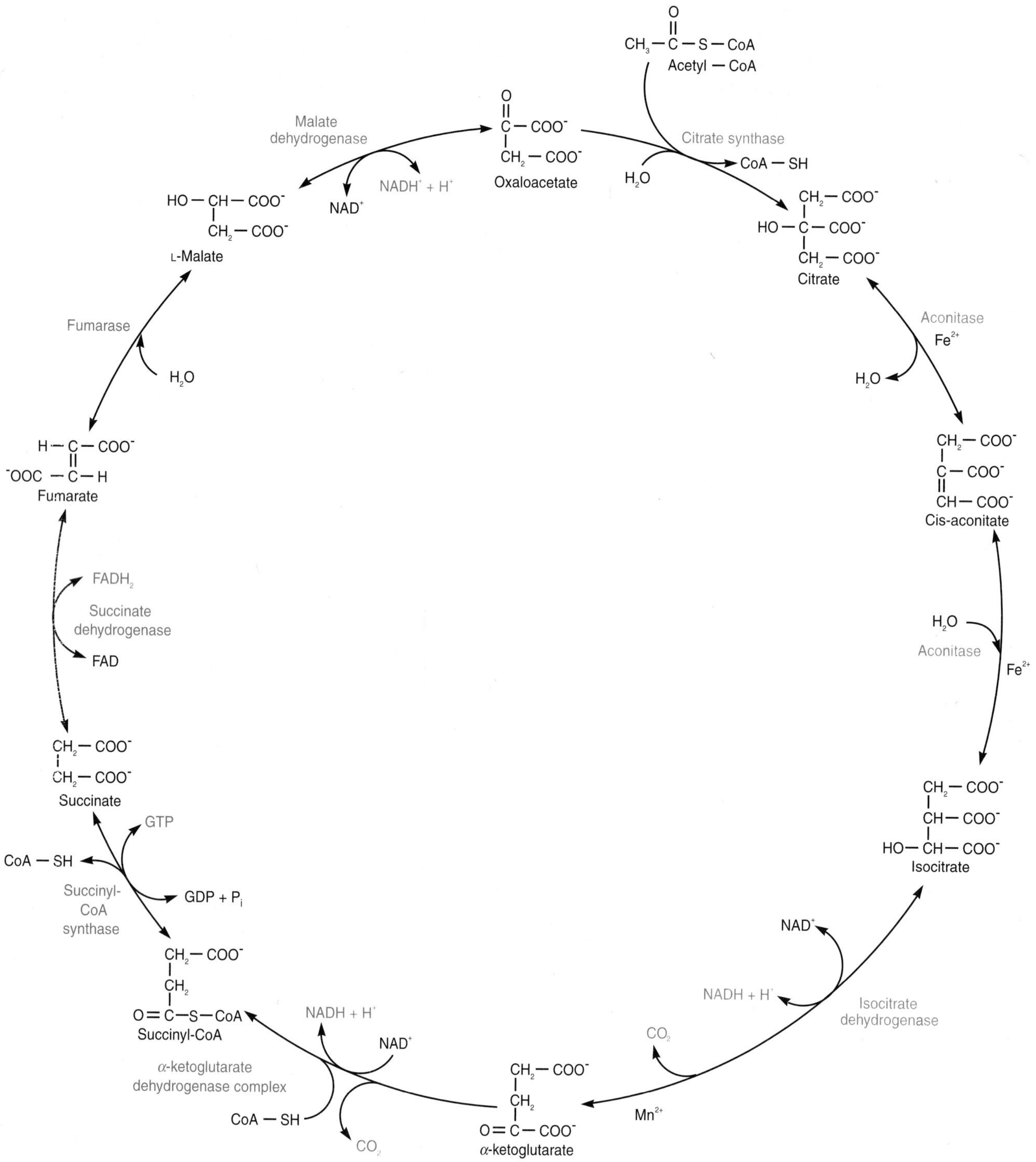

FIGURE IV-4 The Tricarboxylic Acid Cycle (TCA Cycle) Also referred to as the Krebs cycle or the citric acid cycle.

APPENDIX V

Answers to Multiple Choice Questions

Chapter 1

1. D
2. A
3. B
4. C
5. B
6. B
7. C
8. A
9. E
10. A

Chapter 2

1. C
2. A
3. E
4. A
5. B
6. C
7. B
8. D
9. E
10. A

Chapter 3

1. A
2. A
3. E
4. B
5. B
6. C
7. E
8. C
9. D
10. A

Chapter 4

1. B
2. B
3. C
4. B
5. D
6. B
7. E
8. A
9. D
10. B

Chapter 5

1. C
2. D
3. A
4. B
5. B
6. C
7. E
8. D
9. C
10. A

Chapter 6

1. D
2. C
3. D
4. E
5. B
6. A
7. D
8. D
9. D
10. E

Chapter 7

1. B
2. A
3. A
4. A
5. C
6. B
7. B
8. C
9. D
10. D

Chapter 8

1. C
2. A
3. D
4. A
5. B
6. D
7. A
8. B
9. A
10. B

Chapter 9

1. C
2. C
3. E
4. B
5. B
6. C
7. B
8. B
9. B
10. D

Chapter 10

1. E
2. B
3. E
4. B
5. D
6. B
7. C
8. D
9. B
10. E

Chapter 11

1. E
2. B
3. E
4. B
5. D
6. A
7. D
8. B
9. C
10. D

Chapter 12

1. C
2. A
3. B
4. A, C
5. A
6. B
7. A, B, E
8. A, B
9. C
10. A, B

Chapter 13

1. C
2. B
3. E
4. A
5. C
6. E
7. D
8. C
9. A
10. A

Chapter 14

1. D
2. A
3. B
4. B
5. D
6. B
7. A
8. D
9. E
10. A

Chapter 15

1. B
2. E
3. A
4. B
5. A
6. E
7. A
8. C
9. D
10. C

Chapter 16

1. E
2. E
3. D
4. D
5. B
6. D
7. D
8. A
9. B
10. D

Chapter 17

1. D
2. C
3. E
4. D
5. A
6. D
7. C
8. A
9. C
10. C

Chapter 18

1. A
2. E
3. A
4. D
5. E
6. C
7. A
8. C
9. A
10. A

Chapter 19

1. C
2. A
3. D
4. D
5. A
6. C
7. C
8. D
9. D
10. A

Chapter 20

1. A
2. B
3. A
4. B
5. E
6. B
7. B
8. E
9. C
10. E

Chapter 21

1. D
2. C
3. A
4. B
5. A
6. B
7. D
8. D
9. A
10. C

Chapter 22

1. E
2. E
3. A
4. E
5. B
6. A
7. C
8. A
9. D
10. D

Chapter 23

1. B
2. E
3. C
4. A
5. A
6. C
7. D
8. C
9. E
10. B

Chapter 24

1. E
2. C
3. E
4. A
5. B
6. A
7. A
8. C
9. D
10. D

Chapter 25

1. C
2. A
3. B
4. D
5. A
6. D
7. C
8. D
9. C
10. E

Chapter 26

1. D
2. D
3. C
4. B
5. C
6. B
7. A
8. B
9. D
10. C

Chapter 27

1. B
2. C
3. C
4. D
5. C
6. E
7. A
8. D
9. A
10. B

Chapter 28

1. E
2. A
3. C
4. E
5. C
6. C
7. C
8. A
9. A
10. E

Chapter 29

1. D
2. D
3. A
4. B
5. C
6. A
7. E
8. A
9. E
10. E

Chapter 30

1. A
2. A
3. C
4. D
5. A
6. D
7. C
8. C
9. B
10. A

Chapter 31

1. B
2. B
3. A
4. A
5. C
6. E
7. C
8. C
9. B
10. E

Chapter 32

1. B
2. C
3. D
4. E
5. B
6. B
7. C
8. D
9. D
10. E

GLOSSARY

ABC transport systems A type of active transport system that requires ATP as an energy source (***A**TP **B**inding-**C**assette*).

abscess A localized collection of pus within a tissue.

A-B toxin Exotoxin composed of an active subunit (A-subunit) and a binding subunit (B-subunit).

acellular Not composed of cells, therefore not living.

acetyl-CoA Product of the transition reaction; a precursor metabolite used in fatty acid synthesis.

acid-fast staining A procedure used to stain certain microorganisms, particularly members of the genus *Mycobacterium,* that do not readily take up dyes used in microbiology.

acidic amino acids Amino acids with more carboxyl (—COOH) than amino (—NH_2) groups.

acidophiles Organisms that grow optimally at a pH below 5.5.

acquired resistance Development of antimicrobial resistance in a previously sensitive organism; occurs through spontaneous mutation or acquisition of new genetic information.

acridine orange A fluorescent dye that binds DNA and can be used to determine the total number of microorganisms in a sample.

actin Protein that makes up actin filaments of eukaryotic cells; it can rapidly assemble and subsequently disassemble to cause motion.

actin filaments Cytoskeletal structures of eukaryotic cells that enable the cell cytoplasm to move.

actinomycetes Filamentous bacteria; many are valuable in the production of antibiotics.

activated macrophages Macrophages stimulated by cytokines to enlarge and become metabolically active, with greatly increased capability to kill and degrade intracellular organisms and materials.

activated sludge method A method of sewage treatment in which wastes are degraded by complex populations of aerobic microorganisms.

activated T cell T cell activated by exposure to antigen in conjunction with required accessory signals.

activation energy Initial energy required to break a chemical bond.

activator-binding site Sequence of DNA that precedes an ineffective promoter; binding of an activator to this site enhances the ability of RNA polymerase to initiate transcription at that promoter.

active immunity Protective immunity produced by an individual in response to an antigenic stimulus.

active site Site on an enzyme molecule to which substrate binds; also known as the catalytic site.

active transport Energy-consuming process by which molecules are carried across cell boundaries; can accumulate compounds against a concentration gradient.

acute infections Infections in which the symptoms and signs have a rapid onset and are usually severe, often with fever, but short-lived.

acute inflammation Short-term inflammatory response, marked by a prevalence of neutrophils.

acute phase response Changes in the blood that occur early during an infection, with the production of acute phase proteins and cells that contribute to the inflammatory response.

acylated homoserine lactone (AHL) Small molecules that can move freely in and out of a cell; provides cells with a mechanism of assessing cell density (quorum sensing).

adaptive immune response Immune response that depends on the recognition and elimination of antigens by antigen-specific lymphocytes.

adaptive immunity Host defenses that develop throughout life; involves B cells and T cells.

ADCC (antibody-dependent cellular cytotoxicity) Killing of target cells by macrophages, granulocytes, or natural killer cells that contact the target via their Fc receptors binding to Fc of antibodies attached to the target.

adenosine diphosphate (ADP) The acceptor of free energy in a cell; that energy is used to add an inorganic phosphate (P_i) to ADP, generating ATP.

adenosine triphosphate (ATP) The energy currency of a cell, serving as the ready and immediate donor of free energy.

adherence A necessary first step in colonization and infection, in which the pathogen attaches to host cells to avoid being removed from the body.

adhesin Component of a microorganism that is used to bind to surfaces.

adhesion molecule Molecule on the surface of a cell that allows that cell to adhere to other cells.

adjuvant Substance that increases the immune response to antigen.

ADP Abbreviation for adenosine diphosphate.

adsorption Attachment of one substance to the surface of another.

aerobic respiration Metabolic process in which electrons are transferred from the electron transport chain to molecular oxygen (O_2).

aerosol Material dispersed into the air as a fine mist.

aerotaxis Movement toward or away from molecular oxygen.

aerotolerant anaerobes Organisms that can grow in the presence of O_2 but never use it as a terminal electron acceptor; also called obligate fermenters.

affinity maturation The "fine-tuning" of the fit of an antibody molecule for an antigen; it is due to mutations that occur as activated B cells multiply.

aflatoxin Potent toxin made by species of *Aspergillus;* may contaminate peanuts and other grains.

agar Polysaccharide extracted from marine algae; used to solidify microbiological media.

agarose Highly purified form of agar used in gel electrophoresis.

agar slant Microbiological medium that has been solidified with agar and stored in a tube that was held at a shallow angle as the medium solidified, creating a larger surface area.

agglutination Clumping together of cells or particles.

AIDS Acquired immunodeficiency syndrome.

AIDS-related complex (ARC) A group of symptoms, fever, fatigue, diarrhea, and weight loss, that herald the onset of AIDS.

alga (pl. **algae)** A primitive photosynthetic eukaryotic organism.

alkalophiles Organisms that grow optimally at a pH above 8.5.

alkylating agent Chemical that adds alkyl groups, short chains of carbon atoms, to purines and pyrimidines; promotes mutations.

alkyl group Short chain or single carbon atom such as a methyl group (—CH_3).

allele One form of a gene.

allergen Antigen that causes an allergy.

allergic rhinitis Hay fever; sneezing, runny nose, teary eyes resulting from exposure of a sensitized person to inhaled antigen; an IgE-mediated allergic reaction.

allergy Hypersensitivity, especially of the IgE-mediated type.

allograft Organ or tissue graft transplanted between genetically nonidentical members of the same species.

allosteric site Site on an allosteric enzyme that binds an effector molecule; binding alters the activity of the enzyme.

alpha (α) hemolysis Type of hemolysis observed on blood agar, characterized by zone of greenish clearing around the colonies.

alternative pathway Pathway of complement activation initiated by the binding of a complement protein (C3b) to cell surfaces.

amalgam Mixture of mercury with other metals to form a paste that hardens; used to fill cavities in teeth.

amino acids Subunits of a protein molecule.

aminoglycosides Group of antimicrobial medications that interferes with protein synthesis.

amino terminal (or **N terminal**) The end of the protein molecule that has an unbonded —NH_2 group.

ammonification The reactions that result in the release of ammonia (NH_3) from organic nitrogen-containing molecules.

amphibolic pathways Metabolic pathways that play roles in both catabolism and anabolism.

amylases Enzymes that digest starches.

anabolism Cellular processes that use the energy stored in ATP to synthesize and assemble subunits such as amino acids; synonymous with biosynthesis.

anaerobic Containing no molecular oxygen (O_2).

anaerobic respiration Metabolic process in which electrons are transferred from the electron transport chain to an inorganic terminal electron acceptor other than O_2.

analytical study An epidemiological study done to identify specific risk factors associated with developing a certain disease.
anamnestic response (See *secondary response.*)
anaphylaxis Allergic reaction caused by IgE; generalized hypersensitive reaction to an allergen that can cause a profound drop in blood pressure.
anaplerotic reactions Chemical reactions that bypass certain steps of the central metabolic pathways; they are used to replenish some of the intermediates drawn off for biosynthesis.
anion Negatively charged ion.
anneal Form a double-stranded duplex from two complementary strands of DNA.
anoxic Devoid of O_2.
anoxygenic phototrophs Photosynthetic bacteria that use hydrogen sulfide or organic compounds rather than water as a source of electrons for reducing power; they do not generate O_2.
antagonistic In antimicrobial therapy, a combination of antimicrobial medications in which the action of one interferes with the action of the other.
antenna complex Complex in photosynthetic organisms composed of hundreds of light-gathering pigments; acts as a funnel, capturing light energy and transferring it to reaction-center chlorophyll.
antibacterial drug Chemical used to treat bacterial infections.
antibiogram Antibiotic susceptibility pattern; used to distinguish different bacterial strains.
antibiotic Chemical produced by certain molds and bacteria that kills or inhibits the growth of other microorganisms.
antibiotic-associated colitis Intestinal disease caused by overgrowth of toxin-producing strains of *Clostridium difficile;* typically, occurs when a person is taking antimicrobial medications.
antibody Immunoglobulin protein produced by the body in response to a substance and that reacts specifically with that substance.
anticodon Sequence of three nucleotides in a tRNA molecule that is complementary to a particular codon in mRNA.
antigen Molecule that reacts specifically with an antibody or immune lymphocyte.
antigen-antibody complex Linked group of antibodies bound to antigen.
antigen-binding sites Regions at the ends of the two arms of an antibody molecule that recognize specific antigen; there are two identical antigen-binding sites on each monomer of antibody.
antigen-presenting cells (APCs) Cells such as B cells, macrophages, and dendritic cells that can present exogenous antigen to helper T cells.
antigenic determinant Part of an antigen molecule that binds the specific antibody; an epitope.
antigenic drift Slight changes that occur in the antigens of a virus; specific antibodies made to the antigen before the change occurred are only partially protective.
antigenic shift Major changes that can occur in the antigens of a virus.
antigenic variation Routine alteration by an organism in the characteristics of certain of its surface proteins.
antigen presentation Process in which cells display antigen in the groove of MHC molecules for inspection by T cells.
antimicrobial drug Chemical used to treat microbial infections; also called an antimicrobial.
antiparallel Term used to describe opposing orientations of the two strands of DNA in the double helix; one strand is oriented in the 5′ to 3′ direction and its complement is oriented in the 3′ to 5′ direction.
antisense strand Complement to the sense (or plus) strand of RNA; also called the minus (−) strand.
antiseptic A disinfectant that is non-toxic enough to be used on skin.
antiserum A preparation of serum containing protective antibodies.
antitoxin An antibody preparation that protects against a given toxin.
aplastic anemia Potentially lethal condition in which the body is unable to make blood cells.
apoptosis Programmed cell death.
arbovirus Arthropod-borne virus. One of a large group of RNA viruses carried by insects and mites that act as biological vectors.
Archaea One of the two domains of prokaryotes; most, but not all, archaea grow in extreme environments.
arteriosclerosis Condition characterized by thickening and loss of elasticity of the walls of arteries; "hardening of the arteries."
arthropod Classification grouping of invertebrate animals that includes insects, ticks, lice, and mites.
Arthus reaction Hypersensitivity reaction caused by immune complexes and neutrophils.
artificial wetland method Method of sewage treatment in which sewage is channeled into successive ponds where both aerobic and anaerobic degradation occurs.
artificially acquired immunity Active or passive immunity acquired through artificial means such as vaccination or administration of immune serum globulin.
aseptic Free of microorganisms and viruses; sterile.
aseptic technique Use of specific methods and sterile materials to exclude contaminating microorganisms from an environment.
asexual Reproduction not preceded by the union of cells or genetic exchange.
A-site (or **aminoacyl site**) Site on the ribosome to which tRNAs enter to donate their amino acid; acceptor site.
asthma Immediate respiratory allergy resulting from mediator release from mast cells in the lower airways.
astrobiology Study of life in the universe.
atomic force microscope Type of scanning probe microscope that has a tip mounted so it can bend in response to the slightest force between the tip and the sample.
ATP Abbreviation for adenosine triphosphate.
ATP synthase Protein complex that harvests the energy of a proton motive force to synthesize ATP.
attack rate Proportional number of cases developing in a population exposed to an infectious agent.
attenuated vaccine Vaccine composed of a weakened form of a disease-causing microorganism or virus that is generally unable to cause disease; the vaccine strain is able to replicate.
auramine A fluorescent dye that can be used to stain members of the genus *Mycobacterium.*
autoantibodies Antibodies that bind to "self" proteins.
autoclave Device employing steam under pressure used for sterilizing materials that are stable to heat and moisture.
autoimmune disease Disease produced as a result of an immune reaction against one's own tissues.
autolyze To spontaneously disintegrate as a result of enzymes within the cell.
autoradiography The use of film to detect a radioactive molecule.
autotroph Organism that can use CO_2 as its main source of carbon.
auxotroph Mutant microorganism that requires an organic growth factor.
avirulent Lacking disease-causing attributes.
a_w Abbreviation for water activity.
axial filaments Characteristic structure of motility found in spirochetes.
axon The long thin extension of a nerve cell.
azoles Large family of chemically synthesized medications, some of which have antifungal activity.

---

bacillus (pl. **bacilli**) Cylindrical-shaped bacterium; also referred to as a rod.
bacitracin Antimicrobial medication that inhibits cell wall biosynthesis by interfering with the transport of peptidoglycan precursors across the cytoplasmic membrane.
bacteremia Bacteria circulating in the bloodstream.
Bacteria One of the two domains of prokaryotes; all medically important prokaryotes are in the domain *Bacteria.*
bactericidal Able to kill bacteria.
bacteriochlorophyll Type of chlorophyll used by purple and green bacteria; absorbs wavelengths of light that penetrate to greater depths and are not used by other photosynthetic organisms.
bacteriocins Proteins made by bacteria that kill certain other bacteria.
bacteriophage A virus that infects bacteria; often abbreviated to phage.
bacteriorhodopsin Pigment of some prokaryotes that absorbs energy from sunlight and uses it to expel protons from the cell, generating a proton gradient.
bacteriostatic Able to inhibit the growth of bacteria.
balanced pathogenicity Host parasite relationship in which the parasite persists in the host without causing excessive harm.
barophiles Bacteria that can grow under high pressure.
basal body Structure that anchors the flagella to the cell wall and cytoplasmic membrane.
base Refers to the purine or pyrimidine ring structure found in nucleic acids.
base analog Compound that resembles a purine or pyrimidine base closely enough to be incorporated into DNA in place of a natural base.
base-pairing The hydrogen bonding of adenine (A) to thymine (T) and cytosine (C) to guanine (G); occurs between two complementary strands of DNA.
basement membrane Thin layer of fibrous material that underlies epithelial cells.
basic amino acids Amino acids with more basic ($—NH_3^+$) groups than acid ($—COO^-$) groups.
basophil Leukocyte with large dark-staining granules that contain histamine and other mediators of inflammation; receptors on cell surfaces bind monomers of IgE.
B-cell receptor Membrane-bound derivative of the antibody that a B cell is programmed to make; it enables the B cell to recognize a specific antigen.
B cells Lymphocytes programmed to produce antibody molecules.

beta- (β) hemolysis Type of hemolysis observed on blood agar that is characterized by a clear zone around a colony.

beta- (β) lactam drugs Group of antimicrobial medications that inhibit peptidoglycan synthesis and have a shared chemical structure called a β-lactam ring.

bilayer membrane (or **unit membrane**) Double layer of phospholipid molecules that forms the major structure of the cytoplasmic (plasma) membrane.

bile Yellow-colored fluid produced by the liver that aids in the absorption of nutrients from the intestine.

binary fission Asexual process of reproduction in which one cell divides into two independent daughter cells.

binding protein Protein that functions in the ABC transport system; resides immediately outside of the cytoplasmic membrane to deliver a given molecule to a specific transport complex within the membrane.

binomial system System of naming each species of organism with two Latin words.

biochemical oxygen demand (BOD) Measure of the amount of biologically degradable organic material in water.

biocide Compound such as a disinfectant that is toxic to many forms of life, including microorganisms.

biodiversity Diversity in the number of species inhabiting an ecosystem and their evenness of distribution.

biofilm Polysaccharide-encased community of microorganisms.

bioinformatics Developing and using computer technology to store, retrieve, and analyze nucleotide sequence data.

bioleaching Conversion of metals to a soluble form due to the metabolic oxidation of insoluble metal sulfides by microorganisms.

biological vector Organism that acts as a host for a pathogen before it is transmitted to another organism; the pathogen can multiply to high numbers within it.

bioluminescence Biological production of light.

biomass Total weight of all organisms in any particular environment.

bioremediation Process that uses microorganisms to degrade harmful chemicals.

biosphere The sum of all the regions of the earth where life exists.

biotechnology The use of microbiological and biochemical techniques to solve practical problems and produce more useful products.

biotype A strain that has a characteristic biochemical pattern different from other strains; also called a biovar.

blood agar Type of rich agar medium that contains red blood cells and can be used to detect hemolysis.

blood-brain barrier Property of the central nervous system blood vessels that restricts passage of infectious agents and certain molecules (such as medications) into the brain and spinal cord.

blunt end The type of DNA ends generated by a restriction enzyme that cuts directly in the middle of the recognition sequence.

BOD Abbreviation for biochemical oxygen demand.

boil Painful localized collection of pus within the skin and subcutaneous tissue; a furuncle.

bonds Forces which hold atoms or molecules together.

bone marrow Soft material that fills bone cavities and contains stem cells for all blood cells.

botulinum toxin Toxin produced by *Clostridium botulinum* that can cause a fatal paralysis in people who consume it.

bright-field microscope Type of light microscope that illuminates the field of view evenly.

brine Salty water; used to cure fish and meats.

broad host range plasmid A plasmid which can replicate in a wide variety of unrelated bacteria.

broad-spectrum antimicrobials Antimicrobials that inhibit or kill a wide range of microorganisms, often including both Gram-positive and Gram-negative bacteria.

Bt-toxin Protein crystal naturally produced by the bacterium *Bacillus thuringiensis* as it forms endospores; toxic to insect larvae that consume it.

bubo Enlarged, tender lymph node characteristic of plague and some venereal diseases.

bubonic plague Form of plague that typically develops when *Yersinia pestis* is injected via the bite of an infected flea.

budding Asexual reproductive technique that involves a pushing out of a part of the parent cell that eventually gives rise to a new daughter cell.

buffer Substance in a solution that acts to prevent changes in pH.

bulking Overgrowth of filamentous microorganisms in sewage at treatment facilities; interferes with the separation of the solid sludge from the liquid effluent.

burst size Number of newly formed virus particles released from a single cell.

---

calcofluor white Fluorescent dye that binds to a component of certain cells, including fungi, causing them to fluoresce bright blue.

Calvin cycle Metabolic pathway used by many autotrophs to incorporate CO_2 into an organic form; also called the Calvin-Benson cycle.

cAMP Abbreviation for cyclic AMP.

cancer Abnormally growing cells that can spread from their site of origin; malignant tumors.

candidiasis Fungal diseases caused by *Candida albicans.*

candle jar Closed jar in which a lit candle converts some of the O_2 in air to CO_2 and water vapor; used to cultivate capnophiles.

CAP Abbreviation for cyclic AMP-activating protein.

cap Methylated guanine derivative added to the 5′ end of eukaryotic mRNA before transcription is complete.

capnophiles Organisms that require increased concentrations of CO_2 (5% to 10%) and approximately 15% oxygen.

capsid Protein coat that surrounds the nucleic acid of a virus.

capsule Glycocalyx that is distinct and gelatinous; sometimes correlated with an organism's ability to cause disease.

carbapenems Group of antimicrobial medications that interferes with peptidoglycan synthesis; very resistant to inactivation by β-lactamases.

carbohydrate Compounds containing principally carbon, hydrogen, and oxygen atoms in a ratio of 1:2:1.

carbon fixation Process of converting inorganic carbon (CO_2) to an organic form; in photosynthetic organisms, the dark or light-independent reactions.

carboxyl terminal (or **C terminal**) The end of the protein molecule that has an unbonded —COOH group.

carbuncle Painful infection of the skin and subcutaneous tissues; manifests as a cluster of boils.

carcinogen A chemical or radiation that causes cancer.

cariogenic Causing dental caries, tooth decay.

carotenoids Accessory pigment found in a wide variety of photosynthetic organisms that increases the efficiency of light capture by absorbing wavelengths of light not absorbed by chlorophylls; mammals can use one of the carotenoids (beta-carotene) as a source of vitamin A.

carrier (1) Type of protein found in cell membranes that transports certain compounds across the membrane; may also be called a permease or transporter protein. (2) A human or other animal that harbors a pathogen without noticeable ill effects.

carrier cell A virus-infected cell that extrudes virions as it multiplies.

carrier state State of infection in which the agent can be detected in body fluids without causing disease symptoms.

cascade In biology, a series of reactions that, once started, continues to the final step by each step triggering the next in a special order; activation of complement is an example.

caseous necrosis Type of localized tissue death having a cheeselike consistency, characteristic of tuberculosis and certain other chronic infectious diseases.

catabolism Cellular processes that harvest the energy released during the breakdown of compounds such as glucose and use that energy to synthesize ATP, the energy currency of all cells.

catabolite Product of catabolism.

catabolite repression The mechanism by which cells decrease the expression of genes that encode certain degradative enzymes in the presence of a compound such as glucose.

catalase Enzyme that breaks down hydrogen peroxide (H_2O_2) to produce water (H_2O) and oxygen gas (O_2).

catalyst Substance that speeds up the rate of a chemical reaction without being altered or depleted in the process.

cations Positively charged ions.

CD markers Abbreviation for cluster of differentiation markers.

CD4 lymphocytes T lymphocytes bearing the CD4 markers; helper T cells are CD4 cells.

CD8 lymphocytes T lymphocytes bearing the CD8 markers; cytotoxic T cells are CD8 cells.

cDNA DNA obtained by using reverse transcriptase to synthesize DNA from an RNA template *in vitro;* lacks introns that characterize eukaryotic DNA.

cell culture (or **tissue culture**) Cultivation of animal or plant cells in the laboratory.

cell envelope The layers surrounding the contents of the cell; includes the cytoplasmic membrane, cell wall, and capsule (if present).

cell wall Rigid barrier that surrounds a cell, keeping the contents from bursting out; in prokaryotes, peptidoglycan provides rigidity to the cell wall.

cell-mediated immunity (CMI) (See *cellular immunity.*)

cellular immunity (also called cell-mediated immunity or CMI) The immune response mediated by T lymphocytes (T cells).

cellulose Polymer of glucose subunits; principal structural component of plant cell walls.

central metabolic pathways Glycolysis, the TCA cycle, and the pentose phosphate pathway.
cephalosporins Group of antimicrobial medications that interfere with peptidoglycan synthesis.
cestode Tapeworm.
chain terminator A dideoxynucleotide; when this molecule is incorporated into a growing strand of DNA, no additional nucleotides can be added, and elongation of the strand ceases.
challenge In immunology, to give an antigen to provoke an immunologic response in a subject previously sensitized to the antigen.
chancre Sore resulting from an ulcerating infection; the "hard chancre" of primary syphilis is typically firm and painless.
chaperones Proteins that help other proteins fold properly.
chemical bond Force that holds atoms together to form molecules.
chemically defined media Bacteriological media composed of ingredients of known chemical composition; generally used for specific experiments when nutrients must be precisely controlled.
chemiosmotic gradient Accumulation of protons on one side of a membrane due to expulsion of protons by the electron transport chain; used by prokaryotes to power the synthesis of ATP, fuel certain transport processes, and drive the rotation of flagella; also called the proton motive force.
chemiosmotic theory The theory that a proton gradient is formed by the electron transport chain and is then used to power the synthesis of ATP.
chemoautotrophs Organisms that use chemicals as a source of energy and CO_2 as the major source of carbon.
chemoheterotrophs Organisms that use chemicals as a source of energy, and organic compounds as a source of carbon.
chemokine Cytokine important in chemotaxis of immune cells.
chemolithoautotrophs Organisms that obtain energy by degrading reduced inorganic compounds such as hydrogen gas (H_2), and use CO_2 as a source of carbon.
chemolithotrophs Organisms that obtain energy by degrading reduced inorganic chemicals such as hydrogen gas (H_2); in general, chemolithotrophs are chemolithoautotrophs.
chemoorganoheterotrophs Organisms that obtain both energy and carbon from organic compounds.
chemoorganotrophs Organisms that obtain energy by degrading organic compounds such as glucose; in general, chemoorganotrophs are chemoorganoheterotrophs.
chemostat Device used to grow bacteria in the laboratory that allows nutrients to be added and waste products to be removed continuously.
chemotaxis Directed movement of an organism in response to a certain chemical in the environment.
chemotherapeutic agent Chemical used as a therapeutic medication to treat a disease.
chemotrophs Organisms that obtain energy by degrading chemical compounds.
chickenpox Disease caused by the herpesvirus, varicella.
chloramphenicol Antimicrobial medication that interferes with protein synthesis.
chlorophylls The primary light-absorbing pigments used in photosynthesis.
chloroplasts Organelles in photosynthetic eukaryotic cells that harvest the energy of sunlight and use it to synthesize ATP, which is then used to fuel the synthesis of organic compounds.
chlorosomes Structures of green bacteria in which the accessory pigments are located.
chocolate agar Type of agar medium that contains red blood cells that have been heated under controlled conditions to lyse them, releasing their nutrients; used to culture fastidious bacteria.
cholesterol Sterol found in animal cell membranes; provides rigidity to eukaryotic membranes.
chorea Constant complex, rapid, jerky involuntary movements; an occasional sequel to untreated *Streptococcus pyogenes* infections.
chromatin Complex of histones and DNA that make up the chromosomes of eukaryotic cells.
chromosome Array of genes responsible for the determination and transmission of hereditary characteristics.
chronic infections Infections that develop slowly and persist for months or years.
chronic inflammation Long-term inflammatory response, marked by the prevalence of macrophages, giant cells, and granulomas.
cilium (pl. **cilia**) Short, projecting hairlike organelle of locomotion, similar to a flagellum.
circulative transmission Transmission of viruses to plants by insects within which the virus circulates but does not multiply.
cirrhosis A chronic progressive condition affecting the liver characterized by formation of strands of scar tissue; various causes, but commonly due to alcoholism.
citric acid cycle Metabolic pathway that incorporates acetyl-CoA, ultimately generating CO_2 and reducing power, also known as the tricarboxylic acid (TCA) cycle and the Krebs cycle.
clade Subtype of a virus such as human immunodeficiency virus (HIV), defined by similar amino acid sequences of their envelope proteins.
class Collection of similar orders; a collection of several classes makes up a phylum.
class switching The process that allows a B cell to change the antibody class it is programmed to make; through class switching plasma cells that descend from the B cell can make antibodies other than IgM.
classical pathway Pathway of complement activation initiated by specific antigen-antibody interaction.
classification Process of arranging organisms into similar or related groups, primarily to provide easy identification and study.
clonal selection and expansion Selection and activation of a lymphocyte by interaction of antigen and specific antigen receptor on the lymphocyte surface, causing the lymphocyte to proliferate to form an expanded clone.
clonal deletion Elimination of lymphocytes that have an antigen receptor that binds to normal host molecules.
clone Group of cells derived from a single cell.
closed system Batch system (such as a tube or flask of broth, or an agar plate) used for growing microorganisms; nutrients are not replenished and wastes are not removed.
clusters of differentiation (CD) marker Molecules on the surface of T cells and other white blood cells that are used by scientists to distinguish subsets of cells.
CMI Abbreviation for cell-mediated immunity.
CO_2 fixation Process of converting inorganic carbon (CO_2) to an organic form.
coagulase Non-enzymatic product of *Staphylococcus aureus* that clots plasma.
coccus (pl. **cocci**) Spherical-shaped bacterial cell.
codon Set of three nucleotides.
coenzyme Non-protein organic compounds that assist some enzymes, acting as a loosely bound carrier of small molecules or electrons.
cofactor Non-protein component required for the activity of some enzymes.
cohesive ends Single-stranded overhangs generated when DNA is digested with a restriction enzyme that cuts asymmetrically within the recognition sequence; sticky ends.
cohort group Population with a known exposure to a specific risk factor that is followed over time in a prospective study.
coliforms (See *total coliform.*)
colonization Establishment of a site of reproduction of microbes on a material, animal, or person without necessarily resulting in tissue invasion or damage.
colony Population of bacterial cells arising from a single cell.
colony blotting Technique that uses a probe to detect a given DNA sequence in colonies growing on an agar plate.
colony-forming unit A unit that gives rise to a single colony; may be a single cell or multiple cells attached to one another.
colony-stimulating factors A group of cytokines that direct the formation of the various types of blood cells from stem cells.
combination therapy Administration of two or more antimicrobial medications simultaneously to prevent growth of mutants that might be resistant to one of the antimicrobials.
commensalism Relationship between two organisms in which one partner benefits from the association and the other is unaffected.
commercially sterile Free of all microorganisms capable of growing under normal storage conditions; the endospores of some thermophiles may remain.
common-source epidemic Outbreak of disease due to contaminated food, water, or other single source of infectious agent.
communicable diseases Diseases that are spread from an infected animal or person to another animal or person.
communities All of the living organisms in a given area.
competent Condition in which a bacterial cell is capable of taking up and integrating fragments of DNA into its chromosome.
competitive inhibition Type of enzyme inhibition that occurs when the inhibitor competes with the normal substrate for binding to the active site.
complement system Series of serum proteins involved with innate immunity; complement proteins can be rapidly activated, contributing to protective outcomes including inflammation, lysis of foreign cells, and opsonization.
complementary Describes bases in nucleic acid which hydrogen bond to one another; A (adenine) is complementary to T (thymine), and G (guanine) is complementary to C (cytosine).
complex medium Medium for growing bacteria that has some ingredients of unknown chemical composition.
compound microscope Microscope that employs two magnifying lenses—an objective lens and an ocular lens; the lenses in combination visually

enlarge an object by a factor equal to the product of each lens's magnification.

condenser lens Lens of a microscope that is used to focus the illumination; positioned between the light source and the specimen and does not affect the magnification.

conditional lethal mutant Mutant that under some environmental conditions will grow, with lethal results, but under other conditions will not grow.

confocal scanning laser microscope Type of microscope that focuses a laser beam to illuminate a given point on one vertical plane of a specimen; after successive regions and planes have been scanned, a computer can construct a three-dimensional image of a thick structure.

congenital A condition existing from the time of birth.

conidia Asexual spores borne on hyphae; produced by fungi and bacteria of the genus *Streptomyces*.

conjugate vaccine A vaccine composed of a polysaccharide antigen covalently attached to a large protein molecule; this type of vaccine converts what would be a T-independent antigen into a T-dependent antigen.

conjugation Mechanism of gene transfer in bacteria that involves cell-to-cell contact.

conjugative plasmid Plasmid that carries the genes for sex pili and can transfer copies of itself to other bacteria during conjugation.

constant region That part of the antibody molecule that does not vary in amino acid sequences among molecules of the same immunoglobulin class.

co-stimulatory molecules Surface proteins expressed by dendritic cells and macrophages when the cell senses molecules that signify an invading microbe or tissue damage; they facilitate activation of T cells that recognize the antigen presented by the antigen-presenting cell (APC).

constitutive enzyme An enzyme that is constantly synthesized.

contact dermatitis A T-cell-mediated inflammation of the skin occurring in sensitized individuals as a result of contact with the particular antigen; a form of delayed hypersensitivity.

contagious diseases Diseases that are highly communicable and are spread from one host to another very readily.

continuous culture Method used to maintain cells in a state of uninterrupted growth by continuously adding nutrients and removing waste products; a type of open system.

convalescence Period of recuperation and recovery from an illness.

convergent evolution Process of evolution when two genetically different organisms develop similar environmental adaptations.

corepressor Molecule that binds to an inactive repressor and, as a consequence, enables it to function as a repressor.

cortex Layer of the endospore that helps maintain the core in a dehydrated state, protecting it from the effects of heat.

counterstain In a differential staining procedure, the stain applied to impart a contrasting color to bacteria that do not retain the primary stain.

covalent bond Strong chemical bond formed by the sharing of electrons between atoms.

critical instruments Medical instruments such as needles and scalpels that come into direct contact with body tissue.

cross-contamination Transfer of pathogens from one item to another.

cross-sectional study Study that surveys a range of people to determine the prevalence of characteristics including disease, risk factors associated with disease, or previous exposure to a disease-causing agent.

croup Acute obstruction of the larynx occurring mainly in infants and young children, often resulting from respiratory syncytial or other viral infection.

crown gall tumor A tumor on a plant caused by *Agrobacterium tumefaciens*.

CSF Abbreviation for colony-stimulating factor.

curd Coagulated milk proteins, produced during cheese-making.

cyclic AMP-activating protein (CAP) Protein that binds to cAMP to promote gene transcription.

cyclic photophosphorylation Type of photophosphorylation in which electrons are returned directly to the chlorophyll; used to synthesize ATP without generating reducing power.

cyst Dormant resting protozoan cell characterized by a thickened cell wall.

cysticercus (pl. **cysticerci**) Cystlike larval form of tapeworms.

cystitis Inflammation of the urinary bladder.

cytochromes Proteins that carry electrons, usually as members of electron transport chains.

cytokine Low molecular weight regulatory protein made by cells that affect the behavior of other cells; cytokines attach to specific cytokine receptors and are essential for communication between cells.

cytokine receptor Type of surface receptor that binds a chemokine.

cytopathic effect Observable change in a cell *in vitro* produced by viral action such as lysis of the cell.

cytoplasm Viscous fluid within a cell.

cytoplasmic membrane Thin, fluid, lipid bilayer that surrounds the cytoplasm and defines the boundary of a cell.

cytoskeleton Dynamic filamentous network that provides structure and shape to eukaryotic cells.

cytotoxic Kills cells.

cytotoxic T cells Type of lymphocyte programmed to destroy corrupt "self" cells.

cytotoxin Toxin that damages a variety of different cell types.

---

danger model Hypothesis that suggests that the immune system mounts a response against foreign material only if it is associated with tissue damage, microbial products, or other signs of "danger."

dark-field microscope Type of microscope that directs light toward the specimen at an angle, so that only light scattered by the specimen enters the objective lens; materials in the specimen stand out as bright objects against a dark background.

dark reactions Process of carbon fixation in photosynthetic organisms; the ATP used to drive the process is obtained in the light reactions; the dark reactions are called the light-independent reactions.

dark repair Enzymes of DNA repair that do not depend on visible light.

death phase Stage in which the number of viable bacteria in a population decreases at an exponential rate.

decarboxylation Removal of carbon dioxide from a chemical.

decimal reduction time Time required for 90% of the organisms to be killed under specific conditions; D value.

decontamination Treatment to reduce the number of disease-causing organisms to a level that is considered safe.

defensins Short antimicrobial peptides produced naturally by a variety of eukaryotic cells to fight infections.

degerm Treatment used to decrease the number of microbes in an area, usually skin.

degranulation Release of mediators from granules in the cell, as histamine is released from mast cells.

dehydration synthesis Chemical reaction in which H_2O is removed with the result that two molecules are joined together.

dehydrogenation Oxidation reaction in which both an electron and an accompanying proton are removed.

delayed hypersensitivity Hypersensitivity caused by cytokines released from sensitized T lymphocytes; reactions occur within 48 to 72 hours after exposure of a sensitized individual to antigen.

denaturation (1) Disruption of the three-dimensional structure of a protein molecule. (2) The separation of the complementary strands of DNA.

denaturing gradient gel electrophoresis (DGGE) A procedure that gradually denatures double-stranded nucleic acid during gel electrophoresis and, as a consequence, separates similar-sized fragments according to their melting point, which is related to the nucelotide sequence.

dendritic cells Antigen-presenting cells that play an essential role in activation of naive T cells.

denitrification Bacterial conversion of nitrate to gaseous nitrogen by anaerobic respiration.

dental plaque A biofilm on teeth.

deoxyribonucleic acid (DNA) Macromolecule in the cell that carries the genetic information.

deoxyribose A 5-carbon sugar molecule found in DNA.

depth filter Type of filter with complex, tortuous passages that allow the suspending fluid pass through while retaining microorganisms.

dermatophytes Certain moldlike fungi that live on the skin and can be responsible for disease of the hair, nails, and skin.

dermis The layer of skin that underlies the epidermis.

descriptive study Type of study that seeks to characterize a disease outbreak by determining the characteristics of the persons involved and the place and time of the outbreak.

dessication Dehydration.

detritus Fresh or partially degraded organic matter used by decomposers.

diapedesis Movement of leukocytes from blood vessels into tissues in response to a chemotactic stimulus during inflammation.

diatomaceous earth Sedimentary soil composed largely of the skeletons of diatoms; contains large amounts of silicon.

diauxic growth Two-step growth frequency observed when bacteria are growing in media containing two carbon sources.

diazotroph Organism that can fix nitrogen.

dichotomous key Flowchart of tests used for identifying an organism; each test gives either a positive or negative result.

dideoxy chain termination method A technique used to determine the nucleotide sequence of a strand of DNA; in the procedure, a small amount of chain terminator (a dideoxynucleotide) is added to an *in vitro* synthesis reaction.

dideoxynucleotide (ddNTP) Nucleotide that lacks the 3′ OH group, the portion required for the addition of subsequent nucleotides during DNA synthesis.

differential media Culture media that contain certain ingredients such as sugars in combination with pH indicators; used to distinguish among organisms based on their metabolic traits.

differential staining Type of staining procedure used to distinguish one group of bacteria from another by taking advantage of the fact that certain bacteria have distinctly different chemical structures in some of their components.

differentiate In cell development, a change in a cell associated with the acquisition of distinct morphological and functional properties.

diffusion Movement of substances from a region of high concentration to a region of low concentration.

digesting Treating with an enzyme such as a restriction enzyme, thereby generating degradation products, such as restriction fragments.

diluent Sterile solution used to make dilutions.

dimorphic Able to assume two forms, as the yeast and mold forms of pathogenic fungi.

diphtheroids Gram-positive cells that are club-shaped and arranged to form V-shapes and palisades; the typical microscopic morphology of *Corynebacterium.*

diplococci Cocci that typically occur in pairs.

directly observed therapy Method used to ensure that patients comply with their antimicrobial therapy; health care workers routinely visit patients in the community and watch them take their medications.

direct microscopic count Method of determining the number of bacteria in a measured volume of liquid by counting them microscopically using special glass slides.

direct selection Technique of selecting mutants by plating organisms on a medium on which the desired mutants but not the parent will grow.

disaccharide Carbohydrate molecule consisting of two monosaccharide molecules.

disease Process resulting in tissue damage or alteration of function, producing body changes noticeable by physical examination or laboratory tests.

disinfection Process of reducing or eliminating pathogenic microorganisms or viruses in or on a material so that they are no longer a hazard.

disinfection by-product (DBPs) Compounds formed when chlorine or other disinfectants react with naturally-occurring chemicals in water.

disseminate To spread.

disseminated intravascular coagulation Devastating condition in which clots form in small blood vessels, leading to failure of vital organs.

division Taxonomic rank that groups similar classes; also called a phylum. A collection of similar divisions makes up a kingdom.

DNA Abbreviation for deoxyribonucleic acid.

DNA-based vaccine Vaccine composed of segments of naked DNA from infectious organisms that can be introduced directly into muscle tissue; the host tissue expresses the DNA for a short time, producing the microbial antigens encoded by the DNA. Vaccines of this type are still in developmental stages.

DNA cloning Procedure by which DNA is inserted into a replicon such as a plasmid or bacteriophage, which is then introduced into cells where the replicon can replicate. (See *gene cloning.*)

DNA fingerprinting The use of characteristic patterns in the nucleotide sequence of DNA to match a specimen to a probable source.

DNA gyrase Enzyme that helps relieve the tension in DNA caused by the unwinding of the two strands of the DNA helix.

DNA library Collection of cloned molecules that together encompass the entire genome of an organism of interest; each clone can be viewed as one "book" of the total genetic information of the organism of interest.

DNA ligase Enzyme that forms covalent bonds between adjacent fragments of DNA.

DNA-mediated transformation Process of gene transfer in which DNA is transferred as a "naked" molecule.

DNA microarray (See *microarray.*)

DNA polymerases Enzymes that synthesize DNA; they use one strand as a template to generate the complementary strand.

DNA probe A piece of DNA, labeled in some manner, that is used to identify the presence of homologous DNA by hybridizing to its complement.

DNA replication Duplication of a DNA molecule.

DNA sequencing Determining the sequence (order) of nucleotide bases in a strand of DNA.

domain (1) Level of taxonomic classification above the kingdom level; there are three domains—*Bacteria, Archaea,* and *Eucarya.* (2) Distinct globular regions that characterize immunoglobulin molecules.

donor Refers to the cell that donates DNA in DNA transfer.

double-blind Type of study where neither the physicians nor the patients know who is receiving the actual treatment.

doubling time Time it takes for the number of cells in population to double; the generation time.

downstream Direction toward the 3′ end of an RNA molecule or the analogous (+) strand of DNA.

droplet transmission Transmission of infectious agents through inhalation of respiratory droplets.

Durham tube Small inverted tube placed in a broth of sugar-containing media that is used to detect gas production by a microorganism.

D value Abbreviation for the decimal reduction time.

dysentery Condition characterized by crampy abdominal pain and bloody diarrhea.

---

eclipse period Time during which viruses exist within the host cell separated into their protein and nucleic acid components.

ecological niche The role that an organism plays in a particular ecosystem.

ecosystem An environment and the organisms that inhabit it.

eczema Condition characterized by a blistery skin rash, with weeping of fluid and formation of crusts, usually due to an allergy.

edema Swelling of tissues caused by accumulation of fluid.

edible vaccine Vaccine created by transferring genes encoding key antigens from infectious agents into plants. Vaccines of this type are still in developmental stages.

effector Regulatory molecule that binds to the allosteric site of an enzyme; the binding alters the shape of the enzyme, altering its affinity for the substrate.

effector T cell A descendent of an activated T cell that has become armed with the ability to produce specific cytokines and other substances, endowing the cell with specific protective attributes.

electrochemical gradient A separation of charged ions across the membrane.

electron Negatively charged component of an atom that orbits the nucleus.

electron microscope Microscope that uses electrons instead of light and can magnify images in excess of 100,000×.

electron transport chain Series of electron carriers that transfer electrons from donors such as NADH to acceptors such as oxygen, ejecting protons in the process.

electrophoresis Technique that uses an electric current to separate either DNA fragments or proteins.

electroporation Process of treating cells with an electric current to introduce DNA into them.

element A substance that is composed of a single type of atom.

elementary body Small dense-appearing infectious form of *Chlamydia* species that is released upon death and rupture of the host cell.

elephantiasis Massive enlargement of the legs and/or external genitalia due to lymphatic obstruction, caused by the inflammatory response to larval roundworms such as *Wuchereria bancrofti.*

ELISA Abbreviation for enzyme-linked immunosorbent assay.

Embden-Meyerhof pathway Metabolic pathway that oxidizes glucose to pyruvate, generating ATP and reducing power; also known as glycolysis and the glycolytic pathway.

emerging diseases Diseases that have increased in incidence in the past two decades.

encephalitis Inflammation of the brain.

endemic Constantly present in a population.

endergonic Chemical reaction that requires a net input of energy because the products have more free energy than the reactants.

endocarditis Inflammation of the heart valves or lining of the heart chambers.

endocytosis Process through which cells take up particles by enclosing them in a vesicle pinched off from the cell membrane.

endogenous antigen An antigen produced within a given host cell.

endogenous pyrogen Fever-inducing substance (such as cytokines) made by the body.

endonuclease An enzyme which cleaves bonds internally in the backbone of DNA.

endoplasmic reticulum (ER) Organelle of eukaryotes where macromolecules destined for the external environment of other organelles are synthesized.

endosome Vesicle formed when a cell takes up material from the surrounding environment using the process of endocytosis.

endospore A kind of resting cell, characteristic of a limited number of bacterial species; highly resistant to heat, radiation, and disinfectants.

endosymbiont Microorganism that resides within another cell, providing a benefit to the host cell.

endosymbiont theory Theory that the ancestors of mitochondria and chloroplasts were bacteria that had been residing within other cells in a mutually beneficial partnership.

endothelial cell Cell type that lines the blood and lymph vessels.

endotoxic shock Septic shock that occurs as a result of endotoxin (lipopolysaccharide) circulating in the bloodstream.

endotoxin Lipopolysaccharide, a toxic component of the outer membrane of Gram-negative cells that can elicit symptoms such as fever and shock; lipid A is the molecule responsible for the toxic effects of endotoxin.

end product inhibition Inhibition of gene activity by the end product of a biosynthetic pathway.

energy The capacity to do work.

energy source Compound that is oxidized by a cell to release energy; also called an electron donor.

enrichment culture Culture method that provides conditions to enhance the growth of one particular organism in a mixed population.

enterics A common name for members of the family *Enterobacteriaceae.*

enterobacteria (See *enterics.*)

enterotoxin Poisonous substance, usually of bacterial origin, that acts on the intestinal lining cells to cause diarrhea and vomiting.

Entner-Doudoroff pathway Pathway that converts glucose to pyruvate and glyceraldehyde-3-phosphate by producing 6-phosphogluconate and then dehydrating it.

entropy The degree of disorder in a system.

enveloped viruses Viruses that have a double layer of lipid surrounding their nucleocapsid.

enzyme A protein that functions as a catalyst.

enzyme-linked immunosorbent assay (ELISA) Technique used for detecting and quantifying specific antigens or antibodies by using an antibody labeled with an enzyme.

enzyme-substrate complex Transient form that occurs in an enzyme-mediated reaction, as the enzyme converts a substrate into a product.

eosinophil A type of white blood cell; thought to be primarily important in expelling parasitic worms from the body.

EPA Abbreviation for Environmental Protection Agency, a federal agency.

epidemic A disease or other occurrence whose incidence is higher than expected within a region or population.

epidemiology The study of factors influencing the frequency and distribution of diseases.

epidermis The outermost layer of skin.

epithelial cell Cell type that lines the surfaces of the body.

epitope Region of an antigen recognized by antibodies and antigen receptors on lymphocytes.

ergosterol Sterol found in fungal cell membranes; the target of many antifungal drugs.

ergot Poisonous substance produced by the fungus that causes rye smut.

erythrocytes Red blood cells.

E-site (or **exit site)** Site on the ribosome from which tRNAs exit after donating their amino acid to the adjacent tRNA.

ester bond Covalent bond formed between a —COOH group and an —OH group with the removal of H_2O.

ethambutol Antimycobacterial drug that inhibits enzymes required for synthesis of mycobacterial cell wall components.

ethidium bromide Mutagenic dye that binds to nucleic acid by intercalating between the bases; ethidium bromide-stained DNA is fluorescent when viewed with UV light.

eubacteria Term formerly used to describe those prokaryotes that are now separated into the Domain *Bacteria.*

Eucarya Name of the domain comprising eukaryotic organisms.

eukaryote Organism composed of one or more eukaryotic cells.

eukaryotic cell Complex cell type differing from a prokaryotic cell mainly in having a nuclear membrane.

eutrophic A nutrient-rich environment supporting the excessive growth of algae and other autotrophs.

evolutionary chronometer A molecule such as rRNA that can be used to measure the time elapsed since two organisms diverged from a common ancestor.

exanthem A skin rash.

excision repair Mechanism of DNA repair in which a fragment of single-stranded DNA containing mismatched bases is cut out.

exergonic Describes a chemical reaction that releases energy because the starting compounds have more free energy than the products.

exfoliatin A bacterial toxin that causes sloughing of the outer epidermis.

exocytosis Process by which eukaryotic cells expel material; membrane-bound vesicles inside the cell fuse with the plasma membrane, releasing their contents to the external medium.

exoenzyme Enzyme that acts outside the cell that produces it.

exoerythrocytic Occurring outside the red blood cells, as the developmental cycle in malaria that occurs in the liver.

exogenous antigen An antigen that originated outside of a given host cell.

exogenous pyrogen Fever-inducing substance (such as bacterial endotoxin) made from an external source.

exons Portions of eukaryotic genes that are expressed; interrupted by introns.

exotoxin Soluble poisonous protein substance released by a microorganism.

experimental study Type of study done to assess the effectiveness of measures to prevent or treat disease.

exponential phase Stage of growth of a bacterial culture in which cells are multiplying exponentially; log phase.

expression vectors Vectors that facilitate transcription and translation of cloned DNA.

external node Point on a phylogenetic tree that represents a named species that still exists.

external transmission (or **temporary transmission)** Refers to transmission of viruses to plants by insects in which the virus is associated with the external mouthparts of the insect.

extrachromosomal DNA in a cell that is not part of the chromosome.

extremophiles Organisms that live under extremes of temperature, barometric pressure, or other environmental conditions.

extrinsic factors In food microbiology, environmental conditions, such as the temperature and atmosphere, that influence the rate of microbial growth.

Fab (fragment antigen-binding) region Portion of an antibody molecule that binds to the antigen.

facilitated diffusion Transport process that enables movement of impermeable compounds from one side of the membrane to the other by exploiting a concentration gradient; does not require expenditure of energy by the cell.

facultative Flexible with respect to growth conditions; for example, able to live with or without O_2.

facultative anaerobe Organism that grows best in the presence of oxygen (O_2), but can grow in its absence.

FAD Abbreviation for flavin adenine dinucleotide, an electron carrier.

fallopian tube The tubes that convey ova from the ovaries to the uterus.

FAME Stands for fatty acid methyl ester; a component of a technique that identifies bacteria based on their cellular fatty acid composition.

family Taxonomic group between order and genus.

fasciitis Inflammation of the fascia, bands of fibrous tissue that underlie the skin and surround muscle and body organs.

fastidious Exacting; refers to organisms that require growth factors.

fatty acid A molecule consisting of long chains of carbon atoms bonded to hydrogen atoms with an acidic group (–COOH) at one end.

F^- cell Recipient bacterial cell in conjugation.

F^+ cell Donor bacterial cell in conjugation, transfers the F plasmid.

F plasmid (See *fertility plasmid.*)

Fc portion of antibody Crystallizable end of the constant region of an immunoglobulin molecule; responsible for binding to Fc receptors on cells, for initiating the classical pathway of complement activation, and for other biological functions.

fecal coliforms Thermotolerant coliform bacteria.

fecal-oral transmission Transmitting organisms that colonize the intestine by ingesting fecally contaminated material.

feedback inhibition Inhibition of the first enzyme of a biosynthetic pathway by the end product of that pathway; also called allosteric or end product inhibition.

feeding tolerance Lack of immune response to a specific antigen resulting from introducing the antigen orally.

fermentation Metabolic process in which the final electron acceptor is an organic compound.

fertility plasmid (or **F plasmid)** Plasmid found in donor cells of *E. coli* which codes for the sex pilus and makes the cell F^+.

fever An increase in internal body temperature to 37.8°C or higher.

fibronectin Glycoprotein occurring on the surface of cells and also in a circulating form that adheres tightly to medical devices; certain pathogens attach to it to initiate colonization.

filterable viruses The old terminology for viruses.

fimbria (pl. **fimbriae)** Type of pilus that enables cells to attach to a specific surface.

first-line antimicrobials In antimycobacterial drug therapy, the antimicrobials that are preferred because they are most effective as well as least toxic.

first-line defenses The barriers that separate and shield the interior of the body from the surrounding environment.

flagellin Protein subunits that make up the filament of flagella.

flagellum (pl. **flagella)** (1) In prokaryotic cells, a long protein appendage composed of subunits of flagellin that provides a mechanism of motility. (2) In eukaryotic cells, a long whiplike appendage composed of microtubules in a 9 + 2 arrangement that provides a mechanism of locomotion.

flavin adenine dinucleotide (FAD) A derivative of the vitamin riboflavin that functions as an electron carrier.

flavoprotein A flavin-containing electron carrier that functions in the electron transport chain.

flow cytometer Instrument that counts cells in a suspension by measuring the scattering of light by individual cells as they pass by a laser.

fluid mosaic model Model that describes the dynamic nature of the cytoplasmic membrane.

fluke Short, non-segmented, bilaterally symmetrical flatworm.

fluorescence-activated cell sorter (FACS) Machine that sorts fluorescent-labeled cells in a mixture by passing single cells in a stream past photodetectors.

fluorescence *in situ* hybridization (FISH) A procedure that uses a fluorescently labeled probe to detect specific nucleotide sequences within intact cells affixed to a microscope slide.

fluorescence microscope Special type of microscope used to observe cells that have been stained or tagged with fluorescent dyes.

fluoroquinolones Group of antimicrobial drugs that interferes with nucleic acid synthesis.

follicular dendritic cells Specialized cells that appear to retain antigen in small amounts, using it to continually rejuvenate the memory response of adaptive immunity.

fomites Inanimate objects such as books, tools, or towels that can act as transmitters of pathogenic microorganisms or viruses.

foodborne intoxication Disease resulting from ingestion of food that contains a toxin produced by a microorganism.

foraminifera Protozoa that have silicon or calcium in their cell walls.

forespore Portion of the endospore formed during the process of sporulation that will ultimately become the core of the endospore.

fowl cholera Worldwide septicemic illness of wild and domestic fowl, caused by *Pasteurella multocida;* focus of the discovery by Pasteur that an attenuated organism could be used as a vaccine.

fragmentation Form of asexual reproduction in which a filament composed of a string of cells breaks apart, forming multiple reproductive units.

frameshift mutation Mutation resulting from the addition or deletion of a number of nucleotides not divisible by three.

free energy Amount of energy that can be gained by breaking the bonds of a chemical; does not include the energy that is always lost as heat.

freeze-etching Process used to prepare specimens for transmission electron microscopy that allows the shape of underlying regions within structures of a cell to be viewed.

fruiting body With respect to myxobacteria, a complex aggregate of cells, visible to the naked eye, produced when nutrients or water are depleted.

fungemia Fungi circulating in the bloodstream.

fungicide Kills fungi; used to describe the effects of some antimicrobial chemicals.

fungistatic Able to inhibit the growth of fungi.

fungus (pl. fungi) A non-photosynthetic eukaryotic heterotroph.

furuncle A boil; a localized skin infection that penetrates into the subcutaneous tissue, usually caused by *Staphylococcus aureus.*

GALT Abbreviation for gut-associated lymphoid tissue.

gametes Haploid cells that fuse with other gametes to form the diploid zygote in sexual reproduction.

gamma globulin Portion of blood serum proteins that contains IgG.

ganglion (pl. **ganglia)** Small body near the spinal column representing a bulge in a peripheral nerve at the site where the sensory nerve cells are located.

gas chromatography Technique of separating and identifying gaseous components of a substance.

gastroenteritis Acute inflammation of the stomach and intestines; often applied to the syndrome of nausea, vomiting, diarrhea, and abdominal pain.

gas vesicles Small rigid compartments produced by some aquatic bacteria that provide buoyancy to the cell; gases, but not water, flow freely into the vesicles, thereby decreasing the density of the cell.

G + C content Percentage of guanine plus cytosine in double-stranded DNA; also called the GC content.

gel electrophoresis Technique that uses electric current to separate either DNA fragments or proteins according to size by drawing them through a slab of gel, which has the consistency of very firm gelatin.

gene The functional unit of a genome.

gene cloning Procedure by which genes are inserted into a replicon such as a plasmid or bacteriophage, which is then introduced into cells where the replicon can replicate.

gene fusion The joining of two genes.

gene library Sum total of all of the genes of an organism that have been inserted into cloning vectors.

generalized transducing phage Bacteriophage that is capable of transferring any part of the bacterial chromosome from one cell to another. (By contrast, a specialized transducing phage transfers only specific parts of the genome.)

generalized transduction Transfer of any bacterial gene to another bacterium by a phage.

general paresis Group of symptoms arising from nervous system damage, usually occurring 10 to 20 years after contracting syphilis; often manifest by emotional instability, memory loss, hallucinations, abnormalities of the eyes, and paralysis.

general secretory pathway Primary mechanism bacterial cells use to secrete proteins; proteins destined for secretion are recognized by their characteristic sequence of amino acids that make up the amino terminal end.

generation time Time it takes for the number of cells in a population to double; doubling time.

genetic engineering Process of deliberately altering an organism's genetic information by changing its nucleic acid sequences.

genetic reassortment Exchange of genetic information following two different segmented viruses infecting the same cell.

genetic recombination The joining together of genes from different organisms.

genetics The study of the function and transfer of genes.

genome Complete set of genetic information in a cell.

genome mining Searching genomic databases; for example, companies might search genomic databases to locate ORFs that may encode proteins of medical value.

genomic island Mobile genetic elements in the chromosome that are transferred as a unit and code for traits that benefit the organism under certain circumstances. They include pathogenicity islands and antibiotic resistance islands.

genomics Study and analysis of the nucleotide sequence of DNA.

genotype The sequence of nucleotides in the DNA of an organism.

genus (pl. **genera)** Category of related organisms, usually containing several species. The first name of an organism in the Binomial System of Nomenclature.

germicide Agent that kills microorganisms and inactivates viruses.

germination Sum total of the biochemical and morphological changes that an endospore or other resting cell undergoes before becoming a vegetative cell.

giant cell Very large cell with many nuclei, formed by the fusion of many macrophages during a chronic inflammatory response; found in granulomas.

gingivitis Inflammation of the gums.

global control The simultaneous regulation of numerous unrelated genes.

glucans Polysaccharides composed of repeating subunits of glucose; involved in formation of dental plaque.

glucose-salts Type of chemically defined medium that contains only glucose and certain inorganic salts; supports the growth of *E. coli.*

glycan chain High molecular weight linear polymer of alternating subunits of *N*-acetylglucosamine and *N*-acetylmuramic acid that serves as the backbone of the peptidoglycan molecule.

glycocalyx Gel-like layer that surrounds some cells and generally functions as a mechanism of either protection or attachment.

glycogen Polysaccharide composed of glucose molecules.

glycolipids Lipids that have various sugars attached.

glycolysis Metabolic pathway that oxidizes glucose to pyruvate, generating ATP and reducing power; also called the Embden-Meyerhoff pathway and the glycolytic pathway.

glycolytic pathway Glycolysis.

glycoproteins Proteins with covalently bonded sugar molecules.

glycosylase An enzyme that removes oxidized guanine from DNA by breaking a bond between deoxyribose and the oxidized guanine.

goblet cells Mucus-secreting epithelial cells.

Golgi apparatus Series of membrane-bound flattened sacs within eukaryotic cells that serve as the site where macromolecules synthesized in the endoplasmic reticulum are modified before they are transported to other destinations.

Gram-negative Bacteria that lose the crystal violet in the Gram stain procedure and therefore stain pink; the cell wall of these organisms is composed of a thin layer of peptidoglycan surrounded by an outer membrane.

Gram-positive Bacteria that retain the crystal violet stain in the Gram stain procedure and therefore stain purple; the cell wall of these organisms is composed of a thick layer of peptidoglycan.

Gram stain Staining technique that divides bacteria into one of two groups, Gram-positive or Gram-negative, on the basis of color; among bacteria, the staining reaction correlates well with cell wall structure.

granulation tissue New tissue formed during healing of an injury, consisting of small, red, translucent nodules containing abundant blood vessels.
granulocytes White blood cells characterized by the presence of prominent granules; basophil granules stain dark with basophilic dyes, eosinophils stain bright red with eosinophilic dyes, and neutrophils do not take up either stain.
granuloma Found in a chronic inflammatory response, collections of lymphocytes and stages of macrophages; an attempt by the body to wall off and contain persistent organisms and antigens.
griseofulvin Antifungal medication that appears to interfere with the action of tubulin, a necessary factor in nuclear division.
group translocation Type of transport process that chemically alters a molecule during its passage through the cytoplasmic membrane.
growth curve Growth pattern observed when cells are grown in a closed system; consists of five stages—lag phase, log phase (or exponential phase), stationary phase, death phase, and the phase of prolonged decline.
growth factors Compounds that a particular bacterium cannot synthesize and therefore must be included in a medium which supports the growth of that organism.
gumma Localized area of chronic inflammation and necrosis in tertiary syphilis, often manifest as a swelling.

HAART Highly active antiretroviral therapy; a cocktail of medications that act at different sites during replication of human immunodeficiency virus.
hairy leukoplakia Whitish patch, usually appearing on the tongue of individuals with severe immunodeficiency, thought to be caused by reactivation of latent Epstein-Barr virus (EBV) infection.
half-life Time it takes for one-half of the original number of molecules of a compound to be eliminated or degraded.
halophile Organism that prefers or requires a high salt (NaCl) medium.
haploid Containing only a single set of genes.
hapten Substance that can combine with specific antibodies but cannot incite the production of those antibodies unless it is attached to a large carrier molecule.
haustoria Specialized hypha of parasitic fungi that can penetrate plant or animal cell walls.
heavy chain The two higher molecular weight polypeptide chains that make up an antibody molecule; the type of heavy chain dictates the class of antibody molecule.
helicase Enzyme that unwinds the DNA helix ahead of the replication fork.
helminth A parasitic worm.
helper T cells Type of lymphocyte programmed to activate B cells and macrophages, and assist other aspects of adaptive immunity.
hemagglutination Clumping of red blood cells.
hemagglutination inhibition Immunological test used to detect antibodies against certain viruses which naturally cause red blood cells to agglutinate; antibodies that bind the virus inhibit the usual agglutination.
hemagglutinin A protein important in the virulence of the influenza virus.
hematopoietic stem cells Bone marrow cells that give rise to all blood cells.
hemolytic disease of the newborn (HDN) Disease of the fetus or newborn caused by transplacental passage of maternal antibodies against the baby's red blood cells, resulting in red cell destruction; usually anti-Rhesus (Rh) antibodies are involved and the disease is called Rh disease; also called erythroblastosis fetalis.
hemolytic uremic syndrome (HUS) Serious condition characterized by red cell breakdown and kidney failure; a sequel to infection by certain Shiga toxin-producing strains of *Shigella dysenteriae* and *Escherichia coli.*
hepatitis Inflammation of the liver; various causes, but commonly the result of viral infection, particularly by the hepatitis viruses.
hepatitis B virus An enveloped DNA virus with an unusual mode of replication involving reverse transcriptase; cause of hepatitis B.
herd immunity Phenomenon that occurs when a critical concentration of immune hosts prevents the spread of an infectious agent.
hermaphroditic Having both male and female reproductive structures in the same organism.
herpes zoster Another name for shingles; a disease that results from reactivation of the herpesvirus causing chickenpox.
heterocyst Specialized non-photosynthetic cells of cyanobacteria within which nitrogen fixation occurs.
heterophile antibody Antibody that reacts with the red blood cells of another animal.
heterotroph Organism that obtains carbon from an organic compound such as glucose.
Hfr cells (high frequency of recombination cells) Rare cells in the F^+ population that can transfer their chromosome to an F^- cell.
high-copy-number plasmid Plasmid whose numbers in the cell range from 50 to 500.
high efficiency particulate air (HEPA) filters Special filters that remove from air nearly all particles, including microorganisms, that have a diameter greater than 0.3 μm.
high-energy phosphate bond Bond that joins a phosphate group to a molecule and releases a relatively high amount of energy when hydrolyzed; denoted by the symbol ~.
high-level disinfectant Chemical used to destroy all viruses and vegetative cells, but not endospores.
high-temperature-short-time (HTST) method Most common pasteurization protocol; using this method, milk is pasteurized by holding it at 72°C for 15 seconds.
histamine A substance found in basophil and mast cell granules that upon release can cause dilation and increased permeability of blood vessel walls and other effects; a mediator of inflammation.
HIV disease The illness caused by human immunodeficiency virus, marked by gradual impairment of the immune system, ending in AIDS.
HLA Abbreviation for human leukocyte antigen.
homologous With respect to DNA, stretches that have similar or identical nucleotide sequences and probably encode similar characteristics.
homologous recombination Genetic recombination between stretches of similar or identical nucleotide sequences.
homoserine lactone (HSL) Freely diffusible molecule that is used by certain types of bacteria to sense the density of cells within their population.
hook Curved structure that connects the filament of the flagella to the cell surface.
hops Flowers of the vinelike hop plant; they are added to wort to impart a desirable bitter flavor to beer and contribute antibacterial substances.
horizontal evolution With respect to antimicrobial resistance, the acquisition of resistance through gene transfer.
horizontal gene transfer Transmission of DNA from one bacterium to another through conjugation, DNA-mediated transformation, or transduction; also called lateral gene transfer.
horizontal transmission Transfer of a pathogen from one person to another through contact, ingestion of food or water, or via a living agent such as an insect.
host Organism on or in which smaller organisms or viruses live, feed, and reproduce; a definitive host is an animal in which the sexually mature form of a parasite occurs; an intermediate host is an animal in which the asexual developmental stages of a parasite occur.
host cell In immunology, one of the body's own cells.
host range The range of cell types that a pathogen can infect.
HSV-1 (herpes simplex virus-1) Member of the herpes family of viruses that causes cold sores and other types of infection.
HSV-2 (herpes simplex virus-2) Member of the herpes family of viruses; principal cause of genital herpes.
HTST Abbreviation for high-temperature-short-time pasteurization.
Human Genome Project The undertaking begun in 1990 to determine the sequence of the human genome.
human leukocyte antigen (HLA) Human MHC molecules.
humoral immune response Antibody response.
hybridization The annealing of two complementary strands of DNA from different sources to create a hybrid double-stranded molecule.
hybridoma Cell made by fusing a lymphocyte, such as an antibody-producing B cell, with a cancer cell.
hydrogenation Reduction reaction in which an electron and an accompanying proton is added to a molecule.
hydrogen bond Weak attraction between a positively-charged hydrogen atom of one compound and a negatively charged atom of another compound; the charges of the two atoms are due to polar covalent bonds.
hydrolysis Chemical reaction in which a molecule is broken down as H_2O is added.
hydrophilic Water loving; soluble in water.
hydrophobic bonds Weak bonds formed between molecules as a result of their mutual repulsion of water molecules.
hyperimmune globulin Immunoglobulin prepared from the sera of donors with large amounts of antibodies to certain diseases, such as tetanus; used to prevent or treat the disease.
hypersensitivity Also termed allergy; heightened immune response to antigen.
hyperthermophiles Organisms that have an optimum growth temperature between 70°C and 110°C.
hypervariable regions Small areas in the Fab portion of the immunoglobulin light and heavy polypeptide chains that bind the antigenic epitope.
hypha (pl. hyphae) Threadlike structure that characterizes the growth of most fungi and some bacteria such as members of the genus *Streptomyces.*

hyposensitization (or **desensitization**) Form of therapy for immediate IgE-mediated allergies in which extremely small but increasing amounts of antigen are injected regularly over a period of months, directing the response from IgE to IgG.
hypoxic Deficient in oxygen.

ID_{50} The number of organisms that, when administered, will cause infection in approximately 50% of hosts.
IFN Abbreviation for interferons.
IgA proteases Enzymes that degrade IgA; they may have other roles as well.
illness Period of time during which symptoms and signs of disease occur.
immune complex Complex of antigen and antibody bound together, often with some complement components included.
immune serum globulin Immunoglobulin G portion of pooled plasma from many donors, containing a wide variety of antibodies; used to provide passive protection.
immunity Protection against infectious agents and other substances.
immunoassay Tests using immunological reagents such as antigens and antibodies.
immunocompromised A host with weaknesses or defects in the innate or adaptive defenses.
immunodeficiency Inability to produce a normal immune response to antigen.
immunodiffusion tests Precipitation reactions carried out in agarose or other gels.
immunoelectrophoresis Technique for separating proteins by subjecting the mixture to an electric current followed by diffusion and precipitation in gels using antibodies against the separated proteins.
immunofluorescence Technique used to identify particular antigens microscopically in cells by the binding of a fluorescent antibody to the antigen.
immunogen Antigen that induces an immune response.
immunoglobulin Glycoprotein molecules that react specifically with the substance that induced their formation; antibodies.
immunological tolerance (See *tolerance.*)
immunology The study of immunity, or protection against infectious and other agents, and conditions arising from the mechanisms involved in immunity, such as hypersensitivities.
immunosuppression Non-specific suppression of acquired immune responses.
immunotherapy Techniques used to modify the immune system action for a favorable effect.
inactivated vaccine Vaccine composed of killed bacteria, inactivated virus, or fractions of the agent; the agent in the vaccine is unable to replicate.
inapparent (or **subclinical**) **infections** Infections in which symptoms do not occur or are mild enough to go unnoticed.
incidence rate Number of new cases of a disease within a specific time period in a given population.
inclusion body Microscopically visible structure within a cell representing the site at which an infecting virus replicates; can occur within the nucleus or the cytoplasm.
incubation period Interval between entrance of a pathogen into a susceptible host and the onset of illness caused by that pathogen.
index case First identified case of a disease in an epidemic.
indirect contact Means of transmitting infectious disease via fomites.
indirect selection Technique for isolating mutants and identifying organisms unable to grow on a medium on which the parents do grow; often involves replica plating.
induced With respect to gene expression, a gene product that is synthesized only under certain conditions.
induced mutation Mutation that results from the organism being treated with an agent that alters its DNA.
inducer Substance that activates transcription of certain genes.
inducible enzyme Enzyme synthesized only when a substrate on which it can act is present.
induction Process by which a prophage is excised from the host cell DNA; activation of gene transcription.
infection Growth and multiplication of a parasitic organism or virus in or on the body of the host with or without the production of disease.
infectious disease Disease caused by a microbial or viral infection.
infectious dose Number of microorganisms or viruses sufficient to establish an infection; often expressed as ID_{50} in which 50% of the hosts are infected.
inflammation Innate response to injury characterized by swelling, heat, redness, and pain in the affected area.
initiation complex Complex of a 30S ribosomal subunit, a tRNA that carries f-Met, and elongation factors that comes together at a start codon on mRNA and begins the process of translation.
innate immunity Immunity that is not affected by prior contact with the infectious agent or other material involved and is not mediated by lymphocytes.
innate resistance Resistance of an organism to an antimicrobial medication due to the inherent characteristics of that type organism; also called intrinsic resistance.
inner membrane (1) In prokaryotic cells, the cytoplasmic membrane of Gram-negative bacteria. (2) In eukaryotic cells, the membrane on the interior side of an organelle that has a double membrane.
inorganic A compound that contains no C—C bonds.
insert DNA that is (or will be) joined to a vector to create a recombinant DNA molecule.
insertion mutation Mutation resulting from the integration of a transposon into a gene.
insertion sequence (IS) Short piece of DNA that has the ability to move from one site on a DNA molecule to another; simplest type of transposable element.
insulin-dependent diabetes mellitus (IDDM) Diabetes caused by autoimmune destruction of pancreatic cells by cytotoxic T cells.
intercalating agents Agents that insert themselves between two nucleotides in opposite strands of a DNA double helix.
interference microscope Type of light microscope that employs special optical devices to cause the specimen to appear as a three-dimensional image; an example is the Nomarski differential interference contrast microscope.
interferons Cytokines that induce cells to resist viral replication.
interleukins Cytokines produced by leukocytes.
intermediate fibers Component of the eukaryotic cell cytoskeleton.
intermediate-level disinfectant Type of chemical used to destroy all vegetative bacteria including mycobacteria, fungi, and most, but not all, viruses.
internal node Branch point on a phylogenetic tree that represents an ancestor to modern organisms.
intranuclear inclusion body Structure found within the nucleus of cells infected with certain viruses such as the cytomegalovirus.
intrinsic resistance (See *innate resistance.*)
intron Part of the eukaryotic chromosome that does not code for a protein; removed from the RNA transcript before the mRNA is translated.
inverted repeat Sequence of nucleotides on one strand of DNA that is identical to DNA on another strand when both are read in the same direction, that is, 5′ to 3′; associated with transposable elements.
in vitro In a test tube or other container as opposed to inside a living plant or animal.
in vivo Inside a living plant or animal as opposed to a test tube or other container.
ion Charged atom or molecule.
ionic bond Bond formed by the attraction of positively charged atoms or molecules to negatively charged ones.
IS Abbreviation for insertion sequence.
isomer Molecule with the same number and types of atoms as another but differing in its structure.
isotope Form of an element that differs in atomic weight from the form most common in nature.

Jarisch-Herxheimer reaction Abrupt but transitory worsening of symptoms after starting effective antibacterial treatment, thought to be caused by substances released by the death of the bacteria.

---

keratin A water-repelling protein found in hair, nails, and the outermost cells of the epidermis.
kinetic energy Energy of motion.
kingdom Taxonomic rank that groups several phyla or divisions; a collection of similar kingdoms makes up a domain.
Kirby-Bauer disc diffusion test Procedure used to determine whether a bacterium is susceptible to concentrations of an antimicrobial usually present in the bloodstream of an individual receiving the antimicrobial.
Koch's Postulates Group of criteria used to determine the cause of an infectious disease by culturing the agent and reproducing the disease.
Koplik spots Lesions of the oral cavity caused by measles virus that resemble a grain of salt on a red base.
Krebs cycle Metabolic pathway that incorporates acetyl-CoA, and generates CO_2 and reducing power; also called the tricarboxylic acid (TCA) cycle and the citric acid cycle.

---

labeled Tagged with a detectable marker such as a radioactive isotope, a fluorescent dye, or an enzyme.
***lac* operon** Operon that encodes the proteins required for the degradation of lactose; it has served as one of the most important models for studying gene regulation.

lactic acid bacteria Group of Gram-positive bacteria that generate lactic acid as a major end product of their fermentative metabolism.

lactoferrin Iron-binding protein found in leukocytes, saliva, mucus, milk, and other substances; helps defend the body by depriving microorganisms of iron.

lactose Disaccharide consisting of one molecule of glucose and one of galactose.

***lacZ′* gene** Gene used to visually determine whether or not a vector contains a fragment inserted into a multiple cloning site.

lagging strand Strand of double-stranded DNA that must be synthesized as a series of discontinuous fragments because of its 5′ to 3′ orientation with respect to the replication fork.

lagooning Sewage treatment method in which sewage is channeled into shallow lagoons, during which time it is degraded by anaerobic and/or aerobic organisms.

lag phase Stage in the growth of a bacterial culture characterized by extensive macromolecule and ATP synthesis but no increase in the number of viable cells.

laminar flow hood Biological safety cabinet in which laboratory personnel work with potentially dangerous airborne pathogens; a continuous flow of incoming and outgoing air is filtered through HEPA filters to contain microorganisms within the cabinet.

Lancefield grouping Classification of β-hemolytic streptococci based on serological identification.

latent infection Infection in which the infectious agent is present but not active.

latent stage The intracellular state of a virus in which infectious virions are not being produced.

lateral gene transfer (See *horizontal gene transfer.*)

leading strand Strand of double-stranded DNA that, because of its 5′ to 3′ orientation with respect to the replication fork, is synthesized continuously.

leaky Refers to a mutation in which the mutant gene codes for a protein that is partially functional.

lecithin Component of mammalian cell membranes; attacked by the α-toxin of *Clostridium perfringens* and other lecithinases.

lectin pathway Pathway of complement activation initiated by binding of mannan-binding lectins to microbial cell walls.

leghemoglobin Protein synthesized by leguminous plants that carries O_2 within a *Rhizobium*-harboring nodule.

lethal dose (LD) Concentration of an infectious agent that causes death; often expressed as LD_{50}, the concentration of substances in which 50% of the hosts are killed by the agent.

leukemia Cancer of the leukocytes (white blood cells).

leukocidins Substances that kill white blood cells.

leukocytes White blood cells.

leukotrienes Substances active in inflammation, leading to chemotaxis and increased vascular permeability; produced by mast cells, basophils, and macrophages.

L-forms Bacterial variants that have lost the ability to synthesize the peptidoglycan portion of their cell wall.

lichen Organism composed of a fungus in a symbiotic association with either a green alga or a cyanobacterium.

ligand A specific molecule that binds to a given receptor.

light chain The two lighter molecular weight polypeptide chains that make up an antibody molecule.

light-dependent reactions Processes used by phototrophs to harvest energy from sunlight; the energy-gathering component of photosynthesis.

light-independent reactions Stage of photosynthesis in which the ATP generated in the light-dependent reactions is used to fix CO_2; also called dark reactions.

light microscope Microscope that uses visible light to observe objects.

light reactions (See *light-dependent reactions.*)

light repair Process by which bacteria repair UV damage to their DNA only in the presence of light.

lincosamides Group of antimicrobials that interferes with protein synthesis.

lipid One of a diverse group of organic substances all of which are relatively insoluble in water, but soluble in alcohol, ether, chloroform, or other fat solvents.

lipid A Portion of lipopolysaccharide (LPS) that anchors the molecule in the lipid bilayer of the outer membrane of Gram-negative cells; it plays an important role in the body's ability to recognize the presence of invading bacteria, but is also responsible for the toxic effects of LPS.

lipopolysaccharide (LPS) Molecule formed by bonding of lipid to polysaccharide; a part of the outer membrane of Gram-negative bacteria.

lipoprotein Macromolecule formed by the bonding of lipid to protein.

lipoteichoic acids Component of the Gram-positive cell wall that is linked to the cytoplasmic membrane.

localized infections Infections limited to one site in or on the body, as a furuncle.

locus Position on the chromosome.

log phase Stage of growth of a bacterial culture in which the cells are multiplying exponentially.

low-copy-number plasmid Plasmid whose numbers in the cell are one or two copies.

low-level disinfectants Type of chemical used to destroy fungi, enveloped viruses, and vegetative bacteria except mycobacteria.

LPS Abbreviation for lipopolysaccharide.

luciferase Enzyme that catalyzes the chemical reactions that produce bioluminescence.

lymph Clear yellow liquid that flows within lymphatic vessels; generally contains lymphocytes and may contain globules of fat.

lymphadenopathy syndrome (LAS) Marked generalized enlargement of lymph nodes that often occurs at the end of the period of clinical well-being in HIV disease.

lymphangitis Inflammation of lymphatic vessels.

lymphatic vessels Vessels that carry lymph, which is collected from the fluid that bathes the body's tissues.

lymphocyte Small, round, or oval white blood cell with a large nucleus and a small amount of cytoplasm; involved in adaptive immunity.

lymphoid tissues and organs Collections of lymphocytes and related cells involved in immune responses.

lymphokines Cytokines secreted by lymphocytes.

lysate Remains of cells and virions that are released after lysis of cells.

lyse To burst.

lysogenic conversion Modification of the properties of a cell resulting from expression of intracellular phage DNA.

lysogens Bacteria that carry a prophage integrated into their chromosome.

lysosome Membrane-bound structure in eukaryotic cells that contains powerful degradative enzymes.

lysozyme Enzyme that degrades the peptidoglycan layer of the bacterial cell wall.

MacConkey agar Type of selective and differential bacteriological medium used to isolate certain Gram-negative rods such as those that typically reside in the intestine.

macroenvironment Overall environment in which an organism lives.

macrolides Group of antimicrobial medications that interfere with protein synthesis.

macromolecule Very large molecule composed of repeating subunits.

macrophages Large mononuclear phagocytes of the tissues; professional phagocytes of the mononuclear phagocyte system that can engulf and destroy microorganisms and other extraneous materials, function as antigen-presenting cells, and carry out ADCC (antibody-dependent cellular cytotoxicity).

magnetotaxis Movement by bacterial cells containing magnetite crystals in response to a magnetic field.

major histocompatibility complex (MHC) Cluster of genes coding for key cell surface proteins important in antigen presentation.

malaise Vague feeling of uneasiness or discomfort.

malignant tumor Abnormal growth of cells no longer under normal control that have the potential to spread to other parts of the body.

MALT Abbreviation for mucosal-associated lymphoid tissue.

mannan-binding lectins (MBLs) Pattern-recognition molecules the body uses to detect polymers of mannose, which are typically found on microbial but not mammalian cells.

mast cells Granule-containing tissue cells similar in appearance and function to the basophils of the blood, with receptors for the Fc portion of IgE; important in the inflammatory response and immediate allergic reactions.

MBC Abbreviation for minimum bactericidal concentration.

M cells Specialized epithelial cells lying over Peyer's patches that collect material in the intestine and transfer it to the lymphoid tissues beneath.

mechanical vector Organism such as a fly that physically moves contaminated material from one location to another.

mechanisms of pathogenicity Methods that pathogens use to evade host defenses and cause damage.

medium (pl. **media**) Any material used for growing organisms.

megakaryocyte The large blood cell from which platelets arise.

meiosis Process in eukaryotic cells by which the chromosome number is reduced from diploid ($2N$) to haploid ($1N$).

melting Denaturating of double-stranded DNA.

membrane attack complex (MAC) Complex of certain components of the complement system that forms pores in the cell membrane, resulting in lysis of the cell.

membrane-damaging toxin Toxin that disrupts plasma membranes of eukaryotic cells.

membrane filtration A technique used to determine the number of bacteria in a liquid sample that has a relatively low number of organisms; concentrates bacteria by filtration before they are plated.

membrane proteins Specialized proteins embedded in the membrane bilayer; some function as receptors and others function as transport proteins.

memory cells Lymphocytes specific for an antigen that persist in the body after an immune response to that antigen; upon subsequent exposure to the same antigen, they must differentiate and usually proliferate to become effector cells.

memory lymphocytes Long-lived descendants of activated lymphocytes that can quickly respond when specific antigen is encountered again.

memory response (See *secondary response.*)

meninges Membranes covering the brain and spinal cord.

meningitis Inflammation of the meninges.

merozoite Stage in the life cycle of certain protozoa, such as the malaria-causing *Plasmodium* species.

mesophiles Bacteria that grow most rapidly at temperatures between 20°C and 45°C.

messenger RNA (mRNA) Single-stranded RNA synthesized during transcription from DNA that binds to ribosomes and directs the synthesis of protein.

metabolism Sum total of all the chemical reactions in a cell.

metabolite Any product of metabolism.

metachromatic granules Polyphosphate granules found in the cytoplasm of some bacteria that appear as different colors when stained with a basic dye.

methanogens Group of *Archaea* that generate energy by oxidizing hydrogen gas, using CO_2 as a terminal electron acceptor; this process generates methane (CH_4).

MHC Abbreviation for major histocompatibility complex.

MHC molecules Molecules on the surface of cells used to present antigen to T cells; the MHC molecules, encoded by the major histocompatibility complex (MHC), are also involved in the immunological rejection of transplanted tissue and organs.

MIC Abbreviation for minimum inhibitory concentration.

microaerophiles Organisms that require small amounts of oxygen (2% to 10%) for growth, but are inhibited by higher concentrations.

microarray A solid support that contains a fixed pattern of numerous different single-stranded nucleic acid fragments of known sequences.

microenvironment Environment immediately surrounding an individual microorganism.

microtiter plate A small tray containing numerous wells, usually 96.

microtubules Cytoskeleton structures of a eukaryotic cell that form mitotic spindles, cilia, and flagella; long hollow cylinders composed of tubulin.

microvillus (pl. **microvilli**) Tiny cylindrical process from luminal surfaces of cells such as those lining the intestine; increases surface area of the cell.

mineralization Conversion from organic to inorganic form; stabilization.

minimum bactericidal concentration (MBC) Lowest concentration of a specific antimicrobial medication that kills 99.9% of cells in a culture of a given strain of bacteria.

minimum inhibitory concentration (MIC) Lowest concentration of a specific antimicrobial medication that prevents the growth of an organism *in vitro.*

minus (–) strand (1) The DNA strand that is used as a template for RNA synthesis. (2) The complement to the plus (or sense) stand of RNA. Also called the antisense strand.

miracidium First larval form of a fluke, hatching from the ovum as a ciliated organism.

mismatch repair Repair mechanism in which a repair enzyme recognizes improperly hydrogen-bonded bases and excises a short stretch of nucleotides containing these bases.

mitochondrion Organelle in eukaryotic cells in which the majority of ATP synthesis occurs.

mitogen Substance that induces mitosis; causes proliferation of cells.

mitosis Nuclear division process in eukaryotic cells that ensures the daughter cells receive the same number of chromosomes as the original parent.

MMWR Abbreviation for *Morbidity and Mortality Weekly Report,* published by the Centers for Disease Control and Prevention (CDC).

mobilize (plasmids) To prepare DNA for transfer by conjugation.

mold A filamentous fungus.

mole Amount of a chemical in grams that contains 6.023×10^{23} molecules; it is equal to the molecular weight of the chemical, or the sum of the atomic weight of all the atoms in a molecule of that chemical.

molecular postulates Group of criteria used to determine the cause of an infectious disease by using genetic and other molecular techniques.

molecular weight Relative weight of an atom or molecule based on a scale in which the H atom is assigned the weight of 1.0.

molecule Chemical consisting of two or more atoms held together by chemical bonds.

monobactams Group of antimicrobial medications that interferes with peptidoglycan synthesis; very resistant to β-lactamases.

monocistronic RNA transcript that encodes one gene.

monoclonal antibodies Antibodies with a single specificity produced *in vitro* by lymphocytes that have been fused with a type of malignant myeloma cell.

monocytes Mononuclear phagocytes of the blood; part of the mononuclear phagocyte system of professional phagocytes.

monomer Repeating subunit of a polymer.

mononuclear phagocyte system (MPS) System of mononuclear cells (monocytes and macrophages) scattered throughout the body that are highly efficient at phagocytosis; formerly known as the reticuloendothelial system.

monosaccharide A sugar; a simple carbohydrate generally having the formula $C_nH_{2n}O_n$, where n can vary in number from three to eight.

morbidity Illness; most often expressed as the rate of illness in a given population at risk.

mordant Substance that increases the affinity of cellular components for a dye.

morphology Form or shape of a particular organism or structure.

mortality Death; most often expressed as a rate of death in a given population at risk.

most probable number (MPN) method Statistical estimate of cell numbers based on the theory of probability; a sample is successively diluted to determine the point at which subsequent dilutions receive no cells.

M protein A protein found in the cell walls of Group A streptococci that is associated with virulence.

mRNA Messenger RNA.

mucociliary escalator Moving layer of mucus and cilia lining the respiratory tract that traps bacteria and other particles and moves them into the throat.

mucosa (See *mucous membrane.*)

mucosal-associated lymphoid tissue (MALT) Lymphoid tissue present in the mucosa of the respiratory, gastrointestinal, and genitourinary tracts.

mucous membrane Epithelial barrier that is coated with mucus.

multiple-cloning site Small sequence of DNA that contains several unique restriction enzyme recognition sites into which foreign DNA can be cloned.

mushroom Filamentous multicelled fungus with macroscopic fruiting bodies.

mutagen Any agent that increases the frequency at which DNA is altered (mutated).

mutant Organism that has a changed nucleotide sequence or arrangement of nucleotides in its DNA.

mutation Modification in the base sequence of DNA in a gene resulting in an alteration in the protein encoded by the gene.

mutualism A symbiotic association in which both partners benefit.

myasthenia gravis Autoimmune disease characterized by muscle weakness, caused by autoantibodies.

mycelium (pl. **mycelia**) Tangled, matlike mass of fungal hyphae.

mycology The study of fungi.

mycorrhiza Symbiotic relationship between certain fungi and the roots of plants.

mycosis (pl. **mycoses**) Disease caused by a fungus.

***N*-acetylglucosamine (NAG)** One of the two alternating subunits of the glycan chains that make up peptidoglycan.

NAD/NADH Abbreviations for the oxidized/reduced forms of nicotinamide adenine dinucleotide, a diffusible electron carrier.

NADP/NADPH Abbreviations for the oxidized/reduced forms of nicotinamide adenine dinucleotide, a diffusible electron carrier.

narrow host range plasmid Plasmid that only replicates in one or a few closely related species of bacteria.

narrow-spectrum antimicrobials Antimicrobial medications that inhibit or kill a limited range of bacteria.

National Molecular Subtyping Network for Foodborne Disease Surveillance (See *PulseNet.*)

natural killer cell (See *NK cell.*)

natural selection Selection by the environment of those cells best able to grow in that environment.

naturally acquired immunity Active or passive immunity acquired through natural means such as exposure to a disease-causing agent, breastfeeding, or transfer of IgG to a fetus *in utero.*

necrotic Dead; refers to dead cells or tissues in contact with living cells, as necrotic tissue in wounds.

negative staining Staining technique that employs an acidic dye to stain the background against which colorless cells can be seen.

negative (–) strand (See *minus (–) strand.*)
Negri body Viral inclusion body characteristic of rabies.
nematodes Roundworms.
neurotoxin Toxin that damages the nervous system.
neurotransmitter Any of a group of substances released from the terminations of nerve cells when they are stimulated; they cross to the adjacent cell and cause it to be excited or inhibited.
neutralization tests Tests in which antibodies neutralize viruses by preventing them from infecting cells or neutralize toxins by binding to them and making them nontoxic.
neutron Uncharged component of an atom found in the nucleus.
neutrophiles Organisms that can live and multiply within the range of pH 5 (acidic) to pH 8 (basic) and have a pH optimum near neutral (pH 7).
neutrophils (See *polymorphonuclear neutrophils.*)
nitrification Conversion of ammonia (NH_3) to nitrate (NO_3^-).
nitrogen fixation Conversion of nitrogen gas to ammonia.
NK cell Large granular, non-T, non-B lymphocyte that can kill cells to which antibody has bound and cells that do not bear MHC class I molecules on the surface.
Nomarski differential interference contrast microscope Type of microscope that has a device for separating light into two beams that pass through the specimen and then recombine; light waves are out of phase when they recombine, resulting in the three-dimensional appearance of material in the specimen.
nomenclature System of assigning names to organisms; a component of taxonomy.
non-communicable diseases Disease that cannot be transmitted from one individual to another.
non-competitive inhibition Type of enzyme inhibition that results from a molecule binding to the enzyme at a site other than the active site.
non-conjugative plasmid Plasmid that lacks some of the genetic information required for its transfer to other bacteria by conjugation.
non-critical instruments Medical instruments and surfaces such as stethoscopes and countertops that only come into contact with unbroken skin.
non-cyclic photophosphorylation Type of photophosphorylation in which high-energy electrons are drawn off to generate reducing power, electrons must still be returned to chlorophyll, but they must come from a source such as water.
non-polar covalent bond Bond formed by sharing electrons between atoms that have equal attraction for the electrons.
nonsense mutation A mutation which generates a stop codon, resulting in a shortened protein.
normal microbial flora That group of microorganisms that colonizes the body surfaces but does not usually cause disease; also called normal flora.
Northern blotting Procedure that is similar in principle to a Southern blotting, except that it uses a nucleic acid probe to detect sequences of RNA.
nosocomial infection Infection acquired during hospitalization.
notifiable diseases Group of diseases that are reported to the CDC by individual states; typically these diseases are of relatively high incidence or otherwise a potential danger to public health.
nuclear envelope Double membrane that separates the nucleus from the cytoplasm in eukaryotic cells.
nucleic acids hybridization (See *hybridization.*)
nucleic acids Ribonucleic acid (RNA) and deoxyribonucleic acid (DNA).
nucleocapsid Viral nucleic acid and its protein coat.
nucleoid Region of a prokaryotic cell containing the DNA.
nucleolus Region within the nucleus where ribosomal RNAs are synthesized.
nucleosome Unit of the chromatin of eukaryotic cells that consists of a complex of histones around which the linear DNA wraps twice.
nucleotide array technology Use of a solid support to which a two-dimensional arrangement of numerous different single-stranded DNA fragments of known sequences has been attached; each fragment functions as a probe.
nucleotides Basic subunits of ribonucleic or deoxyribonucleic acid consisting of a purine or pyrimidine covalently bonded to ribose or deoxyribose, which is covalently bound to a phosphate molecule.
nucleus Membrane-bound organelle in a eukaryotic cell that contains chromosomes and the nucleolus.
nuisance bloom Odiferous scum caused when buoyant cyanobacteria cells float to the surface of a body of stagnant water, and then lyse and decay.
numerical taxonomy Method of classification based on the phenotypes of prokaryotes; determines the relatedness of different organisms based on the percentage of characteristics that two groups have in common.

O antigen Antigenic polysaccharide portion of lipopolysaccharide, the molecule that makes up the outer leaflet of the outer membrane of Gram-negative bacteria.
objective lens Lens of a compound microscope that is closest to the specimen.
obligate aerobes Organisms with an absolute requirement for oxygen.
obligate anaerobes Organisms that cannot multiply if O_2 is present; they are often killed by traces of O_2 because of its toxic derivatives.
obligate fermenters Organisms that can grow in the presence of O_2 but never use it as a terminal electron acceptor; also called aerotolerant anaerobes.
obligate intracellular parasites Organisms that grow only inside living cells.
occlusion bodies Masses of viruses inside or outside cells.
ocular lens Lens of a compound microscope that is closest to the eye.
oil A liquid fat.
Okazaki fragment Nucleic acid fragment synthesized as a result of the discontinuous replication of the lagging strand of DNA.
oligonucleotide Short chain of nucleotides.
oligosaccharide Short chain of monosaccharide subunits joined together by covalent bonds; shorter than a polysaccharide.
oligotrophic environment A nutrient-poor environment.
oligotrophs Organisms that can grow in a nutrient-poor environment.
oncogene Gene whose activity is involved in turning a normal cell into a cancer cell.
open reading frame (ORF) Stretch of DNA, generally longer than 300 base pairs, that has a reading frame beginning with a start codon and ending with a stop codon; it suggests that the region encodes a protein.
open system Method used to maintain cells in a state of continuous growth by continuously adding nutrients and removing waste products; also called a continuous culture.
operator Region located immediately downstream of a promoter to which a repressor can bind; binding of the repressor to the operator effectively prevents RNA polymerase from progressing past that region and blocks transcription.
operon Group of linked genes that are controlled as a single unit.
opine Unusual amino acid derivative; a portion of the Ti plasmid of *Agrobacterium tumefaciens* is transferred to plant cells and directs the plant cells to synthesize this compound.
opportunist Organism that causes disease only in hosts with impaired defense mechanisms or when introduced into an unusual location; also called an opportunistic pathogen.
opsonization Enhanced phagocytosis, usually caused by coating of the particle to be ingested with either antibody or complement components.
opthalmia neonatorum Eye infection of newborns usually caused by *Neisseria gonorrhoeae* or *Chlamydia trachomatis,* acquired from infected mothers during the birth process.
optical isomer (or **stereoisomer)** Mirror image of a compound.
optimal proportion Relative proportions of antigen and antibody at which both are fully incorporated in a precipitate.
optimum growth temperature Temperature at which a microorganism multiplies most rapidly.
oral tolerance Decreased reactivity of immune cells resulting from feeding an antigen.
order Taxonomic classification between class and family.
organ A structure composed of different tissues coordinated to perform a specific function.
organelle A structure within a cell that performs a specific function.
organic A compound in which a carbon atom is covalently bonded to another carbon or hydrogen atom.
organic matter Material that contains carbon atoms bonded to other carbon atoms.
origin of replication Distinct region of a DNA molecule at which replication is initiated.
origin of transfer Short stretch of nucleotides, a part of which is transferred first when a plasmid is transferred to a recipient cell; necessary for plasmid transfer.
osmosis Movement of water across a membrane from a dilute solution to a more concentrated solution.
osmotic pressure Pressure exerted by water on a membrane due to a difference in the concentration of molecules on each side of the membrane.
osmotolerant Organisms that can tolerate relatively high salt concentrations, up to approximately 10% NaCl.
O-specific polysaccharide side chain The portion of LPS that is directed away from the membrane, at the end opposite of Lipid A; because its composition varies, it can sometimes be used to identify species or strains.
outbreak Cluster of cases occurring during a brief time interval and affecting a specific population; may herald the onset of an epidemic.

outer membrane (1) In prokaryotic cells, the unique lipid bilayer of Gram-negative cells that surrounds the peptidoglycan layer. (2) In eukaryotic cells, the membrane on the cytoplasmic side of organelles that have double membranes.

oxazolidinones Group of antimicrobial drugs that interferes with protein synthesis.

oxidase test Rapid biochemical test used to detect the activity of cytochrome *c* oxidase.

oxidation Removal of an electron.

oxidation-reduction reactions Chemical reactions in which one or more electrons is transferred from one molecule to another; the compound that loses electrons becomes oxidized and the chemical that gains electrons becomes reduced.

oxidative phosphorylation Synthesis of ATP from ADP and inorganic phosphate using the energy of a proton motive force, which is generated by harvesting chemical energy.

oxygenic photosynthesis Photosynthetic reaction that releases oxygen.

---

palindrome Two stretches of DNA on opposite strands that are identical when oriented in the same direction, that is, 5′ to 3′ or 3′ to 5′.

pandemic A worldwide epidemic.

para-aminobenzoic acid (PABA) Intermediate in the pathway for folic acid synthesis in bacteria; sulfa drugs have a similar structure to PABA.

parasitism Association in which one organism, the parasite, benefits at the expense of the other organism, the host.

parent strain Refers to the original strain of a bacterium used in an experiment; term is often used in place of wild-type strain.

passive diffusion Process in which molecules flow freely into and out of a cell so that the concentration of any particular molecule is the same on the inside as it is on the outside of the cell.

passive immunity Protective immunity resulting from the transfer of antibody-containing serum produced by other individuals or animals.

pasteurization Process of heating food or other substances under controlled conditions of time and temperature to kill pathogens and reduce the total number of microorganisms without damaging the substance.

pathogen Organism or virus causing a disease.

pathogenesis Process by which disease develops.

pathogenicity islands Stretches of DNA in bacteria that code for virulence factors; a pathogenicity island can be transferred as a unit to another bacterium, endowing the recipient with the ability to produce the encoded virulence factors.

pattern recognition Method by which the innate immune system recognizes invading microbes or tissue damage; the system uses receptors and other molecules that bind lipopolysaccharide, peptidoglycan, and other molecular patterns associated with invading microbes or tissue damage.

peliosis hepatis Serious condition characterized by formation of blood-filled cysts in the liver, caused by *Bartonella henselae;* usually a complication of AIDS or other severe immunodeficiency.

penicillin Antibiotic that interferes with the synthesis of the peptidoglycan portion of bacterial cell walls.

penicillin-binding proteins (PBPs) Target of β-lactam antimicrobial drugs; their role in bacteria is peptidoglycan synthesis.

penicillin enrichment Method for increasing the relative proportion of auxotrophic mutants in a population by killing off the growing prototrophic cells with penicillin.

pentamer Polymer composed of five monomeric structural units.

pentose phosphate pathway Metabolic pathway that initiates the degradation of glucose, generating reducing power in the form of NADPH, and two precursor metabolites.

peptide bond Covalent bond formed between the —COOH group of one amino acid and the $—NH_2$ group of another amino acid; characteristic of proteins.

peptide interbridge Component of the peptidoglycan layer of Gram-positive bacteria; the short chain of amino acids that links the peptide side chains of adjacent *N*-acetylmuramic acid molecules.

peptide vaccine Vaccine composed of key antigenic peptides from disease-causing microbes. Vaccines of this type are still in developmental stages.

peptidyl site (or **P-site**) Site on the ribosome to which the tRNA that temporarily carries the elongating amino acid chain resides.

peptidoglycan Macromolecule found only in bacteria that provides rigidity to the bacterial cell wall. The basic structure of peptidoglycan is an alternating series of two major subunits *N*-acetylmuramic acid (NAM) and *N*-acetylglucosamine (NAG); chains of these alternating subunits, are cross-linked by peptide chains.

peptone Common component of bacteriological media; consists of proteins originating from any of a variety of sources that have been hydrolyzed to amino acids and short peptides by treatment with enzymes, acids, or alkali.

perforin Molecule produced by T-cytotoxic cells and NK cells; functions in killing target cells by forming a pore through the target cell membrane.

periplasm (or **periplasmic gel**) Gel that fills the region between the outer membrane and the cytoplasmic membrane in Gram-negative bacteria.

peristalsis The rhythmic contractions of the intestinal tract that propel food and liquid.

peritrichous flagella Distribution of flagella over the entire surface of a cell.

peroxidase enzymes Enzymes found in neutrophil granules, saliva, and milk that together with hydrogen peroxide and halide ions make up an effective antimicrobial system.

persistent Refers to infection in which the causative agent remains in the body for long periods of time, often without causing symptoms of disease.

petechia (pl. **petechiae**) Small purplish spot on the skin or mucous membrane caused by hemorrhage.

Petri dish Two-part dish of glass or plastic often used to contain medium solidified with agar, on which bacteria are grown.

Peyer's patches Collections of lymphoid cells in the gastrointestinal tract; part of the mucosal-associated lymphoid tissue (MALT).

pH Scale of 0 to 14 that expresses the acidity or alkalinity of a solution.

phage Shortened term for bacteriophage.

phage induction Process by which phage DNA is excised from bacterial DNA.

phagocytes Cells that specialize in engulfing and digesting microbes and cell debris.

phagocytosis (v. **phagocytize**) The process by which certain cells ingest particulate matter by surrounding and enveloping those materials, bring them into the cell in a membrane-bound vesicle.

phagolysosome Membrane-bound vacuole generated when a phagosome fuses with a lysosome.

phagosome Membrane-bound vacuole that contains the material engulfed by a phagocyte.

phase-contrast microscope Type of light microscope that employs special optical devices to amplify the difference in the refractive index of a cell and the surrounding medium, increasing the contrast of the image.

phase variation The reversible and random alteration of expression of certain bacterial structures such as fimbriae by switching on and off the genes that encode those structures.

phenotype The properties of a cell determined by the expression of the genotype.

phenotypic mixing Exchange of protein coats by two viruses when two virions infect the same cell.

phospholipase Membrane-damaging toxin that enzymatically removes the polar head group on phospholipids.

phospholipid Lipid that has a phosphate molecule as part of its structure.

phosphotransferase system Type of group translocation in which the transported molecule is phosphorylated as it passes through the cytoplasmic membrane.

photoautotrophs Organisms that use light as the energy source and CO_2 as the major carbon source.

photoheterotrophs Organisms that use light as the energy source and organic compounds as the carbon source.

photooxidation Chemical reaction occurring as a result of absorption of light energy in the presence of oxygen.

photophosphorylation Synthesis of ATP from ADP and inorganic phosphate using the energy of a proton motive force, which is generated by harvesting radiant energy.

photoreactivation (or **light repair**) Breakage of the covalent bonds joining thymine dimers in the light, thereby restoring the DNA to its original state.

photosynthesis Reactions used to harvest the energy of light to synthesize ATP, which is then used to power CO_2 fixation.

photosystems Protein complexes within which chlorophyll and other light-gathering pigments are organized; located in special photosynthetic membranes.

phototaxis Directed movement in response to variations in light.

phototrophs Organisms that use light as a source of energy.

phycobiliproteins Light-harvesting pigments of cyanobacteria; they absorb energy from wavelengths of light that are not well absorbed by chlorophyll.

phylogenetic tree Type of diagram that depicts the evolutionary heritage of organisms.

phylogeny Evolutionary relatedness of organisms.

phylum (pl. **phyla**) Collection of similar classes; a collection of similar phyla makes up a kingdom; a phylum may also be called a division.

phytoplankton Floating and swimming algae and photosynthetic prokaryotic organisms of lakes and oceans.

pilus (pl. **pili**) Hairlike appendages on many Gram-negative bacteria that function in conjugation and for attachment.

pinocytosis Process by which eukaryotic cells take in liquid and small particles from the surrounding environment by internalizing and pinching off small pieces of their own membrane, bringing along a small volume of liquid and any material attached to the membrane.

plankton Primarily microscopic organisms floating freely in most waters.

plaque (1) Clear area in a monolayer of cells. (2) In dentistry, a polysaccharide-encased community of bacteria (a biofilm) that adheres to a tooth surface.

plasma Fluid portion of non-clotted blood.

plasma cell End cell of the B-cell series, fully differentiated to produce and secrete large amounts of antibody.

plasma membrane Semipermeable membrane that surrounds the cytoplasm in a cell; cytoplasmic membrane.

plasmid Small extrachromosomal circular DNA molecule that replicates independently of the chromosome; often codes for antibiotic resistance.

plasmolysis Process in which water diffuses out of a cell, causing the cytoplasm to dehydrate and shrink from the cell wall.

plate count Method used to determine the number of viable cells in a specimen by determining the number of colonies that arise when the specimen is added to an agar medium.

platelets (or **thrombocytes**) Small cell fragments in the blood that are essential for blood clotting; arise from large bone marrow cells called megakaryocytes.

pleomorphic Bacteria that characteristically vary in shape.

pleurisy Inflammation of the pleura, membranes that line the lung and chest cavity; often marked by a sharp pain associated with breathing.

plus (+) strand (1) The DNA strand that is complementary to the strand used as a template for RNA synthesis. (2) Of the two RNA molecules that can theoretically be transcribed from double-stranded DNA, the one that can be translated to make a protein; also called the sense strand.

PMN Abbreviation for polymorphonuclear neutrophil.

pneumonia Inflammation of the lungs accompanied by filling of the air sacs with fluids such as pus and blood.

pneumonic plague Disease that develops when *Yersinia pestis* infects the lungs.

point mutation Mutation in which only a single base pair is involved.

polar covalent bond Bond formed by sharing electrons between atoms that have unequal attraction for the electrons.

polarity (1) The degree of affinity that an atom has for electrons; this results in positive or negative charges on atoms in a molecule. (2) The 5′ to 3′ directionality of a nucleic acid fragment. (3) The transfer of DNA from one cell to another in an exclusive direction, for example from an F^+ cell to an F^- cell.

poly A tail Series of approximately 200 adenine derivatives that are added to the 3′ end of an mRNA transcript in eukaryotic cells; thought to stabilize the transcript and enhance translation.

polycistronic (or **polygenic**) An mRNA molecule that carries more than one gene.

polygenic (1) A trait encoded by more than one location on the chromosome. (2) An mRNA molecule that carries more than one gene.

polymer Large molecules formed by the joining together of repeating small molecules (subunits).

polymerase chain reaction (PCR) Method used to create millions of copies of a given region of DNA in only a matter of hours.

polymorphic Having different distinct forms.

polymorphonuclear neutrophils (PMNs) Phagocytic cells that together with the macrophages are known as "professional phagocytes"; the nuclei of these cells are segmented and composed of several lobes.

polymyxin B Type of antimicrobial medication that damages cytoplasmic membranes.

polypeptide Chain of amino acids joined by peptide bonds; also called a protein.

polyprotein A single chain of amino acids that comprises multiple different proteins.

polyribosome Assembly of multiple ribosomes attached to a single mRNA molecule; also called a polysome.

polysaccharide Long chains of monosaccharide subunits.

polysaccharide vaccine Vaccine composed of polysaccharides, which make up the capsule of certain organisms; it generally elicits only an IgM response, provides no memory, and elicits a poor response in young children.

polyunsaturated fatty acid Fatty acid that contains numerous double bonds.

porins Proteins in the outer membrane of Gram-negative bacteria that form channels through which small molecules can pass.

portal of entry Place of entry of microorganisms into the host.

portal of exit Place where infectious agents leave the host to find a new host.

positive selection Process that permits only those T cells that recognize MHC molecules to some extent to develop further.

positive (+) strand (See *plus (+) strand.*)

potential energy Stored energy; it can exist in a variety of forms including chemical bonds, a rock on the top of a hill, and water behind a dam.

pour-plate method Method of inoculating an agar medium with bacteria while the agar is liquid and then pouring it into a Petri dish, where the agar hardens; the colonies grow both on the surface and within the medium.

precipitation reaction Reaction of an antibody with a soluble antigen to form an insoluble substance.

precursor metabolites Metabolic intermediates produced in catabolic pathways that can be siphoned off and used in anabolic pathways.

preservation The process of inhibiting the growth of microorganisms in products to delay spoilage.

prevalence Total number cases, both old and new, in a given population at risk at a point in time.

primary culture Cells taken and grown directly from the tissues of an animal.

primary immune response Immune response that occurs upon first exposure to an antigen.

primary infection Infection in a previously healthy individual, such as measles in a child who has not had measles before.

primary lymphoid organs Organs in which lymphocytes mature; the thymus and bone marrow.

primary metabolites Compounds synthesized by a cell during the log phase.

primary pathogen Microorganism or virus that is able to cause disease in an otherwise healthy individual.

primary producers Organisms that convert CO_2 into organic compounds; by doing so, they sustain other life forms, including humans.

primary response The response that marks the adaptive immune system's first encounter with a particular antigen.

primary stain First dye applied in a multistep differential staining procedures; generally stains all cells.

primary structure Refers to the sequence of amino acids in a protein.

primary treatment In treatment of wastewater, a physical process designed to remove materials that will settle out.

primase Enzyme that synthesizes small fragments of RNA to serve as primers for DNA synthesis during DNA replication.

primer RNA molecule that initiates the synthesis of DNA.

prion Infectious protein that has no nucleic acid.

probe In nucleic acid hybridization, a single-stranded piece of nucleic acid that has been tagged with a detectable marker; it is used to identify the homologous nucleic by hybridizing to its complement.

productive infection Virus infection in which more virions are produced.

professional phagocytes Macrophages and polymorphonuclear leukocytes; these routinely and efficiently ingest and destroy foreign material.

proglottid One of the segments that make up most of the body of a tapeworm.

pro-inflammatory cytokines Any of a group of cytokines that contribute to the inflammatory response.

prokaryote Single-celled organism that does not contain a membrane-bound nucleus nor any other membrane-bound organelles.

prokaryotic cell Cell characterized by lack of a nuclear membrane and the absence of membrane-bound organelles.

promoter Nucleotide sequence to which RNA polymerase binds to initiate transcription.

propagated epidemic Outbreak of disease in which the infectious agent is transmitted to others, resulting in steadily increasing numbers of people becoming ill.

prophage Latent form of a temperate phage whose DNA has been inserted into the host's DNA.

prophylaxis Prevention of disease.

prospective study Study that looks ahead to see if the risk factors identified by a retrospective study predict a tendency to develop the disease.

protease Enzyme that degrades protein; the protease that is encoded by HIV is the target of several anti-HIV medications.

protein Macromolecule containing one or more polypeptide chains.

protein A Protein produced by *Staphylococcus aureus* that inhibits phagocytosis of the organism by binding to the Fc portion of antibodies.

protein subunit vaccine Vaccine composed of key protein antigens or antigenic fragments of an infectious agent, rather than whole cells or viruses.

proteome The inventory of proteins encoded by a genome.

proteomics The study of the proteome.

protist Designation for eukaryotic organisms other than plants, animals, and fungi; may be unicellular or multicellular.

proton Positively charged component of an atom found in the nucleus.

proton motive force Form of energy generated by the electron transport chain, which expels protons to create a chemiosmotic gradient.

proton pump Complex of electron carriers in the electron transport chain that ejects protons from the cell.

proto-oncogene A type of gene involved in tumor formation; it codes for a protein that activates transcription.

protoplast Gram-positive cell from which the rigid cell wall has been removed.

prototroph Organism that has no organic growth requirements other than a source of carbon and energy.

protozoa Group of single-celled eukaryotic organisms.

provirus Latent form of a virus in which the viral DNA is incorporated into the chromosome of the host.

pseudomembranous colitis Disease of the colon caused by *Clostridium difficile* in which patches called pseudomembranes, composed of dead epithelium, inflammatory cells and clotted blood, form on the intestinal lining.

pseudopods Transient armlike extensions formed by phagocytes and protozoa; they surround and enclose extracellular material, including bacteria, during the process of phagocytosis.

P-site (or **peptidyl site**) Site on the ribosome where the tRNA that temporarily carries the elongating amino acid chain resides.

psychrophile Microorganism that grows best between –5°C and 15°C.

psychrotroph Organism that has an optimum temperature between 20°C and 30°C.

pseudomembranous colitis Disease of the colon caused by *Clostridium difficile* in which patches called pseudomembranes, composed of dead epithelium, inflammatory cells and clotted blood, form on the intestinal lining.

puerperal fever Childbed fever; infection of the uterus following childbirth, commonly caused by *Streptococcus pyogenes.*

pulsed-field gel electrophoresis Type of gel electrophoresis that is used to separate very large fragments of DNA.

PulseNet Surveillance network established by the Centers for Disease Control and Prevention to facilitate the tracking of foodborne disease outbreaks; catalogues the RFLPs of certain pathogenic organisms. Also called the National Molecular Subtyping Network for Foodborne Disease Surveillance.

pure culture A population of organisms descended from a single cell.

purine Component of RNA and DNA; the two major purines are adenine and guanine.

pus Thick, opaque, often yellowish material that forms at the site of infection, made up of dead neutrophils and tissue debris.

putrefaction Digestion of proteins by enzymes to yield foul-smelling products.

pyelonephritis Infection of the kidneys.

pyoderma Any skin disease characterized by production of pus.

pyogenic Pus-producing.

pyrimidine Component of RNA and DNA; the three major pyrimidines are thymidine, cytosine, and uracil.

pyrogens Fever-inducing substances.

pyruvate End product of glycolysis; a precursor metabolite used in the synthesis of amino acids.

---

quaternary ammonium compounds Cationic (positively charged) detergents that are non-toxic enough to be used to disinfect food preparation surfaces; also called quats.

quaternary structure Level of structure of a protein molecule resulting from the interaction of one or more protein chains.

quinone A lipid-soluble electron carrier that functions in the electron transport chain.

quorum sensing Communication between bacteria by means of small molecules, permitting the bacteria to sense when there is an adequate quorum or number of organisms present to activate certain genes.

---

radial immunodiffusion test Quantitative antigen-antibody precipitation in gel test in which one reactant is distributed throughout the gel and the other reactant diffuses into the gel, producing a ring of precipitation.

rDNA DNA that encodes ribosomal RNA (rRNA).

reactive oxygen A form of oxygen that is highly toxic to cells because it damages DNA.

reading frames Grouping of a stretch of nucleotides into sequential triplets; an mRNA molecule has three reading frames, but only one is typically used in translation.

receptor Type of membrane protein that binds to specific molecules in the environment, providing a mechanism for the cell to sense and adjust to its surroundings.

receptor-mediated endocytosis Type of pinocytosis that allows cells to internalize extracellular ligands that bind to the cell's receptors.

recognition sequence The DNA sequence recognized by a particular restriction enzyme.

recombinant DNA molecule DNA molecule created by joining DNA from two different sources *in vitro;* a vector-insert chimera is a recombinant DNA molecule.

recombinant vaccines Subunit vaccines produced by genetic engineering.

redox reactions Transfer of electrons from one compound to another; one compound becomes reduced and the other becomes oxidized.

reducing agents Compounds that readily donate electrons to another compound, thereby reducing the other compound.

reducing power Reduced electron carriers such as NADH, NADPH, and $FADH_2$; their bonds contain a form of usable energy.

reduction Process of adding electrons to a molecule.

refraction Bending of light rays that occurs when light passes from one medium to another.

regulatory gene Gene that functions in the control of the rate of synthesis of other gene products.

regulatory protein Protein that binds to DNA, either blocking or enhancing the function of RNA polymerase.

regulatory T cells Type of lymphocyte that helps control the immune response.

regulon Set of related genes that are transcribed as separate units but are controlled by the same regulatory protein.

replica plating Technique for the simultaneous transfer of organisms in separated colonies from one medium to another medium.

replication fork In DNA synthesis, the site at which the double helix is being unwound to expose the single strands that can function as templates.

replicon Piece of DNA that is capable of replicating; contains an origin of replication.

reporter gene Gene that has a detectable phenotype and can be fused to a gene of interest, providing a mechanism by which to monitor the expression of the gene of interest.

repressible enzyme Enzyme whose synthesis can be turned off by certain conditions.

repressor Protein that binds to the operator site and prevents transcription.

reservoir Source of a disease-causing organism.

resident flora Normal flora that typically inhabit body sites for extended periods.

resistance plasmid (or **R plasmid)** Plasmid that carries genetic information for resistance to one or more antimicrobial medications and heavy metals.

resolve To clearly separate.

respiration Sum total of metabolic steps in the degradation of foodstuffs when the electron acceptor is an inorganic compound.

respire To use the processes of respiration.

response regulator Regulatory protein of a two-component regulatory system; receives a phosphoryl group from the membrane-spanning sensor.

restriction enzyme Type of enzyme that recognizes and cleaves a specific sequence of DNA.

restriction fragment length polymorphism (RFLP) Pattern of fragment sizes obtained by digesting DNA with one or more restriction enzymes.

restriction fragments Fragments generated when DNA is cut with restriction enzymes.

reticulate body Fragile, replicating, non-infectious intracellular form of *Chlamydia* species.

reticuloendothelial system (RES) (See *mononuclear phagoctye system [MPS].*)

retrospective study Type of study done following a disease outbreak; compares the actions and events surrounding clinical cases with those of controls.

retroviruses Group of viruses that carry their genetic information as single-stranded RNA; they have the enzyme reverse transcriptase, which forms a DNA copy that is then integrated into the host cell chromosome.

reverse transcriptase Enzyme that synthesizes double-stranded DNA complementary to an RNA template.

reversion Process by which a second mutation corrects a defect caused by an earlier mutation.

Reye's syndrome Often fatal condition characterized by vomiting, coma, and brain and liver damage, mostly occurring in children treated with aspirin for influenza or chickenpox.

RFLP Abbreviation for restriction fragment length polymorphism.

rheumatoid arthritis Severe crippling autoimmune disease of the joints, caused by cytokines from inflammatory Th1 cells and immune complexes.

rhizosphere Zone around plant roots containing organic materials exuded by the roots.

rhodamine Fluorescent dye that binds to a compound found in the cell walls of members of the genus *Mycobacterium.*

rhuMab (recombinant human monoclonal antibody) Hybrid recombinant anti-IgE molecule being tested in the treatment of asthma.

ribonucleic acid (RNA) Macromolecules in a cell that play a role in converting the information coded by the DNA into amino acid sequences in protein.

ribose A 5-carbon sugar found in RNA.

ribosomal RNA (rRNA) Type of RNA present in ribosomes; the nucleotide sequences of these are increasingly being used to classify and, in some cases, identify microorganisms.

ribosome Structure that facilitates the joining of amino acids during the process of translation; composed of protein and ribosomal RNA.
ribosome-binding site Sequence of nucleotides in mRNA to which a ribosome binds; the first time the codon for methionine (AUG) appears after that site, translation generally starts.
ribotyping Technique used to distinguish among related strains; detects RFLPs in ribosomal RNA genes.
ribozymes RNA molecules that have a catalytic function.
rifamycins Group of antimicrobial medications that block transcription.
risk factors Specific conditions associated with high frequencies of disease.
RNA Abbreviation for ribonucleic acid.
RNA polymerase Enzyme that catalyzes the synthesis of RNA using a DNA template.
RNases Enzymes that degrade RNA.
rod Cylindrical-shaped bacterium; also called a bacillus.
rolling circle replication Mechanism of DNA replication in which a single strand of DNA is synthesized.
rough endoplasmic reticulum Organelle where proteins destined for locations other than the cytoplasm are synthesized.
roundworm (or **nematode)** A helminth that has a cylindrical, tapered body; a nematode.
R plasmids Plasmids that encode resistance to one or more antimicrobial medications and heavy metals.
rRNA Ribosomal RNA.
RTF Abbreviation for resistance transfer factor.
rubisco Enzyme that initiates the Calvin cycle by joining CO_2 to the 5-carbon compound ribulose-1,5-bisphosphate.

---

salinity Amount of salt in a solution.
SALT Skin-associated lymphoid tissues.
sanitization Process of substantially reducing the microbial populations on objects to achieve acceptably safe public health levels.
saprophyte Organism that takes in nutrients from dead and decaying matter.
saturated Refers to a fatty acid that contains no double bonds.
scanning electron microscope (SEM) Type of electron microscope that scans a beam of electrons back and forth over the surface of a specimen; used for observing surface details, but not internal structures of cells.
scavenger receptor Receptor on phagocytes that facilitates the engulfment of various materials that have charged molecules on their surface.
schizogony Process of multiple fission in which the nucleus divides a number of times before individual daughter cells are produced.
schizont Multinucleate stage in the development of certain protozoa, such as the ones that cause malaria.
scolex Attachment organ of a tapeworm, the head end.
scrapie Common name for a neurological disease of sheep thought to be caused by a prion.
sebum Oily secretion of the sebaceous glands of the skin.
secondary response (or **memory response)** Enhanced immune response that occurs upon second or subsequent exposure to specific antigen, caused by the rapid activation of long-lived memory cells; anamnestic response.
secondary infection Infection that occurs along with or immediately following another infection, usually as a result of the first infection.
secondary lymphoid organs Peripheral lymphoid organs throughout the body where mature lymphocytes function in immune responses; their locations include the adenoids, tonsils, spleen, appendix, and lymph nodes, among others.
secondary metabolites Metabolic products synthesized during late-log and stationary phase.
secondary structure Refers to the arrangement of amino acids in a protein; the two major arrangements are helices and sheets.
secondary treatment In treatment of wastewater, a biological process designed to convert most of the suspended solids to microbial mass and inorganic compounds.
segmented virus Virus that has a genome consisting of multiple different nucleic acid fragments.
selectable marker Gene that encodes a selectable phenotype such as antibiotic resistance.
selective enrichment Method of increasing the relative proportion of one particular species in a broth culture by including a selective agent that inhibits the growth of other species.
selectively permeable membrane Membrane that allows some but not other molecules to pass through freely.
selective medium Culture medium that inhibits the growth of certain microorganisms and therefore favors the growth of desired microorganisms.
selective toxicity Causing greater harm to a pathogen than to the host.
self-assembly Spontaneous formation of a complex structure from its component molecules without the aid of enzymes.
self-transmissible plasmid Plasmid that codes for all of the information necessary for its own transfer.
semiconservative replication Type of nucleic acid replication that results in each of the two double-stranded molecules containing one of the original strands (the template strand) and one newly synthesized strand.
semicritical instruments Medical instruments such as endoscopes that come into contact with mucous membranes, but do not penetrate body tissues.
semipermeable Describes material that allows the passage of some but not other molecules.
sense strand Of the two RNA molecules that can theoretically be transcribed from double-stranded DNA, the one that can be translated to make a protein; also called the plus (+) strand.
sensitization Prior immunization; allergic reactions to an antigen occur only in sensitized individuals who have been exposed to that particular antigen.
sepsis A bloodstream infection.
septic shock An array of effects including fever, drop in blood pressure, and disseminated intravascular coagulation, that results from infection of the bloodstream or circulating endotoxin.
septicemia Acute illness caused by infectious agents or their products circulating in the bloodstream; blood poisoning.
septic shock Array of symptoms including fever, drop in blood pressure, and disseminated intravascular coagulation that results when substances associated with bacteria, such as lipopolysaccharide, circulate in the bloodstream.
septic tank A large tank used for individual sewage treatment systems; wastes are collected in the tank and degraded by anaerobic organisms, with the organic compounds in the resulting fluid degraded in a drainage field by aerobic organisms.
serial dilutions Series of dilutions, usually twofold or tenfold, used to determine the titer or concentration of a substance in solution.
seroconversion Change from negative serum without specific antibodies to serum positive for specific antibodies.
serogroup Microorganisms within a species that are the same antigenically as determined by specific antisera.
serology Use of serum antibodies to detect and measure antigens, or conversely, the use of antigens to detect serum antibodies.
serotype A strain that has a characteristic antigenic structure that differs from other strains; also called a serovar.
serum Fluid portion of blood that remains after blood clots.
sex pilus Thin protein appendage required for attachment of one bacterium to another prior to DNA transfer by conjugation.
shake tube Tube of agar medium that has been uniformly inoculated with a bacterial culture in order to determine the oxygen requirement of that organism.
shingles (or **herpes zoster)** Condition resulting from the reactivation of the varicella-zoster virus.
shock Condition with multiple causes characterized by low blood pressure and circulation of the blood inadequate to sustain normal function of vital organs; septic shock results from growth of microorganisms in the body; toxic shock results from a circulating exotoxin.
siderophore Iron-binding substance produced by bacteria to scavenge iron.
sigma (σ) factor Component of RNA polymerase that recognizes the promoter.
signal sequence Characteristic series of hydrophobic amino acids at the amino terminal end of a protein destined for secretion; functions as a tag, directing transport of the protein through the membrane.
signal transduction Process that transmits information from outside of a cell to the inside, allowing that cell to respond to changing environmental conditions.
signature sequences Characteristic sequences in the genes that encode ribosomal RNA that can be used to classify or identify certain organisms.
signs Effects of a disease observed by examining the patient.
similarity coefficient Numerical value that can be used to classify prokaryotes based on their phenotypic characteristics.
simple diffusion Movement of molecules or ions from a region of high concentration to a region of low concentration; does not involve transport proteins.
simple staining Staining technique that employs a basic dye to impart color to cells.
single-cell protein (SCP) Use of microorganisms such as yeast and bacteria as a protein source.
site-specific recombination Mechanism by which a piece of DNA becomes part of a larger piece of DNA; involves identical sequences on each piece of DNA.
size standard In gel electrophoresis of DNA, a series of DNA fragments of known sizes added to a lane of the gel to be used as a basis for later size comparison.
skin-associated lymphoid tissue (SALT) Secondary lymphoid tissue consisting of collections of lymphoid cells under the skin.

slime layer Type of glycocalyx that is diffuse and irregular.
slime mold Terrestrial organism that is similar to the fungi but not related genetically.
slow infection An infection that takes a long period of time before symptoms appear.
smear In a staining procedure, the film obtained by placing a drop of a liquid containing a microbe on a glass microscope slide and allowing it to air dry.
smooth endoplasmic reticulum Organelle of eukaryotic cells that is the site of lipid synthesis and degradation and calcium ion storage.
solute Dissolved molecules.
SOS repair Complex, inducible repair process used to repair highly damaged DNA.
Southern blotting Technique to detect a given nucleotide sequence in DNA fragments that have been separated by gel electrophoresis and transferred to a membrane filter.
specialized transduction Transfer of only specific bacterial genes by phage from one bacterium to another.
species Group of related isolates or strains; the basic unit of taxonomy. In the binomial nomenclature scheme, the second name given to an organism.
spheroplast Gram-negative cell from which the peptidoglycan component of the cell wall has been removed; retains some portions of the outer membrane.
spikes (or **attachment proteins**) Structures on the outside of the virion that bind to host cell receptors.
spirillum (pl. **spirilla**) Curved rod long enough to form spirals.
spirochete Type of long helical cell with a flexible cell wall and an axial filament.
splicing Process that removes introns from eukaryotic precursor RNA to generate mRNA.
spoilage Biochemical changes in foods that are perceived as undesirable.
spontaneous generation Discredited theory that organisms can arise from non-living matter.
spontaneous mutation Mutation that occurs naturally without the addition of mutagenic agents.
spore Type of differentiated, specialized cell formed by certain organisms; includes some types of dormant cells that are resistant to adverse conditions and the reproductive structures formed by fungi.
sporozoite Elongated infectious form of certain protozoa; for example, in malaria, the form entering the body from a mosquito bite, infectious for liver cells.
sporulation In bacteria, a complex, highly ordered sequence of morphological changes during which a bacterial vegetative cell produces a specialized cell greatly resistant to environmental adversity; eukaryotes can also experience sporulation.
spread plate Technique used to cultivate bacteria by uniformly spreading a suspension of cells onto the surface of an agar plate.
sputum Material coughed from the lungs.
start codon Codon at which translation is initiated; in prokaryotes, typically the first AUG after a ribosome-binding site.
starter cultures Strains of microorganisms added to a food to initiate the fermentation process.
stationary phase Stage of growth of a culture in which the number of viable cells remains constant.
stereoisomer (or **optical isomer**) Mirror image of a compound.
sterilant A chemical used to destroy all microorganisms and viruses in a product, rendering it sterile.
sterile Completely free of all microorganisms and viruses; an absolute term.
sterilization The process of destroying or removing all microorganisms and viruses through physical or chemical means.
steroid Type of lipid with a specific four-membered ring structure.
sticky ends (See *cohesive ends.*)
stock culture Culture stored for use as an inoculum in later procedures.
stop codon Codon that does not code for an amino acid and is not recognized by a tRNA; signals the end of the protein.
strain Population of cells descended from a single cell.
streak plate Simplest and most commonly used technique for isolating bacteria; a series of successive streak patterns is used to sequentially dilute an inoculum on the surface of an agar plate.
streptococcal pyrogenic exotoxins (SPEs) Family of genetically related poisonous proteins produced by certain strains of *Streptococcus pyogenes,* responsible for scarlet fever, toxic shock, and "flesh-eating" necrotizing fasciitis.
stromatolite Coral-like mat of filamentous microorganisms.
structural isomers Molecules that contain the same elements but in different arrangements that are not mirror images; structural isomers have different names.
subclinical Infection or disease with no apparent symptoms.
substrate (1) Substance on which an enzyme acts to form products. (2) Surface on which an organism will grow.
substrate-level phosphorylation Transfer of the high-energy phosphate from a phosphorylated compound to ADP to form ATP.
sucrose Disaccharide consisting of a molecule of glucose bonded to fructose; common table sugar.
sugar-phosphate backbone Series of alternating sugar and phosphates moieties of a DNA molecule.
sulfa drugs Group of antimicrobial drugs that inhibit folic acid synthesis.
sulfanilamide Antimicrobial drug that inhibits folic acid synthesis; one of the sulfa drugs.
sulfate-reducers Group of obligate anaerobes that use sulfate (SO_4^{2-}) as a terminal electron acceptor, producing hydrogen sulfide as an end product.
S unit Unit of measurement that expresses the sedimentation rate of a compound; reflects the mass and density of the compound; "S" stands for Svedberg.
superantigens Molecules that stimulate T lymphocytes by binding to MHC class II molecules and to part of the T-cell receptor distinct from the antigen-binding site, resulting in activation of many T cells, overproduction of cytokines, severe reactions, and sometimes fatal shock.
superficial mycoses Fungal infections that affect the hair, skin, or nails.
superoxide (O_2^-) Toxic derivative of O_2.
superoxide dismutase Enzyme that degrades superoxide to produce hydrogen peroxide.
surface receptors Proteins in the membrane of a cell to which certain signal molecules bind; they enable the inner workings of the cell to sense and respond to signals outside of the cell.
swarmer cells Motile cells of sheathed bacteria that disperse to new locations.
symbiosis The living together of two dissimilar organisms or symbionts.
symptoms Effects of a disease experienced by the patient.
syncytium (pl. **syncytia**) Multinucleate body formed by the fusion of cells.
synergistic Describes the acting together of agents to produce an effect greater than the sum of the effects of the individual agents.
synergistic infection An infection in which two or more species of pathogens act together to produce an effect greater than the sum of effects if each pathogen were acting alone.
synthetic medium Medium in which the chemical composition and quantity of every component is known.
systemic infection Infection in which the infectious agent spreads throughout the body.
systemic mycoses Fungal infections that affect the tissues deep in the body.

---

tandem repeat Repetitive core sequence located in regions between human genes; probes that bind to tandem repeats are used in DNA fingerprinting.
tapeworm (or **cestode**) A helminth that has a segmented, ribbon-shaped body; a cestode.
***Taq* polymerase** Heat-stable DNA polymerase of the thermophilic bacterium *Thermus aquaticus.*
target cell In immunology, cell that is the direct recipient of a T cell's effector functions.
target DNA In the PCR procedure, the region to be amplified.
tautomeric shift Movement of H atoms from one site on a nitrogenous base to another on DNA; alters the hydrogen-bonding properties and therefore, may result in mutations.
taxa Groups into which organisms are classified.
taxonomy The science that studies organisms in order to arrange them into groups; those organisms with similar properties are grouped together and separated from those that are different. Taxonomy encompasses identification, classification, and nomenclature.
T_C cells Effector form of a cytotoxic T cell; it induces apoptosis in infected or cancerous "self" cells.
T-cell receptor Molecule on a T cell that enables the T cell to recognize a specific antigen.
T cells Lymphocytes that mature in the thymus; they originate from stem cells in bone marrow, differentiate in the thymus, and move through the bloodstream to secondary lymphoid organs where they are responsible for cellular immune responses and function as helper cells in the antibody response.
T-dependent antigens Antigens that evoke an antibody response only with the participation of T-helper cells.
T-DNA Portion of the Ti plasmid of *Agrobacterium tumefaciens* that is transferred into a plant cell.
teichoic acids Component of the Gram-positive cell wall, composed of chains of a common subunit, either ribitol-phosphate or glycerol-phosphate, to which various sugars and D-alanine are usually attached.
temperate phage Bacteriophage that can either become integrated into the host cell DNA as a prophage or replicate outside the host chromosome leading to cell lysis.

template Strand of nucleic acid that a polymerase uses to synthesize a complementary strand.
terminal electron acceptor Chemical that is ultimately reduced as a consequence of chemotrophic metabolism.
tertiary structure Level of structure of a protein described by its three-dimensional nature; two major shapes exist, globular and fibrous.
tertiary treatment In treatment of wastewater, any purification process beyond secondary treatment, generally designed to remove nitrates and phosphates.
tetracyclines Group of antimicrobial medications that interfere with protein synthesis.
T_H cells Effector form of a helper T cell; it activates B cells and macrophages, and releases cytokines that stimulate other aspects of the immune system.
therapeutic index Ratio of minimum toxic dose to minimum effective dose of a medication.
thermophile Organism with an optimum growth temperature between 45°C and 70°C.
thrush Infection of the mouth by *Candida albicans.*
thylakoids Membrane-bound disclike structures within the stroma of chloroplasts; they contain chlorophyll.
thymine dimer Two adjacent thymine molecules on the same strand of DNA joined together through covalent bonds.
thymus Primary lymphoid organ, located in the upper chest, in which T lymphocytes mature.
T-independent antigens Antigens that can activate B cells without the assistance of a T-helper cell.
Ti plasmid (See *tumor-inducing plasmid.*)
tissue culture Culture of plant or animal cells that grows in an enriched medium outside the plant or animal.
titer Measure of the concentration of a substance in solution; for example, the amount of a specific antibody in serum, usually measured as the highest dilution of serum that will test positive for antibody.
tolerance Specific unresponsiveness of the adaptive immune system that reflects its ability to ignore any given molecule, such as a normal cellular protein.
toll-like receptors (TLRs) A group of surface receptors that recognize specific compounds unique to microbes, enabling the cell to sense the presence of invading microbes and then alert other components of the host's defenses.
total coliforms Facultative, non-spore-forming, Gram-negative rods that ferment lactose, producing acid and gas within 48 hours at 35°C; because most typically reside in the intestine, they are used as indicators of fecal pollution.
toxemia Circulation of toxins in the bloodstream.
toxin Poisonous chemical substance.
toxoid Modified form of a toxin that is no longer toxic but is able to stimulate the production of antibodies that will neutralize the toxin.
trace elements Elements that are required in very minute amounts by all cells; they include cobalt, zinc, copper, molybdenum, and manganese.
trachoma Potentially serious chronic eye disease caused by certain strains of *Chlamydia trachomatis.*
transamination Transfer of an amino group from an amino acid to another organic compound; converts the recipient compound to an amino acid.
transcript Fragment of RNA, synthesized using one of the two strands of DNA as a template.
transcription Process of transferring genetic information coded in DNA into messenger RNA (mRNA).
transcytosis Transport of a substance across a cell border; a cell takes up the substance from one side of the border and then releases it to the other side.
transduction Mechanism of gene transfer between bacteria in which bacterial DNA is transferred inside a phage.
transfer RNA (tRNA) Type of RNA that delivers the appropriate amino acid to the ribosome during translation.
transferrin An iron-binding protein found in blood and tissue fluids.
transformed cells Bacterial or animal cells containing inheritable changes.
transfusion reaction Reaction characterized by fever, low blood pressure, pain, nausea, and vomiting, resulting from the transfusion of immunologically incompatible blood.
transgenic Plants and animals into which new DNA has been introduced.
transient expression Expression of a gene for a short period of time. Often refers to expression of genes introduced into cells and not integrated into the genome.
transient flora Microorganisms that are only temporary residents of body sites.
transition step Step in metabolism that links glycolysis to the TCA cycle; converts pyruvate to acetyl-CoA.
translation Process by which genetic information in the messenger RNA directs the order of amino acids in protein.
translocation Advancement of a ribosome a distance of one codon during translation.
transmissible spongiform encephalopathies Group of fatal neurodegenerative diseases of humans and animals in which brain tissue develops spongelike holes.
transmission electron microscope (TEM) Type of microscope that directs a beam of electrons at a specimen; used to observe fine details of cell structure.
transport protein Type of protein found in cell membranes that functions in the transport of certain compounds across the membrane; may be called a permease or a carrier.
transport systems Mechanisms used to transport small molecules across the cytoplasmic membrane.
transposable element (or **transposon**) Gene that moves from one DNA molecule to another within the same cell or from one site on a DNA molecule to another site on the same molecule.
transposition Movement of a piece of DNA from one site in a molecule to another site in the same cell.
trematodes Flatworms known as flukes.
tricarboxylic acid (TCA) cycle Metabolic pathway that incorporates acetyl-CoA, ultimately generating CO_2 and reducing power, also called the Krebs cycle and the citric acid cycle.
trichomes Filamentous multicellular associations of cyanobacteria that may or may not be enclosed within a sheath.
trickling filter method Treatment method for small sewage plants in which a rotating arm sprays sewage onto a bed of rocks coated with a biofilm of organisms that aerobically degrades the wastes.
triglyceride Molecule consisting of three molecules of the same or different fatty acids bonded to glycerol.
trimethoprim Antimicrobial medication that interferes with folic acid synthesis.
tRNA Transfer RNA.
trophozoite Vegetative feeding form of some protozoa.
tubercle Granuloma formed in tuberculosis.
tumble Rolling motion of a motile cell that is caused by an abrupt change in the direction of rotation of flagella.
tumor-inducing (Ti) plasmid Plasmid of *Agrobacterium tumefaciens* that enables the organism to cause tumors in plants; a derivative of the plasmid is used as a vector by scientists to introduce DNA into plants.
tumor necrosis factors (TNFs) A group of cytokines that play an important role in the inflammatory response and other aspects of immunity.
turbidity Cloudiness; the turbidity of a bacterial suspension is proportional to the number of cells in that suspension.
tyndallization Repeated cycles of heating and incubation to kill spore-forming bacteria.
type III secretions system Mechanism by which bacterial pathogens transfer gene products directly into host cells.

---

ubiquity Widespread prevalence.
ultra-high-temperature (UHT) method A method that uses heat to render a product free of all microorganisms that can grow under normal storage conditions.
ultraviolet (UV) light Electromagnetic radiation with wavelengths between 175 and 350 nm; invisible.
uncoating In virology, the separation of the protein coat from the nucleic acid of the virion.
unsaturated Refers to a fatty acid with one or more double bonds.
upstream Direction toward the 5′ end of either an RNA molecule or the analogous (+) strand of DNA.
urea $CO(NH_2)_2$ A waste product of protein catabolism by the body's cells; present in various body fluids, notably urine.
urticaria Hives; an allergic skin reaction characterized by the formation of itchy red swellings.
UV Abbreviation for ultraviolet light.

---

vaccine Preparation of attenuated or inactivated microorganisms or viruses or their components used to immunize a person or animal against a particular disease.
vancomycin Antimicrobial medication that interferes with peptidoglycan synthesis.
variable region The portion of an antibody molecule that contains the antigen-binding sites; tremendous variation exists between the amino acid sequences of variable regions in different antibody molecules.
vector (1) In molecular biology, a piece of DNA that acts as a carrier of a cloned fragment of DNA. (2) In epidemiology, any living organism that can carry a disease-causing microbe; most commonly arthropods such as mosquitoes and ticks.
vegetative cell Typical, actively multiplying cell.
vehicle Inanimate carrier of an infectious agent from one host to another.
vertical evolution Acquisition of antimicrobial resistance through spontaneous mutation.
vertical transmission Transfer of a pathogen from a pregnant woman to the fetus, or from a mother to her infant during childbirth.
vibrio (pl. **vibrios**) Short, curved rod-shaped bacterial cell.
villus (pl. **villi**) Narrow protrusion from a membrane such as the intestinal lining.

viremia Viruses circulating in the bloodstream.
virion Viral particle in its inert extracellular form.
viroid Piece of RNA that does not have a protein coat but does replicate within living cells.
virulence Relative ability of a pathogen to overcome body defenses and cause disease.
virulence determinants Arsenal of mechanisms of pathogenicity of a given microbe.
virus Acellular or non-living agent composed of nucleic acid surrounded by a protein coat.
vitamin One of a group of organic compounds found in small quantities in natural foodstuffs that are necessary for the growth and reproduction of an organism; usually converted into coenzymes.
volutin Storage form of phosphate found inside certain bacterial cells; because granules of volutin exhibit characteristic staining with the dye methylene blue, they are called metachromatic granules.

---

water activity (a_w) Quantitative measure of the water available.
water molds Non-photosynthetic members of the heterokons; similar to the fungi but not related genetically.
Western blotting Procedure that uses a labeled antibody to detect specific proteins; similar in principle to a Southern blot.
whey Liquid portion that remains after milk proteins coagulate during cheese-making.
wide host range plasmid Plasmid that can replicate in unrelated bacteria.
wild type Form of an organism that is isolated from nature.

---

yeast Unicellular fungus.
yeast artificial chromosome (YAC) Vector that can be used to clone segments of DNA up to a million nucleotides in length into the yeast *Saccharomyces cerevisiae.*
yeast two-hybrid system A tool for studying protein-protein interactions; it relies on two yeast proteins that can work in concert to activate a reporter gene.

---

zone of inhibition Region around a chemical saturated disc where bacteria are unable to grow due to adverse effects of the compound in the disc.
zoonosis (pl. **zoonoses**) Disease of animals that can be transmitted to humans.
zooplankton Floating and swimming small animals and protozoa found in marine environments, usually in association with the phytoplankton.
zygote Diploid cell formed by the sexual fusion of two haploid cells.

CREDITS

Photographs

Table of Contents Part Openers

1: © Science VU/Visuals Unlimited; 2: © Dr. Gopal Murti/SPL/Custom Medical Stock Photo; 3: © David M. Phillips/Visuals Unlimited; 4: © SPL/ Photo Researchers; 5: © Grant Heilman Photography.

Chapter 1

Opener: © Science VU/Visuals Unlimited; 1.2: Courtesy of Milton P. Gordon and Syed Tanveer Haider; 1.3: © Bettmann/Corbis; 1.5: © Kathy Talaro/Visuals Unlimited; 1.6: © Cabisco/Visuals Unlimited; 1.7a: © Dr. John D. Cunningham/ Visuals Unlimited ; 1.7b: © C. Shih & R. Kessel/Visuals Unlimited; 1.8: © Manfred Kage/Peter Arnold; 1.9a: © K.G. Murti/Visuals Unlimited; 1.9b: © Thomas Broker/Phototake; 1.9c: © K.G. Murti/Visuals Unlimited; 1.10: © U.S. Department of Agriculture/Dr. Diemer; 1.11: © Stanley B. Prusiner/Visuals Unlimited; Box 1.1, Fig. 1: Courtesy of Milton P. Gordon and Syed Tanveer Haider; Box 1.1, Fig. 2: Courtesy of Dr. Heide N. Schulz/Max Planck Institute for Marine Microbiology; Box 1.1, Fig. 3: Courtesy of Reinhard Rachel and Harald Huber, University of Regensburg, Germany.

Chapter 2

Opener: © Scott Camazine/Photo Researchers, Inc.; Pros 2.1a: © Mark Antman/The Image Works; Pros 2.1b: © SIU/Peter Arnold.

Chapter 3

Opener: © Terry Beveridge/Biological Photo Service; 3.1: Courtesy of Leica, Inc., Deerfield, FL; Table 3.1a: From S. T. Williams, M.E. Sharpe and J.G. Holt (Eds.), *Bergey's Manual of Systematic Bacteriology, Vol. 4*. © 1989 Williams and Wilkins Co.,Baltimore. Micrograph from T. Cross, University of Bradford, Bradford, U.K.; Table 3.1b: © Wim van Egmond/Visuals Unlimited; Table 3.1c: © P. Johnson/Photo Researchers, Inc.; Table 3.1d: © T. E. Adams/ Visuals Unlimited; Table 3.1e: © Evans Roberts; Table 3.1f: Courtesy of Michael W. Davidson/National High Magnetic Field Lab; Table 3.1g: © R. Kessel & C. Shih/Visuals Unlimited; Table 3.1h: © David M. Phillips/Visuals Unlimited; Table 3.1i: © Torunn Berge/Photo Researchers, Inc.; 3.2a,b: © W. A. Jensen; 3.3a: © Richard Megna/Fundamental Photographs; 3.4: © Wim van Egmond/Visuals Unlimited ; 3.5: © P. Johnson/Photo Researchers, Inc.; 3.6: © T. E. Adams/Visuals Unlimited; 3.7: © Evans Roberts; 3.8a,b: Courtesy of Michael W. Davidson/National High Magnetic Field Lab; 3.10a: © R. Kessel & C. Shih/Visuals Unlimited; 3.10b: © H. Aldrich/Visuals Unlimited; 3.11: © David M. Phillips/Visuals Unlimited; 3.12: © Torunn Berge/Photo Researchers, Inc.; 3.14: © Leon J. Le beau/Biological Photo Service; 3.15: © John D. Cunningham/Visuals Unlimited; 3.16: © Dr. Gladden Willis/Visuals Unlimited/Getty; 3.17: © Jack M. Bostrack/Visuals Unlimited; 3.18: © E. Chan/Visuals Unlimited; 3.19a: Courtesy of Molecular Probes, Eugene, OR; 3.19b: © Richard L. Moore/Biological Photo Service; 3.19c: © Evans Roberts; 3.20a,b: © David M. Phillips/Visuals Unlimited; 3.20c: © Dennis Kunkel/Phototake; 3.20d: © Veronika Burmeister/Visuals Unlimited; 3.20e,f: © David M. Phillips/Visuals Unlimited; 3.21a: Courtesy of Walther Stoeckenius; 3.21b: Courtesy of James T. Staley; 3.22a (top): © George Musil/Visuals Unlimited; 3.22a (bottom): © David M. Phillips/ Visuals Unlimited; 3.22b: © R. Kessel & C. Shih/Visuals Unlimited; 3.22c: © Oliver Mecks/Photo Researchers, Inc; 3.23b: Courtesy of L. Santo, H. Hohl, and H. Frank, Journal of Bacteriology 99:824, 1969. American Society for Microbiology; 3.31: Courtesy of Dale C. Birdsell; Table 3.5: © Leon J. Le beau/Biological Photo Service; 3.33c,d: © Terry Beveridge, University of Guelph; 3.35: Courtesy of Dr. Edwin S. Boatman; 3.36a: Courtesy of K.J. Cheng and J. W. Costerton; 3.36b: Courtesy of A. Progulske and S.C. Holt, *Journal of Bacteriology*, 143:1003-1018, 1980; 3.37a: © Fred Hossler/Visuals Unlimited; 3.37b: © Science VU/Visuals Unlimited; 3.40: © D. Blackwill and D. Maratea/Visuals Unlimited; 3.41a: Courtesy of Dr. Charles Brinton, Jr.; 3.41b: © U.S. Department of Agriculture/Harley W. Moon; 3.42a: © CNRI/SPL/Photo Researchers, Inc.; 3.42b: © Dr. Gopal Murti/SPL/Photo Researchers; 3.44: Courtesy of Dr. Edwin S. Boatman ; 3.45: Courtesy of J.F.M. Hoeniger, *J. Bacteriol.* 96:1835,1968. American Society for Microbiology; 3.47c: Courtesy of Thomas Fritsche; 3.52b: © Garry T. Cole/ Biological Photo Service; 3.53b: © Keith Porter/Photo Researchers, Inc.; 3.54: Courtesy of Lewis K. Shumway; 3.55: © R. Bolendar & D. Fawcett/ Visuals Unlimited; 3.56: Courtesy of Charles J. Flickinger.

Chapter 4

Opener: Courtesy of Dr. Eshel Ben-Jacob; 4.2: © Dr. Dennis Kunkel/ Visuals Unlimited; 4.3: Courtesy of the Center for Biofilm Engineering, Montana State University-Bozeman, Image by P. Stoodley; 4.4: © Michael Gabridge/Visuals Unlimited; 4.5: © Fred Hossler/Visuals Unlimited; 4.11a: © Christine Case/Visuals Unlimited; 4.11b: © L. M. Pope and D. R. Grote/ Biological Photo Service; 4.12: © Dr. Elmer Koneman/Visuals Unlimited; 4.14: Courtesy of Thermoforma, Forma Scientific Division; 4.19a: © Dennis Kunkel/Phototake; 4.19b: © Kathy Talaro/Visuals Unlimited; 4.21: © Richard Megna/Fundamental Photographs.

Chapter 5

Opener: © Southern Illinois University/Photo Researchers, Inc.; 5.1a: © Yoav Levy/Phototake; 5.1c: © Rosenfeld Images/LTD/SPL/Photo Researchers, Inc.; 5.1b: © Rosenfeld Images/LTD/SPL/Photo Researchers, Inc.; 5.1d: © Bob Daemmrich/The Image Works; 5.1e: © Nieto/Herrican/Photo Researchers, Inc.; 5.4a,b: Evans Roberts; 5.6: © Pall/Visuals Unlimited; 5.8: © Dennis Kunkel/Phototake.

Chapter 6

Opener: © Brock May/Photo Researchers, Inc.; 6.2: © Farrell Grehan/Photo Researchers, Inc.; 6.3a: © Photodisc Vol. Series 74, photo by Robert Glusie; 6.3b: © Jane Burton/Bruce Coleman, Inc; 6.9b,c: From Voet: Biochemistry, 1/e, 1990/ John Wiley & Sons; 6.21a,b: © Brian Moeskau/McGraw-Hill; 6.21c: © Dennis Strete/Fundamental Photographs; 6.21d: © Photodisc/ McGraw-Hill; 6.21e: © Brian Moeskau/McGraw-Hill; 6.21f: © Dennis Strete/Fundamental Photographs.

Chapter 7

Opener: © D. Struthers/Toney Stone Images/Getty; 7.4: From J. Cairns, "The Chromosome of E. coli" in Cold Spring Harbor Symposia on Quantitative Biology, 77. © 1963 by Cold Spring Harbor Laboratory Press.

Chapter 8

Opener: © Dr. Gopal Murti/SPL/Custom Medical Stock Photo; 8.6: © Matt Meadows/Peter Arnold, Inc; 8.23: Courtesy of C. Brinton, Jr. and J. Carnahan.

Chapter 9

Opener: © Jean Claude Revy/Phototake; 9.2: © Richard T. Nowitz/Photo Researchers, Inc.; 9.7: Courtesy of Pamela Silver and Jason Karana, Harvard Medical School, Dana Farber Cancer Institute. Photo provided by

Howell Martin; 9.11: Dr. R. Rachel, and Prof. Dr. K.O. Stetter, University of Regensburg, Lehrstuhl fuer Mikrobiologie, Regensburg, Germany.; 9.12: Courtesy of Rosetta Inpharmatics © 2002 Rosetta Inpharmatics, Inc. All rights reserved.; 9.17: Reprinted with permission from Edvotek, Inc.; 9.20: © Simon Fraser/SPL/Photo Researchers, Inc.; 9.21: © Jean Claude Revy/Phototake.

Chapter 10

Opener: © Meckes/Ottawa/Photo Researchers, Inc.; 10.2a: © George Wilder/Visuals Unlimited; 10.2b,c: Courtesy of Dr. Thomas R. Fritsche, M.D., Ph.D., Clinical Microbiology Division, University of Washington, Seattle; 10.3a: © E. Koneman/Visuals Unlimited; 10.3b: © Biophoto Associates/Photo Researchers, Inc.; 10.4a: © Ray Otero/Visuals Unlimited; 10.4b,c: © Dennis Strete/Fundamental Photographs; 10.6a: Courtesy of bioMerieux, Inc.; 10.6b: Courtesy of Becton, Dickinson and Company; 10.10: Courtesy of Patricia Exekiel Moor; 10.11, 10.12: Evans Roberts.

Chapter 11

Opener: © F. Widdel/Visuals Unlimited; 11.1a: © F. Widdel/Visuals Unlimited; 11.1b: © Ralph Robinson/Visuals Unlimited; 11.2a: © Thomas Tottleben/Tottleben Scientific Company; 11.2b: © David M. Phillips/Visuals Unlimited; 11.3: © John Walsh/Photo Researchers, Inc.; 11.4a: Courtesy of Dr. Heinrich Kaltwasser. From ASM News 53(2): Cover, 187; 11.4b: From M. P. Starr et al (Eds.), *The Prokaryotes.* Springer-Verlag.; 11.5: From J. G. Holt (Ed.), *The Shorter Bergey's Manual of Determinative Bacteriology*, 8/e, 1977. Williams and Wilkins Co., Baltimore; 11.6a: Courtesy of Isao Inouye, University of Tsukuba, Mark A. Shneegurt, Wichita State University and Cyanosite (www.cyanosite.bio.purdue.edu/index.html); 11.6b: © M. I. Walker/Photo Researchers, Inc.; 11.7, 11.8: Courtesy of Wayne Carmichael, Wright State University, Mark A. Schneegurt, Wichita State University and Cyanosite (www.cyanosite.bio.purdue.edu/index.html); 11.9a: Courtesy of J. T. Staley and J. P. Dalmasso; 11.9b: Courtesy of Dr. James Staley; 11.10: © John D. Cunningham/Visuals Unlimited; 11.11: © Dennis Kunkel/Phototake; 11.12: © Evans Roberts; 11.13: © CNRI/Phototake; 11.15a: © Eric Grave/Photo Researchers, Inc.; 11.15b: © Soad Tabaqchali/Visuals Unlimited; 11.16a,b: Courtesy of Harold L. Sadoff; 11.17a: Courtesy of Mary F. Lampe; 11.17b: © Patricia L. Grilione/Phototake; 11.18: From S. T. Williams, M.E. Sharpe and J.G. Holt (Eds.), *Bergey's Manual of Systematic Bacteriology, Vol. 4.* © 1989 Williams and Wilkins Co., Baltimore. Micrograph from T. Cross, University of Bradford, Bradford, U.K.; 11.19, 11.20a: © John D. Cunningham/Visuals Unlimited; 11.20b: From N. R. Krieg and J. G. Holt (Eds.), *Bergey's Manual of Systematic Bacteriology*, Vol. 1, 1984. Williams and Wilkins Co., Baltimore; 11.21, 11.22: Courtesy of J. T. Staley and J. P. Dalmasso; 11.23: From J.T. Staley, M.P. Bryant, N. Pfennig, and J.G. Holt (Eds.) *Bergey's Manual of Systematic Bacteriology, Vol. 3.* © 1989 Williams and Wilkins Co., Baltimore; 11.24: © Alfred Pasieka/Peter Arnold, Inc.; 11.25a: Courtesy of Amy Cheng Vollmer, Swarthmore College; 11.25a: © Kenneth Lucas/Biological Photo Service; 11.26: Courtesy of Betsy L. Williams; 11.27: © Michael Gabridge/Visuals Unlimited; 11.28: © Alfred Pasieka/Peter Arnold, Inc.; 11.29: Courtesy of R. R. Friis, *J. Bacteriol.* 110:706, 1972. American Society for Microbiology; 11.30: © Wayne P. Armstrong, Life Sciences Department, Palomar College; 11.31: Dr. R. Rachel, and Prof. Dr. K.O. Stetter, University of Regensburg, Lehrstuhl fuer Mikrobiologie, Regensburg, Germany.; 11.32: US Geological Survey, Photo by David E. Wieprecht.

Chapter 12

Opener : © John D. Cunningham/Visuals Unlimited; 12.2a: © Cabisco/Visuals Unlimited; 12.2b: © John D. Cunningham/Visuals Unlimited; 12.3: © Martha Nester; 12.5: © David M. Phillips/Visuals Unlimited; 12.6: © Arthur M. Siegelman/Visuals Unlimited; 12.7a,b,c: Courtesy of Fritz Schoenknecht; 12.9a: © E. Chan/Visuals Unlimited; 12.9b: © Inga Spence/Tom Stack & Associates; 12.9c: © Bob Pool/Tom Stack & Associates; 12.10: © A.B. Dowsette/SPL/Photo Researchers; 12.13a: © Martha Nester; 12.13b: © Bruce Iverson; 12.14, 12.15b,c,d: © Martha Nester; 12.16: © Carolina Biological Supply/Phototake; 12.18, 12.20, 12.21: Courtesy of Sam Eng and Fritz Schoenknecht.

Chapter 13

Opener: © Oliver Mecks/Photo Researchers, Inc; 13.1a: Courtesy of Harold Fisher, University of Rhode Island and Robley Williams, University of California Berkeley; 13.1b: © Dennis Kunkel/Phototake; 13.1c: © Thomas Broker/Phototake; 13.8: Courtesy of Harold Fisher; 13.12a: © Prof. L. Caro/SPL/Photo Researchers; 13.12b: Courtesy of Dr. Rafael Martinez, University of California, Los Angeles; 13.12c: © Oliver Mecks/Photo Researchers, Inc.

Chapter 14

Opener: © Scott Camazine/Photo Researchers, Inc.; 14.1a: © CDC/Science Source/Photo Researchers; 14.1b: © K. G. Murti/Visuals Unlimited; 14.1c: Courtesy of Dr. Frederick A. Murphy, Centers for Disease Control and prevention; 14.6b: © Dr. Jack Griffith; 14.12: © Michael Gabridge/Custom Medical Stock; 14.13a,b,c: Courtesy of M. Cooney; 14.14a: © Terry Hazen/Visuals Unlimited; 14.14b: © E. Chan/Visuals Unlimited; 14.15: Courtesy of Fred Williams, National Exposure Research Laboratory/U.S. EPA; 14.16: Courtesy of M. Cooney; 14.17a: © Dean Glawe/Biological Photo Service; 14.17b: © Bruce Iverson; 14.17c: © Dean Glawe/Biological Photo Service; 14.18: © Science VU/Visuals Unlimited; 14.19: © Barbara J. Miller/Biological Photo Service; 14.20a: © BSIP/Photo Researchers.

Chapter 15

Opener: © David M. Phillips/Visuals Unlimited; 15.8b: Reprinted from Wendell F. Rosse et al., "Immune Lysis of Normal Human and Parozysmal Nocturnal Hemoglobinuria (PNH) Red Blood Cells," *Journal of Experimental Medicine*, 123:969, 1996. Rockefeller University Press; 15.10: © Meckes/Ottawa/SPL/Photo Researchers, Inc.

Chapter 16

Opener: © Lennart Nilsson/Boehringer Ingelheim International GMBH; 16.10a: Courtesy of Dr. James W. Vardiman; 16.10b: © NIBSCS/SPL/Photo Researchers; 16.10c: © D. Fawcett/Visuals Unlimited.

Chapter 17

Opener: © Kevin Noran/Tony Stone/Getty; 17.1a: © SPL/Photo Researchers; 17.1b: © Dag Sundberg/Photographer's Choice/Getty Images; 17.1c: © BSIP/Phototake; 17.1d: © SPL/Photo Researchers; 17.3: © Jean Claude Revy - ISM/Phototake; 17.5: © Dr. Dan Schadler/Oglethorpe University; 17.9: © Science VU/Wellcome/Visuals Unlimited; 17.10: © Centers for Disease Control; 17.12: © Bob Coyle/McGraw-Hill; 17.13: Courtesy of Genelabs Diagnostics.

Chapter 18

Opener: © Mario Tama/Getty Images; 18.2: © STU/Custom Medical Stock; 18.6: © Bart's Medical Library/Phototake; 18.8: © Kenneth E. Greer/Visuals Unlimited; 18.9: © SIU/Visuals Unlimited.

Chapter 19

Opener: © SPL/Photo Researchers; 19.4: Courtesy of Chihiro Sasakawa, University of Tokyo; 19.5: Courtesy of Mark A. Jepson, from Trends in Microbiology (98)v6:359-365, "Studying M cells and their role in infection"; M.A. Jepson and M.A. Clark, Elsevier Press; 19.7: Courtesy of Pascale F. Cossart, From B. Finlay and P. F. Cossart, Science 276:720, April 4, 1997.

Chapter 20

Opener: © Gianni Tortoli/Photo Researchers; 20.1a(i): © Photodisc/McGraw-Hill; 20.1a(ii): © Corbis Digital Stock CD/McGraw-Hill; 20.1b(i): © Photodisc/McGraw-Hill; 20.1b(ii): Courtesy of University of Nebraska/Department of Entomology; 20.1b(iii): © Photodisc/McGraw-Hill; 20.1b(iv): © Kent Wood/Photo Researchers; 20.1b(v): © Photodisc/McGraw-Hill; 20.3a, b: © Cameramann International; 20.9: © WHO, Geneva Switzerland; 20.11: © B. Seitz/Photo Researchers.

Chapter 21

Opener: © SPL/Photo Researchers; 21.5a,b: Reprinted with permission of Robert L. Perkins from A. S. Klainer and R. L. Perkins, Journal of Infectious Diseases, 122:4, 1970 © University of Chicago Press; 21.10: © Fred Marsik/

Visuals Unlimited; 21.11: Courtesy bioMerieux, St. Louis, MO ; 21.12a, b: AB Biodisk.

Chapter 22

Opener: © SPL/Photo Researchers; 22.1: Courtesy of Karen A. Holbrook; 22.2a: © Carroll H. Weiss/Camera M.D. Studios; 22.2b: © Carroll H. Weiss/Camera M.D. Studios; 22.2c: Courtesy of Glenn D. Roberts, Mayo Clinic; 22.3: © SPL/Photo Researchers, Inc.; 22.4: Courtesy of National Institute Slide Bank/The Welcome Center for Medical Sciences; 22.5: © SPL/Photo Researchers; 22.6: © Evans Roberts; 22.8: © Ken Greer/Visuals Unlimited; 22.9: Courtesy of Rocky Mountain Laboratory, Hamilton, Montana, CDC; 22.11: © Ed Reschke/Peter Arnold, Inc.; 22.12: © SPL/Photo Researchers; 22.13: © Charles W. Stratton/Visuals Unlimited; 22.15: © C. C. Duncan/Medical Images, Inc.; 22.17: © John D. Cunningham/Visuals Unlimited; 22.18: © Carroll H. Weiss/Camera M.D. Studios; 22.19: © Oliver Mecks/Photo Researchers, Inc; 22.20: © Lowell Georgia/Photo Researchers, Inc; 22.21: © Dr. P. Marazzi/SPL/Photo Researchers, Inc; 22.22: © Carroll H. Weiss/Camera M.D. Studios; 22.24: © CNRI/SPL/Photo Researchers, Inc.; 22.25a: © Dr. P. Marazzi/SPL/Photo Researchers, Inc; 22.25b: © Evans Roberts; 22.26a: © Dr. P. Marazzi/SPL/Photo Researchers, Inc; 22.26b: © A.M. Siegelman/Visuals Unlimited.

Chapter 23

Opener: © Moore/Custom Medical Stock Photo; 23.3: © Michael English/Medical Images, Inc.; 23.4: © Evans Roberts; 23.5: © Kenneth E. Greer/Visuals Unlimited; 23.6a: © Leonard Morse, M.D./Medical Images, Inc.; 23.6b: © Carroll H. Weiss/Camera M.D. Studios; 23.6c: © A.M. Siegelman/Visuals Unlimited; 23.7: Courtesy of National Institute Slide Bank/The Welcome Center for Medical Sciences; 23.8: © A.M. Siegelman/Visuals Unlimited; 23.10, 23.11: Courtesy of National Institute Slide Bank/The Welcome Center for Medical Sciences; 23.12: Courtesy of Dr. John Slack; 23.13: © Kenneth E. Greer/Visuals Unlimited; 23.14: © Leonard Morse, M.D./Medical Images, Inc.

Chapter 24

Opener: © Mediscan/Visuals Unlimited; 24.2, 24.5: © Evans Roberts; 24.7: © SPL/Photo Researchers; 24.8: Courtesy Smith & Nephew Ent.; 24.9: © A.B. Dowsette/SPL/Photo Researchers; 24.10: © Evans Roberts; 24.11a,b: © St. Francis Hospital/Cameramann International; 24.12a: © Evans Roberts; 24.12b: © Larry Jensen/Visuals Unlimited; 24.13: Courtesy of J.B. Baseman; from P.C. Hu, A.M. Collier, and J.B. Baseman "J. Exp. Med." 145:1328, 1977. Rockefeller University Press.; 24.14: Courtesy of Dr. Kenneth Bromberg; 24.17: © Biophoto Associates/Photo Researchers, Inc.; 24.18a: © John D. Cunningham/Visuals Unlimited; 24.18b: © CNRI/Phototake; 24.19: © SPL/Photo Researchers; 24.20: © Science VU/Visuals Unlimited; 24.23a: Centers for Disease Control; 24.23b: © E. Chan/Visuals Unlimited; 24.25a,b: © Evans Roberts.

Chapter 25

Opener: © Garry Watson/Photo Researchers, Inc; 25.3: © Fred Hossler/Visuals Unlimited; 25.5a,b, 25.6a: From S. Schluger, R.A. Yaodels and R.C. Page, "Periodontal Disease," 1977. © Lea & Febiger, Philadelphia; 25.6b: © Evans Roberts; 25.9: © Frederick C. Skvara, M.D.; 25.10: © Science VU/Visuals Unlimited; 25.12: © Veronika Burmeister/Visuals Unlimited; 25.14: Courtesy of Philippe J. Sansonette, M.D., Professeur Institut Pasteur; 25.15: © David M. Rollins/Visuals Unlimited; 25.16: © Moredun Animal Health Ltd./Photo Researchers, Inc.; 25.17: © Science Source/Photo Researchers, Inc.; 25.22: © P.M. Motta & F. M. Magliocca/SPL/Photo Researchers, Inc.; 25.23: © Michael Abbey/Photo Researchers, Inc.; 25.24: © Oliver Meckers/Photo Researchers, Inc.

Chapter 26

Opener: © Kwangshin Kim/Photo Researchers, Inc.; 26.3: © Science VU/Fred Marsik/Visuals Unlimited; 26.4: © Custom Medical Stock Photo; 26.5: Centers for Disease Control; 26.8: © Biological Photo Service/Terraphotographics; 26.9: © Biophoto Associates/Photo Researchers, Inc.; 26.10: Courtesy of Stanley Falkow; 26.11: Courtesy of Morris D. Cooper, Ph.D., Professor of Medical Microbiology, Southern Illinois University School of Medicine, Springfield, IL; 26.12: Courtesy of National Institute Slide Bank/The Welcome Center for Medical Sciences; 26.13: Courtesy of S. Eng and F. Schoenknecht; 26.14: Courtesy of Thomas Diepgen, University Heidelberg; 26.15: © Carroll H. Weiss/Camera M.D. Studios; 26.16: © L. Winograd/Biological Photo Service; 26.17a: © Carroll H. Weiss/Camera M.D. Studios; 26.17b: © Harvey Blank, M.d./Camera M.D. Studios; 26.18: Courtesy of National Institute Slide Bank/The Welcome Center for Medical Sciences; 26.19: © Biophoto Associates/Photo Researchers, Inc.; 26.22: © David M. Phillips/Visuals Unlimited.

Chapter 27

Opener: © Dr. Linda Stannard, UCT/Science Photo Library/Photo Researchers; 27.4: © John Durham/SPL/Photo Researchers, Inc.; 27.6: © Kenneth Greer/Visuals Unlimited; 27.7: © Mary K. Stallone/MediChrome/The Stock Shop; 27.9: © Palo Koch/Photo Researchers, Inc; 27.10: © John D. Cunningham/Visuals Unlimited; 27.11: © Science VU/Dr. Soad Tabaqchali/Visuals Unlimited; 27.14: Courtesy of National Institute Slide Bank/The Welcome Center for Medical Sciences; 27.15: © Evans Roberts; 27.16: © Bettmann/Corbis; 27.18a: © Tektoff-BM/CNRI/SPL/Photo Researchers, Inc.; 27.18b: © Tobey Sanford; 27.19: © Evans Roberts; 27.20: © Mary K. Stallone/MediChrome/The Stock Shop; 27.21: © Cabisco/Visuals Unlimited; 27.22: © Dr. Terry Kreeger/Visuals Unlimited.

Chapter 28

Opener: © Dr. Tony Brain/SPL/Photo Researchers, Inc; 28.2: © Kenneth Greer/Visuals Unlimited; 28.4: © Science Source/Photo Researchers, Inc; 28.6: © A.M. Siegelman/Visuals Unlimited; 28.7a, b: Courtesy of Joe Hinnebusch, From Hinnebusch, B.J., Perry, R.D., and Schwan, T.G., Science 273:367, 19 July 1996.; 28.9a: © Ed Reschke; 28.9b: © Jacquin Carrillo-Farga/Science Source/Photo Researchers, Inc.

Chapter 29

Opener: © Manfred Kage/Peter Arnold, Inc.; 29.2: Courtesy of Stuart Fischman, D.M.D; 29.12: © St. Mary's Hospital Medical School/SPL/Photo Researchers, Inc.; 29.13: © Cecil H. Fox/Photo Researchers; 29.14a: © E. Koneman/Visuals Unlimited; 29.14c: Courtesy of Dr. Thomas R. Fritsche, M.D., Ph.D., Clinical Microbiology Division, University of Washington, Seattle; 29.15: © Dr. F.C. Skvara/Peter Arnold, Inc.; 29.16: © Paula Inhad/Custom Medical Stock Photo; 29.17: Courtesy of Dr. Edwin P. Ewuing, Jr./Centers for Disease Control.

Chapter 30

Opener: © Grant Heilman Photography; 30.4: From Y. Cohen and E. Rosenberg, "Microbial Mats," Fig. 1a, pg. 4, 1989, American Society for Microbiology; 30.5: © SPL/Photo Researchers; 30.8: © Nancy Pearsall; 30.11a: © WHOI-D. Foster/Visuals Unlimited; 30.12a: © Stephan Imhof/Philipps-Universität ; 30.12b: © R.L. Peterson/Biological Photo Service; 30.13b: © John D. Cunningham/Visuals Unlimited; Table 30.1: Courtesy of J.P. Dalmasso.

Chapter 31

Opener: © Myrleen Cate/PhotoEdit; 31.7: Courtesy of IDEXX Laboratories, Inc.; 31.8: © Alan L. Detrick/Photo Researchers, Inc.; 31.9: © Phil Degginger/Color-Pic, Inc.; 31.11a,b: © Science VU/Visuals Unlimited.

Chapter 32

Opener: © Michael Newman/PhotoEdit; 32.1: © Paul Webster/Tony Stone/Getty; 32.2a,b,c: © Martha Nester; 32.3a,b,c: Courtesy of the Wisconsin Milk Marketing Board; 32.6a,b,c,d,e,f: © Martha Nester; 32.7a: © Rachael Epstein/PhotoEdit; 32.7b: © William J. Weber/Visuals Unlimited; 32.8a,b: © Felicia Martinez/PhotoEdit.

Line Art and Text

Chapter 1

TA1.1: FRANK & ERNEST © reprinted by permission of Newspaper Enterprise Association, Inc.; Figure 1.4: Adapted from WHO, 1993. TEN YEARS OF PROGESS 1984-1993. The Programme for Vaccine Development.

Chapter 2
TA2.1: FRANK & ERNEST © reprinted by permission of Newspaper Enterprise Association, Inc.

Chapter 3
Chapter 3 cartoon: By permission of John Deering and Creators Syndicate, Inc.

Chapter 4
Figure 4.8: Finkel, S.E., Zinser, E.R., and Kolter, R., (2000) Long-Term Survival and Evolution in the Stationary Phase. In: G. Stor and R. Hengis-Aronis (ed.), BACTERIAL STRESS RESPONSES. ASM Press, Washington, D.C.; Figure 4.20: Table excerpt from STANDARD METHODS FOR THE EXAMINATION OF WATER AND WASTEWATER, 18th edition, The American Water Works Association, Denver, CO.

Chapter 6
Figure 6.23: Adapted from a figure by Ken Nealson, Jet Propulsion Laboratory, California Institute of Technology, Pasadena, CA.; Table 6.8 Adapted from a table to Kendall Gray, University of Washington.

Chapter 7
TA7.1: FRANK & ERNEST © reprinted by permission of Newspaper Enterprise Association, Inc.

Chapter 8
TA8.1: FRANK & ERNEST © reprinted by permission of Newspaper Enterprise Association, Inc.

Chapter 9
TA9.1: FRANK & ERNEST © reprinted by permission of Newspaper Enterprise Association, Inc.

Chapter 10
Figure 10.1: Adapted from G.J. Olsen and C.R. Woese "Ribosomal RNA: A Key to Phylogeny" FASEB Journal, 7:113-123, 1993; Figure 10.7: Adapted from Sigma-Aldrich, http://www.sigma-aldrich.com; Figure 10.13: Source: The Ribosomal Database Project.

Chapter 14
Chapter 14 cartoon: By permission of John L. Hart FLP, and Creators Syndicate, Inc.; Figure 14.4: Based on Sherris Medical Microbiology Textbook

Chapter 15
Figure 15.2: Adapted from Mims, et al. *Pathogenesis of Infectious Disease*, fourth edition (1995) Academic Press.

Chapter 17
Table 17.4: Table adapted from CDC, *MMWR* Vol. 51 (2), 31-33, January 18, 2002. www.cdc.gov/nip/recs/childschedule.pdf.

Chapter 19
Figure 19.12: Adapted from *Arousing the Fury of the Immune System*, 1998 Howard Hughes Medical Institute.

Chapter 20
Figure 20.2: Source: CDC, *MMWR* 45(6): 135, 1996; Figure 20.4: Source: Summary of Notifiable Diseases, United States, 1997. *MMWR* 46 (No. 54-001); Figure 20.6: Source: CDC, *MMWR* 44(48): 901, 1995; Figure 20.7: Source: Incidence of Foodborne Illness: Preliminary Data from the Foodborne Disease Active Surveillance Network (FoodNet), United States, 1998 *MMWR* 48(09): 189-195; Figure 20.8: Source: CDC, *MMWR* (49)4, February 2000; Figure 20.10: Source: http://www.whitehouse.gov/WH/EOP/OSTP/CISET/html/ciset.html.

Chapter 21
Figure 21.1: From Rolinson, George, N., (1998), *Journal of Antimicrobial Chemotherapy* 41, 489-603.

Chapter 22
Chapter 22 cartoon: By permission of John Deering and Creators Syndicate, Inc.; Figure 22.10: Source: CDC, *MMWR* 42(53): 48, October 21, 1994. Summary of Notifiable Disease, United States, 1993; Figure 22.14: Source: CDC, *MMWR* Summary of Notifiable Disease, United States 1997. 46(54): 42, November 20, 1998; Figure 22.23: Source: CDC. Summary of Notifiable Disease, United States, 1997. *MMWR* 46(54): 54, November 20, 1998; CDC, *MMWR* 49(51 & 52): 1165, Table III; CDC, *MMWR* 50(51 & 52): 1167, Table III.

Chapter 23
Chapter 23, Case Presentation: Source: Centers for Disease Control and Prevention. 1999, *Morbidity and Mortality Weekly Report* 48:98.

Chapter 24
Figure 24.22: From www.cdc.gov/ncidod/disease/hanta/hps/nofrasmes/casemap.htm.

Chapter 25
TA25.1: FRANK & ERNEST © reprinted by permission of Newspaper Enterprise Association, Inc.; Figure 25.11: Source: CDC, 1999, Summary of Notifiable Diseases, United States, 1998. *MMWR* 47(53): 1-93; CDC, *MMWR* 49(51 & 52): 1165, Table III; CDC, *MMWR* 50(51 & 52): 1167, Table III; Figure 25.18:
Source: CDC 1999. Summary of Notifiable Diseases, United States, 1998. *MMWR* 47(53): 1-93; CDC, *MMWR* 50(51 & 52): 1174; Figure 25.21: Source: CDC 1999. Summary of Notifiable Diseases, United States, 1998. *MMWR* 47(53): 1-93; *MMWR* 50(51 & 52): 1163, 1166, Tables II and III, and corresponding tables in vols. 49, 48, 47, 46, and 45 of the same publication.

Chapter 26
Figure 26.6: Source: CDC 1994. Summary of Notifiable Diseases, United States, 1993. *MMWR* 42(53): 57; Figure 26.21: From www.unaids.org/bangkok2004.

Chapter 27
Figure 27.3: Source: CDC 1998, 1999. *MMWR* 47(46): 993; and Summary of Notifiable Diseases, United States, 1998. *MMWR* 47(53): viii, 38; Figure 27.5: Source: Schuchat, Anne et al. Bacterial Meningitis in the United States in 1995. 1997. *The New England Journal of Medicine* 337(14): 970; Figure 27.8: Source: CDC 1993, 1999. Summary of Notifiable Diseases, United States, 1992, 1998. *MMWR* 41(55): 41 and 47(53): 49; Figure 27.12: Source: www.cdc.gov/mmwr/preview/mmwrhtml/mm5345a4.htm; Figure 27.17: Source: CDC, 1993, 1999. Summary of Notifiable Diseases, United States, 1992, 1998. *MMWR* 41(55): 46, 47(53): 54.

Chapter 28
Figure 28.5: Source: DCD, 1994. Summary of Notifiable Diseases, 1993, *MMWR* 42(53): 62, CDC, *MMWR* 51(9): 182-184; Figure 28.10: Source: WHO; Figure 28.12: Source: www.cdc.gov/ncidod/emergplan/box23.html

Chapter 29
Case Presentation, Chapter 29: Source: Centers for Disease Control and Prevention, 1996, *Morbidity and Mortality Weekly Report* 45(6): 122; Figure 29.1: Adapted from United Nations HIV/AIDS Program as reported in the *Seattle Times News*, Tuesday, November 24, 1998; Figure 29.9: Adapted from CDC. HIV/AIDS Surveillance I Women, L264 slide series, slide#1, and *HIV/AIDS Surveillance Report* 1999; 11(No. 1): 3; Figure 29.10: Source: CDC, *HIV/AIDS Surveillance Report* 1999; 11(No. 1): 36.

Chapter 30
Figure 30.12: From *The Living World* by Johnson. Reprinted by permission of The McGraw-Hill Companies.

INDEX

Page numbers followed by *t* and *f* indicate tables and figures, respectively. References preceded by A denote pages within the appendices.

A

D

E

F

G

H

I

M

N

O

Q

R

S

U

V

W

X

Y

Z